For Reference

Not to be taken from this room

The College Blue Book®

36th Edition

Distance Learning Programs

The College Blue Book®

36th Edition

Distance Learning Programs

MACMILLAN REFERENCE USA
A part of Gale, Cengage Learning

GALE
CENGAGE Learning™

Detroit • New York • San Francisco • New Haven, Conn • Waterville, Maine • London

GALE
CENGAGE Learning™

The College Blue Book, 36th Edition
Volume 6

Project Editor: Bohdan Romaniuk

Editorial Support Services: Wayne Fong

Composition and Electronic Prepress: Gary Leach

Manufacturing: Rita Wimberley

Product Management: Jenai Mynatt

For product information and technology assistance, contact us at **Gale Customer Support, 1-800-877-4253.**
For permission to use material from this text or product, submit all requests online at **www.cengage.com/permissions.**
Further permissions questions can be emailed to **permissionrequest@cengage.com**

Gale
27500 Drake Rd.
Farmington Hills, MI, 48331-3535

ISBN-13: 978-0-02-866074-5 (6 vol. set)
ISBN-10: 0-02-866074-9 (6 vol. set)
ISBN-13: 978-0-02-866080-6 (vol. 6)
ISBN-10: 0-02-866080-3 (vol. 6)

ISSN 1556-0570

This title is also available as an e-book.
ISBN-13: 978-0-02-866142-1 (set)
ISBN-10: 0-02-866142-7 (set)
Contact your Gale sales representative for ordering information.

Printed in the United States of America
1 2 3 4 5 6 7 12 11 10 09 08

TABLE OF CONTENTS

HOW TO USE THIS GUIDE   1

WHAT IS DISTANCE LEARNING?   3

IS DISTANCE LEARNING RIGHT FOR YOU?   11

WHAT CAN YOU STUDY VIA DISTANCE LEARNING?   19

WHO OFFERS DISTANCE EDUCATION?   25

SELECTING A GOOD DISTANCE LEARNING PROGRAM   29

TAKING STANDARDIZED ADMISSIONS TESTS   35

APPLYING FOR ADMISSION TO DEGREE PROGRAMS   41

PAYING FOR YOUR EDUCATION   47

SUCCEEDING AS A DISTANCE LEARNER   55

ADDITIONAL RESOURCES   61

GLOSSARY   71

INSTITUTION PROFILES   77

IN-DEPTH DESCRIPTIONS   330

CONSORTIUM IN-DEPTH DESCRIPTION   536

INSTITUTIONS OFFERING DEGREE AND CERTIFICATE PROGRAMS INDEX   541

NON-DEGREE-RELATED COURSE SUBJECT AREAS INDEX   631

GEOGRAPHICAL LISTING OF DISTANCE LEARNING PROGRAMS INDEX   733

HOW TO USE THIS GUIDE

INSTITUTION PROFILES AND SPECIAL MESSAGES

Here, in alphabetical order, you'll find more than 900 institutions offering postsecondary education at a distance. Each profile covers such items as accreditation information, availability of financial aid, degrees and awards offered, course subject areas offered outside of degree programs, and the person or office to contact for program information. In addition, there are **Special Messages** from institutions about new programs or special events.

For each institution, specific degrees and award programs are listed, followed by a list of subjects for which individual courses (undergraduate, graduate, and noncredit) are offered.

INSTITUTIONAL INFORMATION

The sections here describe overall characteristics of an institution and its distance learning offerings, featuring key facts and figures about the institutions, including:

- institution Web site,
- background information on the institution,
- the type of accreditation held by the institution,
- when distance learning courses were first offered at the institution,
- the number of students enrolled in distance learning courses,
- the availability of financial aid,
- services available to distance learners, and
- the person or office to contact for more information about the institution's distance learning courses.

DEGREES AND AWARDS

This part of the profile lists each program leading to a degree or certificate that can be completed entirely at a distance. Programs are grouped by the level of award: associate degrees, baccalaureate degrees, graduate degrees, undergraduate certificates, and graduate certificates.

COURSE SUBJECT AREAS OFFERED OUTSIDE OF DEGREE PROGRAMS

Listed here are the general subject areas in which the institution offers courses at a distance. Subjects are divided into those offered for undergraduate credit and for graduate credit and those that are noncredit. Note that this is not a listing of course titles; you will need to contact the institution for a detailed list of courses offered.

IN-DEPTH DESCRIPTIONS OF DISTANCE LEARNING PROGRAMS

Additional details on distance learning offerings are provided by participating institutions and consortia. Each two-page entry provides details on delivery media, programs of study, special programs, credit options, faculty, students, admission, tuition and fees, financial aid, and applying.

An institution's absence from this section does not constitute an editorial decision on the part of Peterson's. Rather, this section is an open forum for institutions to expand upon information provided in the **Institution Profiles and Special Messages** section of the book. The descriptions are arranged alphabetically by institution name.

CONSORTIUM IN-DEPTH DESCRIPTION

The organization listed in this section represents a consortium of institutions offering distance learning programs. This consortium has been formed so that an expanded set of distance learning options can be offered beyond the resources available through any single member institution. The consortium does not have a central application process and/or does not directly award credits and degrees. Applications are processed, and credits and conferred degrees are awarded, through one of the member institutions. Further, the consortium generally is not directly granted accreditations; rather, credits and degrees reflect the accreditation of the awarding institution. The reader should obtain specific information directly from the consortium.

APPENDIX

The **Appendix** lists resources that can give you more information on subjects presented in previous sections of this guide.

GLOSSARY

With the **Glossary**, you'll be able to learn all the pertinent terms from A to Z.

INDEXES

If you are interested in locating a certificate or degree program in a specific field of study, refer to the index of **Institutions Offering Degree and Certificate Programs.** Here you'll find institutions offering everything from accounting to theological and ministerial studies.

If it is individual courses you're looking for, the index of **Non-Degree-Related Course Subject Areas** will guide you to institutions offering credit and noncredit courses at either the undergraduate or graduate level.

The **Geographical Listing of Distance Learning Programs** lets you find programs that are offered by institutions that are located near you. Keep in mind that most institutions' offerings are available nationally, and sometimes internationally. See individual listings for details.

DATA COLLECTION PROCEDURES

The information provided in these profiles was collected during the summer of 2008 by way of a survey posted online for colleges and universities. With minor exceptions, all data included in this edition have been submitted by officials at the schools themselves. In addition, many of the institutions that submitted data were contacted directly by the Peterson's research staff to verify unusual figures, resolve discrepancies, and obtain additional data. All usable information received in time for publication has been included. The omission of any particular item from an index or profile listing signifies that the item is either not applicable to that institution or that data were not available. Although Peterson's has every reason to believe that the information presented in this guide is accurate, students should check with each college or university to verify such figures as tuition and fees, which may have changed since the publication of this guide.

CRITERIA FOR INCLUSION IN THIS BOOK

In the research for this guide, the following definition of distance learning was used: a planned teaching/learning experience in which teacher and students are separated by physical distance and use any of a wide spectrum of media. This definition is based on the one developed by the University of Wisconsin Extension.

The College Blue Book: Distance Learning Programs profiles more than 900 institutions of higher education currently offering courses or entire programs at a distance. To be included, all U.S. institutions must have full accreditation or candidate-for-accreditation (preaccreditation) status granted by an institutional or specialized accrediting body recognized by the U.S. Department of Education or the Council for Higher Education Accreditation. The six U.S. regional accrediting associations are: the New England Association of Schools and Colleges, Middle States Association of Colleges and Schools, North Central Association of Colleges and Schools, Northwest Commission on Colleges and Universities, Southern Association of Colleges and Schools, and Western Association of Schools and Colleges. Approval by state educational agencies is conferred separately on some distance education courses. Canadian institutions must be chartered and authorized to grant degrees by the provincial government, be affiliated with a chartered institution, or be accredited by a recognized U.S. accrediting body.

WHAT IS DISTANCE LEARNING?

One student is a busy professional who needs to update work-related skills by taking a couple of computer applications courses in his spare time. Another student, a working mother, never finished her bachelor's degree and would love to have that diploma and get a better job. A third student attends a local community college, but what he'd really like is a degree offered by a four-year institution halfway across the country—without moving. Another would-be student is employed full-time in a field in which a master's degree, perhaps even a doctorate, would really give her career a boost. What all these diverse people have in common is an already full life. For them, disrupting family and work by commuting to sometimes distant on-campus classes on a rigid schedule is simply not a workable option. Instead, students like these are turning to distance learning in order to pursue their educational goals. For many people, and perhaps you, distance learning is a blessing—it means you can get the education you need, which might otherwise be difficult or impossible to obtain in the traditional manner.

What, exactly, is distance learning (also called distance education)? Broadly defined, distance learning is the delivery of educational programs to students who are off site. In a distance learning course, the instructor is not in the same place as the student; the students may be widely separated by geography and time; and the instructor and students communicate with each other using various means, from the U.S. mail to the Internet. Students that take a distance education course are called distance learners, whether they live 300 miles from the university or right across the street.

Distance learning makes use of many technologies, and courses are structured in many different ways. Adding to the variety of distance learning programs provided by traditional institutions of higher education are programs offered by new types of institutions, many worthy, others known as diploma mills, that help to fuel the growth in distance education. With so many technologies, courses, programs, and institutions involved in distance education, your distance learning options can be confusing at first. However, it's critical that you understand what distance education involves and which institutions offer a solid education *before* you enroll. That way you'll be sure that you spend your effort, time, and money wisely on a reputable education.

In this section, we'll give you an overview of distance learning; in "Is Distance Learning Right for You?", we'll help you determine whether or not distance education is right for you; and then in later sections we'll give you enough background and guidance so you can make an informed choice when selecting a program. We'll also provide suggestions for handling the application process, paying for your education, and making the most of your distance learning experience.

A BRIEF HISTORY OF DISTANCE EDUCATION

In the last five to ten years, distance education has mushroomed, so it's easy to think of it as a completely recent phenomenon. However, today's distance education, based primarily on video and Internet technologies, has its roots in the correspondence courses that arose in the late 1800s. Instructors would send print materials to students by mail, and students would do their assignments and return them by mail. Correspondence courses were asynchronous; that is, the student was not tied to the instructor's timetable. He or she would do the work when it was convenient. Correspondence courses still exist, mostly for single courses, but they have lost ground over the last seventy years to more modern technologies. The first generation of technology that began to supplant correspondence courses was radio in the 1930s, followed by broadcast television in the 1950s and 1960s. Radio and television courses provided one-way communication, and so they were most suitable for delivering information from the faculty to the students. Typically, there was only minimal interaction between instructor and students, and no interaction at all among students. Another constraint on radio and television courses was time. Broadcast courses are synchronous; students had to be listening to the radio or watching television when the course was broadcast, or they would miss the class.

By about 1960, the advent of cable television, audiocassette recorders, and videocassette recorders solved the time problem posed by the earlier broadcast courses. Courses could be broadcast over cable channels several times so students could watch at their convenience. With a VCR or tape recorder, a student could record a lecture or class session when it was broadcast and view or hear it at any time. In fact, recorders made broadcasting unnecessary. The content of a course could be recorded on an audiocassette or videotape and sent to students, who could listen or view it when they had time. Although recording technology provided convenience for students, because courses are asynchronous, it did not solve the major drawback of broadcast courses—the lack of interaction among faculty members and students.

Beginning in the 1980s, the personal computer, two-way audio and videoconferencing, and the Internet greatly expanded the scope of distance education. With these new technologies, much more information could be conveyed from the faculty to students. More importantly, two-way communication became possible, using interactive video technology or e-mail, newsgroups, bulletin boards, and chat rooms on the Internet. Today, distance education makes use of a wide range of technologies.

INSTRUCTIONAL TECHNOLOGIES IN DISTANCE LEARNING

Today's distance learning courses can be divided into several main categories according to the primary technologies they use to deliver instruction: print-based courses, audio-based courses, video-based courses, and Internet-based courses. The audio, video, and Internet courses all have variations that are synchronous—classes take place at specific times only—and asynchronous—classes that occur at flexible times that may be more convenient for the student.

PRINT-BASED COURSES

Correspondence courses use print materials as the medium of instruction. Students receive the materials by mail at the start of the course and return completed assignments by mail. Sometimes fax machines are used to speed up the delivery of assignments, and the telephone can be used if communication between instructor and student is necessary. Patti Iversen, who lives in Montana, completed part of her Bachelor of Science in Nursing degree from the University of Mary in North Dakota by correspondence course. "The correspondence courses offered no direct contact with the instructor or other students," she recalls. "I purchased a syllabus and book and was otherwise on my own." In addition to the lack of interaction between instructor and students, correspondence courses have the disadvantage of being slow. The low-tech nature of a print-based course means lots of delay between assignments and feedback. Of course, the low-tech nature of the course is an advantage, too. Students don't have to invest in expensive technology and can do their work anywhere. Even though print materials continue to play a very important role in distance learning, they are now usually supplemented by more modern instructional technologies.

AUDIO-BASED COURSES

Audio-based courses may involve two-way communication, as in audio or phone conferencing; or they may involve one-way communication, including radio broadcast and prerecorded audiotapes sent to students. Fritz J. Messere, associate professor and coordinator of broadcasting at the State University of New York at Oswego, recalls the first time, in 1981, he was involved in teaching a course that used phone conferencing. Once a week, faculty members and students from ten universities as well as representatives from the Federal Communications Commission "met" for a class. "The first three weeks were chaotic," recalls Messere. "We didn't know who was talking." However, they worked out a plan in which a different faculty member moderated the session each week by asking questions. At midsession there was a break, followed by a round-robin discussion, in which each site participated in a predetermined sequence.

According to the National Center for Education Statistics of the U.S. Department of Education, audio-based technologies are not widely used today, with only about 12 percent of institutions of higher learning reporting their use as the primary means of delivering a course. Instead, audio technologies may be used to supplement the main technology used in the course. For example, in an Internet-based distance education course, students and professors may call one another periodically.

VIDEO-BASED COURSES

Video-based technologies include two-way interactive video conferencing, one-way video with two-way audio, one-way live video, and one-way prerecorded videotapes provided to students. Of these, two-way interactive video and prerecorded videotapes are the most popular. Of the institutions of higher learning surveyed by the U.S. Department of Education, 54 percent used two-way interactive video and 47 percent used prerecorded videotapes as the primary mode of instructional delivery in their distance education courses.

Two-Way Interactive Video

A course taught by means of two-way interactive video takes place simultaneously in two or more sites. The instructor is located in the home site with a group of students, and other students are located in satellite sites, often with a facilitator to help out. Each site has TV monitors or large screens on which the instructor and students can be viewed. One student in a biology of horticulture course at the University of Cincinnati described the technology used in her course: "Both [home and satellite] classrooms are set up with cameras and two video screens each, which show what is going on in both classrooms. There is a technical assistant present in each location, one on the main campus to set things up and work with the camera, etc., and another in the remote location to set equipment up and to adjust settings should there be any problems." The course itself was conducted as a lecture: "For the most part, the instructor lectures, with students occasionally asking or answering questions. When any student speaks in class, they press a button on a little apparatus on the desk in front of them, which makes the camera point to them as they speak and allows their voice to be transmitted to the other location." Quizzes and exams are faxed to the satellite site and faxed back or mailed by an assistant when they are completed. Like the best classroom teaching, two-way interactive video works well when the instructor is comfortable with "performing" on camera. "You have to keep students at all sites involved with you by making the lecture as entertaining as possible," says Dr. Larry Anthony, coordinator of the addiction studies baccalaureate program based at the University of Cincinnati. "I've had to adapt my teaching to the medium. For example, instead of using overheads as I might in a regular classroom, I'm more inclined to use a series of PowerPoint slides because they're more entertaining."

Two-way interactive video bridges geographical distances but not time. Students must be in a particular place at a particular time to take the course.

Prerecorded Video

A far less sophisticated, though almost as popular, means of instruction is prerecorded videotape. Each course session is videotaped and mailed to off-site students. To supplement this, the course may have a Web site where notes and assignments are posted, or these may be mailed to the off-site students along with the tapes. If students have any questions, they can call or e-mail the instructor after they view the tape. For many students, the lack of interactivity is made up for by the benefit of "attending" class at their own convenience. Nicole DeRaleau, who is studying for a Master of Engineering degree at Worcester Polytechnic Institute in Massachusetts, says, "Watching the videotaped class is really not very different from sitting in class, except that I can't raise my hand and ask questions." On the other hand, she points out that the asynchronous nature of prerecorded video is an advantage: "I can watch half a class at one sitting, and the other half at a later time. I often work late, and I don't have to worry about missing class."

The time and place dimensions of various distance learning instructional technologies.

	Specific place	Any place
Any time (asynchronous)		◆ Online courses (newsgroups, bulletin boards, Web sites, e-mail) ◆ CD-ROMs, DVDs ◆ Videotapes ◆ Audiotapes ◆ Correspondence courses
Specific time (synchronous)	◆ Two-way interactive videoconferencing ◆ Two-way interactive audioconferencing ◆ Traditional on-campus classes	◆ Online course (interactive computer conferencing, chat rooms, MUDs, MOOs) ◆ Radio broadcasts ◆ TV broadcasts, satellite, and cable

INTERNET-BASED COURSES

Today many distance learning courses, called online courses or e-learning, are offered over the Internet. Some online courses use synchronous, "real-time" instruction based primarily on interactive computer conferencing or chat rooms. However, most Internet-based courses use asynchronous instruction, making use of online course management systems, Web sites, e-mail, electronic mailing lists, newsgroups, bulletin boards, and messaging programs.

In asynchronous online courses, instructors post instructional material and assignments, including text, images, video, audio, and even interactive simulations, on the course Web site. Using messaging systems, newsgroups, or bulletin boards, they can start online discussions by posting a comment or question; students can log on using a password and join the discussion at their convenience. In some courses there may be periodic "real-time" interaction in chat rooms or interactive environments like MUDS (multiple-user dungeons) and MOOs (multiple-object orientations). Feedback and guidance to individual students can be done by e-mail or telephone. Note that most of the interaction in an online course is text-based; instructors and students communicate primarily through the keyboarded word. Joanne Simon, who is earning a Master of Business Administration degree from the University of Phoenix Online, describes the setup of her courses: "We use newsgroup folders—the main classroom, a chat room, a course material folder, an assignment folder, and four study group folders. We post a minimum of three messages per day to the main folder in which that week's readings are discussed. In those messages we encourage other students to share ideas, experiences, and opinions on various topics . . . ." Besides this seminar-style interaction, there are many assignments, according to Simon. "We also submit weekly summaries, one graded group assignment, and two personal assignments weekly." Needless to

say, students must have a computer with the appropriate software and Internet access in order to take an Internet-based course. The cost of technology aside, online distance learning programs have considerable advantages. Because the course material stays online for a period of time, students can log on at their own convenience. "There are time stamps on everything they submit," says Michael S. Ameigh, Assistant Provost for Distance Learning and Information Resources and Associate Professor of Communication Studies at the State University of New York at Oswego. "I can see that students are often working in the middle of the night." This flexibility is one of the main attractions of online courses for students, but it can also be its main disadvantage. "It's a common misperception that online courses can be dropped into and out of," says Claudine SchWeber, Assistant Vice President for Distance Education and Lifelong Learning at the University of Maryland University College. Without class sessions to attend at scheduled times, the impetus to log on and do course work must come from within, which requires a great deal of self-discipline.

To help ensure that students keep up, many instructors structure the learning environment by setting weekly deadlines for reading lectures and completing assignments, requiring group projects, and making participation in online discussions mandatory. "I personally contact students who do not participate," says Fritz Messere, who has been teaching broadcasting and business courses online for several years. "Students must interact with me in order to pass the course." At the University of Phoenix Online, students are required to log on to a course and post messages five days out of seven as one of the requirements for passing. In online courses with participation requirements, the amount of interaction between the faculty and students is far greater than in a large lecture class held on campus. There's no lying low in the back of the classroom in a well-run online course.

MIXING THE TECHNOLOGIES

Many courses use a combination of technologies as well as print materials. For example, at Southwest Texas State University, a course in geography for elementary and high school teachers begins with a videoconference, with the instructor introducing himself or herself and outlining the course requirements. A printed study guide with all assigned readings and activities is distributed to all participants at the first session. Teachers who cannot get to a videoconferencing site are sent a videocassette of the first session along with the study guide. After the first session, the course moves online. Using chat rooms, threaded discussions, and e-mail, participants do their assignments and group projects and interact online. Assignments are snail-mailed to the faculty member. Finally, the class concludes with another synchronous videoconference or recorded videotape.

This course may be unusual in that it combines two of the major distance learning technologies, but it is not unusual to find courses that use one of the major technologies and supplement it with another. For example, e-mail is used for individual student-instructor communication in most courses, even if the course is conducted by two-way interactive videotape or prerecorded video.

FUTURE TRENDS

Today, online instruction, two-way interactive video, and one-way prerecorded video are the most popular instructional technologies in distance education. According to the Department of Education's National Center for Education Statistics, colleges and universities are planning to increase their use of Internet-based instruction and two-way interactive video. Prerecorded video is likely to decrease in popularity. The explosive growth in distance learning in the last five years has come primarily from online courses, and that is likely to continue. With better databases and other sources of information continuing to appear on the Internet, ease of access to reliable data will increase. Also, high bandwidth technologies make individualized, customized, and live video interactions possible, with lengthy video programming available. Online distance learning is also causing a shift to a more collaborative learning model. "Because of the nature of online resources and communication, the faculty is no longer the one authoritative voice," explains Claudine SchWeber of the University of Maryland University College. An undergraduate there agrees. "Students learn from each other as well as from the instructor and course materials," she commented. "Instructors who are comfortable with online technology . . . create a classroom environment that is interactive, inviting, stimulating, motivating, and lively." Another interesting trend to note is the incorporation of the new instructional technologies in conventional, classroom-based courses. "What we are finding is that our distance technology is having an impact on the way we teach on-campus courses to undergraduate and graduate students," comments McRae C. Banks, head of the department of management and professor of entrepreneurship at Worcester Polytechnic Institute in Massachusetts. "As one example, some faculty members have students take online quizzes before each class period . . . . Before the professor goes into class, he or she knows what areas the students understand and what areas are troubling them. Now more time can be spent where the students are having difficulty." Other professors hold office hours or help sessions in chat rooms when they are at home or out of town at conferences. Still others require students to respond to each class lecture by posting a comment to a discussion group. "For us, the bottom line is finding ways to enhance the educational experience for students," says Banks.

WHAT CAN YOU LEARN VIA DISTANCE EDUCATION?

The short answer is almost anything. You can take a single course in almost any field, or earn a certificate or degree in many fields, by distance education. Next, we'll give you an overview of what's available, and in "What Can You Study via Distance Learning?" we'll discuss these programs in more detail.

COURSE OFFERINGS

According to the National Center for Education Statistics, an estimated 54,470 different distance education courses were offered in academic year 1997–1998, the last year for which reliable figures are available. That number has undoubtedly increased considerably since then. As you can see in Figure 1-1, most of these courses were college-level, credit-granting courses at the undergraduate level, and about one quarter were at the graduate/first-professional level. Fewer than one tenth were noncredit-granting courses.

According to Figure 1-2, of the courses offered, the greatest number can be found in fields that are part of a general undergraduate education, such as English, humanities, and the social and behavioral sciences; physical and life sciences; and mathematics. However, in the fields of education, engineering, and library and information sciences, more courses are offered at the graduate/first-professional level than at the undergraduate level. According to the Department of Education, there are three likely reasons for this: the emphasis on graduate education in these fields, the suitability of course content for distance education, and the likelihood that groups of students would be located in particular places, such as a school district or engineering firm, to receive broadcast or interactive video courses.

DEGREE AND CERTIFICATE PROGRAMS

Many institutions of higher learning simply offer a smorgasbord of distance education courses that can be taken for credit. An increasing number of institutions, however, have taken distance education to the next step; they have begun to offer undergraduate and graduate certificate and degree programs that can be completed entirely by distance education. For example, a student with an associate degree from a local community college can go on to earn a baccalaureate degree from a four-year institution by distance learning, without relocating. Or a working professional can earn a master's degree or professional certificate on a part-time basis through distance learning. Recently, there has been a phenomenal increase in the number of degree and certificate programs available through distance learning. Unlike individual course offerings, degree and certificate programs are more likely to be offered at the graduate and first-professional level than at the undergraduate level, as you can see in Figure 1-3. Most degree and certificate programs are in the fields of liberal/general studies, business and management, health professions, education, and engineering.

**Figure 1–1: Distance Education Course Offerings
in 1997–1998 (by level)**

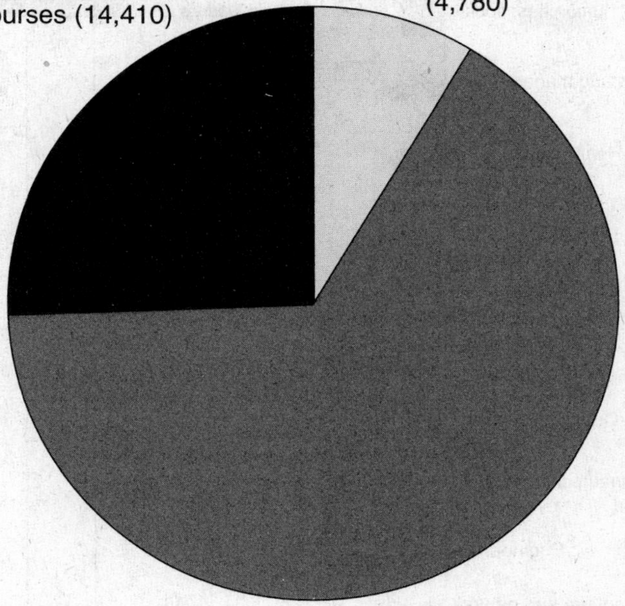

Graduate/first-
professional credit
courses (14,410)

Noncredit courses
(4,780)

Undergraduate credit
courses (35,550)

Source: Data from U.S. Department of Education, National Center for Education
Statistics, Postsecondary Education Quick Information System, *Survey on
Distance Education at Postsecondary Education Institutions*, 1998-1999,
p. 19.

WHO OFFERS DISTANCE LEARNING?

The better question might be, "Who doesn't?" With lifelong learning becoming commonplace and communications technologies improving rapidly, the demand for distance education has grown dramatically, and with it the number and variety of providers. The first group of providers consists of the traditional colleges, universities, graduate schools, community colleges, technical schools, and vocational schools. These providers range from schools only their neighbors have heard of to household names like Stanford, Virginia Tech, and the University of California, to name just a few. The challenges posed by distance education have forced colleges and universities to be creative in their approaches. Some schools have formed partnerships with cable companies, public broadcasting services, satellite broadcasters, and online education companies to deliver high-quality distance education. Colleges and universities also partner with corporations to deliver courses and degree programs to employees. For example, the University of Cincinnati's College of Pharmacy offers courses and a master's degree program via distance learning to employees of Procter & Gamble Pharmaceuticals Norwich, New York, location as well as other P&G sites.

Many schools have formed consortia, or collaborative groups, within a state or region or even internationally, which enables students to take courses as needed from all the participating institutions. An example of a consortium is the University of

Texas (UT) TeleCampus, which does not confer degrees but supports the participating University of Texas campuses, which do award degrees.

A few colleges and universities are virtual, meaning they don't have a campus. These schools offer most or all of their instruction by means of distance education, providing complete degree programs. The University of Phoenix Online and Walden University are two well-known examples.

Finally, there are many online purveyors of noncredit distance education courses on subjects that range from candlemaking and beauty secrets to C++ programming and Spanish. These courses may be fun and even instructive, but they won't contribute to your formal educational credentials.

We'll discuss the providers of distance education more fully in "Who Offers Distance Education?"

HOW EFFECTIVE IS DISTANCE LEARNING?

There is a great deal of interest in the effectiveness of distance learning. Research into this subject is largely anecdotal and much of it is out-of-date, given the rapid development of instructional technology in the last few years. However, Thomas L. Russell, in a widely quoted report entitled *The No Significant Difference Phenomenon*, concluded from a review of 355 research studies

**Figure 1–2: Distance Education Course Offerings
by Field of Study, 1997–1998**

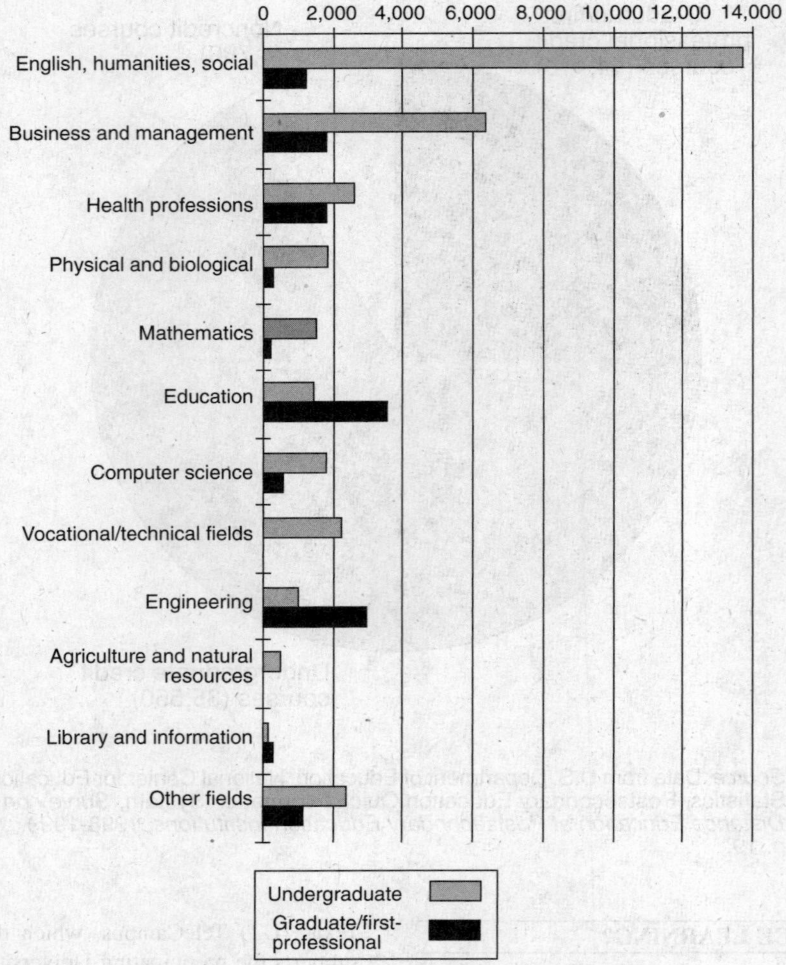

Source: Data from U.S. Department of Education, National Center for Education
Statistics, Postsecondary Education Quick Information System, *Survey on
Distance Education at Postsecondary Education Institutions*, 1998-1999,
p. 25.

and summaries published between 1928 and 1999 that the learning outcomes (test scores and course grades) of distance learning and traditional students are similar. In addition, Russell found that distance learners themselves have positive attitudes toward distance education and are generally satisfied with it. There are a number of questions regarding the effectiveness of distance education that have not yet been answered by the research. For example, how do the different learning styles of students relate to the use of particular technologies? How do individual differences among students affect their ability to learn by distance education? Why do more students drop out of distance education courses than drop out of traditional courses? What types of content are most suitable for distance learning? Common sense suggests that distance education is more effective for some people than for others, the different instructional technologies are more effective with different types of learners, and some subjects are more suitable for distance education than other subjects.

Some educators are not fans of distance education, believing that technology, no matter how sophisticated, cannot substitute the face-to-face interactions of a community of teachers and learners. Even proponents of distance learning concede that students who have the time and money for a traditional on-campus education should go for it. "Technology can't provide the intangible experiences of campus life, especially on the undergraduate level," comments Robert V. Steiner, who directs the distance learning project at Columbia University's Teachers College. "However, distance education is extremely helpful for adult learners who need to get their education in a flexible manner."

Barbara Lockee, Virginia Tech's distance learning program developer and an assistant professor of instructional technology, agrees. "Distance education has the increased potential to reach new audiences that haven't had access to higher education," says Lockee. "Because of the changing needs of our work force, people who are employed need ongoing, lifelong education. So new higher-ed participants are in their 30s and beyond, and many probably have their undergraduate degree but need skills to be successful in the information age."

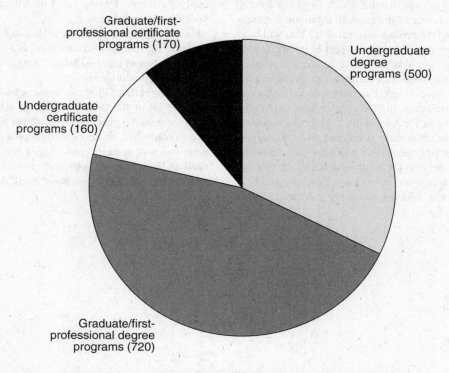

**Figure 1–3: Distance Education Degree
and Certificate Programs, 1997–1998**

Graduate/first-
professional certificate
programs (170)

Undergraduate
certificate
programs (160)

Undergraduate
degree
programs (500)

Graduate/first-
professional degree
programs (720)

Source: Data from U.S. Department of Education, National Center for Education
Statistics, Postsecondary Education Quick Information System, *Survey on
Distance Education at Postsecondary Education Institutions*, 1998-1999,
p. 34.

Distance education may have benefits beyond accessibility, flexibility, and convenience. For example, when asked to compare the experiences of teaching a course to a single classroom of students and by two-way interactive video, Larry Anthony indicated that the students in the distance learning course had the richer experience. "We were hearing from people in different parts of the country," he explained. "In addiction studies, there are different cultural issues and problems in different places. In terms of diversity, the distance learning class was great." Kevin Ruthen, who earned a Master of Science degree in information resource management from Syracuse University, also thought that distance education had added to the value of his degree: "The students and professors . . . were all different ages, from many professional fields, and from many regions of the world," he recalls. "I learned a tremendous amount and gained many different perspectives due to this diversity as opposed to what would be, in my opinion, a less diverse class environment in an on-campus class."

PURSUING YOUR EDUCATION BY DISTANCE LEARNING

Still interested in distance learning? Then the next question is: What's involved in finding a reputable distance education program and getting in? A lot. The first, and perhaps the most important part of this process, is a combination of introspection and research. You are going to have to assess yourself and what's out there to find a good match. You'll have to answer questions like: What are my professional goals? What are my interests and abilities? Which courses or certificate or degree programs will help me achieve my goals? Am I prepared for higher education in this field? What must I do to improve my qualifications? Do I have the motivation, personal characteristics, and skills that will enable me to learn at a distance? In "Is Distance Learning Right for You?", we will help you assess the advantages and disadvantages of distance learning as well as your strengths and weaknesses; this will enable you to decide whether or not distance education is for you. Then in "What Can You Study via Distance Learning?", we'll describe the different degree and certificate programs that are available, what's involved in transferring credits, and how you may be able to earn credits for prior learning and life experience. In "Who Offers Distance Education?", we'll describe the various types of distance learning providers. We'll give you suggestions on how to find out more about programs and institutions.

Once you've done your research on distance education programs, on what basis should you evaluate them? In addition to finding out the all-important accreditation status of the programs in which you are interested, you'll have to find out what each program is really like and whether it's a good match for you. Will the program help you achieve your educational and professional goals? Is the instructional technology a comfortable match for you? "Selecting a Good Distance Learning Program" discusses these issues and provides a checklist of factors you should consider when you evaluate distance education programs.

Once you've identified the programs to which you will apply, what standardized qualifying exams, if any, will you need to take? What should you do to prepare for the SAT*, Graduate Record Examinations (GRE®), or one of the graduate admissions examinations used by many of the professional schools? You will have to find out what each program requires as part of its application and what the deadlines are. You may have to write a personal statement so that the admissions committee can evaluate your background. You will have to ask instructors or colleagues to write letters of recommendation. In "Taking Standardized Admissions Tests" and "Applying for Admission to Degree Programs" we will describe the process in more detail and give you suggestions on how to prepare applications that will gain you admission.

How are you going to pay for your education? If you are planning to attend part-time while working, that may not be a problem. But for full-time students, financing a distance degree program can be complicated. You will have to figure out how much money you will need, find possible sources of aid, and apply for them. "Paying for Your Education" covers financing your distance education.

Finally, in "Succeeding as a Distance Learner," some of the students we interviewed and surveyed will share more of their experiences and offer additional advice on succeeding in a distance education program.

In the pages that follow, there are many suggestions for accomplishing all of the tasks involved in selecting and applying to distance learning programs. Not all the advice will be applicable to everyone. Still, this book will provide you with an overview of what you will need to know. And it will indicate what you will need to find out on your own to ensure that your distance education does all that you hope it will do.

---

*SAT is a registered trademark of the College Board, which was not involved in the production of, and does not endorse, this book.

GRE® is a registered trademark of Educational Testing Service (ETS). This book is not endorsed or approved by ETS.

IS DISTANCE LEARNING RIGHT FOR YOU?

Distance learning can satisfy a wide range of needs for many people in diverse circumstances, but it's not for everyone. Some students don't have the study skills or self-discipline to succeed as a distance learner. Others are interested in a field of study or a degree that is not offered via distance learning. Still, for most people distance learning has the potential to open up new possibilities in higher education. For many adult students, the advantages of distance learning far outweigh the disadvantages. In this section, we'll discuss the pros and cons of distance learning and help you assess whether or not distance learning is right for you.

THE ADVANTAGES OF DISTANCE LEARNING

Distance learning has many benefits. That's why distance-learning programs meet the needs of so many different people of all ages, genders, professions, and educational backgrounds.

As you read the following list of distance learning benefits, ask yourself if any of them provide a way to overcome an obstacle that is standing in your way when you think about going back to school. Do any of these advantages make continuing your education a real possibility right now, rather than a vague goal for sometime in the future?

Here are the benefits of distance learning in general:

- **Distance learning breaks down time barriers.** In most distance learning programs, you don't have to be at a certain place at a certain time. You can learn when it's convenient for you, so you can fit your education into a busy work and home life. You only take as many courses as you can handle at a time, and sometimes you can start whenever you like instead of at the beginning of a semester.
- **Distance learning breaks down geographical barriers.** Whether you are logging on to a course from your own computer at home or traveling a short distance to a satellite classroom, distance education makes your geographical distance from a college or university irrelevant. Students who live in remote areas, who don't have time to commute to a campus, and who travel a lot on business benefit from this aspect of distance education.
- **Distance learning goes at your own pace.** Distance learning is ideal for students who like to set their own pace and who learn best on their own. As you work through course material, you can spend more time on difficult concepts and less time on easier ones. Although you are likely to have weekly or other periodic deadlines, as long as you make them, you can approach the work at a pace that suits your schedule.
- **Distance learning can save money.** Although the tuition and fees for distance learning courses are usually comparable to those charged for on-campus courses, you can save money on child care, gas, parking, and other commuting costs. In addition, you generally don't have to take time off from work to attend class.
- **Distance learning fits individual needs.** You can often tailor a program to fit your particular educational and professional goals and take courses from various institutions if necessary.
- **Distance learning provides freedom of choice.** Since you are not confined to schools within easy commuting distance, you are able to consider distance learning programs at reputable colleges and universities around the country and the world.
- **Distance learning teaches more than just the course material.** Depending on the type of program you take, distance learning can improve your computer, Internet, reading, writing, and oral communication skills, which benefits you no matter what kind of career you pursue.
- **Distance learning broadens your perspective.** Often, your classmates will be from diverse backgrounds and places. You will interact with a more diverse group of people than you would normally find on most campuses.

Refer to Figure 2-1 for the specific advantages of each of the major distance learning instructional technologies.

THE DISADVANTAGES OF DISTANCE LEARNING

Before you think that distance learning is the solution to all problems of access to education, know that it does have its drawbacks. Consider whether or not any of the following general disadvantages would cause you to eliminate distance learning from your education plans. For disadvantages specific to a particular instructional technology, refer to Figure 2-1.

- **Distance learning requires a high degree of discipline and self-motivation.** Dropout rates are higher for distance learning programs than for campus-based programs. No doubt, some dropouts are students who did not realize that distance learning requires as much, if not more, time than a traditional on-campus class. For older distance education students, it's easy for work or family needs to take priority over education. Many distance learners drop out because the distance course is the easiest thing to let go of when things get too hectic.
- **Distance learning can be lonely.** Some people need the face-to-face interaction that a traditional classroom provides. Even though instructors may try to overcome social isolation in distance learning courses, for some students there is simply not enough social contact to keep them enthusiastic and motivated.
- **Distance learning can take longer.** Because distance learning is self-motivated, it's easier to give in to other demands on your time and postpone taking courses, increasing the time it takes to complete a degree program.
- **Distance learning students may get poor student services.** On-campus students have convenient access to the library, academic advisers, job placement services, tutoring, and student centers. Many distance learning programs offer student services

Figure 2-1: Specific Advantages and Disadvantages of the
Major Distance Learning Technologies

Distance Learning Technology	Advantages	Disadvantages
Online	▲Course work can be done at any time of day or night. ▲Any computer with Internet access can be used. ▲Courses can easily be taken from more than one school. ▲Computer skills are developed. ▲There are no commuting costs.	▼Lots of self-discipline and motivation are needed. ▼A computer with Internet access is needed. ▼Social interaction is on line only.
Two-way interactive videoconferencing	▲There is access to courses at distant campuses. ▲Social interaction is most similar to that of a traditional classroom. ▲There is no cost to the student for technology.	▼Classes are held at particular times and places.
Videotapes of class sessions	▲Course work can be done at any time of day or night. ▲Any TV and VCR can be used. ▲There are no commuting costs.	▼Lots of self-discipline and motivation are needed. ▼Social interaction is minimal. ▼Distance learners are several days behind on-campus class.

such as online library access and registration, but in most schools the services still can't compare to those available to on-campus students.

- **Distance learning students miss the college experience.** College campuses offer a lot more than classes, with cultural and sports activities, dorm life, faculty-student interaction, and the opportunity to form lifelong friendships. Although this is not an important consideration for most older distance learners, younger students that pursue an undergraduate education may find the on-campus experience too valuable to pass up.
- **A traditional college degree is a better choice to meet some future goals.** Although distance learning is becoming more mainstream and is usually accepted by employers, as long as it is from a reputable institution, it is still regarded by some in the traditional academic community as inferior. Thus, a traditional degree may be more valuable if you are considering applying in the future to the more prestigious graduate and professional programs, including law school and medical school.

ASSESSING YOURSELF

With the advantages and disadvantages of distance learning in mind, you should take some time to honestly answer the following questions. Consider your own goals, circumstances, personality, skills, social support, and comfort with technology to determine whether or not you are a good candidate for distance learning.

GOALS

What are your educational and professional goals?

First you must determine your educational and professional goals. Ask yourself what you would like to be doing in five or ten

years, and then determine what courses or degree programs will help you achieve your goals. Do you need a course to update your skills, a certificate to provide professional credentials, or a degree to solidify or advance your professional standing?

For example, when Head Start announced that an associate degree in early childhood education would soon be a requirement for its teachers, Angela Butcher had a problem. Butcher, who teaches at Jackson-Vinton Community Action Head Start in Ohio, just had a high school diploma. "I was so scared of losing my job. Going to a college campus (the closest is 45 minutes away) after working 8 hours a day and finding a sitter for my two children because my husband works second shift—it was just impossible to even think about doing it. Then my director received a brochure about the distance learning program at the University of Cincinnati and asked if I would like to give college a shot that way." Butcher continues, "I felt this was a true gift to help me to [keep] the profession that is dear to me."

For Butcher, the goal was crystal clear and the means of achieving that goal fell into place quite nicely. However, for any student, it's important to know what you hope to accomplish by undertaking any degree program. "Make sure you have your goals defined," advises Scott Garrod, a Master of Business candidate at Syracuse University. "Then the decision between a distance or traditional [program] will be easy." Keep in mind that in some fields a distance education degree is not as acceptable as it is in others. Although most business employers don't make any distinctions between distance and on-campus degrees, as long as they are from reputable institutions, in academia and some professions employers may not be so accommodating. Be sure you understand what academic credentials will carry weight in the field in which you are interested.

Why are you considering distance education?

Do you have a busy schedule full of commitments to work, family, and community? If so, your top reason for enrolling in a distance education course or program may be the flexibility it offers. The ability to do course work at your own convenience is the key consideration for most distance learners.

"My schedule does not permit consistent attendance in a traditional classroom," comments one 46-year-old undergraduate. "As a consultant, I may be required to spend up to 60 hours at a client site . . . . As a parent, I have many commitments that would take priority over my attending class." She continues, "The online program at the University of Maryland University College offers me maximum flexibility in which to pursue my educational goals without interfering with the rest of my crazy schedule." Another student, Kimberly Foreman, who is studying for a Master of Healthcare Administration from Seton Hall University's online program in New Jersey, investigated several programs. "Traditional on-campus evening classes interfered with work and family obligations. The weekend programs still required that I be at a certain place at a certain time, and this was also inconvenient," she explains. "I wanted flexibility and a program that allowed me to be self-directed but still have interaction with faculty members and classmates." The online program she found at Seton Hall met her needs.

Some students need the flexibility of distance education because their work involves a great deal of travel. "With my job, travel is a requirement . . . sometimes unpredictable travel," says Scott Garrod of Syracuse University. "So a distance learning program that was not classroom-dependent was a great alternative." Another student, Paul Nashawaty, explains, "My profession has me traveling around and moving from place to place." Nashawaty, who is earning a Master of Business Administration from Worcester Polytechnic Institute in Massachusetts, concluded, "It would be very difficult for me to transfer from school to school."

Other students enroll in distance education courses and programs because they live too far from the institutions of higher learning that offer the education they need. These are students for whom the word "distance" in distance learning has a literal meaning. "My husband is a farmer, so my family is not mobile," explains Patti Iversen, a nurse who lives in Montana and is working on a Master of Science in Nursing degree (family nurse-practitioner) from Gonzaga University in Spokane, Washington. "I live in a rural community and the closest colleges and universities are 250 to 300 miles from my home. I did not want to leave my family for extended periods of time in order to meet my educational and career objectives." For Iversen, distance learning was the only way to achieve her goals.

"I wanted a degree from a respected and vigorous program but didn't want to move my family or quit my job," says Lara Hollenczer, a marketing manager who lives in Maryland and is pursuing a master's degree in communications management from Syracuse University in New York. Distance learning provided Hollenczer the means to earn the degree she wanted without disrupting her work and family life. So, when you consider taking a course or enrolling in a degree program, ask yourself whether flexibility of time and place is critical for you. If flexibility is one of your top needs, distance learning may be the right choice for you.

PERSONAL ATTITUDES AND SKILLS

Are you prepared to do as much work as you would have to do in a traditional course, and perhaps more?

Many people believe that distance learning is an easier or faster way to earn a degree. This is because in recent years many fraudulent distance-learning schools have sprung up, promising degrees in little or no time for little or no work. These diploma mills have given rise to the false perception that distance learning degrees are somehow easier to earn than degrees earned the traditional way. However, distance learning courses and degree programs offered by reputable schools require just as much time and effort as their on-campus counterparts.

"Some students think that an online course is cybersurfing for credit," says Michael S. Ameigh, Assistant Provost for Distance Learning and Information Resources and Associate Professor of Communication Studies at the State University of New York at Oswego. "But an online course is actually more work than if students took the course in the classroom." That's because online instructors often require a certain amount of participation from students in order to pass the course, whereas most classroom instructors do not demand participation from students beyond completing the assignments and exams. So, at the beginning of each course, Ameigh tries to weed out students who think that online learning is easier than conventional courses. He provides a six-minute "welcome document," a streaming media PowerPoint presentation with narration that gives an overview of what the course covers and what he expects of students. In courses taken by distance learners and on-campus students, instructors make no distinctions between distance learners and traditional students when it comes to the course work that they must do. For example, in Gonzaga University's undergraduate and graduate nursing programs, "Course requirements for students at a distance are identical to those for their on-campus colleagues," according to Dale Ann Abendroth, Assistant Professor of Nursing.

From the student's perspective, a high-quality distance education course is as rigorous as a traditional course. "Certainly the expectations of the instructor and the volume of readings and assignments were as stringent, or even more so, than on-site courses I have taken," comments a high school librarian of her Rutgers University postgraduate course in critical issues for the wired classroom. "Be prepared for a great deal of work. It seems to me that more work is assigned than in a 'regular' class, so students shouldn't perceive distance learning as an easy way out. It isn't!"

Do you have the time-management skills necessary to juggle work, home, and school responsibilities?

As we have seen, a distance learning course or program takes as much time as a traditional one, and sometimes more. So ask yourself, do you have enough time to take a distance learning course or courses? Will you be able to juggle your course work, professional work, family obligations, and community activities to make time for all your responsibilities? "I've seen students register for four or five classes in a semester and try to work full-time," says Patti Wolf, Assistant Academic Director and Assistant Professor of Computer Science at the University of Maryland University College. "Many of these students have underestimated the time required for their online courses and ended up doing poorly." Wolf adds, "You should expect to spend as much time online (or otherwise preparing for class) as you would in a traditional classroom." Distance learner Patti Iversen advises students to "be realistic about the amount of time that will be needed for study and travel, if required [for programs with residency periods]."

In addition to having enough time to do the course work, students have to be able to plan their time, make a schedule, and stick to it. "The biggest problem I see among my students is an inability to budget their time," says Wolf. "They get to the third week of class and realize that it's Saturday night and they haven't done their homework."

Iversen agrees. "Failure to adequately anticipate and plan for the rigors of independent learning leads to frustration and poor outcomes," she warns. Even though many courses, like Wolf's, are set up in weekly blocks to help students pace themselves, it's still up to the student to make time to log on or watch the videotape and do the assignments.

Do you have the discipline and self-motivation to work regularly if you don't have to show up for class at a given time and place?

When we asked students and faculty members what personal qualities a distance learner needs, most people mentioned discipline and self-motivation as the keys to success. "Success as a distance learner requires more self-discipline and greater ability to learn autonomously than site-based learning," claims distance learner Patti Iversen. M.B.A. candidate Paul Nashawaty echoes her remarks, "You must keep on top of the workload and try not to slack off," he says. "Discipline is my number-one factor for success in this program." A University of Maryland University College undergraduate agrees, "Students [must] have the discipline to complete course work studies and assignments on time and independently without the in-person reminders that come with regularly scheduled class meetings." When you are considering distance education, ask yourself whether or not you have the qualities needed to see it through. According to Denise Petrosino, a certified public accountant working on a master's in organizational management from the University of Phoenix Online, "As long as you are goal-oriented and self-motivated, you can do it."

Do you have the initiative and assertiveness needed to succeed in a distance learning environment?

Initiative and assertiveness are qualities needed for success in distance learning. Students need to take the initiative to ask questions and resolve problems that the instructor may not be able to perceive.

In addition, students in distance learning courses need to be assertive in order to make themselves known to the instructor and to other students. For example, in an online course, a student who never participates in threaded discussions tends to "disappear." "In the online environment, students have to be assertive," says Michael S. Ameigh of the State University of New York at Oswego. "Otherwise we don't know who they are." Similarly, in a prerecorded video course, a student who never contacts the instructor has little presence in the instructor's mind. Of course, initiative and assertiveness are pluses for traditional on-campus students, too. The student who speaks up in class is more likely to have a good learning experience and succeed in a course than the student who sits silently in the back of the room. For many adults, maturity brings assertiveness. "My students are a professional

group," says Dale Ann Abendroth, Assistant Professor of Nursing at Gonzaga University. "It's rare that I have a wallflower in a course."

YOUR ACADEMIC AND PROFESSIONAL SKILLS

Do you have sound study skills, including reading, researching, writing papers, and taking exams?

Good study skills are a necessary prerequisite for distance learning. In fact, many institutions that offer distance learning courses and degree programs require that students have taken at least some college-level courses before they enroll in a distance education degree program. For example, some distance education bachelor's programs prefer students with an associate degree from a community college or a certain minimum number of undergraduate credit hours. In this way, they ensure that students are ready to tackle course work via distance learning without needing much help with basic study skills.

For graduate programs, it is simply assumed that students have the necessary study skills and are ready to undertake graduate-level work. Laurie Noe, a doctoral candidate in management of children and youth programs at Nova Southeastern University, explains, "You are required to produce papers, take tests, conduct research, and formulate and state your opinions just as if you were in a traditional setting."

Do you have good communication skills? Can you present yourself well in writing? Can you speak up on camera?

Good communication skills—reading, writing, listening, and speaking—are necessary to succeed in all types of distance learning courses and programs. However, different distance learning technologies emphasize different communication skills.

"Online students have to be reasonably articulate in the written mode of communication," explains Claudine SchWeber, Assistant Vice President for Distance Education and Lifelong Learning at the University of Maryland University College. That's because virtually all communication in an online course takes place through the written word, therefore you must be comfortable with reading messages and responding in writing.

For some people, this is ideal. "Students who are petrified to talk in class often find it easy to communicate in writing online. They can make well-reasoned, thought-out responses to the discussion," explains Patti Wolf of the University of Maryland University College. "One of the things that happens online is that people who talk little in the classroom feel more comfortable and tend to communicate well," says Karen Novick, Director of Professional Development Studies at Rutgers University in New Jersey. Robert V. Steiner, who directs the distance learning project at Teachers College, Columbia University, also agrees. "For some students, online learning may provide a more comfortable environment in which to express themselves. Students can reflect on what they want to say before they post a message." On the other hand, some students are simply more visual and more oriented to getting information via television rather than the written word. For them, two-way interactive video is a more comfortable way to communicate. It's easier for these students to speak up and communicate with people they can see and hear rather than to write messages to unseen students and instructors. "Once students get used to being on camera, they react fairly normally," says Larry Anthony, Director of the Addiction Studies Program at the University of Cincinnati. Of course, students who take courses via video still need written communication skills because most of their assignments and exams are in writing.

If you are pursuing a degree or certificate to improve your professional standing, do you have the background that may be required?

Many graduate-level professional programs require that students have worked in the field for several years before they apply. For example, many programs that offer a Master in Business Administration prefer students who have demonstrated their professional capabilities through several years of work. Graduate-level work in other fields, such as nursing, social work, and education, often requires related work experience. Be sure you have the necessary professional background for the programs you are considering.

SOCIAL FACTORS

Do you have the support of your family and employers?

As you have realized by now, a distance learning course or program can be challenging. Taking such a course or program means that you will be working harder than ever, so having the backing of your family and employer can be very helpful. "It's important to have a good support group behind you," says Barbara Rosenbaum, who is working on a master's degree in communications management from Syracuse University. "My husband, friends, family, and colleagues helped me keep my energy and focus up." Distance learner Patti Iversen agrees. "A local support network is a valuable asset in helping to overcome the occasional slump in motivation that occurs over time."

Are you comfortable with the social interaction that is characteristic of distance learning? Can you overcome or accept the social isolation that often occurs?

The issue of social interaction and isolation is complex because different factors, including instructional technology, personality, and life circumstances, influence how each person reacts to the social element of distance learning.

Instructional technology. As we saw when we discussed communication skills, each distance learning technology draws on particular skills. Similarly, each distance learning technology offers a different type of social interaction. Let's look at each major distance learning technology to get a better idea of how it affects the social elements of distance education.

The technology that offers a social experience most similar to that of the conventional classroom is two-way interactive video. Even though the students may be geographically distant from one another, communication is in real time, people can see one another, and the feeling of social isolation is minimized. Kenneth Wachter, Professor of Demography at the University of California at Berkeley, offered an advanced postgraduate course in mathematical demography via two-way interactive video to students at Berkeley and the University of California at Los Angeles. He was delighted by how the two groups of students were brought together. "The thing that works best is the human back and forth," says Wachter.

Online courses can also offer social interaction, but in a new and, to some, unfamiliar form. "At first it is strange e-mailing someone you don't know. However, you get to know the person via e-mail just as you would talking or writing a letter," explains an undergraduate at the University of Maryland University College. "In the cybercafes that are provided for classmates, we talk about class work, movies, music, time management, and sports. It helps bring the class together socially." Denise Petrosino, who is enrolled in a master's program in organizational management at the University of Phoenix Online, agrees. "If you have a fear of limited interaction with the teacher and students, you can put that aside because I believe that we learn more about our teacher and classmates in the online program than in the live classroom," says Petrosino. "The reason I say this is because you get to read all correspondence between students and teacher."

In courses in which class videotapes are mailed to off-site students, the sense of social isolation is the most pronounced. That's because these courses often do not provide a means for ongoing discussion between off-site students, on-site students, and instructors. "The professors do not know much about the distance students' personalities, or even what they look like," explains Nicole DeRaleau, who lives in Connecticut and is a Master of Engineering student at Worcester Polytechnic Institute in Massachusetts. "Their interaction with us is minimal, and the closest form of personal interaction may be a telephone call, which is almost always initiated by the student." Note that some courses that rely on videotapes for instructional delivery are now moving online as well, establishing class bulletin boards on which discussions can take place, thus improving the social interaction of the off-site students.

Personality. The second factor that influences how social interaction and social isolation are perceived is an individual's personality—one person's social isolation is another person's cherished privacy. For some people, the type of interaction that characterizes distance learning is not enough to overcome a sense of social isolation. "Eye contact, vocal inflection, body language—all these elements of communication are missing [online]," explains Robert V. Steiner, who directs the distance learning project at Teachers College, Columbia University. "For some people, the sense of isolation can be significant." Joanne Simon, a student at the University of Phoenix Online who actually prefers online classes to traditional classes, admits, "I like to talk, so for me, the social interaction is lacking." Another distance learner thinks that people who are "social butterflies" will find the social interactions of distance learning unfulfilling.

On the other hand, people who are not especially extroverted may find distance learning suits them. They can participate, especially in online courses, without risking too much personal revelation.

Personal circumstances. How important is social interaction? Clearly, there must be enough interaction to facilitate learning. But for many adult students, the lack of social interaction is simply not a problem.

"For the most part, I feel detached from the class itself, and that is okay," says Brigit Dolan, a nurse who lives in Boise, Idaho, and is enrolled in Gonzaga University's Master of Science in Nursing program in Spokane, Washington. In this program, students are required to attend classes three times per semester. The remaining classes are mailed to them on videotape. "I feel okay to share my ideas and experiences when I'm there, but I'm fulfilled enough in other areas of my life that I don't yearn for that much interaction from my school life .... I just do my work, communicate with my professors and classmates occasionally, and that's about it." Like Brigit Dolan, most adult students are not looking for the social life and collegiality that are characteristics of the on-campus undergraduate experience. A librarian taking a postgraduate course at Rutgers University explains, "I don't think social interaction is a high priority in the kind of postgrad courses I take; we all have jobs and personal lives, and time is precious." Carla Gentry, a nurse enrolled in a distance learning master's program, agrees. "At my stage in life, I am not going to school for the social benefits."

How well do you work with others?

After the discussion of social interaction and social isolation, you may wonder why working well with others is important in the distance learning environment. The reason is that many instructors try to overcome the potential social isolation of the distance education course by assigning group work, thus forcing people to interact with each other.

Doing a group project in a distance learning class is challenging. The first challenge is to coordinate the activities of a group of people who are extremely busy, geographically distant from one another, and doing their work at different hours of the day and night. The second challenge is to get a group of distance learners to work together. "Since distance learners are so independent and self-motivated, they also like to do things their own way," says Brigit Dolan, who finds group projects the most challenging aspect of distance education. Trust, cooperation, and flexibility are key.

TECHNOLOGY ISSUES

Do you have the technical skills, or the willingness to acquire these skills, that may be required of a distance learning program?

Those of you who see yourselves as technologically challenged may have been dismayed by the discussion in "What Is Distance Learning?" of the technology involved in many distance learning courses. Don't be. Remember that the technology is just a tool, a means to an end, and it can be learned.

In fact, some distance learning technology is not particularly advanced from the user's point of view. For example, in two-way interactive video courses, all you have to do is learn to activate the microphone (some even activate automatically when you speak) and watch the video monitors. For prerecorded video, you just pop the videocassette into the VCR and turn on the TV. Online courses do involve a little more technological savvy. However, consider the experience of one librarian who was taking a traditional on-campus postgraduate course at Rutgers University. "My first online course was thrust upon me," she recalls. The instructor, who developed a serious health problem that prevented her from coming in to class, gave students the option of continuing online. "I, on my own, would never have chosen this mode; I was too computer-illiterate at that time. However, I quickly found that the technical skills required were really not onerous at all and that I could master them easily .... If I can succeed—no spring chicken with little technology experience—anyone can." Denise Petrosino agrees. "You do not have to be a technical genius to go to school online. If you have a computer, can log onto the Web, and know how to use e-mail, you are set."

Do you have or are you willing to gain access to the necessary equipment, which may include a computer, VCR, television, or fax machine?

Most people own a television and VCR, so these are not usually items that a new distance learner needs to purchase. However, investing in the proper computer hardware and software for a distance education program can be costly. Even if you already own a computer with Internet access, you may have to upgrade your hardware or Internet browser or purchase additional software in order to meet the minimum technical requirements of a course.

Can you tolerate dealing with technology problems?

Technology sometimes fails, and distance learners have to learn how to cope when it does. Many schools offer technical support for distance learners, and sometimes problems can be solved quickly. But if your computer system crashes for a week, you'll have to find other alternatives until you can fix the problem. "Students should be comfortable with the technology triad—fax, phone, and computer," says Claudine SchWeber of the University of Maryland University College. "Then if one goes down, they have other channels of communication."

A MINI SELF-ASSESSMENT

If you do an Internet search using the phrase "distance learning self-assessment," you will find dozens of brief quizzes designed to evaluate whether or not distance learning suits your personality, skills, and learning style. Most are posted on the Web sites of colleges and universities that offer distance education courses. For example, the Community College of Baltimore County's self-assessment test can be found at www.ccbcmd.edu/distance/access.html, and St. Louis Community College offers its self-assessment at www.stlcc.edu/Distance_Learning/Distance_Learning_Quiz.html.

For your convenience, we've provided a brief self-assessment. Although most of the online quizzes focus on Internet-based courses, this assessment is broader. Take it and see how you do!

DISTANCE LEARNING SELF-ASSESSMENT

1. When I think about how I learn, I think:
   (A) I learn best independently. I am self-motivated and like to work at my own pace. I don't need a lot of handholding.
   (B) I like to work independently, but I like to get some feedback once in a while on how I'm doing. I don't need a lot of support, just a little help every once in a while.
   (C) I can work independently, but I want to know where I stand. I like to be in an interactive situation where I get regular feedback on how I am doing.
   (D) I need lots of interaction with my teachers and peers. I like the give and take of the classroom setting. It keeps me engaged in my classes.
2. When I think about learning through different media, such as the Internet or videoconferencing, I think:
   (A) It would be exciting to be able to do my work through a different medium. The idea of sitting in a classroom does nothing for me.

(B) I am open to the idea of trying something different, like an Internet class. I would like to see how it would work for me.

(C) I'm not sure that I would be ready to work that independently. When I think of furthering my education, I see myself in a more traditional setting.

(D) I absolutely want a traditional learning experience. I want to be in a classroom setting and experience all that school has to offer.

3. When I think about interacting with my teachers, I think:

(A) I don't really care whether or not I have any face-to-face contact with my teachers. As long as I'm getting the kind of information I need to be successful in my classes, I can be satisfied as a student.

(B) I don't need a great deal of direct contact with my teachers. I'm a good, independent worker. I do want to be able to ask for help and direction when I need it.

(C) I don't need to be in a situation where I have daily conversations with my teachers, but I do like to know that they are there if I need them. I find a good teacher really helps me get excited about a topic.

(D) I really value my contacts with my teachers. I like to be able to engage in a dialogue in the classroom. A good teacher helps me connect to the subject.

4. When I think about trying to do schoolwork at home, I think:

(A) I have a great setup at home, which is conducive to studying. I like the idea of being able to work in my own space and at my own pace.

(B) I can work fairly well at home, I just have to make sure that I don't get too distracted by what is going on around me.

(C) I could work at home, but I really don't see that as an ideal situation. There is too much going on and I would be able to concentrate better in a classroom or library setting.

(D) There is no way I want to learn from home. I want to get out of the house and be in a classroom with other students.

5. When it comes to setting my schedule for learning and studying, I think:

(A) I need as much flexibility as I can get. I've got a lot of other things going on in my life and I'd really like to be able to work at my own pace.

(B) I would like to have some flexibility in scheduling my classes, but I don't want to drag it out either. I want to get through my education as quickly as possible.

(C) I like the idea of having my time fairly structured. If I don't have someone pushing me along, it may take me longer than I want to get through school.

(D) I need to have a structured schedule to keep me on task.

6. When I think about the traditional education experience, I think:

(A) Campus or classroom life doesn't really appeal to me at this stage in my life. I don't need or want the experience, for example, of living in a dorm or sitting in a classroom. I want to find an alternative way of earning my degree or certificate.

(B) I'm not sure if I want to commit to the classroom experience. It may work for me, but I'm willing to look at other ways of earning a degree.

(C) I think I would be happier if I were on a campus somewhere. I think I'd probably regret missing out on the learning experience. I wouldn't rule out the notion of being a commuter, though.

(D) I really want a traditional learning experience where I can get away from home. I'm at a point in my life where that seems to be the logical next step for me.

To evaluate your readiness for distance education, count the number of (A)s, (B)s, (C)s, and (D)s among your responses. If most of your answers were

- (A)—you should carefully investigate distance education as an option for continuing your education.

- (B)—you should investigate whether distance learning programs are suitable for meeting at least part of your educational needs. For example, you may want to complete a significant portion of your academic work through a distance learning program but still allow yourself time for some of your work to be completed in a traditional classroom setting.

- (C)—you're probably better-suited for a traditional campus-based college experience than a distance learning environment. However, some course work through a distance learning program may be a great way to supplement your on-campus course work. You should probably look for a program that will provide you with faculty or mentor feedback on a regular basis.

- (D)—you are clearly suited for a traditional classroom setting where you can have more immediate interaction with your teachers and peers. This is not to say that you may not find distance learning programs useful at some point in the future, but it sounds like you need something more hands-on so you can get immediate feedback in the classroom while enjoying the other benefits of college life.

CONCLUSION

As you have seen in this section, distance learning is not for those who lack motivation or need other people to keep them on task. On the other hand, it is perfectly suited for those who have definite educational and professional goals, are committed to getting an education, are focused and organized, can persevere when things get tough, and need the flexibility that distance education offers.

Finding the time in a busy schedule to successfully complete distance learning courses is a challenge for most adults. It's easy for work and family obligations to take precedence over getting an education. Still, distance learning makes it possible for many adults who cannot regularly attend on-campus classes to get a high-quality education. As one undergraduate distance learner commented, "For working adults (and particularly working parents), distance learning may provide the best means for obtaining an undergraduate or graduate degree from a highly respected university without interfering with life's other commitments."

WHAT CAN YOU STUDY VIA DISTANCE LEARNING?

If you are interested in pursuing your education by distance learning, you are not limited to a few specialized courses or degree programs. Actually, almost every course, certificate, and degree program that you can take on campus is also available in a distance learning format. There are exceptions, of course. Degree programs in subjects that require laboratory work or performance, for example, cannot usually be done completely at a distance. Still, distance education spans a wide range of offerings, from accredited graduate-level degree programs to self-help and hobby courses. Although some programs and courses are limited to residents of certain states or regions, many are available nationwide and internationally.

In this section we will focus on programs and courses offered by institutions of higher education, including technical institutes, community colleges, four-year colleges, and universities. Figure 3-1 shows how higher education is structured in the United States, and how distance learning programs and courses are available at most levels of postsecondary education. The exceptions are some professional degrees, such as doctor of medicine, and postdoctoral study and research. Another partial exception is the law degree (LL.B., J.D.). Although you can acquire a law degree via distance learning, at the time this book was published, no distance learning law program had been accredited by the American Bar Association. Thus, a person with a law degree from an unaccredited distance learning program will not be able to take the bar exam in most states. The accreditation issue is important in many fields besides law, and we will examine it more closely in "Selecting a Good Distance Learning Program." In this section we'll simply give you an overview of the degrees, certificates, and courses that are available via distance learning and guidance on how to find programs and courses of interest to you.

UNDERGRADUATE DEGREE PROGRAMS

Today you can earn an associate or bachelor's degree entirely by distance learning. You may also be able to shorten the time it takes to earn a degree if you transfer college credits from other institutions of higher learning, earn credits through equivalency exams, or present a portfolio of your accomplishments. For adults, earning credits for past academic and other work can cut a year or more off the time it takes to earn an undergraduate degree. So don't be shy about negotiating for credits with the school in which you plan to enroll—the time and money you save may be considerable.

ASSOCIATE DEGREE

The degree conferred by community colleges is the associate degree. Students enrolled full-time can earn an associate degree in two years, but part-time students may take much longer to earn the 60 to 64 credits required. The two most common associate degrees are the Associate of Arts (A.A.) and the Associate of Science (A.S.), although there are many other titles that range from Associate of Business Administration (A.B.A.) to Associate of General Studies (A.G.S.). Distance learning associate degrees are offered in a wide range of fields, including liberal arts, business, computer science, and health professions. Many students who have earned an associate degree go on to apply those credits toward a bachelor's degree.

BACHELOR'S DEGREE

The bachelor's degree is recognized worldwide as the first university degree a student earns. In the United States, the bachelor's degree is conferred by four-year colleges, universities, and technical institutes. Although students enrolled full-time can earn the degree in four years, many actually take up to six years. Part-time students take longer, of course, to earn the 120 to 128 credits required for the bachelor's degree.

In most colleges and universities, the course of study that leads to a bachelor's degree consists of concentrated work in a "major" such as psychology or business and wide-ranging work in a variety of subjects—the liberal arts—to give students a broad foundation of knowledge. However, some bachelor's degree programs focus on intensive study in a particular field without the broad liberal arts background.

The most common bachelor's degrees are the Bachelor of Arts (B.A.) and the Bachelor of Science (B.S.), although there are scores of other titles in use as well. Distance learning bachelor's degrees are offered in many fields, including business, engineering, computer science, economics, English, history, nursing, psychology, and telecommunications. Some colleges and universities offer interdisciplinary degrees, such as environmental studies or arts management, and some permit students to design their own interdisciplinary program.

TRANSFERRING CREDITS

Adult students who have earned some college credits during the course of their career can decrease the time it takes to earn an undergraduate degree by transferring the credits they've earned to a degree program. Many institutions of higher learning will accept transfer credits toward a degree. *Since each school's requirements vary, it's important to check before you enroll.* The school may have rules regarding the maximum number of transfer credits and the types of courses for which credit will be granted. Consult the academic advising office before you register.

EARNING CREDITS BY TAKING EXAMS

It's also possible to earn credit for prior learning if you take examinations to assess your knowledge and skills. For example, if you have worked in the human resources department of a large organization for years, you may know a lot about human resource

Figure 3–1: The Structure of Higher Education in the U.S.

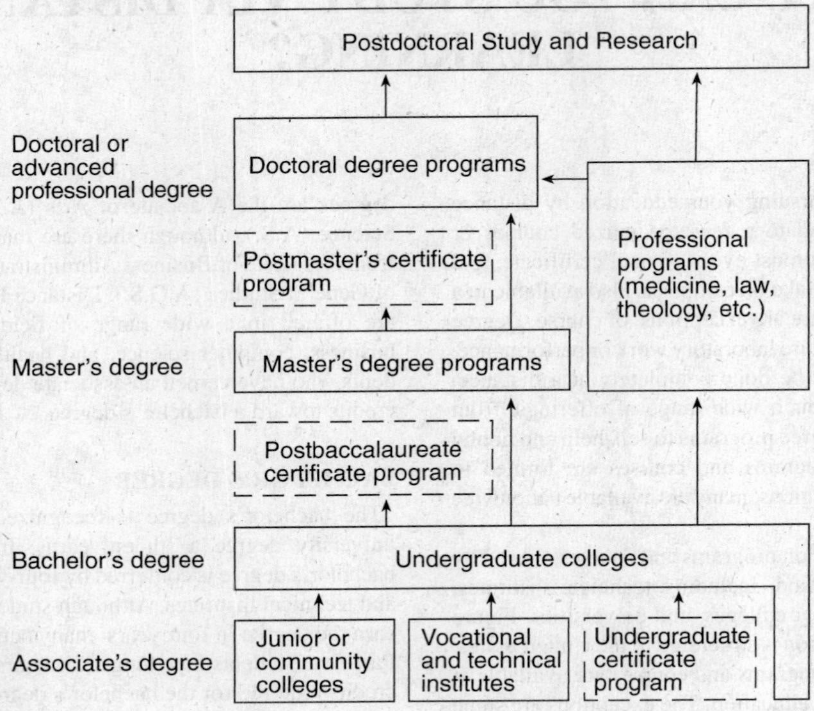

Structure of higher education in the United States. Note that the arrows indicate common pathways of students, but not the only possible pathway. *Source:* Adapted from U.S. Department of Education, National Center for Educational Statistics.

management. If you take and pass a college-level exam in human resource management, you can earn 3 credits toward your degree—without taking a course or paying tuition. Although some schools have developed their own equivalency exams, most schools accept the results of examinations taken through national programs.

CLEP Exams. The most well-known of the national equivalency exam programs is the College-Level Examination Program (CLEP), which is administered by the College Entrance Examination Board and recognized by about 2,900 colleges and universities. Most of the CLEP tests are multiple-choice exams, and some are multiple-choice and essay. There are five general exams: social sciences and history, English composition, humanities, college mathematics, and natural sciences. In addition, there are about thirty specific subject area tests, including American government, Spanish, principles of management, and introductory sociology. A good score on an exam is worth between 3 and 12 credits, it depends on the exam and the credits accepted by your school.

Earning credits by scoring well on equivalency exams can save you both time and tuition money. If you'd like more information about the CLEP exams, visit the College Board Web site at www.collegeboard.org/clep, e-mail them at clep@info.collegeboard.org, or call 800-257-9558.

Excelsior College Examinations. The Excelsior College Examination series, formerly the Regents College Examination series, is similar to the CLEP exams. The series consists of about forty subject area equivalency examinations that are 3 or 4 hours long. Subjects include anatomy and physiology, auditing, organizational behavior, and educational psychology; and the exams are recognized by almost 1,000 colleges and universities. For more information, visit the Excelsior College Web site at www.excelsior.edu, e-mail them at testadmn@excelsior.edu, or call 888-647-2388 (toll-free).

DSSTs. Another series of equivalency exams are the DSSTs. The DSSTs are examinations offered by Prometric. These tests were originally developed for military personnel but are now available for civilians as well. The tests are similar to the CLEP exams, but there are some subject areas not offered by CLEP, such as geography, criminal justice, marketing, technical writing, and ethics in America.

For more information about the DSSTs, you can check the Web site at www.getcollegecredit.com, e-mail them at getcollegecredit@prometric.com, or call 877-471-9860.

GRE Subject Tests. The Graduate Record Examination (GRE) Subject Tests, administered by the Educational Testing Service (ETS), assess knowledge that would ordinarily be acquired during the course of majoring in a subject as an undergraduate. Although they are usually used as entrance exams for graduate schools, some colleges and universities will award undergraduate credit if you get a good score. The subjects include biochemistry, cell and molecular biology; biology; chemistry; computer science; literature in English; mathematics; physics; and psychology.

For more information about the GRE Subject Tests, visit the GRE online site at www.gre.org or call 609-771-7670 or 866-473-4373.

EARNING CREDITS FOR LIFE EXPERIENCE

Many undergraduate degree programs, especially those designed for adults, give credit for knowledge and skills you've gained through life experience. Although the knowledge usually comes through paid employment, it can also be acquired through volunteer work, company or military training courses, travel, recreational activities and hobbies, and reading.

There is a catch, of course—you must document the specifics of what you have learned. It's simply not enough to say that you learned about marketing while selling widgets for XYZ Company. Instead, you must demonstrate what you have learned about pricing, promotion, and product mix; for example, showing plans for a marketing campaign. Thus, to earn credit for life experience, you should assemble a file, or portfolio, of information about your work and other accomplishments. The file may include writing samples, awards, taped presentations or performances, copies of speeches, newspaper articles, official job descriptions, military records, works of art, designs, blueprints, films, or photographs. Your portfolio is then evaluated by an institution's faculty. A student can earn as many as 30 credits—one quarter the number needed for a bachelor's degree—as the result of a good portfolio review. For example, through a portfolio evaluation, a senior marketing executive in her forties earned 30 credits, mostly in marketing and communications, toward her distance learning bachelor's degree from University of Maryland University College. For more information about assessment opportunities for adult learners, check the Web site of the Council for Adult and Experiential Learning (CAEL) at www.cael.org or call 312-499-2600.

Credit for Work Training. Since 1974, thousands of employees have been earning college credit for selected educational programs sponsored by businesses, industry, professional associations, labor unions, and government agencies. The American Council on Education's College Credit Recommendation Service evaluates such programs according to established college-level criteria and recommends college credit for those programs that measure up to these standards. You can check their Web site at www.acenet.edu, e-mail them at credit@ace.nche.edu, or call 866-205-6267.

Credit for Military Training. Service in the military, specialized training, and occupational experience have the potential to earn you college credit. Many military programs have already been evaluated in terms of their equivalency to college credit. The institutions that belong to Servicemembers Opportunity Colleges (SOC) have agreed to assess students' prior learning and accept each other's credits in transfer. To find out more, check the SOC Web site at www.soc.aascu.org, e-mail them at socmail@aascu.org, or call 800-368-5622 (toll-free).

GRADUATE DEGREE PROGRAMS

MASTER'S DEGREE

The master's degree is the first academic or professional degree earned after the bachelor's degree. A traditional, full-time master's degree student may take a year or two to earn the required 30 credits. Part-time students usually take longer; it depends on the design of the degree program. In some master's degree programs, students are simply expected to take advanced-level courses and perhaps pass a culminating exam. In others, original research and a thesis are also required. Some distance learning master's degree programs have a brief residency requirement. Students usually earn a Master of Arts (M.A.), a Master of Science (M.S.), or a Master of Business Administration (M.B.A.) degree.

At the time this book was published, distance learning master's degree programs outnumbered other distance learning degree programs by a considerable margin. Most of these degree programs are professional in nature and are designed for working adults with experience in the field. If you are interested in a master's degree in library science, business, or education, you are in luck. These are fields in which there are many distance master's degree programs from which to choose.

However, if you are looking for a distance learning master's degree program in an academic field, such as English language and literature, chemistry, or ethnic and cultural studies, your choices are far more limited. That's because most master's programs in academic fields are campus based.

Another type of master's degree that is offered via distance learning is the interdisciplinary degree. Some are offered in liberal studies or humanities and are granted for advanced study and a culminating project or thesis. Others combine academic and professional areas of study. Still others are offered in broad subject areas like environmental studies, in which students are expected to design their own course of study based on their particular interests.

In the future, the number of distance academic and interdisciplinary master's degree programs is likely to increase, but far more slowly than the number of professional degree programs, for which the demand is much greater.

DOCTORAL DEGREE

The doctoral degree, the highest degree awarded, is earned after an advanced course of study that usually culminates in original research and a dissertation, an extended written work. The traditional on-campus doctoral student takes four to ten years to complete the degree, but many distance learning doctoral programs are structured to streamline the process. Thus, some doctoral degrees can be earned in as little as three years. Most distance learning doctoral programs, even those offered by virtual universities like the University of Phoenix Online, have a brief residency requirement. The Doctor of Philosophy (Ph.D.) is the most common doctoral degree; it is awarded in fields that range from philosophy to geology to communication. Other frequently awarded doctoral degrees include the Doctor of Education (Ed.D.), Doctor of Business Administration (D.B.A.), Doctor of Engineering (Eng.D.), and Doctor of Psychology (Psy.D.). There are far fewer distance learning doctoral programs than master's programs. However, you can find programs in a wide range of fields, although the number of programs within each field may be limited. You can earn a distance learning doctoral degree in fields as diverse as business, engineering, computer science, counseling psychology, instructional technology, education, human services, library science, English literature, management, pharmacy, and public policy. As with distance learning master's degrees, distance learning doctoral degrees tend to be professional rather than academic. Many of these degree programs are designed with the professional working adult in mind.

EARNING GRADUATE-LEVEL CREDIT FOR KNOWLEDGE AND EXPERIENCE

There is disagreement among institutions of higher education about whether to award graduate-level credit for knowledge acquired outside academia. At present, many graduate schools do not offer credit to students for knowledge and experience acquired before enrollment in the program, no matter how deep or extensive that knowledge and experience may be. However, other less conservative institutions are more open to granting graduate credit for life experience. Check with the schools and programs in which you are interested to see what their policies are.

CERTIFICATE PROGRAMS

Distance learning certificate programs can train you for a new career or give you a foundation in a new subject even if you've already earned a college degree in an entirely different field. A certificate program usually consists of around six to ten courses, all focused on a single profession or subject, and it can be earned at the undergraduate or graduate level. Some schools now offer a portion of a master's or other degree as a certificate. This allows you to take part of the full degree curriculum and either stop at the certification level or proceed through for the entire degree. If this is an option that interests you, be sure to consider the admissions requirements carefully. If you think you may matriculate through to the entire degree, be sure you understand the admissions requirements for each program because they may differ.

PROFESSIONAL CERTIFICATE PROGRAMS

To give you just a few examples of professional certificate programs offered via distance learning, within the engineering profession there are certificates in computer-integrated manufacturing, systems engineering, and fire-protection engineering. In business, there are distance learning certificate programs in information technology and health services management. In education, distance learning certificates include early reading instruction, children's literature, and English as a second language. In health care, certificates include medical assisting, home health nursing, and health-care administration. In law, distance learning certificates are offered in paralegal/legal assistant studies and legal issues for business professionals.

Professional certificate programs are often designed with the help of professional associations and licensing boards, and thus encompass real-world, practical knowledge. Many are designed to prepare students for professional certification or licensure. At the end of the program, the student sits for an exam and earns a state-recognized certificate from a certifying agency or licensing board. *If this is your goal, you should make sure that the certification program you want to take meets the certifying agency or licensing board's requirements.* That way, you won't waste your time or money completing a program that won't help you meet your ultimate professional goals.

CERTIFICATE PROGRAMS IN ACADEMIC SUBJECTS

Less common, but still available via distance learning, are undergraduate and graduate certificate programs in many aca-

demic subjects. At the undergraduate level, you can earn a certificate in areas such as American studies, Chinese language and literature, English composition, creative writing, ethnic and cultural studies, general studies, humanities, and liberal arts and sciences. If you later enroll in an undergraduate degree program, you may be able to apply the credits earned in a certificate program toward your degree.

At the graduate level, you can earn a certificate via distance learning in subjects like biology, English language and literature, geography, physiological psychology, religious studies, and statistics.

INDIVIDUAL COURSES

If you are seeking to update your professional skills, acquire specialized knowledge, earn a few credits toward a degree, or simply take a class for your own pleasure, individual distance learning courses may be for you. Many institutions of higher education venture into distance learning by offering a few classes scattered throughout various departments. As their experience with distance education increases, they begin to offer complete programs of study. Thus, if you are interested in just taking a few courses, you have the widest range of choices. You can find individual courses in subjects that range from accounting to animal sciences and from art history to aviation—and that's just a random sample beginning with the letter *A*.

There are several options that may be open to you when you take an individual course, such as taking the course for credit, taking it without earning credit, or earning Continuing Education Units (CEUs). The option you select depends on your purpose for taking the course.

TAKING A COURSE FOR CREDIT

If you are enrolled in a degree program and need a few credits, taking a distance learning course may help you satisfy your degree requirements. Your own college or university may offer courses via distance learning. In fact, students enrolled in conventional on-campus degree programs sometimes take distance learning courses from their schools when they go home for the summer. For example, Iowa's Drake University offers online summer courses to its students.

If your own institution does not offer suitable distance learning courses, you may be able to take a distance education course from any regionally accredited college or university and get credit for it. You may even be able to save some tuition money if you select a course at a community college or a less expensive four-year college or university. The credits you earn will probably be transferable to the institution in which you are enrolled. *But before you enroll in a course at another college or university, be sure to check with your own school to make sure it will accept the credits.* Many colleges and universities require that you obtain a minimum number of credits from core courses and courses in your major in order to earn their degree. To avoid losing time and money on a course that won't be recognized by your school, it's wise to check with your academic adviser and work out a degree plan before you take courses from other institutions. If you are not currently enrolled in a degree program but think you may be in the future, taking a couple of distance education courses for credit is a good way to see whether or not a distance education degree program is for you. Later you may be able to apply the credits toward your degree.

NONCREDIT COURSES

If learning for the sake of learning or acquiring specific professional knowledge is your goal, taking a distance education course on a noncredit basis may be the way to go. Such courses may help you prepare for a new career or study for professional licensure and certification.

Just as you can audit an on-campus course for a lesser charge than if you were taking the course for credit, you can audit a distance learning course as well. Students who audit a course don't receive a grade, so they are not usually required to turn in assignments or take exams. Still, many do so in order to maximize the learning experience.

CONTINUING EDUCATION UNITS

Distance learning is a good option for working adults whose professions require continuing education, even after they've earned their degree, certificate, or license. Many states mandate continuing education for people in professions such as teaching, nursing, and accounting. For example, New Jersey requires teachers to complete 100 hours of professional development work every five years. Professionals in engineering, business, and computer science may also opt to keep up with developments in their field through distance learning. If you take a distance learning course for professional enhancement, you don't necessarily have to earn regular college credits for it. Instead, you may be able to earn CEUs. The CEU system is a nationally recognized program that provides a standardized measure for accumulating, transferring, and recognizing participation in continuing education programs. One CEU is defined as 10 contact hours of participation in an organized continuing education experience under responsible sponsorship, capable direction, and qualified instruction. Some institutions will permit you to take courses for

continuing education credits rather than for regular credit or no credit. It is still important to take the courses from a properly accredited program, however, so that employers and professional agencies will recognize them.

FINDING PROGRAMS AND COURSES

THE INTERNET

The Internet is an excellent place to start your search for information about distance learning courses and programs. One Internet database is the International Distance Learning Course Finder, provided by International Where and How. When you search for a course, you can specify course subject, course name, country, or institution; and you can narrow the search by language of instruction, mode of instructional technology, and type of credit you are seeking. The Course Finder seems to work well for locating individual courses, but it seems less efficient when asked to locate degree programs.

If you have particular institutions in mind, you can log on to their Web sites to find out about their distance learning courses and degrees. Some of these sites provide distance learning self-assessments and explanations of course delivery systems as well as academic information about courses and programs.

PRINT DIRECTORIES

Print directories are another excellent source of information about distance education courses and degree programs, although one should adhere to this word of caution about using the print directories: There are many directories still in libraries and bookstores that were published just a year or two ago but that are already quite out of date. So many new distance learning courses and degree programs are being offered each year that you must make sure you consult the most recent directories. Otherwise, you may miss the ideal course or program for you.

WHO OFFERS DISTANCE EDUCATION?

As communication technologies have improved and the need for continuous lifelong learning has increased, the nature of postsecondary education has begun to change. Traditional colleges and universities, which used to be the sole purveyors of higher education, now find themselves competing with a range of unconventional providers, including corporate universities, for-profit virtual universities, and unaffiliated distance learning providers. From the student's point of view, the array of institutions that offer distance learning can be confusing. What difference does it make to you whether you take a distance learning course or program from a traditional college, through a consortium of institutions of higher education, from one of the new virtual universities, or from an unaffiliated online provider?

Whether or not the institution matters depends on your purpose. If you just take a few courses for professional development or for your own pleasure and never plan to seek certification or college credit, then your choice of institution is not critical. You can just choose the distance learning provider that seems to have the courses that best suit your informal needs. However, if you plan to earn college credit, professional certification, or a degree, your choice of provider becomes much more important. You must choose an institution whose courses and degrees are widely recognized and accepted in your field. That may mean sticking to the accredited bricks-and-mortar colleges for distance learning programs, or it may mean enrolling in an innovative degree program from a virtual university only a few years old. In this section, we'll describe some of the institutions and partnerships that offer distance learning in order to acquaint you with the variety of providers that exists. In the next section, we will explain some criteria that you can use to evaluate distance education offerings.

TRADITIONAL COLLEGES AND UNIVERSITIES

The most familiar group of distance education providers consists of the traditional colleges, universities, graduate schools, community colleges, technical schools, and vocational schools. In these institutions, distance education arose as individual administrators and faculty members took the initiative to use new technologies to deliver off-campus instruction to students. As the number of courses grew, many institutions developed whole degree programs as the next step.

Among the traditional colleges and universities, public institutions are more likely to offer distance education courses and degree programs than private institutions. In addition, larger institutions are more likely to have distance learning offerings than smaller institutions.

The greatest advantage that most traditional colleges and universities bring to the distance education field is that they are established, well-known institutions with reputable faculty members and lots of experience in education. In other words, they enter the distance learning market with solid educational credentials. If they fall short, it is likely to be in the areas of instructional and information technology. Because a lot of distance education courses are developed ad hoc, the quality of the instructional technology may vary considerably, even from one course to another within the same school. In addition, traditional colleges and universities may fall short in information technology support for faculty members and students. For example, the Gartner Group, an information technology research organization, recommends that organizations have one information technology staff person for every 50 to 75 users. In contrast, colleges and universities report an average of one technical support person for every 150 to 800 users. Recognizing this shortcoming, many colleges and universities have established policies and procedures to set up instructional technology standards and consistency, and they have increased their technical resources and training efforts to support faculty members and students. In addition, because developing quality distance education courses and programs is time-consuming and expensive, colleges and universities have begun to form partnerships to pool their resources. These partnerships, called consortia, have quickly developed into major players in the world of distance higher education.

CONSORTIA

Distance learning consortia are associations or partnerships of higher education institutions that have agreed to cooperate to provide distance learning courses and resources. Most consortia are designed to provide students with a greater selection of both courses and faculty expertise than is available at a single institution. Some consortia also offer centralized student and faculty support services. Just as there are many variations on the basic on-campus program, there are many distance education consortium models too.

It's important to remember that most distance learning consortia are not degree-granting institutions to which the student applies. Though there are exceptions to this, as in the case of Western Governors University and National Technological University (discussed later in the section), students normally apply directly to at least one school in the consortium as a means of accessing the resources of other member institutions.

Almost without exception, accredited universities in consortia have roughly the same application procedures and admissions requirements for distance degree programs as for traditional campus-based programs. In general, minimum grade point averages, standardized test scores of a certain percentile, and letters of recommendation or intent are required for both bachelor's and master's degree programs. The exception is the competency-based program that waives academic credentials and previous schooling and instead uses workplace experience and learned skill-based assessments to place students. So why do you need to know about consortia if you probably will never apply to one? The answer is that by enrolling in a college or university degree program, you may find yourself in a consortium without even realizing it, especially if you attend a state university.

TYPES OF CONSORTIA

Over the last few years, several types of consortia have emerged as the most successful and most popular distance education models. Among them are statewide consortia of public universities and colleges, statewide consortia of public and private institutions, regional consortia, and consortia of peer institutions of higher education.

Statewide Consortia of Public Colleges and Universities. On the tightly focused side of the spectrum, a consortium may consist of the campuses of a single state university system. Students access the distance learning offerings of the various state colleges through a portal sometimes referred to as a virtual university.

A good example of a public statewide consortium is the University of Texas TeleCampus collaboration, which consists of fifteen UT campuses (www.telecampus.utsystem.edu). In collaborative degree plans offered via the TeleCampus, you may apply to one school, take courses from several partner institutions, use centralized support services, and receive a fully accredited degree from the "home" campus to which you originally applied. The TeleCampus serves as both a portal to distance education offerings in the Texas system and as a centralized point of service.

Many other states operate or develop consortia of their public colleges and universities, including Connecticut, Illinois, Kansas, Massachusetts, Michigan, New Jersey, New York, Ohio, Oklahoma, Oregon, South Dakota, and Tennessee. All have arrangements in place whereby students can take some transferable credits online from more than one institution and apply them to a degree at their home institution.

Statewide Consortia of Public and Private Colleges and Universities. Broadening the scope a bit is the statewide consortium that includes both public and private institutions of higher education. Students in the state can use a single Web site to select distance education courses offered by member colleges and universities. If you are enrolled in a degree program at one member institution, you have access to distance learning courses given by other member institutions. Although the consortia members typically work together to maximize the transferability of credits from one college or university to another, it is still usually up to you to ensure that credits earned elsewhere can be applied to your home institution's degree.

For example, Kentucky Virtual Campus (KYVC) encompasses more than fifty institutions in the state of Kentucky, ranging from universities to technical colleges (www.kyvc.org). Each member institution charges its own tuition rates for in-state and out-of-state students. In addition to maintaining a centralized Internet directory of all distance learning courses offered in Kentucky, KYVC offers exceptional student support services. For example, you can fill out a common form to apply online to any of the fifty member institutions. Once you are admitted to the KYVC system, you have centralized online access to every library book in the system as well as online access to the full text of 5,000 journals. If you wish to check out a book, it will be sent to the nearest public library, where you can pick it up free of charge. If there is no library nearby, the book will be sent by courier to your home or office. Your academic records will be maintained by each institution at which you take a course, but also by KYVC, which will keep your complete records from all institutions.

Regional Consortia. Regional consortia include institutions of higher education from more than one state. Such consortia may involve public institutions, private institutions, or a mix of both. The Southern Regional Education Board (SREB) launched the Electronic Campus in 1998 and now offers more than 3,200 courses from 262 colleges and universities in sixteen states (www.electroniccampus.org). The Electronic Campus attempts to guarantee a standard of quality in the courses it lists by reviewing them to make sure they are well set up and supported by adequate services. It does not judge curriculum (it leaves that to member institutions) nor does it list courses in their first year of instruction.

From the Electronic Campus Web site, you can identify distance learning programs and courses that are available from all member institutions. For more detailed information, you can search the site by college or university, discipline, level, and state, including course descriptions and how the programs and courses are delivered. You can also connect directly to a particular college or university to learn about registration, enrollment, and cost.

The Electronic Campus system is administratively decentralized. The acceptance of transfer credits and the use of credits for program requirements are determined by the college or university in which the student is enrolled. Likewise, all institutions set their own levels for in-state and out-of-state tuition, maintain individual student records, and determine policy with respect to access to their own student services. Therefore, if you take three classes from three different institutions you might have to be admitted to all three, pay three different tuition rates, and contact all three institutions for your academic records. A unique model of regional distance education collaboration, consisting of members from nineteen states, is Western Governors University (www.wgu.edu). Unlike most other virtual universities that serve as the hub of a consortium, WGU enrolls its own students and grants its own degrees by assessing students' knowledge through competency-based examinations. WGU does not teach its own courses, but it provides its students with access to courses from member institutions.

Other regional consortia include the National Universities Degree Consortium, a collaboration of ten accredited universities from across the United States (www.nudc.org); and the Canadian Virtual University, which includes seven universities across Canada (www.cvu-uvc.ca). Today, students can even choose to participate in a global consortium like CREAD, the Inter-American network of institutions throughout North, Central, and South America.

Consortia of Peer Institutions of Higher Education. Groups of institutions sometimes form consortia because they have a common orientation or complementary strengths from which students might benefit.

For example, the Jesuit Distance Education Network (JesuitNET) of the Association of Jesuit Colleges and Universities seeks to expand the array of learning options for students on its twenty-four campuses in nineteen states (www.ajcunet.edu). Administrators hope to develop the JesuitNET system so that a student enrolled at any member institution will be able to take fully transferable online courses at any other member institution. Tuition rates will be set by individual colleges and universities. Through its Web site, JesuitNET promotes these schools' online degree and certificate programs as well as individual courses.

PROS AND CONS OF CONSORTIA LEARNING MODELS

One obvious advantage of consortia is the pooling of resources. More university partners translates to more choices in curriculum, and often a shared expense in developing instructional design and technology. Consortia can offer a centralized database or course schedule that allows you to find members' courses easily rather than having to search many institutions' materials and Web sites for what you need. You may also have the chance to choose from among a group of respected faculty members from within the consortia, which allows you to find the teachers with expertise most closely suited to your academic and professional interests. This large sampling of faculty members tends to offer a more diverse worldview in the classroom. And, a consortium can often provide essential student services on a scale not fiscally achievable by a single university. For example, a dozen universities can pool resources for a much broader digital library than any single school could supply on its own.

However, from the student's point of view, consortia can have problems, many of which can be attributed to their relative newness. The most critical of these for students are problems with transferring credits. Other drawbacks may include large class sizes and problems in communication.

Problems with Transferring Credits. One problem that sometimes comes up for students trying to earn an entire degree, or part of a degree, online is that their home institution may require a minimum number of "home" credits, yet it may not offer enough courses via distance learning for a student to meet that minimum. "I am concerned because [my home campus] offers a limited number of online classes," says Andrea Bessel, who is working toward a bachelor's degree in business administration with a concentration in finance. Bessel, who works full time and prefers the convenience of online to on-campus courses, has been taking classes from several institutions in the State University of New York (SUNY) Learning Network (www.sln.suny.edu). "It is great that other SUNY campuses offer more courses," continues Bessel, "but I am concerned about accumulating too many transfer credits—you are only allowed so many."

In the future, this problem is likely to arise less often for several reasons. First, as distance education degree programs become more common and well known, students are likely to search them out and apply directly to the institution that offers them. In contrast, like many other students, Bessel applied to her local state college campus and only later discovered that taking online courses within the statewide system was much more convenient than traveling to class. Second, individual institutions will continue to add to their distance education offerings, broadening the course choices for their "home" students. And third, some state systems and other consortia may eventually decide to liberalize their rules on transfer credit maximums within the consortium as the demand for distance degrees increases.

Indeed, some consortia have already succeeded in solving credit transfer problems, and others are addressing the challenge of reconciling differing credit transfer policies and logistics. *However,*

to ensure that any courses you take will successfully transfer from one institution to another (and ultimately toward your degree), you should secure an academic adviser at the start of your program and investigate the transferability of credits before you register for courses at other institutions within the consortium. Serving as your own adviser brings the risk that some courses may ultimately not transfer toward your degree.

Large Class Size. Because so many students have access to courses in a consortium, online classes may reach an unmanageable size if limits are not placed on the student-to-teacher ratio. Many schools now adopt a ceiling on the number of students allowed in an online class, with teaching assistants or subsections of the course added for each additional set of students. This is vital to the processing of information and interaction required in the successful online course. Faculty members often find that a class of 25 students is quite manageable, but more may become problematic.

Miscommunication. Communication may be difficult in a consortium. The larger the consortium, the more likely that many universities or university systems are involved, and therefore you may need to communicate with several institutions that have differing policies and procedures. Additional communication snags can arise when you try to move your student records from one campus to the next. Some consortia have spent considerable time, effort, and money to make this tedious and laborious process appear seamless to you as a student. For those that have not, you should be prepared to take a proactive stance in helping to see that your records are successfully moved from one department, college, or university to another.

COMPARING THE SINGLE UNIVERSITY TO THE CONSORTIUM

A student who is looking for a learning community with school pride and a great deal of local loyalty may find the multicampus environment of a consortium less desirable than the collegiality of the single university environment. In today's workplace and economy, however, many students opt for the flexibility and increased curriculum choices of a consortium over an individual school. Many consortia have succeeded in creating a sense of community for learners, and many more are attempting to do so. The high level of dialogue in the online environment can often build friendships, connections, and communities not achieved in a traditional environment. A single university can offer you the chance to immerse yourself in one department (of your major, for example), but a consortium can offer a wider variety of choices in mentors and philosophies. As a student, you should think about which you'd prefer.

VIRTUAL UNIVERSITIES

In recent years, the development of communication technology has led to a new type of institution called a virtual university. It's a school without a campus that delivers instruction and degree programs exclusively via technology and usually for a profit. The University of Phoenix Online, Walden University, the United States Open University, and Jones International University are all examples of virtual universities. Some of these institutions have years of experience in distance learning and have evolved as the technologies have changed. For example, Walden University is more than thirty years old, and the University of Phoenix Online was established in 1989 as an offshoot of the University of Phoenix, which was founded in 1976. Others, like the United States Open University, are newly established with a much shorter track record. What most of these institutions have in common is a focus on education for adults. Their course offerings, degree programs, and student services are all geared toward the busy working adult who needs the flexibility of distance education. For example, courses at the University of Phoenix Online are delivered via the Internet. Students take one 5-week course at a time, which allows them to focus their effort intensively on one subject. Student services can be accessed via the university Web site. "We are customer-service oriented," says Russell Paden, regional executive director of academic affairs at the University of Phoenix Online. "We make things easy and convenient for the student." Virtual universities have a mixed reputation in the world of higher education. Although their degrees are accepted by many employers, they are often looked down upon by traditional academics. A few are regionally accredited, some are too new to be accredited, and some are modern versions of the old diploma mills (see "Selecting a Good Distance Learning Program" for more on accreditation).

From a student's point of view, then, the biggest disadvantage of a virtual university may be its less-than-stellar educational repu-

tation, whether deserved or not. A great advantage of the best of these institutions, however, is that they tend to be sophisticated in terms of instructional technology and design and technical support. To the student, this can mean ease, convenience, and flexibility.

THE NEW ONLINE PROVIDERS

The growth of the distance learning market in higher education, continuing education, and training has attracted investors and educators who are eager to provide courses to adults, primarily via the Internet. There are many of these startup ventures, and they take many forms. The following are examples to illustrate:

- The Global Education Network (GEN) offers distance education courses from some of the top colleges in the United States, including Brown, Wellesley, and Williams.
- KaplanCollege.com offers graduate courses for teachers through the John F. Kennedy University.

In the coming years, the new online providers will begin to sort themselves out as some models succeed and some fail. If you are taking courses through your employer or for personal reasons, you may find that one of these companies has courses that meet your needs. If, however, you are looking for a degree program, you are better off sticking with well-established institutions of higher education, at least at present.

SELECTING A GOOD DISTANCE LEARNING PROGRAM

As a prospective distance learning student, you should begin to evaluate programs in which you are interested as much as you would any campus-based, traditional program. The first question, of course, is: Does the curriculum meet your educational and professional goals? If it doesn't, there's not much point in looking into that program any further, however flexible and convenient it seems. If the program does seem to meet your educational needs, then the real work of evaluating it must begin.

Distance education students need to be especially concerned about the quality of the programs they are considering for two main reasons. First, there are a lot of diploma mills out there. As we've seen, there has been a proliferation of distance learning degree programs spurred by the Internet. Many are legitimate, but some are not. As one distance bachelor's degree student put it, "Admission to some online programs consists of nothing more than your name, date of birth, and a check." In fact, to demonstrate how easy it is to set up an online "university" that looks authentic, Emir Mohammed created a Web site for Oxford Open University, a fictitious virtual university, complete with a list of imaginary faculty members with degrees from bogus institutions. So if you run across a school that promises you a degree for little time, effort, or money, be cautious. If it sounds too good to be true, it probably is.

The second reason distance learning students must be especially careful about quality is that in many quarters, distance degrees are still considered the poor relations of degrees earned on campus. "One area of confusion for working adult students is the reaction to distance learning from traditional academia," says Russell Paden, regional executive director of academic affairs for the University of Phoenix Online. "Although attitudes are changing, some in the traditional academic world still think their way is the only way." Robert V. Steiner, who directs the distance learning project at Teachers College, Columbia University, agrees. "For better or worse, justly or not," he says, "there continues to be a perception that distance education degree programs are inferior to traditional programs." Fritz J. Messere, associate professor of broadcasting at the State University of New York at Oswego, thinks that in five or six years, that attitude will change. "When we see what the people with distance degrees actually accomplish in the future, our reluctance to acknowledge that these are real degrees and meaningful educational experiences will disappear."

However, in the meantime you need to evaluate each distance education program that looks promising to ensure that its certificate or degree will be of value to you in the future. What can you do to ensure that a distance credential will be recognized in the academic, professional, and/or business communities? What can you do to assess whether or not the program and the university are of high quality? Basically, you must do a lot of research. You must gather information from the program, university, accrediting agencies, professional associations, faculty, current and former students, and colleagues. Only then can you make an informed decision about whether a program is good as well as right for you.

To guide you in this task, this section describes some of the criteria you should keep in mind as you evaluate each distance education program. *Pay particular attention to the sections on reputation and accreditation.* More than any other factors, a school and program's reputation and accreditation status can serve as benchmarks of quality that will affect the value of your degree.

REPUTATION

"Look for a brand name—a recognized university," suggests Fritz J. Messere of SUNY Oswego. For many students, the reputation of the school is the paramount factor in selecting a program. Sonja Cole, a middle-school media specialist who is enrolled in a continuing professional education program at Rutgers University in New Jersey, explains, "I know that Rutgers has an excellent reputation for academic rigor, so I assumed that their online courses would be just as challenging and stimulating." She continues, "The most important factor to me was the reputation of the school, because distance learning programs are not always taken seriously by administrators and business people . . . . If you can say you took distance courses at a very reputable school, they will be more likely to give you credit." Not only should you consider the reputation of a university in general, you should consider the reputation of a distance degree from a university *in your field*. For example, if you plan to earn a bachelor's degree at a distance to prepare for graduate work, find out whether or not graduate programs in your field will accept an undergraduate distance degree, even from a reputable institution.

"If you are in doubt about the validity of a distance degree in your chosen field, ask around," advises Patti Wolf, assistant professor of computer science at University of Maryland University College. When Wolf was looking for a doctoral program for herself, almost all of her colleagues advised her that a distance degree would not be as well accepted in her chosen career as a traditional degree. Another doctoral student, who is earning an Ed.D. from a relatively new virtual university, regrets that "the one thing I didn't do [was] speak to administrators in local universities to review the reputation of the school I finally chose. Even though the program is still exactly what I wanted and the convenience, schedule, and costs meet my needs, the public perception of this program is not wonderful." Carla Gentry, who is earning a distance master's degree in nursing (nurse-practitioner) at Gonzaga University in Washington, puts the importance of reputation succinctly: "You wouldn't want to spend all that time and money and then find out that the degree isn't worth anything."

ACCREDITATION

The accreditation status of a college, university, or program can give you an indication of its general quality and reputation. But just what does accreditation mean, and how does it affect distance learners?

WHAT IS ACCREDITATION?

In the United States, authority over postsecondary educational institutions is decentralized. The states, not the federal government, have the authority to regulate educational institutions within their borders, and as a consequence, standards and quality vary considerably for "state-approved" schools. You will find many state-approved schools that are not accredited, and many that are.

In order to ensure a basic level of quality, the practice of accrediting institutions arose. Private, nongovernmental educational agencies with a regional or national scope have adopted standards to evaluate whether or not colleges and universities provide educational programs at basic levels of quality. Institutions that seek accreditation conduct an in-depth self-study to measure their performance against the standards. The accrediting agency then conducts an on-site evaluation and either awards accreditation or preaccreditation status—or denies accreditation. Periodically the agency reevaluates each institution to make sure its continued accreditation is warranted. So accreditation is not a one-shot deal—an institution must maintain high standards or it runs the risk of jeopardizing its accreditation status as a result of one of the periodic evaluations.

Seeking accreditation is entirely voluntary on the part of the institution of higher education. The initial accreditation process takes a long time—as much as five or ten years—and it costs money. You can see that a very new school will not have been in operation long enough to be accredited.

INSTITUTIONAL AND SPECIALIZED ACCREDITATION

There are two basic types of accreditation: institutional accreditation and specialized accreditation. Institutional accreditation is awarded to an institution by one of six regional accrediting agencies and many national accrediting agencies, such as the Distance Education and Training Council. The regional accrediting agencies play the largest role in institutional accreditation (see the Appendix for a list of the regional accrediting agencies). If a college or university is regionally accredited, that means that the institution as a whole has met the accrediting agency's standards. Within the institution, particular programs and departments contribute to the institution's objectives at varying levels of quality. There are several benefits of enrolling in a program at a regionally accredited college or university:

- You are assured of a basic level of quality education and services.

- Any credits you earn are more likely to be transferable to other regionally accredited institutions, although we've seen that each institution makes its own decisions on transfer credits on a case-by-case basis.

- Any certificate or degree you earn is more likely to be recognized by other colleges and universities and by employers as a legitimate credential.

- You may qualify for federal loans and grants because regionally accredited institutions are eligible to participate in Title IV financial aid programs (see "Paying for Your Education" for more on financial aid).

In contrast to institutional accreditation, specialized accreditation usually applies to a single department, program, or school that is part of a larger institution of higher education. The accredited unit may be as big as a college within a university or as small as a curriculum within a field of study. Most specialized accrediting agencies review units within institutions that are regionally accredited, although some also accredit freestanding institutions. There are specialized accrediting agencies in almost fifty fields, including allied health, art and design, Bible college education, business, engineering, law, marriage and family therapy, nursing, psychology, and theology. Specialized accreditation may or may not be a consideration for you when you evaluate distance education programs. That's because the role of specialized accreditation varies considerably depending on the field of study. In some professional fields, you must have a degree or certificate from a program with specialized accreditation in order to take qualifying exams or practice the profession. In other fields, specialized accreditation has little or no effect on your ability to work. Thus, it's especially important that you find out what role accreditation plays in your field since it may affect your professional future as well as the quality of your education.

CHECKING ON A SCHOOL AND ITS ACCREDITORS

Since accreditation is awarded by private organizations, any group can hang out a shingle and proclaim itself an accrediting agency. Some diploma mills, for example, have been known to create their own accrediting agency and then proclaim themselves "accredited." So how can you tell (1) if the school or college in which you are interested is regionally accredited, (2) if the program has the specialized accreditation you need, and (3) if the agencies that have accredited the school and program are legitimate? Of course, you can simply ask the school or program, but since accreditation is so important, it's probably a lot wiser to check elsewhere.

First, check with the regional accrediting agency that covers the state in which the school is located. Then check with any specialized accrediting agency that may assess the particular program in which you are interested.

To find out if an accrediting agency is legitimate and nationally recognized, you can consult the Council for Higher Education Accreditation (CHEA), a private agency that accredits the accreditors (www.chea.org). Or you can check with the U.S. Department of Education. Their Web site has a complete list of institutional and specialized accrediting agencies recognized by the federal government (www.ed.gov/admins/finaid/accred/index.html). This Web site will also tell you whether or not accreditation by a particular agency makes the school eligible to participate in federal financial aid programs. A list of regional and specialized accrediting agencies, with contact information, is also provided in the Appendix.

CHECKING ON CANADIAN INSTITUTIONS OF HIGHER EDUCATION

In Canada, as in the United States, there is no centralized governmental accrediting agency. Instead, the provincial governments evaluate the quality of university programs in each province, with a few nationwide agencies evaluating professional programs. To check on a Canadian university, you can contact the appropriate provincial department of education. To get general information about accreditation in Canada, visit the Web site of the Council of Ministers of Education at www.cmec.ca. Their Web site also has contact information and links to the provincial departments of education.

CHECKING ON AN UNACCREDITED INSTITUTION

As we've seen, seeking accreditation is a voluntary process, and some legitimate schools choose not to undertake it. In addition, the newer virtual universities may not have been around long enough to be accredited. So what can you do to make sure a school is legitimate if it is not accredited?

First, you can call the state agency with jurisdiction over higher education in the state in which the school is located. The agency can at least tell you whether or not the school is operating with a legitimate charter, and it may be able to tell you if any complaints have been lodged or legal action taken against it. Second, you can call the school and ask why it is not accredited and whether the school has plans to seek accreditation. If the school tells you it has applied for accreditation, double-check its status with the agency it names. Third, you can consult with people in your field about the school's reputation and the value of its degree. Remember, in some fields, a degree from an unaccredited school or program will bar you from professional licensure and practice. So keep in mind that enrolling in an unaccredited school or program can be risky. If you can avoid it, do so.

ACCREDITATION ISSUES RELATING TO DISTANCE EDUCATION

In the United States during the 1990s, controversy arose over the accreditation of online programs within traditional universities and the accreditation of completely virtual universities. On the one hand, many felt that online degree programs should be evaluated using the same criteria as other degree programs within institutions of higher education. Others thought that new standards were needed to properly evaluate distance education.

Although this issue has not yet been settled, the six regional accrediting agencies have proposed uniform guidelines for evaluating distance education. The impetus for this move is the fact that many distance education programs cross regional borders; the agencies want to ensure that similar standards are adopted across the country. Among the proposed criteria specific to accrediting distance education are faculty control of course content, technical and program support for both faculty members and students, and evaluation and assessment methods for measuring student learning. However, until these or other guidelines are accepted, distance education programs will continue to be evaluated using the same criteria as on-campus programs.

PROGRAM QUALITY

The reputation of a college or university and its accreditation status can give you a broad idea of its standing in the academic and professional world. If you are pursuing a graduate degree or know your field of interest as an undergraduate, it's important to separate the reputation of the program or department in which you are interested from the reputation of the university to which it belongs. Granted, in many cases, both the program and the university will have similar reputations. But in some cases, you may find a below average program at an excellent university or an above average program at a university with a lesser reputation.

Keep in mind that you should be looking for a high-quality curriculum and good faculty; the fact that the program is taught at a distance should be secondary. "I chose this program because it would have been one of my top three choices if I had decided to pursue a full-time [on-campus] master's program," explains Lara Hollenczer, who is earning a distance master's degree in communications management at Syracuse University. Hollenczer suggests talking to professors and current students to get a better idea of a program in which you are interested.

ACADEMIC QUALITY

One way to assess the quality of a program, as we have seen, is to find out whether or not it is accredited by a specialized agency—if that applies in your field. But there are other ways to assess a program's academic quality. First, look at the curriculum. Does it cover what you need to learn? Is the syllabus up to date? For one master's degree student in nursing (family nurse practitioner studies), the quality of the curriculum was the factor that led her to choose Gonzaga University. "I definitely wanted to know that when I graduated I would have a good education and know what I was doing," she explains.

Next, check some of the program's student data. For example, what percentage of students who enroll actually complete the degree? What percentage of students are employed in a field relating to their studies? What are some of the program's graduates doing today? A program with a high completion rate and successful graduates is preferable to one with a high dropout rate.

FACULTY

Second, check out the faculty members. What are their credentials? What are their areas of expertise? Are they well regarded in their field? If the program is professional in nature, look for faculty members with a blend of academic background and professional experience. If the program is academic, you should find out whether tenure-track professors with Ph.D.'s teach both the on-campus and distance courses or if distance courses are relegated to part-time adjunct faculty members and/or assistants. Finally, evaluate whether or not the faculty is experienced both with the course content and with the instructional medium. If a program looks interesting to you, get in touch with a couple of faculty members to discuss it. You can tell a lot about a program by whether or not the faculty members are willing to take some time to talk to prospective students.

EXPERIENCE WITH ADULT LEARNERS

A third area of concern is the program's experience with adult learners. If you're an adult learner and choose to enroll in a college oriented to young undergraduates, you may find yourself struggling to cope. "My concern would be that in some programs the adult learner is an afterthought," says Claudine SchWeber, assistant vice president for distance education and lifelong learning at University of Maryland University College. "Adults are more critical consumers, and that won't fly these days." Working adult students have different needs than full-time on-campus students, and assessing the degree to which a program takes those needs into account can help you decide whether or not a program is a good match for you.

For Robin Barnes, who is pursuing a distance master's degree in nursing (family nurse-practitioner studies) at Gonzaga University, the flexibility of the faculty in dealing with adult students was extremely important. "We were adult learners who had lives and jobs outside of school. If we needed more time for a paper due to work schedules or a family crisis, the instructors were very understanding." Carla Gentry, in the same program, agrees. "The most important factor to me is the flexibility of the program and the staff's willingness to work with my schedule."

INSTRUCTIONAL DESIGN AND TECHNOLOGY

There are several areas that fall under the broad category of instructional design and technology that you should assess for each program you consider.

IS THE INSTRUCTIONAL TECHNOLOGY A GOOD MATCH FOR THE CONTENT?

Your first concern in the area of instructional design and technology should be whether or not the delivery system and the content are a good match. "How can you evaluate whether the technology and content mesh?" asks Robert V. Steiner of Teacher's College, Columbia University. "Online courses are more suitable for knowledge-intensive fields like business and engineering," he points out. "Subjects involving skills development and human interaction are more difficult to convey online." So, for example, in many behavioral sciences courses that involve clinical components, you need to be able to watch human interaction. In many science courses, you need to be able to do lab work. Such courses are more suited to two-way interactive video or on-campus formats than to the online format.

IS THE INSTRUCTIONAL TECHNOLOGY A GOOD MATCH FOR YOU?

Your second consideration is whether or not the instructional technology is a good match for your skills, personality, and learning style. In "Is Distance Learning Right for You?", we covered the pros and cons of the various technologies and described the skills and temperaments best suited to each.

If you are uncertain about your ability to adapt to a program's instructional technology, there are several things you can do. "If possible, take a tour of the technology being used before you enroll," advises Patti Wolf of University of Maryland University College. Many institutional Web sites offer short demos, previews, or tutorials so you can get an idea of what the instructional technology will be like. For example, if you are interested in a distance program at Penn State, you can take a sample course on its World Campus Web site. If the programs in which you are interested do not offer such amenities, ask previous students how the instructional technology worked and what level of expertise is necessary. If technology is an area of particular concern for you, you might even consider a trial run. "I would recommend taking one course before deciding to apply to a school, to see if the style works for the individual," suggests Nicole DeRaleau, an environmental engineering master's degree candidate at Worcester Polytechnic Institute. "If it doesn't work, then perhaps the credits can be transferred and there is no major loss."

HOW RELIABLE IS THE TECHNOLOGY?

On a related note, because distance students depend on technology, it's important that it be reliable. Not only will you depend on your own computer, VCR, or television, but you will depend on the institution's technology, too. Ask current students what their experiences have been. Does the server often go down? Are there frequent problems with camera equipment or satellite transmissions?

If the program is newly formatted for distance education, be prepared for some technological bugs to be worked out on your watch. If the prospect of participating in a maiden voyage is too anxiety-provoking, look for programs that have been running for at least a year.

Last, find out what technical support is offered to students. The best setup is free technical support accessed via an 800-number 24 hours a day, seven days a week.

HOW DO THE FACULTY AND STUDENTS INTERACT?

You should also investigate how the communication and social issues involved in distance learning are dealt with in the programs in which you are interested. (For a review of these issues, see "Is Distance Learning Right for You?") For example, how do students and faculty members communicate? Will you be expected to log on to an online course at specific times or at your convenience? Will you be expected to participate in online discussions a certain number of times during the course? For example, at the University of Phoenix Online, students are expected to log on and participate five days out of seven. At other schools, participation requirements may be program-wide or set by individual instructors.

Another question to ask is: What is done to overcome the distance learner's social isolation? Some programs do little; others rely on group work to forge a community of learning; and still others use a cohort format, in which a group of students enrolls in a program at the same time and proceeds through it together at the same pace.

Pay particular attention to the faculty-to-student ratio in online courses. If there are more than 25 to 30 students per instructor, you're not likely to get much individual attention.

ADVISING AND OTHER SERVICES

Academic advising is one of the most important student services for distance learners, especially if you are seeking to transfer credits or earn credits through examinations or from life experience to apply to a degree. Check what advising services are offered to distance learners, and see how easy they are to access. "I tested academic advising services," reports a distance learning undergraduate at University of Maryland University College. "That was important to me because I've been out of college for such a long time and I needed some help in selecting courses to complete requirements." Advising is also of particular interest to students in a consortium. If you are interested in a program that is part of a consortium, find out if the consortium offers advising or mentoring to help you navigate among institutions and to guide your overall progress.

Other support services that are important to distance education students are libraries, bookstores, administrative support, record keeping, and technical support (discussed above). Many institutions and consortia offer online and telephone access to these services for distance students. In particular, access to an online library is extremely important, especially if you don't live near a good college or university library. Find out what type of access is offered, what the library's resources are, how materials are delivered, and if training on how to use an online library is offered.

If the program in which you are interested is part of a consortium, be sure you understand how each of these student services is handled. In some cases you will have access only to your home institution's services; in other cases you will have access to the services of all member institutions.

Another thing to watch out for is the extent to which the institution as a whole has kept up with an innovative degree program. For example, at many universities, distance learning courses and programs originate in a couple of departments eager to pursue new ways of educating. However, the university's centralized academic and administrative services may lag behind, leaving distance students to struggle with a system not designed for their needs.

As you investigate a program and its services, keep in mind that the way you are treated as a prospective student can tell you something about what you will encounter once enrolled. "Look at the responsiveness of the institution," advises Robert V. Steiner of Teacher's College, Columbia University, "and ask yourself, 'How client-centered is that program?'"

RESIDENCY REQUIREMENT

Some programs, especially doctoral programs, have a residency requirement for distance learning students. The requirement may be several campus visits during the course of a semester, or a brief on-site meeting at the start of a semester. Some residency periods may last up to a week or two. In addition, you may have to travel to campus to take exams, or you may be able to take them locally with a proctor. Be sure you understand what the on-site requirements of a program are, and whether or not you can fulfill them.

TIME FRAMES

Check to see how much time you have to complete a certificate or degree program, and decide whether or not the time frame meets your needs. Some programs have a generous upper limit on the number of years you may take to complete a degree, which allows you to proceed at your own pace. Other programs may be structured on an accelerated or cohort model, with a timetable and lots of interim deadlines. If that's the case, make sure your own schedule can accommodate this. For example, if a program goes year-round and you are usually at a cabin in the woods without Internet access every summer, the program is not a good match for your lifestyle. In addition, if you are considering an accelerated or cohort degree program, make sure you have the support of your family, who may not get much attention from you during this period.

COST

The cost of a distance education degree or certificate program is often the same for on-campus and distance students. However, there are some things you should look out for:

- If you enroll in a consortium, member institutions may charge tuition at different rates.
- If you enroll in a public university, you will probably be charged out-of-state tuition if you are not a state resident.
- Some institutions charge an extra technology fee to cover the costs associated with distance education.
- If there is a residency period, you should plan on spending money for travel, accommodations, and meals.
- If you enroll in an online program, you need to budget for hardware, software, and Internet access as well as books.
- If you are interested in receiving federal financial aid, you must be enrolled in an institution accredited by one of the regional accrediting agencies or certain of the specialized agencies approved by the U.S. Department of Education (check their Web site at www.ed.gov/admins/finaid/accred/index.html).

YOUR PERSONAL CHECKLIST

This section discusses many factors that you can consider when evaluating a distance education program. Here is a checklist to sum up the criteria you should keep in mind:
- ✔ The institution's reputation
- ✔ Institutional (regional) accreditation
- ✔ Specialized accreditation, if applicable
- ✔ The program's quality: curriculum, faculty, and responsiveness to adult learners
- ✔ A good match between instructional technology and content
- ✔ A good match between instructional technology and your skills, personality, and learning style
- ✔ Interaction among students and faculty members
- ✔ Reliability of technology and good technical support
- ✔ Academic advising services
- ✔ Other support services: library, bookstore, administrative support, and record keeping
- ✔ Residency requirements, if any
- ✔ Time frame for completing certificate or degree
- ✔ Cost

Although we have described many factors, in the end there may be only three or four aspects of a program that really concern you. You may be more interested in a program's reputation than in any other factor. Or accreditation may be the most important issue for you. Perhaps you are concerned about finding a good match between your personality and learning style and the instructional design of a program. That is why the self-assessment you did while reading "Is Distance Learning Right for You?" is so crucial, since you can now focus on what's important to you when you evaluate distance programs.

So remember, keep your own educational, professional, and personal needs in the forefront during the selection process. Choosing a good program not only means choosing a high-quality program; it also means choosing a program that's a good match for you.

TAKING STANDARDIZED ADMISSIONS TESTS

For some people, the prospect of taking one of the standardized admissions tests is enough to make them put aside the idea of earning a degree indefinitely. You may be anxious about taking the SAT, Graduate Record Examinations (GRE), or one of the professional exams, but if you have chosen to apply to a program that requires an admissions test, there is no way of avoiding the experience. Many undergraduate programs require the SAT or ACT. Graduate programs often require the GRE or a professional examination, and some require a subject area test and writing assessment as well. Finally, if you are not a native speaker of English, you may need to pass a test of English language proficiency. So unless you've chosen to apply to programs that do not require an examination, you are going to have to take at least one exam—and do well on it.

Note that community colleges and many programs designed specifically for adult learners, including some distance learning programs, do not require a standardized admissions test as part of the application process. Therefore, the first thing you should do is to determine which exam(s), if any, you are expected to take. This information should appear in the packet that accompanies the program's application form. If you do not yet have this material, you should simply call the admissions office or program and ask or check the program's Web site. Once you know which exam you must take, contact the testing service that gives the exam and request registration materials or register online. Information on contacting the testing services appears in the Appendix.

Before we go into detail about the tests, it might be helpful to discuss how an admissions committee might use your score. The role played by the SAT or ACT on the undergraduate level is similar to the GRE or GMAT on the graduate level. These tests provide a benchmark. Essentially, your test score is one of the few objective bits of information in your application that can be used to gauge where you fall in the range of applicants. A few programs, especially the top professional programs that receive many more applicants than they can admit, may use the score as a means of reducing the applicant pool. If your score is below their cutoff, they will not even look at the rest of your application. But most programs are much more flexible in the way they evaluate scores. If your score is low, you may still be considered for admission, especially if your grade point average is high, your work experience is relevant, or your application is otherwise strong. Others will index your exam score and your grade point average to arrive at a more balanced number. Some programs offer a conditional admission when a standardized exam score is low. In order to earn an unconditional admission, you may have to retake the exam to boost your score or achieve a certain GPA in the first courses you take.

Basically, you should regard taking a standardized admissions test as an opportunity to improve your application. And that means you must take the test with plenty of time left to meet application deadlines (see "Taking Standardized Admissions Tests"

and "Applying for Admission to Degree Programs" for more information on applying). That way, if you take the test early and are disappointed with the results, you will have time to retake it. Note that test registration deadlines precede test dates by about six weeks and that you must also allow a few weeks after the testing date for score reporting.

You must also prepare. Thorough preparation, including taking practice tests, can add points to your score by refreshing your memory and giving you experience with test taking. Preparation is especially important if you have been out of school for a long time. As one student who had been out of school for twenty years put it, "Logarithms?! Geometry rules?!" If this sounds like you, you may need to do a quick recap of high school mathematics to do well on the mathematics portion of the SAT, ACT, GRE, or GMAT. And you may have forgotten what test taking is like, but if you study and practice it will help you overcome any weaknesses you may have. We'll discuss ways to prepare for the exams later in this section after we describe the various tests.

UNDERGRADUATE ADMISSIONS TESTS

Bachelor's degree programs that require a standardized admissions test will usually accept either the SAT or the ACT. Some programs will also require SAT Subject Tests in specific subjects.

THE SAT: A TEST OF REASONING

The SAT, which is administered by the Educational Testing Service (ETS) for the College Board, tests your critical reading, writing, and math reasoning skills. These are analytical skills developed over time both in school and at work; the test does not assess your knowledge of specific content areas.

The SAT is a 3-hour-and-45-minute paper test divided into ten sections: three critical reading sections, three math sections, three writing sections, and one unscored experimental section. The 25-minute essay will always be the first section of the test. The unscored section will be an unidentified math, critical reading, or writing multiple choice section.

Critical Reading Sections. The critical reading sections of the SAT test your ability to understand and analyze what you read, see relationships between the parts of a sentence, and understand word meaning in context. In other words, they test your language skills. Two of the critical reading sections last 25 minutes, and the third lasts 20 minutes. There are two types of questions:

- Passage-based reading questions measure your ability to read, understand, and think analytically about a single reading passage or a pair of passages. Reading passages range from 100 to 850 words.
- Sentence-completion questions assess your ability to understand the meaning of words and to recognize correct grammatical patterns.

Math Sections. The math sections of the SAT assess your ability to solve arithmetic, algebra I, algebra II, and geometry problems. The test does not include trigonometry or calculus. Each section lasts 20 or 25 minutes, and there are two main types of questions:

- 44 multiple-choice questions with five choices test your ability to solve math problems.
- 10 questions require a student-generated answer.

Writing Sections. The writing sections include multiple-choice questions and a 25-minute essay. The multiple-choice questions assess your ability to improve sentences and paragraphs and to identify grammatical errors. The short essay assesses your ability to organize and express your ideas clearly. The multiple-choice sections last 25 and 10 minutes and have three main types of questions:

- Improving sentences
- Improving paragraphs
- Identifying sentence errors

Note that you are permitted to bring, in the College Board's words, "almost any four-function, scientific, or graphing calculator" to use on the math sections. According to the College Board, students who use a calculator do slightly better because they do not make computational errors.

Tips for Taking the SAT. It pays to familiarize yourself with the test directions and typical question format beforehand so you don't waste precious testing time trying to figure out what to do (see the section below on test preparation). Because the sections appear in a paper booklet, you can do the questions in a section in any order. For that reason, it makes sense to answer the easy questions first and place a check mark beside the hard questions. Later, if you have time, you can return to the hard questions.

The way the SAT is scored should also influence your approach. First, you are awarded one point for each correct answer. But you lose a fraction of a point for each incorrect answer, except on the student-response questions in the math section. On those questions, you do not lose points for an incorrect answer. If you omit a question, you are not penalized. This means that guessing is only worth it if you can eliminate one or two choices as clearly wrong, improving your odds of picking the correct answer. So if a question and its choices are truly mysterious to you, skip it. The test booklet can be used for computations and notes. Don't make any extra marks on the answer sheet, because it's read by a machine that cannot tell the difference between an answer and a doodle.

THE SAT SUBJECT TESTS

The SAT Subject Tests are 1-hour subject area tests that assess your knowledge of a particular content area taught in high school. The questions are primarily multiple choice. The subject areas include literature in English, U.S. history, world history, two mathematics tests, biology, chemistry, and physics. There are reading-only language tests in French, German, modern Hebrew, Italian, Latin, and Spanish. Finally, there are reading and listening language tests in Chinese, French, German, Japanese, Korean, and Spanish.

THE ACT

The ACT is an admissions exam consisting of four tests: English, reading, mathematics, science, and an optional writing test. The examination takes about 3½ to 4 hours, and it includes 215 multiple-choice questions with either four or five answer choices, as well as an optional 30-minute essay. Since you are not penalized for an incorrect answer on the ACT, you should answer all the questions even if you have to guess.

Unlike the SAT, the ACT is not an aptitude test. Instead, it is based on the high school English, math, and science curriculum. The questions are directly related to what you learned in high school.

GRADUATE ADMISSIONS TESTS

If you apply to graduate school, you may need to take one of the graduate admissions tests. There are two types of Graduate Record Examinations: the General Test, which is usually referred to as the GRE, and the Subject Tests. Each of these tests has a different purpose, and you may need to take more than one of them. If so, try not to schedule two tests on the same day. The experience may be more arduous than you anticipate. Another general admissions test that is sometimes required instead of the GRE is the Miller Analogies Test. In addition, there are specialized exams required for admission to various professional programs.

THE GENERAL TEST (GRE)

According to ETS, the GRE "measures verbal, quantitative, and analytical reasoning skills that have been developed over a long period of time and are not necessarily related to any field of study." Like the SAT, the GRE is a test designed to assess whether you have the aptitude for higher-level study. Even though the GRE may not have subject area relevance, it can indicate that you are capable of doing the difficult reading, synthesizing, and writing demanded of most graduate students.

The test is divided into three separately timed parts, and all the questions are multiple choice: (1) a 30-minute verbal reasoning section with 30 questions, (2) a 45-minute quantitative reasoning section with 28 questions, and (3) an analytical writing section with two questions: an issue task (45 minutes) and an argument task (30 minutes). The parts may be presented in any order. In addition, an unidentified verbal, quantitative, or analytical section that doesn't count in your score may be included. You won't have any way to tell which of the duplicated sections is the "real" one, so you should complete all sections carefully. Finally, another section, on which ETS is still doing research, may also appear. This section will be identified as such and will not count toward your score. ETS tells test takers to plan to spend 2½ to 4 hours at the testing site.

In addition, test takers now encounter a new type of question in both the verbal and quantitative reasoning sections. This is part of the first phase of improvements endorsed by graduate school educators to test validity, provide faculty with better information regarding applicants' performance, address security concerns, increase worldwide access to the test, and make better use of advances in technology and psychometric design.

Verbal Reasoning Section. The thirty questions in the verbal reasoning section of the GRE test your ability to recognize relationships between words and concepts, analyze sentences, and analyze and evaluate written material. In other words, they test your vocabulary and your reading and thinking skills. At present, there are four main types of questions in this section:

- In sentence completion questions, sentences are presented with missing word(s). You are asked to select the word(s) that best complete the sentences. Answering correctly involves figuring out the meanings of the missing words from their context in the sentence.
- Analogy questions present a pair of words or phrases that are related to one another. Your task is to figure out the relationship between the two words or phrases. Then you must select the pair of words or phrases whose relationship is most similar to that of the given pair.
- Reading comprehension questions test your ability to understand a reading passage and synthesize information on the basis of what you've read.
- Antonym questions require you to determine which word or phrase provides the best antonym for the capitalized word. These questions test your vocabulary directly.

The words and reading material on which you are tested in this section come from a wide range of subjects, from daily life to the sciences and humanities.

Quantitative Reasoning Section. This section of the GRE tests your basic mathematical skills and your understanding of elementary mathematical concepts. You will be tested on your ability to reason quantitatively and solve quantitative problems. At present there are three main types of questions in this section:

- Quantitative comparison questions require that you determine which of two quantities is the larger, if possible. If such a determination is not possible, then you must so indicate.
- Data analysis questions provide you with a graph or a table on which to base your solution to a problem.
- Problem-solving questions test a variety of mathematical concepts. They may be word problems or symbolic problems.

The quantitative questions test your knowledge of arithmetic and high school algebra, geometry, and data analysis. They do not cover trigonometry or calculus.

Analytical Writing Section. This section of the GRE tests your critical thinking and analytical writing skills and assesses your ability to articulate and support complex ideas, analyze an argument, and sustain a focused and coherent discussion. It is not meant to assess specific knowledge. There are two separately timed analytical writing tasks:

- The 45-minute "Present Your Perspective on an Issue" prompt asks you to take a position on a topic of general interest and then develop your opinion from any perspective that you choose.
- The 30-minute "Analyze an Argument" topic requires you to critique an argument by assessing the reasonableness of its assumptions, the validity of its logic, and the reliability of its conclusion.

Changes to the analytical writing section may eventually include new, more focused prompts that reduce the possibility of reliance on memorized materials. Analytical writing scores are reported on a 0–6 score scale, in half-point increments.

Tips for Taking the GRE. The GRE is now given only in computer format except in areas of the world where computer-based testing is not available. The test is somewhat different from the old paper-and-pencil test. At the start of each section, you are given questions of moderate difficulty. The computer uses your responses to each question and its information about the test's structure to decide which question to give you next. If your responses continue to be correct, the computer "rewards" you by giving you a harder question. On the other hand, if you answer incorrectly, the next question will typically be easier. In short, the computer uses a cumulative assessment of your performance along with information about the test's design to decide which question you get next.

One result of this format is that you cannot skip a question. The computer needs your answer to a question before it can give you the next one. So you must answer or you get a "no score." In addition, this format means you cannot go back to a previous question to change your answer. The computer has already taken your answer and used it to give you subsequent questions. No backtracking is possible once you've entered and confirmed your answer. This also means that each person's test is different. Even if two people start with the same item set in the basic test section, once they differ on an answer, the subsequent portion of the test will branch differently.

According to ETS, even though people take different tests, their scores are comparable. This is because the characteristics of the questions answered correctly and incorrectly, including their difficulty levels, are taken into account in the calculation of the score. In addition, ETS claims that the computer-based test scores are also comparable to the old paper-and-pencil test scores.

One benefit of the computer-based format is that when you finish, you can cancel the test results—before seeing them—if you feel you've done poorly. If you do decide to keep the test, then you can see your unofficial scores right away. In addition, official score reporting is relatively fast—ten to fifteen days.

A drawback of the format, besides the fact that you cannot skip questions, is that some of the readings, graphs, and questions are too large to appear on the screen in their entirety. You have to scroll up and down to see the whole item. Likewise, referring to a passage or graph while answering a question means that you must scroll up. In addition, you can't underline sentences in a passage or make marks in the margin as you could on the paper test. To make up for this, ETS provides scratch paper that you can use to make notes and do calculations.

To help test takers accustom themselves to the computerized format, ETS provides a tutorial that you may complete before starting on the actual test. The tutorial familiarizes you with the use of a mouse, the conventions of pointing, clicking, and scrolling and the format of the test. If you are familiar with computers, the tutorial will take you less than one-half hour. If you are not, you are permitted to spend more time on it. According to ETS, the system is easy to use, even for a person with no previous computer experience. However, if you are not accustomed to computers, you would be far better off if you practice your basic skills before you get to the testing site. Although in theory a mouse is easy to use, novices often have trouble getting the cursor to go where they want it to go. The last thing you want to deal with while taking the GRE is a wild mouse and accidental clicking on the wrong answers. If it's any consolation, no knowledge of the keyboard is required—everything is accomplished by pointing and clicking.

GRE SUBJECT AREA TESTS

The subject area tests are achievement tests, and they test your content knowledge of particular subjects. There are eight subject area tests, and they are given in paper-and-pencil format only. The subjects include biochemistry, cell and molecular biology; biology; chemistry; computer science; literature in English; mathematics; physics; and psychology. The subject area tests assume a level of knowledge consistent with majoring in a subject or at least having an extensive background in it. ETS suggests allowing about 3½ hours at the testing site for a subject area test.

Unlike the General Test, which is given many times year round, the subject tests are given only three times a year. Keep in mind that because the tests are paper-based, it takes four to six weeks for your scores to be mailed to your designated institutions. Because the tests are given infrequently and score reporting is slow, be sure you plan ahead carefully so your test results will arrive before your deadlines.

MILLER ANALOGIES TEST

The Miller Analogies Test (MAT), which is run by Harcourt Assessment, is accepted by more than 2,300 graduate school programs. It is a test of mental ability given entirely in the form of analogies. For example, the analogies may tap your knowledge of fine arts, literature, mathematics, natural science, and social science.

On the MAT, you have 60 minutes to solve 120 problems. The test is given on an as-needed basis at more than 500 test centers in the United States, Canada, and overseas.

PROFESSIONAL SCHOOL EXAMS

Professional graduate programs are likely to require you to take the appropriate graduate admissions test. The major tests are the Graduate Management Admissions Test (GMAT) for business school applicants; the Law School Admissions Test (LSAT) for law school applicants; and the Medical College Admissions Test (MCAT) for medical school applicants. However, there are also specialized graduate admissions tests in the fields of dentistry, veterinary science, pharmacy, optometry, and education.

Graduate Management Admissions Test. The test most likely to be taken by prospective distance learning students is the GMAT. It is run by the Graduate Management Admissions Council and administered by Pearson VUE. Like the GRE, the GMAT is a computer-based test. It is designed to help schools of business assess applicants' aptitude for graduate level programs in business and management.

The GMAT tests verbal, quantitative, and analytic writing skills:

- In the Verbal section, you will be asked to understand and evaluate written English. There are 41 multiple-choice questions of three basic types: reading comprehension, critical reasoning, and sentence correction. You have 75 minutes to complete this section.

- The Quantitative section tests your basic math skills, understanding of elementary mathematical concepts, and ability to solve quantitative problems. There are 37 multiple-choice questions of two basic types: data sufficiency and problem solving. You have 75 minutes to complete this section.

- The Analytical Writing Assessment measures your ability to think critically and communicate in writing. There are two

essay topics, and you are allowed 30 minutes each to respond. You must analyze an issue and an argument in this section of the test.

TESTS OF ENGLISH LANGUAGE PROFICIENCY

Regardless of whether you're applying to an undergraduate or graduate program, if your native language is not English, you may be required to take the Test of English as a Foreign Language (TOEFL) or Test of Spoken English (TSE) in order to determine your readiness to take courses in English. Both tests are administered by ETS.

The TOEFL is given in computer-based form throughout most of the world. Like the computer-based GRE, the TOEFL does not require previous computer experience. You are given the opportunity to practice on the computer before the test begins. The TOEFL has four sections—listening, reading, structure, and writing—and it lasts about 4 hours.

The TSE evaluates your ability to speak English. During the test, which takes about a half an hour, you answer questions that are presented in written and recorded form. Your responses are recorded; there is no writing required on this test. The TSE is not given in as many locations as the TOEFL, so you may have to travel a considerable distance to take it.

PREPARING FOR A STANDARDIZED TEST

You can improve your scores and reduce your test anxiety by preparing for the exams you need to take. At the very least, preparation will mean that you are familiar with the test instructions and the types of questions you will be asked. If your computer skills need improvement, adequate preparation will mean that you focus on the questions rather than struggle with the mouse when you take the computer-based tests. For achievement tests such as the subject area tests, you will actually need to study content. There are many ways you can prepare for the tests, but whichever method you choose, start early.

- **Practice by taking old tests.** You can check the Web sites of the various tests to download or request practice tests, or you can buy practice test books at a bookstore. You'll find free sample test questions on many other Web sites, including Peterson's (www.petersons.com).

- **Use test-preparation workbooks.** These books give information and test-taking strategies, as well as practice items. There are many workbooks on the market, some with CD-ROMs, that will help you prepare for an admissions test. You'll find a long list of titles to choose from in Peterson's online bookstore at www.petersons.com.

- **Use test-preparation software.** Test-preparation software is becoming more popular as more of the tests shift to computerized format. You can purchase the software in just about any computer software store. You can also take practice tests online at www.petersons.com/testprep.

- **Take a test-preparation course.** If you don't trust yourself to stick with a self-study program using practice tests, workbooks, or software, sign up for a review course such as those given by

Kaplan. Although the courses are much more expensive than the do-it-yourself approach, they may be worth it if they make you study.

- **If your math is rusty, study math content.** According to the College Board, people who study math boost their scores more than people who focus only on test-taking skills.

For a list of test preparation resources, see the Appendix.

REDUCING TEST ANXIETY

The best way to reduce test anxiety is to be thoroughly prepared. If you are well-acquainted with the format, directions, and types of questions you will encounter, you will not need to waste precious testing time puzzling over these aspects of the exam. In addition to thorough preparation, here are some suggestions to reduce the stress of taking the exam.

- Get a good night's rest and don't tank up on caffeinated beverages—they will only make you feel more stressed.
- Make sure you've got all the things you will need, including your admission ticket and proper identification; pencils and erasers if you are taking a paper based test; and a calculator, if one is permitted.
- Dress in layers so you will be prepared for a range of room temperatures.
- Get to the testing site at least a half an hour early. Make sure you know the way and leave yourself plenty of time to get there.
- Pace yourself during the exam. Know how the exam is scored so you can plan your approach.
- Last, try to keep things in perspective. Remember, the exam score is just one item on your application.

We'll discuss the remaining parts of an application in the next section.

APPLYING FOR ADMISSION TO DEGREE PROGRAMS

Now that you have narrowed your selection of programs and ascertained whether or not you need to take a standardized admissions test, it's time to prepare and assemble your applications. If you have not already done so, request an application and information packet from each program to which you plan to apply, download these items from their Web sites, or review them online.

When you look over these materials, you will see that there may be a lot of work involved in applying to a degree program. It may take you a few months to register for and take standardized tests and to assemble and submit all the necessary information, especially if you're an international student or you've been out of school for a few years. Because the process can be complicated and time consuming, you should start well ahead of time. Even if you apply to a certificate program or an associate degree program at a community college, a process that is typically less complicated, you should still make sure to start in time.

DEADLINES

For programs at traditional colleges and universities, application deadlines for fall admission may range from August (one full year prior to your planned enrollment) to late spring or summer for programs with rolling admissions. However, most programs require that you submit your application between January and March of the year in which you wish to start. For certificate programs and at community colleges, the deadlines may be later.

At some of the online universities, students can start their studies at any time of year. For example, at Walden University you can start on the first of any month. At Walden, the deadline for application materials is the first of the month two months prior to the month of enrollment.

Different programs have different deadlines. So be careful when you check the deadlines in the application materials from your various programs. And remember, the deadlines are not suggestions. One student applying to a traditional university who mistook a March deadline for May recalls that "not only would they not consider my application, but they wouldn't refund my application fee, either. I had to reapply the next year and pay again to be considered for their program." So don't be careless about dates—double-check them. Make a checklist like Figure 7-1 to help you keep track of things and stay on top of deadlines.

Application Checklist. Keep track of your applications by inserting a check mark or a completion date in the appropriate column or row. Note that the last four items are financial aid documents, which will be discussed in "Paying for Your Education."

PARTS OF AN APPLICATION

For each program to which you apply, you will have to submit a number of items to make your application complete. For most bachelor's and graduate degree programs, these include:

- Standardized admissions test scores (see "Taking Standardized Admissions Tests")
- An application form
- Your high school, undergraduate, or other transcripts
- Letters of recommendation
- Personal essay(s)

In addition, if you are seeking credit for life experience, an assessment portfolio will be required (see "What Can You Study via Distance Learning?"). A personal interview may be required for some programs, although for most, an interview is optional. A program may require additional items, such as a resume or arts portfolio.

For most associate degree programs at community colleges, the application is much simpler. Typically, it consists of just an application form; you may not even need to submit high school transcripts. For certificate programs, the application may consist of an application form and one or two other items.

Because requirements vary so widely, be sure you read the admissions information thoroughly so you understand what each program expects of you. Since each program may require a slightly different set of items, be sure your checklist reflects this in order to keep track of what you'll need to do.

We'll discuss the main elements of an application below; we'll cover financial aid applications in the next section.

THE APPLICATION FORM

On the application form, you provide basic information such as the program or department to which you are applying; your name, date of birth, social security number, address, and contact information; your citizenship status; your demographic background (usually optional); your current employer and position; your educational background; names of people who are providing references (ask them first!); and admissions test dates. Sometimes the application form also includes a section for applying for financial aid. However, a separate application form for financial aid may be necessary. Be sure you understand what forms you need to submit and to whom if you are applying for aid.

If you use a paper application, you should type the information on the form. If a typewriter is not available, then print your entries neatly. Be sure you do not accidentally omit information, and double-check that there are no spelling errors. "Photocopy the application and fill the copy out," suggests Nicole DeRaleau, a graduate student in engineering at Worcester Polytechnic Institute. "Make sure it is clear and concise, and then copy it onto the actual form."

If you decide to apply online, don't just sit at the computer and dash off the application. Download the application form, fill it in, then proofread it carefully. Only then should you transmit it, being sure to keep a copy. Note that if you apply to an online degree

Figure 7–1: Application Checklist

Item	Program 1	Program 2	Program 3
	Date Due/Date Completed	Date Due/Date Completed	Date Due/Date Completed
Application form			
Test scores requested			
Transcripts requested			
Letters of recommendation solicited			
Letters of recommendation follow-up			
Personal essay(s)			
Application fee			
Other items required (specify)			
Application submitted			
Application follow-up			
FAFSA			
Other financial aid forms			
Financial aid supporting documents			
Financial aid application follow-up			

program and the school does not offer an online application, you should think twice about applying. The lack of an online application is probably indicative of the low level of online student services you can expect once you are enrolled.

Many undergraduate colleges accept a common application form in place of their own. This means that most of the fields you will need to fill in will be the same for all of the schools that accept the common application. You may have to fill out a supplementary form for a college if you use one of these standardized forms. Using a standardized application form lets you concentrate on being organized and writing good essays.

TRANSCRIPTS

As proof of your academic background, you will need to submit official transcripts from each high school (for undergraduate programs), college, and university you have attended, even if you have taken just one course from that institution. To request official transcripts, contact your high school's guidance office or the registrars of your undergraduate college and other institutions you have attended. Be sure to allow two or three months for your request to be processed. It will save time if you call ahead to find out what the fee for each transcript is and what information they need to pull your file and send the transcript to the proper recipient. Then you can enclose a check for that amount with your written request.

Since many schools will send the transcripts directly to the admissions offices of the programs to which you are applying, you may also want to request an unofficial copy of your transcript. You can use this copy for your own reference during the application process.

When you review your transcripts, look for weaknesses that may need explaining, even if they occurred years ago. For example, a low GPA one semester, a very poor grade in a course, or even a below-average overall GPA may hurt your chances of acceptance unless you have a good reason for them. You can explain any shortfalls in your transcripts in your personal essay, cover letter, or addendum to the application.

LETTERS OF RECOMMENDATION

You will probably have to provide letters of recommendation for each program to which you apply. These letters are important, because like the personal essay, they give the members of the admissions committee a more personal view of you than is possible from your grades and test scores. Good letters of recommendation can tremendously increase your chances of admission, and lukewarm letters can harm your application. So it's important to approach the task of choosing and preparing your letter writers in a thoughtful and timely fashion.

In fact, it's a good idea to start asking for references a few months before your application deadline. Professionals and professors are extremely busy people, and the more time that you can give them to work on your recommendation, the better it will reflect who you are. Starting early will also give you an opportunity to follow up with your recommenders well before the application deadlines.

CHOOSING PEOPLE TO WRITE RECOMMENDATIONS

If possible, at least one of your recommendations should be from a teacher or professor, because (1) they are in the best position to judge you as a potential student and (2) members of the admissions committee will consider them peers and so be more inclined to trust their judgment of you.

If you cannot make up the full complement of letters from faculty members or if you are applying to professional programs, you can ask employers or people who know you in a professional capacity to write references for you. In fact, if you are applying to professional programs, having letters of recommendation from those already practicing in the field is a plus.

When you are trying to decide who to ask for recommendations, keep these criteria in mind. The people you ask should

- have a high opinion of you.
- know you well, preferably in more than one context.
- be familiar with your field.
- be familiar with the programs to which you apply.
- have taught a large number of students (or have managed a large number of employees) so they have a good basis upon which to compare you (favorably!) to your peers.
- be known by the admissions committee as someone whose opinion can be trusted.
- have good writing skills.
- be reliable enough to write and mail the letter on time.

A tall order? Yes. It's likely that no one person you choose will meet all these criteria, but try to find people who come close to this ideal.

APPROACHING YOUR LETTER WRITERS

Once you've decided who you plan to ask for references, be diplomatic. Don't simply show up in their offices, ask them to write a letter, and give them the letter of recommendation forms. Plan your approach so that you leave the potential recommender, as well as yourself, a graceful "out" in case the recommender reacts less than enthusiastically.

On your first approach, you should remind the person about who you are (if necessary) and then ask if they think they can write you a good letter of recommendation. This gives the person a chance to say no. If the person agrees, but hesitates or seems to be lukewarm, you can thank them for agreeing to help you. Later, you can write them a note saying that you won't need a letter of recommendation after all. On the other hand, if the person seems genuinely pleased to help you, you can then make an appointment to give them the letter of recommendation forms and the other information they will need.

WAIVING YOUR RIGHT TO SEE A LETTER

The letter of recommendation forms in your application packets contain a waiver. If you sign the waiver, you give up your right to see the letter of recommendation. Before you decide whether or not to sign it, discuss the waiver with each person who is writing you a reference. Some people will write you a reference only if you agree to sign the waiver and they can be sure the letter is confidential. This does not necessarily mean they intend to write a negative letter; instead, it means that they think a confidential letter will carry more weight with the admissions committee. In fact, they are right. A confidential letter usually has more validity in the eyes of the admissions committee. From the committee's point of view, an "open" letter may be less than candid because the letter writer knew you were going to read it. So, in general, it's better for you to waive your right to see a letter. If this makes you anxious in regard to a particular recommender, then do not choose that person to write a letter.

HELPING YOUR LETTER WRITERS

Once a faculty member or employer has agreed to write a letter of recommendation for you, he or she wants to write something positive on your behalf. No matter how great you are, this won't be possible if the letter writer cannot remember you and your accomplishments very well.

So when you meet with your letter writers to give them the letter of recommendation forms, use this opportunity to provide them with information about yourself. Bring a resume that highlights your academic, professional, and personal accomplishments. List the course or courses you took with them, the grades you got, and any significant work you did, such as a big research paper or presentation. The resume can be the basis of a conversation you have with the letter writer that amplifies your notable accomplishments.

What should you do if the letter writer asks *you* to draft the letter? Accept gracefully. Then pretend you are the writer, and craft a letter extolling your virtues and accomplishments in detail. Remember, if the letter writer does not like what you've written, he or she is free to change it in the final draft.

You can help your letter writers by filling in as much of the information as you can on the letter of recommendation forms. It's also a nice gesture to provide stamped, addressed envelopes for the letters if they are to be mailed directly to the programs or to you for inclusion in your application. Be sure your letter writers understand what their deadlines are. In other words, do everything you can to expedite the process, especially since you may be approaching people who are already extremely busy.

Last, send thank-you notes to professors and employers who have come through for you with letters of recommendation. Cementing good relationships now can only help you in the future.

IF YOU'VE BEEN OUT OF SCHOOL FOR YEARS

What should you do if you have been out of school for years and have lost touch with your teachers and professors? There are several things you can do to overcome the problems associated with the passage of time.

First, if a teacher or professor is still at your alma mater, you can get in touch by mail or e-mail, remind the person of who you are, describe what you've done since they taught you and what your plans for school are, and include a resume. Tell the instructor what you remember most about the courses you took with him or her. Most people keep their course records for at least a few years and can look up your grades. If you are still near your high school or undergraduate institution, you can make your approach in person. Once you've made this initial approach, you can then call and ask if the person thinks he or she can write a strong recommendation for you.

Another strategy if you've been out of school for a while is to obtain letters of recommendation from faculty members teaching in the programs to which you plan to apply. In order to obtain such a letter, you may have to take a course in the program before you enroll so that the faculty member gets to know you. Members of an admissions committee will hesitate to reject a candidate who has been strongly recommended by one of their colleagues.

Finally, if you are having trouble recruiting teachers and professors to recommend you, call the programs to which you are applying and ask what their policy is for applicants in your situation. Many programs designed for adult learners, especially the professional programs, allow you to use letters from employers. But remember, if you apply to an academic rather than a professional program, letters from employers will not carry as much weight as letters from faculty members.

THE PERSONAL ESSAY

The application to a degree program is not all numbers and outside evaluations. Schools are also interested in finding out about you as an individual and in more intangible qualities, like your ability to write a good essay. Thus, the personal essay is the part of the application in which you can take control and demonstrate who you are and why you deserve to be admitted. Other parts of your application—test scores, grade point average, and transcripts—may reflect your academic ability, but not much else. The letters of recommendation are beyond your control once you've chosen the writers. But a good personal essay can make you stand out. It can show the qualities that will make you an excellent student and professional. In other words, the essay is your showcase and you should make the most of it. Even if you can write superb prose in your sleep, you still need to know *what* to write. In this section, you'll get a step-by-step guide to preparing the personal essay.

REQUIREMENTS VARY

The essays required of applicants vary widely. For some programs, you may just have to explain in one or two paragraphs why you want to go to that school. For others, you may have to write on a more creative topic, such as the person who influenced you the most. Still for others, such as graduate business programs, the application may call for two, three, or even more essays on different topics. Business schools and programs pay a lot of attention to the personal essay because professional experience is an important criterion for admission, and this is best reflected in the essays.

The admissions committee gleans a lot of information from *what* you write. But they can also tell a lot from *how* you write. If your writing is clear and conveys your ideas effectively, you are demonstrating your ability to communicate. If your writing is free of grammatical and spelling errors, you are demonstrating your attention to detail. Good writing skills are essential for a student in any field, so a poorly written essay can hurt an application. A well-written statement, on the other hand, will help your case.

THINK BEFORE YOU WRITE

Do you remember the self-assessment you did in "Is Distance Learning Right for You?" You answered many difficult questions about your goals, interests, strengths, and weaknesses in order to decide if pursuing an education through distance learning was right for you. If you did an honest and thorough job of assessing yourself then, you will have already thought through many of the issues you will now need to address when you write your personal essay.

Things to Think About. Your self-assessment should make it easier for you to get a handle on issues such as:

- your personal and professional goals and their relationship to your education
- how you came to be interested in a particular field and why you think you are well suited for it
- aspects of your life that make you uniquely qualified to pursue study in this field
- experiences or qualities that distinguish you from other applicants
- unusual hardships or obstacles that you've had to overcome
- unusual accomplishments, whether personal, professional, or academic
- professional experiences that have contributed to your personal growth
- how your skills and personal characteristics would contribute to your success in a distance learning degree program

In addition, when you researched and evaluated programs to which you would apply, you learned a lot about the programs that were good matches for you. In your essay, you may also have to address issues like

- what appeals to you about a particular program.
- how your interests and strengths match their needs.

Be Yourself . . . The most common piece of advice from most admissions directors about writing the personal essay is to be yourself. Remember, you are seeking to be accepted by a program that is a good match for you. If you disguise who you really are in an effort to impress an admissions committee, you are doing yourself—and the school—a disservice. So, be honest. If you demonstrate self-knowledge by presenting your strengths as well as your limitations, your essay will be a true reflection of who you are.

. . . But Be Diplomatic. Honesty is important, but so is diplomacy. Try not to reveal weaknesses in your personality such as laziness, dishonesty, or selfishness. Don't say you want to enroll in a program just because it's online or you know you can get in. Even though these things may be true, they are not reasons with which the admissions committee will necessarily be sympathetic. Instead, frame your points in a positive light: you can fulfill the admission requirements because you have the proper prerequisites, and you know of its reputation for quality online teaching.

WRITE A STRONG OPENING

When you write your essay, put yourself in the position of an admissions committee member who may be reading fifty essays a day. By the end of all this reading, this poor individual may be bored to tears and would be pleased by any essay that simply engages his or her interest. How are you going to accomplish this? By writing an opening that grabs the reader's attention.

Describe an Important Experience. Instead of beginning with, "I want to go to school because . . ." try to engage the reader with something significant. For example, was there an experience that led you to make the decision to pursue your education? If so, describe it.

The opening is also the place where you can set forth any unusual experience you have had that contributed significantly to the person you are today. The experience may be growing up poor, being an Olympic athlete, or moving to the United States at the age of fourteen. Whatever the experience is, show how it has formed your character and life and how it relates to the education you want to pursue now.

Be Specific. What if you have not had a defining moment or experience that sparked your interest in further education? Then write an opening that is specific enough to have some real interest. The key is to remember that specific details are usually more interesting than general statements. Use concrete examples of your successes and action verbs to describe events. Be specific and you'll have a better chance of connecting with your readers.

TELL HOW YOUR STORY INTERSECTS WITH THEIRS

If you apply to several programs, you will be tempted to write a boilerplate essay. Resist the temptation. Admissions committees grow adept at picking out the generic personal statements.

Remember that when you were evaluating programs you were looking for a good match for you. The personal essay is the place where you can explain to the admissions committee why you are a good match for that school. The story of your intellectual and professional development and your goals should culminate in your reasons for choosing this particular program. Your reasons should reflect a knowledge of the program.

Use the Brochure or Catalog as a Resource. You can use the knowledge you've gained from researching the program if you don't know it firsthand to explain why you want to enroll in a program. In particular, the program brochure or catalog can be a good resource when you write this section of the essay. It's important to know what a school has to offer before you write the essay. The admissions committee members will be looking for a good fit for their program.

In addition to identifying the tangible characteristics of a program, you can also get a sense of its philosophy and values from the brochure or catalog.

DESCRIBE YOUR GOALS

In most essays, you will have to explain how a degree will help you achieve your goals. Even if you are not exactly sure what you want to do professionally, describe what you might be interested in doing once you receive the degree. Indicating that you have a purpose in obtaining a degree shows that you are focused and motivated and have a real sense of the possibilities.

EXPLAIN SHORTCOMINGS IN YOUR BACKGROUND

There is a difference of opinion on whether or not the personal essay is the place to explain any weaknesses in your academic or professional preparation if you are not directly asked to do so. Some people think that the essay should concentrate on a positive presentation of your qualifications. They feel that an explanation of poor standardized test scores, for example, belongs in an addendum or cover letter. Others think that the essay is the place to address your application's weaknesses.

Perhaps a good rule of thumb is to address any weaknesses or shortcomings that are directly relevant to your proposed studies in the essay. On the other hand, if the weak spot in your application is not directly related to your field of study, you may prefer to address it in an addendum or cover letter. For example, if when you were a college freshman you had a poor GPA, you can explain this separately. Try to put a positive spin on it, too. Explain, for example, how your GPA in your major was much higher, or how your GPA improved as you matured. Essentially, your decision as to where to address your weaknesses will depend on their importance and relevance to your pursuit of a degree.

EDIT YOUR DRAFTS

Follow the Instructions. When you sit down to draft your essay, the first thing you should make sure is that you are *answering the question posed on the application*. Be sure you read the instructions for each program's personal statement carefully. Small differences in wording can affect how you approach writing the essay.

Don't Write Too Much or Too Little. The second thing you should keep in mind as you begin your draft is the length of the essay. Often, the length is specified. What should you do if length is not specified? Write one to two typed pages. An essay that is shorter than one page does not allow room for you to develop your ideas, and an essay that is longer than two pages becomes a chore for the admissions committee to read. Don't play with font size, either, in order to get the statement to come out the right length. Admissions officers don't really want to read eight-point type. Stick with a basic font, such as Times New Roman, and keep the size between 10 and 12 points. If the essay asks for a specific word count, follow it to the letter. If you come in over or under by 10 words or so, don't worry too much about it. But if you're 100 or more words short or long, you'll have some adding or cutting to do.

Finally, when you write your first draft, do not waste space by repeating information that the admissions committee can get from other parts of your application like your transcript or resume. Use the essay to provide new information or to highlight particular accomplishments.

Review the First Draft. Once you have drafted your essay, read the question again. Has your draft answered the question fully? If the essay is incomplete, go back and fill in the missing material. Then ask people for feedback. Although your spouse and friends may be helpful, you may get more valuable suggestions from faculty members or colleagues who know you and who also know what a personal essay should be like. Ask whether you've included things you should leave out or should add things you've forgotten. Is the tone right? Have you achieved the right balance between boasting and being too modest? Are there any problems with organization, clarity, grammar, or spelling?

Prepare the Final Draft. Once you've revised the essay, set it aside for a couple of days. Then proofread it with a fresh eye. If you are satisfied with your final draft, ask someone else to proofread it for you. The final draft should be absolutely free of grammar and spelling errors, so do not rely on grammar or spellcheckers to find all the errors. Once you are done, be sure to keep backup files as well as a hard copy. Although you won't be able to use the whole essay for all your applications, you may be able to use parts of it. If you do work this way, be absolutely sure when you submit the final essays to different programs that you have not made any embarrassing cutting and pasting mistakes.

Finally, if you submit the statement on separate sheets of paper rather than on the application form itself, put your name, social security number, and the question at the top of the essay and type "see attached essay" on the application form.

MAKE IT YOURS

If after reading this section you are still daunted by the prospect of writing your personal statement, just put the whole task aside for a few days. You will find that the ideas and suggestions you've just read will trigger some mental activity and that soon you will have some ideas of your own to jot down.

Remember, also, that it's not necessary to have an exotic background or a dramatic event to recount in order to write a good essay and gain admission to a program. Admissions committees look for diversity—in gender, race, ethnicity, nationality, and socioeconomic status—to name some obvious characteristics. But they are also looking for people with diverse life experiences to add richness to their student body. Your background, which may seem perfectly ordinary to you, nevertheless has unique and relevant elements that can be assets to the program you choose. Your task is to identify and build upon these elements to persuade the admissions committee that you should be selected.

INTERVIEWS

Interviews are rarely a requirement of the distance education application process. However, if you think you do well in interviews, you can call each program and ask for an interview. A good interview may be an opportunity to sway the admissions committee in your favor. Human nature being what it is, an excellent half-hour interview may loom larger than years of average grades in the minds of those who evaluate your application.

Most interviewers are interested in the way you approach problems, think, and articulate your ideas, and so they will concentrate on questions that will reveal these aspects of your character and not on questions that test your technical knowledge.

They may ask you controversial questions or give you hypothetical problems to solve. Or they may ask about your professional goals, motivation for study, and areas of interest—much of the same material that is in a typical personal essay. Remember that interviewers are interested more in how you think than in what you think.

When you prepare for an interview, it would be helpful if you have already written your personal essay, because the thought processes involved in preparing the essay will help you articulate many of the issues that are likely to come up in an interview. It is also helpful to do your homework on the program, so if the opportunity arises for you to ask questions, you can do so intelligently. Last, be sure you are dressed properly. That means dress as if you are going to a professional job interview.

SUBMITTING YOUR APPLICATION

As we mentioned at the beginning of this section, you should submit your completed applications well before they are due. *Be sure to keep a copy of everything.* That way, you won't lose hours of work if the application gets lost. You can either mail the application to the admissions office or file portions of it online through the programs' Web sites. Remember, however, that some elements of the application, such as the fee and official transcripts, will still need to be mailed in paper form. Note also that most schools that accept online applications simply print them and process them as if they had come in by regular mail.

Try to submit all of your materials at once, which simplifies the task of compiling and tracking your application at the admissions office. If that's impossible, as it is for many students, keep track of missing items and forward them as soon as possible. Remember that if items are missing, your application is likely just to sit in the admissions office.

FOLLOWING UP

It's important that you check up on the status of your applications, especially if you don't receive acknowledgment that an application is complete. Give the admissions office a couple of weeks to process your application, and then call or send an e-mail to find out whether or not it's complete. For some schools, you can check the status of your application online through their Web sites. Usually the missing items are transcripts or letters of recommendation.

IN SUMMARY

Preparing a thorough, focused, and well-written application is one of the most important tasks you will ever undertake. A good application can gain you admission to a program that can help you achieve your goals. "The application process is just one of those hoops you have to jump through to get where you want to go," advises a distance learning student at Gonzaga University. With your destination in mind, work on your applications as if they are the most important things you can possibly be doing, because they are.

PAYING FOR YOUR EDUCATION

Pursuing a certificate or degree can cost a lot of money, but it is usually money well spent. On average, people with undergraduate and graduate degrees make more money than those who do not have these credentials. Still, the question remains: How are you going to pay for school and support yourself (and perhaps your family) at the same time?

Most adult distance learning students solve the problem of paying for their education by continuing to work full-time and attending school part time. As one student put it, "I work and I pay as I go." Although attending part-time does not cut the total cost of your certificate or degree, it does have the advantage of spreading your costs over a longer period and enables you to pay for your education out of your current income. Note, however, that attending school less than half-time will disqualify you from most forms of financial aid.

In this section, we'll discuss ways to pay for your education, both by looking for low-cost alternatives and by finding financial aid. We'll discuss types and sources of aid, where you can find information about financial aid, and the application process. Finally, we'll describe some of the tax issues that may be relevant to students pursuing higher education.

LOOKING FOR LOW-COST ALTERNATIVES

There are ways you can cut the cost of your education, even before you look for sources of financial aid. These include attending a community college rather than a four-year college and attending a public institution of higher education rather than a private one.

COMMUNITY COLLEGE VERSUS FOUR-YEAR COLLEGE

If you are an undergraduate pursuing a bachelor's degree, you could consider enrolling at a community college for your first two years of study. Most community colleges charge less tuition than four-year colleges do. Toward the end of your second year of study, you can apply to a four-year college as a transfer student and complete your bachelor's degree there.

PUBLIC VERSUS PRIVATE COLLEGE OR UNIVERSITY

Since four-year public colleges and universities get most of their support from government funding, they are less expensive than private colleges and universities. Public colleges and universities usually have two scales for tuition and fees—one for out-of-state residents and a much less expensive scale for state residents.

With so much money at stake, and if moving is an option for you, it is definitely worthwhile to find out how you can establish residency in the state in which you plan to get your degree. You may simply have to reside in the state for a year—your first year

of school—in order to be considered a legal resident. But being a resident while a student may not count, and you may have to move to the state a year before you plan to enroll. The legal residency requirements of each state vary, so be sure you have the right information if you decide to pursue this strategy.

TYPES OF FINANCIAL AID

Before we get into a discussion of the various sources of financial aid, it would be helpful to understand some basics. For example, financial aid can be classified in a few ways. First, it can be categorized by type of aid:

- **Grants, scholarships,** and **fellowships** are gifts that do not have to be repaid. These words are used somewhat interchangeably; there is no real difference among them, except that scholarships are usually awarded to undergraduates and fellowships are awarded to graduate students.

- **Loans** are awards that do have to be repaid, with interest, either while you are in school or after you leave school, depending on the terms of the loan. If you consider loans, note that financial aid counselors recommend that your total student debt payment should not exceed 8 to 15 percent of your projected monthly income after you receive your degree.

- **Work-study awards** are amounts you earn through part-time work in a federal aid program.

- **Reimbursements**, generally from employers, repay you for amounts you've already spent on tuition.

You can also classify financial aid according to the reason the student is awarded the aid:

- **Need-based aid** is financial aid awarded on the basis of your financial need. It may take the form of grants, loans, or work-study.

- **Merit-based aid** is funding awarded on the basis of academic merit, regardless of financial need.

A subset of merit-based aid is student profile-based aid—financial aid to students because of their identities. For example, some scholarships are targeted for veterans, minorities, or women; and others are targeted for people with very specific qualifications that the philanthropist wants to reward, such as an Eagle Scout studying labor relations.

A third way to classify financial aid is by its source. The major sources of aid for students are as follows:

- The **federal government**, by far the largest disburser of financial aid—over $50 billion to more than 8.5 million students each year

- **State governments**, some of which have large financial aid programs

• **Private sources of aid**, which include colleges and universities, employers, foundations, service organizations, national scholarship and fellowship programs, home equity loans, and private loan programs

THE LANGUAGE OF FINANCIAL AID

There's some financial aid jargon that you'll have to master in order to understand need-based financial aid programs. Some terms that you'll see frequently include the following:

• **Enrollment status**—Whether you are enrolled full time, three-quarter time, half time, or less than half time in a degree or certificate program. Your status affects your eligibility for most types of aid.

• **Expected Family Contribution (EFC)**—This is the amount you and your family are expected to contribute to the cost of your education per academic year. If you are a dependent, *family* means you and your parents; if you are independent, this means you and your spouse, if you are married. The formula was established by the U.S. Congress to help estimate federal aid amounts for eligible students, and it is used by college financial aid offices as well as the U.S. Department of Education.

• **Cost of attendance**—The total cost—tuition, fees, living expenses, books, supplies, and miscellaneous expenses—of attending a particular school for an academic year. Each school estimates its own cost of attendance, and you can find out what it is if you check your admissions information packet or call the financial aid office. Distance learners should make sure that technology costs are included in the school's cost of attendance and in their own budgets. The cost of transportation, hotels, and meals during residency periods, if any, should also be accounted for in the cost of attendance.

• **Financial need**—The amount of money you need to be given or loaned or that you will earn through work-study in order to attend your school. It is calculated by subtracting your EFC from your cost of attendance:

Cost of Attendance
− Expected Family Contribution
= Financial Need

Note that your financial need will differ from program to program. That's because the cost of attendance will vary from school to school, but your EFC will remain the same, whether you attend the local community college or an expensive private university.

FEDERAL FINANCIAL AID

As we've mentioned, the U.S. government is the largest player in the financial aid arena, and most of your financial aid is likely to come from this source. The federal government provides need-based aid in the form of grants, work-study programs, and loans. Up-to-date information about federal financial aid programs can be found at the U.S. Department of Education's Web site, www.studentaid.ed.gov, or by calling 800-4-FEDAID (toll-free). Eligibility issues relevant to distance learners and some of the basics of federal aid are discussed below. Note that some of these eligibility criteria may change in the future as distance degrees become more common and financial aid programs are modified to reflect the new realities.

ARE YOU ELIGIBLE FOR FEDERAL FINANCIAL AID?

Your financial need is just one criterion used to determine whether or not you are eligible to receive aid from the federal government. In addition, you must

• have a high school diploma or GED or pass a test approved by the Department of Education.

• be enrolled in a degree or certificate program.

• be enrolled in an eligible institution (see below).

• be a U.S. citizen or eligible noncitizen.

• have a Social Security number.

• register with the Selective Service if required.

• maintain satisfactory academic progress once you are in school.

If you have been convicted under federal or state laws of the sale or possession of illegal drugs, you may not be eligible to participate in federal financial aid programs. Call the Federal Student Aid Information Center at 800-4-FEDAID (toll-free) for further information.

If you are not sure if you qualify as an eligible noncitizen, call the financial aid office of the school you plan to attend.

INSTITUTIONAL ELIGIBILITY: AN ISSUE PERTINENT TO DISTANCE LEARNERS

In order to participate in federal financial aid programs, an institution of higher learning must fulfill the criteria established by Congress for the disbursement of Title IV funds, as federal student aid is officially known. There are many complex regulations that establish institutional eligibility. Of these, several may apply to institutions that offer certificates or degrees at a distance. For example, in order to be eligible to participate in federal financial aid programs, an institution must be accredited by an agency—other than the Distance Education and Training Council (DETC)—recognized by the U.S. Department of Education. The reason that schools accredited only by the DETC are not eligible is that they are classified as "correspondence schools," and schools that teach primarily by correspondence are ineligible according to the law. In order to qualify to disburse Title IV aid, an institution must teach at least 50.1 percent of its classes in the traditional classroom or must be classified as an independent study institution rather than a correspondence school. Other requirements for participation in federal financial aid programs involve the academic schedule; for example, there must be a thirty-week academic year, a template that doesn't fit some of the new virtual universities.

The Distance Education Demonstration Program. The rules governing federal aid were originally promulgated to prevent fraud and to assure that funds would be provided to students at schools that met certain standards. However, with the growth of distance education, these regulations are increasingly becoming obstacles to provide aid to students at legitimate but innovative institutions. Recognizing this, Congress established the Distance Education Demonstration Program under the direction of the Department of Education. "The purpose of the Distance Education Demonstration Program is to collect data that will provide some understanding of what constitutes quality in distance education," explains Marianne R. Phelps, former special assistant to the assistant secretary for postsecondary education. "Congress needs information in order to become comfortable with the risks involved in funding distance education." Under this program, the department is permitted to waive some of the Title IV regulations, if necessary, for the fifteen participating institutions of higher education. Eventually, the experiences and data generated by the Distance Education Demonstration Program may provide a basis for a review of current rules and regulations.

Determining the Eligibility Status of an Institution or Program. In the meantime, what can you do to make sure that the school and program in which you are interested are eligible to participate in federal financial aid programs? The simple answer, of course, is call them and ask. However, you can also do some double-checking on your own to confirm what the school tells you.

If you plan to enroll in a regionally accredited traditional college or university, you can safely assume that the institution as a whole is eligible to participate in federal aid programs—since distance certificates and degrees are likely to be a very small proportion of its overall offerings (see "Selecting a Good Distance Learning Program" for a discussion of accreditation). However, because institutions have the discretion to exclude specific programs, you should double-check to see if the school disperses federal aid to students enrolled in programs that interest you. Call the financial aid office and ask. If you are not sure of the accreditation status, and therefore the Title IV status, of the school in which you are interested, first check with the school to find out which agencies, if any, have accredited it. Then visit the Department of Education's Web site to check on the accrediting agencies. The department lists the accrediting agencies of which it approves, and in its short description of each agency, it indicates whether or not the institutions it accredits qualify for Title IV funding. You can then call the accrediting agency to make sure it has indeed accredited the school or program in which you are interested.

FEDERAL AID PROGRAMS

Once you've established the eligibility of the institution and program in which you are interested, you may want to check the federal aid programs in which they participate. Not all schools participate in all the available programs.

Among the federal aid programs are Pell Grants, Federal Supplemental Educational Opportunity Grants, work-study, Federal Family Education Loans (FFEL) and William D. Ford Direct Loans (commonly called Stafford loans), and Perkins Loans.

Pell Grants. Pell Grants, which do not have to be repaid, are awarded to undergraduate students on the basis of need, even if they are enrolled less than half time. In some cases, a student enrolled in a postbaccalaureate teacher certification program may be awarded a Pell Grant. There are no Pell Grants for other graduate students.

The maximum amount of the Pell Grant changes each year and depends on annual funding allocations by Congress. The maximum award for the school year 2006–07 was $4,310. The amount of an award depends on a combination of your financial need, your costs to attend school, your enrollment status as a full-time or part-time student, and whether or not you plan to study for a full academic year or less.

If you are awarded a Pell Grant, the money can be applied directly to your school costs or be paid to you directly or some combination of these methods. Your school must inform you on how it will be disbursing your grant. Disbursements must occur at least once per term or a minimum of twice a year.

Federal Supplemental Educational Opportunity Grants. Federal Supplemental Educational Opportunity Grants (FSEOGs) are awards to undergraduates with exceptional financial need, even if they are enrolled less than half time. These grants generally go to Pell Grant recipients with the lowest EFC. The amount of an FSEOG ranges from $100 to $4,000 per year.

Unlike the Pell Grant program, which provides funds to each eligible student, the FSEOG program is campus-based. This means that the federal government awards each participating institution a certain amount of money, and the school's financial aid office decides how to allocate it. When the school uses up its funding for the year, there are no more FSEOGs awarded. Check with your school to see whether or not it participates in this program.

Federal Work-Study Program. Some colleges and universities participate in the federal work-study program, which provides part-time jobs in public and private nonprofit organizations to both undergraduate and graduate students who demonstrate financial need. The government pays up to 75 percent of your wages, and your employer pays the balance. The value of a work-study job depends on your need, the other elements in your financial aid package, and the amount of money the school has to offer. Not all universities have work-study funds, and some that do have the funds limit their use to undergraduates.

If you receive work-study funds, you may be able to use them in a job that is related to your field. You will have to check with the financial aid office to find out what jobs are available, whether or not you can use the funds in a job you find elsewhere, and what bureaucratic requirements you will have to satisfy.

Stafford Loan Programs (FFEL and Direct Loans). The FFEL program and the William D. Ford Direct Loan Program, commonly called Stafford loans, are two loan programs sponsored by the federal government. Schools generally participate in one of the two programs. The terms and conditions of these loans are similar; the major differences are the source of the funds and some repayment provisions. If you get a FFEL, your funds will come from a bank, credit union, or other participating lender. If you get a Direct Loan, the money comes directly from the federal government.

You are eligible to borrow under these loan programs if you are enrolled at least half time and have financial need remaining after your EFC, Pell Grant eligibility, and aid from other sources are subtracted from your annual cost of attendance. Depending on your need, you may be eligible for a subsidized loan in which the government pays the interest that accrues while you are enrolled at least half time. If you cannot demonstrate sufficient financial need according to government criteria, you may still be able to borrow, but your Stafford loan will be unsubsidized. This means that interest will accrue on the loan while you are still in school unless you arrange to pay it during this period.

In both types of Stafford loans, repayment of the principal as well as future interest begins six months after you are last enrolled on at least a half-time basis. Undergraduates may borrow a maximum of $3,500 to $10,500 per year. Graduate students may borrow up to $18,500 per year up to a maximum of $138,500, which includes any undergraduate loans you may still have. The interest rate varies annually and is set each July. Right now it is capped at 8.25 percent.

Perkins Loan Program. Another source of federal funds is the Perkins Loan program. The Perkins Loan is available to both undergraduate and graduate students who demonstrate exceptional financial need, whether enrolled full-time or part-time, and it is administered by each individual college or university. In some cases, schools reserve Perkins Loans for undergraduates. If you are an undergraduate eligible for a Perkins Loan, you may be able to borrow up to $4,000 per year with a $20,000 maximum. An eligible graduate student may be able to borrow up to $6,000 per year with a $40,000 maximum including undergraduate and graduate Perkins borrowing.

At present, the interest rate is 5 percent, and no interest accrues while you are enrolled in school at least half time. You must start repaying the loan nine months after you are last enrolled on a half-time basis. This loan is the best deal offered by the government.

REPAYING YOUR FEDERAL LOANS

After you graduate, leave school, or drop below half-time status, you will have a grace period of either six or nine months before loan payments start. During the grace period, you will be sent information about payment plans and your first payment due date. You can repay the loan over a maximum of 10 years with a $50 minimum monthly payment, with a graduated plan in which the payments start out low and gradually increase, or with a plan that bases your payments on your income level.

You can also consolidate all your outstanding federal loans into one loan. Having one loan to repay will minimize the chances of administrative error and allow you to write one check per month rather than several.

If you have trouble repaying your federal loans, you may qualify for a deferment or forbearance on your loan. During a deferment, payments are suspended, and if the loan is subsidized, interest does not accrue. During forbearance, payments are postponed or reduced. Repayment assistance may be available if you serve in the military.

STATE AID PROGRAMS

Some states offer financial aid to state residents that attend school in-state, some offer aid to state residents that attend school in-state or elsewhere, and some offer aid to students that attend school in their state regardless of their residency status. Some states, like California, New York, Michigan, Oklahoma, and Texas, have large aid programs. Other states may have little or nothing to offer. Contact your state scholarship office directly to find out what's available and whether you are eligible to apply. Telephone numbers are listed in the Appendix.

PRIVATE SOURCES OF FINANCIAL AID

In addition to the federal government, other organizations provide financial aid to students. These include your school, national and local organizations, private lenders, employers, internships, and cooperative education programs.

THE COLLEGE OR UNIVERSITY

Second only to the federal government in the amount of financial aid disbursed yearly are colleges and universities. Many of these institutions award both need-based and merit-based aid to deserving students. To find out more about the types of aid that the school you are interested in disburses, contact the financial aid office.

NATIONAL AND LOCAL ORGANIZATIONS

Foundations, nonprofit organizations, churches, service and fraternal organizations, professional associations, corporations, unions, and many other national and local organizations award grants to students of higher education. Many of these awards go to students who fit a certain profile, but many of them are open to anyone who applies. The drawback of this type of aid is that you have to locate it and apply on your own.

PRIVATE LENDERS

Many students borrow from private lenders, whether through alternative loan programs, home equity loans, or other types of loans.

Alternative Loan Programs. In addition to the federal loan programs, there are many private alternative loan programs designed to help students. Most private loan programs disburse funds based on your creditworthiness rather than your financial need. Some loan programs target all types of students; others are designed specifically for graduate or professional students. In addition, you can use other types of private loans not specifically designed for education to help finance your degree. For more information, check with your bank and your school's financial aid office.

Home Equity Loans. For students who own their own homes, a home equity loan or line of credit can be an attractive financing alternative to private loan programs. Some of these loans are offered at low rates and allow you to defer payment of the principal for years. In addition, if you use the loan to pay for educational expenses, the interest on the loan is tax deductible.

Credit Cards. Whatever you do, do not use your credit cards to borrow money for school on a long-term basis. The interest rates and finance charges will be high, and the balance will grow astronomically. Credit cards are useful to pay tuition and fees if you (1) can pay the balance in full, (2) expect a student loan to come through shortly, (3) expect your employer to reimburse your costs. Otherwise, avoid them.

INTERNSHIPS AND COOPERATIVE EDUCATION PROGRAMS

In addition to the federal work-study program, there are other employment opportunities that may help you finance your education. Internships with organizations outside the university can provide money as well as practical experience in your field. As an intern, you are usually paid by the outside organization, and you may or may not get credit for the work you do. Although they have been common in the professional programs, such as design and business, for years, lately internships have been growing in popularity in academic programs as well.

In cooperative education programs, you usually alternate periods of full-time work in your field with periods of full-time study. You are paid for the work you do, and you may or may not get academic credit for it as well.

Internship and cooperative education programs may be administered in your department or by a separate office, so you will have to ask to find out.

EMPLOYER REIMBURSEMENT

If you work full time and attend school part time, you may be reimbursed for part or all of your tuition by your employer. Many employers require that you receive a minimum grade in order to qualify for reimbursement. Keep in mind, however, that your employer will withhold taxes and other deductions when it reimburses you, and you will have to make up the difference. Check with your employer before you enroll; some employers reimburse tuition only for job-related courses. Others will not reimburse employees for distance learning courses.

Some large corporations that consider job-related certificate and degrees as forms of employee training may underwrite the entire cost of a program. For example, AT&T pays Denise Petrosino's tuition directly to the University of Phoenix Online. "As long as I maintain a B average, I have 100 percent coverage," explains Petrosino, who is earning a master's degree in organizational management.

LOCATING INFORMATION ABOUT FINANCIAL AID

Finding information about financial aid can be a challenge. There is no one central clearinghouse for information about financial aid for undergraduate and graduate study. You are going to have to check a number of different sources to get the full picture on possible sources of aid that are available for you. We'll discuss a few of them here, but for a list of financial aid resources, see the Appendix.

THE GOVERNMENT

The best source of information on federal aid for students is the U.S. government itself. The federal aid programs are administered by the U.S. Department of Education. You can contact them through their Web site, by telephone, or by mail. (See the Appendix for specifics.) Remember, however, that not all colleges and universities participate in each federal program, so if a particular federal aid program interests you, you will have to contact your school's financial aid office to make sure it's available.

If you are a graduate student, you should note that many agencies of the federal government offer fellowships to graduate students in related fields. Contact the agencies that are relevant to your field of study for further information.

For information on state aid, contact your state agency of higher education (see the Appendix).

THE COLLEGE OR UNIVERSITY

At a small college, the financial aid office is usually the source of all financial aid information. However, at a university, there is more than one office involved with student aid, and thus more than one source of information about it. Each university has a different administrative structure, so you will have to figure out the offices you will most likely need to contact. These may include:

- **The financial aid office.** The university-wide financial aid office is generally the best source of information about federal and private loan programs as well as university-based grants and federal work-study assistance. They may also be able to steer you to other sources of information.

- **The college or school's administrative office.** The next place to check is the administrative office of the college or school to which you are applying. For example, you may be applying for a master's degree in special education. This department may be under the jurisdiction of the College of Education. That office may or may not administer grants to the students of the college. Call to find out.

- **The office of the graduate school.** If you are a graduate student, it pays to check this administrative office; it may or may not have funding to award. If it does, the fellowships or grants are likely to be awarded on a university-wide, competitive basis.

- **The specific program or department to which you are applying.** Often a program brochure describes the types of aid that the department awards its students. If you cannot find this information in the materials you have, then call the program and ask. You'll be able to find out about program aid from this source.

It's important to check with all these offices to see what's available. It's also important to be proactive and call the financial aid office as well as other offices to find out your chances of receiving aid.

THE INTERNET

The Internet is an excellent source of information about all types of financial aid. One of the best places to start your Internet search for financial aid is the Financial Aid Information Page at www.finaid.org. This site has a great deal of information about the different types of financial aid and provides links to other relevant sites as well. It provides a good overview of the financial aid situation. In addition, the site offers several calculators that enable you to estimate many useful figures, including your EFC, projected costs of attendance, and future student loan payments. There are also a number of searchable databases of national scholarships and fellowships on the Internet. One searchable database of financial aid resources can be found on Peterson's Web site (www.petersons.com/finaid), which lists millions of sources of aid totaling billions of dollars. Another scholarship database is FastWeb at www.fastweb.com. On each of these sites, you'll need to answer a questionnaire about your educational background, field of study, and personal characteristics. When you are done, the database is searched to match your data with eligibility requirements of several hundred thousand fellowships and scholarships. You are then given a list of possible fellowships and scholarships to pursue on your own. There is no cost for either of these services.

There are a few things you should beware of when using Internet search services. First, a searchable database is only as good as its index, so you may find yourself getting some odd matches. In addition, most searchable databases of scholarships and fellowships are designed primarily for undergraduates, so the number of potential matches for a graduate student is far fewer than the several hundred thousand sources of aid that a database may contain. Finally, some of these Internet search services charge a fee. Given the amount of free information that's available, both on the Internet and in libraries, it's not necessary to pay for this type of research.

PRINT DIRECTORIES

Although the searchable databases on the Internet are easy to use, it's still a good idea to check print directories of national scholarships, grants, and fellowships. These directories have indexes that make locating potential sources of funds easy. Scholarships, grants, and fellowships are indexed by field of study as well as by type of student. So, for example, you can search for all funding related to the study of Latin America or electrical engineering. Or you can search for funding that is targeted to Hispanic students, disabled students, or adult students. It's a good idea just to browse, too, in case something catches your eye.

There are quite a few directories that you can consult. For undergraduates, Peterson's *Scholarships, Grants, & Prizes* lists many private sources of aid, and Peterson's *College Money Handbook* covers college and university sources of financial aid. For graduate students, the *Annual Register of Grant Support: A Directory of Funding Sources*, published by the National Register Publishing Company, is a comprehensive guide to awards from the government, foundations, and business and professional organizations.

APPLYING FOR FINANCIAL AID

Depending on your personal situation and the requirements of the school, you may have to submit just one or a number of applications for financial aid. If you apply for need-based aid, university merit aid, national scholarships and fellowships, or private loan programs, you will have several application forms to deal with. However many applications you must submit, start the process early.

DEADLINES

"I cannot overemphasize the importance of applying early," says Emerelle McNair, director of scholarships and financial aid at Southern Polytechnic State University in Georgia. "Most awards are made in spring for the following academic year." Be sure you've picked the correct deadlines from your program application information packet. *Students applying for financial aid often have an earlier deadline for the entire application.* If you look for sources of aid outside the program and university, such as national scholarships and fellowships, then it is even more important to start your research early—a full year or more before you plan to enroll.

Remember, it can easily take months to fill out applications and assemble all the supporting data for a financial aid request. You may need to submit income tax forms, untaxed income verification, asset verification, and documents that support any special circumstances you are claiming. For private scholarship applications, you may need to write an essay and provide letters of

recommendation. So give yourself plenty of time to submit the initial application. Later, if you are asked to provide additional information or supporting documents, do so as quickly as possible.

THE FAFSA

The Free Application for Federal Student Aid (FAFSA) is the only form you will need to apply for most federal need-based aid programs and state aid programs as well. FAFSA is used by both undergraduate and graduate students. The FAFSA form is issued annually by the Department of Education at the end of each calendar year (see www.fafsa.ed.gov), and it is available both in paper and online. You use it to report financial data from the previous year in order to be considered for aid in the school year that starts the following fall. It's much easier to fill out the FAFSA if you have already done your federal income tax forms for the year, but since most schools require you to file the FAFSA in January or February, that may be difficult. If your federal income tax return is not done, use estimates so you can file the FAFSA on time. You can amend it later if necessary. Because the FAFSA is designed for undergraduate students who are dependent on their parents, if you are a working adult student you may find you are having difficulty interpreting some of the questions or that the questions do not cover all your circumstances. If there is information about your financial situation that is not elicited by the FAFSA but that you feel is germane to your application, then explain the circumstances in a separate letter to the financial aid office of the schools to which you apply. Suppose, for example, that you have been working full-time for a few years but you are planning to quit your job and attend school full-time. You would complete the FAFSA using the previous year's full-time income figures, but this would not be an accurate reflection of your financial situation during the following school year because your income will drop precipitously. In such a case, you would notify the financial aid office so that it can make a professional judgment as to whether or not your need should be revised upward.

After you submit the FAFSA, you will receive a Student Aid Report (SAR), an acknowledgment that includes a summary of the data you have sent them. Check to make sure the information is accurate and that the schools you have chosen to have the data sent to are correctly listed. If there are errors, make corrections right away. The SAR will also show your EFC, the amount you and your spouse (or parents if you are still a dependent) will be expected to contribute. This information is used by each school to calculate your financial need (cost of attendance minus EFC) and to award need-based aid.

SCHOOL'S FINANCIAL AID APPLICATION FORM OR CSS PROFILE

A school may require that you submit a separate financial aid application in addition to the program application and the FAFSA. If you do not see such a form in the program application packet, call the admissions office to find out whether or not you need to obtain it from another office.

Some schools do not have their own financial aid application form. Instead, they require you to submit a standardized form, the College Scholarship Service's (CSS) Financial Aid PROFILE. This form is similar to the FAFSA, but it is used to award university aid.

THE PROGRAM APPLICATION

For many schools, the program application is the main application for university-based aid. Much of the nonfederal university-based aid for incoming students is determined by the admissions committee's assessment of the merit of program applications. So a strong program application, submitted on time, will improve your chances of getting aid from the program or university. Since you cannot predict which elements of your application will be weighted most heavily by a given admissions committee, do your best on all of them.

NATIONAL AND PRIVATE SCHOLARSHIP AND FELLOWSHIP APPLICATIONS

If you apply for national and/or private scholarships and fellowships, you will have to submit separate applications for each one to the awarding organizations. Follow instructions carefully, making sure you meet all deadlines. Some scholarship applications can be as elaborate as program applications, with letters of recommendation and essays, so allow yourself a lot of time to complete them.

FOLLOWING UP

Just as you do with your program application, follow up with your financial aid applications as well. If you do not receive the SAR, an acknowledgment that your FAFSA form was received, within a few weeks of filing the FAFSA, check on its status. In addition, call the university offices with which you are dealing to make sure everything is proceeding smoothly.

TAX BENEFITS FOR STUDENTS

Whether or not you receive financial aid, there are many recently enacted tax benefits for adults who want to return to school (as well as for parents who send or plan to send their children to college). In effect, these tax cuts make the first two years of college universally available, and they give many more working adults the financial means to go back to school. About 12.9 million students benefit—5.8 million under the HOPE Scholarship tax credit and 7.1 million under the Lifetime Learning tax credit. Countless others benefit from new rules concerning Individual Retirement Accounts (IRAs) and state tuition savings plans as well as from deductions on student loan interest and employer reimbursements for education expenses.

THE HOPE SCHOLARSHIP TAX CREDIT

The HOPE Scholarship tax credit helps make the first two years of college or career school more affordable. Students whose adjusted gross income falls within certain limits receive a 100 percent tax credit for the first $1,000 of tuition and required fees and a 50 percent credit on the second $1,000. This credit is available for tuition and required fees less grants, scholarships, and other tax-free educational assistance. The credit is phased out for joint filers whose adjusted gross income is between $80,000 and $100,000 and for single filers whose adjusted gross income is between $40,000 and $50,000.

The HOPE Scholarship tax credit can be claimed for students who are in their first two years of college or career school and who are enrolled on at least a half-time basis in a degree or certificate program for any portion of the year. The taxpayer can claim a credit for his own tuition expense or for the expenses of his or her spouse or dependent children.

THE LIFETIME LEARNING TAX CREDIT

The Lifetime Learning tax credit is targeted toward adults who want to go back to school, change careers, or take a course or two to upgrade their skills as well as to college juniors, seniors, and graduate and professional degree students. A family may receive a 20 percent tax credit for the first $10,000 of tuition and required fees.

Just like the HOPE Scholarship tax credit, the Lifetime Learning tax credit is available for tuition and required fees less grants, scholarships, and other tax-free educational assistance. The maximum credit is determined on a per-taxpayer (family) basis, regardless of the number of postsecondary students in the family, and it is phased out at the same income levels as the HOPE Scholarship tax credit. Families can claim the Lifetime Learning tax credit for some members of their family and the HOPE Scholarship tax credit for others who qualify in the same year.

INDIVIDUAL RETIREMENT ACCOUNTS

Since January 1, 1998, taxpayers have been able to withdraw funds from an IRA, without penalty, for their own higher education expenses or those of their spouse, child, or even grandchild. However, you do have to pay income taxes on the amount you withdraw.

In addition, for each child under age 18, families may deposit $500 per year into an education IRA in the child's name. Earnings in the education IRA accumulate tax-free, and no taxes are due upon withdrawal if the money is used to pay for postsecondary tuition and required fees (less grants, scholarships, and other tax-free educational assistance), books, equipment, and eligible room and board expenses. Once the child reaches age 30, his or her education IRA must be closed or transferred to a younger member of the family.

A taxpayer's ability to contribute to an education IRA is phased out when the taxpayer is a joint filer with an adjusted gross income between $150,000 and $160,000, or a single filer with an adjusted gross income between $95,000 and $110,000. There are a few restrictions. For example, a student who receives the tax-free distributions from an education IRA may not, in the same year, benefit from the HOPE Scholarship or Lifetime Learning tax credits.

STATE TUITION PLANS

When a family uses a qualified state-sponsored tuition plan to save for college, no tax is due in connection with the plan until the time of withdrawal. Families can now use these plans to save not only for tuition but also for certain room and board expenses for students who attend college on at least a half-time basis. Tuition and required fees paid with withdrawals from a qualified state tuition plan are eligible for the HOPE Scholarship tax credit and Lifetime Learning tax credit.

TAX-DEDUCTIBLE STUDENT LOAN INTEREST

For many graduates, one of the first financial obligations is to repay their student loans. The new student loan interest deduction reduces the burden of the repayment obligation by allowing students or their families to take a tax deduction for interest paid in the first 60 months of repayment on student loans. The deduction is available even if an individual does not itemize other deductions.

The maximum deduction of $2,000 in 2000 rose to $2,500 in 2001 and beyond. It is phased out for joint filers with adjusted gross income between $60,000 and $75,000, and for single filers with adjusted gross income between $40,000 and $55,000.

TAX-DEDUCTIBLE EMPLOYER REIMBURSEMENTS

If you take undergraduate courses and your employer reimburses you for education-related expenses, you may be able to exclude up to $5,250 of employer-provided education benefits from your income. Reimbursement for graduate and professional courses is not eligible for this exclusion and is counted as taxable income.

COMMUNITY SERVICE LOAN FORGIVENESS

This provision excludes from your income any student loan amounts forgiven by nonprofit, tax-exempt charitable, or educational institutions for borrowers who take community-service jobs that address unmet community needs. For example, a recent graduate who takes a low-paying job in a rural school will not owe any additional income tax if in recognition of this service her

college or another charity forgives a loan it made to her to help pay her college costs. This provision applies to loans forgiven after August 5, 1997.

FOR ADDITIONAL INFORMATION

The tax issues relating to higher education are discussed in more detail in Internal Revenue Service Publication 970, *Tax Benefits for Higher Education.* To obtain a copy, visit the Internal Revenue Service Web site at www.irs.gov or call 800-829-3676 (toll-free).

PAYING FOR SCHOOL IS POSSIBLE

You can see that it *is* possible to find the financial aid that will help you pay for school. You will have to be persistent in your search for funds. You may have to spend time working on financial aid research and applications. You may have to borrow money. And once you enter a program, you may have to simplify your lifestyle in order to cut your expenses.

But if you really want to earn a degree or certificate, you can find the financial help that will make it possible. Be realistic about your needs, leave yourself enough time to complete all the paperwork, and do your homework. Now is a good time to look back on all the reasons why you want to continue your education—to remind yourself why it's worth it.

SUCCEEDING AS A DISTANCE LEARNER

Congratulations! You have weathered the selection and application process and you are about to embark on a new phase of your education. As you will soon find out for yourself, taking courses at a distance is not like going to class on campus. Distance learners often have the convenience of setting their own hours and pacing themselves in their studies. As we have seen in previous sections, the instructional technology lends itself to innovative approaches to teaching and learning, including more student participation and collaboration, especially in online courses. You'll find that because you work at a distance you will have more time to reflect about and respond to what you learn as well as to take part in discussions. You may be surprised at the ways in which the community of learning develops in a well-run distance course.

Of course, distance learners face a few challenges unique to the instructional design of distance courses. As a distance learner, you'll be expected to organize your time, work independently as well as collaboratively, take the initiative in your studies, and monitor your own progress, all while mastering the technology and using it as a valuable tool for learning.

So, in addition to the basic study skills you would need to earn any degree—reading, writing, analytical thinking, and test-taking skills—you will need other skills and strategies to succeed at distance learning. In this section we'll give you some suggestions and tips from successful distance learners that will help you become a more effective and successful student yourself.

MASTERING THE TECHNOLOGY

We'll start with technology, because success in distance learning depends first upon reliable technology that you understand how to use. Once you've mastered the technology, it will recede into the background and become something you simply use and even take for granted.

HAVING THE RIGHT EQUIPMENT

Before you start a course, make sure you have the technological tools you will need to participate in discussions and complete assignments. Most programs provide a list of technical requirements ahead of time. If your course is online, get a list of the hardware and software required, and make sure the computer you plan to use is properly equipped and that you have a reliable Internet service provider. If you take a course via broadcast or videotapes, learn how to use your VCR. If you have to buy equipment, don't skimp on specifications to save a few dollars now. The money you spend now to make sure you have the appropriate hardware and software is money well spent, because you'll find it much easier to get your work done properly if you are not struggling with inadequate machinery.

IMPROVING YOUR TECHNOLOGY SKILLS

If you have the proper equipment but think you may not be up to speed technologically, try to improve your technology skills before courses start. As we discussed in "Selecting a Good Distance Learning Program," many colleges offer online tutorials or sample minicourses that you can take if you feel you need some practice with the technology before you actually take your first course. "I am a computer novice and never realized the extent of the computer's online capabilities until I had to learn about it through trial and error," reports a language arts literacy teacher who took a graduate course online from Rutgers University. "This was very frustrating." So if you have the opportunity for a sample course or practice session before courses begin, take it.

TIPS FOR SUCCEEDING WITH TECHNOLOGY

To master the technology involved in your distance courses:

- Make sure you have the appropriate hardware and software for your courses, and don't skimp on the specifications if you need to purchase any items.
- Take a tutorial or sample minicourse ahead of time to familiarize yourself with the instructional technology.
- Allow yourself extra time at the beginning of the course to navigate the technology.
- Keep copies of your assignments and back up your computer files.
- Ask for help when you need it. Well-run distance programs have technological support via telephone seven days a week, 24 hours a day.

Remember, the technology involved in distance learning is a tool that anyone can master—it just may take some effort.

LEARNING ABOUT LIBRARY RESOURCES

Once you've got the technology working for you, the next resource you need to familiarize yourself with is the library. Understanding how to use a library is important to any student's success, but it is especially important for distance students who may not be able to get to a good bricks-and-mortar university library to get the materials they need.

TAKING AN ORIENTATION PROGRAM

One of the first things you should check before courses begin is whether or not a library services orientation program designed for distance students is available. If it is, sign up to take the orientation right away. "An early orientation to library resources, particularly interlibrary loans, is needed for those who can't physically access a library," recommends Kurt Krause, a hotel manager who took an online hospitality management course from

Virginia Tech. Learning about library services through an orientation program will save you time later on when you actually need to do research for a course.

LEARNING WHAT'S AVAILABLE ONLINE

Although the Internet has revolutionized the way we look for and store information, don't make the mistake of thinking that all the information you will need is available on the Internet. True, many journals, databases, catalogs, and newspapers are instantaneously available online, and you can access them directly or through the university library if a subscription is needed. However, the material that's available online is only a fraction of the total resources of a library. Books, for example, are still primarily in print form. Many academic journals provide only abstracts (not full-text articles) online, and a few are not online at all. Reference services may be available only face-to-face or by telephone. And reserve collections may or may not be available online. So one of the first tasks you face is to learn just what you can access online via the university library or directly on the Internet and what you must access in paper, microform, or other physical media.

PLANNING AHEAD TO GET THE MATERIALS YOU NEED

The reason you will need to know what your research resources are fairly early in the game is that you will have to plan ahead if you need to access nondigitized (paper) information at a distance, especially if the material needs to be secured via interlibrary loan. "Because I did not have physical access to a medical library in my community, I had to organize my data collection for assigned papers early in the semester," explains Patti Iversen. "The biggest handicap was the time delay in ordering and receiving full-text articles. A time lapse of three weeks from time of request to delivery of articles was common." You can see the need to plan ahead under these circumstances.

TIPS FOR SUCCEEDING WITH LIBRARY RESOURCES

In order to be prepared for course work, early in the term or, even better, before the term starts:

- **Take a library orientation if one is available.** If there is no formal distance orientation, call the library and ask for an informal orientation.
- **Check your local public and university libraries.** Find out what resources they have and whether or not you can arrange access.
- **Check each course syllabus very early in the term.** Determine whether you can obtain everything you will need online or whether you will have to make other arrangements for some items.
- **Use the reference services of your university library.** Ask for help. Reference librarians are there to help you, even if it's by e-mail or over the phone.

MANAGING YOUR TIME

"If you are a student at any college, there is one thing you just don't have enough of....TIME! Everything is about time," says

Cena Barber, an undergraduate who has taken online courses toward her degree in political science and history at Drake University in Iowa. For students who have family and work responsibilities as well, lack of time is a particularly acute problem. "With life's challenges, kids, family, job—it's hard to keep your studies a high priority," explains Scott Garrod, who is earning a master's degree in business from Syracuse University. "When your four-year-old wants a story read, do you have to study your accounting? That's an easy choice, but it means making up the accounting at a later time."

GENERAL TIPS FOR MANAGING YOUR TIME

Not having enough time is a common problem. Distance learners can approach this problem in several ways:

- **Be realistic about how many courses you can handle.** If you work and/or have a family, you will have relatively little time to spend on schoolwork. Start out with one or two courses at a time, and then if you feel you can increase your courseload, do so. This is especially important if you take a distance course for the first time and don't know exactly what to expect.
- **Set up a regular time to study, but expect to be interrupted.** If you have a study schedule, you are more likely to get your schoolwork done, but be sure to leave some extra time. Unless you live alone, you'll need time for your family commitments. Young kids, especially, don't much care what you are doing when they need a parent, so if possible try to schedule study time when they are not around.
- **Set up a regular place to study.** Although it may be difficult if you are doing schoolwork at home, try to establish a study area that's yours alone to use. If possible, the area should be quiet and free of distractions. "Since you are doing the work at home you can be easily distracted," explains Andrea Bessel, who is earning a bachelor's degree in business administration from the State University of New York at Oswego. "A lot of times something comes up and I end up setting my homework aside, which is not a good habit to get into." So if necessary, do schoolwork at your local public library or from work if your employer permits it.
- **Set priorities on what you have to do.** Make judgments about what you need to do, and then spend your time on activities that are the most important and must be done first. Get used to the fact that you may have to postpone some tasks.
- **Set deadlines.** Distance learning can be very unstructured, so you probably will have to be your own taskmaster. "I have learned that I have to set deadlines for myself," says Brigit Dolan, who is earning a master's degree from Gonzaga University in Washington, "or I will never get anything done."
- **Don't procrastinate.** "Procrastination is your worst enemy," claims Robin Barnes, who earned a master's degree in nursing (family nurse-practitioner) from Gonzaga University.
- **Use time-management tools to help you schedule your time.** Planners, whether paper or electronic, can help you allocate time and keep track of deadlines. "To do" lists can help you manage your short-term commitments.

MANAGING TIME IN ONLINE COURSES

In addition to the lack of time that all students contend with, online distance learners face unique challenges associated with time, namely, managing the flexibility of the online format and dealing with lag time when communicating with students and faculty members.

MANAGING THE FLEXIBILITY OF ONLINE COURSES

Flexibility is a unique advantage that attracts people to asynchronous courses, especially online courses. But flexibility can have a downside as well. "The best thing about distance learning is the freedom to set one's own hours for study and learning. The worst thing about distance learning is the freedom to set one's own hours for study and learning!" exclaims a middle school language arts literacy teacher taking an online graduate course from Rutgers. "Although it hasn't happened to me, it is easy to put aside work and projects for the course when one is not locked into a regular schedule. I can see how one could easily fall behind through a lack of discipline." So you can see that you'll have to use your time-management skills to take advantage of the flexibility and not let it take advantage of you.

MANAGING THE AMOUNT OF TIME SPENT ONLINE

Not only does the flexibility of online courses mean that you need discipline to log on regularly, but once you are connected you have, in theory, as much time as you want to spend on the course. Cena Barber points out, "There is no time limit as to how long the class lasts. It could be five minutes one day and five hours the next." Unless you are careful, it's easy to spend more time than you really have on an online course, so before you log on, decide how much time you have to spend during that session.

GETTING ACCUSTOMED TO THE PACE

Another difference between online and traditional courses that comes as a surprise to many students is the pace at which discussions proceed. In an online course, there is a time interval between when you post a message and when you get a response—in an asynchronous discussion group—or when you send an e-mail and get a reply. Hours, even days, may elapse between exchanges on a topic, and it can take a while to get used to the slow progress of communication.

The time delay sometimes becomes a problem when students work on a group project with deadlines. "Given the time lag, it took ever so much more time to get anything done if you had to collaborate with anyone," explains a library media specialist taking an online postgraduate course from Rutgers. "When would they open the discussion thread? When would they respond? These were frustrations that I hadn't counted on and found difficult to deal with." To solve these problems, groups working on projects often communicate by telephone or in real-time chat rooms.

TIPS FOR MANAGING TIME IN ONLINE COURSES

Given the asynchronous nature of online courses, you will not be able to completely solve the time problems they pose. However, you can minimize or avoid them to some degree.

- **Set a schedule for logging on.** Even though no one may have given you a daily class schedule, you will benefit if you work one out for yourself. "You should become accustomed to getting online on a regular basis," advises Vania McBean, a computer studies major at University of Maryland University College. "I log on each day to see what is new."

- **Limit the amount of time you will spend online at one session.** The limit might be 1 hour, for example. On some days that will be too much time, and on others, too little, but at least you will have a benchmark to aim for.

- **Don't fret about the time delays in asynchronous discussions.** Before you know it, you will have become used to this method of communication and it will no longer seem odd.

- **Use a chat room or the telephone when asynchronous communication becomes too slow.** You can make an appointment to meet in a chat room or have a teleconference if group work needs to be accomplished more efficiently. If e-mailing a fellow student or the instructor takes too long, try telephoning.

MANAGING TIME IN VIDEOTAPED COURSES

Students that take courses in which on-campus lectures are videotaped and mailed to them face a different set of time-management challenges. First, the weekly videotapes may take a considerable amount of time to watch. And second, the taping, duplicating, and delivery time means that distance students lag behind on-campus students in the same course.

SCHEDULING TIME TO WATCH THE VIDEOS

Depending on the course load, students that take videotaped courses may find themselves with 3 to 12 hours or more of videotape to watch each week on top of their assignments. Essentially, the amount of time is the same as it would be if they had to attend classes. Since they don't have to attend classes, inexperienced students may put off watching the videos, thinking they can catch up at a later date. "In the first semester, the learning curve is steep," comments Dale Ann Abendroth, assistant professor of nursing at Gonzaga University. "So I set up my assignments to force students into a pattern of watching the videotapes." If you have a savvy instructor, the assignments will put you on a schedule. If the instructor doesn't take a structured approach, you will need to plan a regular schedule to watch the videos in order to keep up with the course work.

MANAGING THE DELAY BETWEEN DISTANCE AND ON-CAMPUS STUDENTS

In videotaped courses, the distance students are a half-week to a week behind the on-campus students. "It can get a little confusing when reading topics don't correspond with lecture topics because the tapes arrive one week later than the class," explains Carla Gentry, who is earning a Master of Science in Nursing (family nurse-practitioner) from Gonzaga University. If the course also has a Web-based component, the distance students have to cope with joining the Web-based discussion group and receiving the readings before the videotaped lectures arrive.

Schools do try to solve this time-delay problem, with mixed success. "Throughout the semester, we have a one-week lag on assignment due dates (in comparison to the students who are actually in class on campus)," explains Nicole DeRaleau, who is earning a master's degree in engineering from Worcester Polytechnic Institute in Massachusetts. "At the end of the semester, however, we have a one-week disadvantage because the whole class has to turn in final assignments, projects, and finals on the same date in order to get grades done on time," says DeRaleau. "This can be *very* stressful." In contrast, at Gonzaga University's nursing program, distance students are permitted to take their final exams in their local communities a few days later than the on-campus students. "These are logistical problems that both the faculty and students become accustomed to solving," explains Abendroth.

TIPS FOR MANAGING TIME IN VIDEOTAPED COURSES

There are a couple of things you can do to manage your time if you take videotaped courses:

- **Set a schedule for watching the videotapes.** Even though you don't have to show up for class, you still need to put in classroom time in front of your own TV. If you're good at multitasking, you can follow Brigit Dolan's lead. "Sometimes I'm able to pick up my house while listening and taking in the information," explains the graduate student.

- **Keep up with your course work.** Since at times you may need to complete assignments or take exams with less lead time than on-campus students have, it's imperative that you keep up with the work on a regular basis. You may face an end-of-term time crunch, so study regularly throughout the course to minimize its effect.

COMMUNICATING WITH FACULTY

When you are a distance learner you can't just raise your hand and ask a question or stay after class to talk with the instructor. Even in two-way interactive video classes, which are more similar to traditional classes than other distance learning formats, there can be difficulties in communicating with an instructor at a remote location. "It can be a little more inconvenient to speak with your instructor if you need to ask about something you wouldn't ask in front of the whole class," reports a horticulture student taking a two-way interactive video course from the University of Cincinnati.

For students in online and videotaped courses, communicating with an instructor can be slow. "Sometimes you do more self-teaching because you cannot just drop into the instructor's office," explains Robin Barnes. "You may have to wait a day or two for an answer to a question. Have patience and be kind to yourself." However, you can use technology to your advantage in communicating with faculty members. E-mail, for example, is an excellent way to contact a faculty member to find out what his or her expectations are, to clarify assignments, or simply to ask a question. You may not get a response immediately, but most faculty members will answer their e-mail within a day or two. In fact, you should make a point of communicating with your instructor in distance courses. "Be sure to communicate regularly with your professor because [the course] can seem pretty far removed if you are not getting feedback every week or so," advises Sonja Cole, a middle school media specialist taking online courses from Rutgers.

TIPS FOR COMMUNICATING WITH FACULTY MEMBERS

To ensure you get the input an instructor can provide and to make yourself known, here are some strategies for communicating with faculty members:

- **Participate in online discussion groups.** Although your instructor may not comment all the time, he or she is following the class's discussions and will get to know you there.

- **Participate in class discussions in two-way interactive video courses.** It's easy to "hide in the back of the class" if you attend a course in a remote location, but you'll get more out of the class if you respond to the instructor and the class discussion.

- **Be assertive in communicating with your instructors.** "You have to take the initiative," advises a distance learning student. "If you do not make sure that you get the best learning opportunity that you can, no one is going to do that for you." Remember, most faculty members are more than happy to help their students.

- **Use e-mail or the telephone.** If you need to communicate with the instructor privately, use e-mail or the telephone. Most faculty members will respond within a day or two.

REACHING OUT TO YOUR FELLOW STUDENTS

Just as you should take the initiative in communicating with your instructors, you should also be proactive in communicating with fellow students. Communicating with your peers has two benefits: it helps you feel connected to the learning community and it enables you to learn from your fellow students. In addition, establishing good communication with fellow students is key to successful collaborative efforts.

MAKING CONNECTIONS WITH THE LEARNING COMMUNITY

"I have made a conscious effort to build relationships with other students and to keep e-mail contact with them," explains Patti Iversen, a graduate student who lives in Montana and takes distance courses from Gonzaga University in Washington. "This allows each of us the opportunity to get feedback and commiserate." Another student, who is earning a bachelor's degree in information systems management from University of Maryland University College, reports, "My experience with fellow classmates in the online classroom has been very positive. I have found that establishing relationships, despite the fact that they are short-lived, has aided me." During periods when your motivation flags, this connection with others in your courses can help energize you and put you back on track.

TAKING ADVANTAGE OF WHAT YOUR PEERS HAVE TO OFFER

Second, your fellow students can be resources for you. Many distance students are adults with considerable life and professional experience, so they can contribute as much as they learn from the interactions in a course. According to Michael Olsen, who teaches distance courses on the hospitality industry at Virginia Tech, students in his courses "are mature, industry-experienced professionals who come extremely well prepared. They are good contributors and they are not afraid to interact."

Scott Garrod, who is pursuing a master's degree in business from Syracuse University, likes the broad range of people he meets through his distance courses. "You do not develop deep relationships," he explains, "but in a distance program you meet a wider range of individuals across multiple countries and careers."

Since all this knowledge and experience is within easy reach, you should take advantage of it. "You need to read through the responses that others post on the Web, so that you actually gain something from the forum discussion," explains Beth Grote, a Drake University student who took a course online. Some students do more than simply participate in class and in online discussion groups—they form study groups of their own. "You just have to make it a point to form an Internet study group," suggests Robin Barnes. "We would try to converse once a week, more often if we were working on a project."

WORKING ON GROUP PROJECTS

Since instructors often assign group projects in distance courses to help forge a community of learners, you will probably find yourself working with others much more frequently than you did in your past on-campus classes. According to several distance students we surveyed, doing group projects well is one of the most challenging aspects of distance learning. Often the logistics of getting a group of busy working adults in different time zones to meet at an appointed time in a chat room or be available for a conference call can be daunting. In some online courses, separate discussion groups are formed so group members can communicate asynchronously. "You need to have lots of patience and dedication," warns Kevin Ruthen, who earned a master's degree in information resource management from Syracuse University. "Interaction in an online environment can often be more time-consuming than an on-campus meeting."

And the problems of interaction are not limited to time factors. In the online environment, it's sometimes difficult for a group to coalesce and assign roles and tasks to its members. "In one of my courses, members tiptoed around each other, no one wanting to seem overbearing and declare themselves the leader, boss, facilitator, whatever. But we really needed one," explains a library media specialist taking online courses from Rutgers. "It took quite a while for a shakedown to occur so that some work could be accomplished." She continues, "Another problem was what to do about members of the team who were unproductive. It's very hard to prod people over the Internet. On the other hand, since you don't have the opportunity for meandering, off-topic conversations that start in on-site classes, things move swiftly, on schedule."

TIPS FOR COMMUNICATING WELL WITH YOUR PEERS

To make the most of your interactions with your fellow students, you can use these suggestions:

- **Participate.** You should participate in discussions, whether they are in class in two-way interactive video courses or are online. You will get a lot more out of your courses if you take an active part. In addition, you will get to know the other students and they will get to know you.
- **Share your knowledge and experiences.** Don't assume you have nothing to offer. Most adults have plenty of experience and knowledge that can be of value to others.

- **If you need support from other students, ask for it.** Everyone runs into occasional problems in a course, even if the problem is simply feeling overwhelmed by the amount of work you have to do. Communicating with other students can help you solve problems and get back on track, or it can simply make you feel better because you've let off some steam.
- **Use various forms of communication as needed.** Don't feel limited to class time or discussion groups. You can e-mail or call people with whom you'd like to converse in private. Remember, other distance students may feel somewhat disconnected from the group, too, and they will probably welcome an overture from you.
- **Be assertive.** When you work in a group, be assertive about what you can contribute. If the group is not making progress, try to use some of your leadership skills to get things moving.

ENLISTING YOUR FAMILY'S SUPPORT

One of the main benefits of most distance learning courses is that you can take the course from home. But unless you live alone, that means that you are working from a shared space in the presence of your family. Not only do they have to cope with the fact that you have less time for them, but they have to watch you be inaccessible—not an easy task. Therefore you should make sure you enlist the support and cooperation of your family; having their support will make your life—and theirs—much easier.

One distance student has made her education something of a family enterprise. "I work full-time, and I am blessed with a wonderful, supportive husband and the two greatest children one could ever dream of," says LaVonne Johnson, who is earning a master's degree in nursing from Gonzaga University. "We are in this together, everyone helping on some level," she continues. "My husband cooks, cleans, does laundry, and will proof papers if he is the last resort. My thirteen-year-old daughter is a great help around the house and my sixteen-year-old son is always helping with Power Point projects, statistical analyses, and Excel graphs. Needless to say, in return I try really hard not to impact my family any more than they already are, and we get by."

IN CONCLUSION

Distance learning is challenging, but with motivation, self-discipline, and the support of family, coworkers, and fellow students, you can succeed in your courses and earn a certificate or degree if that's your goal. Perhaps the best summation of distance education we encountered from the scores of students we surveyed came from Patti Iversen:

Distance learning isn't for the faint of heart or those who require considerable reinforcement to remain on task. It is sometimes difficult for others to recognize the challenges of the distance learner, as job, family, and community activities all continue as before. Finding a way to carve out of a busy schedule the time necessary to successfully complete courses that seem relatively invisible is a big challenge. At the same time, there is absolutely no way that I could have hoped to accomplish the goal that I have set for myself except as a distance learner. I am able to stretch and grow, professionally and personally, while continuing to live a lifestyle that I value immensely. It isn't always an easy task—it is often rigorous and sometimes frustrating—but distance learning has opened a gate of opportunity for me that previously was inaccessible.

Distance learning can provide that opportunity for you as well.

ADDITIONAL RESOURCES

WHAT IS DISTANCE LEARNING?

You can find countless sources of information about distance learning by doing an Internet search. One Web site that lists links to distance learning resources is dmoz.org/Reference/Education/Distance_Learning. Some other good sources of information include the following:

The Chronicle of Higher Education
1255 23rd Street, NW
Washington, DC 20037
Telephone: 202-466-1000
E-mail: circulation@chronicle.com
Web site: http://chronicle.com

Distance Learning in Higher Education. Council for Higher Education Accreditation, CHEA Update No. 3, June 2000. Available at www.chea.org/Commentary/distance-learning-3.cfm.

Russell, Thomas L. *The No Significant Difference Phenomenon.* Available at teleeducation.nb.ca/nosignificantdifference/.

Survey on Distance Education at Postsecondary Education Institutions, 1997–1998. NCES 2000-13, by Laurie Lewis, Kyle Snow, Elizabeth Farris, Douglas Levin. Bernie Green, project officer. U.S. Department of Education, National Center for Education Statistics, Washington, DC, 1999. Available online at http://nces.ed.gov.

U.S. Distance Learning Association
140 Gould Street
Needham, MA 02494-2397
Telephone: 800-275-5162 (toll-free)
Web site: www.usdla.org

IS DISTANCE LEARNING RIGHT FOR YOU?

Sometimes it helps to have some objective help when you are assessing your goals, aptitudes, strengths, and weaknesses:

National Board for Certified Counselors
3 Terrace Way, Suite D
Greensboro, NC 27403-3660
Telephone: 800-398-5389 (toll-free)
E-mail: nbcc@nbcc.org
Web site: www.nbcc.org

WHAT CAN YOU STUDY VIA DISTANCE LEARNING?

Internet Databases

Peterson's: www.petersons.com/distancelearning

Print Directories

Guide to Distance Learning Programs in Canada 2001. Education International, 2001.

Equivalency Examinations

College Level Examination Program (CLEP)
P.O. Box 6600
Princeton, NJ 08541-6600
Telephone: 609-771-7865
E-mail: clep@info.collegeboard.org
Web site: www.collegeboard.org/clep

CLEP Success. Lawrenceville, NJ: Peterson's, 2007. Lieberman, Leo, et al.

DANTES Subject Standardized Tests (DSSTs)
Telephone: 609-720-6740
E-mail: dantes@chauncey.com *or* exams@voled.doded.mil
Web site: www.chauncey.com/dantes *or* www.voled.doded.mil/dantes/exam

Excelsior College Examination Program (formerly Regents College Examinations)
Test Administration Office
Excelsior College
7 Columbia Circle
Albany, NY 12203-5159
Telephone: 888-647–2388 (toll-free)
E-mail: testadmn@excelsior.edu
Web site: www.excelsior.edu/100.htm

GRE Subject Area Tests
GRE-ETS
P.O. Box 6000
Princeton, NJ 08541-6000
Telephone: 609-771-7670
E-mail: gre-info@ets.org
Web site: www.gre.org

Assessment for Life Experience

Council for Adult and Experiential Learning (CAEL)
55 East Monroe Street, Suite 1930
Chicago, IL 60603
Telephone: 312-499-2600
Web site: www.cael.org

Credit for Work Training

American Council on Education
Center for Adult Learning Educational Credentials
One Dupont Circle NW
Washington, DC 20036
Telephone: 202-939-9475
E-mail: credit@ace.nche.edu
Web site: www.acenet.edu

Credit for Military Training

Servicemembers Opportunities Colleges
1307 New York Avenue NW, fifth floor

Washington, DC 20005-4701
Telephone: 800-368-5622 (toll-free)
E-mail: socmail@aascu.org
Web site: www.soc.aascu.org

SELECTING A GOOD DISTANCE LEARNING PROGRAM

The names and contact information of all agencies recognized by the U.S. Department of Education (www.ed.gov/offices/OPE/accreditation/natlagencies.html) and the Council for Higher Education Accreditation (www.chea.org) are listed below.

Institutional Accrediting Agencies—Regional

Middle States Association of Colleges and Schools

Accredits institutions in Delaware, District of Columbia, Maryland, New Jersey, New York, Pennsylvania, Puerto Rico, and the Virgin Islands.

Jean Avnet Morse, Executive Director
Commission on Higher Education
3624 Market Street
Philadelphia, PA 19104-2680
Telephone: 267-284-5000
Fax: 215-662-5950
E-mail: info@msache.org
Web site: www.msache.org

New England Association of Schools and Colleges

Accredits institutions in Connecticut, Maine, Massachusetts, New Hampshire, Rhode Island, and Vermont.

Barbara E. Brittingham, Director
Commission on Institutions of Higher Education
209 Burlington Road
Bedford, MA 01730-1433
Telephone: 781-271-0022
Fax: 781-271-0950
E-mail: ccook@neasc.org
Web site: www.neasc.org

North Central Association of Colleges and Schools

Accredits institutions in Arizona, Arkansas, Colorado, Illinois, Indiana, Iowa, Kansas, Michigan, Minnesota, Missouri, Nebraska, New Mexico, North Dakota, Ohio, Oklahoma, South Dakota, West Virginia, Wisconsin, and Wyoming.

Sylvia Manning, Executive Director
The Higher Learning Commission
30 North LaSalle Street, Suite 2400
Chicago, IL 60602-2504
Telephone: 800-621-7440
Fax: 312-263-7462
E-mail: smanning@hlcommission.org
Web site: www.ncahigherlearningcommission.org

Northwest Commission on Colleges and Universities

Accredits institutions in Alaska, Idaho, Montana, Nevada, Oregon, Utah, and Washington.

Sandra E. Elman, Executive Director
Commission on Colleges
8060 165th Avenue, NE, Ste 100
Redmond, WA 98052

Telephone: 425-558-4224
Fax: 425-376-0596
E-mail: selman@nwccu.org
Web site: www.nwccu.org

Southern Association of Colleges and Schools

Accredits institutions in Alabama, Florida, Georgia, Kentucky, Louisiana, Mississippi, North Carolina, South Carolina, Tennessee, Texas, and Virginia.

Belle Wheelan, President
Commission on Colleges
1866 Southern Lane
Decatur, GA 30033-4097
Telephone: 404-679-4500
Fax: 404-679-4528
E-mail: bwheelan@sacscoc.org
Web site: www.sacscoc.org

Western Association of Schools and Colleges

Accredits institutions in California, Guam, and Hawaii.

Ralph Wolff, President and Executive Director
Accrediting Commission for Senior Colleges and Universities
985 Atlantic Avenue, Suite 100
Alameda, CA 94501
Telephone: 510-748-9001
Fax: 510-748-9797
E-mail: rwolff@wascsenior.org
Web site: www.wascweb.org

Institutional Accrediting Agencies—Other

Accrediting Council for Independent Colleges and Schools

Sheryl L. Moody, Executive Director
750 First Street, NE, Suite 980
Washington, DC 20002-4241
Telephone: 202-336-6780
Fax: 202-842-2593
E-mail: smoody@acics.org
Web site: www.acics.org

Distance Education and Training Council

Michael P. Lambert, Executive Secretary
1601 Eighteenth Street, NW
Washington, DC 20009-2529
Telephone: 202-234-5100
Fax: 202-332-1386
E-mail: detc@detc.org
Web site: www.detc.org

Specialized Accrediting Agencies

Acupuncture

Dort S. Bigg, Executive Director
Accreditation Commission for Acupuncture and Oriental Medicine
Maryland Trade Center #3
7501 Greenway Center Drive
Suite 820
Greenbelt, MD 20770
Telephone: 301-313-0855
Fax: 301-313-0912

E-mail: acaom1@compuserve.com
Web site: www.acaom.org

Art and Design

Samuel Hope, Executive Director
National Association of Schools of Art and Design
11250 Roger Bacon Drive, Suite 21
Reston, VA 20190
Telephone: 703-437-0700
Fax: 703-437-6312
E-mail: info@arts-accredit.org
Web site: www.arts-accredit.org

Chiropractic

Lee Van Dusen, Executive Director
The Council on Chiropractic Education
8049 North 85th Way
Scottsdale, AZ 85258-4321
Telephone: 480-443-8877
Fax: 480-483-7333
E-mail: cce@cce-usa.org
Web site: www.cce-usa.org

Clinical Laboratory Science

Dianne M. Cearlock, CEO
National Accrediting Agency for Clinical Laboratory Sciences
8410 West Bryn Mawr Avenue, Suite 670
Chicago, IL 60631
Telephone: 312-714-8880
Fax: 312-714-8886
E-mail: dcearlock@naacls.org
Web site: www.naacls.org

Dance

Samuel Hope, Executive Director
National Association of Schools of Dance
11250 Roger Bacon Drive, Suite 21
Reston, VA 20190
Telephone: 703-437-0700
Fax: 703-437-6312
E-mail: info@arts-accredit.org
Web site: www.arts-accredit.org

Dentistry

Anthony Ziebert, Director Commission on Dental
  Accreditation
American Dental Association
211 East Chicago Avenue, 18th Floor
Chicago, IL 60611
Telephone: 312-440-2500
Fax: 312-440-2800
E-mail: education@ada.org
Web site: www.ada.org

Education

Arthur Wise, President
National Council for Accreditation of Teacher Education
2010 Massachusetts Avenue, NW
Washington, DC 20036-1023
Telephone: 202-466-7496
Fax: 202-296-6620
E-mail: info@ncate.org
Web site: www.ncate.org

Engineering

George D. Peterson, Executive Director
Accreditation Board for Engineering and Technology, Inc.
111 Market Place, Suite 1050
Baltimore, MD 21202
Telephone: 410-347-7700
Fax: 410-625-2238
E-mail: info@abet.org
Web site: www.abet.org

Environment

National Environmental Health Science and Protection
  Accreditation Council
720 South Colorado Boulevard, Suite 970-S
Denver, CO 80246-1925
Telephone: 303-756-9090
Fax: 303-691-9490
E-mail: staff@neha.org
Web site: www.neha.org/AccredCouncil.html

Forestry

Terrance Clark, Associate Director of Science and Education
Committee on Education
Society of American Foresters
5400 Grosvenor Lane
Bethesda, MD 20814-2198
Telephone: 301-897-8720 Ext. 119
Fax: 301-897-3690
E-mail: clearkt@safnet.org
Web site: www.safnet.org

Health Services Administration

John S. Lloyd, President and CEO
Commission on Accreditatino of Healthcare Management Edu-
  cation
24k00 14th Street, North
Suite 780
Washington, DC 20001-4510
Telephone: 703-894-0960
Fax: 703-894-0941
E-mail: jlloyds@cahme.org
Web site: http://cahmeweb.org

Interior Design

Holly Mattson, Director
Council for Interior Design Accreditation
60 Monroe Center, NW, Suite 300
Grand Rapids, MI 49503-2920
Telephone: 616-458-0400
Fax: 616-458-0460
E-mail: info@accredit-id.org
Web site: www.accredit-id.org

Journalism and Mass Communications

Susanne Shaw, Executive Director
Accrediting Council on Education in Journalism and Mass
  Communications
School of Journalism
Stauffer-Flint Hall
University of Kansas
Lawrence, KS 66045
Telephone: 785-864-3986
Fax: 785-864-5225

E-mail: sshaw@kuhub.cc.ukans.edu
Web site: www.ukans.edu/~acejmc

Landscape Architecture

Ronald C. Leighton, Accreditation Manager
Landscape Architectural Accreditation Board
American Society of Landscape Architects
636 I Street, NW
Washington, DC 20001-3736
Telephone: 202-898-2444
Fax: 202-898-1185
E-mail: rleighton@asla.org
Web site: www.asla.org/

Law

Hulett H. Askew, Consultant on Legal Education
American Bar Association
321 North Clark Street, 21st Floor
Chicago, Illinois 60610-4714
Phone: 312-988-6746
Fax: 312-988-5681
E-mail: askewh@staff.abanet.org
Web: www.abanet.org/legaled/

Library

Karen O'Brien, Director
Office for Accreditation
American Library Association
50 East Huron Street
Chicago, Illinois 60611
Phone: 800-545-2433 Ext. 2432
Fax: 312-280-2433
E-mail: kobrien@ala.org
Web: www.ala.org/accreditation/

Marriage and Family Therapy

Jeff S. Harmon, Director of Accreditation Services
Commission on Accreditation for Marriage and Family Therapy
  Education
American Association for Marriage and Family Therapy
112 South Alfred Street
Alexandria, Virginia 22314-3061
Phone: 703-253-0459
Fax: 703-253-0508
E-mail: jharmon@aamft.org
Web: www.aamft.org

Medical Illustration

Commission on Accreditation of Allied Health Education
Programs (CAAHEP)
Kathleen Megivern, Executive Director
1361 Park Street
Clearwater, Florida 33756
Phone: 727-210-2350
Fax: 727-210-2354
E-mail: mail@caahep.org
Web: www.caahep.org

Medicine

Liaison Committee on Medical Education (LCME)
In even-numbered years beginning each July 1,
contact:
Dan Hunt, Secretary

Association of American Medical Colleges
2450 N Street, NW
Washington, DC 20037
Phone: 202-828-0596
Fax: 202-828-1125
E-mail: dhunt@aamc.org
Web: www.lcme.org
In odd-numbered years beginning each July 1,
contact:
Barbara Barzansky, Interim Secretary
American Medical Association
Council on Medical Education
515 North State Street
Chicago, Illinois 60610
Phone: 312-464-1690
Fax: 312-464-5830
E-mail: barbara_barzansky@ama-assn.org
Web: www.ama-assn.org

Music

Samuel Hope, Executive Director
National Association of Schools of Music (NASM)
Commission on Accreditation
11250 Roger Bacon Drive, Suite 21
Reston, Virginia 20190
Phone: 703-437-0700
Fax: 703-437-6312
E-mail: info@arts-accredit.org
Web: www.arts-accredit.org

Naturopathic Medicine

Daniel Seitz, Executive Director
Council on Naturopathic Medical Education
P.O. Box 178
Great Barrington, Massachusetts 01230
Phone: 413-528-8877
Fax: 413-528-8880
E-mail: council@cnme.org
Web: www.cnme.org

Nurse Anesthesia

Francis R. Gerbasi, Director of Accreditation and Education
Council on Accreditation of Nurse Anesthesia Educational
  Programs
American Association of Nurse Anesthetists
222 South Prospect Avenue, Suite 304
Park Ridge, Illinois 60068
Phone: 847-692-7050 Ext. 1154
Fax: 847-692-7137
E-mail: fgerbasi@aana.com
Web: www.aana.com

Nurse Education

Jennifer L. Butlin, Director
Commission on Collegiate Nursing Education (CCNE)
One Dupont Circle, NW, Suite 530
Washington, DC 20036-1120
Phone: 202-887-6791
Fax: 202-887-8476
E-mail: jbutlin@aacn.nche.edu
Web: www.aacn.nche.edu/accreditation/index.htm

Nurse Midwifery

Mary Brucker, Chair
ACNM Accreditation Commission
American College of Nurse-Midwives
Nurse-Midwifery Program
8403 Colesville Road, Suite 1550
Silver Spring, Maryland 20910
Phone: 240-485-1800
Fax: 240-485-1818
E-mail: mary_brucker@baylor.edu
Web: www.midwife.org

Jo Anne Myers-Ciecko, Executive Director
Midwifery Education Accreditation Council
P.O. Box 984
La Conner, Washington 98257
Phone: 360-466-2080
Fax: 480-907-2936
E-mail: executivedirector@meacschools.org
Web: www.meacschools.org

Nurse Practitioner

Susan Wysocki, President
National Association of Nurse Practitioners in Women's Health
Council on Accreditation
505 C Street, NE
Washington, DC 20002
Phone: 202-543-9693
Fax: 202-543-9858
E-mail: info@npwh.org
Web: www.npwh.org

Nursing

Sharon J. Tanner, Executive Director
National League for Nursing Accrediting Commission (NLNAC)
61 Broadway, 33rd Floor
New York, New York 10006
Phone: 800-669-1656
Fax: 212-812-0390
E-mail: stanner@nlnac.org
Web: www.nlnac.org

Occupational Therapy

Neil Harvison, Director of Accreditation
American Occupational Therapy Association
4720 Montgomery Lane
P.O. Box 31220
Bethesda, Maryland 20824-1220
Phone: 301-652-2682 Ext. 2912
Fax: 301-652-7711
E-mail: nharvison@aota.org
Web: www.aota.org

Optometry

Joyce L. Urbeck, Administrative Director
Accreditation Council on Optometric Education
American Optometric Association (AOA)
243 North Lindbergh Boulevard
St. Louis, Missouri 63141
Phone: 314-991-4100
Fax: 314-991-4101
E-mail: jlurbeck@aoa.org
Web: www.aoanet.org

Osteopathic Medicine

Konrad C. Miskowicz-Retz, Director
Department of Education
Commission on Osteopathic College Accreditation
American Osteopathic Association
142 East Ontario Street
Chicago, Illinois 60611
Phone: 312-202-8048
Fax: 312-202-8202
E-mail: kretz@osteopathic.org
Web: www.osteopathic.org

Pharmacy

Peter H. Vlasses, Executive Director
Accreditation Council for Pharmacy Education
20 North Clark Street, Suite 2500
Chicago, Illinois 60602-5109
Phone: 312-664-3575
Fax: 312-664-4652
E-mail: pvlasses@acpe-accredit.org
Web: www.acpe-accredit.org

Physical Therapy

Mary Jane Harris, Director
Department of Accreditation
Commission on Accreditation in Physical Therapy Education (CAPTE)
American Physical Therapy Association (APTA)
Trans Potomac Plaza
1111 North Fairfax Street
Alexandria, Virginia 22314
Phone: 703-706-3245
Fax: 703-684-7343
E-mail: maryjaneharris@apta.org
Web: www.apta.org

Physician Assistant Studies

John E. McCarty, Executive Director
Accreditation Review Commission on Education for the Physician Assistant, Inc. (ARC-PA)
12000 Findley Road, Suite 240
Duluth, Georgia 30097
Phone: 770-476-1224
Fax: 770-476-1738
E-mail: arc-pa@arc-pa.org
Web: www.arc-pa.org

Planning

Shonagh Merits, Executive Director
American Institute of Certified Planners/Association of Collegiate Schools of Planning/American Planning Association
Planning Accreditation Board (PAB)
122 South Michigan Avenue, Suite 1600
Chicago, Illinois 60603
Phone: 312-334-1271
Fax: 312-334-1273
E-mail: pab@planning.org
Web: showcase.netins.net/web/pab_fi66/index.htm

Podiatric Medicine

Alan R. Tinkleman, Director
Council on Podiatric Medical Education
American Podiatric Medical Association

9312 Old Georgetown Road
Bethesda, Maryland 20814-1621
Phone: 301-571-9200
Fax: 301-571-4903
E-mail: artinkleman@apma.org
Web: www.cpme.org

Psychology and Counseling

Susan Zlotlow, Director
Office of Program Consultation and Accreditation
American Psychological Association
750 First Street, NE
Washington, DC 20002-4242
Phone: 202-336-5979
Fax: 202-336-5978
E-mail: szlotlow@apa.org
Web: www.apa.org/ed/accreditation

Carol L. Bobby, Executive Director
Council for Accreditation of Counseling and Related Educational Programs
1001 North Fairfax Street, Suite 510
Alexandria, Virginia 22314
Phone: 703-535-5990
Fax: 703-739-6209
E-mail: cacrep@cacrep.org
Web: www.cacrep.org

Public Affairs and Administration

Crystal Calarusse, Executive Director
Commission on Peer Review and Accreditation
National Association of Schools of Public Affairs and Administration
1120 G Street, NW, Suite 730
Washington, DC 20005
Phone: 202-628-8965
Fax: 202-626-4978
E-mail: calarusse@naspaa.org
Web: www.naspaa.org

Public Health

Laura Rasar King, Executive Director
Council on Education for Public Health
800 Eye Street, NW, Suite 202
Washington, DC 20001-3710
Phone: 202-789-1050
Fax: 202-789-1895
E-mail: Lking@ceph.org
Web: www.ceph.org

Rehabilitation Education

Marvin D. Kuehn, Executive Director
Council on Rehabilitation Education (CORE)
Commission on Standards and Accreditation
300 North Martingale Road, Suite 460
Schaumburg, Illinois 60173
Phone: 847-944-1345
Fax: 847-944-1324
E-mail: mkuehn@emporia.edu
Web: www.core-rehab.org

Social Work

Dean Pierce, Director
Commission on Accreditation

Council on Social Work Education
1725 Duke Street, Suite 500
Alexandria, Virginia 22314
Phone: 703-683-8080
Fax: 703-683-8099
E-mail: dpierce@cswe.org
Web: www.cswe.org/cswe

Speech-Language Pathology and Audiology

Patrima L. Tice, Director of Credentialing
American Speech-Language-Hearing Association
2200 Research Boulevard
Rockville, Maryland 20850-3289
Phone: 301-897-5700
Fax: 301-571-0457
E-mail: ptice@asha.org
Web: www.asha.org

Teacher Education

Arthur Wise, President
National Council for Accreditation of Teacher Education
2010 Massachusetts Avenue, NW
Washington, DC 20036-1023
Phone: 202-466-7496
Fax: 202-296-6620
E-mail: ncate@ncate.org
Web: www.ncate.org

Frank B. Murray, President
Teacher Education Accreditation Council (TEAC)
Accreditation Committee
One Dupont Circle, Suite 320
Washington, DC 20036-0110
Phone: 202-466-7236
Fax: 202-466-7238
E-mail: frank@teac.org
Web: www.teac.org

Technology

Elise Scanlon, Executive Director
Accrediting Commission of Career Schools and Colleges of Technology
2101 Wilson Boulevard, Suite 302
Arlington, Virginia 22201
Phone: 703-247-4212
Fax: 703-247-4533
E-mail: escanlon@accsct.org
Web: www.accsct.org

Theater

Samuel Hope, Executive Director
National Association of Schools of Theatre
Commission on Accreditation
11250 Roger Bacon Drive, Suite 21
Reston, Virginia 20190
Phone: 703-437-0700
Fax: 703-437-6312
E-mail: info@arts-accredit.org
Web: www.arts-accredit.org

Theology

Bernard Fryshman, Executive Vice President
Association of Advanced Rabbinical and Talmudic Schools (AARTS)

Accreditation Commission
11 Broadway, Suite 405
New York, New York 10004
Phone: 212-363-1991
Fax: 212-533-5335

Daniel O. Aleshire, Executive Director
Association of Theological Schools in the United States and
  Canada (ATS)
Commission on Accrediting
10 Summit Park Drive
Pittsburgh, Pennsylvania 15275-1103
Phone: 412-788-6505
Fax: 412-788-6510
E-mail: ats@ats.edu
Web: www.ats.edu

Russell Guy Fitzgerald Jr., Executive Director
Transnational Association of Christian Colleges and Schools
  (TRACS)
Accreditation Commission
P.O. Box 328
Forest, Virginia 24551
Phone: 434-525-9539
Fax: 434-525-9538
E-mail: rfitzgerald@tracs.org
Web: www.tracs.org

Veterinary Medicine

Elizabeth Sabin, Assistant Director
Education and Research Division
American Veterinary Medical Association
Council on Education
1931 North Meacham Road, Suite 100
Schaumburg, Illinois 60173
Phone: 847-925-8070
Fax: 847-925-1329
E-mail: esabin@avma.org
Web: www.avma.org

Accreditation in Canada

To get general information about accreditation in Canada, visit
  the Web site of the Council of Ministers of Education. Their
  Web site also has contact information and links to the provincial departments of education.

Council of Ministers of Education, Canada
95 St. Clair Avenue West, Suite 1106
Toronto, Ontario
Canada M4V 1N6
Telephone: 416-962-8100
Fax: 416-962-2800
E-mail: cmec@cmec.ca
Web site: www.cmec.ca

Other Resources for Evaluating Programs

Bear, Mariah P., John Bear, and John B. Bear. *Bear's Guide to
  Earning Degrees Nontraditionally, 13th ed.*

Ten Speed Press, 1999.

*Quality on the Line: Benchmarks for Success in Internet-Based
  Distance Education.* Washington, DC: The Institute for Higher
  Education Policy, March 2000. Available at www.ihep.com/
  qualityonline.pdf.

TAKING STANDARDIZED ADMISSIONS TESTS

SAT

For information about the SAT, contact the College Board:

SAT Program
The College Board
P.O. Box 025505
Miami, FL 33102
Telephone: 866-756-7346 (in the U.S.);
  212-713-7789 (international)
E-mail: sat@info.collegeboard.org
Web site: www.collegeboard.org

The College Board offers free preparation advice and practice
tests. The Web site also offers other test-preparation materials,
including books, videos, and software, for a charge. Order at
www.collegeboard.org or call 609-771-7243:

ACT

ACT Registration
P.O. Box 414
Iowa City, IA 52243-0414
Telephone: 319-337-1270
Web site: www.act.org/aap

The Web site offers test-preparation strategies, sample questions, and information about other ACT resources.

ACT Inc., *The Real ACT Prep Guide.* Lawrenceville, NJ:
  Peterson's, 2007.

GRE

For information about the GRE, contact the Educational
Testing Service:

GRE-ETS
P.O. Box 6000
Princeton, NJ 08541-6000
Telephone: (609) 771-7670
E-mail: gre-info@ets.org
Web site (GRE Online): www.gre.org

The Web site offers a lot of material that can be downloaded:
information bulletins, practice tests, descriptions of the subject
area tests, and preparation software. Order from ETS at
www.gre.org:

GRE Big Book

GRE Powerprep Software. Includes test preparation for both
  the General Test and the Writing Assessment.

GRE Practicing to Take the General Test

Practice Books for Subject Area Tests

MAT

Harcourt Assessment
19500 Bulverde Rd.
San Antonio, TX 78259
Telephone: (800) 211-8378 (toll-free)
Web site: www.milleranalogies.com

GMAT

GMAT
Distribution and Receiving Center
225 Phillips Boulevard
Ewing, NJ 08628-7435

Telephone: 609-771-7330
E-mail: gmat@ets.org
Web site (MBA Explorer): www.gmac.com

TOEFL

Information on the TOEFL can be obtained from the Educational Testing Service:

TOEFL
P.O. Box 6151
Princeton, NJ 08541-6151
Telephone: 609-771-7100
E-mail: toefl@ets.org
Web site: www.toefl.org

APPLYING FOR ADMISSION TO DEGREE PROGRAMS

Davidson, Wilma, and Susan McCloskey. *Writing a Winning College Application Essay.* Lawrenceville, NJ: Peterson's, 2002.

Hayden, Thomas C. *Insider's Guide to College Admissions.* Lawrenceville, NJ: Peterson's, 2000.

Stelzer, Richard J. *How to Write a Winning Personal Statement for Graduate and Professional School, 3rd ed.* Princeton, NJ: Peterson's, 1997. Lots of suggestions, both from the author and admissions representatives of graduate and professional schools, along with many sample essays.

PAYING FOR YOUR EDUCATION

General Information

Financial Aid Information Page (www.finaid.org). The best place to start an Internet search for financial aid information.

National Association of Student Financial Aid Administrators (www.nasfaa.org). Lots of essays explain various aspects of financial aid, including educational tax credits.

State Residency

Todd, Daryl F., Jr. *How to Cut Tuition: The Complete Guide to In-State Tuition.* Linwood, NJ: Atlantic Educational Publishing, 1997.

Federal Aid

Federal Student Aid Information Center
P.O. Box 84
Washington, DC 20044-0084
Telephone: 800-4-FED-AID (toll-free) (general information, assistance, and publications)
Web sites:
General information and home page: www.ed.gov/studentaid

For a copy of *Financial Aid: The Student Guide:* www.ed.gov/ prog_info/SFA/StudentGuide.

For the FAFSA, go to FAFSA Online: www.fafsa.ed.gov.

For more on the Distance Education Demonstration Program: www.ed.gov/offices/OPE/PPI/DistEd/proginfo.html.

State Agencies of Higher Education

Alabama: 334-242-2274
Alaska: 907-465-6741

Arizona: 602-229-2591
Arkansas: 800-547-8839 (toll-free)
California: 916-526-7590
Colorado: 303-866-2723
Connecticut: 860-947-1855
Delaware: 800-292-7935 (toll-free)
District of Columbia: 202-698-2400
Florida: 888-827-2004 (toll-free)
Georgia: 770-724-9030 or 404-656-5969
Hawaii: 808-956-8213
Idaho: 208-334-2270
Illinois: 800-899-4722 (toll-free)
Indiana: 317-232-2350
Iowa: 515-242-3344
Kansas: 785-296-3517
Kentucky: 800-928-8926 (toll-free)
Louisiana: 800-259-5626 (toll-free)
Maine: 800-228-3734 (toll-free)
Maryland: 410-260-4565
Massachusetts: 617-727-9420
Michigan: 877-323-2287 (toll-free)
Minnesota: 800-657-3866 (toll-free)
Mississippi: 601-432-6997
Missouri: 800-473-6757 (toll-free)
Montana: 800-537-7508 (toll-free)
Nebraska: 402-471-2847
Nevada: 775-687-9228
New Hampshire: 603-271-2555
New Jersey: 800-792-8670 (toll-free)
New Mexico: 800-279-9777 (toll-free)
New York: 800-642-6234 (toll-free)
North Carolina: 800-600-3453 (toll-free)
North Dakota: 701-328-4114
Ohio: 888-833-1133 (toll-free)
Oklahoma: 800-858-1840 (toll-free)
Oregon: 800-452-8807 (toll-free)
Pennsylvania: 800-692-7392 or 7435(toll-free)
Rhode Island: 800-922-9855 (toll-free)
South Carolina: 803-737-2260
South Dakota: 605-773-3134
Tennessee: 800-342-1663 (toll-free)
Texas: 800-242-3062 (toll-free)
Utah: 800-418-8757 (toll-free)
Vermont: 800-642-3177 (toll-free)
Virginia: 804-786-1690
Washington: 360-753-7850
West Virginia: 888-825-5707 (toll-free)
Wisconsin: 608-267-2206
Wyoming: 307-777-7763
Guam: 671-475-0457
Northern Marianas: 670-234-6128
Puerto Rico: 787-724-7100
Republic of Palau: 680-488-2471
Virgin Islands: 340-774-4546

CSS Financial Aid Profile

Contact the College Scholarship Service at www.collegeboard.org or 305-829-9793.

Grants, Fellowships, and Scholarships

AJR Newslink (www.newslink.org). Awards, grants, and scholarships for journalism students.

Annual Register of Grant Support: A Directory of Funding Sources. Wilmette, IL.: National Register Publishing Company.

College Money Handbook 2009. Lawrenceville, NJ: Peterson's, 2008.

Corporate Foundation Profiles. New York: Foundation Center, 1999 (http://fdncenter.org or 212-620-4230).

FastWeb (http://fastweb.com). Online searchable database of scholarships and fellowships.

Petersons.com. Online searchable database of scholarships and fellowships.

Scholarships, Grants, & Prizes 2009. Lawrenceville, NJ: Peterson's, 2008.

Cooperative Education

Re, Joseph M. *Earn and Learn.* Octameron Associates, 1997.

Credit Reporting Agencies

It's a good idea to check your credit rating before you apply for any loans. Call first to find out if there is a fee.

Experian
P.O. Box 9530
Allen, TX 75013
Telephone: 888-397-3742 (toll-free)

Equifax
P.O. Box 105873
Atlanta, GA 30348
Telephone: 800-685-1111 (toll-free)

CSC Credit Services
Consumer Assistance Center
P.O. Box 674402
Houston, TX 77267-4402
Telephone: 800-759-5979 (toll-free)

Trans Union Corporation
P.O. Box 390
Springfield, PA 19064-0390
Telephone: 800-888-4213 (toll-free)

Tax Issues

Educational Expenses, IRS Publication 508.

Tax Benefits for Higher Education. IRS Publication 970.

To get a copy of these publications, visit the Internal Revenue Service Web site at www.irs.ustreas.gov/prod/forms_pubs/pubs or call 800-829-3676 (toll-free).

Women, Minority Students, Disabled Students, and Veterans

Bruce-Young, Doris M., and William C. Young. *Higher Education Money Book for Women and Minorities.* Young Enterprises International, 1997.

Minority and Women's Complete Scholarship Book; plus Scholarships for Religious Affiliations and People with Disabilities. Sourcebooks, 1998.

Olson, Elizabeth A. *Dollars for College (Women).* Garrett Park Press, 1995.

Saludos Web Education Center (www.saludos.com). Internships and scholarships targeted to Hispanic Americans as well as those not considering race or ethnicity.

Schlachter, Gail Ann, and R. David Weber. *Financial Aid for African Americans.* Reference Service Press, 1997.

Schlachter, Gail Ann, and R. David Weber. *Financial Aid for the Disabled and Their Families.* Reference Service Press, 1998.

Schlachter, Gail Ann, and R. David Weber. *Financial Aid for Veterans, Military Personnel, and Their Dependents.* Reference Service Press, 1996.

Schlachter, Gail Ann. *Directory of Financial Aid for Women.* Reference Service Press, 1997.

International Students

Funding for U.S. Study—A Guide for International Students and Professionals and *Financial Resources for International Study.* New York: Institute of International Education (www.iiebooks.org).

SUCCEEDING AS A DISTANCE LEARNER

Bruno, Frank J. *Going Back to School: College Survival Strategies for Adult Students.* New York, Arco, 1998.

GLOSSARY

accreditation—in the United States, the process by which private, nongovernmental educational agencies with regional or national scope certify that colleges and universities provide educational programs at basic levels of quality

ACT—a standardized undergraduate admissions test that is based on the typical high school curriculum

associate degree—a degree awarded upon the successful completion of a prebaccalaureate-level program, usually consisting of two years of full-time study at the college level

asynchronous—not simultaneous or concurrent; for example, discussion groups in online courses are asynchronous because students can log on and post messages at any time

audioconferencing—electronic meeting in which participants in remote locations can communicate with one another using phones

bachelor's degree—a degree awarded upon the successful completion of about four years of full-time study at the college level

bandwidth—the width of frequencies required to transmit a communications signal without too much distortion; video, animation, and sound require more bandwidth than text

broadband—a high-speed, high-capacity transmission channel carried on coaxial or fiber-optic cable; it has a higher *bandwidth* than telephone lines and so can transmit more data more quickly than telephone lines

broadcast radio and television—radio and television programs sent out over the airwaves; one of the earliest distance learning technologies still used today

browser—a computer program used to view, download, upload, or otherwise access documents (sites) on the World Wide Web

bulletin board—a site on the Internet where people can post messages

cable television—television programming transmitted over optical fiber, coaxial, or twisted pair (telephone) cables

CD-ROM—compact disc, read-only memory; an optical storage technology that allows you to store and play back data

certificate—an educational credential awarded upon completion of a structured curriculum, typically including several courses but lasting for a period of time less than that required for a degree

certification—the awarding of a credential, usually by a professional or industry group, usually after a course of study and the passing of an exam

chat room—a site on the Internet in which people can communicate synchronously by typing messages to one another

CLEP—the College Level Examination Program, administered by the College Board, that tests students' subject knowledge in order to award college-level credit for noncollegiate learning

common application form—a standardized basic admissions application form, available online, that is used by many colleges

consortium—a group of colleges and universities that pool resources to enable students to take courses as needed from all participating institutions

continuing education unit—10 contact hours of participation in an organized continuing education program; a nationwide, standardized measure of continuing education courses

correspondence course—individual or self-guided study by mail from a college or university for which credit is typically granted through written assignments and proctored examinations; also referred to as *independent study*

correspondence school—a school whose primary means of delivering instruction is via *correspondence courses*

cost of attendance—the total cost, including tuition, fees, living expenses, books, supplies, and miscellaneous expenses, of attending a particular school for an academic year

distance learning—the delivery of educational programs to students who are off site; also called *distance education*

doctoral degree—the highest degree awarded upon demonstrated mastery of a subject, including the ability to do scholarly research

DSSTs—a series of equivalency examinations used originally by the U.S. Department of Defense but now available to civilians as well

DVD—digital video disc; an optical storage technology that allows you to store and retrieve audio and video data

e-learning—distance learning via the Internet; sometimes called *online learning*

e-mail—text or other messages sent over the Internet

enrollment status—whether a student is enrolled full-time, three-quarter-time, half-time, or less than half-time in a degree or certificate program

equivalency examination—an examination similar to the final exam of a college-level course; if you pass, you may be awarded college-level credit; for example, the CLEP and DSST exams

Excelsior College Examinations—a series of equivalency examinations administered by Excelsior College; formerly the Regents College Examinations

Expected Family Contribution (EFC)—the amount a student and his or her family are expected to contribute to the cost of the student's education per academic year

FAFSA—the Free Application for Federal Student Aid; needed to apply for federal aid programs

fax machine—a telecopying device that transmits written or graphic material over telephone lines to produce a hard copy at a remote location

Federal Supplemental Educational Opportunity Grant (FSEOG)—a federal grant awarded to students that demonstrate the greatest financial need

Federal Work-Study Program—provides part-time jobs in public and private nonprofit organizations to both undergraduate and graduate students who demonstrate financial need; the government pays up to 75 percent of the student's wages, and the employer pays the balance

fellowship—monies to be used for a student's education that does not have to be repaid; also called a *grant* or *scholarship*

financial need—the amount of money a student needs to be given or loaned or to earn through work-study, in order to attend school for one year, calculated by subtracting Expected Family Contribution (EFC) from cost of attendance

first-professional degree—a degree awarded upon the successful completion of a program of study (for which a bachelor's degree is normally the prerequisite) that prepares a student for a specific profession

GMAT—the Graduate Management Admissions Test, a standardized test used by many graduate programs in business

graduate degree—a degree awarded upon the successful completion of a program of study at the postbaccalaureate level; usually a master's or doctoral degree

grant—monies to be used for a student's education that do not have to be repaid; also called a *scholarship* or *fellowship*

GRE General Test—the Graduate Record Examinations General Test, which tests verbal, quantitative, and analytical skills; usually taken by prospective graduate students

GRE Subject Area Tests—examinations that assess knowledge usually acquired in college-level courses

instructional design—the way course content is organized for the learner; it varies from one distance technology to another

Internet—the global computer network of networks that allows for the transmission of words, images, and sound to anyone with an Internet connection; one of the major instructional delivery systems for distance learning

Internet service provider (ISP)—a company such as AOL or Earthlink that serves as a gateway to the Internet; by subscribing to its service, an individual can connect to the Internet

life experience—a basis for earning college credit, usually demonstrated by means of a portfolio

LSAT—the Law School Admissions Test, taken by law school applicants

master's degree—a degree awarded upon the successful completion of a program of study beyond the baccalaureate level that typically requires one or two years of full-time study

MAT—the Miller Analogies Test, a standardized admissions test used by some graduate programs

MCAT—the Medical College Admissions Test, taken by medical school applicants

merit-based aid—funding awarded on the basis of academic merit, regardless of financial need

modem—MOdulator DEModulator; a device that allows a computer to connect with other computers (and therefore the Internet) over telephone lines; the faster the modem speed, the faster data is transmitted

need-based aid—financial aid awarded on the basis of financial need; it may take the form of grants, loans, or work-study

online course—a course offered primarily over the Internet

online learning—distance learning via the Internet; sometimes called *e-learning*

Pell Grant—a federal grant that is awarded to students on the basis of financial need

Perkins Loan—a loan offered by the federal government to students with exceptional financial need

PowerPoint—a software program that enables the user to prepare slides with text, graphics, and sound; often used by instructors in their class presentations

PROFILE®—the financial aid application service of the College Board is a standardized financial aid application form used by many colleges and universities

SAT—a standardized undergraduate admissions test

SAT Subject Tests—subject area tests that assess high school–level knowledge; used by some schools for undergraduate admissions

satellite television—programming beamed to an orbiting satellite, then retrieved by one or more ground-based satellite dishes

scholarship—monies to be used for a student's education that do not have to be repaid; also called a *grant* or *fellowship*

Stafford Loan—a subsidized or unsubsidized loan that is offered by the federal government

streaming video—high *bandwidth* video data transmission

synchronous—occurring simultaneously, in real time

Title IV funds—federal money disbursed to eligible students through eligible, accredited institutions of higher learning or directly from the government

TOEFL—the Test of English as a Foreign Language, taken by students who are not native speakers of English

two-way interactive video—two-way communication of video and audio signals so that people in remote locations can see and hear one another

videoconferencing—one-way video and two-way audio transmission, or two-way video transmission conducted via satellite; instructors and students can communicate between remote locations

videotaped lecture—recording of an on-campus lecture or class session; usually mailed to distance learners enrolled in the course

virtual university—a college or university that offers most or all of its instruction exclusively via technology and usually for a profit

whiteboard—a program that allows multiple users at their own computers to draw and write comments on the same document

work-study award—an amount a student earns through part-time work as part of the Federal Work-Study Program

Institution Profiles

This section contains factual profiles of institutions, with a focus on their distance learning programs. Each profile covers such items as accreditation information, availability of financial aid, degree and certificate programs offered, non-degree-related course topics offered, and whom to contact for program information.

The profile information presented here was collected during the summer of 2008 via an online survey for distance learning programs and is arranged alphabetically.

ABILENE CHRISTIAN UNIVERSITY
Abilene, Texas
Instructional Technology
http://www.acu.edu/distanceeducation
Abilene Christian University was founded in 1906. It is accredited by Southern Association of Colleges and Schools. It first offered distance learning courses in 1996. In fall 2007, there were 250 students enrolled in distance learning courses. Institutionally administered financial aid is available to distance learners.
Services Distance learners have accessibility to academic advising, bookstore, campus computer network, career placement assistance, e-mail services, library services, tutoring.
Contact Mr. William Horn, Director of Graduate Recruiting, Abilene Christian University, ACU Box 29000, Admissions and Recruiting, Abilene, TX 79699-9201. Telephone: 325-674-2656. Fax: 325-674-2130. E-mail: hornw@acu.edu.

DEGREES AND AWARDS
Certificate Conflict Resolution and Reconciliation
MA Conflict Resolution and Reconciliation
MEd Curriculum and Instruction; Higher Education; Leadership of Learning; Special Education
MS Organizational and Human Resource Development (OHRD)

COURSE SUBJECT AREAS OFFERED OUTSIDE OF DEGREE PROGRAMS
Undergraduate—biblical and other theological languages and literatures; biblical studies; business/corporate communications; communication and media; economics; education; English.
Graduate—biblical studies; education; human development, family studies, and related services.

ACADEMY OF ART UNIVERSITY
San Francisco, California
http://online.academyart.edu
Academy of Art University was founded in 1929. It is accredited by Accrediting Council for Independent Colleges and Schools. It first offered distance learning courses in 2002. In fall 2007, there were 5,445 students enrolled in distance learning courses. Institutionally administered financial aid is available to distance learners.
Services Distance learners have accessibility to academic advising, bookstore, campus computer network, career placement assistance, e-mail services, tutoring.
Contact Admissions, Academy of Art University, 79 New Montgomery Street, San Francisco, CA 94105. Telephone: 800-544-2787. E-mail: info@academyart.edu.

DEGREES AND AWARDS
AA Advertising; Animation and Visual Effects; Computer Arts/New Media; Digital Arts and Communications; Fashion; Fine Art; Graphic Design; Illustration; Industrial Design; Interior Architecture and Design; Motion Pictures and Television; Photography
BFA Advertising; Animation and Visual Effects; Computer Arts/New Media; Digital Arts and Communications; Fashion; Fine Art; Graphic Design; Illustration; Industrial Design; Interior Architecture and Design; Motion Pictures and Television; Photography
MFA Advertising; Animation and Visual Effects; Computer Arts/New Media; Fashion; Fine Art; Graphic Design; Illustration; Industrial Design; Interior Architecture and Design; Motion Pictures and Television; Photography

COURSE SUBJECT AREAS OFFERED OUTSIDE OF DEGREE PROGRAMS
Undergraduate—apparel and textiles; design and applied arts; film/video and photographic arts; fine and studio art; graphic communications; interior architecture; visual and performing arts.
Graduate—apparel and textiles; design and applied arts; film/video and photographic arts; fine and studio art; graphic communications; interior architecture; visual and performing arts.

ACADIA UNIVERSITY
Wolfville, Nova Scotia, Canada
Division of Continuing and Distance Education
http://conted.acadiau.ca
Acadia University was founded in 1838. It is provincially chartered. It first offered distance learning courses in 1968. In fall 2007, there were 1,200 students enrolled in distance learning courses. Institutionally administered financial aid is available to distance learners.
Services Distance learners have accessibility to academic advising, bookstore, campus computer network, e-mail services, library services, tutoring.
Contact Ms. Brenda Harris, Student Services Representative, Acadia University, Division of Continuing and Distance Education, 38 Crowell Drive, Wolfville, NS B4P 2R6, Canada. Telephone: 800-565-6568. Fax: 902-585-1068. E-mail: continuing.education@acadiau.ca.

DEGREES AND AWARDS
Programs offered do not lead to a degree or other formal award.

COURSE SUBJECT AREAS OFFERED OUTSIDE OF DEGREE PROGRAMS
Undergraduate—accounting and computer science; biology; business administration, management and operations; business/commerce; business/corporate communications; business, management, and marketing related; chemistry; computer programming; computer science; economics; education; educational/instructional media design; education related; English; English composition; English language and literature related; experimental psychology; fine and studio art; foods, nutrition, and related services; geological and earth sciences/geosciences; gerontology; health psychology; history; languages (foreign languages related); liberal arts and sciences, general studies and humanities; linguistic, comparative, and related language studies; marketing; microbiological sciences and immunology; multi-/interdisciplinary studies related; nutrition sciences; philosophy; physics; political science and government; psychology; social sciences; sociology; special education.
Graduate—educational assessment, evaluation, and research; educational/instructional media design; education related.
Non-credit—area studies; creative writing; English as a second language; entrepreneurial and small business operations; mathematics; music; parks, recreation, and leisure related.

ADAMS STATE COLLEGE
Alamosa, Colorado
Extended Studies
http://exstudies.adams.edu
Adams State College was founded in 1921. It is accredited by North Central Association of Colleges and Schools. It first offered distance learning courses in 1978. In fall 2007, there were 590 students enrolled in distance learning courses. Institutionally administered financial aid is available to distance learners.
Services Distance learners have accessibility to academic advising, bookstore, e-mail services, library services.
Contact Mr. Walter Roybal, Student Advisor, Adams State College, Extended Studies, 208 Edgemont Boulevard, Alamosa, CO 81102. Telephone: 800-548-6679. Fax: 719-587-7974. E-mail: ascadvisor@adams.edu.

DEGREES AND AWARDS
AA General Education requirements
AS General Education requirements
BA Business Administration; Interdisciplinary Studies; Sociology
BS Business Administration

COURSE SUBJECT AREAS OFFERED OUTSIDE OF DEGREE PROGRAMS
Undergraduate—business/commerce; business/corporate communications; business, management, and marketing related; business/managerial economics; criminal justice and corrections; criminology; English composition; English language and literature related; finance and financial

management services; history; human resources management; legal studies (non-professional general, undergraduate); legal support services; medieval and Renaissance studies; sociology.
Graduate—biology; education; educational/instructional media design; education (specific subject areas); technology education/industrial arts.
Non-credit—accounting and related services; business/commerce; computer software and media applications; creative writing; data processing; entrepreneurial and small business operations; gerontology; linguistic, comparative, and related language studies; sales, merchandising, and related marketing operations (general); sales, merchandising, and related marketing operations (specialized).
See full description on page 330.

AIB COLLEGE OF BUSINESS
Des Moines, Iowa
http://www.aib.edu/onlineEducation
AIB College of Business was founded in 1921. It is accredited by North Central Association of Colleges and Schools. It first offered distance learning courses in 2001. In fall 2007, there were 425 students enrolled in distance learning courses. Institutionally administered financial aid is available to distance learners.
Services Distance learners have accessibility to academic advising, bookstore, campus computer network, career placement assistance, e-mail services, library services, tutoring.
Contact Dale Engle, Admissions Representative, AIB College of Business, 2500 Fleur Drive, Des Moines, IA 50321. Telephone: 800-444-1921. Fax: 515-244-6773. E-mail: engled@aib.edu.

DEGREES AND AWARDS
AAS Accounting and Business Leadership; Accounting and Financial Services; Accounting and Information Technology; Accounting; Business Administration and Financial Services; Business Administration and Leadership; Business Administration–Sales and Marketing; Business Administration; Office and Business Administration; Travel and Hospitality Management; Travel and Hospitality Management/Business Admin; Voice Captioning
BS Accounting; Business Administration

COURSE SUBJECT AREAS OFFERED OUTSIDE OF DEGREE PROGRAMS
Undergraduate—accounting and related services; business administration, management and operations; business/commerce; business, management, and marketing related; business operations support and assistant services; computer software and media applications; data entry/microcomputer applications; economics; English; English composition; entrepreneurial and small business operations; finance and financial management services; human resources management; industrial and organizational psychology; international business; marketing; mathematics; mathematics and statistics related; psychology; public relations, advertising, and applied communication related; sociology; technical and business writing.

ALBANY STATE UNIVERSITY
Albany, Georgia
http://www.asurams.edu
Albany State University was founded in 1903. It is accredited by Southern Association of Colleges and Schools. It first offered distance learning courses in 2000. In fall 2007, there were 60 students enrolled in distance learning courses. Institutionally administered financial aid is available to distance learners.
Services Distance learners have accessibility to academic advising, career placement assistance, e-mail services, library services, tutoring.
Contact Ms. Natalie Regina Knox, Coordinator, Off-Campus Programs, Albany State University, 504 College Drive, Albany, GA 31701. Telephone: 229-430-4721. E-mail: natalie.knox@asurams.edu.

DEGREES AND AWARDS
Programs offered do not lead to a degree or other formal award.

COURSE SUBJECT AREAS OFFERED OUTSIDE OF DEGREE PROGRAMS
Undergraduate—criminal justice and corrections; education; social work.
Graduate—business, management, and marketing related.

ALCORN STATE UNIVERSITY
Alcorn State, Mississippi
Office of Academic Technologies
http://blackboard.alcorn.edu
Alcorn State University was founded in 1871. It is accredited by Southern Association of Colleges and Schools. It first offered distance learning courses in 1997. In fall 2007, there were 898 students enrolled in distance learning courses. Institutionally administered financial aid is available to distance learners.
Services Distance learners have accessibility to academic advising, e-mail services, library services.
Contact Mr. Prashant D. Shinde, Director of Academic Technology, Alcorn State University, 1000 ASU Drive, #569, Alcorn State, MS 39096-7500. Telephone: 601-877-6142. Fax: 601-877-6256. E-mail: prashant@alcorn.edu.

DEGREES AND AWARDS
MSN Nursing

COURSE SUBJECT AREAS OFFERED OUTSIDE OF DEGREE PROGRAMS
Undergraduate—curriculum and instruction; education (specific subject areas); nursing.
Graduate—accounting and related services; environmental/environmental health engineering.

ALLEN COLLEGE
Waterloo, Iowa
http://www.allencollege.edu/
Allen College was founded in 1989. It is accredited by North Central Association of Colleges and Schools. It first offered distance learning courses in 2000. In fall 2007, there were 450 students enrolled in distance learning courses. Institutionally administered financial aid is available to distance learners.
Services Distance learners have accessibility to academic advising, bookstore, campus computer network, career placement assistance, e-mail services, library services, tutoring.
Contact Lisa Doreen Brodersen, EdD, Professor of Nursing, Web Education Coordinator, Allen College, 1825 Logan Avenue, Waterloo, IA 50703. Telephone: 319-226-2034. Fax: 319-226-2075. E-mail: broderld@ihs.org.

DEGREES AND AWARDS
BSN Nursing–Bachelor of Science in Nursing
MSN Nursing

ALLEN COUNTY COMMUNITY COLLEGE
Iola, Kansas
http://www.allencc.edu
Allen County Community College was founded in 1923. It is accredited by North Central Association of Colleges and Schools. It first offered distance learning courses in 2001. In fall 2007, there were 1,100 students enrolled in distance learning courses. Institutionally administered financial aid is available to distance learners.
Services Distance learners have accessibility to academic advising, bookstore, career placement assistance, e-mail services, library services.
Contact Regena M. Bailey Aye, Online Coordinator, Allen County Community College, PO Box 66, Burlingame, KS 66413. Telephone: 785-654-2416 Ext. 204. E-mail: rbailey@allencc.edu.

DEGREES AND AWARDS
Programs offered do not lead to a degree or other formal award.

COURSE SUBJECT AREAS OFFERED OUTSIDE OF DEGREE PROGRAMS

Undergraduate—agricultural business and management; agriculture; allied health and medical assisting services; American literature (United States and Canadian); behavioral sciences; biological and physical sciences; biology; business administration, management and operations; business/commerce; business, management, and marketing related; business/managerial economics; cell biology and anatomical sciences; computer and information sciences; computer software and media applications; criminal justice and corrections; data entry/microcomputer applications; economics; English; English composition; geography and cartography; health and physical education/fitness; history; mathematics; music; nutrition sciences; philosophy; physical sciences; political science and government; psychology; psychology related; sociology; speech and rhetoric; statistics.

ALPENA COMMUNITY COLLEGE
Alpena, Michigan
http://www.alpenacc.edu

Alpena Community College was founded in 1952. It is accredited by North Central Association of Colleges and Schools. It first offered distance learning courses in 1997. In fall 2007, there were 207 students enrolled in distance learning courses. Institutionally administered financial aid is available to distance learners.

Services Distance learners have accessibility to academic advising, bookstore, e-mail services, library services, tutoring.

Contact Dr. Mark Curtis, Vice President of Instruction, Alpena Community College, 665 Johnson Street, Alpena, MI 49707. Telephone: 989-358-7443. Fax: 989-358-7561. E-mail: curtism@alpenacc.edu.

DEGREES AND AWARDS

Certificate Corrections Officer Academic program

COURSE SUBJECT AREAS OFFERED OUTSIDE OF DEGREE PROGRAMS

Undergraduate—computer/information technology administration and management; computer systems networking and telecommunications; construction trades related; criminal justice and corrections; electrical and electronic engineering technologies; English composition; fine and studio art; health and medical administrative services; philosophy; political science and government; psychology; sociology.

Non-credit—construction trades related; work and family studies.

AMBERTON UNIVERSITY
Garland, Texas
http://www.amberton.edu/

Amberton University was founded in 1971. It is accredited by Southern Association of Colleges and Schools. It first offered distance learning courses in 1992. In fall 2007, there were 800 students enrolled in distance learning courses. Institutionally administered financial aid is available to distance learners.

Services Distance learners have accessibility to academic advising, bookstore, library services.

Contact Dr. Jo Lynn Loyd, Vice President, Strategic Services, Amberton University, 1700 Eastgate Drive, Garland, TX 75041. Telephone: 972-279-6511 Ext. 126. Fax: 972-279-9773. E-mail: jloyd@amberton.edu.

DEGREES AND AWARDS

BBA Management
MA Professional Development
MBA Management
MS Human Relations and Business

COURSE SUBJECT AREAS OFFERED OUTSIDE OF DEGREE PROGRAMS

Undergraduate—accounting and related services; business administration, management and operations.

Graduate—business administration, management and operations; counseling psychology.

THE AMERICAN COLLEGE
Bryn Mawr, Pennsylvania
http://www.theamericancollege.edu/

The American College was founded in 1927. It is accredited by Middle States Association of Colleges and Schools. It first offered distance learning courses in 1961. In fall 2007, there were 30,000 students enrolled in distance learning courses. Institutionally administered financial aid is available to distance learners.

Services Distance learners have accessibility to academic advising, bookstore, e-mail services, library services.

Contact Office of Student Services, The American College, 270 South Bryn Mawr Avenue, Bryn Mawr, PA 19010. Telephone: 888-263-7265. Fax: 610-526-1465. E-mail: studentservices@theamericancollege.edu.

DEGREES AND AWARDS

Certificate CFP(r) Certification Curriculum; Pensions and Executive Compensation

Diploma Chartered Advisor for Senior Living (CASL) designation; Chartered Financial Consultant (ChFC(r)) designation; Chartered Leadership Fellow(r) (CLF(r)) designation; Chartered Life Underwriter (CLU(r)) designation; LUTC Fellow Designation; Registered Employee Benefits Consultant(r) (REBC(r)) designation; Registered Health Underwriter(r) (RHU(r)) designation

Advanced Graduate Diploma Chartered Advisor in Philanthropy(r)(CAP) designation

Graduate Certificate Asset Management; Business Succession Planning; Charitable Planning; Estate Planning and Taxation; Financial Planning–Graduate Financial Planning track

MSFS Financial Services
MSM Leadership

COURSE SUBJECT AREAS OFFERED OUTSIDE OF DEGREE PROGRAMS

Undergraduate—business administration, management and operations; business/commerce; finance and financial management services; gerontology; human resources management; insurance; sales, merchandising, and related marketing operations (specialized); social psychology.

Graduate—business administration, management and operations; business/commerce; finance and financial management services; human resources management; insurance.

AMERICAN GRADUATE UNIVERSITY
Covina, California
http://www.agu.edu/

American Graduate University was founded in 1969. It is accredited by Distance Education and Training Council. It first offered distance learning courses in 1975. In fall 2007, there were 972 students enrolled in distance learning courses. Institutionally administered financial aid is available to distance learners.

Services Distance learners have accessibility to academic advising, bookstore, library services.

Contact Ms. Marie J. Sirney, Executive Vice President, American Graduate University, 733 North Dodsworth Avenue, Covina, CA 91724. Telephone: 626-966-4576 Ext. 1003. Fax: 626-915-1709. E-mail: mariesirney@agu.edu.

DEGREES AND AWARDS

MA Acquisition Management–Master of Acquisition Management; Contract Management–Master of Contract Management; Project Management–Master of Project Management

MBA Acquisition and Contracting concentration or Project Management concentration

MSM Supply Management

COURSE SUBJECT AREAS OFFERED OUTSIDE OF DEGREE PROGRAMS

Graduate—accounting and related services; business administration, management and operations; business/corporate communications; business/managerial economics.

AMERICAN INTERCONTINENTAL UNIVERSITY ONLINE
Hoffman Estates, Illinois
http://www.aiuonline.edu

American InterContinental University Online was founded in 1970. It is accredited by Southern Association of Colleges and Schools. It first offered distance learning courses in 2001. In fall 2007, there were 22,173 students enrolled in distance learning courses. Institutionally administered financial aid is available to distance learners.

Services Distance learners have accessibility to academic advising, bookstore, career placement assistance, e-mail services, library services, tutoring.

Contact Richard Kennedy, Vice President of Admissions, American InterContinental University Online, 5550 Prairie Stone Parkway, Suite 400, Hoffman Estates, IL 60192. Telephone: 877-701-3800. Fax: 866-647-9403. E-mail: info@aiuonline.edu.

DEGREES AND AWARDS

AAB Business concentration; Completion Program; Criminal Justice Administration concentration; Healthcare Administration concentration; Human Resources concentration; Information Systems concentration; Medical Coding and Billing concentration; Visual Communication concentration

BA Visual Communication–Digital Design concentration (completion program); Visual Communication–Web Design concentration (completion program)

BBA Accounting and Finance concentration (completion program); Healthcare Management concentration (completion program); Human Resource Management concentration (completion program); International Business concentration (completion program); Management concentration (completion program); Marketing concentration (completion program); Operations Management concentration (completion program); Organizational Psychology and Development concentration (completion program); Project Management concentration (completion program)

BS Criminal Justice, Special Populations concentration

BST Information Technology and Bachelor of Information Technology (BIT), Computer Forensics concentration (completion program); Information Technology and Bachelor of Information Technology (BIT), Internet Security concentration (completion program); Information Technology–Bachelor of Information Technology (BIT)–Computer Systems concentration (completion program); Information Technology–Bachelor of Information Technology (BIT)–Network Administration concentration (completion program); Information Technology–Bachelor of Information Technology (BIT)–Programming concentration (completion program)

MBA Accounting and Finance concentration (10-month program); Finance concentration (10 month program); Healthcare Management concentration (10-month program); Human Resource Management concentration (10-month program); International Business concentration (10-month program); Management concentration (10-month program); Marketing concentration (10-month program); Operations Management concentration (10-month program); Organizational Psychology and Development concentration (10-month program); Project Management concentration (10-month program)

MEd Curriculum and Instruction concentration (10-month program); Educational Assessment and Evaluation concentration (10-month program); Instructional Technology concentration (10-month program); Leadership of Educational Organizations concentration (10-month program)

MIT IT Project Management concentration (10 month program); Internet Security concentration (10-month program)

COURSE SUBJECT AREAS OFFERED OUTSIDE OF DEGREE PROGRAMS

Undergraduate—business, management, and marketing related; computer/information technology administration and management; criminal justice and corrections; design and applied arts.

Graduate—business administration, management and operations; computer/information technology administration and management; educational administration and supervision.

See full description on page 332.

AMERICAN PUBLIC UNIVERSITY SYSTEM
Charles Town, West Virginia
http://www.apus.edu/

American Public University System was founded in 1991. It is accredited by Distance Education and Training Council. It first offered distance learning courses in 1993. In fall 2007, there were 16,700 students enrolled in distance learning courses. Institutionally administered financial aid is available to distance learners.

Services Distance learners have accessibility to academic advising, bookstore, campus computer network, e-mail services, library services, tutoring.

Contact Ms. Terry Grant, Director, Enrollment Management and Retention, American Public University System, 111 West Congress Street, Charles Town, WV 25414. Telephone: 877-468-6268 Ext. 3720. E-mail: tgrant@apus.edu.

DEGREES AND AWARDS

AA General Studies

BA Criminal Justice; Emergency and Disaster Management; English; Family Development; Fire Science Management; History; Homeland Security; Hospitality Management; International Relations; Legal Studies; Management; Marketing; Military History, Military Management, Intelligence Studies; Philosophy; Political Science; Psychology; Religion; Security Management; Sociology; Transportation and Logistics Management

BBA Business Administration

BS Environmental Studies; Information Technology Management; Middle Eastern Studies; Public Health; Space Studies; Sports and Health Sciences

MA Criminal Justice; Emergency and Disaster Management; History; Homeland Security; Humanities; International Relations and Conflict Resolution; Military Studies; National Security Studies; Political Science; Security Management; Sports Management; Strategic Intelligence; Transportation and Logistics Management

MAM Management

MBA Business Administration

MPA Public Administration

MS Environmental Policy and Management; Space Studies

MS/MPH Public Health

COURSE SUBJECT AREAS OFFERED OUTSIDE OF DEGREE PROGRAMS

Undergraduate—area studies; business administration, management and operations; computer/information technology administration and management; criminal justice and corrections; English; English composition; health and medical administrative services; history; human development, family studies, and related services; human resources management; international business; international relations and affairs; liberal arts and sciences, general studies and humanities; management information systems; military studies; military technologies; philosophy; philosophy and religious studies related; political science and government; psychology; public administration; public policy analysis.

Graduate—business/commerce; criminal justice and corrections; ethnic, cultural minority, and gender studies; history; international relations and affairs; military studies; military technologies; public administration and social service professions related; transportation and materials moving related.

See full description on page 334.

AMERICAN UNIVERSITY
Washington, District of Columbia
http://www.american.edu/distanceed/

American University was founded in 1893. It is accredited by Middle States Association of Colleges and Schools. It first offered distance learning courses in 2004.

Services Distance learners have accessibility to academic advising, bookstore, campus computer network, career placement assistance, e-mail services, library services.

Contact Distance Education Coordinator, American University, Washington, DC 20016. E-mail: distanceed@american.edu.

DEGREES AND AWARDS

Programs offered do not lead to a degree or other formal award.

COURSE SUBJECT AREAS OFFERED OUTSIDE OF DEGREE PROGRAMS

Undergraduate—anthropology; chemistry; communication and journalism related; criminology; education; health and physical education/fitness; international relations and affairs; political science and government; psychology.

Graduate—accounting and related services; communication and journalism related; criminology; education; international relations and affairs; political science and government; psychology.

AMRIDGE UNIVERSITY
Montgomery, Alabama
Extended Learning Program
http://www.amridgeuniversity.edu

Amridge University was founded in 1967. It is accredited by Southern Association of Colleges and Schools. It first offered distance learning courses in 1993. In fall 2007, there were 725 students enrolled in distance learning courses. Institutionally administered financial aid is available to distance learners.

Services Distance learners have accessibility to academic advising, bookstore, library services, tutoring.

Contact Rick Johnson, Admissions Advisor and Counselor, Amridge University, 1200 Taylor Road, Montgomery, AL 36117. Telephone: 800-351-4040 Ext. 7513. Fax: 334-387-3878. E-mail: rickjohnson@amridgeuniversity.edu.

DEGREES AND AWARDS

AA Liberal Studies

BA Biblical Studies

BS Business Administration/General Business; Business Administration/Information Communication; Business Administration/Information Systems Management; Human Development; Human Resource Leadership; Liberal Studies; Management Communication; Ministry/Bible; Public Safety and Business/Organization Security; Public Safety and Criminal Justice; Public Safety and Homeland Security

MA Behavioral Leadership and Management; Biblical Studies; Marriage and Family Therapy; Practical Theology; Professional Counseling

MDiv Marriage and Family Therapy; Ministerial Leadership; Ministry; Pastoral Counseling; Professional Counseling

MS Leadership and Management; Ministerial Leadership; Pastoral Counseling

DMin Christian Ministry; Family Therapy

PhD Biblical Studies; Family Therapy

COURSE SUBJECT AREAS OFFERED OUTSIDE OF DEGREE PROGRAMS

Undergraduate—human services; liberal arts and sciences, general studies and humanities; missionary studies and missiology; pastoral counseling and specialized ministries; philosophy and religious studies related; religious studies; theological and ministerial studies.

Graduate—human services; missionary studies and missiology; pastoral counseling and specialized ministries; philosophy and religious studies related; religious studies; theological and ministerial studies.

Non-credit—human services; liberal arts and sciences, general studies and humanities; missionary studies and missiology; pastoral counseling and specialized ministries; philosophy and religious studies related; religious studies; theological and ministerial studies.

See full description on page 336.

ANDERSON UNIVERSITY
Anderson, Indiana
http://www.anderson.edu/sot/academics/onlinemts/index.html

Anderson University was founded in 1917. It is accredited by North Central Association of Colleges and Schools. It first offered distance learning courses in 1999. In fall 2007, there were 30 students enrolled in distance learning courses. Institutionally administered financial aid is available to distance learners.

Services Distance learners have accessibility to academic advising, bookstore, campus computer network, e-mail services, library services.

Contact Dr. John H. Aukerman, Director of Distance Education, Anderson University, 1100 East 5th Street, Anderson, IN 46012. Telephone: 765-641-4530. Fax: 765-641-3005. E-mail: jhaukerman@anderson.edu.

DEGREES AND AWARDS

MA Christian Ministries

ANDOVER NEWTON THEOLOGICAL SCHOOL
Newton Centre, Massachusetts
http://www.ants.edu

Andover Newton Theological School was founded in 1807. It is accredited by New England Association of Schools and Colleges. It first offered distance learning courses in 1999. In fall 2007, there were 175 students enrolled in distance learning courses. Institutionally administered financial aid is available to distance learners.

Services Distance learners have accessibility to academic advising, bookstore, campus computer network, e-mail services, library services.

Contact Dr. Jeffrey Jones, Director of Distance Learning, Andover Newton Theological School, 210 Herrick Road, Newton Centre, MA 02459. Telephone: 617-964-1100 Ext. 291. E-mail: jjones@ants.edu.

DEGREES AND AWARDS

Programs offered do not lead to a degree or other formal award.

COURSE SUBJECT AREAS OFFERED OUTSIDE OF DEGREE PROGRAMS

Graduate—biblical studies; history; pastoral counseling and specialized ministries; religious education; religious studies; theological and ministerial studies; theology and religious vocations related.

Non-credit—biblical studies; religious education; religious studies.

ANGELO STATE UNIVERSITY
San Angelo, Texas
http://www.angelo.edu/

Angelo State University was founded in 1928. It is accredited by Southern Association of Colleges and Schools. It first offered distance learning courses in 2000. In fall 2007, there were 903 students enrolled in distance learning courses. Institutionally administered financial aid is available to distance learners.

Services Distance learners have accessibility to academic advising, campus computer network, e-mail services, library services.

Contact Dr. Nancy Allen, Associate Vice President, Angelo State University, 2601 West Avenue North, ASU Station #11008, San Angelo, TX 76909. Telephone: 325-942-2723 Ext. 298. Fax: 325-942-2128. E-mail: nancy.allen@angelo.edu.

DEGREES AND AWARDS

BSN Nursing–Bachelor of Science in Nursing
MSN Nursing

ANNE ARUNDEL COMMUNITY COLLEGE
Arnold, Maryland
Distance Learning Center
http://www.aacc.edu/virtualcampus

Anne Arundel Community College was founded in 1961. It is accredited by Middle States Association of Colleges and Schools. It first offered distance learning courses in 1981. In fall 2007, there were 3,923 students enrolled in distance learning courses. Institutionally administered financial aid is available to distance learners.

Services Distance learners have accessibility to academic advising, bookstore, campus computer network, career placement assistance, e-mail services, library services, tutoring.

Contact Ms. Patty McCarthy-O'Neill, Distance Learning Coordinator, Anne Arundel Community College, 101 College Parkway, Arnold, MD 21012-1895. Telephone: 410-777-2514. Fax: 410-777-2691. E-mail: pmmccarthyoneill@aacc.edu.

DEGREES AND AWARDS

AA Transfer Studies
AAS Business Management; General Technology
AS Business Administration transfer

COURSE SUBJECT AREAS OFFERED OUTSIDE OF DEGREE PROGRAMS

Undergraduate—accounting and related services; allied health and medical assisting services; applied mathematics; behavioral sciences; biological and physical sciences; business administration, management and operations; business, management, and marketing related; business/managerial economics; chemistry; communication and media; computer and information sciences; computer science; criminal justice and corrections; developmental and child psychology; economics; English composition; finance and financial management services; geography and cartography; health and physical education/fitness; history; hospitality administration; intercultural/multicultural and diversity studies; legal studies (non-professional general, undergraduate); legal support services; marketing; mathematics and statistics related; philosophy; political science and government; social psychology; social sciences related; sociology; statistics.

Non-credit—business, management, and marketing related; computer and information sciences; finance and financial management services; health services/allied health/health sciences; history; languages (foreign languages related).

ANTIOCH UNIVERSITY MCGREGOR
Yellow Springs, Ohio
http://www.mcgregor.edu

Antioch University McGregor was founded in 1988. It is accredited by North Central Association of Colleges and Schools. It first offered distance learning courses in 1988. In fall 2007, there were 128 students enrolled in distance learning courses. Institutionally administered financial aid is available to distance learners.

Services Distance learners have accessibility to academic advising, bookstore, campus computer network, e-mail services, library services.

Contact Mr. Seth Gordon, Enrollment Services Manager, Antioch University McGregor, 800 Livermore Street, Yellow Springs, OH 45387. Telephone: 937-769-1825. Fax: 937-769-1804. E-mail: sgordon@mcgregor.edu.

DEGREES AND AWARDS

MA Community Change and Civic Leadership; Community College Management; Conflict Resolution; Individualized Liberal and Professional Studies (various self-designed topics); Intercultural Conflict Management

COURSE SUBJECT AREAS OFFERED OUTSIDE OF DEGREE PROGRAMS

Graduate—business administration, management and operations; education.

APPALACHIAN STATE UNIVERSITY
Boone, North Carolina
http://www.appstate.edu/

Appalachian State University was founded in 1899. It is accredited by Southern Association of Colleges and Schools. It first offered distance learning courses in 1960. In fall 2007, there were 1,400 students enrolled in distance learning courses. Institutionally administered financial aid is available to distance learners.

Services Distance learners have accessibility to academic advising, bookstore, campus computer network, career placement assistance, e-mail services, library services.

Contact Ms. Cynthia Weaver, Director, Office of Extension and Distance Education, Appalachian State University, Office of Extension and Distance Education, PO Box 32054, Boone, NC 28608. Telephone: 800-355 4084. E-mail: extension@appstate.edu.

DEGREES AND AWARDS

Graduate Certificate Distance Education–Online Teaching and Learning; Gerontology
MA Educational Media, New Media and Global Education

ARAPAHOE COMMUNITY COLLEGE
Littleton, Colorado
Educational Technology
http://www.arapahoe.edu

Arapahoe Community College was founded in 1965. It is accredited by North Central Association of Colleges and Schools. It first offered distance learning courses in 1985. In fall 2007, there were 1,856 students enrolled in distance learning courses. Institutionally administered financial aid is available to distance learners.

Services Distance learners have accessibility to academic advising, bookstore, campus computer network, e-mail services, library services.

Contact Lee Christopher, eLearning Manager, Arapahoe Community College, 5900 South Santa Fe Drive, Littleton, CO 80160. Telephone: 303-797-5965. Fax: 303-797-5700 Ext. 6700. E-mail: lee.christopher@arapahoe.edu.

DEGREES AND AWARDS
Programs offered do not lead to a degree or other formal award.

COURSE SUBJECT AREAS OFFERED OUTSIDE OF DEGREE PROGRAMS

Undergraduate—accounting and computer science; accounting and related services; allied health and medical assisting services; allied health diagnostic, intervention, and treatment professions; alternative and complementary medical support services; alternative and complementary medicine and medical systems; American literature (United States and Canadian); American Sign Language (ASL); anthropology; apparel and textiles; applied mathematics; architecture related; area, ethnic, cultural, and gender studies related; astronomy and astrophysics; audiovisual communications technologies; behavioral sciences; biochemistry, biophysics and molecular biology; bioethics/medical ethics; biology; business administration, management and operations; business/corporate communications; business, management, and marketing related; chemistry; clinical child psychology; clinical/medical laboratory science and allied professions; clinical psychology; cognitive psychology and psycholinguistics; cognitive science; communication and journalism related; communication and media; communications technology; comparative literature; computer and information sciences; computer and information sciences and support services related; computer/information technology administration and management; computer programming; computer science; computer software and media applications; computer systems analysis; computer systems networking and telecommunications; criminal justice and corrections; economics; education; educational administration and supervision; educational assessment, evaluation, and research; educational/instructional media design; educational psychology; education related; education (specific levels and methods); education (specific subject areas); electrical and electronic engineering technologies; engineering technologies related; English; English as a second language; English composition; English language and literature related; English literature

(British and Commonwealth); entrepreneurial and small business operations; ethnic, cultural minority, and gender studies; family psychology; film/video and photographic arts; finance and financial management services; funeral service and mortuary science; geography and cartography; geological and earth sciences/geosciences; geological/geophysical engineering; graphic communications; ground transportation; health aides/attendants/orderlies; health and medical administrative services; health and physical education/fitness; health/medical preparatory programs; health professions related; health psychology; health services/allied health/health sciences; history; hospitality administration; human development, family studies, and related services; information science/studies; journalism; languages (Romance languages); languages (South Asian); legal professions and studies related; legal research and advanced professional studies; legal studies (non-professional general, undergraduate); legal support services; liberal arts and sciences, general studies and humanities; management information systems; marketing; mathematics; mathematics and computer science; mathematics and statistics related; medical basic sciences; medical clinical sciences/graduate medical studies; medical illustration and informatics; mental and social health services and allied professions; music; nursing; personality psychology; pharmacology and toxicology; pharmacy, pharmaceutical sciences, and administration; philosophy; physics; political science and government; psychology; public health; public relations, advertising, and applied communication related; publishing; real estate; sales, merchandising, and related marketing operations (general); sales, merchandising, and related marketing operations (specialized); security and protective services related; social and philosophical foundations of education; sociology; special education; speech and rhetoric; teaching assistants/aides; technical and business writing; vehicle maintenance and repair technologies; visual and performing arts.

ARIZONA WESTERN COLLEGE
Yuma, Arizona
http://www.azwestern.edu
Arizona Western College was founded in 1962. It is accredited by North Central Association of Colleges and Schools. It first offered distance learning courses in 1992. In fall 2007, there were 2,573 students enrolled in distance learning courses. Institutionally administered financial aid is available to distance learners.
Services Distance learners have accessibility to academic advising, bookstore, campus computer network, e-mail services, library services.
Contact Bryan Doak, Interim Vice President for Student Services, Arizona Western College, PO Box 929, Yuma, AZ 85366-0929. Telephone: 928-344-7617. Fax: 928-344-7543. E-mail: bryan.doak@azwestern.edu.

DEGREES AND AWARDS
AD Administration of Justice; Business Administration; Education

COURSE SUBJECT AREAS OFFERED OUTSIDE OF DEGREE PROGRAMS
Undergraduate—accounting and related services; business/commerce; computer and information sciences; criminal justice and corrections; English; fire protection; liberal arts and sciences, general studies and humanities.

ARKANSAS STATE UNIVERSITY–BEEBE
Beebe, Arkansas
http://www.asub.edu/dlweb
Arkansas State University–Beebe was founded in 1927. It is accredited by North Central Association of Colleges and Schools. It first offered distance learning courses in 1999. In fall 2007, there were 814 students enrolled in distance learning courses. Institutionally administered financial aid is available to distance learners.
Services Distance learners have accessibility to academic advising, bookstore, career placement assistance, e-mail services, library services, tutoring.

Contact Chris Boyett, Director of Distance Learning, Arkansas State University–Beebe, PO Box 1000, Beebe, AR 72012. Telephone: 501-882-4442. Fax: 501-882-4412. E-mail: jcboyett@asub.edu.

DEGREES AND AWARDS
AA Liberal Arts–Associate of Arts in Liberal Arts

COURSE SUBJECT AREAS OFFERED OUTSIDE OF DEGREE PROGRAMS
Undergraduate—accounting and related services; agricultural business and management; business administration, management and operations; business/corporate communications; business, management, and marketing related; communication and media; computer and information sciences; computer programming; creative writing; criminal justice and corrections; data entry/microcomputer applications; developmental and child psychology; ecology, evolution, and population biology; economics; English; English composition; geography and cartography; geological and earth sciences/geosciences; history; mathematics; music; philosophy; physical sciences; political science and government; psychology; sociology; statistics; visual and performing arts.

ARKANSAS STATE UNIVERSITY–MOUNTAIN HOME
Mountain Home, Arkansas
http://www.asumh.edu
Arkansas State University–Mountain Home was founded in 2000. It is accredited by North Central Association of Colleges and Schools. It first offered distance learning courses in 2000. In fall 2007, there were 280 students enrolled in distance learning courses. Institutionally administered financial aid is available to distance learners.
Services Distance learners have accessibility to academic advising, bookstore, campus computer network, e-mail services, library services, tutoring.
Contact Mr. Scott Raney, Director of Student Services, Arkansas State University–Mountain Home, 1600 South College Street, Mountain Home, AR 72653. Telephone: 870-508-6168. Fax: 870-508-6284. E-mail: sraney@asumh.edu.

DEGREES AND AWARDS
AA General degree

COURSE SUBJECT AREAS OFFERED OUTSIDE OF DEGREE PROGRAMS
Undergraduate—accounting and computer science; biology; business administration, management and operations; comparative literature; computer science; dramatic/theater arts and stagecraft; economics; English composition; health professions related; history; languages (classics and classical); liberal arts and sciences, general studies and humanities; mathematics.

ARKANSAS TECH UNIVERSITY
Russellville, Arkansas
Virtual Learning Center
http://elearn.atu.edu/
Arkansas Tech University was founded in 1909. It is accredited by North Central Association of Colleges and Schools. It first offered distance learning courses in 1996. In fall 2007, there were 1,847 students enrolled in distance learning courses. Institutionally administered financial aid is available to distance learners.
Services Distance learners have accessibility to academic advising, bookstore, campus computer network, career placement assistance, e-mail services, library services.
Contact Admissions Office, Arkansas Tech University, ATU, Doc Bryan 141, Russellville, AR 72801-2222. Telephone: 479-968-0343. E-mail: tech.enroll@atu.edu.

DEGREES AND AWARDS
AS Early Childhood Education
BS Early Childhood Education; Emergency Administration and Management

MS College Student Personnel

COURSE SUBJECT AREAS OFFERED OUTSIDE OF DEGREE PROGRAMS

Undergraduate—agricultural business and management; biology; business administration, management and operations; computer and information sciences; educational/instructional media design; education related; education (specific levels and methods); education (specific subject areas); electrical, electronics and communications engineering; English language and literature related; health and medical administrative services; history; hospitality administration; journalism; marketing; mathematics; mechanic and repair technologies related; music; nursing; physical sciences; political science and government; psychology; rehabilitation and therapeutic professions; security and protective services related.

Graduate—educational administration and supervision; educational/instructional media design; education related; education (specific subject areas); journalism.

ARLINGTON BAPTIST COLLEGE
Arlington, Texas
Distance Education Department
http://www.abconline.edu/

Arlington Baptist College was founded in 1939. It is accredited by Association for Biblical Higher Education. It first offered distance learning courses in 1994. In fall 2007, there were 73 students enrolled in distance learning courses. Institutionally administered financial aid is available to distance learners.
Services Distance learners have accessibility to academic advising, bookstore, campus computer network, e-mail services, library services.
Contact Janie Taylor, Registrar, Arlington Baptist College, 3001 West Division Street, Arlington, TX 76012. Telephone: 817-461-8741 Ext. 105. Fax: 817-274-1138. E-mail: jtaylor@abconline.org.

DEGREES AND AWARDS
Programs offered do not lead to a degree or other formal award.

COURSE SUBJECT AREAS OFFERED OUTSIDE OF DEGREE PROGRAMS

Undergraduate—biblical studies; education related; pastoral counseling and specialized ministries; philosophy and religious studies related; theological and ministerial studies.
Non-credit—biblical studies; theological and ministerial studies.

ASSEMBLIES OF GOD THEOLOGICAL SEMINARY
Springfield, Missouri
Office of Continuing Education
http://www.agts.edu

Assemblies of God Theological Seminary was founded in 1972. It is accredited by North Central Association of Colleges and Schools. It first offered distance learning courses in 1980. In fall 2007, there were 21 students enrolled in distance learning courses. Institutionally administered financial aid is available to distance learners.
Services Distance learners have accessibility to academic advising, bookstore, campus computer network, e-mail services, library services, tutoring.
Contact Rev. Joel Triska, Distance Learning Specialist, Assemblies of God Theological Seminary, 1435 North Glenstone Avenue, Springfield, MO 65802. Telephone: 800-467-2487 Ext. 1046. Fax: 417-268-1009. E-mail: jtriska@agts.edu.

DEGREES AND AWARDS
Programs offered do not lead to a degree or other formal award.

COURSE SUBJECT AREAS OFFERED OUTSIDE OF DEGREE PROGRAMS

Graduate—biblical and other theological languages and literatures; biblical studies; history; missionary studies and missiology; pastoral counseling and specialized ministries; philosophy and religious studies related; religious studies; theological and ministerial studies; theology and religious vocations related.

ATHABASCA UNIVERSITY
Athabasca, Alberta, Canada
http://www.athabascau.ca

Athabasca University was founded in 1970. It is provincially chartered. It first offered distance learning courses in 1972. In fall 2007, there were 37,000 students enrolled in distance learning courses. Institutionally administered financial aid is available to distance learners.
Services Distance learners have accessibility to academic advising, bookstore, campus computer network, e-mail services, library services, tutoring.
Contact Information Centre, Athabasca University, 1 University Drive, Athabasca, AB T9S 3A3, Canada. Telephone: 800-788-9041. Fax: 780-675-6437. E-mail: inquire@athabascau.ca.

DEGREES AND AWARDS
BA Anthropology (3 year); Anthropology (4 year); Canadian Studies (3 year); Canadian Studies (4 year); English (3 year); English (4 year); French (3 year); French (4 year); History (3 year); History (4 year); Human Resources Management/Marketing (3 year); Human Resources Management/Marketing (4 year); Human Resources and Labour Relations; Humanities (3 year); Humanities (4 year); Information Systems (3 year); Information Systems (4 year); Labour Studies (3 year); Labour Studies (4 year); Management post-Diploma (3 year); Management post-Diploma (4 year); Political Economy (3 year); Political Economy (4 year); Political Science (3 year); Political Science (4 year); Psychology (3 year); Psychology (4 year); Sociology (3 year); Sociology (4 year); Women's Studies (3 year); Women's Studies (4 year)
BComm Accounting; E-Commerce; Financial Service
BGS Applied Studies; Arts and Science
BN Nursing–Post-LPN; Nursing–Post-RN
BPA Communication Studies; Criminal Justice; Governance, Law, and Management; Human Services
BS Computing and Information Systems–post-Diploma; Computing and Information Systems; Health Administration post-Diploma; Health Administration; Human Science–post-Diploma; Human Science
Certificate Accounting; Accounting, advanced; Administration; Career Development; Computers and Management Information Systems; Computing and Information Systems; Counseling Women; E-Commerce; English Language Studies; Financial Services; French Language Proficiency; Health Development Administration; Heritage Resources Management; Human Resources and Labour Relations; Labour Studies; Marketing; Public Administration
Diploma Arts; Inclusive Education
Advanced Graduate Diploma Distance Education (Technology); Heritage Resources Management; Management; Nursing–Nursing Practice, advanced; Project Management
MA Integrated Studies
MBA Business Administration; Energy Elective; Policing Elective; Project Management
MCDCC Counseling
MCH Health Studies–Master of Health Studies
MDE Distance Education
MN Nursing
MSIS Information Systems
EdD Education

COURSE SUBJECT AREAS OFFERED OUTSIDE OF DEGREE PROGRAMS

Undergraduate—accounting and related services; anthropology; astronomy and astrophysics; biological and biomedical sciences related; biological and physical sciences; biology; business administration, management and operations; business/commerce; business/corporate communications; business, management, and marketing related; business/managerial economics; chemistry; communication and journalism related; communication and media; communication disorders sciences and services; communications technology; community health services; community organization and advocacy; community psychology; comparative literature; computer and information sciences; computer and information sciences and support services related; computer/information technology administration and management; computer programming; computer science; computer software and media applications; computer systems analysis; computer systems networking and telecommunications; counseling psychology; creative writing; criminal justice and corrections; criminology; data processing; demography and population; developmental and child psychology; economics; educational assessment, evaluation, and research; English; English as a second language; English composition; environmental control technologies; finance and financial management services; fine and studio art; foods, nutrition, and related services; geography and cartography; geological and earth sciences/geosciences; health and medical administrative services; health/medical preparatory programs; health professions related; history; human development, family studies, and related services; human resources management; human services; industrial and organizational psychology; international relations and affairs; journalism; legal studies (non-professional general, undergraduate); linguistic, comparative, and related language studies; management information systems; marketing; mathematics; mathematics and computer science; mental and social health services and allied professions; music; natural resources conservation and research; natural resources management and policy; nursing; philosophy; philosophy and religious studies related; physical sciences; physiological psychology/psychobiology; plant sciences; political science and government; psychology; psychology related; public administration; public health; public policy analysis; public relations, advertising, and applied communication related; sales, merchandising, and related marketing operations (general); social sciences; sociology; statistics.

Graduate—accounting and related services; agricultural business and management; business administration, management and operations; business/corporate communications; business, management, and marketing related; business/managerial economics; community health services; community organization and advocacy; community psychology; computer and information sciences; computer and information sciences and support services related; computer/information technology administration and management; computer science; computer systems analysis; counseling psychology; curriculum and instruction; developmental and child psychology; economics; educational administration and supervision; educational assessment, evaluation, and research; educational psychology; education related; health/medical preparatory programs; health professions related; history; human development, family studies, and related services; human resources management; human services; industrial and organizational psychology; information science/studies; international business; international relations and affairs; management information systems; management sciences and quantitative methods; marketing; mathematics and computer science; mental and social health services and allied professions; nursing; philosophy; political science and government; psychology; public administration; public administration and social service professions related; public health; public policy analysis; public relations, advertising, and applied communication related; sales, merchandising, and related marketing operations (general); sales, merchandising, and related marketing operations (specialized); social sciences; social sciences related; social work; sociology; special education; taxation.

Non-credit—accounting and related services; anthropology; astronomy and astrophysics; biology; building/construction finishing, management, and inspection; business administration, management and operations; business/commerce; business/corporate communications; business, management, and marketing related; business/managerial economics; business operations support and assistant services; chemistry; city/urban, community and regional planning; clinical psychology; communication and media; communication disorders sciences and services; communications technology; community health services; community organization and advocacy; community psychology; computer and information sciences; computer/information technology administration and management; computer programming; computer science; computer software and media applications; computer systems analysis; counseling psychology; criminal justice and corrections; criminology; data entry/microcomputer applications; data processing; developmental and child psychology; economics; educational administration and supervision; educational assessment, evaluation, and research; educational/instructional media design; educational psychology; education related; English; English as a second/foreign language (teaching); English as a second language; English composition; environmental control technologies; ethnic, cultural minority, and gender studies; finance and financial management services; fine and studio art; foods, nutrition, and related services; geological and earth sciences/geosciences; gerontology; health professions related; history; human development, family studies, and related services; human resources management; human services; industrial and organizational psychology; international business; international relations and affairs; journalism; liberal arts and sciences, general studies and humanities; linguistic, comparative, and related language studies; management information systems; management sciences and quantitative methods; marketing; mathematics; mathematics and computer science; medical basic sciences; mental and social health services and allied professions; music; nursing; philosophy; philosophy and religious studies related; physical sciences; political science and government; psychology; public administration; public administration and social service professions related; public health; public policy analysis; public relations, advertising, and applied communication related; radio, television, and digital communication; sales, merchandising, and related marketing operations (general); sales, merchandising, and related marketing operations (specialized); school psychology; science technologies related; science, technology and society; social and philosophical foundations of education; social psychology; social sciences; social sciences related; social work; sociology; statistics; taxation.

See full description on page 338.

ATHENS TECHNICAL COLLEGE
Athens, Georgia
http://www.athenstech.edu
Athens Technical College was founded in 1958. It is accredited by Southern Association of Colleges and Schools. It first offered distance learning courses in 1995. In fall 2007, there were 700 students enrolled in distance learning courses. Institutionally administered financial aid is available to distance learners.
Services Distance learners have accessibility to academic advising, campus computer network, career placement assistance, e-mail services, library services, tutoring.
Contact Mr. Dennis Ashworth, Vice President of Information Technology, Athens Technical College, 800 US Highway 29 North, Athens, GA 30601-1500. Telephone: 706-355-5167. E-mail: dashworth@athenstech.edu.

DEGREES AND AWARDS
Programs offered do not lead to a degree or other formal award.

COURSE SUBJECT AREAS OFFERED OUTSIDE OF DEGREE PROGRAMS

Undergraduate—accounting and related services; allied health and medical assisting services; biochemistry, biophysics and molecular biology; biology/biotechnology laboratory technician; business/commerce; chemistry; computer and information sciences; construction trades; cosmetology and related personal grooming services; criminal justice and corrections; economics; education related; electrical/electronics maintenance and repair technology; English composition; health/medical preparatory programs; hospitality administration; legal studies (non-professional general, undergraduate); marketing; mathematics; mechanic and repair technologies related; plumbing and related water supply services; psychology; psychology related; technical and business writing; veterinary biomedical and clinical sciences.

Non-credit—accounting and computer science; allied health and medical assisting services; business, management, and marketing related; computer programming; computer software and media applications; creative writing; data entry/microcomputer applications; English language and literature related; family and consumer economics; gerontology; real estate; teaching assistants/aides; technical and business writing.

ATLANTIC UNIVERSITY
Virginia Beach, Virginia
http://www.atlanticuniv.edu/

Atlantic University was founded in 1930. It is accredited by Distance Education and Training Council. It first offered distance learning courses in 1985. In fall 2007, there were 175 students enrolled in distance learning courses. Institutionally administered financial aid is available to distance learners.

Services Distance learners have accessibility to academic advising, e-mail services, library services.

Contact Mr. Gregory Deming, Director of Admissions, Atlantic University, 215 67th Street, Virginia Beach, VA 23451. Telephone: 757-631-8101 Ext. 7173. Fax: 757-631-8096. E-mail: admissions@atlanticuniv.edu.

DEGREES AND AWARDS

MA Transpersonal Studies
MFA Visionary Art and Consciousness

COURSE SUBJECT AREAS OFFERED OUTSIDE OF DEGREE PROGRAMS

Graduate—alternative and complementary medical support services; alternative and complementary medicine and medical systems; biblical studies; counseling psychology; creative writing; education related; fine and studio art; movement and mind-body therapies; peace studies and conflict resolution; philosophy and religious studies related; psychology related; religious studies; visual and performing arts.

Non-credit—alternative and complementary medical support services; alternative and complementary medicine and medical systems; biblical studies; counseling psychology; creative writing; education related; fine and studio art; movement and mind-body therapies; peace studies and conflict resolution; philosophy and religious studies related; psychology related; religious studies; visual and performing arts.

AUBURN UNIVERSITY
Auburn University, Alabama
Distance Learning/Outreach Technology
http://www.auburn.edu/auonline

Auburn University was founded in 1856. It is accredited by Southern Association of Colleges and Schools. It first offered distance learning courses in 1975. In fall 2007, there were 1,000 students enrolled in distance learning courses. Institutionally administered financial aid is available to distance learners.

Services Distance learners have accessibility to academic advising, bookstore, campus computer network, career placement assistance, e-mail services, library services.

Contact Distance Learning, Auburn University, 305 O.D. Smith Hall, Auburn University, AL 36849. Telephone: 334-844-3103. Fax: 334-844-3118.

DEGREES AND AWARDS

Certificate Dietary Management
EMBA Business Administration; Physicians Executive MBA
MA Early Childhood Intervention
MAE Aerospace Engineering; Foreign Language
MBA Business Administration
MBA/M Acc Accountancy
MBA/MSMIS Management Information Systems
MCE Chemical Engineering; Civil Engineering
MCSE Computer Science and Engineering
MEd Collaborative Teacher and Early Childhood Education; Music; Rehabilitation Counseling
MISE Industrial and Systems Engineering
MME Materials Engineering; Mechanical Engineering
MS Hotel and Restaurant Management
PharmD Pharmacy

COURSE SUBJECT AREAS OFFERED OUTSIDE OF DEGREE PROGRAMS

Undergraduate—agriculture; animal sciences; communication and media; communication disorders sciences and services; computer science; film/video and photographic arts; geography and cartography; health and physical education/fitness; political science and government; speech and rhetoric.

Graduate—accounting and related services; aerospace, aeronautical and astronautical engineering; business administration, management and operations; civil engineering; civil engineering technology; computer science; education; education related; education (specific levels and methods); education (specific subject areas); engineering-related fields; engineering science; foods, nutrition, and related services; pharmacy, pharmaceutical sciences, and administration; special education.

Non-credit—animal sciences; computer/information technology administration and management; construction management; data processing; dietetics and clinical nutrition services; engineering; foods, nutrition, and related services; veterinary biomedical and clinical sciences.

See full description on page 340.

AUSTIN PEAY STATE UNIVERSITY
Clarksville, Tennessee
http://www.apsu.edu/

Austin Peay State University was founded in 1927. It is accredited by Southern Association of Colleges and Schools. It first offered distance learning courses in 1996. In fall 2007, there were 5,427 students enrolled in distance learning courses. Institutionally administered financial aid is available to distance learners.

Services Distance learners have accessibility to academic advising, bookstore, campus computer network, career placement assistance, e-mail services, library services, tutoring.

Contact Mr. Mike Dunn, APSU Online Advisor, Austin Peay State University, PO Box 4717, Clarksville, TN 37044. Telephone: 931-221-6484. Fax: 931-221-6485. E-mail: dunnm@apsu.edu.

DEGREES AND AWARDS

AS Liberal Arts
BA Communication Arts (BA or BS)
BN Nursing–RN to BSN
BPS Regents Online degree program
BS Computer Science–Information Systems; Criminal Justice–Homeland Security; Political Science; Professional Studies
MA Corporate Communication; Military History; Psychology–Industrial/Organizational Psychology
MS Health Service Administration
MSM Management

COURSE SUBJECT AREAS OFFERED OUTSIDE OF DEGREE PROGRAMS

Undergraduate—astronomy and astrophysics; health and physical education/fitness; mathematics and computer science; psychology; public administration; sociology; speech and rhetoric.

Graduate—communication and journalism related; health and physical education/fitness.

AVILA UNIVERSITY
Kansas City, Missouri
http://www.avila.edu/

Avila University was founded in 1916. It is accredited by North Central Association of Colleges and Schools. It first offered distance learning courses in 1999. In fall 2007, there were 100 students enrolled in distance learning courses. Institutionally administered financial aid is available to distance learners.

Services Distance learners have accessibility to academic advising, bookstore, campus computer network, e-mail services, library services.

Contact Dr. Steve Iliff, Dean of the School of Professional Studies, Avila University, 11901 Wornall Road, Kansas City, MO 64145. Telephone: 816-501-3763. Fax: 816-941-4650. E-mail: steve.iliff@avila.edu.

DEGREES AND AWARDS
Programs offered do not lead to a degree or other formal award.

COURSE SUBJECT AREAS OFFERED OUTSIDE OF DEGREE PROGRAMS

Undergraduate—biological and physical sciences; business administration, management and operations; business, management, and marketing related; economics; English language and literature related; health and medical administrative services; international business; multi-/interdisciplinary studies related; psychology.

AZUSA PACIFIC UNIVERSITY
Azusa, California
http://online.apu.edu/

Azusa Pacific University was founded in 1899. It is accredited by Western Association of Schools and Colleges. It first offered distance learning courses in 1999. In fall 2007, there were 1,750 students enrolled in distance learning courses. Institutionally administered financial aid is available to distance learners.

Services Distance learners have accessibility to bookstore, e-mail services, library services.

Contact Dr. Bruce Simmerok, Director of Distance Learning and Continuing Education, Azusa Pacific University, 901 East Alosta Avenue, Azusa, CA 91702-7000. Telephone: 626-815-5038. E-mail: bsimmerok @apu.edu.

DEGREES AND AWARDS
Certificate Library Media Teaching
MA Educational Technology
MAE Library Science–School Librarianship

COURSE SUBJECT AREAS OFFERED OUTSIDE OF DEGREE PROGRAMS

Undergraduate—computer science; history; religious studies.
Graduate—computer science; educational administration and supervision; educational assessment, evaluation, and research; educational/instructional media design; education (specific subject areas); nursing; theological and ministerial studies.

BAKER COLLEGE OF FLINT
Flint, Michigan
Baker College OnLine
http://online.baker.edu

Baker College of Flint was founded in 1911. It is accredited by North Central Association of Colleges and Schools. It first offered distance learning courses in 1994. In fall 2007, there were 12,124 students enrolled in distance learning courses. Institutionally administered financial aid is available to distance learners.

Services Distance learners have accessibility to academic advising, bookstore, campus computer network, career placement assistance, e-mail services, library services, tutoring.

Contact Mr. Chuck J. Gurden, Vice President, Graduate and Online Admissions, Baker College of Flint, 1116 West Bristol Road, Flint, MI 48507. Telephone: 800-469-3165. Fax: 810-766-2051. E-mail: cgurde01@baker.edu.

DEGREES AND AWARDS
ABA Business Administration
BBA Business Administration
BGS General Studies
BS Psychology
MBA Business Administration
MSCS Information Systems

COURSE SUBJECT AREAS OFFERED OUTSIDE OF DEGREE PROGRAMS

Undergraduate—business administration, management and operations; computer/information technology administration and management.
See full description on page 342.

BAKKE GRADUATE UNIVERSITY
Seattle, Washington

Bakke Graduate University was founded in 1990. It is accredited by Transnational Association of Christian Colleges and Schools. It first offered distance learning courses in 1995. In fall 2007, there were 6 students enrolled in distance learning courses. Institutionally administered financial aid is available to distance learners.

Services Distance learners have accessibility to academic advising, e-mail services, library services.

Contact Mrs. Judi Melton, Registrar, Bakke Graduate University, 1013 Eighth Avenue, Seattle, WA 98104. Telephone: 206-264-9100 Ext. 14. Fax: 206-264-8828. E-mail: judim@bgu.edu.

DEGREES AND AWARDS
Programs offered do not lead to a degree or other formal award.

COURSE SUBJECT AREAS OFFERED OUTSIDE OF DEGREE PROGRAMS

Graduate—biblical studies; religious studies; theological and ministerial studies; theology and religious vocations related; urban studies/affairs.

BALL STATE UNIVERSITY
Muncie, Indiana
School of Continuing Education and Public Service
http://www.bsu.edu/distance

Ball State University was founded in 1918. It is accredited by North Central Association of Colleges and Schools. It first offered distance learning courses in 1984. In fall 2007, there were 3,646 students enrolled in distance learning courses. Institutionally administered financial aid is available to distance learners.

Services Distance learners have accessibility to academic advising, bookstore, campus computer network, career placement assistance, e-mail services, library services.

Contact Ms. Diane K. Watters, Marketing Director, Ball State University, School of Extended Education, Carmichael Hall, Room 200, Muncie, IN 47306. Telephone: 765-285-9042. Fax: 765-285-7161. E-mail: dbuck@ bsu.edu.

DEGREES AND AWARDS
AA General Program
AS Business Administration Management
BGS General Studies
BSN Nursing
Certificate Certificate in Web Applications
License Gifted and Talented Education
MA Career and Technical Education; Physical Education–Coaching specialization; Technology Education
MAE Educational Administration and Supervision; Elementary Education
MBA Business Administration
MSN Nursing

COURSE SUBJECT AREAS OFFERED OUTSIDE OF DEGREE PROGRAMS

Undergraduate—geography and cartography; health services/allied health/health sciences; political science and government; real estate.
Graduate—English as a second/foreign language (teaching); special education.

BALTIMORE CITY COMMUNITY COLLEGE
Baltimore, Maryland
http://www.bccc.edu

Baltimore City Community College was founded in 1947. It is accredited by Middle States Association of Colleges and Schools. It first offered distance learning courses in 1992. In fall 2007, there were 1,403 students enrolled in distance learning courses. Institutionally administered financial aid is available to distance learners.

Services Distance learners have accessibility to bookstore, campus computer network, e-mail services, library services, tutoring.

Contact Karen McClaskey, Student Support Manager, Baltimore City Community College, 2901 Liberty Heights Avenue, Baltimore, MD 21215. Telephone: 410-462-7625. Fax: 410-462-8252. E-mail: kmcclaskey@bccc.edu.

DEGREES AND AWARDS

AA Buisness Management; Dietetic Technician; General Studies; Law Enforcement

COURSE SUBJECT AREAS OFFERED OUTSIDE OF DEGREE PROGRAMS

Undergraduate—accounting and related services; bilingual, multi-lingual, and multicultural education; biological and physical sciences; biology; business administration, management and operations; business/commerce; computer software and media applications; criminal justice and corrections; curriculum and instruction; economics; English composition; hospitality administration; microbiological sciences and immunology; psychology; sociology; special education; technical and business writing.

Non-credit—accounting and related services; business administration, management and operations; computer software and media applications; personal and culinary services related.

BALTIMORE HEBREW UNIVERSITY
Baltimore, Maryland
http://www.bhu.edu/

Baltimore Hebrew University was founded in 1919. It is accredited by Middle States Association of Colleges and Schools. It first offered distance learning courses in 2005. In fall 2007, there were 10 students enrolled in distance learning courses. Institutionally administered financial aid is available to distance learners.

Services Distance learners have accessibility to library services.

Contact Dr. Barbara G. Zirkin, Dean/Chief Academic Officer, Baltimore Hebrew University, 5800 Park Heights Avenue, Baltimore, MD 21215. Telephone: 410-578-6900. Fax: 410-578-6940. E-mail: bzirkin@bhu.edu.

DEGREES AND AWARDS

Programs offered do not lead to a degree or other formal award.

COURSE SUBJECT AREAS OFFERED OUTSIDE OF DEGREE PROGRAMS

Graduate—biblical studies; education (specific subject areas); history.

BAPTIST BIBLE COLLEGE OF PENNSYLVANIA
Clarks Summit, Pennsylvania
http://academics.bbc.edu

Baptist Bible College of Pennsylvania was founded in 1932. It is accredited by Association for Biblical Higher Education. It first offered distance learning courses in 1998. In fall 2007, there were 50 students enrolled in distance learning courses. Institutionally administered financial aid is available to distance learners.

Services Distance learners have accessibility to academic advising, bookstore, e-mail services, library services.

Contact Mr. Kai-Chun Cheng, Distance Learning Facilitator, Baptist Bible College of Pennsylvania, 538 Venard Road, Clarks Summit, PA 18411. Telephone: 570-585-9408. Fax: 570-585-4057. E-mail: kccheng@bbc.edu.

DEGREES AND AWARDS

MCP Counseling Ministries
MDiv Master of Divinity
MMin Master of Ministry
MS Biblical Ministry
MSE Christian School Education

THE BAPTIST COLLEGE OF FLORIDA
Graceville, Florida
Division of Distance Learning
http://www.baptistcollege.edu

The Baptist College of Florida was founded in 1943. It is accredited by Southern Association of Colleges and Schools. It first offered distance learning courses in 1999. In fall 2007, there were 200 students enrolled in distance learning courses. Institutionally administered financial aid is available to distance learners.

Services Distance learners have accessibility to academic advising, bookstore, campus computer network, career placement assistance, e-mail services, library services, tutoring.

Contact Dr. David Coggins, Director of Distance Learning, The Baptist College of Florida, 5400 College Drive, Graceville, FL 32440. Telephone: 850-263-3261 Ext. 482. Fax: 850-263-7506. E-mail: jdcoggins@baptistcollege.edu.

DEGREES AND AWARDS

AD Divinity
BS Biblical Studies

COURSE SUBJECT AREAS OFFERED OUTSIDE OF DEGREE PROGRAMS

Undergraduate—biblical studies; counseling psychology; philosophy and religious studies related.

BARCLAY COLLEGE
Haviland, Kansas
Home College Program
http://www.barclaycollege.edu

Barclay College was founded in 1917. It is accredited by Association for Biblical Higher Education. It first offered distance learning courses in 1993. In fall 2007, there were 21 students enrolled in distance learning courses. Institutionally administered financial aid is available to distance learners.

Services Distance learners have accessibility to academic advising, bookstore, e-mail services, library services.

Contact Dr. Glenn Leppert, Registrar, Barclay College, 607 North Kingman, Haviland, KS 67059-0288. Telephone: 620-862-5252 Ext. 46. Fax: 620-862-5242. E-mail: registrar@barclaycollege.edu.

DEGREES AND AWARDS

Programs offered do not lead to a degree or other formal award.

COURSE SUBJECT AREAS OFFERED OUTSIDE OF DEGREE PROGRAMS

Undergraduate—behavioral sciences; biblical studies; education related; English; English composition; mathematics; missionary studies and missiology; physical sciences; psychology; religious/sacred music; sociology; theological and ministerial studies.

BARTON COUNTY COMMUNITY COLLEGE
Great Bend, Kansas
http://bartonline.org

Barton County Community College was founded in 1969. It is accredited by North Central Association of Colleges and Schools. It first offered distance learning courses in 1998. In fall 2007, there were 5,000 students enrolled in distance learning courses. Institutionally administered financial aid is available to distance learners.

Services Distance learners have accessibility to academic advising, bookstore, campus computer network, e-mail services, library services, tutoring.

Contact Wynn Butler, Executive Director, Distance Education, Barton County Community College, PO Box 2463, BartOnline, Fort Riley, KS 66442. Telephone: 877-620-6606. E-mail: butlerw@bartonccc.edu.

DEGREES AND AWARDS

AA General degree
AAS General degree

AGS General Studies
AS General degree

COURSE SUBJECT AREAS OFFERED OUTSIDE OF DEGREE PROGRAMS

Undergraduate—accounting and computer science; biochemistry, biophysics and molecular biology; chemistry; communication and journalism related; computer and information sciences; English; health psychology; history; physical science technologies; sociology; statistics.

BEACON UNIVERSITY
Columbus, Georgia
http://www.beacon.edu

Beacon University was founded in 1993. It is accredited by Transnational Association of Christian Colleges and Schools. It first offered distance learning courses in 1993. In fall 2007, there were 225 students enrolled in distance learning courses. Institutionally administered financial aid is available to distance learners.

Services Distance learners have accessibility to academic advising, bookstore, campus computer network, career placement assistance, e-mail services, library services.

Contact Cindy Winkles, Admission Officer, Beacon University, 6003 Veterans Parkway, Columbus, GA 31909. Telephone: 706-323-5364 Ext. 258. Fax: 706-323-5891. E-mail: cindy.winkles@beacon.edu.

DEGREES AND AWARDS
MDiv Master of Divinity

COURSE SUBJECT AREAS OFFERED OUTSIDE OF DEGREE PROGRAMS

Undergraduate—biblical studies; biological and physical sciences; business administration, management and operations; business, management, and marketing related; English composition; English language and literature related; English literature (British and Commonwealth); mathematics; philosophy and religious studies related; psychology; psychology related; religious studies; speech and rhetoric.

Graduate—biblical and other theological languages and literatures; biblical studies; business administration, management and operations; business, management, and marketing related; philosophy; psychology; psychology related.

Non-credit—biblical and other theological languages and literatures; biblical studies; biological and physical sciences; business administration, management and operations; business, management, and marketing related; English composition; English language and literature related; mathematics; philosophy and religious studies related; psychology; psychology related; religious studies; speech and rhetoric.

BEAUFORT COUNTY COMMUNITY COLLEGE
Washington, North Carolina
Distance Education Center
http://www.beaufortccc.edu

Beaufort County Community College was founded in 1967. It is accredited by Southern Association of Colleges and Schools. It first offered distance learning courses in 1995. In fall 2007, there were 500 students enrolled in distance learning courses. Institutionally administered financial aid is available to distance learners.

Services Distance learners have accessibility to academic advising, bookstore, campus computer network, career placement assistance, e-mail services, library services, tutoring.

Contact Penny Sermons, Director, Learning Resources Center/Distance Learning, Beaufort County Community College, PO Box 1069, Washington, NC 27889. Telephone: 252-940-6243. Fax: 252-946-9575. E-mail: pennys@beaufortccc.edu.

DEGREES AND AWARDS
Programs offered do not lead to a degree or other formal award.

COURSE SUBJECT AREAS OFFERED OUTSIDE OF DEGREE PROGRAMS

Undergraduate—accounting and related services; allied health diagnostic, intervention, and treatment professions; business administration, management and operations; computer and information sciences; education; English; health/medical preparatory programs; human services; liberal arts and sciences, general studies and humanities; management information systems; nursing; psychology; psychology related; social psychology; sociology.

Non-credit—accounting and related services; business/corporate communications; computer and information sciences; computer software and media applications.

BELHAVEN COLLEGE
Jackson, Mississippi
http://online.belhaven.edu/index.htm

Belhaven College was founded in 1883. It is accredited by Southern Association of Colleges and Schools. It first offered distance learning courses in 2006. In fall 2007, there were 39 students enrolled in distance learning courses. Institutionally administered financial aid is available to distance learners.

Services Distance learners have accessibility to academic advising, campus computer network, e-mail services, library services.

Contact Jenny Mixon, Director of Graduate and Online Admission, Belhaven College, 1500 Peachtree Street, Box 279, Jackson, MS 39202. Telephone: 601-965-7043. Fax: 601-968-8946. E-mail: jmixon@belhaven.edu.

DEGREES AND AWARDS
AA General Studies
BS Management

COURSE SUBJECT AREAS OFFERED OUTSIDE OF DEGREE PROGRAMS

Undergraduate—business administration, management and operations.

BELLEVUE COMMUNITY COLLEGE
Bellevue, Washington
Telecommunications Program–Distance Learning Department
http://distance-ed.bcc.ctc.edu

Bellevue Community College was founded in 1966. It is accredited by Northwest Commission on Colleges and Universities. It first offered distance learning courses in 1980. In fall 2007, there were 3,100 students enrolled in distance learning courses. Institutionally administered financial aid is available to distance learners.

Services Distance learners have accessibility to academic advising, bookstore, campus computer network, e-mail services, library services, tutoring.

Contact Liz Anderson, Director of Distance Education, Bellevue Community College, 3000 Landerholm Circle SE, Bellevue, WA 98007-6484. Telephone: 425-564-2438. Fax: 425-564-5564. E-mail: landerso@bcc.ctc.edu.

DEGREES AND AWARDS
AA General Studies
AAS Transfer degree for Business Students; Transfer degree
Certificate of Achievement Business Intelligence Developer
Certificate Bookkeeping–Paraprofessional Accounting program; Business Intelligence Analyst; Business Software Specialist–Business Technology Systems; Introductory C++ Programming

COURSE SUBJECT AREAS OFFERED OUTSIDE OF DEGREE PROGRAMS

Undergraduate—accounting and related services; American literature (United States and Canadian); anthropology; archeology; astronomy and astrophysics; atmospheric sciences and meteorology; biology; botany/plant biology; business administration, management and operations; business/commerce; business/corporate communications; business, management, and marketing related; business operations support and assistant services; chemistry; communication and media; comparative literature; computer and information sciences; computer and information sciences and support services related; computer programming; computer science; computer software and media applications; creative writing; criminology; developmental and child psychology; ecology, evolution, and population biology; economics; education; English; English composition; English language and literature related; English literature (British and Commonwealth); entrepreneurial and small business operations; fire protection; geography and cartography; geological and earth sciences/geosciences; health professions related; history; liberal arts and sciences, general studies and humanities; management information systems; marketing; mathematics; mathematics and statistics related; medieval and Renaissance studies; music; natural sciences; nutrition sciences; philosophy; physical sciences; physical sciences related; plant sciences; political science and government; psychology; psychology related; social psychology; social sciences; social sciences related; sociology; speech and rhetoric.

BELLEVUE UNIVERSITY
Bellevue, Nebraska
Online Programs
http://www.bellevue.edu
Bellevue University was founded in 1965. It is accredited by North Central Association of Colleges and Schools. It first offered distance learning courses in 1996. In fall 2007, there were 3,000 students enrolled in distance learning courses. Institutionally administered financial aid is available to distance learners.
Services Distance learners have accessibility to academic advising, campus computer network, e-mail services, library services.
Contact Admissions Counselor, Bellevue University. Telephone: 800-756-7920. E-mail: info@bellevue.edu.

DEGREES AND AWARDS
BA Leadership; Liberal Studies
BS Accounting; Adult Education; Advertising Management; Behavioral Science; Business Information Systems; Business; Computer Information Systems in Business; Computer Information Systems; Corporate Communication; Corrections Administration and Management; Criminal Justice Administration; Culinary Arts; Gaming and Simulation; Healthcare Management; Human and Social Services Administration; Information Technology; Investigations; Legal Studies; Logistics Management; Long Term Care Administration; Management Information Systems; Management of Health Informatics; Management of Human Resources; Management; Marketing Management; Organizational Systems Management; Security Management; Software Development; Technical Sales; Web Technologies; World Security and Strategic Studies
BSBA Business Administration
EMBA Executive Master of Business Administration
MA Human Capital Management; Human Services; Leadership; Management
MBA Business Administration
MHA Healthcare Administration
MPA Public Administration
MS Acquisition and Contract Management; Clinical Counseling; Computer Information Systems; Human Services; Instructional Design and Development; Management of Information Systems; Organizational Performance; Security Management

COURSE SUBJECT AREAS OFFERED OUTSIDE OF DEGREE PROGRAMS
Undergraduate—accounting and computer science; American literature (United States and Canadian); biological and physical sciences; business administration, management and operations; business/commerce; business, management, and marketing related; business/managerial economics; communication and media; comparative literature; computer and information sciences; computer and information sciences and support services related; computer/information technology administration and management; computer programming; computer software and media applications; computer systems analysis; computer systems networking and telecommunications; English; English literature (British and Common-

wealth); finance and financial management services; fine and studio art; health and medical administrative services; human resources management; human services; management information systems; management sciences and quantitative methods; marketing; sales, merchandising, and related marketing operations (specialized).
Graduate—accounting and computer science; business administration, management and operations; business/commerce; business/corporate communications; business, management, and marketing related; business/managerial economics; health and medical administrative services; management information systems; management sciences and quantitative methods; sales, merchandising, and related marketing operations (specialized).
See full description on page 344.

BELMONT TECHNICAL COLLEGE
St. Clairsville, Ohio
http://www.btc.edu
Belmont Technical College was founded in 1971. It is accredited by North Central Association of Colleges and Schools. It first offered distance learning courses in 1999. In fall 2007, there were 167 students enrolled in distance learning courses. Institutionally administered financial aid is available to distance learners.
Services Distance learners have accessibility to academic advising, bookstore, campus computer network, career placement assistance, e-mail services, library services, tutoring.
Contact Catherine L. Bennett, Associate Dean of Learning, Information Services, and Technology, Belmont Technical College, 120 Fox Shannon Place, St. Clairsville, OH 43950. Telephone: 740-695-9500 Ext. 1088. Fax: 740-695-2247. E-mail: cbennett@btc.edu.

DEGREES AND AWARDS
AAS Information Technology and Information Services Library Paraprofessional

COURSE SUBJECT AREAS OFFERED OUTSIDE OF DEGREE PROGRAMS
Undergraduate—accounting and computer science; accounting and related services; computer and information sciences; computer and information sciences and support services related; computer programming; computer science; computer software and media applications; English; English composition; English language and literature related; health services/allied health/health sciences; information science/studies; library assistant; library science related; philosophy; physical sciences; psychology; sociology; statistics; technical and business writing.

BENEDICTINE UNIVERSITY
Lisle, Illinois
Benedictine University was founded in 1887. It is accredited by North Central Association of Colleges and Schools.
Contact Online Programs, Benedictine University, 5700 College Road, Lisle, IL 60532-0900. Telephone: 866-295-3104.

DEGREES AND AWARDS
MBA Business Administration; Online Finance; Online Healthcare Administration; Online International Business; Online Marketing
MEd Reading and Literacy
MPH Online Administration of Health Care Institutions; Online Disaster Management; Online Health Education; Online Health Policy; Online MPH

BERGEN COMMUNITY COLLEGE
Paramus, New Jersey
Center for Distance Learning
http://www.bergen.edu/dlearning
Bergen Community College was founded in 1965. It is accredited by Middle States Association of Colleges and Schools. It first offered distance learning courses in 1974. In fall 2007, there were 2,509 students enrolled in distance learning courses. Institutionally administered financial aid is available to distance learners.
Services Distance learners have accessibility to academic advising, bookstore, e-mail services, library services, tutoring.

Contact Ms. Kathy Morley, Distance Learning Supervisor, Bergen Community College, 400 Paramus Road, Paramus, NJ 07652. Telephone: 201-612-5288. Fax: 201-612-8225. E-mail: kmorley@bergen.edu.

DEGREES AND AWARDS
Programs offered do not lead to a degree or other formal award.

COURSE SUBJECT AREAS OFFERED OUTSIDE OF DEGREE PROGRAMS
Undergraduate—accounting and related services; American literature (United States and Canadian); anthropology; business administration, management and operations; computer programming; computer science; criminal justice and corrections; developmental and child psychology; dramatic/theater arts and stagecraft; education; educational psychology; English composition; finance and financial management services; foods, nutrition, and related services; geological and earth sciences/geosciences; history; journalism; philosophy; philosophy and religious studies related; political science and government; psychology; religious studies; social psychology; social sciences; sociology; speech and rhetoric; visual and performing arts.

BERKELEY COLLEGE
West Paterson, New Jersey
http://www.berkeleycollege.edu/
Berkeley College was founded in 1931. It is accredited by Middle States Association of Colleges and Schools. It first offered distance learning courses in 2001. In fall 2007, there were 477 students enrolled in distance learning courses. Institutionally administered financial aid is available to distance learners.
Services Distance learners have accessibility to academic advising, bookstore, campus computer network, career placement assistance, e-mail services, library services, tutoring.
Contact Mr. David Bertone, Senior Director, Enrollment, Berkeley College, 44 Rifle Camp Road, West Paterson, NJ 07424. Telephone: 800-446-5400. Fax: 973-278-2431. E-mail: online@berkeleycollege.edu.

DEGREES AND AWARDS
AAS Business Administration; Financial Services; Health Services Administration–Medical Insurance, Billing, and Coding; Health Services Administration; International Business; Justice Studies–Criminal Justice
BS Business Administration; Justice Studies–Criminal Justice; Management

COURSE SUBJECT AREAS OFFERED OUTSIDE OF DEGREE PROGRAMS
Undergraduate—accounting and related services; American literature (United States and Canadian); anthropology; area, ethnic, cultural, and gender studies related; biological and physical sciences; business administration, management and operations; business/commerce; business, management, and marketing related; business/managerial economics; communication and media; computer software and media applications; criminal justice and corrections; criminology; data entry/microcomputer applications; economics; English composition; English language and literature related; entrepreneurial and small business operations; ethnic, cultural minority, and gender studies; finance and financial management services; health and medical administrative services; history; human resources management; industrial and organizational psychology; intercultural/multicultural and diversity studies; international business; legal studies (non-professional general, undergraduate); liberal arts and sciences, general studies and humanities; management sciences and quantitative methods; marketing; mathematics and statistics related; multi-/interdisciplinary studies related; philosophy; philosophy and religious studies related; physical sciences related; political science and government; psychology; public relations, advertising, and applied communication related; sales, merchandising, and related marketing operations (general); sales, merchandising, and related marketing operations (specialized); security and protective services related; social sciences related; sociology; statistics.

BERKELEY COLLEGE–NEW YORK CITY CAMPUS
New York, New York
http://www.berkeleycollege.edu/
Berkeley College–New York City Campus was founded in 1936. It is accredited by Middle States Association of Colleges and Schools. It first offered distance learning courses in 1998. In fall 2007, there were 557 students enrolled in distance learning courses. Institutionally administered financial aid is available to distance learners.
Services Distance learners have accessibility to academic advising, bookstore, campus computer network, career placement assistance, e-mail services, library services, tutoring.
Contact Ms. Valerie Nebeling, Director, Admissions, Berkeley College–New York City Campus, 44 Rifle Camp Road, West Paterson, NJ 07424. Telephone: 800-446-5400. Fax: 973-278-2431. E-mail: online@berkeleycollege.edu.

DEGREES AND AWARDS
AAS Business Administration–Information Systems Management; Business Administration–Management; Business Administration–Marketing; Health Services Administration–Medical Insurance, Billing, and Coding; Health Services Administration; International Business
BBA Business Administration–Information Systems Management; Business Administration–Management; Business Administration–Marketing; Business, general; Health Services Administration; International Business

COURSE SUBJECT AREAS OFFERED OUTSIDE OF DEGREE PROGRAMS
Undergraduate—accounting and related services; American literature (United States and Canadian); anthropology; area, ethnic, cultural, and gender studies related; behavioral sciences; biological and physical sciences; business administration, management and operations; business/commerce; business, management, and marketing related; business/managerial economics; communication and media; computer software and media applications; criminology; data entry/microcomputer applications; economics; English composition; English language and literature related; entrepreneurial and small business operations; ethnic, cultural minority, and gender studies; finance and financial management services; health and medical administrative services; history; human resources management; industrial and organizational psychology; intercultural/multicultural and diversity studies; international business; legal studies (non-professional general, undergraduate); liberal arts and sciences, general studies and humanities; management sciences and quantitative methods; marketing; mathematics and statistics related; multi-/interdisciplinary studies related; philosophy; philosophy and religious studies related; physical sciences related; political science and government; psychology; public relations, advertising, and applied communication related; sales, merchandising, and related marketing operations (general); sales, merchandising, and related marketing operations (specialized); security and protective services related; social sciences related; sociology; statistics.

BERKELEY COLLEGE–WESTCHESTER CAMPUS
White Plains, New York
http://www.berkeleycollege.edu/
Berkeley College–Westchester Campus was founded in 1945. It is accredited by Middle States Association of Colleges and Schools. It first offered distance learning courses in 1998. In fall 2007, there were 89 students enrolled in distance learning courses. Institutionally administered financial aid is available to distance learners.
Services Distance learners have accessibility to academic advising, bookstore, campus computer network, career placement assistance, e-mail services, library services, tutoring.
Contact Mr. David Bertone, Senior Director, Enrollment, Berkeley College–Westchester Campus, 44 Rifle Camp Road, West Paterson, NJ 07424. Telephone: 800-446-5400. Fax: 973-278-2431. E-mail: online@berkeleycollege.edu.

DEGREES AND AWARDS
AAS Business Administration–Information Systems Management; Business Administration–Management; Business Administration–Marketing; Health

Services Administration–Medical Insurance, Billing, and Coding; Health Services Administration; International Business

BBA Business Administration–Information Systems Management; Business Administration–Management; Business Administration–Marketing; Business, general; Health Services Management; International Business

COURSE SUBJECT AREAS OFFERED OUTSIDE OF DEGREE PROGRAMS

Undergraduate—accounting and related services; American literature (United States and Canadian); anthropology; area, ethnic, cultural, and gender studies related; biological and physical sciences; business administration, management and operations; business/commerce; business, management, and marketing related; business/managerial economics; communication and media; computer software and media applications; criminology; data entry/microcomputer applications; economics; English composition; English language and literature related; entrepreneurial and small business operations; ethnic, cultural minority, and gender studies; finance and financial management services; health and medical administrative services; history; human resources management; industrial and organizational psychology; intercultural/multicultural and diversity studies; international business; legal studies (non-professional general, undergraduate); liberal arts and sciences, general studies and humanities; management sciences and quantitative methods; marketing; mathematics and statistics related; multi-/interdisciplinary studies related; philosophy; philosophy and religious studies related; physical sciences related; political science and government; psychology; public relations, advertising, and applied communication related; sales, merchandising, and related marketing operations (general); sales, merchandising, and related marketing operations (specialized); security and protective services related; social sciences related; sociology; statistics.

BETHEL COLLEGE
McKenzie, Tennessee
http://www.bethel-college.edu/

Bethel College was founded in 1842. It is accredited by Southern Association of Colleges and Schools. It first offered distance learning courses in 1998. In fall 2007, there were 1,022 students enrolled in distance learning courses. Institutionally administered financial aid is available to distance learners.

Services Distance learners have accessibility to academic advising, bookstore, career placement assistance, e-mail services, library services, tutoring.

Contact Mrs. Lisa Vaughn, Director of Student Affairs, Educational Outreach, Bethel College, 325 Cherry Avenue, McKenzie, TN 38201. Telephone: 731-352-4000. Fax: 731-352-4069. E-mail: vaughnl@bethel-college.edu.

DEGREES AND AWARDS

BS Management and Organizational Development
MBA Business Administration

COURSE SUBJECT AREAS OFFERED OUTSIDE OF DEGREE PROGRAMS

Undergraduate—education.
Graduate—education.

BETHUNE-COOKMAN UNIVERSITY
Daytona Beach, Florida
School of Graduate and Professional Studies
http://cookman.edu/schoolof graduate and professionalstudies

Bethune-Cookman University was founded in 1904. It is accredited by Southern Association of Colleges and Schools. Institutionally administered financial aid is available to distance learners.
Services Distance learners have accessibility to academic advising, bookstore, campus computer network, career placement assistance, e-mail services, library services, tutoring.
Contact Mrs. Sonja Lewis Lucas, Director of Marketing and Public Relations, Bethune-Cookman University, 640 Dr. Mary McLeod Bethune

Boulevard, Daytona Beach, FL 32114. Telephone: 386-481-2344. Fax: 386-481-2380. E-mail: lewiss@cookman.edu.

DEGREES AND AWARDS

MS Transformative Leadership; Transformative Leadership; Transformative Leadership

BEULAH HEIGHTS UNIVERSITY
Atlanta, Georgia
http://www.beulah.org/

Beulah Heights University was founded in 1918. It is accredited by Association for Biblical Higher Education. It first offered distance learning courses in 2000. In fall 2007, there were 200 students enrolled in distance learning courses. Institutionally administered financial aid is available to distance learners.
Services Distance learners have accessibility to academic advising, bookstore, campus computer network, e-mail services, library services.
Contact Jacquelyn Armstrong, Registrar, Beulah Heights University, 892 Berne Street SE, PO Box 18145, Atlanta, GA 30316. Telephone: 404-627-2681 Ext. 104. Fax: 404-627-0702. E-mail: jackie.armstrong@beulah.org.

DEGREES AND AWARDS
Programs offered do not lead to a degree or other formal award.

COURSE SUBJECT AREAS OFFERED OUTSIDE OF DEGREE PROGRAMS

Undergraduate—applied mathematics; biblical and other theological languages and literatures; biblical studies; communication and media; computer science; English; ethnic, cultural minority, and gender studies; human development, family studies, and related services; liberal arts and sciences, general studies and humanities; mathematics; pastoral counseling and specialized ministries; philosophy; political science and government; religious education.
Graduate—biblical and other theological languages and literatures.

BLACKHAWK TECHNICAL COLLEGE
Janesville, Wisconsin
http://www.blackhawk.edu

Blackhawk Technical College was founded in 1968. It is accredited by North Central Association of Colleges and Schools. It first offered distance learning courses in 2000. In fall 2007, there were 250 students enrolled in distance learning courses. Institutionally administered financial aid is available to distance learners.
Services Distance learners have accessibility to academic advising, bookstore, campus computer network, career placement assistance, e-mail services, library services.
Contact Linda Brown, High School Community Relations Specialist, Blackhawk Technical College, 6004 South County Road G, Janesville, WI 53546-9458. Telephone: 608-757-7670. Fax: 608-743-4407. E-mail: lbrown@blackhawk.edu.

DEGREES AND AWARDS
AS Accounting

COURSE SUBJECT AREAS OFFERED OUTSIDE OF DEGREE PROGRAMS

Undergraduate—accounting and related services; allied health and medical assisting services; business administration, management and operations; business, management, and marketing related; business operations support and assistant services; computer and information sciences and support services related; computer programming; computer systems networking and telecommunications; criminal justice and corrections; culinary arts and related services; dental support services and allied professions; education (specific levels and methods); electromechanical and instrumentation and maintenance technologies; fire protection; health and medical administrative services; heating, air conditioning, ventilation and refrigeration maintenance technology; legal support services; marketing; mechanical engineering related technologies; nursing.

Non-credit—apparel and textiles; business operations support and assistant services; computer software and media applications; crafts, folk art and artisanry; creative writing; criminal justice and corrections; drafting/design engineering technologies; English as a second language; film/video and photographic arts; fire protection; foods, nutrition, and related services; human development, family studies, and related services; languages (foreign languages related); leatherworking and upholstery; real estate; sales, merchandising, and related marketing operations (specialized); woodworking.

BLACK HILLS STATE UNIVERSITY
Spearfish, South Dakota
Extended Services and Instructional Technology
http://www.bhsu.edu/Academics/DistanceLearning/tabid/109/Default.aspx

Black Hills State University was founded in 1883. It is accredited by North Central Association of Colleges and Schools. It first offered distance learning courses in 1994. In fall 2007, there were 1,074 students enrolled in distance learning courses. Institutionally administered financial aid is available to distance learners.

Services Distance learners have accessibility to academic advising, bookstore, campus computer network, career placement assistance, e-mail services, library services.

Contact Joyce Holzer, Senior Secretary, Black Hills State University, Educational Outreach, 1200 University Street, Unit 9508, Spearfish, SD 57799-9508. Telephone: 605-642-6258. Fax: 605-642-6031. E-mail: joyceholzer@bhsu.edu.

DEGREES AND AWARDS
AA General Studies
Advanced Graduate Diploma Curriculum and Instruction
MS Strategic Leadership

COURSE SUBJECT AREAS OFFERED OUTSIDE OF DEGREE PROGRAMS

Undergraduate—accounting and computer science; biblical and other theological languages and literatures; business administration, management and operations; business/commerce; business, management, and marketing related; developmental and child psychology; economics; educational psychology; education related; English; English composition; finance and financial management services; geography and cartography; human resources management; international business; languages (foreign languages related); library science related; marketing; mathematics; psychology; psychology related; social sciences; sociology; technical and business writing.

Graduate—business, management, and marketing related; developmental and child psychology; education; educational assessment, evaluation, and research; educational/instructional media design; education related; hospitality administration.

BLACKSTONE CAREER INSTITUTE
Allentown, Pennsylvania
http://www.blackstone.edu

Blackstone Career Institute first offered distance learning courses in 2001. In fall 2007, there were 1,422 students enrolled in distance learning courses. Institutionally administered financial aid is available to distance learners.

Contact Emily Eider, Assistant Director of Education, Blackstone Career Institute, 1011 Brookside Road, Suite 300, Allentown, PA 18106. Telephone: 610-871-0031 Ext. 212. E-mail: eeider@blackstone.edu.

DEGREES AND AWARDS
Programs offered do not lead to a degree or other formal award.

COURSE SUBJECT AREAS OFFERED OUTSIDE OF DEGREE PROGRAMS

Non-credit—allied health and medical assisting services; legal support services.

BLESSING-RIEMAN COLLEGE OF NURSING
Quincy, Illinois
http://www.brcn.edu

Blessing-Rieman College of Nursing was founded in 1985. It is accredited by North Central Association of Colleges and Schools. In fall 2007, there were 30 students enrolled in distance learning courses. Institutionally administered financial aid is available to distance learners.

Contact Rachel Cramsey, Registrar, Blessing-Rieman College of Nursing, PO Box 7005, Broadway at 11th, Quincy, IL 62305-7005. Telephone: 217-228-5520 Ext. 6962. Fax: 217-223-1781. E-mail: rcramsey@brcn.edu.

DEGREES AND AWARDS
Programs offered do not lead to a degree or other formal award.

COURSE SUBJECT AREAS OFFERED OUTSIDE OF DEGREE PROGRAMS
Undergraduate—nursing.

BLOOMFIELD COLLEGE
Bloomfield, New Jersey
http://www.bloomfield.edu/

Bloomfield College was founded in 1868. It is accredited by Middle States Association of Colleges and Schools. It first offered distance learning courses in 1997. In fall 2007, there were 203 students enrolled in distance learning courses. Institutionally administered financial aid is available to distance learners.

Services Distance learners have accessibility to campus computer network, e-mail services, library services.

Contact Dr. Marion Terenzio, Vice President for Academic Affairs, Bloomfield College, 467 Franklin Street, Bloomfield, NJ 07003. Telephone: 973-748-9000 Ext. 226. Fax: 973-743-3998. E-mail: marion_terenzio@bloomfield.edu.

DEGREES AND AWARDS
Programs offered do not lead to a degree or other formal award.

COURSE SUBJECT AREAS OFFERED OUTSIDE OF DEGREE PROGRAMS

Undergraduate—business administration, management and operations; computer/information technology administration and management; education; English; history; psychology.

BLOOMSBURG UNIVERSITY OF PENNSYLVANIA
Bloomsburg, Pennsylvania
School of Graduate Studies
http://www.bloomu.edu

Bloomsburg University of Pennsylvania was founded in 1839. It is accredited by Middle States Association of Colleges and Schools. It first offered distance learning courses in 1983. In fall 2007, there were 125 students enrolled in distance learning courses. Institutionally administered financial aid is available to distance learners.

Services Distance learners have accessibility to academic advising, bookstore, campus computer network, career placement assistance, e-mail services, library services.

Contact Mr. Thomas Fletcher, Director, Corporate and Continuing Education, Bloomsburg University of Pennsylvania, 700 West Main Street, Bloomsburg, PA 17815-1301. Telephone: 570-389-5161. Fax: 570-389-5060. E-mail: tfletche@bloomu.edu.

DEGREES AND AWARDS
MS Instructional Technology Education Specialist; Radiologist Assistant

COURSE SUBJECT AREAS OFFERED OUTSIDE OF DEGREE PROGRAMS

Undergraduate—business, management, and marketing related; nursing; statistics.

Graduate—business, management, and marketing related; curriculum and instruction; educational/instructional media design.

Non-credit—communications technologies and support services related.

BLUE MOUNTAIN COMMUNITY COLLEGE
Pendleton, Oregon
Distance Education–Extended Programs
http://www.bluecc.edu/

Blue Mountain Community College was founded in 1962. It is accredited by Northwest Commission on Colleges and Universities. It first offered distance learning courses in 1982. In fall 2007, there were 375 students enrolled in distance learning courses. Institutionally administered financial aid is available to distance learners.

Services Distance learners have accessibility to academic advising, bookstore, campus computer network, library services, tutoring.

Contact Mr. Bruce Kauss, Distance Education Specialist, Blue Mountain Community College, PO Box 100, Pendleton, OR 97801. Telephone: 541-278-5763. Fax: 541-278-5841. E-mail: bkauss@bluecc.edu.

DEGREES AND AWARDS
Programs offered do not lead to a degree or other formal award.

COURSE SUBJECT AREAS OFFERED OUTSIDE OF DEGREE PROGRAMS
Undergraduate—accounting and related services; American literature (United States and Canadian); anthropology; applied mathematics; archeology; biology; business/commerce; business, management, and marketing related; business operations support and assistant services; criminology; developmental and child psychology; teaching assistants/aides.

BLUE RIDGE COMMUNITY COLLEGE
Flat Rock, North Carolina
http://www.blueridge.edu

Blue Ridge Community College was founded in 1969. It is accredited by Southern Association of Colleges and Schools. It first offered distance learning courses in 1998. In fall 2007, there were 860 students enrolled in distance learning courses. Institutionally administered financial aid is available to distance learners.

Services Distance learners have accessibility to academic advising, bookstore, career placement assistance, e-mail services, library services.

Contact Ms. Alice F. Crisp, Director for Instructional Technology and Distance Learning Support, Blue Ridge Community College, 180 West Campus Drive, Flat Rock, NC 28731. Telephone: 828-694-1890. Fax: 828-694-1690. E-mail: alicec@blueridge.edu.

DEGREES AND AWARDS
AAS Marketing and Retailing

COURSE SUBJECT AREAS OFFERED OUTSIDE OF DEGREE PROGRAMS
Undergraduate—American Sign Language (ASL); business administration, management and operations; business, management, and marketing related; business operations support and assistant services; computer and information sciences; computer/information technology administration and management; computer programming; computer software and media applications; computer systems networking and telecommunications; criminal justice and corrections; education; education related; education (specific levels and methods); education (specific subject areas); English; English composition; entrepreneurial and small business operations; health and physical education/fitness; history; human development, family studies, and related services; marketing; mathematics and statistics related; mechanical engineering related technologies; psychology; sales, merchandising, and related marketing operations (general); sales, merchandising, and related marketing operations (specialized); social sciences related; special education; teaching assistants/aides.

Non-credit—accounting and computer science; business/commerce; business, management, and marketing related; communication and media; community health services; computer and information sciences; computer/information technology administration and management; computer programming; computer software and media applications; computer systems networking and telecommunications; creative writing; criminal justice and corrections; education related; film/video and photographic arts; health and medical administrative services; languages (foreign languages related); legal support services; marketing; sales, merchandising, and related marketing operations (specialized); technical and business writing.

BOISE STATE UNIVERSITY
Boise, Idaho
Division of Extended Studies
http://www.boisestate.edu/distance

Boise State University was founded in 1932. It is accredited by Northwest Commission on Colleges and Universities. It first offered distance learning courses in 1980. In fall 2007, there were 5,647 students enrolled in distance learning courses. Institutionally administered financial aid is available to distance learners.

Services Distance learners have accessibility to academic advising, bookstore, campus computer network, career placement assistance, e-mail services, library services, tutoring.

Contact Betty Miller, Course Administration and Student Services Coordinator, Boise State University, 1910 University Drive, Distance Education Department, Division of Extended Studies, Boise, ID 83725-1120. Telephone: 208-426-5622. Fax: 208-426-3467. E-mail: distanceed@boisestate.edu.

DEGREES AND AWARDS
Graduate Certificate Human Performance Technology; Online Teaching; School Technology Coordination; Technology Integration
MET Educational Technology
MS Instructional and Performance Technology
MSE Educational Technology

COURSE SUBJECT AREAS OFFERED OUTSIDE OF DEGREE PROGRAMS
Undergraduate—accounting and related services; anthropology; behavioral sciences; biological and physical sciences; business, management, and marketing related; chemistry; computer and information sciences and support services related; criminal justice and corrections; curriculum and instruction; economics; education; educational/instructional media design; electrical and electronic engineering technologies; English composition; geological and earth sciences/geosciences; health and medical administrative services; history; human resources management; languages (foreign languages related); languages (Romance languages); mathematics; music; nursing; philosophy; physics; psychology; social work; sociology; technical and business writing; visual and performing arts related.

Graduate—criminal justice and corrections; educational/instructional media design; education related; health and medical administrative services; human resources management; management sciences and quantitative methods; social work.

BOWLING GREEN STATE UNIVERSITY
Bowling Green, Ohio
http://online.bgsu.edu

Bowling Green State University was founded in 1910. It is accredited by North Central Association of Colleges and Schools. It first offered distance learning courses in 1998. In fall 2007, there were 1,562 students enrolled in distance learning courses. Institutionally administered financial aid is available to distance learners.

Services Distance learners have accessibility to academic advising, bookstore, campus computer network, career placement assistance, e-mail services, library services, tutoring.

Contact Ms. Connie Molnar, Director, Distance Education, Bowling Green State University, 14 College Park, Bowling Green, OH 43403. Telephone: 419-372-7900. Fax: 419-372-8667. E-mail: cmolnar@bgsu.edu.

DEGREES AND AWARDS
BLS Liberal Studies–Bachelor of Liberal Studies online degree program
BS Technological Education, advanced
BSN Nursing–RN to BSN completion

Graduate Certificate Food and Nutrition; International Scientific and Technical Communication; Ohio Reading Endorsement program; Quality Systems
MA English
MBA Executive Master of Organization Development
MEd Assistive Technology specialization
MS Criminal Justice
PhD Technology Management

COURSE SUBJECT AREAS OFFERED OUTSIDE OF DEGREE PROGRAMS

Undergraduate—allied health and medical assisting services; American literature (United States and Canadian); applied mathematics; architecture; biblical studies; biology; business/commerce; business, management, and marketing related; communication and journalism related; communication and media; communications technology; computer and information sciences; computer programming; computer science; computer software and media applications; computer systems networking and telecommunications; creative writing; educational/instructional media design; English; English composition; English literature (British and Commonwealth); environmental control technologies; environmental/environmental health engineering; ethnic, cultural minority, and gender studies; film/video and photographic arts; foods, nutrition, and related services; geography and cartography; geological and earth sciences/geosciences; health and medical administrative services; history; hospitality administration; human development, family studies, and related services; human resources management; information science/studies; international/global studies; languages (East Asian); languages (Germanic); languages (Modern Greek); languages (Romance languages); liberal arts and sciences, general studies and humanities; library science related; mathematics; music; nursing; philosophy; philosophy and religious studies related; political science and government; psychology; public health; public relations, advertising, and applied communication related; social sciences; social work; sociology; technical and business writing; technology education/industrial arts.
Graduate—American literature (United States and Canadian); biology; building/construction finishing, management, and inspection; computer software and media applications; construction engineering technology; creative writing; education; educational assessment, evaluation, and research; English; English literature (British and Commonwealth); family and consumer sciences/human sciences; foods, nutrition, and related services; gerontology; languages (Romance languages); mathematics; psychology; quality control and safety technologies; special education; speech and rhetoric; technical and business writing; technology education/industrial arts.
Non-credit—business/commerce; computer and information sciences and support services related; computer software and media applications; construction trades related; health professions related.

BRADLEY UNIVERSITY
Peoria, Illinois
Division of Continuing Education and Professional Development
http://www.bradley.edu/classes/
Bradley University was founded in 1897. It is accredited by North Central Association of Colleges and Schools. It first offered distance learning courses in 1985. In fall 2007, there were 361 students enrolled in distance learning courses. Institutionally administered financial aid is available to distance learners.
Services Distance learners have accessibility to academic advising, bookstore, campus computer network, career placement assistance, e-mail services, library services.
Contact Andy Kindler, Associate Registrar, Bradley University, 1501 West Bradley Avenue, Peoria, IL 61625. Telephone: 309-677-3106. Fax: 309-677-2715. E-mail: akindler@bradley.edu.

DEGREES AND AWARDS
Programs offered do not lead to a degree or other formal award.

COURSE SUBJECT AREAS OFFERED OUTSIDE OF DEGREE PROGRAMS

Undergraduate—business, management, and marketing related; communication and media; computer and information sciences; education; English; family and consumer sciences/human sciences; international business; nursing; psychology; social work; sociology; theological and ministerial studies.
Graduate—education; electrical and electronic engineering technologies; nursing; political science and government.

BRAZOSPORT COLLEGE
Lake Jackson, Texas
http://www.brazosport.edu/
Brazosport College was founded in 1968. It is accredited by Southern Association of Colleges and Schools. It first offered distance learning courses in 1997. In fall 2007, there were 700 students enrolled in distance learning courses. Institutionally administered financial aid is available to distance learners.
Services Distance learners have accessibility to academic advising, bookstore, campus computer network, e-mail services, library services.
Contact Mr. Terry Comingore, Director, Learning Assistance, Distance Learning, and Instructional Media, Brazosport College, 500 College Drive, Lake Jackson, TX 77566. Telephone: 979-230-3318. Fax: 979-230-3443. E-mail: terry.comingore@brazosport.edu.

DEGREES AND AWARDS
Programs offered do not lead to a degree or other formal award.

COURSE SUBJECT AREAS OFFERED OUTSIDE OF DEGREE PROGRAMS

Undergraduate—accounting and related services; business administration, management and operations; business, management, and marketing related; chemistry; computer and information sciences; economics; English composition; fine and studio art; geography and cartography; history; mathematics; nutrition sciences; political science and government; psychology.

BRENAU UNIVERSITY
Gainesville, Georgia
Department of Distance Learning
http://online.brenau.edu
Brenau University was founded in 1878. It is accredited by Southern Association of Colleges and Schools. It first offered distance learning courses in 1998. In fall 2007, there were 338 students enrolled in distance learning courses. Institutionally administered financial aid is available to distance learners.
Services Distance learners have accessibility to academic advising, bookstore, campus computer network, career placement assistance, e-mail services, library services, tutoring.
Contact Miss Melissa Holman, Online Student Coordinator, Brenau University, 500 Washington Street SE, Gainesville, GA 30501. Telephone: 770-718-5327. Fax: 770-718-5329. E-mail: mholman1@brenau.edu.

DEGREES AND AWARDS
BBA Business Administration; Marketing
BSN Nursing–RN to BSN
MBA Accounting; Business Administration; Healthcare Management; Management Studies, advanced
MEd Early Childhood Education; Middle Grades Education

COURSE SUBJECT AREAS OFFERED OUTSIDE OF DEGREE PROGRAMS

Undergraduate—accounting and related services; allied health and medical assisting services; American literature (United States and Canadian); anthropology; astronomy and astrophysics; business administration, management and operations; business/commerce; business/corporate communications; business, management, and marketing related; business/managerial economics; communication and media; community health services; computer and information sciences; criminal justice and corrections; criminology; curriculum and instruction; design and applied arts; developmental and child psychology; economics; education; educational administration and supervision; educational assessment, evaluation, and research; educational/instructional media design; educational psychology; education related; education (specific levels and methods); education (specific subject areas); English; English composition; English language and literature related; geography and cartography; health/medical preparatory programs; health professions related; history; human development, family studies, and related services; human resources management; information science/studies; international business; journalism; legal studies (non-professional general, undergraduate); liberal arts and sciences, general studies and humanities; linguistic, comparative, and related language studies; management information systems; management sciences and quantitative methods; marketing; mathematics; mathematics and statistics related; museum studies; music; nursing; peace studies and conflict resolution; pharmacology and toxicology; philosophy; political science and government; psychology; psychology related; public administration; public administration and social service professions related; public relations, advertising, and applied communication related; sales, merchandising, and related marketing operations (specialized); social and philosophical foundations of education; social sciences; sociology; special education; statistics; taxation; technical and business writing; visual and performing arts related.

Graduate—accounting and related services; allied health diagnostic, intervention, and treatment professions; business administration, management and operations; business/commerce; business/corporate communications; business, management, and marketing related; business/managerial economics; computer and information sciences; economics; education; educational administration and supervision; educational assessment, evaluation, and research; educational psychology; education related; finance and financial management services; health and medical administrative services; health professions related; international business; management information systems; management sciences and quantitative methods; marketing; nursing; rehabilitation and therapeutic professions; sales, merchandising, and related marketing operations (general); sales, merchandising, and related marketing operations (specialized); taxation.

See full description on page 346.

BRIDGEWATER STATE COLLEGE
Bridgewater, Massachusetts
Distance Learning and Technology Programs
http://www.bridgew.edu/distance
Bridgewater State College was founded in 1840. It is accredited by New England Association of Schools and Colleges. It first offered distance learning courses in 1996. In fall 2007, there were 2,500 students enrolled in distance learning courses. Institutionally administered financial aid is available to distance learners.
Services Distance learners have accessibility to bookstore, campus computer network, e-mail services, library services.
Contact Dr. Mary W. Fuller, EdD, Director of Continuing and Distance Education, Bridgewater State College, John Joseph Moakley Center for Technological Applications, Burrill Avenue, Bridgewater, MA 02325. Telephone: 508-531-6145. Fax: 508-531-6121. E-mail: mfuller@bridgew.edu.

DEGREES AND AWARDS
MEd Educational Leadership

COURSE SUBJECT AREAS OFFERED OUTSIDE OF DEGREE PROGRAMS
Undergraduate—anthropology; business/corporate communications; business/managerial economics; communication and media; communication disorders sciences and services; computer/information technology administration and management; criminology; curriculum and instruction; education; educational administration and supervision; educational assessment, evaluation, and research; English composition; entrepreneurial and small business operations; ethnic, cultural minority, and gender studies; geography and cartography; geological and earth sciences/

geosciences; history; music; political science and government; psychology; sociology; special education; technical and business writing.

Graduate—communication and media; economics; educational administration and supervision; linguistic, comparative, and related language studies; psychology; special education.

Non-credit—accounting and related services; allied health and medical assisting services; business administration, management and operations; business/commerce; business, management, and marketing related; business/managerial economics; business operations support and assistant services; communication and media; computer systems analysis; creative writing; finance and financial management services; health and medical administrative services; information science/studies; sales, merchandising, and related marketing operations (specialized).

BRIGHAM YOUNG UNIVERSITY
Provo, Utah
Independent Study
http://elearn.byu.edu
Brigham Young University was founded in 1875. It is accredited by Northwest Commission on Colleges and Universities. It first offered distance learning courses in 1961. In fall 2007, there were 100,000 students enrolled in distance learning courses. Institutionally administered financial aid is available to distance learners.
Services Distance learners have accessibility to academic advising, bookstore, e-mail services, library services, tutoring.
Contact Shannon Ogden, Advertising Coordinator, Brigham Young University, 206 Harman Building, PO Box 21514, Provo, UT 84602-1514. Telephone: 800-914-8931. Fax: 801-422-0102. E-mail: shannon.ogden@byu.edu.

DEGREES AND AWARDS
Programs offered do not lead to a degree or other formal award.

COURSE SUBJECT AREAS OFFERED OUTSIDE OF DEGREE PROGRAMS
Undergraduate—accounting and related services; American literature (United States and Canadian); anthropology; astronomy and astrophysics; biological and biomedical sciences related; biology; botany/plant biology; business administration, management and operations; business/corporate communications; business, management, and marketing related; chemical engineering; chemistry; civil engineering; communication and media; communication disorders sciences and services; curriculum and instruction; dance; developmental and child psychology; dramatic/theater arts and stagecraft; economics; education; educational administration and supervision; educational psychology; education related; English composition; film/video and photographic arts; fine and studio art; food science and technology; geography and cartography; geological and earth sciences/geosciences; health and physical education/fitness; history; information science/studies; languages (Germanic); languages (Middle/Near Eastern and Semitic); languages (Romance languages); liberal arts and sciences, general studies and humanities; marketing; mathematics and statistics related; microbiological sciences and immunology; music; nursing; philosophy; philosophy and religious studies related; physical sciences; physics; political science and government; psychology; religious education; religious studies; social work; sociology; special education; speech and rhetoric; statistics; technology education/industrial arts; visual and performing arts; zoology/animal biology.

Graduate—education.

Non-credit—computer and information sciences; computer software and media applications; creative writing; English language and literature related; history; human development, family studies, and related services; religious studies.

BRISTOL COMMUNITY COLLEGE
Fall River, Massachusetts
Distance Learning
http://dl.bristolcc.edu

Bristol Community College was founded in 1965. It is accredited by New England Association of Schools and Colleges. It first offered distance learning courses in 1999. In fall 2007, there were 1,520 students enrolled in distance learning courses. Institutionally administered financial aid is available to distance learners.

Services Distance learners have accessibility to academic advising, bookstore, campus computer network, e-mail services, library services, tutoring.

Contact April Bellafiore, Assistant Dean of Instructional Learning Technologies, Bristol Community College, 777 Elsbree Street, Fall River, MA 02720. Telephone: 508-678-2811 Ext. 2387. E-mail: april.bellafiore@bristolcc.edu.

DEGREES AND AWARDS

AS Computer Information Systems/Computer Programming; Computer Information Systems/Multimedia and Internet
Certificate Computer Programming; Desktop Publishing Technology; Information Technology Fluency; Multimedia Communications; Web Page Development, basic

COURSE SUBJECT AREAS OFFERED OUTSIDE OF DEGREE PROGRAMS

Undergraduate—accounting and computer science; accounting and related services; American Sign Language (ASL); biology; business/commerce; computer and information sciences; computer and information sciences and support services related; computer/information technology administration and management; computer programming; computer science; computer software and media applications; computer systems analysis; computer systems networking and telecommunications; criminal justice and corrections; criminology; data entry/microcomputer applications; data processing; economics; education; English; English composition; English literature (British and Commonwealth); geography and cartography; history; information science/studies; management information systems; mathematics; mathematics and statistics related; philosophy; psychology; psychology related; social sciences; social sciences related; sociology; statistics; technical and business writing.
Non-credit—health and medical administrative services.

BROCK UNIVERSITY
St. Catharines, Ontario, Canada
Centre for Adult Studies and Distance Learning, Faculty of Education
http://adult.ed.brocku.ca

Brock University was founded in 1964. It is provincially chartered. It first offered distance learning courses in 1993. In fall 2007, there were 500 students enrolled in distance learning courses. Institutionally administered financial aid is available to distance learners.

Services Distance learners have accessibility to academic advising, bookstore, campus computer network, career placement assistance, e-mail services, library services.

Contact Sandra Plavinskis, Coordinator of B.Ed. in Adult Education Degree and Certificate Programs, Brock University, Centre for Adult Education and Community Outreach, Faculty of Education, St. Catharines, ON L2S 3A1, Canada. Telephone: 905-688-5550 Ext. 4308. Fax: 905-984-4842. E-mail: adulted@brocku.ca.

DEGREES AND AWARDS

BEd Adult Education (BEd in Adult Education)
Certificate Adult Education

COURSE SUBJECT AREAS OFFERED OUTSIDE OF DEGREE PROGRAMS

Undergraduate—education; education related.

BROOME COMMUNITY COLLEGE
Binghamton, New York
http://www.sunybroome.edu/

Broome Community College was founded in 1946. It is accredited by Middle States Association of Colleges and Schools. It first offered distance learning courses in 1998. In fall 2007, there were 1,131 students enrolled in distance learning courses. Institutionally administered financial aid is available to distance learners.

Services Distance learners have accessibility to campus computer network, e-mail services, library services.

Contact Martin J. Guzzi, Registrar, Broome Community College, PO Box 1017, Binghamton, NY 13902. Telephone: 607-778-5527. Fax: 607-778-5294. E-mail: guzzi_m@sunybroome.edu.

DEGREES AND AWARDS

AAS Computer Technology; Early Childhood; Medical Lab Technology
AS Human Services; Liberal Arts–General Studies

COURSE SUBJECT AREAS OFFERED OUTSIDE OF DEGREE PROGRAMS

Undergraduate—anthropology; biology; business/commerce; computer science; English composition; health professions related; history; nursing; physical sciences; psychology; social sciences; sociology.

BROWARD COMMUNITY COLLEGE
Fort Lauderdale, Florida
Instructional Technology
http://www.broward.edu/elearning

Broward Community College was founded in 1960. It is accredited by Southern Association of Colleges and Schools. It first offered distance learning courses in 1978. In fall 2007, there were 5,459 students enrolled in distance learning courses. Institutionally administered financial aid is available to distance learners.

Services Distance learners have accessibility to academic advising, bookstore, e-mail services, library services, tutoring.

Contact Lisa M. Ciardulli, Director of e-Learning Programs and Services, Broward Community College, 3501 Southwest Davie Road, Building 17, Room 226, Davie, FL 33314. Telephone: 954-201-6567. Fax: 954-201-6398. E-mail: lciardul@broward.edu.

DEGREES AND AWARDS

AA Liberal Arts
AAS Accounting Technology; Business Administration
AS Accounting Technology; Business Administration

COURSE SUBJECT AREAS OFFERED OUTSIDE OF DEGREE PROGRAMS

Undergraduate—accounting and related services; anthropology; biology; business/commerce; computer science; developmental and child psychology; economics; education related; English composition; entrepreneurial and small business operations; geography and cartography; geological and earth sciences/geosciences; health and physical education/fitness; history; languages (Romance languages); legal studies (non-professional general, undergraduate); marketing; mathematics and statistics related; nursing; philosophy; philosophy and religious studies related; psychology; sociology; statistics.

BRYANT AND STRATTON ONLINE
Lackawanna, New York
http://www.bryantstratton.edu

Bryant and Stratton Online is accredited by Middle States Association of Colleges and Schools. It first offered distance learning courses in 1997. In fall 2007, there were 850 students enrolled in distance learning courses. Institutionally administered financial aid is available to distance learners.

Services Distance learners have accessibility to academic advising, bookstore, career placement assistance, e-mail services, library services, tutoring.

Contact Admissions, Bryant and Stratton Online, Sterling Park, 200 Redtail, Orchard Park, NY 14127. Telephone: 716-677-8800 Ext. 241. Fax: 716-677-8899. E-mail: online@bryantstratton.edu.

DEGREES AND AWARDS

AAS Criminal Justice; Human Resources Specialist; Medical Administrative Assistant
AD Accounting Online; Business Online; Information Technology Online; Paralegal Online
BBA Business Administration

COURSE SUBJECT AREAS OFFERED OUTSIDE OF DEGREE PROGRAMS

Undergraduate—accounting and related services; business administration, management and operations; business/commerce; business/corporate communications; computer/information technology administration and management; computer programming; computer software and media applications; computer systems networking and telecommunications; legal support services.

BRYN ATHYN COLLEGE OF THE NEW CHURCH
Bryn Athyn, Pennsylvania
Bryn Athyn College of the New Church was founded in 1876. It is accredited by Middle States Association of Colleges and Schools. It first offered distance learning courses in 2007. In fall 2007, there were 10 students enrolled in distance learning courses. Institutionally administered financial aid is available to distance learners.
Services Distance learners have accessibility to academic advising, campus computer network, e-mail services.
Contact Rev. Scott I. Frazier, Instructor, Bryn Athyn College of the New Church, PO Box 717, Bryn Athyn, PA 19009-0717. Telephone: 267-502-4875. Fax: 267-502-2658. E-mail: scott.frazier@brynathyn.edu.

DEGREES AND AWARDS
Programs offered do not lead to a degree or other formal award.

COURSE SUBJECT AREAS OFFERED OUTSIDE OF DEGREE PROGRAMS
Undergraduate—education; religious studies.
Graduate—religious studies.

BUENA VISTA UNIVERSITY
Storm Lake, Iowa
Centers
http://centers.bvu.edu
Buena Vista University was founded in 1891. It is accredited by North Central Association of Colleges and Schools. It first offered distance learning courses in 1975. In fall 2007, there were 1,418 students enrolled in distance learning courses. Institutionally administered financial aid is available to distance learners.
Services Distance learners have accessibility to academic advising, bookstore, campus computer network, career placement assistance, e-mail services, library services.
Contact Marge Welch, Associate Dean for Professional and Online Studies, Buena Vista University, 610 West 4th Street, Storm Lake, IA 50588. Telephone: 712-749-2250. Fax: 712-749-1470. E-mail: welchm @bvu.edu.

DEGREES AND AWARDS

BA Business; Elementary Education; English; History; Information Management; Political Science–Criminal Justice; Social Sciences
Certification Education–Middle School Education; Education–Secondary Education; Special Education–Instructional Specialist I
MSE Guidance and Counseling–School Guidance and Counseling

COURSE SUBJECT AREAS OFFERED OUTSIDE OF DEGREE PROGRAMS
Undergraduate—accounting and related services; business administration, management and operations; business/commerce; business, man-

agement, and marketing related; criminal justice and corrections; criminology; education; education related; education (specific levels and methods); education (specific subject areas); English; entrepreneurial and small business operations; finance and financial management services; health and medical administrative services; history; human services; management information systems; political science and government; psychology; psychology related; social sciences; social sciences related; sociology; special education.
Graduate—education related.

BUENA VISTA UNIVERSITY
Storm Lake, Iowa
Master of Education
http://www.bvu.edu/learn
Buena Vista University was founded in 1891. It is accredited by North Central Association of Colleges and Schools. It first offered distance learning courses in 2004. In fall 2007, there were 278 students enrolled in distance learning courses. Institutionally administered financial aid is available to distance learners.
Services Distance learners have accessibility to academic advising, bookstore, campus computer network, career placement assistance, e-mail services, library services, tutoring.
Contact Laura Harris, BVU Online, Buena Vista University, 610 West 4th Street, Storm Lake, IA 50588. Telephone: 712-749-1893. Fax: 712-749-1241. E-mail: harrisl@bvu.edu.

DEGREES AND AWARDS

MEd Curriculum and Instruction–Effective Teaching and Instructional Leadership emphasis; Curriculum and Instruction–Teaching English as a Second Language emphasis

COURSE SUBJECT AREAS OFFERED OUTSIDE OF DEGREE PROGRAMS

Undergraduate—accounting and related services; business administration, management and operations; business/commerce; business/corporate communications; business, management, and marketing related; business/managerial economics; communication and journalism related; communication and media; criminal justice and corrections; curriculum and instruction; education; English; English composition; finance and financial management services; marketing; political science and government; psychology.
Graduate—curriculum and instruction; education; English as a second/foreign language (teaching).

BUFFALO STATE COLLEGE, STATE UNIVERSITY OF NEW YORK
Buffalo, New York
http://www.buffalostate.edu/offices/ir
Buffalo State College, State University of New York was founded in 1867. It is accredited by Middle States Association of Colleges and Schools. It first offered distance learning courses in 1998. In fall 2007, there were 499 students enrolled in distance learning courses. Institutionally administered financial aid is available to distance learners.
Services Distance learners have accessibility to academic advising, bookstore, career placement assistance, e-mail services, library services.
Contact Meghan Pereira, Instructional Technology Specialist, Buffalo State College, State University of New York, 1300 Elmwood Avenue, BC 113, Buffalo, NY 14222. Telephone: 716-878-3877. Fax: 716-878-3131. E-mail: pereirme@buffalostate.edu.

DEGREES AND AWARDS

CAGS Adult Education; Creative Studies; Human Resource Development
MS Adult Education; Creative Studies

COURSE SUBJECT AREAS OFFERED OUTSIDE OF DEGREE PROGRAMS

Undergraduate—business, management, and marketing related; communication and media; computer science; design and applied arts; dietetics and clinical nutrition services; education; education related; English; English composition; history; political science and government. **Graduate**—education related.

BURLINGTON COLLEGE
Burlington, Vermont
Independent Degree Program (IDP)
http://www.burlingtoncollege.edu
Burlington College was founded in 1972. It is accredited by New England Association of Schools and Colleges. It first offered distance learning courses in 1993. In fall 2007, there were 28 students enrolled in distance learning courses. Institutionally administered financial aid is available to distance learners.
Services Distance learners have accessibility to academic advising, career placement assistance, e-mail services, library services, tutoring.
Contact Ms. Laryn Runco, Director of Admissions and Public Relations, Burlington College, 95 North Avenue, Burlington, VT 05401. Telephone: 802-862-9616 Ext. 104. Fax: 802-660-4331. E-mail: admissions@ burlington.edu.

DEGREES AND AWARDS
BA Cinema Studies; Fine Arts; Gender Studies; Human Services; Individualized major/Interdisciplinary Studies; Inter-American Studies; Legal and Justice Studies; Psychology; Transpersonal Psychology; Writing and Literature

COURSE SUBJECT AREAS OFFERED OUTSIDE OF DEGREE PROGRAMS
Undergraduate—comparative literature; counseling psychology; creative writing; developmental and child psychology; educational psychology; ethnic, cultural minority, and gender studies; experimental psychology; fine and studio art; history; human development, family studies, and related services; human services; liberal arts and sciences, general studies and humanities; multi-/interdisciplinary studies related; philosophy; psychology; sociology.

BURLINGTON COUNTY COLLEGE
Pemberton, New Jersey
Distance Learning Office
http://staff.bcc.edu/distance
Burlington County College was founded in 1966. It is accredited by Middle States Association of Colleges and Schools. It first offered distance learning courses in 1978. In fall 2007, there were 1,548 students enrolled in distance learning courses. Institutionally administered financial aid is available to distance learners.
Services Distance learners have accessibility to academic advising, bookstore, career placement assistance, e-mail services, library services, tutoring.
Contact Kathleen Devone, Coordinator of Distance Learning, Burlington County College, 601 Pemberton-Browns Mills Road, Pemberton, NJ 08068. Telephone: 609-894-9311 Ext. 1790. Fax: 609-894-4189. E-mail: dlearn@bcc.edu.

DEGREES AND AWARDS
AA Liberal Arts
AAS Liberal Arts and Sciences
AS Business Management

COURSE SUBJECT AREAS OFFERED OUTSIDE OF DEGREE PROGRAMS
Undergraduate—accounting and related services; American literature (United States and Canadian); anthropology; biology; communication and media; computer and information sciences; computer software and media applications; criminal justice and corrections; culinary arts and related services; developmental and child psychology; ecology, evolution, and population biology; educational psychology; English; English composition; film/video and photographic arts; fine and studio art; food science and technology; history; hospitality administration; languages (Romance languages); management sciences and quantitative methods;

marketing; mathematics; mathematics and statistics related; psychology; psychology related; social sciences; social sciences related; sociology; statistics.

BUTLER COMMUNITY COLLEGE
El Dorado, Kansas
http://www.butlercc.edu/
Butler Community College was founded in 1927. It is accredited by North Central Association of Colleges and Schools. It first offered distance learning courses in 1998. In fall 2007, there were 2,000 students enrolled in distance learning courses. Institutionally administered financial aid is available to distance learners.
Services Distance learners have accessibility to academic advising, bookstore, e-mail services, library services, tutoring.
Contact Ms. Meg McGranaghan, Director, Instructional Technology, Butler Community College, 901 South Haverhill Road, El Dorado, KS 67042. Telephone: 316-322-3345. Fax: 316-322-3315. E-mail: megmcg @butlercc.edu.

DEGREES AND AWARDS
AA History; Liberal Arts; Philosophy and Religion
AAS Marketing and Management
AGS Liberal Arts
AS History; Liberal Arts; Software Development

COURSE SUBJECT AREAS OFFERED OUTSIDE OF DEGREE PROGRAMS
Undergraduate—accounting and related services; allied health and medical assisting services; applied mathematics; astronomy and astrophysics; behavioral sciences; business, management, and marketing related; chemistry; computer programming; criminal justice and corrections; criminology; data entry/microcomputer applications; developmental and child psychology; drafting/design engineering technologies; economics; English composition; fine and studio art; gerontology; health and physical education/fitness; health professions related; history; human development, family studies, and related services; human resources management; marketing; mathematics; mathematics and statistics related; music; nursing; nutrition sciences; philosophy; philosophy and religious studies related; physical sciences; physical sciences related; physics; political science and government; psychology; social sciences; social sciences related; sociology; speech and rhetoric.
Non-credit—nursing.

CABRILLO COLLEGE
Aptos, California
Instruction, Transfer and Distance Education
http://www.cabrillo.edu/services/disted/
Cabrillo College was founded in 1959. It is accredited by Western Association of Schools and Colleges. It first offered distance learning courses in 1994. In fall 2007, there were 3,600 students enrolled in distance learning courses. Institutionally administered financial aid is available to distance learners.
Services Distance learners have accessibility to academic advising, bookstore, career placement assistance, e-mail services, library services, tutoring.
Contact Francine Van Meter, Director, Teaching and Learning Center, Cabrillo College, 6500 Soquel Drive, Aptos, CA 95003. Telephone: 831-479-6191. Fax: 831-479-5721. E-mail: francine.vanmeter@ cabrillo.edu.

DEGREES AND AWARDS
AA Liberal Arts

COURSE SUBJECT AREAS OFFERED OUTSIDE OF DEGREE PROGRAMS
Undergraduate—accounting and computer science; accounting and related services; allied health and medical assisting services; anthropology; biological and biomedical sciences related; biological and physical sciences; business/commerce; cell biology and anatomical sciences;

communication and journalism related; computer and information sciences; computer science; criminal justice and corrections; culinary arts and related services; English; English composition; film/video and photographic arts; fire protection; foods, nutrition, and related services; geography and cartography; geological and earth sciences/geosciences; health professions related; history; journalism; languages (Romance languages); legal studies (non-professional general, undergraduate); library science related; mathematics; music; philosophy; philosophy and religious studies related; physical sciences; real estate; sociology; visual and performing arts related.

CALDWELL COMMUNITY COLLEGE AND TECHNICAL INSTITUTE
Hudson, North Carolina
http://www.cccti.edu

Caldwell Community College and Technical Institute was founded in 1964. It is accredited by Southern Association of Colleges and Schools. It first offered distance learning courses in 1989. In fall 2007, there were 1,200 students enrolled in distance learning courses. Institutionally administered financial aid is available to distance learners.
Services Distance learners have accessibility to academic advising, bookstore, career placement assistance, e-mail services, library services, tutoring.
Contact Jennifer S. Sime, Director, Distance Learning, Caldwell Community College and Technical Institute, 2855 Hickory Boulevard, Hudson, NC 28638-2397. Telephone: 828-726-2707. Fax: 828-759-4632. E-mail: jsime@cccti.edu.

DEGREES AND AWARDS
Programs offered do not lead to a degree or other formal award.

COURSE SUBJECT AREAS OFFERED OUTSIDE OF DEGREE PROGRAMS
Undergraduate—accounting and related services; biological and biomedical sciences related; biological and physical sciences; biology; business administration, management and operations; business/commerce; business/corporate communications; business operations support and assistant services; communication and media; computer and information sciences; educational psychology; English; English composition; fine and studio art; fire protection; history; human development, family studies, and related services; liberal arts and sciences, general studies and humanities; marketing; mathematics; music; physical sciences; psychology; social sciences; sociology; technical and business writing.
Non-credit—accounting and related services; business administration, management and operations; business/corporate communications; business/managerial economics; business operations support and assistant services; computer and information sciences and support services related; computer/information technology administration and management; computer software and media applications; creative writing; criminal justice and corrections; finance and financial management services; health/medical preparatory programs; linguistic, comparative, and related language studies; peace studies and conflict resolution; sales, merchandising, and related marketing operations (specialized); technical and business writing.

CALIFORNIA INSTITUTE OF INTEGRAL STUDIES
San Francisco, California
Transformative Studies
http://www.ciis.edu

California Institute of Integral Studies was founded in 1968. It is accredited by Western Association of Schools and Colleges. It first offered distance learning courses in 1993. In fall 2007, there were 150 students enrolled in distance learning courses. Institutionally administered financial aid is available to distance learners.
Services Distance learners have accessibility to academic advising, bookstore, campus computer network, e-mail services, library services.
Contact Ms. Allyson Werner, Admissions Counselor for the School of Consciousness and Transformation, California Institute of Integral Studies, 1453 Mission Street, San Francisco, CA 94103. Telephone: 415-575-6155. Fax: 415-575-1268. E-mail: awerner@ciis.edu.

DEGREES AND AWARDS
MA Transformative Leadership
PhD Transformative Studies

COURSE SUBJECT AREAS OFFERED OUTSIDE OF DEGREE PROGRAMS
Graduate—area studies; community organization and advocacy; ecology, evolution, and population biology; ethnic, cultural minority, and gender studies; philosophy and religious studies related; religious studies; sociology.
Non-credit—area studies; community organization and advocacy; ecology, evolution, and population biology; ethnic, cultural minority, and gender studies; philosophy and religious studies related; religious studies; sociology.

See full description on page 348.

CALIFORNIA NATIONAL UNIVERSITY FOR ADVANCED STUDIES
Northridge, California
http://www.cnuas.edu/

California National University for Advanced Studies was founded in 1993. It is accredited by Distance Education and Training Council. It first offered distance learning courses in 1993. In fall 2007, there were 450 students enrolled in distance learning courses. Institutionally administered financial aid is available to distance learners.
Services Distance learners have accessibility to academic advising, bookstore, campus computer network, e-mail services.
Contact Dr. Lolly Horn, CEO and Vice President for Academic Affairs, California National University for Advanced Studies, 8550 Balboa Boulevard, Suite 210, Northridge, CA 91325. Telephone: 800-782-2422. Fax: 818-830-2418. E-mail: lhorn@mail.cnuas.edu.

DEGREES AND AWARDS
BS Business Administration; Computer Science; Engineering; Quality Assurance Science
Certificate Human Resource Management Practice
MBA Business Administration
MEM Engineering Management
MHRM Human Resources
MS Engineering

COURSE SUBJECT AREAS OFFERED OUTSIDE OF DEGREE PROGRAMS
Undergraduate—accounting and related services; business administration, management and operations; business/corporate communications; business/managerial economics; computer and information sciences; economics; electrical and electronic engineering technologies; engineering; environmental/environmental health engineering; finance and financial management services; human resources management; international business; management information systems; marketing; mechanical engineering; quality control and safety technologies.
Graduate—accounting and related services; business administration, management and operations; computer and information sciences; computer engineering; electrical and electronic engineering technologies; engineering; engineering/industrial management; environmental/environmental health engineering; human resources management; management information systems; marketing; mechanical engineering.

CALIFORNIA POLYTECHNIC STATE UNIVERSITY, SAN LUIS OBISPO
San Luis Obispo, California
Distance Education–Extended University Programs and Services
http://www.continuing-ed.calpoly.edu

California Polytechnic State University, San Luis Obispo was founded in 1901. It is accredited by Western Association of Schools and Colleges. It first offered distance learning courses in 1998. In fall 2007, there were 45 students enrolled in distance learning courses. Institutionally administered financial aid is available to distance learners.
Services Distance learners have accessibility to academic advising, bookstore, campus computer network, e-mail services.

Contact Ms. Patricia-Ann Stoneman, Director of Academic Programs, California Polytechnic State University, San Luis Obispo, 1 Grand Avenue, Continuing Education, San Luis Obispo, CA 93407. Telephone: 805-756-2053. Fax: 805-756-5933. E-mail: pstonema@calpoly.edu.

DEGREES AND AWARDS
Programs offered do not lead to a degree or other formal award.

COURSE SUBJECT AREAS OFFERED OUTSIDE OF DEGREE PROGRAMS
Undergraduate—applied mathematics.
Graduate—education.
Non-credit—business administration, management and operations; business/corporate communications; business, management, and marketing related; computer and information sciences; management information systems; mathematics.

CALIFORNIA STATE UNIVERSITY, CHICO
Chico, California
Center for Regional and Continuing Education
http://rce.csuchico.edu/online
California State University, Chico was founded in 1887. It is accredited by Western Association of Schools and Colleges. It first offered distance learning courses in 1975. In fall 2007, there were 2,076 students enrolled in distance learning courses. Institutionally administered financial aid is available to distance learners.
Services Distance learners have accessibility to academic advising, bookstore, campus computer network, e-mail services, library services, tutoring.
Contact Mr. Jeffrey S. Layne, Program Director, California State University, Chico, Chico, CA 95929-0250. Telephone: 530-898-6105. Fax: 530-898-4020. E-mail: jlayne@csuchico.edu.

DEGREES AND AWARDS
BA Liberal Studies; Social Science
BS Computer Science
BSN Nursing
MN Nursing
MS Computer Science

COURSE SUBJECT AREAS OFFERED OUTSIDE OF DEGREE PROGRAMS
Undergraduate—agriculture; anthropology; area, ethnic, cultural, and gender studies related; behavioral sciences; communication and media; community health services; curriculum and instruction; dance; education; English; ethnic, cultural minority, and gender studies; geography and cartography; health and medical administrative services; history; human development, family studies, and related services; liberal arts and sciences, general studies and humanities; neuroscience; nursing; political science and government; psychology; religious studies; social sciences; social work; sociology.
Graduate—computer science; education; nursing.

CALIFORNIA STATE UNIVERSITY, DOMINGUEZ HILLS
Carson, California
Distance Learning
http://dominguezonline.csudh.edu
California State University, Dominguez Hills was founded in 1960. It is accredited by Western Association of Schools and Colleges. It first offered distance learning courses in 1974. In fall 2007, there were 4,000 students enrolled in distance learning courses. Institutionally administered financial aid is available to distance learners.
Services Distance learners have accessibility to academic advising, bookstore, campus computer network, e-mail services, library services, tutoring.
Contact Registration Department, California State University, Dominguez Hills, College of Extended and International Education, 1000 East

Victoria Street, Carson, CA 90747. Telephone: 877-GO-HILLS. Fax: 310-516-3971. E-mail: eeinfo@csudh.edu.

DEGREES AND AWARDS
BS Applied Studies; Nursing completion program; Quality Assurance
Certificate of Completion Quality Assurance
Certificate Assistive Technology; Community College Teaching; Production and Inventory Control; Purchasing
CCCPE Administrative Medical Specialist with Medical Billing and Coding Certificate; Advanced Coding for the Physician's Office; Advanced Hospital Coding and CCS Prep; Advanced Paralegal Certificate; Medical Billing and Coding; Medical Transcription; Paralegal Certificate; Technical Writing
MA Humanities; Negotiation, Conflict Resolution, and Peacebuilding
MBA Business Administration
MPA Public Administration
MS Nursing; Quality Assurance

COURSE SUBJECT AREAS OFFERED OUTSIDE OF DEGREE PROGRAMS
Undergraduate—biology; education; educational administration and supervision; education related; landscape architecture; music; physics.
Non-credit—accounting and related services; alternative and complementary medicine and medical systems; business/corporate communications; business, management, and marketing related; communication and journalism related; computer and information sciences; computer/information technology administration and management; design and applied arts; dietetics and clinical nutrition services; education; educational administration and supervision; environmental control technologies; film/video and photographic arts; finance and financial management services; fine and studio art; gerontology; graphic communications; health and medical administrative services; history; human resources management; mathematics; museum studies; music; personal and culinary services related; psychology related; quality control and safety technologies; sales, merchandising, and related marketing operations (general); sales, merchandising, and related marketing operations (specialized).
See full description on page 350.

CALIFORNIA STATE UNIVERSITY, EAST BAY
Hayward, California
Online Campus
http://www.csueastbay.edu/ecat/current/i-140online.html
California State University, East Bay was founded in 1957. It is accredited by Western Association of Schools and Colleges. It first offered distance learning courses in 1998. In fall 2007, there were 200 students enrolled in distance learning courses. Institutionally administered financial aid is available to distance learners.
Services Distance learners have accessibility to academic advising, bookstore, campus computer network, career placement assistance, e-mail services, library services, tutoring.
Contact Dr. Nan Chico, Director, Online and Hybrid Support Center, California State University, East Bay, OHSC, LI 2800, Hayward, CA 94542. Telephone: 510-885-4384. Fax: 510-885-4498. E-mail: nan.chico@csueastbay.edu.

DEGREES AND AWARDS
BA Human Development
BS Recreation
MSE Option in Online Teaching and Learning

CALIFORNIA STATE UNIVERSITY, NORTHRIDGE
Northridge, California
Distance Learning
http://tsengcollege.csun.edu/online.html
California State University, Northridge was founded in 1958. It is accredited by Western Association of Schools and Colleges. It first offered distance learning courses in 1998. In fall 2007, there were 350 students enrolled in distance learning courses. Institutionally administered financial aid is available to distance learners.
Services Distance learners have accessibility to academic advising, bookstore, campus computer network, e-mail services, library services.

Contact Karena Senchack, Distance Learning Program Manager, California State University, Northridge, College of Extended Learning, 18111 Nordhoff Street, Mail Code 8401, Northridge, CA 91330-8401. Telephone: 818-677-6405. Fax: 818-677-6408. E-mail: karena.senchack@csun.edu.

DEGREES AND AWARDS
CCCPE Communication Disorders and Science–CEUs in Communication Disorders and Science
MAE Educational Administration
MS Communication Disorders and Sciences
MSE Engineering Management

COURSE SUBJECT AREAS OFFERED OUTSIDE OF DEGREE PROGRAMS
Non-credit—communication disorders sciences and services.

CALIFORNIA STATE UNIVERSITY, SACRAMENTO
Sacramento, California
Distance and Distributed Education
http://www.csus.edu/atcs/
California State University, Sacramento was founded in 1947. It is accredited by Western Association of Schools and Colleges. It first offered distance learning courses in 1986. In fall 2007, there were 3,000 students enrolled in distance learning courses. Institutionally administered financial aid is available to distance learners.
Services Distance learners have accessibility to academic advising, bookstore, campus computer network, e-mail services, library services, tutoring.
Contact Dr. Jean-Pierre Raymond Bayard, Director of Academic Technology and Creative Services, California State University, Sacramento, 6000 J Street, Sacramento, CA 95819. Telephone: 916-278-3370. Fax: 916-278-5143. E-mail: bayardj@csus.edu.

DEGREES AND AWARDS
Programs offered do not lead to a degree or other formal award.

COURSE SUBJECT AREAS OFFERED OUTSIDE OF DEGREE PROGRAMS
Undergraduate—accounting and related services; anthropology; business/corporate communications; business, management, and marketing related; clinical/medical laboratory science and allied professions; computer and information sciences; computer software and media applications; criminal justice and corrections; economics; foods, nutrition, and related services; geological and earth sciences/geosciences; gerontology; health and physical education/fitness; history; human development, family studies, and related services; journalism; languages (Romance languages); management information systems; mathematics; medieval and Renaissance studies; music; nursing; psychology; real estate; sales, merchandising, and related marketing operations (general); sociology; special education; statistics.
Graduate—business, management, and marketing related; educational assessment, evaluation, and research; educational/instructional media design; electrical, electronics and communications engineering; nursing; public policy analysis.

CALIFORNIA STATE UNIVERSITY, SAN BERNARDINO
San Bernardino, California
http://www.csusb.edu/
California State University, San Bernardino was founded in 1965. It is accredited by Western Association of Schools and Colleges. It first offered distance learning courses in 1988. In fall 2007, there were 13,634 students enrolled in distance learning courses. Institutionally administered financial aid is available to distance learners.
Services Distance learners have accessibility to academic advising, bookstore, e-mail services, library services.
Contact Dr. James Michael Monaghan, Director of Distributed Learning, California State University, San Bernardino, 5500 University Parkway, San Bernardino, CA 92407. Telephone: 909-537-7439. Fax: 909-537-7637. E-mail: monaghan@csusb.edu.

DEGREES AND AWARDS
BSN Nursing–Online RN to BSN
MA Criminal Justice; Education–Career and Technical Education (EVOC); Education–Instructional Technology (ETEC); Education–Reading Education (ERDG); Education–Special Education—Level II credential ESPE
MPA Public Administration
MSN Nursing

COURSE SUBJECT AREAS OFFERED OUTSIDE OF DEGREE PROGRAMS
Undergraduate—accounting and computer science; accounting and related services; Air Force J.R.O.T.C/R.O.T.C; allied health and medical assisting services; American literature (United States and Canadian); area, ethnic, cultural, and gender studies related; astronomy and astrophysics; bilingual, multilingual, and multicultural education; business administration, management and operations; business, management, and marketing related; clinical child psychology; cognitive psychology and psycholinguistics; communication and journalism related; communication and media; communications technology; community health services; criminal justice and corrections; economics; education; educational/instructional media design; education related; education (specific subject areas); English; ethnic, cultural minority, and gender studies; finance and financial management services; languages (foreign languages related); liberal arts and sciences, general studies and humanities; mathematics; multi-/interdisciplinary studies related; nursing; political science and government; psychology; social work; visual and performing arts.
Graduate—allied health diagnostic, intervention, and treatment professions; communication and media; communications technology; criminal justice and corrections; education; educational/instructional media design; education (specific subject areas); public administration.
Non-credit—education related.

CALIFORNIA STATE UNIVERSITY, SAN MARCOS
San Marcos, California
Extended Studies
http://www.csusm.edu/el
California State University, San Marcos was founded in 1990. It is accredited by Western Association of Schools and Colleges. It first offered distance learning courses in 1997. In fall 2007, there were 400 students enrolled in distance learning courses. Institutionally administered financial aid is available to distance learners.
Services Distance learners have accessibility to academic advising, bookstore, campus computer network, career placement assistance, e-mail services, library services, tutoring.
Contact Ms. Veronica Martinelli, Credit Programs Coordinator, California State University, San Marcos, 333 South Twin Oaks Valley Road, San Marcos, CA 92096. Telephone: 760-750-8717. Fax: 760-750-3138. E-mail: vmartine@csusm.edu.

DEGREES AND AWARDS
BS Kinesiology
BSN Accelerated Program; Nursing–RN to BSN
Certificate Biotechnology Laboratory Technician; Construction Supervision; Paralegal Studies; Preparation for Clinical Nurse Faculty

COURSE SUBJECT AREAS OFFERED OUTSIDE OF DEGREE PROGRAMS
Undergraduate—accounting and computer science; allied health and medical assisting services; applied mathematics; business administration, management and operations; business operations support and assistant services; computer and information sciences and support services related; computer programming; education (specific subject areas); mathematics; social work.
Graduate—education related; education (specific subject areas).
Non-credit—accounting and computer science; business/commerce; communication and journalism related; community health services; comparative literature; computer and information sciences; dramatic/theater arts and stagecraft; English as a second language; family and consumer

economics; fine and studio art; health/medical preparatory programs; health services/allied health/health sciences; languages (foreign languages related); mathematics; nursing; philosophy; psychology related; work and family studies.

CALVIN COLLEGE
Grand Rapids, Michigan
http://www.calvin.edu/
Calvin College was founded in 1876. It is accredited by North Central Association of Colleges and Schools. It first offered distance learning courses in 1995. In fall 2007, there were 30 students enrolled in distance learning courses. Institutionally administered financial aid is available to distance learners.
Services Distance learners have accessibility to academic advising, bookstore, campus computer network, career placement assistance, e-mail services, library services.
Contact Ms. Cindi Hoekstra, Graduate Program Coordinator, Calvin College, 3201 Burton Street SE, Grand Rapids, MI 49546. Telephone: 616-526-6158. E-mail: choekstr@calvin.edu.

DEGREES AND AWARDS
Programs offered do not lead to a degree or other formal award.

COURSE SUBJECT AREAS OFFERED OUTSIDE OF DEGREE PROGRAMS
Graduate—educational administration and supervision.

CALVIN THEOLOGICAL SEMINARY
Grand Rapids, Michigan
http://www.calvinseminary.edu
Calvin Theological Seminary was founded in 1876. It first offered distance learning courses in 2001. In fall 2007, there were 45 students enrolled in distance learning courses. Institutionally administered financial aid is available to distance learners.
Services Distance learners have accessibility to academic advising, campus computer network, e-mail services, library services, tutoring.
Contact Rev. Greg Janke, Director of Admissions, Calvin Theological Seminary, 3233 Burton Street SE, Grand Rapids, MI 49546. Telephone: 616-957-7035. Fax: 616-957-8621. E-mail: gjanke0@calvinseminary.edu.

DEGREES AND AWARDS
MA New Church Development

COURSE SUBJECT AREAS OFFERED OUTSIDE OF DEGREE PROGRAMS
Graduate—biblical and other theological languages and literatures; biblical studies; missionary studies and missiology; pastoral counseling and specialized ministries; religious education; religious/sacred music; religious studies; theological and ministerial studies; theology and religious vocations related.

CAMPBELLSVILLE UNIVERSITY
Campbellsville, Kentucky
http://www.campbellsville.edu/
Campbellsville University was founded in 1906. It is accredited by Southern Association of Colleges and Schools. It first offered distance learning courses in 1999. In fall 2007, there were 212 students enrolled in distance learning courses. Institutionally administered financial aid is available to distance learners.
Services Distance learners have accessibility to academic advising, bookstore, campus computer network, career placement assistance, e-mail services, library services.
Contact Ms. Karla Deaton, Coordinator of Academic Outreach, Campbellsville University, 1 University Drive, Campbellsville, KY 42718-2799. Telephone: 270-789-5078. Fax: 270-789-5550. E-mail: krdeaton@campbellsville.edu.

DEGREES AND AWARDS
MSE Special Education

COURSE SUBJECT AREAS OFFERED OUTSIDE OF DEGREE PROGRAMS
Undergraduate—religious studies; social work.
Graduate—educational administration and supervision; religious studies; social work.

CAMPBELL UNIVERSITY
Buies Creek, North Carolina
http://www.campbell.edu
Campbell University was founded in 1887. It is accredited by Southern Association of Colleges and Schools. It first offered distance learning courses in 2000. In fall 2007, there were 1,200 students enrolled in distance learning courses. Institutionally administered financial aid is available to distance learners.
Services Distance learners have accessibility to academic advising, bookstore, campus computer network, e-mail services, library services.
Contact Mrs. Jane B. Strother, Director, Distance Education, Campbell University, PO Box 264, Buies Creek, NC 27506. Telephone: 910-814-4739. Fax: 910-814-4736. E-mail: strotherj@campbell.edu.

DEGREES AND AWARDS
Programs offered do not lead to a degree or other formal award.

COURSE SUBJECT AREAS OFFERED OUTSIDE OF DEGREE PROGRAMS
Undergraduate—accounting and related services; American literature (United States and Canadian); biblical studies; business administration, management and operations; business/corporate communications; English composition; fine and studio art; geography and cartography; history; mathematics and computer science; political science and government; psychology; sociology; statistics.

CANISIUS COLLEGE
Buffalo, New York
On-Line Master of Science in Physical Education
http://www.canisius.edu/physed/online
Canisius College was founded in 1870. It is accredited by Middle States Association of Colleges and Schools. It first offered distance learning courses in 2002. In fall 2007, there were 350 students enrolled in distance learning courses. Institutionally administered financial aid is available to distance learners.
Services Distance learners have accessibility to academic advising, bookstore, campus computer network, career placement assistance, e-mail services, library services, tutoring.
Contact Timothy M. Sawicki, EdD, Associate Professor and Program Director, Canisius College, 2001 Main Street (KAC-217), Buffalo, NY 14208-1098. E-mail: sawickit@canisius.edu.

DEGREES AND AWARDS
MS Ed On-Line Master of Science in Physical Education

COURSE SUBJECT AREAS OFFERED OUTSIDE OF DEGREE PROGRAMS
Graduate—behavioral sciences; community health services; curriculum and instruction; developmental and child psychology; education; educational administration and supervision; educational assessment, evaluation, and research; educational psychology; education related; education (specific levels and methods); education (specific subject areas); family psychology; health and physical education/fitness; social work; student counseling and personnel services.
See full description on page 352.

CAPE COD COMMUNITY COLLEGE
West Barnstable, Massachusetts
Distance and Learning Technology
http://learning.capecod.mass.edu

Cape Cod Community College was founded in 1961. It is accredited by New England Association of Schools and Colleges. It first offered distance learning courses in 1993. In fall 2007, there were 750 students enrolled in distance learning courses. Institutionally administered financial aid is available to distance learners.

Services Distance learners have accessibility to academic advising, bookstore, campus computer network, career placement assistance, e-mail services, library services, tutoring.

Contact Greg Masterson, Director of Distance Learning, Cape Cod Community College, 2240 Iyanough Road, West Barnstable, MA 02668. Telephone: 508-375-4040 Ext. 4345. Fax: 508-375-4041. E-mail: gmasters@capecod.edu.

DEGREES AND AWARDS
Programs offered do not lead to a degree or other formal award.

COURSE SUBJECT AREAS OFFERED OUTSIDE OF DEGREE PROGRAMS
Undergraduate—business administration, management and operations; computer software and media applications; developmental and child psychology; economics; English composition; fine and studio art; history; marketing; mathematics; natural sciences; nursing; psychology; psychology related; social sciences; sociology.
Non-credit—dental support services and allied professions.

CAPE FEAR COMMUNITY COLLEGE
Wilmington, North Carolina
http://cfcc.edu

Cape Fear Community College was founded in 1959. It is accredited by Southern Association of Colleges and Schools. It first offered distance learning courses in 1988. In fall 2007, there were 2,188 students enrolled in distance learning courses. Institutionally administered financial aid is available to distance learners.

Services Distance learners have accessibility to academic advising, bookstore, campus computer network, career placement assistance, e-mail services, library services, tutoring.

Contact Dr. Larolyn Zylicz, Department Chair, Distance Learning, Cape Fear Community College, 411 North Front Street, Wilmington, NC 28401. Telephone: 910-362-7245. Fax: 910-362-7152. E-mail: lzylicz@cfcc.edu.

DEGREES AND AWARDS
AA General Studies; General Studies

COURSE SUBJECT AREAS OFFERED OUTSIDE OF DEGREE PROGRAMS
Undergraduate—accounting and computer science; business, management, and marketing related; computer/information technology administration and management; health services/allied health/health sciences; human services; legal studies (non-professional general, undergraduate); marketing.
Non-credit—business/commerce.

CAPELLA UNIVERSITY
Minneapolis, Minnesota
http://www.capella.edu/

Capella University was founded in 1993. It is accredited by North Central Association of Colleges and Schools. It first offered distance learning courses in 1993. In fall 2007, there were 17,203 students enrolled in distance learning courses. Institutionally administered financial aid is available to distance learners.

Services Distance learners have accessibility to academic advising, bookstore, career placement assistance, library services, tutoring.

Contact Enrollment Services, Capella University, 225 South Sixth St, 9th Floor, Minneapolis, MN 55402. Telephone: 888-227-3552 Ext. 3. Fax: 612-977-5060. E-mail: info@capella.edu.

DEGREES AND AWARDS
BS Business; Information Technology; Public Safety
MBA Business
MS Education; Human Services; Information Technology; Organization and Management; Psychology; Public Safety
PhD Education; Human Services; Information Technology; Organization and Management; Psychology; Public Safety
Psy D Psychology

COURSE SUBJECT AREAS OFFERED OUTSIDE OF DEGREE PROGRAMS
Graduate—business administration, management and operations; business/corporate communications; business, management, and marketing related; clinical psychology; computer/information technology administration and management; computer systems networking and telecommunications; counseling psychology; criminal justice and corrections; education; educational administration and supervision; educational/instructional media design; educational psychology; human resources management; human services; industrial and organizational psychology; international business; marketing; psychology; sales, merchandising, and related marketing operations (general); school psychology.
See full description on page 354.

CAPITAL COMMUNITY COLLEGE
Hartford, Connecticut
Distance Learning Class
http://ccc.commnet.edu/

Capital Community College was founded in 1946. It is accredited by New England Association of Schools and Colleges. It first offered distance learning courses in 1998. In fall 2007, there were 295 students enrolled in distance learning courses. Institutionally administered financial aid is available to distance learners.

Services Distance learners have accessibility to academic advising, bookstore, career placement assistance, library services, tutoring.

Contact Mr. Michael Kriscenski, Distance Learning Counselor, Capital Community College, 950 Main Street, Hartford, CT 06103. Telephone: 860-906-5040. E-mail: mkriscenski@ccc.commnet.edu.

DEGREES AND AWARDS
AS Computer Information System; General Studies

COURSE SUBJECT AREAS OFFERED OUTSIDE OF DEGREE PROGRAMS
Undergraduate—allied health diagnostic, intervention, and treatment professions; behavioral sciences; biology; business administration, management and operations; business/commerce; business, management, and marketing related; computer/information technology administration and management; computer software and media applications; developmental and child psychology; English; English language and literature related; English literature (British and Commonwealth); family psychology; genetics; health services/allied health/health sciences; history; human development, family studies, and related services; human resources management; human services; languages (Romance languages); library assistant; linguistic, comparative, and related language studies; marketing; political science and government; psychology; social sciences; sociology.

CARDINAL STRITCH UNIVERSITY
Milwaukee, Wisconsin
College of Education
http://www.stritch.edu/

Cardinal Stritch University was founded in 1937. It is accredited by North Central Association of Colleges and Schools. It first offered distance learning courses in 1995. In fall 2007, there were 60 students enrolled in distance learning courses. Institutionally administered financial aid is available to distance learners.

Services Distance learners have accessibility to academic advising, bookstore, campus computer network, career placement assistance, e-mail services, library services.

Contact Judy Wendorf, Director of University Outreach and Professional Development, Cardinal Stritch University, 6801 North Yates Road, Milwaukee, WI 53217-3985. Telephone: 414-410-4428. E-mail: jawendorf@stritch.edu.

DEGREES AND AWARDS
BS Public Safety Management
MA Special Education
MBA Business Administration
MEd Education; Instructional Technology

COURSE SUBJECT AREAS OFFERED OUTSIDE OF DEGREE PROGRAMS
Graduate—education; educational administration and supervision.
Non-credit—business administration, management and operations; computer software and media applications; creative writing; family and consumer sciences/human sciences business services.

CARLOW UNIVERSITY
Pittsburgh, Pennsylvania
http://www.carlow.edu/
Carlow University was founded in 1929. It is accredited by Middle States Association of Colleges and Schools. It first offered distance learning courses in 1995. In fall 2007, there were 2,405 students enrolled in distance learning courses. Institutionally administered financial aid is available to distance learners.
Services Distance learners have accessibility to academic advising, bookstore, campus computer network, career placement assistance, e-mail services, library services, tutoring.
Contact Nola Coulson, Coordinator, Instructional Technology, Carlow University, 3333 Fifth Avenue, Pittsburgh, PA 15213. Telephone: 412-578-6338. Fax: 412-578-6595. E-mail: coulsonna@carlow.edu.

DEGREES AND AWARDS
Programs offered do not lead to a degree or other formal award.

COURSE SUBJECT AREAS OFFERED OUTSIDE OF DEGREE PROGRAMS
Undergraduate—accounting and computer science; biology; business, management, and marketing related; chemistry; computer science; education; English; information science/studies; management information systems; mathematics; nursing; philosophy; political science and government; psychology; social psychology; social work; sociology; special education.
Graduate—business, management, and marketing related; counseling psychology; education; nursing; special education.

CARL SANDBURG COLLEGE
Galesburg, Illinois
http://www.sandburg.edu
Carl Sandburg College was founded in 1967. It is accredited by North Central Association of Colleges and Schools. It first offered distance learning courses in 1986. In fall 2007, there were 250 students enrolled in distance learning courses. Institutionally administered financial aid is available to distance learners.
Services Distance learners have accessibility to bookstore, campus computer network, e-mail services, library services.
Contact Carol Kreider, Director of Admissions, Carl Sandburg College, 2400 Tom L. Wilson Boulevard, Galesburg, IL 61401. Telephone: 309-341-5234. Fax: 309-344-3291. E-mail: ckreider@sandburg.edu.

DEGREES AND AWARDS
Programs offered do not lead to a degree or other formal award.

COURSE SUBJECT AREAS OFFERED OUTSIDE OF DEGREE PROGRAMS
Undergraduate—accounting and related services; cell biology and anatomical sciences; computer software and media applications; English;

English composition; fine and studio art; geography and cartography; health services/allied health/health sciences; music; psychology; sociology.

CARROLL COMMUNITY COLLEGE
Westminster, Maryland
http://www.carrollcc.edu
Carroll Community College was founded in 1993. It is accredited by Middle States Association of Colleges and Schools. It first offered distance learning courses in 1993. In fall 2007, there were 485 students enrolled in distance learning courses. Institutionally administered financial aid is available to distance learners.
Services Distance learners have accessibility to academic advising, bookstore, library services.
Contact Ms. Janenne Corcoran, Director of Advising, Counseling, and Admissions, Carroll Community College, 1601 Washington Road, Westminster, MD 21157. Telephone: 410-386-8405. Fax: 410-386-8446. E-mail: jcorcoran@carrollcc.edu.

DEGREES AND AWARDS
Programs offered do not lead to a degree or other formal award.

COURSE SUBJECT AREAS OFFERED OUTSIDE OF DEGREE PROGRAMS
Undergraduate—accounting and related services; allied health and medical assisting services; atmospheric sciences and meteorology; biology; business administration, management and operations; business/corporate communications; business, management, and marketing related; computer and information sciences; computer/information technology administration and management; computer programming; computer systems networking and telecommunications; criminal justice and corrections; economics; educational assessment, evaluation, and research; education related; English composition; health and physical education/fitness; history; legal studies (non-professional general, undergraduate); legal support services; management information systems; marketing; mathematics; music; nursing; nutrition sciences; philosophy; psychology; social psychology; statistics; taxation; technical and business writing.
Non-credit—accounting and related services; business administration, management and operations; business/commerce; business, management, and marketing related; business operations support and assistant services; computer programming; computer software and media applications; computer systems networking and telecommunications; creative writing; family and consumer economics; finance and financial management services; gerontology; graphic communications; health and medical administrative services; languages (Romance languages); legal studies (non-professional general, undergraduate); legal support services; technical and business writing; veterinary biomedical and clinical sciences.

CARROLL UNIVERSITY
Waukesha, Wisconsin
http://www.cc.edu/academics/online
Carroll University was founded in 1846. It is accredited by North Central Association of Colleges and Schools. It first offered distance learning courses in 1995. In fall 2007, there were 167 students enrolled in distance learning courses. Institutionally administered financial aid is available to distance learners.
Services Distance learners have accessibility to academic advising, bookstore, campus computer network, career placement assistance, e-mail services, library services, tutoring.
Contact Ms. Tina Knopp, Director of Admissions, Carroll University, 100 North East Avenue, Waukesha, WI 53186. Telephone: 262-524-7518. Fax: 262-650-4851. E-mail: twood@cc.edu.

DEGREES AND AWARDS
Programs offered do not lead to a degree or other formal award.

COURSE SUBJECT AREAS OFFERED OUTSIDE OF DEGREE PROGRAMS
Undergraduate—accounting and computer science; business, management, and marketing related; communication and media; computer

science; economics; English; finance and financial management services; history; philosophy; religious education; sociology.

Graduate—computer science; computer software and media applications; education (specific subject areas).

THE CATHOLIC DISTANCE UNIVERSITY
Hamilton, Virginia
http://www.cdu.edu/

The Catholic Distance University was founded in 1983. It is accredited by Distance Education and Training Council. It first offered distance learning courses in 1983. In fall 2007, there were 1,000 students enrolled in distance learning courses. Institutionally administered financial aid is available to distance learners.

Services Distance learners have accessibility to academic advising, bookstore, campus computer network, e-mail services, library services.

Contact Ms. Carol Ciullo, Director of Admissions, The Catholic Distance University, 120 East Colonial Highway, Hamilton, VA 20158. Telephone: 888-254-4238 Ext. 700. Fax: 540-338-4788. E-mail: cciullo @cdu.edu.

DEGREES AND AWARDS
BA Theology
Certification Advanced Catechist Certificate
Diploma Catechetical Diploma
MA Theology

COURSE SUBJECT AREAS OFFERED OUTSIDE OF DEGREE PROGRAMS
Undergraduate—biblical and other theological languages and literatures; philosophy and religious studies related; theological and ministerial studies; theology and religious vocations related.
Graduate—biblical and other theological languages and literatures; philosophy and religious studies related; religious education; religious studies; theological and ministerial studies; theology and religious vocations related.
Non-credit—biblical and other theological languages and literatures; philosophy and religious studies related; religious education; religious studies; theological and ministerial studies; theology and religious vocations related.

CAYUGA COUNTY COMMUNITY COLLEGE
Auburn, New York
http://www.cayuga-cc.edu/

Cayuga County Community College was founded in 1953. It is accredited by Middle States Association of Colleges and Schools. It first offered distance learning courses in 1998. In fall 2007, there were 800 students enrolled in distance learning courses. Institutionally administered financial aid is available to distance learners.

Services Distance learners have accessibility to academic advising, bookstore, career placement assistance, e-mail services, library services, tutoring.

Contact Ed Kowalski, Director of Online Programs, Cayuga County Community College, 197 Franklin Street, Auburn, NY 13021. Telephone: 315-255-1743. Fax: 315-255-2117. E-mail: kowalskie@cayuga-cc.edu.

DEGREES AND AWARDS
AA Liberal Arts and Humanities
AAS Business Administration; Criminal Justice/Corrections; Criminal Justice/Police
AS Business Administration; Liberal Arts and Sciences/Mathematics and Sciences

COURSE SUBJECT AREAS OFFERED OUTSIDE OF DEGREE PROGRAMS
Undergraduate—accounting and related services; anthropology; biological and physical sciences; biology; business administration, management and operations; business/commerce; computer science; computer systems networking and telecommunications; economics; English; health

and physical education/fitness; history; mathematics; political science and government; psychology; social psychology; social sciences; social sciences related; statistics.

CENTENNIAL COLLEGE
Scarborough, Ontario, Canada

Centennial College is provincially chartered. It first offered distance learning courses in 1993. In fall 2007, there were 1,400 students enrolled in distance learning courses. Institutionally administered financial aid is available to distance learners.

Services Distance learners have accessibility to academic advising, bookstore, campus computer network, career placement assistance, e-mail services, library services, tutoring.

Contact Ms. Meera Mather, Chair, Centennial College, Scarborough, ON M1G 3T8, Canada. Telephone: 416-289-5000 Ext. 2505. E-mail: mmather@centennialcollege.ca.

DEGREES AND AWARDS
Programs offered do not lead to a degree or other formal award.

COURSE SUBJECT AREAS OFFERED OUTSIDE OF DEGREE PROGRAMS
Undergraduate—accounting and computer science; area, ethnic, cultural, and gender studies related; biology; business administration, management and operations; business, management, and marketing related; computer and information sciences; human resources management; languages (foreign languages related); marketing; mathematics; teaching assistants/aides.
Graduate—education; English as a second/foreign language (teaching); English as a second language; hospitality administration.
Non-credit—computer/information technology administration and management; computer programming; computer systems networking and telecommunications; finance and financial management services.

CENTRAL ARIZONA COLLEGE
Coolidge, Arizona
Instructional Technology
http://www.centralaz.edu

Central Arizona College was founded in 1961. It is accredited by North Central Association of Colleges and Schools. It first offered distance learning courses in 1994. In fall 2007, there were 1,800 students enrolled in distance learning courses. Institutionally administered financial aid is available to distance learners.

Services Distance learners have accessibility to academic advising, bookstore, campus computer network, e-mail services, library services, tutoring.

Contact Mrs. Alfreda Poynter, Director of Admissions, Central Arizona College, 8470 North Overfield Road, Coolidge, AZ 85228. Telephone: 800-237-9814. Fax: 520-494-5529. E-mail: alfreda.poynter@centralaz. edu.

DEGREES AND AWARDS
Programs offered do not lead to a degree or other formal award.

COURSE SUBJECT AREAS OFFERED OUTSIDE OF DEGREE PROGRAMS
Undergraduate—anthropology; cell biology and anatomical sciences; education; English composition; fine and studio art; history; human development, family studies, and related services; languages (Romance languages); legal studies (non-professional general, undergraduate); mathematics and statistics related; philosophy and religious studies related; sociology.

CENTRAL BIBLE COLLEGE
Springfield, Missouri
http://www.cbcag.edu/

Central Bible College was founded in 1922. It is accredited by Association for Biblical Higher Education. It first offered distance learning courses in 2001. In fall 2007, there were 100 students enrolled in distance learning courses. Institutionally administered financial aid is available to distance learners.

Services Distance learners have accessibility to academic advising, bookstore, campus computer network, e-mail services, library services.

Contact Dr. Leo Theriot, Director, Center for LifeLong Learning, Central Bible College, 3000 North Grant Avenue, Springfield, MO 65803. Telephone: 417-833-2551 Ext. 1277. Fax: 417-833-0854. E-mail: ltheriot@cbcag.edu.

DEGREES AND AWARDS
Programs offered do not lead to a degree or other formal award.

COURSE SUBJECT AREAS OFFERED OUTSIDE OF DEGREE PROGRAMS
Undergraduate—biblical studies; education.
Non-credit—biblical and other theological languages and literatures; biblical studies.

CENTRAL CAROLINA COMMUNITY COLLEGE
Sanford, North Carolina
http://www.cccc.edu/de
Central Carolina Community College was founded in 1962. It is accredited by Southern Association of Colleges and Schools. It first offered distance learning courses in 1997. In fall 2007, there were 1,300 students enrolled in distance learning courses. Institutionally administered financial aid is available to distance learners.
Services Distance learners have accessibility to academic advising, bookstore, campus computer network, career placement assistance, e-mail services, library services, tutoring.
Contact Mr. Brian S. Merritt, Distance Education Counselor, Central Carolina Community College, 1105 Kelly Drive, Sanford, NC 27330. Telephone: 919-718-7511. Fax: 919-718-7380. E-mail: bmerritt@cccc.edu.

DEGREES AND AWARDS
AA General Studies
AAS Applied Science–Diploma in Applied Science and Associate in Applied Science; Applied Science–Diploma in Applied Science and Associate in Applied Science
AS General Studies
Certificate Various Subjects–BioQuality, Entrepreneur, Human Resources Management; Various Subjects–Income Tax Preparer, Library Services, Manager Trainee; Various Subjects–Medical Transcription, Networking, News Writing; Various Subjects–Payroll Accounting, Photo Journalism, Small Business Financial Advisor I and II

COURSE SUBJECT AREAS OFFERED OUTSIDE OF DEGREE PROGRAMS
Undergraduate—accounting and related services; agriculture; American literature (United States and Canadian); anthropology; biblical studies; biological and physical sciences; biomedical/medical engineering; biotechnology; business/commerce; business, management, and marketing related; business operations support and assistant services; chemistry; communication and journalism related; computer programming; computer science; criminal justice and corrections; dental support services and allied professions; dramatic/theater arts and stagecraft; economics; education; electrical and electronic engineering technologies; English; health and physical education/fitness; history; journalism; languages (foreign languages related); library science related; marketing; mathematics; sociology.
Non-credit—clinical/medical laboratory science and allied professions; computer and information sciences; criminal justice and corrections; English as a second language; management information systems.

CENTRAL CONNECTICUT STATE UNIVERSITY
New Britain, Connecticut
http://www.ccsu.edu/
Central Connecticut State University was founded in 1849. It is accredited by New England Association of Schools and Colleges. It first offered distance learning courses in 1992. In fall 2007, there were 70 students enrolled in distance learning courses. Institutionally administered financial aid is available to distance learners.
Services Distance learners have accessibility to bookstore, campus computer network, career placement assistance, e-mail services, library services, tutoring.

Contact Sherry Pesino, Assistant Director, Media Services, Central Connecticut State University, 1615 Stanley Street, New Britain, CT 06050-4010. Telephone: 860-832-2028. Fax: 860-832-2039. E-mail: pesinos@ccsu.edu.

DEGREES AND AWARDS
MS Data Mining

COURSE SUBJECT AREAS OFFERED OUTSIDE OF DEGREE PROGRAMS
Undergraduate—geography and cartography.

CENTRALIA COLLEGE
Centralia, Washington
Distance Learning
http://cconline.centralia.edu
Centralia College was founded in 1925. It is accredited by Northwest Commission on Colleges and Universities. It first offered distance learning courses in 1975. In fall 2007, there were 400 students enrolled in distance learning courses. Institutionally administered financial aid is available to distance learners.
Services Distance learners have accessibility to academic advising, bookstore, campus computer network, career placement assistance, e-mail services, library services, tutoring.
Contact Eric Richardson, Program Coordinator, eLearning, Centralia College, 600 Centralia College Boulevard, Centralia, WA 98531. Telephone: 360-736-9391 Ext. 374. E-mail: erichardson@centralia.edu.

DEGREES AND AWARDS
AA Criminal Justice

COURSE SUBJECT AREAS OFFERED OUTSIDE OF DEGREE PROGRAMS
Undergraduate—accounting and related services; anthropology; business administration, management and operations; business, management, and marketing related; chemistry; computer software and media applications; criminal justice and corrections; developmental and child psychology; education; English; English composition; geography and cartography; geological and earth sciences/geosciences; health and physical education/fitness; history; human development, family studies, and related services; liberal arts and sciences, general studies and humanities; library science related; management information systems; mathematics; philosophy; political science and government; psychology; real estate; social sciences; sociology; statistics.
Non-credit—computer and information sciences; computer programming; computer software and media applications; computer systems analysis; data entry/microcomputer applications; management information systems; sales, merchandising, and related marketing operations (specialized).

CENTRAL MICHIGAN UNIVERSITY
Mount Pleasant, Michigan
Off-Campus Programs
http://www.cel.cmich.edu/default.html
Central Michigan University was founded in 1892. It is accredited by North Central Association of Colleges and Schools. It first offered distance learning courses in 1971. In fall 2007, there were 8,000 students enrolled in distance learning courses. Institutionally administered financial aid is available to distance learners.
Services Distance learners have accessibility to academic advising, bookstore, campus computer network, career placement assistance, e-mail services, library services, tutoring.
Contact Ms. Marnie Roestel, Coordinator of Recruitment Services, Central Michigan University, 802 Industrial Drive, Mount Pleasant, MI 48858. Telephone: 800-950-1144 Ext. 3937. E-mail: roest1m@cmich.edu.

DEGREES AND AWARDS
BS Administration–Building Code Administration; Administration–Organizational Administration; Community Development, Community

Services major; Community Development, Health Sciences major; Community Development, Public Administration major

MA Education

MAE Educational Leadership, Charter School Administration emphasis

MBA MIS concentration and SAP emphasis; Value Driven Organization

MS Administration–General Administration concentration; Administration–Health Services Administration concentration; Administration–Human Resource Administration; Administration–Information Resource Management concentration; Administration–Leadership concentration; Administration–Public Administration concentration; Nutrition and Dietetics

DHA Healthcare Administration

COURSE SUBJECT AREAS OFFERED OUTSIDE OF DEGREE PROGRAMS

Undergraduate—accounting and computer science; allied health and medical assisting services; architecture related; behavioral sciences; building/construction finishing, management, and inspection; business administration, management and operations; business/commerce; business/corporate communications; business, management, and marketing related; business/managerial economics; business operations support and assistant services; community health services; community organization and advocacy; construction management; construction trades; economics; family and consumer sciences/human sciences; family and consumer sciences/human sciences related; health and medical administrative services; health and physical education/fitness; health professions related; health services/allied health/health sciences; human development, family studies, and related services; human resources management; human services; industrial and organizational psychology; marketing; multi-/interdisciplinary studies related; political science and government; psychology; psychology related; public administration; public administration and social service professions related; public policy analysis; work and family studies.

Graduate—accounting and computer science; behavioral sciences; business administration, management and operations; business/commerce; business/corporate communications; business, management, and marketing related; business/managerial economics; communication and journalism related; communications technology; computer and information sciences; computer and information sciences and support services related; computer systems analysis; curriculum and instruction; dietetics and clinical nutrition services; economics; education (specific levels and methods); education (specific subject areas); entrepreneurial and small business operations; finance and financial management services; food science and technology; foods, nutrition, and related services; health and medical administrative services; health professions related; hospitality administration; human resources management; management information systems; management sciences and quantitative methods; marketing; multi-/interdisciplinary studies related; nutrition sciences; political science and government; public administration; public administration and social service professions related; public policy analysis; public relations, advertising, and applied communication related; sales, merchandising, and related marketing operations (general).

See full description on page 356.

CENTRAL NEW MEXICO COMMUNITY COLLEGE
Albuquerque, New Mexico
http://www.cnm.edu/depts/dl

Central New Mexico Community College was founded in 1965. It is accredited by North Central Association of Colleges and Schools. It first offered distance learning courses in 1997. In fall 2007, there were 1,686 students enrolled in distance learning courses. Institutionally administered financial aid is available to distance learners.

Services Distance learners have accessibility to academic advising, bookstore, campus computer network, career placement assistance, e-mail services, library services, tutoring.

Contact Ms. Xeturah Woodley, Executive Director, Central New Mexico Community College, Distance Learning Office, 525 Buena Vista SE, Albuquerque, NM 87106. Telephone: 505-224-3317. Fax: 505-224-3321. E-mail: xwoodley@cnm.edu.

DEGREES AND AWARDS
AAS Business Administration; Office Administration

COURSE SUBJECT AREAS OFFERED OUTSIDE OF DEGREE PROGRAMS

Undergraduate—accounting and related services; biology; building/construction finishing, management, and inspection; business administration, management and operations; business/commerce; business, management, and marketing related; business/managerial economics; business operations support and assistant services; clinical/medical laboratory science and allied professions; communication and media; computer and information sciences; computer programming; creative writing; criminal justice and corrections; culinary arts and related services; data processing; economics; English; English composition; entrepreneurial and small business operations; fire protection; foods, nutrition, and related services; information science/studies; international business; legal studies (non-professional general, undergraduate); mathematics; microbiological sciences and immunology; nursing; philosophy; psychology; real estate; sales, merchandising, and related marketing operations (general); sociology; speech and rhetoric.

CENTRAL OREGON COMMUNITY COLLEGE
Bend, Oregon
Open Campus Distance Learning Program
http://www.cocc.edu/

Central Oregon Community College was founded in 1949. It is accredited by Northwest Commission on Colleges and Universities. It first offered distance learning courses in 1996. In fall 2007, there were 260 students enrolled in distance learning courses. Institutionally administered financial aid is available to distance learners.

Services Distance learners have accessibility to academic advising, bookstore, campus computer network, e-mail services, library services, tutoring.

Contact Barbara Klett, Instructional Technology Coordinator, Central Oregon Community College, 2600 NW College Way, Bend, OR 97701. Telephone: 541-383-7785. E-mail: bklett@cocc.edu.

DEGREES AND AWARDS
Programs offered do not lead to a degree or other formal award.

COURSE SUBJECT AREAS OFFERED OUTSIDE OF DEGREE PROGRAMS

Undergraduate—allied health and medical assisting services; business administration, management and operations; computer and information sciences; English composition; English literature (British and Commonwealth); geological and earth sciences/geosciences; health and physical education/fitness; health services/allied health/health sciences; history; liberal arts and sciences, general studies and humanities; library science; mathematics; nursing.

CENTRAL TEXAS COLLEGE
Killeen, Texas
Distance Education and Educational Technology
http://online.ctcd.edu

Central Texas College was founded in 1967. It is accredited by Southern Association of Colleges and Schools. It first offered distance learning courses in 1972. In fall 2007, there were 16,028 students enrolled in distance learning courses. Institutionally administered financial aid is available to distance learners.

Services Distance learners have accessibility to academic advising, bookstore, career placement assistance, library services, tutoring.

Contact Mrs. Angela Dawn Reese, Coordinator, Recruiting and Retention, Central Texas College, PO Box 1800, Killeen, TX 76540. Telephone: 254-526-1104. Fax: 254-526-1751. E-mail: angela.reese@ctcd.edu.

DEGREES AND AWARDS
AA Interdisciplinary Studies; Social Science

AAS Applied Management with Computer Applications (non-Texas students only); Applied Management; Applied Technology; At-Risk

Youth Specialization; Business Management Marketing and Sales Management; Business Management; Chemical Dependency specialization; Computer Science–Information Technology; Criminal Justice Corrections specialization; Criminal Justice; Executive Assistant; Homeland Security and Emergency Management; Hospitality Management–Food and Beverage Management; Hospitality Management; Office Management; Social Work

AGS General Studies

AS Business Administration

Certificate At-Risk Youth Specialization; Business Management Marketing and Sales; Business Management; Chemical Dependency specialization; Criminal Justice Addictions; Criminal Justice Corrections specialization; Criminal Justice Studies specialization; Homeland Security and Emergency Management; Hospitality Management–Food and Beverage Management; Hospitality Management–Property Management Advanced; Hospitality Management–Rooms Division; Information Center Specialist; Medical Office Specialist; Medical Transcription; Microsoft System Administrator; Office Assistant; Office Management Levels 1&2; Software Applications Specialist

COURSE SUBJECT AREAS OFFERED OUTSIDE OF DEGREE PROGRAMS

Undergraduate—accounting and computer science; accounting and related services; allied health and medical assisting services; American literature (United States and Canadian); anthropology; applied mathematics; area, ethnic, cultural, and gender studies related; biblical studies; business administration, management and operations; business/corporate communications; business, management, and marketing related; business/managerial economics; business operations support and assistant services; clinical child psychology; communication and media; community psychology; computer and information sciences; computer and information sciences and support services related; computer programming; computer science; computer software and media applications; computer systems analysis; computer systems networking and telecommunications; counseling psychology; criminal justice and corrections; criminology; culinary arts and related services; developmental and child psychology; economics; education; English; English composition; English language and literature related; English literature (British and Commonwealth); entrepreneurial and small business operations; ethnic, cultural, minority, and gender studies; family and consumer sciences/human sciences; family psychology; fine and studio art; fire protection; foods, nutrition, and related services; geography and cartography; health and physical education/fitness; health professions related; history; hospitality administration; human resources management; legal studies (non-professional general, undergraduate); management information systems; marketing; mathematics; mathematics and computer science; mathematics and statistics related; mental and social health services and allied professions; military studies; multi-/interdisciplinary studies related; music; nursing; philosophy; philosophy and religious studies related; political science and government; psychology; psychology related; public administration; real estate; sales, merchandising, and related marketing operations (specialized); social sciences; social sciences related; social work; sociology; statistics; technical and business writing.

CENTRAL VIRGINIA COMMUNITY COLLEGE
Lynchburg, Virginia
Learning Resources
http://www.cvcc.vccs.edu

Central Virginia Community College was founded in 1966. It is accredited by Southern Association of Colleges and Schools. It first offered distance learning courses in 1984. In fall 2007, there were 1,669 students enrolled in distance learning courses. Institutionally administered financial aid is available to distance learners.

Services Distance learners have accessibility to academic advising, bookstore, campus computer network, e-mail services, library services, tutoring.

Contact Susan S. Beasley, Distance Education Coordinator, Central Virginia Community College, 3506 Wards Road, Lynchburg, VA 24502. Telephone: 434-832-7742. Fax: 434-832-7880. E-mail: beasleys@cvcc.vccs.edu.

DEGREES AND AWARDS
AAS Medical Laboratory Technology

COURSE SUBJECT AREAS OFFERED OUTSIDE OF DEGREE PROGRAMS

Undergraduate—accounting and related services; allied health and medical assisting services; applied mathematics; astronomy and astrophysics; biology; business operations support and assistant services; chemistry; computer and information sciences; economics; education related; English; English composition; health professions related; history; information science/studies; library science related; marketing; music; philosophy; political science and government; psychology; religious studies; sociology; speech and rhetoric; technical and business writing.

CENTRAL WASHINGTON UNIVERSITY
Ellensburg, Washington
Center for Learning Technologies
http://www.cwu.edu/~media/

Central Washington University was founded in 1891. It is accredited by Northwest Commission on Colleges and Universities. It first offered distance learning courses in 1996. In fall 2007, there were 1,530 students enrolled in distance learning courses. Institutionally administered financial aid is available to distance learners.

Services Distance learners have accessibility to academic advising, bookstore, campus computer network, career placement assistance, e-mail services, library services.

Contact Tracy Terrell, Registrar, Central Washington University, Mitchell Hall, 400 East University Way, Ellensburg, WA 98926-7465. Telephone: 509-963-3076. Fax: 509-963-3022. E-mail: reg@cwu.edu.

DEGREES AND AWARDS
MS Physical Education, Health, and Leisure Studies

COURSE SUBJECT AREAS OFFERED OUTSIDE OF DEGREE PROGRAMS

Undergraduate—accounting and related services; anthropology; biology; business administration, management and operations; business/commerce; chemistry; communication and journalism related; computer/information technology administration and management; criminal justice and corrections; economics; education; English; family and consumer sciences/human sciences related; geography and cartography; history; human resources management; management information systems; marketing; nutrition sciences; philosophy and religious studies related; psychology; sociology.

Graduate—accounting and related services; business administration, management and operations; education; health and physical education/fitness.

CENTRAL WYOMING COLLEGE
Riverton, Wyoming
Distance Education and Extended Studies
http://www.cwc.edu

Central Wyoming College was founded in 1966. It is accredited by North Central Association of Colleges and Schools. It first offered distance learning courses in 1983. In fall 2007, there were 719 students enrolled in distance learning courses. Institutionally administered financial aid is available to distance learners.

Services Distance learners have accessibility to academic advising, bookstore, campus computer network, e-mail services, library services, tutoring.

Contact Retha Reinke, Distance Education Technician, Central Wyoming College, 2660 Peck Avenue, Riverton, WY 82501. Telephone: 307-855-2124. Fax: 307-855-2097. E-mail: rreinke@cwc.edu.

DEGREES AND AWARDS
Programs offered do not lead to a degree or other formal award.

COURSE SUBJECT AREAS OFFERED OUTSIDE OF DEGREE PROGRAMS

Undergraduate—accounting and related services; anthropology; area, ethnic, cultural, and gender studies related; atmospheric sciences and meteorology; biology; chemistry; communication and media; computer and information sciences; computer science; data entry/microcomputer applications; economics; education (specific subject areas); English composition; fine and studio art; geography and cartography; health and physical education/fitness; languages (American Indian/Native American); library science; mathematics; mechanics and repair; music; nursing; political science and government; psychology; religious studies; social sciences; sociology; vehicle maintenance and repair technologies; zoology/animal biology.

Non-credit—agricultural and domestic animal services; air transportation; animal sciences; applied horticulture/horticultural business services; area, ethnic, cultural, and gender studies related; botany/plant biology; business operations support and assistant services; computer software and media applications; culinary arts and related services; dance; data entry/microcomputer applications; design and applied arts; dramatic/theater arts and stagecraft; electrical and power transmission installation; electrical/electronics maintenance and repair technology; English composition; film/video and photographic arts; finance and financial management services; fine and studio art; food science and technology; foods, nutrition, and related services; graphic communications; health and physical education/fitness; health professions related; health services/allied health/health sciences; history; landscape architecture; languages (foreign languages related); mechanics and repair; medical basic sciences; mental and social health services and allied professions; movement and mind-body therapies; music; neuroscience; nutrition sciences; personal and culinary services related; precision metal working; psychology; vehicle maintenance and repair technologies; veterinary biomedical and clinical sciences; visual and performing arts; visual and performing arts related; wildlife and wildlands science and management; woodworking.

CERRITOS COLLEGE
Norwalk, California
Distributed Education Program
http://www.cerritos.edu/de

Cerritos College was founded in 1956. It is accredited by Western Association of Schools and Colleges. It first offered distance learning courses in 1985. In fall 2007, there were 9,000 students enrolled in distance learning courses. Institutionally administered financial aid is available to distance learners.

Services Distance learners have accessibility to academic advising, bookstore, e-mail services, library services, tutoring.

Contact Yvette Juarez, Program Assistant, Distance Education, Cerritos College, 11110 Alondra Boulevard, Norwalk, CA 90650. Telephone: 562-860-2451 Ext. 2405. Fax: 562-467-5091. E-mail: yjuarez@cerritos.edu.

DEGREES AND AWARDS

Programs offered do not lead to a degree or other formal award.

COURSE SUBJECT AREAS OFFERED OUTSIDE OF DEGREE PROGRAMS

Undergraduate—anthropology; business/commerce; business operations support and assistant services; curriculum and instruction; data entry/microcomputer applications; English composition; history; journalism; legal studies (non-professional general, undergraduate); management information systems; radio, television, and digital communication; sociology; woodworking; zoology/animal biology.

CERRO COSO COMMUNITY COLLEGE
Ridgecrest, California
Cerro Coso Online
http://cconline.cerrocoso.edu

Cerro Coso Community College was founded in 1973. It is accredited by Western Association of Schools and Colleges. It first offered distance learning courses in 1997. In fall 2007, there were 3,000 students enrolled in distance learning courses. Institutionally administered financial aid is available to distance learners.

Services Distance learners have accessibility to academic advising, bookstore, career placement assistance, library services, tutoring.

Contact Lori Olivera, Program Manager, Cerro Coso Community College, 4090 West Line Street, Bishop, CA 93514. Telephone: 888-537-6932. Fax: 760-872-5310. E-mail: lolivera@cerrocoso.edu.

DEGREES AND AWARDS

AA Business Administration; Humanities; Liberal Arts; Social Sciences
AS Administration of Justice; Business Administration; Computer Information Systems; Digital Media Arts; Management; Small Business Management/Entrepreneurship
Certificate Teaching–Online Teaching

COURSE SUBJECT AREAS OFFERED OUTSIDE OF DEGREE PROGRAMS

Undergraduate—anthropology; computer programming; criminal justice and corrections; English; human development, family studies, and related services; mathematics; music; sales, merchandising, and related marketing operations (general); speech and rhetoric.

CHADRON STATE COLLEGE
Chadron, Nebraska
Extended Campus Programs
http://www.csc.edu/distancelearning

Chadron State College was founded in 1911. It is accredited by North Central Association of Colleges and Schools. It first offered distance learning courses in 1991. In fall 2007, there were 700 students enrolled in distance learning courses. Institutionally administered financial aid is available to distance learners.

Services Distance learners have accessibility to academic advising, bookstore, campus computer network, career placement assistance, e-mail services, library services, tutoring.

Contact Ms. Jodi Banzhaf, Distance Learning Coordinator, Chadron State College, 1000 Main Street, Chadron, NE 69337. Telephone: 800-600-4099. Fax: 308-432-6473. E-mail: elrep@csc.edu.

DEGREES AND AWARDS

BA Business Administration/Management Information Systems; Business Administration/Management; Business Administration/Marketing; Business, general; Library Information Management; Psychology
BS Math
MAE Math
MBA Business Administration
MEd Educational Technology; Math
MS Organizational Management, Human Services option

COURSE SUBJECT AREAS OFFERED OUTSIDE OF DEGREE PROGRAMS

Undergraduate—accounting and computer science; accounting and related services; applied mathematics; biological and physical sciences; business administration, management and operations; business/commerce; business/corporate communications; business, management, and marketing related; business/managerial economics; computer and information sciences; criminology; developmental and child psychology; economics; education; educational administration and supervision; educational assessment, evaluation, and research; educational/instructional media design; educational psychology; education related; education (specific levels and methods); education (specific subject areas); English composition; English literature (British and Commonwealth); family and consumer sciences/human sciences; family and consumer sciences/human sciences related; geography and cartography; history; housing and human environments; human development, family studies, and related services; human resources management; human services; industrial and organizational psychology; information science/studies; legal professions and studies related; legal studies (non-professional general, undergraduate); liberal arts and sciences, general studies and humanities; library science; library science related; management information systems; management sciences and quantitative methods; marketing; mathematics; mathematics and computer science; mathematics and statistics related; philosophy; philosophy and religious studies related; physical sciences; physical sciences related; physiological psychology/psychobiology; psychology; psychology related; real estate; sales, merchandising, and related marketing operations (general); sales, merchandising, and related marketing operations (specialized); social sciences; social sciences related; social work; sociology; special education; statistics; technical and business writing.

Graduate—accounting and computer science; accounting and related services; business administration, management and operations; business/commerce; business, management, and marketing related; business/managerial economics; counseling psychology; curriculum and instruction; economics; education; educational administration and supervision; educational assessment, evaluation, and research; educational/instructional media design; educational psychology; education related; education (specific levels and methods); education (specific subject areas); English; history; human resources management; industrial and organizational psychology; management information systems; management sciences and quantitative methods; marketing; mathematics; mathematics and computer science; mathematics and statistics related; psychology; psychology related; sales, merchandising, and related marketing operations (general); sales, merchandising, and related marketing operations (specialized); school psychology; special education; statistics; technology education/industrial arts.

Non-credit—education related.

CHAMINADE UNIVERSITY OF HONOLULU
Honolulu, Hawaii
http://www.chaminade.edu/

Chaminade University of Honolulu was founded in 1955. It is accredited by Western Association of Schools and Colleges. It first offered distance learning courses in 1997. In fall 2007, there were 762 students enrolled in distance learning courses. Institutionally administered financial aid is available to distance learners.

Services Distance learners have accessibility to academic advising, bookstore, campus computer network, e-mail services, library services.

Contact Skip Lee, Director of Accelerated Undergraduate Program, Chaminade University of Honolulu, 3140 Waialae Avenue, Honolulu, HI 96816-1578. Telephone: 808-735-4851. Fax: 808-735-4766. E-mail: slee@chaminade.edu.

DEGREES AND AWARDS
Programs offered do not lead to a degree or other formal award.

COURSE SUBJECT AREAS OFFERED OUTSIDE OF DEGREE PROGRAMS

Undergraduate—accounting and related services; anthropology; business administration, management and operations; criminal justice and corrections; dramatic/theater arts and stagecraft; economics; education; English; English composition; finance and financial management services; history; mathematics; music; philosophy; philosophy and religious studies related; physics; political science and government; psychology; religious studies; sociology.

Graduate—criminal justice and corrections; education; religious studies.

CHARTER OAK STATE COLLEGE
New Britain, Connecticut
http://www.charteroak.edu/

Charter Oak State College was founded in 1973. It is accredited by New England Association of Schools and Colleges. It first offered distance learning courses in 1992. In fall 2007, there were 2,071 students enrolled in distance learning courses. Institutionally administered financial aid is available to distance learners.

Services Distance learners have accessibility to academic advising, bookstore, e-mail services, library services, tutoring.

Contact Peggy Intravia, Associate, Academic Affairs, Charter Oak State College, 55 Paul J. Manafort Drive, New Britain, CT 06053-2150. Telephone: 860-832-3837. Fax: 860-832-3999. E-mail: mintravia@charteroak.edu.

DEGREES AND AWARDS
AA General Studies
AS General Studies
BA General Studies
BS General Studies

COURSE SUBJECT AREAS OFFERED OUTSIDE OF DEGREE PROGRAMS

Undergraduate—accounting and related services; American literature (United States and Canadian); behavioral sciences; biology/biotechnology laboratory technician; business administration, management and operations; business, management, and marketing related; cognitive psychology and psycholinguistics; communication and media; computer and information sciences; computer systems networking and telecommunications; criminology; educational administration and supervision; educational/instructional media design; English language and literature related; finance and financial management services; foods, nutrition, and related services; forensic psychology; genetics; geological and earth sciences/geosciences; health services/allied health/health sciences; management information systems; marketing; mathematics; mathematics and statistics related; philosophy and religious studies related; psychology; psychology related; public administration; public administration and social service professions related; social sciences related; sociology; speech and rhetoric; statistics.

Non-credit—health professions related; nursing; pharmacy, pharmaceutical sciences, and administration.

See full description on page 358.

CHATHAM UNIVERSITY
Pittsburgh, Pennsylvania
http://www.chatham.edu/ccps

Chatham University was founded in 1869. It is accredited by Middle States Association of Colleges and Schools. It first offered distance learning courses in 2005. In fall 2007, there were 211 students enrolled in distance learning courses. Institutionally administered financial aid is available to distance learners.

Services Distance learners have accessibility to academic advising, bookstore, campus computer network, career placement assistance, e-mail services, library services, tutoring.

Contact Sarah Wojdylak, Admissions Support Specialist, College for Continuing and Professional Studies, Chatham University, College for Continuing and Professional Studies, Woodland Road, Pittsburgh, PA 15232. Telephone: 412-365-1148. Fax: 412-365-1720. E-mail: ccps@chatham.edu.

DEGREES AND AWARDS
BSN Nursing–RN to BSN
Graduate Certificate Infant Mental Health
MA Master of Professional Writing; Wellness Program
MFA Creative Writing
MHS Health Science
DH Sc Nursing–Doctor of Nursing Practice
OTD Professional Doctor of Occupational Therapy

COURSE SUBJECT AREAS OFFERED OUTSIDE OF DEGREE PROGRAMS

Undergraduate—accounting and related services; behavioral sciences; biochemistry, biophysics and molecular biology; biology; business, management, and marketing related; business/managerial economics; chemistry; communication and journalism related; computer and information sciences and support services related; creative writing; dance; economics; education; engineering; English; environmental design; film/video and photographic arts; history; human services; interior architecture; international business; languages (Romance languages); legal professions and studies related; marketing; mathematics; museum studies; music; nursing;

physics; political science and government; psychology; religious studies; social work; visual and performing arts.

Graduate—accounting and related services; biology; business administration, management and operations; business operations support and assistant services; counseling psychology; creative writing; education; film/video and photographic arts; interior architecture; landscape architecture; nursing; physical sciences; teaching assistants/aides.

Non-credit—computer software and media applications; nursing.

CHEMEKETA COMMUNITY COLLEGE
Salem, Oregon
Chemeketa Online
http://online.chemeketa.edu
Chemeketa Community College was founded in 1955. It is accredited by Northwest Commission on Colleges and Universities. It first offered distance learning courses in 1979. In fall 2007, there were 8,229 students enrolled in distance learning courses. Institutionally administered financial aid is available to distance learners.
Services Distance learners have accessibility to academic advising, bookstore, e-mail services, library services, tutoring.
Contact Secretary, Chemeketa Community College, 4000 Lancaster Drive NE, PO Box 14007, Salem, OR 97309-7070. Telephone: 503-399-7873. E-mail: col@chemeketa.edu.

DEGREES AND AWARDS
AA Oregon Transfer
AAS Accounting; Fire Protection Technology–Fire Prevention; Fire Protection Technology–Fire Suppression; Hospitality Management; Management; Speech/Language Pathology Assistant; Tourism and Travel Management
AGS General Studies
AS Business
Certificate of Completion Computer Assisted Drafting (CAD); Oregon Transfer Module
Certificate Business Software; Hospitality Management; Speech/Language Pathology Assistant; Tourism and Travel Management

COURSE SUBJECT AREAS OFFERED OUTSIDE OF DEGREE PROGRAMS
Undergraduate—accounting and related services; allied health and medical assisting services; American literature (United States and Canadian); anthropology; applied mathematics; archeology; area, ethnic, cultural, and gender studies related; astronomy and astrophysics; biological and biomedical sciences related; biological and physical sciences; biology; business administration, management and operations; business/commerce; business/corporate communications; business, management, and marketing related; business operations support and assistant services; chemistry; computer and information sciences; computer and information sciences and support services related; computer programming; computer science; computer software and media applications; computer systems networking and telecommunications; creative writing; criminal justice and corrections; criminology; curriculum and instruction; data entry/microcomputer applications; developmental and child psychology; drafting/design engineering technologies; economics; education; education related; English composition; ethnic, cultural minority, and gender studies; fine and studio art; fire protection; foods, nutrition, and related services; geography and cartography; geological and earth sciences/geosciences; health and physical education/fitness; health professions related; history; hospitality administration; human development, family studies, and related services; information science/studies; liberal arts and sciences, general studies and humanities; management information systems; mathematics; mathematics and computer science; mathematics and statistics related; music; philosophy; philosophy and religious studies related; physical sciences; physical sciences related; political science and government; psychology; psychology related; religious studies; sales, merchandising, and related marketing operations (general); sales, merchandising, and related marketing operations (specialized); social sciences; social sciences related; sociology; speech and rhetoric; statistics; technical and business writing.

CHICAGO STATE UNIVERSITY
Chicago, Illinois
http://www.csu.edu/
Chicago State University was founded in 1867. It is accredited by North Central Association of Colleges and Schools. It first offered distance learning courses in 1999. In fall 2007, there were 813 students enrolled in distance learning courses. Institutionally administered financial aid is available to distance learners.
Services Distance learners have accessibility to academic advising, bookstore, campus computer network, e-mail services, library services, tutoring.
Contact Janice Gilmore, Secretary, Chicago State University, Office of Distance Learning, NAL-457, 9501 South King Drive, Chicago, IL 60628. Telephone: 773-995-2960. Fax: 773-995-2580. E-mail: jgilmore@csu.edu.

DEGREES AND AWARDS
Programs offered do not lead to a degree or other formal award.

COURSE SUBJECT AREAS OFFERED OUTSIDE OF DEGREE PROGRAMS
Undergraduate—accounting and computer science; accounting and related services.

CINCINNATI CHRISTIAN UNIVERSITY
Cincinnati, Ohio
Correspondence Department
http://www.ccuniversity.edu/elearn
Cincinnati Christian University was founded in 1924. It is accredited by Association for Biblical Higher Education. It first offered distance learning courses in 1980. In fall 2007, there were 172 students enrolled in distance learning courses. Institutionally administered financial aid is available to distance learners.
Services Distance learners have accessibility to academic advising, bookstore, campus computer network, e-mail services, library services, tutoring.
Contact Ms. Suzanne Faber, Administrative Assistant to the Dean of Distance Education and Institutional Research, Cincinnati Christian University, 2700 Glenway Avenue, Cincinnati, OH 45204-3200. Telephone: 513-244-8475. Fax: 513-244-8123. E-mail: suzanne.faber@ccuniversity.edu.

DEGREES AND AWARDS
Programs offered do not lead to a degree or other formal award.

COURSE SUBJECT AREAS OFFERED OUTSIDE OF DEGREE PROGRAMS
Undergraduate—biblical and other theological languages and literatures; biblical studies; education; history.
Graduate—biblical and other theological languages and literatures; biblical studies; counseling psychology; education; history; religious studies.

CINCINNATI STATE TECHNICAL AND COMMUNITY COLLEGE
Cincinnati, Ohio
http://www.cincinnatistate.edu
Cincinnati State Technical and Community College was founded in 1966. It is accredited by North Central Association of Colleges and Schools. It first offered distance learning courses in 1994. In fall 2007, there were 1,460 students enrolled in distance learning courses. Institutionally administered financial aid is available to distance learners.
Services Distance learners have accessibility to academic advising, bookstore, campus computer network, e-mail services, library services.
Contact Ms. Gaby Boeckermann, Director of Admissions, Cincinnati State Technical and Community College, 3520 Central Parkway, Cincinnati, OH 45223. Telephone: 513-569-1550. E-mail: gaby.boeckermann@cincinnatistate.edu.

DEGREES AND AWARDS
Programs offered do not lead to a degree or other formal award.

COURSE SUBJECT AREAS OFFERED OUTSIDE OF DEGREE PROGRAMS
Undergraduate—accounting and related services; allied health and medical assisting services; applied horticulture/horticultural business services; business administration, management and operations; business/commerce; business operations support and assistant services; civil engineering technology; communication and media; computer and information sciences; computer/information technology administration and management; computer software and media applications; computer systems networking and telecommunications; data processing; engineering technologies related; health and medical administrative services; health professions related; history; information science/studies; management information systems; mechanical engineering related technologies; sociology.

CITRUS COLLEGE
Glendora, California
Distance Education
http://www.citruscollege.com
Citrus College was founded in 1915. It is accredited by Western Association of Schools and Colleges. It first offered distance learning courses in 1996. In fall 2007, there were 2,000 students enrolled in distance learning courses. Institutionally administered financial aid is available to distance learners.
Services Distance learners have accessibility to academic advising, bookstore, campus computer network, e-mail services, library services, tutoring.
Contact Ms. Lari Kirby, Distance Education Supervisor, Citrus College, 1000 West Foothill Boulevard, Glendora, CA 91741-1899. Telephone: 626-914-8569. E-mail: online@citruscollege.edu.

DEGREES AND AWARDS
Programs offered do not lead to a degree or other formal award.

COURSE SUBJECT AREAS OFFERED OUTSIDE OF DEGREE PROGRAMS
Undergraduate—accounting and computer science; anthropology; astronomy and astrophysics; behavioral sciences; biological and physical sciences; biology; business/commerce; communication and media; computer and information sciences; computer programming; criminal justice and corrections; economics; English; English composition; history; journalism; liberal arts and sciences, general studies and humanities; mathematics; music; philosophy; political science and government; psychology; psychology related; real estate; social sciences; sociology.

CITY COLLEGES OF CHICAGO, HAROLD WASHINGTON COLLEGE
Chicago, Illinois
Center for Distance Learning
http://cdl.ccc.edu
City Colleges of Chicago, Harold Washington College was founded in 1962. It is accredited by North Central Association of Colleges and Schools. In fall 2007, there were 3,531 students enrolled in distance learning courses. Institutionally administered financial aid is available to distance learners.
Services Distance learners have accessibility to bookstore, campus computer network, e-mail services, library services, tutoring.
Contact Marcia Turner, Assistant Dean, City Colleges of Chicago, Harold Washington College, 6343 South Halsted Street, Center for Distance Learning, Chicago, IL 60621. Telephone: 773-487-3707. Fax: 312-553-5987. E-mail: mturner36@ccc.edu.

DEGREES AND AWARDS
Programs offered do not lead to a degree or other formal award.

COURSE SUBJECT AREAS OFFERED OUTSIDE OF DEGREE PROGRAMS
Undergraduate—accounting and related services; biology; business administration, management and operations; business, management, and marketing related; communication and journalism related; creative writing; developmental and child psychology; English composition; languages (foreign languages related); mathematics; mathematics and computer science; mathematics and statistics related; military studies; multi-/interdisciplinary studies related; music; nutrition sciences; philosophy and religious studies related; physical sciences related; psychology related; public relations, advertising, and applied communication related; school psychology; security and protective services related; social work; sociology; speech and rhetoric; statistics; visual and performing arts.

CITY UNIVERSITY OF SEATTLE
Bellevue, Washington
Distance Learning Option
http://www.cityu.edu
City University of Seattle was founded in 1973. It is accredited by Northwest Commission on Colleges and Universities. It first offered distance learning courses in 1985. In fall 2007, there were 600 students enrolled in distance learning courses. Institutionally administered financial aid is available to distance learners.
Services Distance learners have accessibility to academic advising, bookstore, e-mail services, library services, tutoring.
Contact Office of Admissions, City University of Seattle, 11900 NE First Street, Bellevue, WA 98005. Telephone: 800-422-4898. Fax: 425-709-5361. E-mail: info@cityu.edu.

DEGREES AND AWARDS
AS General Studies
BA Psychology–Applied Psychology
BS Accounting; Business Administration (Information Systems/Technology emphasis); Business Administration (Marketing emphasis); Business Administration (Project Management emphasis); Business Administration–E-Commerce emphasis (Bulgaria); Business Administration–General Management emphasis; Business Administration–Human Resource emphasis; Business Administration–Individualized Study emphasis; Computer Systems (Networking/Telecommunications emphasis); General Studies
Certificate Accounting; Marketing; Networking/Telecommunications; Project Management
Graduate Certificate Financial Management; General Management; Information Systems; Marketing; Project Management; Technology Management
MA Leadership
MEd Reading and Literacy
MS Project Management; Technology Management
See full description on page 360.

CLACKAMAS COMMUNITY COLLEGE
Oregon City, Oregon
Learning Resources
http://dl.clackamas.edu
Clackamas Community College was founded in 1966. It is accredited by Northwest Commission on Colleges and Universities. It first offered distance learning courses in 1997. In fall 2007, there were 9,422 students enrolled in distance learning courses. Institutionally administered financial aid is available to distance learners.
Services Distance learners have accessibility to academic advising, bookstore, campus computer network, career placement assistance, e-mail services, library services, tutoring.
Contact Debra Carino, Director of Distance Learning, Clackamas Community College, 19600 South Molalla Avenue, Oregon City, OR 97045. Telephone: 503-657-6958 Ext. 5198. E-mail: debrac@clackamas.edu.

DEGREES AND AWARDS
Programs offered do not lead to a degree or other formal award.

COURSE SUBJECT AREAS OFFERED OUTSIDE OF DEGREE PROGRAMS

Undergraduate—accounting and computer science; accounting and related services; allied health and medical assisting services; astronomy and astrophysics; biology; building/construction finishing, management, and inspection; business administration, management and operations; business, management, and marketing related; chemistry; computer science; criminal justice and corrections; education; English composition; English literature (British and Commonwealth); environmental/ environmental health engineering; human development, family studies, and related services; legal professions and studies related; mathematics; music; physics; speech and rhetoric; technical and business writing.

CLARION UNIVERSITY OF PENNSYLVANIA
Clarion, Pennsylvania
Extended Studies and Distance Learning Department
http://www.clarion.edu/academic/distance/index.shtml

Clarion University of Pennsylvania was founded in 1867. It is accredited by Middle States Association of Colleges and Schools. It first offered distance learning courses in 1996. In fall 2007, there were 2,307 students enrolled in distance learning courses. Institutionally administered financial aid is available to distance learners.

Services Distance learners have accessibility to academic advising, bookstore, campus computer network, e-mail services, library services, tutoring.

Contact Ms. Lynne M. Lander Fleisher, Associate Director, Clarion University of Pennsylvania, Office of Extended Programs, 840 Wood Street, Clarion, PA 16214. Telephone: 814-393-2778. Fax: 814-393-2779. E-mail: lfleisher@clarion.edu.

DEGREES AND AWARDS

AA Arts and Sciences

AS Early Childhood Education

BLS Liberal Studies

BS Liberal Studies, Library Science concentration

BSN Nursing

Certification Early Childhood Directors Credential Program; Education–Graduate PA Secondary Teacher certification program; Instructional Technology Specialist

Endorsement CPA Exam Eligibility Program; Radiologic Sciences Prerequisite program

MA Rehabilitative Science

MBA Business Administration

MLS Library Science

MS Mass Media Arts and Journalism

MSN Nursing–Family Nurse Practitioner

COURSE SUBJECT AREAS OFFERED OUTSIDE OF DEGREE PROGRAMS

Undergraduate—atmospheric sciences and meteorology; biology; chemistry; communication and media; computer science; economics; education related; English composition; health and physical education/ fitness; languages (foreign languages related); legal professions and studies related; library science; music; nursing; philosophy; psychology; real estate; visual and performing arts related.

Graduate—business administration, management and operations; communication and journalism related; communication and media; education; library science; nursing; rehabilitation and therapeutic professions.

Non-credit—real estate.

See full description on page 362.

CLARKSON COLLEGE
Omaha, Nebraska
Office of Distance Education
http://www.clarksoncollege.edu

Clarkson College was founded in 1888. It is accredited by North Central Association of Colleges and Schools. It first offered distance learning courses in 1986. In fall 2007, there were 601 students enrolled in distance learning courses. Institutionally administered financial aid is available to distance learners.

Services Distance learners have accessibility to academic advising, bookstore, campus computer network, career placement assistance, e-mail services, library services, tutoring.

Contact Admissions, Clarkson College, 101 South 42nd Street, Omaha, NE 68131-2379. Telephone: 800-647-5500. Fax: 402-552-6057. E-mail: admiss@clarksoncollege.edu.

DEGREES AND AWARDS

AD Health Information Management

BS Health Care Business–Health Information Management major; Health Care Business–Informatics major; Health Care Business–Management major; Medical Imaging

BSN Nursing–RN to BSN

Certificate Health Information Management–Foundations; Health Information Management–HIM; PACS Administrator; PACS Manager

MS Health Care Business Leadership

MSN Adult Nurse Practitioner; Family Nurse Practitioner; Nursing Education; Nursing Health Care Leadership

CLARK STATE COMMUNITY COLLEGE
Springfield, Ohio
Alternative Methods of Instructional Delivery
http://www.clarkstate.edu/dlearning.html

Clark State Community College was founded in 1962. It is accredited by North Central Association of Colleges and Schools. It first offered distance learning courses in 1996. In fall 2007, there were 2,160 students enrolled in distance learning courses. Institutionally administered financial aid is available to distance learners.

Services Distance learners have accessibility to academic advising, bookstore, campus computer network, career placement assistance, e-mail services, library services, tutoring.

Contact Amy Sues, Coordinator of Advising, Clark State Community College, PO Box 570, Springfield, OH 45501-0570. Telephone: 937-328-3867. Fax: 937-328-3853. E-mail: suesa@clarkstate.edu.

DEGREES AND AWARDS

AA University Transfer

AAS Medical Laboratory Technology; Nursing–Registered Nursing; Physical Therapist Assistant

AS University Transfer

COURSE SUBJECT AREAS OFFERED OUTSIDE OF DEGREE PROGRAMS

Undergraduate—accounting and computer science; agricultural business and management; allied health and medical assisting services; applied horticulture/horticultural business services; behavioral sciences; biological and biomedical sciences related; biological and physical sciences; biology; biology/biotechnology laboratory technician; business administration, management and operations; business/commerce; business, management, and marketing related; cell biology and anatomical sciences; chemistry; communication and media; computer and information sciences and support services related; computer software and media applications; creative writing; English; English composition; geological and earth sciences/geosciences; health professions related; history; nursing; psychology; psychology related; sociology; technical and business writing.

Non-credit—transportation and materials moving related.

CLATSOP COMMUNITY COLLEGE
Astoria, Oregon
http://www.clatsopcc.edu

Clatsop Community College was founded in 1958. It is accredited by Northwest Commission on Colleges and Universities. It first offered distance learning courses in 1986. In fall 2007, there were 142 students enrolled in distance learning courses. Institutionally administered financial aid is available to distance learners.

Services Distance learners have accessibility to bookstore, e-mail services, library services.

Contact Kirsten Horning, Distance Education Coordinator, Clatsop Community College, 1680 Lexington Avenue, Astoria, OR 97103. Telephone: 503-338-2341. Fax: 503-325-5738. E-mail: khorning@clatsopcc.edu.

DEGREES AND AWARDS
Programs offered do not lead to a degree or other formal award.

COURSE SUBJECT AREAS OFFERED OUTSIDE OF DEGREE PROGRAMS
Undergraduate—business administration, management and operations; criminal justice and corrections; English language and literature related; history; mathematics; nursing; psychology; sociology.

CLEAR CREEK BAPTIST BIBLE COLLEGE
Pineville, Kentucky
http://www.ccbbc.edu/OnlineClasses/default.asp

Clear Creek Baptist Bible College was founded in 1926. It is accredited by Association for Biblical Higher Education. It first offered distance learning courses in 2002. In fall 2007, there were 75 students enrolled in distance learning courses. Institutionally administered financial aid is available to distance learners.

Services Distance learners have accessibility to academic advising, bookstore, career placement assistance, e-mail services, library services.

Contact Rev. Billy Howell, Director of Admissions, Clear Creek Baptist Bible College, 300 Clear Creek Road, Pineville, KY 40977. Telephone: 606-337-3196 Ext. 103. Fax: 606-337-2372. E-mail: bhowell@ccbbc.edu.

DEGREES AND AWARDS
Programs offered do not lead to a degree or other formal award.

COURSE SUBJECT AREAS OFFERED OUTSIDE OF DEGREE PROGRAMS
Undergraduate—biblical studies; theological and ministerial studies; theology and religious vocations related.

Non-credit—biblical studies; theological and ministerial studies; theology and religious vocations related.

CLEMSON UNIVERSITY
Clemson, South Carolina
Distance Education, Educational Technology Services
http://ccit.clemson.edu/departments/CRLT/distance_education/

Clemson University was founded in 1889. It is accredited by Southern Association of Colleges and Schools. It first offered distance learning courses in 1988. In fall 2007, there were 2,840 students enrolled in distance learning courses. Institutionally administered financial aid is available to distance learners.

Services Distance learners have accessibility to academic advising, bookstore, campus computer network, career placement assistance, e-mail services, library services.

Contact Kathy Hoellen, Director, Teaching and Learning Technologies, Clemson University, 433 Brackett Hall, PO Box 342803, Clemson, SC 29634-2803. Telephone: 864-653-0379. Fax: 864-656-0750. E-mail: hoellen@clemson.edu.

DEGREES AND AWARDS
BS Nursing

MCSM Construction Science and Management

MEngr Electrical Engineering

MS Human Resource Development; Nursing; Youth Development

PhD Educational Leadership

COURSE SUBJECT AREAS OFFERED OUTSIDE OF DEGREE PROGRAMS
Undergraduate—astronomy and astrophysics; business/commerce; communication and media; construction management; economics; electrical and electronic engineering technologies; English composition; marketing; mathematics; music; nutrition sciences; parks, recreation and leisure; physics; sociology.

Graduate—agriculture; animal sciences; business administration, management and operations; communication and media; construction management; electrical and electronic engineering technologies; English; history; human resources management; nutrition sciences; statistics.

Non-credit—accounting and related services; allied health and medical assisting services; building/construction finishing, management, and inspection; business/commerce; business, management, and marketing related; business operations support and assistant services; communication and media; computer and information sciences; computer programming; computer software and media applications; computer systems networking and telecommunications; construction engineering technology; creative writing; data entry/microcomputer applications; data processing; English composition; languages (Romance languages); legal professions and studies related; mathematics; publishing; teaching assistants/aides; technical and business writing.

CLEVELAND COMMUNITY COLLEGE
Shelby, North Carolina
Distance Learning Program
http://www.clevelandcommunitycollege.edu

Cleveland Community College was founded in 1965. It is accredited by Southern Association of Colleges and Schools. It first offered distance learning courses in 1999. In fall 2007, there were 1,500 students enrolled in distance learning courses. Institutionally administered financial aid is available to distance learners.

Services Distance learners have accessibility to academic advising, bookstore, e-mail services, library services.

Contact Jody Ledford, Distance Learning Coordinator, Cleveland Community College, 137 South Post Road, Shelby, NC 28152. Telephone: 704-484-4000 Ext. 4111. Fax: 704-484-4036. E-mail: ledford@clevelandcommunitycollege.edu.

DEGREES AND AWARDS
Programs offered do not lead to a degree or other formal award.

COURSE SUBJECT AREAS OFFERED OUTSIDE OF DEGREE PROGRAMS
Undergraduate—accounting and computer science; American literature (United States and Canadian); biology; biology/biotechnology laboratory technician; biotechnology; business administration, management and operations; business, management, and marketing related; business/managerial economics; computer/information technology administration and management; computer programming; computer software and media applications; computer systems networking and telecommunications; economics; education; English composition; fire protection; history; holocaust and related studies; human development, family studies, and related services; music; psychology; sociology; teaching assistants/aides.

Non-credit—fire protection.

CLEVELAND INSTITUTE OF ELECTRONICS
Cleveland, Ohio
http://www.cie-wc.edu

Cleveland Institute of Electronics was founded in 1934. It is accredited by Distance Education and Training Council. It first offered distance learning courses in 1941. In fall 2007, there were 2,400 students enrolled in distance learning courses. Institutionally administered financial aid is available to distance learners.

Services Distance learners have accessibility to academic advising, bookstore, e-mail services, library services, tutoring.

Contact Guidance Counselor, Cleveland Institute of Electronics, 1776 East 17th Street, Cleveland, OH 44114. Telephone: 216-781-9400. Fax: 216-781-0331. E-mail: instruct@cie-wc.edu.

DEGREES AND AWARDS

AAS Computer Information Technology and Systems Management; Electronic Engineering Technology

Diploma A+ Certification and Computer Technology; Broadcast Engineering; Computer Programming with Java and C#; Electronics Engineering; Electronics Technology and Advanced Troubleshooting; Electronics Technology with Digital Microprocessor Lab; Electronics Technology with FCC License Preparation; Electronics Technology with Laboratory; Industrial Electronics with PLC Technology; Network+ Certification and Computer Technology; Wireless and Electronic Communications

Specialized diploma Introduction to Home Automation Installation

COURSE SUBJECT AREAS OFFERED OUTSIDE OF DEGREE PROGRAMS

Undergraduate—communication and media; computer engineering; electrical and electronic engineering technologies; engineering; social sciences related.

Non-credit—accounting and computer science; computer/information technology administration and management; computer programming; computer science; computer software and media applications; data entry/microcomputer applications; electrical and power transmission installation; electrical/electronics maintenance and repair technology; mechanical engineering related technologies; mechanic and repair technologies related; mechanics and repair.

CLEVELAND STATE COMMUNITY COLLEGE
Cleveland, Tennessee
Instructional Computer Technology Center of Emphasis
http://www.clevelandstatecc.edu

Cleveland State Community College was founded in 1967. It is accredited by Southern Association of Colleges and Schools. It first offered distance learning courses in 1998. In fall 2007, there were 800 students enrolled in distance learning courses. Institutionally administered financial aid is available to distance learners.

Services Distance learners have accessibility to academic advising, bookstore, campus computer network, career placement assistance, e-mail services, library services, tutoring.

Contact Dr. Spencer Culbreth, Vice President of Academic Affairs, Cleveland State Community College, 3535 Adkisson Drive, Cleveland, TN 37312. Telephone: 423-472-4171 Ext. 381. E-mail: sculbreth@clevelandstatecc.edu.

DEGREES AND AWARDS
Programs offered do not lead to a degree or other formal award.

COURSE SUBJECT AREAS OFFERED OUTSIDE OF DEGREE PROGRAMS

Undergraduate—accounting and related services; allied health and medical assisting services; biblical and other theological languages and literatures; biological and physical sciences; business/commerce; computer and information sciences; data entry/microcomputer applications; education; English composition; history; mathematics; music; pharmacology and toxicology; physics; psychology; sociology; speech and rhetoric; statistics; technical and business writing; technology education/industrial arts.

CLEVELAND STATE UNIVERSITY
Cleveland, Ohio
Off-Campus Academic Programs
http://www.csuohio.edu/elearning

Cleveland State University was founded in 1964. It is accredited by North Central Association of Colleges and Schools. It first offered distance learning courses in 1994. In fall 2007, there were 1,105 students enrolled in distance learning courses. Institutionally administered financial aid is available to distance learners.

Services Distance learners have accessibility to academic advising, bookstore, campus computer network, career placement assistance, e-mail services, library services, tutoring.

Contact Mr. Paul E. Bowers, Director of eLearning, Cleveland State University, Rhodes Tower 203, 2121 Euclid Avenue, Cleveland, OH 44115. Telephone: 216-875-9624. Fax: 216-687-9733. E-mail: p.bowers@csuohio.edu.

DEGREES AND AWARDS
BSN Nursing–RN to BSN completion
Certificate Bioethics
Endorsement Computer/Technology
Graduate Certificate Adult Learning and Development; Bioethics; Research Administration
MEd Adult Learning and Development; Educational Technology
MS Health Science
MSN Forensic Nursing
MSW Social Work

COURSE SUBJECT AREAS OFFERED OUTSIDE OF DEGREE PROGRAMS

Undergraduate—accounting and computer science; accounting and related services; area, ethnic, cultural, and gender studies related; bioethics/medical ethics; biological and biomedical sciences related; biology; chemistry; city/urban, community and regional planning; civil engineering; communication and journalism related; communication and media; computer and information sciences; computer engineering; computer programming; computer science; computer software and media applications; education; electrical and electronic engineering technologies; engineering; engineering-related fields; engineering technology; English; geography and cartography; geological and earth sciences/geosciences; history; linguistic, comparative, and related language studies; nursing; pharmacy, pharmaceutical sciences, and administration; philosophy; public administration; public administration and social service professions related; social work; special education; urban studies/affairs.

Graduate—accounting and related services; area, ethnic, cultural, and gender studies related; bioethics/medical ethics; chemical engineering; city/urban, community and regional planning; civil engineering; computer engineering; crafts, folk art and artisanry; curriculum and instruction; education; educational assessment, evaluation, and research; education related; education (specific levels and methods); education (specific subject areas); electrical, electronics and communications engineering; engineering; engineering/industrial management; engineering related; engineering-related fields; engineering-related technologies; environmental/environmental health engineering; health and medical administrative services; health/medical preparatory programs; health professions related; health services/allied health/health sciences; industrial engineering; linguistic, comparative, and related language studies; manufacturing engineering; mechanical engineering; mechanical engineering related technologies; nursing; philosophy; philosophy and religious studies related; public administration; public administration and social service professions related; social work; special education; student counseling and personnel services; technology education/industrial arts; urban studies/affairs.

Non-credit—accounting and related services; business administration, management and operations; business/commerce; business/corporate communications; computer software and media applications; computer systems networking and telecommunications; data entry/microcomputer applications; education related; entrepreneurial and small business operations; family and consumer economics; film/video and photographic arts; foods, nutrition, and related services; health and physical education/fitness; health professions related; human development, family studies, and related services; journalism; languages (foreign languages related); legal support services; management information systems; public health; sales, merchandising, and related marketing operations (specialized); technology education/industrial arts.

CLINTON COMMUNITY COLLEGE
Plattsburgh, New York
http://www.clinton.edu/onlinelearning
Clinton Community College was founded in 1969. It is accredited by Middle States Association of Colleges and Schools. It first offered distance learning courses in 2000. In fall 2007, there were 300 students enrolled in distance learning courses. Institutionally administered financial aid is available to distance learners.
Services Distance learners have accessibility to academic advising, bookstore, campus computer network, career placement assistance, e-mail services, library services, tutoring.
Contact Prof. Vicky Sloan, Distance Learning Coordinator, Clinton Community College, 136 Clinton Point Drive, Plattsburgh, NY 12901. Telephone: 518-562-4281. E-mail: vicky.sloan@clinton.edu.

DEGREES AND AWARDS
AA Liberal Arts/Humanities and Social Science
AAS Business
AS Business Administration

COURSE SUBJECT AREAS OFFERED OUTSIDE OF DEGREE PROGRAMS
Undergraduate—accounting and related services; applied mathematics; biological and physical sciences; business administration, management and operations; business/corporate communications; computer and information sciences; computer programming; criminal justice and corrections; economics; English; history; human development, family studies, and related services; human services; liberal arts and sciences, general studies and humanities; music; political science and government; psychology; sociology; statistics.

COASTLINE COMMUNITY COLLEGE
Fountain Valley, California
Distance Learning Department
http://www.coastline.edu/
Coastline Community College was founded in 1976. It is accredited by Western Association of Schools and Colleges. It first offered distance learning courses in 1976. In fall 2007, there were 11,000 students enrolled in distance learning courses. Institutionally administered financial aid is available to distance learners.
Services Distance learners have accessibility to academic advising, bookstore, e-mail services, library services, tutoring.
Contact Distance Learning Department, Coastline Community College, 11460 Warner Avenue, Fountain Valley, CA 92708. Telephone: 714-241-6216. E-mail: dlearning@coastline.edu.

DEGREES AND AWARDS
AA American Studies; Arts and Humanities; Business Administration; Economics; Gerontology; History; Human Services; Liberal Studies; Science and Math; Social and Behavioral Sciences

COURSE SUBJECT AREAS OFFERED OUTSIDE OF DEGREE PROGRAMS
Undergraduate—anthropology; astronomy and astrophysics; biological and biomedical sciences related; biology; business administration, management and operations; business/commerce; business/corporate communications; business operations support and assistant services; cell biology and anatomical sciences; chemistry; communication and journalism related; communication and media; computer and information sciences; computer programming; computer software and media applications; construction engineering technology; developmental and child psychology; ecology, evolution, and population biology; economics; electrical and electronic engineering technologies; English; English composition; gerontology; health and medical administrative services; history;

human services; information science/studies; international business; journalism; languages (foreign languages related); languages (Romance languages); legal support services; liberal arts and sciences, general studies and humanities; library science related; linguistic, comparative, and related language studies; management information systems; mathematics; mathematics and statistics related; philosophy; philosophy and religious studies related; political science and government; psychology; sales, merchandising, and related marketing operations (general); sales, merchandising, and related marketing operations (specialized); social sciences related; sociology; special education; statistics; visual and performing arts.
Non-credit—English as a second language.

COGSWELL POLYTECHNICAL COLLEGE
Sunnyvale, California
http://www.cogswell.edu/fireScience.html
Cogswell Polytechnical College was founded in 1887. It is accredited by Western Association of Schools and Colleges. It first offered distance learning courses in 1981. In fall 2007, there were 73 students enrolled in distance learning courses. Institutionally administered financial aid is available to distance learners.
Services Distance learners have accessibility to academic advising, e-mail services, library services.
Contact Ms. Milla Zlatanov, Data Manager, Cogswell Polytechnical College, 1175 Bordeaux Drive, Sunnyvale, CA 94089. Telephone: 408-541-0100 Ext. 133. Fax: 408-747-0764. E-mail: mzlatanov@cogswell.edu.

DEGREES AND AWARDS
BS Fire Administration, Fire Prevention and Technology

COURSE SUBJECT AREAS OFFERED OUTSIDE OF DEGREE PROGRAMS
Undergraduate—fire protection; public administration; security and protective services related.

COLLEGE OF EMMANUEL AND ST. CHAD
Saskatoon, Saskatchewan, Canada
http://usask.ca/stu/emmanuel
College of Emmanuel and St. Chad was founded in 1879. It is provincially chartered. It first offered distance learning courses in 1995. In fall 2007, there were 11 students enrolled in distance learning courses. Institutionally administered financial aid is available to distance learners.
Services Distance learners have accessibility to academic advising, bookstore, campus computer network, library services.
Contact Ms. Colleen Walker, Registrar, College of Emmanuel and St. Chad, 114 Seminary Crescent, Saskatoon, SK S7N 0X3, Canada. Telephone: 306-975-1558. Fax: 306-934-2683. E-mail: colleen.walker@usask.ca.

DEGREES AND AWARDS
Programs offered do not lead to a degree or other formal award.

COURSE SUBJECT AREAS OFFERED OUTSIDE OF DEGREE PROGRAMS
Graduate—biblical and other theological languages and literatures; biblical studies; theological and ministerial studies; theology and religious vocations related.

COLLEGE OF MOUNT ST. JOSEPH
Cincinnati, Ohio
http://www.msj.edu/
College of Mount St. Joseph was founded in 1920. It is accredited by North Central Association of Colleges and Schools. It first offered distance learning courses in 1997. In fall 2007, there were 75 students enrolled in distance learning courses. Institutionally administered financial aid is available to distance learners.
Services Distance learners have accessibility to academic advising, bookstore, campus computer network, career placement assistance, e-mail services, library services, tutoring.

Contact Ms. Peggy Minnich, Director of Admissions, College of Mount St. Joseph, 5701 Delhi Road, Cincinnati, OH 45233. Telephone: 513-244-4814. E-mail: peggy_minnich@mail.msj.edu.

DEGREES AND AWARDS
Programs offered do not lead to a degree or other formal award.

COURSE SUBJECT AREAS OFFERED OUTSIDE OF DEGREE PROGRAMS
Undergraduate—business administration, management and operations; education; legal support services; music; political science and government; social psychology.
Graduate—business administration, management and operations; education.

THE COLLEGE OF ST. SCHOLASTICA
Duluth, Minnesota
Graduate Studies
http://grad.css.edu
The College of St. Scholastica was founded in 1912. It is accredited by North Central Association of Colleges and Schools. It first offered distance learning courses in 1986. In fall 2007, there were 244 students enrolled in distance learning courses. Institutionally administered financial aid is available to distance learners.
Services Distance learners have accessibility to academic advising, bookstore, campus computer network, career placement assistance, e-mail services, library services, tutoring.
Contact Tonya J. Roth, Graduate Recruitment Counselor, The College of St. Scholastica, 1200 Kenwood Avenue, Duluth, MN 55811. Telephone: 218-723-6285. Fax: 218-733-2275. E-mail: gradstudies@css.edu.

DEGREES AND AWARDS
BA Health Information Management Degree completion; Nursing–RN to BA completion
Certificate Educational Technology; Graduate Teaching Licensure; Healthcare Informatics; Information Technology Leadership
MA Health Information Management; Information Technology Leadership
MEd Curriculum and Instruction; Educational Media and Technology; Graduate Teaching Licensure

COURSE SUBJECT AREAS OFFERED OUTSIDE OF DEGREE PROGRAMS
Undergraduate—biology; computer and information sciences; economics; gerontology; health and medical administrative services; music; nursing; psychology.
Graduate—biology; curriculum and instruction; health and medical administrative services; library science related; music; nursing.

COLLEGE OF SAN MATEO
San Mateo, California
http://www.collegeofsanmateo.edu
College of San Mateo was founded in 1922. It is accredited by Western Association of Schools and Colleges. It first offered distance learning courses in 1977. In fall 2007, there were 1,515 students enrolled in distance learning courses. Institutionally administered financial aid is available to distance learners.
Services Distance learners have accessibility to academic advising, bookstore, campus computer network, career placement assistance, e-mail services, library services, tutoring.
Contact Betty Fleming, Distance Learning Coordinator, College of San Mateo, 1700 West Hillsdale Boulevard, San Mateo, CA 94402-3784. Telephone: 650-524-6933. Fax: 650-574-6345. E-mail: fleming@smccd.edu.

DEGREES AND AWARDS
Programs offered do not lead to a degree or other formal award.

COURSE SUBJECT AREAS OFFERED OUTSIDE OF DEGREE PROGRAMS
Undergraduate—accounting and related services; anthropology; astronomy and astrophysics; business/commerce; business/corporate communications; chemistry; computer programming; English composition; film/video and photographic arts; health and physical education/fitness; languages (Romance languages); legal studies (non-professional general, undergraduate); marketing; mathematics; philosophy; political science and government; psychology; sociology.

COLLEGE OF SOUTHERN MARYLAND
La Plata, Maryland
Distance Learning Department
http://www.csmd.edu
College of Southern Maryland was founded in 1958. It is accredited by Middle States Association of Colleges and Schools. It first offered distance learning courses in 1980. In fall 2007, there were 2,063 students enrolled in distance learning courses. Institutionally administered financial aid is available to distance learners.
Services Distance learners have accessibility to academic advising, bookstore, campus computer network, career placement assistance, e-mail services, library services, tutoring.
Contact Paul Toscano, Distance Learning Coordinator, College of Southern Maryland, 8730 Mitchell Road, PO Box 910, La Plata, MD 20646-0910. Telephone: 301-934-7615. Fax: 301-934-7699. E-mail: info@csmd.edu.

DEGREES AND AWARDS
AA Arts and Sciences–Applied Science and Technology; Arts and Sciences–Arts and Humanities; Arts and Sciences–Social Sciences; Arts and Sciences; General Studies
AAS Computer Programming; Information Services Technology–Web Developer; Information Services Technology; Management Development
AS Business Administration–Technical Management; Business Administration
Certificate Accounting, advanced; Accounting, basic; Computer Skills for Managers; General Studies; Information Services Technology; Management Development–Marketing; Management Development; Web Developer

COURSE SUBJECT AREAS OFFERED OUTSIDE OF DEGREE PROGRAMS
Undergraduate—accounting and related services; astronomy and astrophysics; biology; business/commerce; business/corporate communications; communication and media; computer systems analysis; computer systems networking and telecommunications; creative writing; criminal justice and corrections; economics; educational psychology; education related; English composition; fine and studio art; geography and cartography; health and physical education/fitness; history; human development, family studies, and related services; human resources management; information science/studies; international business; languages (Romance languages); legal studies (non-professional general, undergraduate); marketing; mathematics; mathematics and statistics related; philosophy; philosophy and religious studies related; physics; political science and government; psychology; sociology; statistics; technical and business writing.
Non-credit—computer/information technology administration and management; education; health professions related; nursing.

COLLEGE OF THE ALBEMARLE
Elizabeth City, North Carolina
Distance Education
http://www.albemarle.edu
College of The Albemarle was founded in 1960. It is accredited by Southern Association of Colleges and Schools. It first offered distance learning courses in 1993. In fall 2007, there were 1,000 students enrolled in distance learning courses. Institutionally administered financial aid is available to distance learners.
Services Distance learners have accessibility to academic advising, bookstore, campus computer network, career placement assistance, e-mail services, library services, tutoring.

Contact Jerry Oliver, Distance Education Coordinator, College of The Albemarle, PO Box 2327, Elizabeth City, NC 27906-2327. Telephone: 252-335-0821 Ext. 2313. Fax: 252-337-6710. E-mail: joliver@albemarle.edu.

DEGREES AND AWARDS
AAS Business Administration; Criminal Justice

COURSE SUBJECT AREAS OFFERED OUTSIDE OF DEGREE PROGRAMS
Undergraduate—accounting and related services; biology; business administration, management and operations; business/commerce; business/corporate communications; computer and information sciences; computer science; economics; education related; electrical and electronic engineering technologies; English composition; English literature (British and Commonwealth); fine and studio art; health and physical education/fitness; history; human development, family studies, and related services; legal studies (non-professional general, undergraduate); marketing; mathematics and statistics related; psychology; sociology.
Non-credit—accounting and related services; business administration, management and operations; business/commerce; business/corporate communications; business, management, and marketing related; business operations support and assistant services; communication and media; computer and information sciences; computer engineering; computer/information technology administration and management; computer programming; computer science; computer software and media applications; computer systems networking and telecommunications; data entry/microcomputer applications; data processing; educational administration and supervision; English; English composition; gerontology; human services; information science/studies; management information systems; mental and social health services and allied professions; public administration; public administration and social service professions related; sales, merchandising, and related marketing operations (specialized); technical and business writing.

COLLEGE OF THE SEQUOIAS
Visalia, California
http://www.cos.edu
College of the Sequoias was founded in 1925. It is accredited by Western Association of Schools and Colleges. It first offered distance learning courses in 1997. In fall 2007, there were 1,100 students enrolled in distance learning courses. Institutionally administered financial aid is available to distance learners.
Services Distance learners have accessibility to academic advising, bookstore, e-mail services, library services.
Contact Deborah L. Nolan, PhD, Distance Education Coordinator, College of the Sequoias, 915 South Mooney Boulevard, Visalia, CA 93277. Telephone: 559-737-6132. E-mail: deborahn@cos.edu.

DEGREES AND AWARDS
Programs offered do not lead to a degree or other formal award.

COURSE SUBJECT AREAS OFFERED OUTSIDE OF DEGREE PROGRAMS
Undergraduate—accounting and related services; behavioral sciences; business/commerce; computer and information sciences; computer software and media applications; criminal justice and corrections; education; English composition; foods, nutrition, and related services; history; human development, family studies, and related services; legal support services; mathematics; music; nursing; psychology; real estate; sociology; speech and rhetoric; teaching assistants/aides; visual and performing arts.

COLLEGE OF THE SISKIYOUS
Weed, California
Distance Learning
http://www.siskiyous.edu/distancelearning/
College of the Siskiyous was founded in 1957. It is accredited by Western Association of Schools and Colleges. It first offered distance learning

courses in 1975. In fall 2007, there were 748 students enrolled in distance learning courses. Institutionally administered financial aid is available to distance learners.
Services Distance learners have accessibility to academic advising, bookstore, career placement assistance, e-mail services, library services, tutoring.
Contact Nancy Shepard, Telecommunications Specialist, College of the Siskiyous, 800 College Avenue, Weed, CA 96094. Telephone: 530-938-5520. E-mail: shepard@siskiyous.edu.

DEGREES AND AWARDS
AA Early Childhood Education

COURSE SUBJECT AREAS OFFERED OUTSIDE OF DEGREE PROGRAMS
Undergraduate—accounting and related services; business/commerce; business/corporate communications; computer science; English composition; English language and literature related; English literature (British and Commonwealth); family and consumer economics; family psychology; health and physical education/fitness; history; liberal arts and sciences, general studies and humanities; mathematics; nursing; nutrition sciences; political science and government; psychology; social sciences; student counseling and personnel services; teaching assistants/aides.

COLORADO MOUNTAIN COLLEGE DISTRICT SYSTEM
Glenwood Springs, Colorado
Educational Technology
http://www.coloradomtn.edu/distlearn/
Colorado Mountain College District System first offered distance learning courses in 1985. In fall 2007, there were 800 students enrolled in distance learning courses. Institutionally administered financial aid is available to distance learners.
Services Distance learners have accessibility to bookstore, e-mail services, library services.
Contact Mr. Daryl D. Yarrow, Distance Learning Coordinator, Colorado Mountain College District System, 831 Grand Avenue, Glenwood Springs, CO 81601. Telephone: 800-621-8559 Ext. 8336. Fax: 970-947-8307. E-mail: distance@coloradomtn.edu.

DEGREES AND AWARDS
Programs offered do not lead to a degree or other formal award.

COURSE SUBJECT AREAS OFFERED OUTSIDE OF DEGREE PROGRAMS
Undergraduate—accounting and related services; anthropology; astronomy and astrophysics; biology; business/commerce; business/corporate communications; chemistry; computer science; computer software and media applications; developmental and child psychology; economics; education related; English composition; fine and studio art; geography and cartography; health professions related; history; hospitality administration; languages (foreign languages related); library science related; mathematics and statistics related; philosophy; physics; psychology; social psychology; sociology; statistics.

COLORADO STATE UNIVERSITY
Fort Collins, Colorado
College of Business
http://www.CSUdistanceMBA.com
Colorado State University was founded in 1870. It is accredited by North Central Association of Colleges and Schools. It first offered distance learning courses in 1967. In fall 2007, there were 711 students enrolled in distance learning courses. Institutionally administered financial aid is available to distance learners.
Services Distance learners have accessibility to academic advising, bookstore, campus computer network, career placement assistance, e-mail services, library services.
Contact Mr. Matt Leland, MBA Program Coordinator, Colorado State University, College of Business, 1270 Campus Delivery, 162 Rockwell

Hall, Fort Collins, CO 80523-1270. Telephone: 800-491-4622 Ext. 1. Fax: 970-491-3481. E-mail: matt.leland@colostate.edu.

DEGREES AND AWARDS

MBA Business Administration–Distance MBA program; Distance MBA

COURSE SUBJECT AREAS OFFERED OUTSIDE OF DEGREE PROGRAMS

Graduate—accounting and related services; business administration, management and operations; business/commerce; business/corporate communications; business, management, and marketing related; business/managerial economics; computer systems networking and telecommunications; finance and financial management services; human resources management; international business; management information systems; management sciences and quantitative methods; marketing; statistics.

See full description on page 364.

COLORADO STATE UNIVERSITY
Fort Collins, Colorado
Division of Continuing Education
http://www.learn.colostate.edu

Colorado State University was founded in 1870. It is accredited by North Central Association of Colleges and Schools. It first offered distance learning courses in 1967. In fall 2007, there were 1,696 students enrolled in distance learning courses. Institutionally administered financial aid is available to distance learners.

Services Distance learners have accessibility to academic advising, bookstore, library services.

Contact Ms. Frances Betts, Program Coordinator, Colorado State University, Continuing Education, 1040 Campus Delivery, Fort Collins, CO 80523-1040. Telephone: 970-491-0675. Fax: 970-491-7885. E-mail: frances.betts@colostate.edu.

DEGREES AND AWARDS

BA Liberal Arts

BS Agricultural and Resource Economics; Fire and Emergency Services Administration; Human Development and Family Studies

Certificate of Completion Mediation; Teaching with Technology and Distance Learning certificate; Veterinary Medicine Online

Certificate Apparel and Merchandising (graduate); Apparel and Merchandising; Apparel and Merchandising; Applied Statistics and Data Analysis; Child Care Training; Community-Based Development; Core Business Competencies; Ergonomics, basic; Fire and Emergency Services Administration (FESA); Natural Resources and the Environment; Pesticide Application Training; Postsecondary Teaching; Residential Interiors; School/Community Safety; Seed Analysis Training; Six Sigma eBlack Belt (20 weeks); Six Sigma eGreen Belt (12 weeks); Statistical Theory and Method

EMBA Business Administration

MAg Agricultural Extension Education specialization; Integrated Resource Management (IRM)

MBA Business Administration

MCS Computer Science

ME Biomedical Engineering specialization; Civil Engineering; Electrical and Computer Engineering (Telecommunications); Mechanical Engineering (Engineering Management program); Mechanical Engineering (Ind Engg and Operations Res program); Mechanical Engineering (Materials Engineering); Systems Engineering specialization (in development)

MEd Adult Education and Training (AET); Education and Human Resource Studies (Organizational Performance and Change–OPC); Educational Leadership, Renewal, and Change

MS Apparel and Merchandising; Mechanical Engineering (Engineering Management program); Mechanical Engineering (Ind Engg and Operations Res program); Mechanical Engineering (Materials Engineering); Rangeland Ecosystem Science; Statistics

MSW Social Work–Advanced Standing; Social Work

PhD Community College Leadership (CCL); Educational Leadership, Renewal, and Change; Mechanical Engineering (Ind Engg and Operations Res program)

COURSE SUBJECT AREAS OFFERED OUTSIDE OF DEGREE PROGRAMS

Undergraduate—accounting and computer science; agricultural production; agriculture; animal sciences; anthropology; biology; business/commerce; computer science; construction management; design and applied arts; developmental and child psychology; economics; education; engineering; engineering technologies related; English; English composition; ethnic, cultural minority, and gender studies; finance and financial management services; fine and studio art; fishing and fisheries sciences and management; foods, nutrition, and related services; geography and cartography; health and physical education/fitness; landscape architecture; marketing; mathematics; music; natural resources conservation and research; plant sciences; psychology; social sciences; sociology; speech and rhetoric; statistics; wildlife and wildlands science and management.

Graduate—agriculture; business administration, management and operations; civil engineering; computer science; drafting/design engineering technologies; education; education related; fishing and fisheries sciences and management; human resources management; human services; mathematics; mechanical engineering; natural resources management and policy; social work; statistics; wildlife and wildlands science and management.

Non-credit—accounting and computer science; animal sciences; business/commerce; business, management, and marketing related; community health services; community organization and advocacy; community psychology; construction management; education; environmental design; environmental/environmental health engineering; health and physical education/fitness; human resources management; information science/studies; legal support services; management sciences and quantitative methods; social sciences; veterinary biomedical and clinical sciences.

See full description on page 366.

COLORADO TECHNICAL UNIVERSITY COLORADO SPRINGS
Colorado Springs, Colorado
http://www.ctuonline.edu

Colorado Technical University Colorado Springs was founded in 1965. It is accredited by North Central Association of Colleges and Schools. It first offered distance learning courses in 2003. Institutionally administered financial aid is available to distance learners.

Services Distance learners have accessibility to academic advising, bookstore, campus computer network, career placement assistance, e-mail services, library services, tutoring.

Contact Admissions Department, Colorado Technical University Colorado Springs, 4435 North Chestnut Street, Suite E, Colorado Springs, CO 80907. Telephone: 800-416-8904. E-mail: info@ctuonline.edu.

DEGREES AND AWARDS

AS Accounting; Business Administration; Criminal Justice; General Studies; Information Technology; Medical Billing and Coding; Paralegal Studies

BS Accounting; Criminal Justice; Information Technology, Network Management concentration; Information Technology, Security concentration; Information Technology, Software Systems Engineering concentration

BSBA Finance concentration; Health Care Management concentration; Human Resource Management concentration; Information Technology concentration; International Business concentration; Management concentration; Marketing concentration; Project Management concentration

EMBA Executive Master of Business Administration

MBA Accounting concentration; Finance concentration; Health Care Management concentration; Human Resource Management concentration; Insurance and Risk Management concentration; Logistics and Supply Chain Management concentration; Marketing concentration; Mediation and Dispute Resolution concentration; Operations Management concentration; Technology Management concentration

MSM Business Management concentration; Criminal Justice concentration; Information Systems Security concentration; Information Technology Management concentration; Project Management concentration
See full description on page 368.

COLUMBIA COLLEGE
Columbia, Missouri
http://www.ccis.edu/online
Columbia College was founded in 1851. It is accredited by North Central Association of Colleges and Schools. It first offered distance learning courses in 2000. In fall 2007, there were 6,851 students enrolled in distance learning courses. Institutionally administered financial aid is available to distance learners.
Services Distance learners have accessibility to academic advising, bookstore, campus computer network, career placement assistance, e-mail services, library services.
Contact Ms. Marilyn Whitehead, Director of Administration, Columbia College, 1001 Rogers Street, Attention: Online Campus, Columbia, MO 65216. Telephone: 573-875-7459. Fax: 573-875-7445. E-mail: mawhitehead@ccis.edu.

DEGREES AND AWARDS
AA General Studies
AGS General Studies
AS Business Administration; Criminal Justice; Environmental Studies; Fire Science Administration; Human Services
BA American Studies; Business Administration; Criminal Justice; General Studies; History; Human Services; Psychology; Sociology
BS Business Administration
MAT Education
MBA Business Administration
MSCJ Criminal Justice Administration

COURSE SUBJECT AREAS OFFERED OUTSIDE OF DEGREE PROGRAMS
Undergraduate—accounting and related services; American literature (United States and Canadian); anthropology; area, ethnic, cultural, and gender studies related; astronomy and astrophysics; behavioral sciences; biological and biomedical sciences related; business administration, management and operations; business/commerce; business, management, and marketing related; chemistry; computer and information sciences; criminal justice and corrections; curriculum and instruction; economics; education; English literature (British and Commonwealth); entrepreneurial and small business operations; history; marketing; mathematics; mathematics and computer science; multi-/interdisciplinary studies related; philosophy and religious studies related; political science and government; psychology; psychology related; sales, merchandising, and related marketing operations (general); social sciences related; social work; sociology.
Graduate—business administration, management and operations; business, management, and marketing related; business/managerial economics; criminal justice and corrections; education; educational assessment, evaluation, and research.

COLUMBIA-GREENE COMMUNITY COLLEGE
Hudson, New York
Educational Technology Center
http://blackboard.sunycgcc.edu/
Columbia-Greene Community College was founded in 1969. It is accredited by Middle States Association of Colleges and Schools. It first offered distance learning courses in 1995. In fall 2007, there were 176 students enrolled in distance learning courses. Institutionally administered financial aid is available to distance learners.
Services Distance learners have accessibility to campus computer network, e-mail services, library services.
Contact Ms. Carol Doerfer, Assistant Dean, Columbia-Greene Community College, Room 110, 4400 Route 23, Hudson, NY 12534. Telephone: 518-828-4181 Ext. 3350. Fax: 518-828-8543. E-mail: doerfer@sunycgcc.edu.

DEGREES AND AWARDS
Programs offered do not lead to a degree or other formal award.

COURSE SUBJECT AREAS OFFERED OUTSIDE OF DEGREE PROGRAMS
Undergraduate—business administration, management and operations; computer programming; developmental and child psychology; English composition; psychology; sociology.

COLUMBIA INTERNATIONAL UNIVERSITY
Columbia, South Carolina
Distance Education Center
http://www.ciu.edu/distance
Columbia International University was founded in 1923. It is accredited by Association for Biblical Higher Education. It first offered distance learning courses in 1978. In fall 2007, there were 900 students enrolled in distance learning courses. Institutionally administered financial aid is available to distance learners.
Services Distance learners have accessibility to academic advising, bookstore, campus computer network, career placement assistance, e-mail services, library services.
Contact Mrs. Alisa Fulton, Assessment and Student Services Coordinator, Columbia International University, 7435 Monticello Road, Columbia, SC 29203. Telephone: 803-807-5731. Fax: 803-223-2502. E-mail: distance@ciu.edu.

DEGREES AND AWARDS
Programs offered do not lead to a degree or other formal award.

COURSE SUBJECT AREAS OFFERED OUTSIDE OF DEGREE PROGRAMS
Undergraduate—biblical studies; missionary studies and missiology; religious studies; theological and ministerial studies; theology and religious vocations related.
Graduate—anthropology; biblical and other theological languages and literatures; biblical studies; curriculum and instruction; education; educational administration and supervision; education related; history; languages (classics and classical); linguistic, comparative, and related language studies; missionary studies and missiology; religious studies; theological and ministerial studies; theology and religious vocations related.
Non-credit—anthropology; biblical studies; education; educational psychology; languages (classics and classical); missionary studies and missiology; religious studies; theological and ministerial studies; theology and religious vocations related.

COLUMBIA SOUTHERN UNIVERSITY
Orange Beach, Alabama
http://www.columbiasouthern.edu
Columbia Southern University was founded in 1993. It is accredited by Distance Education and Training Council. It first offered distance learning courses in 1993. In fall 2007, there were 9,400 students enrolled in distance learning courses. Institutionally administered financial aid is available to distance learners.
Services Distance learners have accessibility to academic advising, bookstore, library services.
Contact Admissions Department, Columbia Southern University, 25326 Canal Road, Orange Beach, AL 36561. Telephone: 251-981-3771. Fax: 251-981-3815. E-mail: admissions@columbiasouthern.edu.

DEGREES AND AWARDS
AA General Education
AAS Business; Criminal Justice; Fire Science
BS Business Administration; Criminal Justice Administration; Environmental Management; Fire Science; Health Care Administration; Hospitality and Tourism; Human Resource Management; Information Technology; Marketing; Occupational Safety and Health; Psychology
MBA Business Administration

MS Criminal Justice Administration; Occupational Safety and Health
DBA Business Administration

COLUMBIA UNIVERSITY
New York, New York
Columbia Video Network
http://www.cvn.columbia.edu

Columbia University was founded in 1754. It is accredited by Middle States Association of Colleges and Schools. It first offered distance learning courses in 1986. In fall 2007, there were 475 students enrolled in distance learning courses. Institutionally administered financial aid is available to distance learners.

Services Distance learners have accessibility to academic advising, bookstore, campus computer network, career placement assistance, e-mail services, library services.

Contact Online Recruiter, Columbia University, 530 Mudd Building, MC 4719, 500 West 120th Street, New York, NY 10027. Telephone: 212-854-6447. Fax: 212-854-2325. E-mail: info@cvn.columbia.edu.

DEGREES AND AWARDS

Certificate of Achievement Business and Technology; Civil Engineering; Financial Engineering; Industrial Engineering; Information Systems; Intelligent Systems; Manufacturing Engineering; Materials Science and Engineering; Mathematics–Applied Mathematics; Multimedia Networking; Nanotechnology; Networking and Systems; New Media Engineering; Operations Research; Telecommunications; Wireless and Mobile Communications

Advanced Graduate Diploma Computer Science; Electrical Engineering; Industrial Engineering and Operations Research; Mechanical Engineering

MS Applied Physics; Biomedical Engineering; Chemical Engineering; Civil Engineering–Construction Engineering and Management; Civil Engineering; Computer Science; Earth and Environmental Engineering; Engineering and Management Systems; Finance–Methods in Finance; Materials Science and Engineering; Mathematics–Applied Mathematics

MSEE Electrical Engineering

MSME Mechanical Engineering

COURSE SUBJECT AREAS OFFERED OUTSIDE OF DEGREE PROGRAMS

Graduate—applied mathematics; biomedical/medical engineering; chemical engineering; civil engineering; computer science; electrical, electronics and communications engineering; engineering/industrial management; environmental/environmental health engineering; materials science; mechanical engineering.

Non-credit—applied mathematics; chemical engineering; civil engineering; computer science; engineering; engineering/industrial management; environmental/environmental health engineering; materials science; mechanical engineering.

COLUMBUS STATE COMMUNITY COLLEGE
Columbus, Ohio
Global Campus
http://www.cscc.edu

Columbus State Community College was founded in 1963. It is accredited by North Central Association of Colleges and Schools. It first offered distance learning courses in 1980. In fall 2007, there were 8,000 students enrolled in distance learning courses. Institutionally administered financial aid is available to distance learners.

Services Distance learners have accessibility to academic advising, bookstore, campus computer network, career placement assistance, e-mail services, library services, tutoring.

Contact Dr. Leslie King, Administrator for Instructional Technologies and Distance Learning, Columbus State Community College, Center for Teaching and Learning Innovation, 339 Cleveland Avenue, Columbus, OH 43215. Telephone: 614-287-2589. Fax: 614-287-5123. E-mail: lking01@cscc.edu.

DEGREES AND AWARDS

AA General Studies
AAS Business Management; Marketing
CCCPE Direct Marketing Certificate; Geographic Information Systems; Health Care Manager Certificate; International Commerce Certificate; Purchasing; Supply Chain Management

COURSE SUBJECT AREAS OFFERED OUTSIDE OF DEGREE PROGRAMS

Undergraduate—accounting and related services; allied health and medical assisting services; allied health diagnostic, intervention, and treatment professions; American literature (United States and Canadian); anthropology; biological and biomedical sciences related; business administration, management and operations; business/corporate communications; chemistry; communication and journalism related; comparative literature; computer and information sciences; computer programming; computer software and media applications; construction management; counseling psychology; creative writing; culinary arts and related services; developmental and child psychology; drafting/design engineering technologies; dramatic/theater arts and stagecraft; economics; engineering mechanics; engineering technologies related; English; English composition; English language and literature related; English literature (British and Commonwealth); environmental control technologies; ethnic, cultural minority, and gender studies; finance and financial management services; foods, nutrition, and related services; geography and cartography; graphic communications; health and medical administrative services; health and physical education/fitness; health professions related; history; hospitality administration; human resources management; languages (Romance languages); legal studies (non-professional general, undergraduate); legal support services; marketing; mathematics; mechanical engineering related technologies; mental and social health services and allied professions; natural sciences; nursing; nutrition sciences; philosophy; philosophy and religious studies related; political science and government; psychology; public relations, advertising, and applied communication related; quality control and safety technologies; sales, merchandising, and related marketing operations (general); science technologies related; social sciences related; sociology; speech and rhetoric; technical and business writing; vehicle maintenance and repair technologies; visual and performing arts related.

COLUMBUS STATE UNIVERSITY
Columbus, Georgia
Instructional Technology Services
http://www.colstate.edu

Columbus State University was founded in 1958. It is accredited by Southern Association of Colleges and Schools. It first offered distance learning courses in 1991. In fall 2007, there were 800 students enrolled in distance learning courses. Institutionally administered financial aid is available to distance learners.

Services Distance learners have accessibility to academic advising, bookstore, campus computer network, career placement assistance, e-mail services, library services.

Contact Sandra K. Stratford, Instructional Technology Services Coordinator, Columbus State University, 4225 University Avenue, Columbus, GA 31907. Telephone: 706-568-2043. Fax: 706-568-2459. E-mail: stratford_sandra@colstate.edu.

DEGREES AND AWARDS

BS Information Technology
MEd Accomplished Teaching
MS Computer Science–Applied Computer Science

COURSE SUBJECT AREAS OFFERED OUTSIDE OF DEGREE PROGRAMS

Undergraduate—computer science; education; psychology.
Graduate—computer programming; education (specific subject areas).

COMMUNITY COLLEGE OF BEAVER COUNTY
Monaca, Pennsylvania
http://www.ccbc.edu
Community College of Beaver County was founded in 1966. It is accredited by Middle States Association of Colleges and Schools. It first offered distance learning courses in 1998. In fall 2007, there were 500 students enrolled in distance learning courses. Institutionally administered financial aid is available to distance learners.
Services Distance learners have accessibility to academic advising, bookstore, campus computer network, e-mail services, library services, tutoring.
Contact Registrar, Community College of Beaver County, One Campus Drive, Registrar's Office, Building 1, Monaca, PA 15061-2588. Telephone: 724-775-8561 Ext. 253. Fax: 724-775-4687. E-mail: dan.slater @ccbc.edu.

DEGREES AND AWARDS
Programs offered do not lead to a degree or other formal award.

COURSE SUBJECT AREAS OFFERED OUTSIDE OF DEGREE PROGRAMS
Undergraduate—accounting and computer science; air transportation; American literature (United States and Canadian); behavioral sciences; business administration, management and operations; business, management, and marketing related; business/managerial economics; cognitive psychology and psycholinguistics; computer and information sciences; computer programming; computer science; computer software and media applications; criminal justice and corrections; developmental and child psychology; economics; education; English; English composition; English literature (British and Commonwealth); fine and studio art; history; liberal arts and sciences, general studies and humanities; mathematics; nursing; nutrition sciences; philosophy; psychology; psychology related; social psychology; social sciences; social sciences related; sociology; statistics; technical and business writing.
Non-credit—accounting and computer science; business administration, management and operations; business/commerce; business/corporate communications; business, management, and marketing related; business/managerial economics; business operations support and assistant services; computer and information sciences; computer science; computer software and media applications; entrepreneurial and small business operations; graphic communications.

COMMUNITY COLLEGE OF DENVER
Denver, Colorado
Distance Learning
http://www.ccd.edu/OnlineLearning/
Community College of Denver was founded in 1970. It is accredited by North Central Association of Colleges and Schools. It first offered distance learning courses in 1986. In fall 2007, there were 2,000 students enrolled in distance learning courses. Institutionally administered financial aid is available to distance learners.
Services Distance learners have accessibility to academic advising, bookstore, e-mail services, library services, tutoring.
Contact Jeanne Stroh, Director for Online Learning, Community College of Denver, Campus Box 900, PO Box 173363, Denver, CO 80217-3363. Telephone: 303-352-3302. Fax: 303-556-6319. E-mail: jeanne.stroh@ ccd.edu.

DEGREES AND AWARDS
AA Behavioral Sciences; Business Administration; Economics; English/ Literature; Liberal Arts; Psychology; Sociology
AGS Generalist
AS Biology; Chemistry; Generalist; Pre-Dental; Pre-Engineering; Pre-Pharmacy; Pre-Physical Therapy; Pre-Physician; Pre-Physics

COURSE SUBJECT AREAS OFFERED OUTSIDE OF DEGREE PROGRAMS
Undergraduate—accounting and related services; anthropology; astronomy and astrophysics; biology; business administration, management and operations; business/corporate communications; business, management,

and marketing related; chemistry; comparative literature; computer/ information technology administration and management; computer software and media applications; creative writing; economics; education (specific levels and methods); education (specific subject areas); English; English composition; entrepreneurial and small business operations; fine and studio art; geography and cartography; geological and earth sciences/ geosciences; health/medical preparatory programs; history; human development, family studies, and related services; liberal arts and sciences, general studies and humanities; mathematics; microbiological sciences and immunology; nursing; philosophy; philosophy and religious studies related; physics; political science and government; psychology; religious studies; sales, merchandising, and related marketing operations (general); sociology; speech and rhetoric; teaching assistants/aides; technical and business writing; veterinary biomedical and clinical sciences.
Non-credit—business administration, management and operations; business/commerce; business, management, and marketing related; business operations support and assistant services; computer and information sciences; computer programming; computer software and media applications; crafts, folk art and artisanry; education; family psychology; film/video and photographic arts; finance and financial management services; fine and studio art; food science and technology; foods, nutrition, and related services; health aides/attendants/orderlies; languages (foreign languages related); languages (Romance languages); music; parks, recreation and leisure; personal and culinary services related; personality psychology; publishing; real estate.

CONCEPTION SEMINARY COLLEGE
Conception, Missouri
http://www.conceptionabbey.edu
Conception Seminary College was founded in 1886. It is accredited by North Central Association of Colleges and Schools. Institutionally administered financial aid is available to distance learners.
Contact Br. Paul Sheller, OSB, Director of Admissions and Vocation Promotion, Conception Seminary College, PO Box 502, Conception, MO 64433. Telephone: 660-944-2886. Fax: 660-944-2829. E-mail: vocations@conception.edu.

DEGREES AND AWARDS
Programs offered do not lead to a degree or other formal award.

COURSE SUBJECT AREAS OFFERED OUTSIDE OF DEGREE PROGRAMS
Undergraduate—biblical studies; theological and ministerial studies.
Graduate—biblical studies; theological and ministerial studies.

CONCORDIA COLLEGE–NEW YORK
Bronxville, New York
CUENET (Concordia University Education Network)
http://www.concordia-ny.edu
Concordia College–New York was founded in 1881. It is accredited by Middle States Association of Colleges and Schools. It first offered distance learning courses in 1995. In fall 2007, there were 36 students enrolled in distance learning courses. Institutionally administered financial aid is available to distance learners.
Contact Prof. Sherry Fraser, Dean of the College, Concordia College–New York, 171 White Plains Road, Bronxville, NY 10708. Telephone: 914-337-9300 Ext. 2211. Fax: 914-395-4500. E-mail: sherry.fraser@ concordia-ny.edu.

DEGREES AND AWARDS
Programs offered do not lead to a degree or other formal award.

COURSE SUBJECT AREAS OFFERED OUTSIDE OF DEGREE PROGRAMS
Undergraduate—biblical studies; education; religious studies; social work.

CONCORDIA UNIVERSITY, ST. PAUL
St. Paul, Minnesota
http://www.csp.edu

Concordia University, St. Paul was founded in 1893. It is accredited by North Central Association of Colleges and Schools. It first offered distance learning courses in 1998. In fall 2007, there were 640 students enrolled in distance learning courses. Institutionally administered financial aid is available to distance learners.

Services Distance learners have accessibility to academic advising, bookstore, campus computer network, e-mail services, library services, tutoring.

Contact Ms. Kimberly Craig, Director, Graduate and Degree Completion Admissions, Concordia University, St. Paul, 275 Syndicate Street North, Saint Paul, MN 55104-5494. Telephone: 800-333-4705. Fax: 651-603-6320. E-mail: craig@csp.edu.

DEGREES AND AWARDS

BA Child Development; Criminal Justice; Family Life Education; Human Resource Management; Information Technology Management; Marketing Management; Organizational Management and Leadership; Public Safety and Security

MA Christian Outreach; Human Services–Criminal Justice Leadership emphasis; Human Services–Family Life Education emphasis; Organizational Management–Sports Management emphasis; Organizational Management; Organizational Management, Human Resources emphasis

MAE Differentiated Instruction; Early Childhood

MBA Business Administration

COURSE SUBJECT AREAS OFFERED OUTSIDE OF DEGREE PROGRAMS

Undergraduate—business/commerce; developmental and child psychology; education; human development, family studies, and related services; sociology.

Graduate—business/commerce; developmental and child psychology; education; human development, family studies, and related services; sociology.

Non-credit—business/commerce; communication and media; fine and studio art; mathematics and computer science; social sciences.

CONCORDIA UNIVERSITY WISCONSIN
Mequon, Wisconsin
Continuing Education Division
http://www.cuw.edu/elearning

Concordia University Wisconsin was founded in 1881. It is accredited by North Central Association of Colleges and Schools. It first offered distance learning courses in 1994. In fall 2007, there were 1,100 students enrolled in distance learning courses. Institutionally administered financial aid is available to distance learners.

Services Distance learners have accessibility to academic advising, bookstore, campus computer network, career placement assistance, e-mail services, library services, tutoring.

Contact Sarah Pecor, Director of E-Learning, Concordia University Wisconsin, 12800 North Lake Shore Drive, Mequon, WI 53097. Telephone: 262-243-4257. Fax: 262-243-4459. E-mail: sarah.pecor@cuw.edu.

DEGREES AND AWARDS

BA Business Management

BSN Nursing–BSN completion for RN's

MBA Business Administration

MS Curriculum and Instruction; Education Administration; Education Counseling; Reading; Rehabilitation Science

MSN Nursing

COURSE SUBJECT AREAS OFFERED OUTSIDE OF DEGREE PROGRAMS

Undergraduate—accounting and related services; business, management, and marketing related; computer science; economics; finance and financial management services; history; management sciences and quantitative methods; marketing; nursing.

Graduate—business administration, management and operations; curriculum and instruction; educational administration and supervision; educational psychology; education related; nursing.

CONNORS STATE COLLEGE
Warner, Oklahoma
Academics and Technology
http://www.connorsstate.edu/disted

Connors State College was founded in 1908. It is accredited by North Central Association of Colleges and Schools. It first offered distance learning courses in 1997. In fall 2007, there were 900 students enrolled in distance learning courses. Institutionally administered financial aid is available to distance learners.

Contact Dr. JoLynn Digranes, Executive Vice President, Connors State College, RR 1, Box 1000, Warner, OK 74469. Telephone: 918-463-2931 Ext. 6215. E-mail: jdigran@connorsstate.edu.

DEGREES AND AWARDS

Programs offered do not lead to a degree or other formal award.

COURSE SUBJECT AREAS OFFERED OUTSIDE OF DEGREE PROGRAMS

Undergraduate—agricultural business and management; business administration, management and operations; business, management, and marketing related; business/managerial economics; computer and information sciences; fine and studio art; geography and cartography; languages (Romance languages); mathematics; physical sciences; political science and government; social sciences; sociology.

CORBAN COLLEGE
Salem, Oregon
Business & Organizational Leadership and Family Studies
http://www.corban.edu/adultdegree/onlineprogs.html

Corban College was founded in 1935. It is accredited by Northwest Commission on Colleges and Universities. It first offered distance learning courses in 1994. In fall 2007, there were 130 students enrolled in distance learning courses. Institutionally administered financial aid is available to distance learners.

Services Distance learners have accessibility to academic advising, bookstore, campus computer network, e-mail services, library services, tutoring.

Contact Ms. Nancy L. Martyn, Dean of Adult Degree Programs, Corban College, Adult Degree Programs, 5000 Deer Park Drive SE, Salem, OR 97316. Telephone: 503-375-7590. Fax: 503-375-7583. E-mail: nmartyn@corban.edu.

DEGREES AND AWARDS

BS Business–Business and Organizational Leadership; Psychology/Family Studies

COURSE SUBJECT AREAS OFFERED OUTSIDE OF DEGREE PROGRAMS

Undergraduate—biblical studies; business administration, management and operations; counseling psychology; history; human development, family studies, and related services; liberal arts and sciences, general studies and humanities; marketing; mathematics; physical sciences; psychology related; religious studies; theological and ministerial studies.

See full description on page 370.

CORNING COMMUNITY COLLEGE
Corning, New York
Open Learning Program
http://www.corning-cc.edu

Corning Community College was founded in 1956. It is accredited by Middle States Association of Colleges and Schools. It first offered distance learning courses in 1996. In fall 2007, there were 500 students enrolled in distance learning courses. Institutionally administered financial aid is available to distance learners.

Services Distance learners have accessibility to academic advising, bookstore, campus computer network, career placement assistance, e-mail services, library services, tutoring.

Contact Sarah C. Weisman, Associate Dean of Learning Resources, Corning Community College, 1 Academic Drive, Corning, NY 14830-3297. Telephone: 607-962-9385. Fax: 607-962-9466. E-mail: sweisma1@corning-cc.edu.

DEGREES AND AWARDS
Programs offered do not lead to a degree or other formal award.

COURSE SUBJECT AREAS OFFERED OUTSIDE OF DEGREE PROGRAMS
Undergraduate—accounting and related services; applied mathematics; business administration, management and operations; business/managerial economics; business operations support and assistant services; chemistry; computer programming; computer science; computer software and media applications; computer systems networking and telecommunications; design and applied arts; economics; education; educational assessment, evaluation, and research; English; English composition; English language and literature related; fine and studio art; graphic communications; health and physical education/fitness; history; hospitality administration; human services; mathematics; nutrition sciences; philosophy; psychology; social psychology; sociology.

COVENANT THEOLOGICAL SEMINARY
St. Louis, Missouri
External Studies Office
http://www.covenantseminary.edu/attending/distance.asp
Covenant Theological Seminary was founded in 1956. It is accredited by North Central Association of Colleges and Schools. It first offered distance learning courses in 1989. In fall 2007, there were 115 students enrolled in distance learning courses. Institutionally administered financial aid is available to distance learners.
Services Distance learners have accessibility to academic advising, bookstore, campus computer network, career placement assistance, e-mail services, library services, tutoring.
Contact Mr. Jeremy Kicklighter, Director of Admissions, Covenant Theological Seminary, 12330 Conway Road, St. Louis, MO 63141. Telephone: 800-264-8064. Fax: 314-434-4819. E-mail: admissions@covenantseminary.edu.

DEGREES AND AWARDS
Graduate Certificate Biblical and Theological Studies
MA Theological Studies

COURSE SUBJECT AREAS OFFERED OUTSIDE OF DEGREE PROGRAMS
Graduate—biblical studies; missionary studies and missiology; religious education; religious studies; theological and ministerial studies; theology and religious vocations related.
Non-credit—biblical studies; missionary studies and missiology; religious education; religious studies; theological and ministerial studies; theology and religious vocations related.

CRAFTON HILLS COLLEGE
Yucaipa, California
Distance Education Office
http://www.craftonhills.edu
Crafton Hills College was founded in 1972. It is accredited by Western Association of Schools and Colleges. It first offered distance learning courses in 1980. In fall 2007, there were 737 students enrolled in distance learning courses. Institutionally administered financial aid is available to distance learners.
Services Distance learners have accessibility to academic advising, bookstore, campus computer network, e-mail services, library services.
Contact Ms. Trelisa Glazatov, Distance Education Systems Administrator, Crafton Hills College, 441 West 8th Street, San Bernardino, CA 92401. Telephone: 909-384-4318. Fax: 909-885-3035. E-mail: tglazato@sbccd.cc.ca.us.

DEGREES AND AWARDS
Programs offered do not lead to a degree or other formal award.

COURSE SUBJECT AREAS OFFERED OUTSIDE OF DEGREE PROGRAMS
Undergraduate—anthropology; astronomy and astrophysics; biology; business administration, management and operations; developmental and child psychology; economics; geography and cartography; geological and earth sciences/geosciences; health and physical education/fitness; history; human development, family studies, and related services; philosophy and religious studies related; political science and government; real estate; religious studies; social psychology; sociology.

CROSSROADS COLLEGE
Rochester, Minnesota
http://www.crossroadscollege.edu/
Crossroads College was founded in 1913. It is accredited by Association for Biblical Higher Education. It first offered distance learning courses in 2007. In fall 2007, there were 10 students enrolled in distance learning courses. Institutionally administered financial aid is available to distance learners.
Services Distance learners have accessibility to academic advising, campus computer network, e-mail services.
Contact Mrs. Barb Ackland, Compass Admissions Advisor, Crossroads College, 920 Mayowood Road SW, Rochester, MN 55902. Telephone: 507-535-3307. Fax: 507-288-9046. E-mail: backland@crossroadscollege.edu.

DEGREES AND AWARDS
BS Ministry
CCCPE Bible and Theology

COURSE SUBJECT AREAS OFFERED OUTSIDE OF DEGREE PROGRAMS
Undergraduate—liberal arts and sciences, general studies and humanities; theological and ministerial studies.
Non-credit—liberal arts and sciences, general studies and humanities; theological and ministerial studies.

CROWN COLLEGE
St. Bonifacius, Minnesota
Crown College Online
http://www.crown.edu
Crown College was founded in 1916. It is accredited by Association for Biblical Higher Education. It first offered distance learning courses in 2000. In fall 2007, there were 200 students enrolled in distance learning courses. Institutionally administered financial aid is available to distance learners.
Services Distance learners have accessibility to academic advising, bookstore, campus computer network, career placement assistance, e-mail services, library services, tutoring.
Contact Heather Downs, Recruitment Manager, Crown College, 8700 College View Drive, St. Bonifacius, MN 55375. Telephone: 952-446-4100. Fax: 952-446-4149. E-mail: downsh@crown.edu.

DEGREES AND AWARDS
AS Christian Ministries
BS Christian Ministry
MA Christian Studies; Educational Leadership; Intercultural Studies; Ministry Leadership; Organizational Leadership

COURSE SUBJECT AREAS OFFERED OUTSIDE OF DEGREE PROGRAMS
Undergraduate—missionary studies and missiology; pastoral counseling and specialized ministries; philosophy and religious studies related; religious education; religious studies.
Graduate—biblical studies; business administration, management and operations; business/managerial economics; business operations support and assistant services; education; educational administration and super-

vision; education related; missionary studies and missiology; philosophy and religious studies related; theological and ministerial studies.

CULVER-STOCKTON COLLEGE
Canton, Missouri
http://www.culver.edu/

Culver-Stockton College was founded in 1853. It is accredited by North Central Association of Colleges and Schools. It first offered distance learning courses in 2002. In fall 2007, there were 62 students enrolled in distance learning courses. Institutionally administered financial aid is available to distance learners.

Services Distance learners have accessibility to academic advising, bookstore, campus computer network, career placement assistance, e-mail services, library services, tutoring.

Contact Dr. R. Joseph Dieker, Dean of Academic Affairs, Culver-Stockton College, One College Hill, Canton, MO 63435. Telephone: 573-288-6325. Fax: 573-288-6616. E-mail: jdieker@culver.edu.

DEGREES AND AWARDS
BS Business Administration; Management Information Systems

COURSE SUBJECT AREAS OFFERED OUTSIDE OF DEGREE PROGRAMS
Undergraduate—astronomy and astrophysics; biology; business administration, management and operations; computer and information sciences; management information systems; nursing.

CUMBERLAND COUNTY COLLEGE
Vineland, New Jersey
Multimedia and Distance Learning Services
http://www.cccnj.edu

Cumberland County College was founded in 1963. It is accredited by Middle States Association of Colleges and Schools. It first offered distance learning courses in 1990. In fall 2007, there were 100 students enrolled in distance learning courses. Institutionally administered financial aid is available to distance learners.

Services Distance learners have accessibility to academic advising, bookstore, campus computer network, career placement assistance, e-mail services, library services, tutoring.

Contact Michael R. Farinelli, Senior Manager, Multimedia Support Services, Cumberland County College, College Drive, PO Box 1500, Vineland, NJ 08362-0517. Telephone: 856-691-8600 Ext. 303. Fax: 856-691-9489. E-mail: mfarinelli@cccnj.edu.

DEGREES AND AWARDS
Programs offered do not lead to a degree or other formal award.

COURSE SUBJECT AREAS OFFERED OUTSIDE OF DEGREE PROGRAMS
Undergraduate—anthropology; business administration, management and operations; clinical child psychology; economics; English composition; history; languages (foreign languages related); psychology; sociology; speech and rhetoric.

CUYAHOGA COMMUNITY COLLEGE
Cleveland, Ohio
http://www.tri-c.edu/distancelearning/Pages/Home.aspx

Cuyahoga Community College was founded in 1963. It is accredited by North Central Association of Colleges and Schools. It first offered distance learning courses in 1990. In fall 2007, there were 10,000 students enrolled in distance learning courses. Institutionally administered financial aid is available to distance learners.

Services Distance learners have accessibility to academic advising, bookstore, campus computer network, career placement assistance, e-mail services, library services.

Contact Ms. Patricia McKee, Information Support Specialist, Cuyahoga Community College, 2900 Community College Avenue, MMC 56, Cleveland, OH 44115. Telephone: 216-987-4257. Fax: 216-987-3675. E-mail: patricia.mckee@tri-c.edu.

DEGREES AND AWARDS
Programs offered do not lead to a degree or other formal award.

COURSE SUBJECT AREAS OFFERED OUTSIDE OF DEGREE PROGRAMS
Undergraduate—accounting and computer science; allied health and medical assisting services; American literature (United States and Canadian); anthropology; archeology; area, ethnic, cultural, and gender studies related; biology; business administration, management and operations; chemistry; computer and information sciences; dietetics and clinical nutrition services; economics; education; English; English composition; English language and literature related; geological and earth sciences/geosciences; graphic communications; health aides/attendants/orderlies; health services/allied health/health sciences; history; hospitality administration; human services; information science/studies; journalism; languages (foreign languages related); legal professions and studies related; legal support services; manufacturing engineering; materials engineering; mathematics; music; nursing; philosophy; physical sciences; physics; plant sciences; political science and government; psychology; public administration; real estate; social sciences; sociology; speech and rhetoric; urban studies/affairs; veterinary biomedical and clinical sciences.

DAEMEN COLLEGE
Amherst, New York
http://www.daemen.edu

Daemen College was founded in 1947. It is accredited by Middle States Association of Colleges and Schools. It first offered distance learning courses in 1999. In fall 2007, there were 1,200 students enrolled in distance learning courses. Institutionally administered financial aid is available to distance learners.

Services Distance learners have accessibility to academic advising, bookstore, campus computer network, e-mail services, library services.

Contact Ms. Cheryl Littlejohn, Distance Learning Coordinator, Daemen College, 4380 Main Street, BC211A, Amherst, NY 14226. Telephone: 716-839 8532. Fax: 716-839 8261. E-mail: clittlej@daemen.edu.

DEGREES AND AWARDS
Programs offered do not lead to a degree or other formal award.

COURSE SUBJECT AREAS OFFERED OUTSIDE OF DEGREE PROGRAMS
Undergraduate—American Sign Language (ASL); business/commerce; computer software and media applications; education; English composition; entrepreneurial and small business operations; health and medical administrative services; health/medical preparatory programs; health professions related; linguistic, comparative, and related language studies; nursing; psychology; sociology.
Graduate—medical clinical sciences/graduate medical studies; nursing.

DAKOTA STATE UNIVERSITY
Madison, South Dakota
Extended Programs
http://www.departments.dsu.edu/disted/

Dakota State University was founded in 1881. It is accredited by North Central Association of Colleges and Schools. It first offered distance learning courses in 1991. In fall 2007, there were 718 students enrolled in distance learning courses. Institutionally administered financial aid is available to distance learners.

Services Distance learners have accessibility to academic advising, bookstore, campus computer network, career placement assistance, e-mail services, library services, tutoring.

Contact Ms. Susan Eykamp, Distance Education Specialist, Extended Programs, Dakota State University, 820 North Washington Avenue,

Technology Classroom Building, Madison, SD 57042-1799. Telephone: 800-641-4309. Fax: 605-256-5095. E-mail: dsuinfo@dsu.edu.

DEGREES AND AWARDS

AA General Studies
AS Health Information Technology
BBA Management Information Systems
BS Health Information Administration
MS Educational Technology; Information Assurance and Computer Security
MSIS Information Systems
DSc IS Information Systems

COURSE SUBJECT AREAS OFFERED OUTSIDE OF DEGREE PROGRAMS

Undergraduate—accounting and related services; communications technology; computer and information sciences; computer and information sciences and support services related; computer/information technology administration and management; computer programming; computer science; computer systems analysis; education related; English; English composition; English language and literature related; fine and studio art; health and medical administrative services; health and physical education/fitness; human resources management; information science/studies; mathematics; music; psychology; sociology; special education; speech and rhetoric.
Graduate—computer and information sciences; computer and information sciences and support services related; educational/instructional media design; education related; information science/studies.

DALLAS BAPTIST UNIVERSITY
Dallas, Texas
Dallas Baptist University Online (DBU Online)
http://online.dbu.edu

Dallas Baptist University was founded in 1965. It is accredited by Southern Association of Colleges and Schools. It first offered distance learning courses in 1998. In fall 2007, there were 1,614 students enrolled in distance learning courses. Institutionally administered financial aid is available to distance learners.
Services Distance learners have accessibility to academic advising, bookstore, campus computer network, career placement assistance, e-mail services, library services, tutoring.
Contact Ms. Judy Yi, Online Student Coordinator, Dallas Baptist University, Online Education, 3000 Mountain Creek Parkway, Dallas, TX 75211-9299. Telephone: 800-460-8188. Fax: 214-333-5373. E-mail: online@dbu.edu.

DEGREES AND AWARDS

AA General degree
ABS Associate of Biblical Studies
BA Biblical Studies
BAS Christian Ministries; Communication; Health Care Management; Interdisciplinary Studies–8 concentrations; Psychology; Sociology
BBA Management Information Systems; Management; Marketing
BBS Business Administration; Management Information Systems; Management; Marketing
Certificate E-Business
MACE Business Ministry Concentration; Childhood Ministry Concentration; Christian Education–Childhood Ministry; Dual MACE/MBA; General concentration
MAM Human Resource Management; Management, general
MBA Dual MBA/MACE; E-Business; Finance; International Business; Management Information Systems; Management; Marketing
MEd Educational Leadership; Higher Education

COURSE SUBJECT AREAS OFFERED OUTSIDE OF DEGREE PROGRAMS

Undergraduate—accounting and related services; American literature (United States and Canadian); atmospheric sciences and meteorology; biblical studies; biological and physical sciences; biology; business administration, management and operations; business/corporate communications; business, management, and marketing related; business/

managerial economics; communication and journalism related; communication and media; communications technologies and support services related; communications technology; community health services; computer and information sciences; computer science; computer software and media applications; computer systems analysis; computer systems networking and telecommunications; creative writing; criminal justice and corrections; criminology; economics; education; education related; English; English composition; English language and literature related; family psychology; finance and financial management services; fine and studio art; geological and earth sciences/geosciences; graphic communications; health and physical education/fitness; health professions related; history; human resources management; international agriculture; liberal arts and sciences, general studies and humanities; management information systems; marketing; mathematics; mathematics and statistics related; missionary studies and missiology; natural sciences; personality psychology; philosophy; philosophy and religious studies related; political science and government; psychology; psychology related; public health; religious education; religious studies; sales, merchandising, and related marketing operations (general); social psychology; social sciences; social sciences related; sociology; speech and rhetoric; statistics; theological and ministerial studies.
Graduate—accounting and related services; business administration, management and operations; business/commerce; business/corporate communications; business, management, and marketing related; business/managerial economics; computer and information sciences; computer/information technology administration and management; computer software and media applications; computer systems analysis; computer systems networking and telecommunications; criminal justice and corrections; criminology; curriculum and instruction; economics; education; educational administration and supervision; educational assessment, evaluation, and research; educational/instructional media design; education related; English as a second/foreign language (teaching); entrepreneurial and small business operations; finance and financial management services; human resources management; information science/studies; international business; liberal arts and sciences, general studies and humanities; management information systems; management sciences and quantitative methods; marketing; missionary studies and missiology; philosophy and religious studies related; religious education; religious studies; sales, merchandising, and related marketing operations (general); statistics; theological and ministerial studies.

DALLAS CHRISTIAN COLLEGE
Dallas, Texas
http://www.dallas.edu/Online/index.cfm

Dallas Christian College was founded in 1950. It is accredited by Association for Biblical Higher Education. It first offered distance learning courses in 2001. In fall 2007, there were 80 students enrolled in distance learning courses. Institutionally administered financial aid is available to distance learners.
Services Distance learners have accessibility to academic advising, bookstore, e-mail services, library services.
Contact Mrs. Crystal Laidacker, Registrar/Advisor for Online Students, Dallas Christian College, 2700 Christian Parkway, Dallas, TX 75234. Telephone: 800-688-1029 Ext. 140. E-mail: claidacker@dallas.edu.

DEGREES AND AWARDS

Programs offered do not lead to a degree or other formal award.

COURSE SUBJECT AREAS OFFERED OUTSIDE OF DEGREE PROGRAMS

Undergraduate—behavioral sciences; biblical and other theological languages and literatures; biblical studies; biology; community psychology; English composition; history; philosophy and religious studies related; theological and ministerial studies; theology and religious vocations related.

DALLAS COUNTY COMMUNITY COLLEGE DISTRICT
Dallas, Texas
Dallas TeleCollege
http://dallastelecollege.dcccd.edu

Dallas County Community College District is accredited by Southern Association of Colleges and Schools. It first offered distance learning courses in 1972. In fall 2007, there were 12,000 students enrolled in distance learning courses. Institutionally administered financial aid is available to distance learners.

Services Distance learners have accessibility to academic advising, bookstore, campus computer network, e-mail services, library services, tutoring.

Contact Mrs. Angela Auzenne, Public Information Director, Dallas County Community College District, 9596 Walnut Street, Dallas, TX 75243-2112. Telephone: 972-669-6657. Fax: 972-669-6409. E-mail: aauzenne@dcccd.edu.

DEGREES AND AWARDS

AA Liberal Arts and General Studies

AS Business; General Studies

COURSE SUBJECT AREAS OFFERED OUTSIDE OF DEGREE PROGRAMS

Undergraduate—accounting and related services; anthropology; astronomy and astrophysics; biology; business operations support and assistant services; computer and information sciences; computer and information sciences and support services related; computer engineering; computer/information technology administration and management; computer programming; computer science; computer software and media applications; computer systems analysis; computer systems networking and telecommunications; creative writing; data entry/microcomputer applications; data processing; developmental and child psychology; drafting/design engineering technologies; economics; education; education related; English as a second language; English composition; health and medical administrative services; health professions related; history; human development, family studies, and related services; human resources management; journalism; liberal arts and sciences, general studies and humanities; marketing; mathematics; mathematics and computer science; mathematics and statistics related; music; philosophy; philosophy and religious studies related; physical sciences; physical sciences related; psychology; real estate; social sciences; social sciences related; sociology; speech and rhetoric.

DANIEL WEBSTER COLLEGE
Nashua, New Hampshire
http://www.dwc.edu/de

Daniel Webster College was founded in 1965. It is accredited by New England Association of Schools and Colleges. It first offered distance learning courses in 2000. Institutionally administered financial aid is available to distance learners.

Services Distance learners have accessibility to academic advising, bookstore, campus computer network, career placement assistance, e-mail services, library services, tutoring.

Contact Distance Programs, Daniel Webster College, 20 University Drive, Nashua, NH 03063. Telephone: 800-325-6876.

DEGREES AND AWARDS

ABA Business Administration

AGS General Studies

BS Business and Management; Organizational Leadership; Social Sciences

Certificate Client-Server Application Development; Computer Programming–C/UNIX Programming; Computer Programming–MS Windows Programming; Computer Programming–UNIX Systems Administration; Computer Science–PC Networking; Webmaster Technology

MBA MBA for Aviation Professionals

DANVILLE COMMUNITY COLLEGE
Danville, Virginia
Learning Resource Center
http://www.dcc.vccs.edu

Danville Community College was founded in 1967. It is accredited by Southern Association of Colleges and Schools. It first offered distance learning courses in 1990. In fall 2007, there were 1,200 students enrolled in distance learning courses. Institutionally administered financial aid is available to distance learners.

Services Distance learners have accessibility to academic advising, bookstore, career placement assistance, e-mail services, library services.

Contact Dr. Chris Ezell, Vice President of Instruction and Student Services, Danville Community College, 1008 South Main Street, Danville, VA 24541. Telephone: 434-797-8410. Fax: 434-797-8514. E-mail: cezell@dcc.vccs.edu.

DEGREES AND AWARDS
Programs offered do not lead to a degree or other formal award.

COURSE SUBJECT AREAS OFFERED OUTSIDE OF DEGREE PROGRAMS

Undergraduate—accounting and related services; allied health and medical assisting services; allied health diagnostic, intervention, and treatment professions; behavioral sciences; biological and biomedical sciences related; biology; business administration, management and operations; business/commerce; business, management, and marketing related; business operations support and assistant services; communication and media; community health services; computer programming; computer science; computer software and media applications; criminal justice and corrections; criminology; dental support services and allied professions; dentistry and oral sciences (advanced/graduate); design and applied arts; developmental and child psychology; drafting/design engineering technologies; education; educational/instructional media design; education (specific levels and methods); English; English composition; English language and literature related; English literature (British and Commonwealth); foods, nutrition, and related services; geography and cartography; graphic communications; health and physical education/fitness; health professions related; history; human development, family studies, and related services; marketing; mathematics; mathematics and computer science; music; natural sciences; nursing; nutrition sciences; political science and government; psychology; social psychology; social sciences; sociology; theological and ministerial studies.

DARTON COLLEGE
Albany, Georgia
Office of Distance Learning
http://online.darton.edu

Darton College was founded in 1965. It is accredited by Southern Association of Colleges and Schools. It first offered distance learning courses in 1993. In fall 2007, there were 3,000 students enrolled in distance learning courses. Institutionally administered financial aid is available to distance learners.

Services Distance learners have accessibility to academic advising, bookstore, campus computer network, career placement assistance, e-mail services, library services, tutoring.

Contact Mrs. Kay Bell, Enrollment Counselor, Darton College, 2400 Gillionville Road, Albany, GA 31707. Telephone: 229-317-6815. E-mail: kayano.bell@darton.edu.

DEGREES AND AWARDS

AA English; Foreign Language; History; Speech

AAS Histologic Technology; Management; Office Administration (Administrative Support); Paralegal

AS Business Administration; Business Education; Computer Information Systems; Criminal Justice; Early Childhood Education; Economics; General Studies; Health Information Management; Health Information Technology; Health Information Technology; Medical Laboratory Technology; Medical Technology; Office Administration (Secretarial Science); Political Science; Pre-Law; Psychology; Social Work; Sociology; Teacher

Education (Middle Grades); Teacher Education (Secondary Education); Teacher Education (Special Education)

Certificate of Completion Accounting; Addictions Counseling; Criminal Justice Management; General Management; Management and Marketing; Marketing; Teachers Communications and Crisis Skills; Technology

Certificate Histology; Medical Coding

COURSE SUBJECT AREAS OFFERED OUTSIDE OF DEGREE PROGRAMS

Undergraduate—accounting and computer science; accounting and related services; allied health and medical assisting services; allied health diagnostic, intervention, and treatment professions; American literature (United States and Canadian); applied mathematics; biological and biomedical sciences related; business administration, management and operations; business/commerce; cell biology and anatomical sciences; clinical/medical laboratory science and allied professions; communication and media; computer software and media applications; computer systems networking and telecommunications; criminal justice and corrections; economics; education; education related; education (specific levels and methods); education (specific subject areas); English; English composition; English literature (British and Commonwealth); finance and financial management services; health and medical administrative services; health and physical education/fitness; health/medical preparatory programs; health professions related; health services/allied health/ health sciences; history; languages (East Asian); languages (foreign languages related); languages (Germanic); languages (Romance languages); liberal arts and sciences, general studies and humanities; linguistic, comparative, and related language studies; mathematics; mathematics and computer science; mathematics and statistics related; music; philosophy; philosophy and religious studies related; physical sciences; physiology, pathology and related sciences; political science and government; psychology; social work; sociology; speech and rhetoric; statistics.

Non-credit—business administration, management and operations; business/corporate communications; business, management, and marketing related; computer software and media applications; creative writing; finance and financial management services; real estate; sales, merchandising, and related marketing operations (specialized); technical and business writing.

See full description on page 372.

DAWSON COMMUNITY COLLEGE
Glendive, Montana
Continuing and Extension Education Department
http://www.dawson.edu

Dawson Community College was founded in 1940. It is accredited by Northwest Commission on Colleges and Universities. It first offered distance learning courses in 1990. In fall 2007, there were 20 students enrolled in distance learning courses. Institutionally administered financial aid is available to distance learners.

Services Distance learners have accessibility to academic advising, bookstore, career placement assistance, library services.

Contact Mrs. MaryAnn Vester, Director of Continuing Education and Outreach, Dawson Community College, 300 College Drive, Glendive, MT 59330. Telephone: 406-377-3396 Ext. 409. Fax: 406-377-8132. E-mail: mare@dawson.edu.

DEGREES AND AWARDS
AA General Studies
AAS Business Management; Human Services; Law Enforcement

COURSE SUBJECT AREAS OFFERED OUTSIDE OF DEGREE PROGRAMS
Undergraduate—agricultural business and management; agriculture; American literature (United States and Canadian); anthropology; biology; business administration, management and operations; communication and media; computer software and media applications; creative writing;

criminal justice and corrections; developmental and child psychology; English composition; fine and studio art; human services; psychology; sociology.

DAYTONA STATE COLLEGE
Daytona Beach, Florida
Interactive Telecommunications Services
http://online.DaytonaState.edu

Daytona State College was founded in 1958. It is accredited by Southern Association of Colleges and Schools. It first offered distance learning courses in 1974. In fall 2007, there were 4,000 students enrolled in distance learning courses. Institutionally administered financial aid is available to distance learners.

Services Distance learners have accessibility to academic advising, bookstore, campus computer network, e-mail services, library services, tutoring.

Contact Dr. Robert Saum, Director, Florida Online and Faculty Technology Resource Area, Daytona State College, PO Box 2811, 1200 West International Speedway Boulevard, Daytona Beach, FL 32120-2811. Telephone: 386-506-3484. Fax: 386-506-4601. E-mail: saumr@ daytonastate.edu.

DEGREES AND AWARDS
AA Liberal Arts (In State); Liberal Arts (Out of State)
AAS Business Administration (Out of State); Business Administration (in state)
AS Business Administration (Out of State); Business Administration (in state)
BAS Management and Supervision (In State); Management and Supervision (Out of State)

COURSE SUBJECT AREAS OFFERED OUTSIDE OF DEGREE PROGRAMS
Undergraduate—accounting and computer science; allied health and medical assisting services; behavioral sciences; biological and physical sciences; business, management, and marketing related; computer programming; criminal justice and corrections; developmental and child psychology; economics; education; English; English language and literature related; history; languages (foreign languages related); mathematics; music; philosophy; radio, television, and digital communication; visual and performing arts.

DE ANZA COLLEGE
Cupertino, California
Distance Learning Center
http://distance.deanza.edu

De Anza College was founded in 1967. It is accredited by Western Association of Schools and Colleges. It first offered distance learning courses in 1974. In fall 2007, there were 2,200 students enrolled in distance learning courses. Institutionally administered financial aid is available to distance learners.

Services Distance learners have accessibility to academic advising, bookstore, campus computer network, career placement assistance, library services, tutoring.

Contact Ann Leever, Instructional Associate, De Anza College, 21250 Stevens Creek Boulevard, Cupertino, CA 95014. Telephone: 408-864-8969. Fax: 408-864-8245. E-mail: information@deanza.edu.

DEGREES AND AWARDS
Programs offered do not lead to a degree or other formal award.

COURSE SUBJECT AREAS OFFERED OUTSIDE OF DEGREE PROGRAMS
Undergraduate—accounting and related services; allied health and medical assisting services; anthropology; area studies; biology; business administration, management and operations; computer and information sciences; computer programming; computer systems networking and telecommunications; developmental and child psychology; economics; English; English composition; ethnic, cultural minority, and gender

studies; foods, nutrition, and related services; graphic communications; history; human development, family studies, and related services; intercultural/multicultural and diversity studies; journalism; legal professions and studies related; legal studies (non-professional general, undergraduate); mathematics; mathematics and statistics related; music; philosophy and religious studies related; political science and government; psychology; real estate; religious studies; social psychology; social sciences; sociology; statistics; visual and performing arts; visual and performing arts related.

DEFIANCE COLLEGE
Defiance, Ohio
Design for Leadership
http://www.defiance.edu/pages/design_leadership.html
Defiance College was founded in 1850. It is accredited by North Central Association of Colleges and Schools. It first offered distance learning courses in 1971. In fall 2007, there were 35 students enrolled in distance learning courses. Institutionally administered financial aid is available to distance learners.
Services Distance learners have accessibility to academic advising, campus computer network, career placement assistance, e-mail services, library services, tutoring.
Contact Dr. Marian R. Plant, Coordinator, Design for Leadership, Defiance College, 701 North Clinton Street, Defiance, OH 43512. Telephone: 419-783-2465. Fax: 419-784-0426. E-mail: design@defiance.edu.

DEGREES AND AWARDS
AA Religious Education
BA Religious Education
Certificate African American Ministry Leadership module; Church Education; Youth Ministry Leadership Module

COURSE SUBJECT AREAS OFFERED OUTSIDE OF DEGREE PROGRAMS
Undergraduate—biblical studies; religious education; theology and religious vocations related.

DELAWARE COUNTY COMMUNITY COLLEGE
Media, Pennsylvania
Distance Learning
http://www.dccc.edu/dl
Delaware County Community College was founded in 1967. It is accredited by Middle States Association of Colleges and Schools. It first offered distance learning courses in 1980. In fall 2007, there were 2,000 students enrolled in distance learning courses. Institutionally administered financial aid is available to distance learners.
Services Distance learners have accessibility to academic advising, bookstore, campus computer network, e-mail services, library services, tutoring.
Contact Alexander Plachuta, Director of Distance Learning, Delaware County Community College, 901 South Media Line Road, Media, PA 19063. Telephone: 610-359-5158. E-mail: distance@dccc.edu.

DEGREES AND AWARDS
AA General Studies
AAB Business Administration

COURSE SUBJECT AREAS OFFERED OUTSIDE OF DEGREE PROGRAMS
Undergraduate—accounting and related services; American literature (United States and Canadian); anthropology; area, ethnic, cultural, and gender studies related; area studies; astronomy and astrophysics; atmospheric sciences and meteorology; biological and physical sciences; biology; business administration, management and operations; business/commerce; business/corporate communications; business, management, and marketing related; business/managerial economics; business operations support and assistant services; clinical psychology; community psychology; comparative literature; computer and information sciences;

computer and information sciences and support services related; computer engineering; computer/information technology administration and management; computer programming; computer science; computer software and media applications; computer systems networking and telecommunications; construction engineering technology; construction trades related; counseling psychology; creative writing; criminal justice and corrections; data entry/microcomputer applications; data processing; demography and population; developmental and child psychology; economics; educational psychology; English; English composition; ethnic, cultural minority, and gender studies; family and consumer sciences/human sciences; finance and financial management services; food science and technology; geography and cartography; history; human development, family studies, and related services; human resources management; information science/studies; journalism; legal studies (non-professional general, undergraduate); liberal arts and sciences, general studies and humanities; management information systems; management sciences and quantitative methods; marketing; mathematics; mathematics and computer science; nursing; pharmacy, pharmaceutical sciences, and administration; philosophy; philosophy and religious studies related; physics; psychology; psychology related; public relations, advertising, and applied communication related; religious studies; sales, merchandising, and related marketing operations (general); sales, merchandising, and related marketing operations (specialized); science technologies related; science, technology and society; social psychology; social sciences; social sciences related; sociology.
Non-credit—computer and information sciences; computer and information sciences and support services related; computer engineering; computer programming; computer science; computer software and media applications; computer systems analysis; computer systems networking and telecommunications.

DELAWARE TECHNICAL & COMMUNITY COLLEGE, JACK F. OWENS CAMPUS
Georgetown, Delaware
http://www.dtcc.edu/
Delaware Technical & Community College, Jack F. Owens Campus was founded in 1967. It is accredited by Middle States Association of Colleges and Schools. It first offered distance learning courses in 1985. In fall 2007, there were 2,000 students enrolled in distance learning courses.
Services Distance learners have accessibility to academic advising, bookstore, campus computer network, career placement assistance, e-mail services, library services, tutoring.
Contact Dr. Michael A. Mills, Director of E-Learning, Delaware Technical & Community College, Jack F. Owens Campus, 100 Campus Drive, Dover, DE 19901. Telephone: 302-857-1750. Fax: 302-739-6822. E-mail: mmills@dtcc.edu.

DEGREES AND AWARDS
AAS Office Administration

COURSE SUBJECT AREAS OFFERED OUTSIDE OF DEGREE PROGRAMS
Undergraduate—accounting and related services; agricultural business and management; agriculture; agriculture and agriculture operations related; applied mathematics; business administration, management and operations; computer science; criminal justice and corrections; economics; educational/instructional media design; English as a second language; English composition; human services; mathematics; psychology; sociology; statistics; technical and business writing.

DENVER SEMINARY
Littleton, Colorado
http://www.denverseminary.edu
Denver Seminary was founded in 1950. It is accredited by North Central Association of Colleges and Schools. It first offered distance learning courses in 1988. In fall 2007, there were 140 students enrolled in distance learning courses. Institutionally administered financial aid is available to distance learners.
Services Distance learners have accessibility to academic advising, bookstore, career placement assistance, library services.

Contact Dr. Venita Doughty, Director of Educational Technology, Denver Seminary, 6399 South Santa Fe Drive, Littleton, CO 80120. Telephone: 303-762-6933. Fax: 303-761-8060. E-mail: venita.doughty@denverseminary.edu.

DEGREES AND AWARDS
Programs offered do not lead to a degree or other formal award.

COURSE SUBJECT AREAS OFFERED OUTSIDE OF DEGREE PROGRAMS
Graduate—biblical and other theological languages and literatures; biblical studies; history; philosophy and religious studies related; religious education; religious studies; theological and ministerial studies.

DEPAUL UNIVERSITY
Chicago, Illinois
Office of Distance Learning
http://www.depaul.edu/admission/types_of_admission/index.asp

DePaul University was founded in 1898. It is accredited by North Central Association of Colleges and Schools. It first offered distance learning courses in 1996. In fall 2007, there were 2,079 students enrolled in distance learning courses. Institutionally administered financial aid is available to distance learners.

Services Distance learners have accessibility to academic advising, bookstore, campus computer network, career placement assistance, e-mail services, library services, tutoring.

Contact Admissions, DePaul University, One East Jackson Boulevard, Chicago, IL 60604-2287. Telephone: 312-362-8300. E-mail: admission@depaul.edu.

DEGREES AND AWARDS
BA Liberal Arts, general
Certificate Certificate of Mastery in Prior Learning Assessment; Prior Learning Assessment; Professional in Human Resources; Project Management; e-Financial Planning
MA Information Technology
MS Computer Science; Computer, Information, and Network Security; E-Commerce Technology; Information Systems; Instructional Technology Systems; Public Service Management; Software Engineering; Telecommunication Systems

COURSE SUBJECT AREAS OFFERED OUTSIDE OF DEGREE PROGRAMS
Undergraduate—computer science; information science/studies.
Graduate—computer programming; computer science; computer systems networking and telecommunications; information science/studies; nursing.
Non-credit—alternative and complementary medical support services; finance and financial management services; human resources management; management sciences and quantitative methods.

DEPAUL UNIVERSITY
Chicago, Illinois
School for New Learning
http://www.snl.depaul.edu

DePaul University was founded in 1898. It is accredited by North Central Association of Colleges and Schools. It first offered distance learning courses in 1996. In fall 2007, there were 762 students enrolled in distance learning courses. Institutionally administered financial aid is available to distance learners.

Services Distance learners have accessibility to academic advising, bookstore, campus computer network, career placement assistance, e-mail services, library services, tutoring.

Contact Academic Advisor, DePaul University, School for New Learning, 25 East Jackson Boulevard, 2nd Floor, Chicago, IL 60604. Telephone: 866-765-3678. Fax: 312-362-8809. E-mail: snladvising@depaul.edu.

DEGREES AND AWARDS
BA Individually designed focus area

COURSE SUBJECT AREAS OFFERED OUTSIDE OF DEGREE PROGRAMS
Undergraduate—liberal arts and sciences, general studies and humanities; science, technology and society; social sciences related.
See full description on page 374.

DESALES UNIVERSITY
Center Valley, Pennsylvania
http://www.desales.edu/access

DeSales University was founded in 1964. It is accredited by Middle States Association of Colleges and Schools. It first offered distance learning courses in 1998. In fall 2007, there were 200 students enrolled in distance learning courses. Institutionally administered financial aid is available to distance learners.

Services Distance learners have accessibility to academic advising, bookstore, campus computer network, e-mail services, library services.

Contact Mrs. Deborah L. Booros, Dean of Lifelong Learning, DeSales University, 2755 Station Avenue, Allentown, PA 18034. Telephone: 610-282-1100 Ext. 1550. E-mail: deborah.booros@desales.edu.

DEGREES AND AWARDS
BAS Management and Marketing

COURSE SUBJECT AREAS OFFERED OUTSIDE OF DEGREE PROGRAMS
Undergraduate—accounting and computer science; biology; business administration, management and operations; business, management, and marketing related; classical and ancient studies; comparative literature; computer science; criminal justice and corrections; criminology; economics; English; English composition; English language and literature related; English literature (British and Commonwealth); entrepreneurial and small business operations; finance and financial management services; history; human resources management; industrial and organizational psychology; marketing; mathematics; mathematics and statistics related; music; philosophy; philosophy and religious studies related; psychology; religious education; sales, merchandising, and related marketing operations (general); social sciences; sociology; statistics; theology and religious vocations related.

DEVRY UNIVERSITY ONLINE
Oakbrook Terrace, Illinois
http://www.devry.edu/online

DeVry University Online was founded in 2000. It is accredited by North Central Association of Colleges and Schools. In fall 2007, there were 12,276 students enrolled in distance learning courses. Institutionally administered financial aid is available to distance learners.

Services Distance learners have accessibility to academic advising, bookstore, career placement assistance, e-mail services, library services.

Contact Sarah Penn, Director of Admissions Online, DeVry University Online, 1200 East Diehl Road, Naperville, IL 60563. Telephone: 630-645-6170. E-mail: spenn@devry.edu.

DEGREES AND AWARDS
AAS Accounting; Electronics and Computer Technology; Health Information Technology; Network Systems Administration; Web Graphic Design
BS Computer Engineering Technology; Computer Information Systems; Electronics Engineering Technology; Game and Simulation Programming; Network and Communications Management; Technical Management
BSBA Business Administration
MAFM Accounting and Financial Management
MBA Business Administration
MHRM Human Resource Management
MISM Information Systems Management
MPA Public Administration
MPM Project Management
MS Educational Technology
MSEE Electrical Engineering
MTM Network and Communications Management

COURSE SUBJECT AREAS OFFERED OUTSIDE OF DEGREE PROGRAMS

Undergraduate—accounting and related services; area, ethnic, cultural, and gender studies related; biological and biomedical sciences related; business/commerce; communication and media; computer and information sciences; creative writing; economics; English composition; legal studies (non-professional general, undergraduate); liberal arts and sciences, general studies and humanities; marketing; mathematics; taxation; technical and business writing.

Graduate—accounting and related services; business/commerce; communication and media; communications technology; computer and information sciences; computer systems networking and telecommunications; economics; entrepreneurial and small business operations; finance and financial management services; health professions related; human resources management; marketing; mathematics; public administration; taxation.

See full description on page 376.

DICKINSON STATE UNIVERSITY
Dickinson, North Dakota
http://www.dsu.nodak.edu/

Dickinson State University was founded in 1918. It is accredited by North Central Association of Colleges and Schools. It first offered distance learning courses in 1998. In fall 2007, there were 643 students enrolled in distance learning courses. Institutionally administered financial aid is available to distance learners.

Services Distance learners have accessibility to academic advising, bookstore, campus computer network, career placement assistance, e-mail services, library services, tutoring.

Contact Ms. Marty Odermann-Gardner, Director, Dickinson State University, 291 Campus Drive, CB 183, Dickinson, ND 58601. Telephone: 701-483-2166. Fax: 701-483-2028. E-mail: marty.odermann.gardner@dsu.nodak.edu.

DEGREES AND AWARDS
AA General Program

AS Agricultural Sales and Services–Equine option

BA Composite Social Science; English

BPS University Studies

BS Accounting; Business Administration; Computer Science; Computer Technology Management; Education–Elementary Education; Finance; Finance; History; Human Resource Management; Human Resource Management; International Business; International Business; Secondary Education–Composite Social Science; Secondary Education–English; Secondary Education–History; Secondary Education–Math

BSAST Applied Science in Technology (BAST); Applied Science in Technology

BUS University Studies

DINÉ COLLEGE
Tsaile, Arizona
http://www.dinecollege.edu

Diné College was founded in 1968. It is accredited by North Central Association of Colleges and Schools. It first offered distance learning courses in 2005. In fall 2007, there were 250 students enrolled in distance learning courses. Institutionally administered financial aid is available to distance learners.

Services Distance learners have accessibility to academic advising, campus computer network, e-mail services, library services.

Contact Shirleen Philips-Benally, Distance Education Coordinator, Diné College, 1228 Yucca Street, PO Box 580, Shiprock, NM 87420. Telephone: 505-368-3518. E-mail: spbenally@dinecollege.edu.

DEGREES AND AWARDS
Programs offered do not lead to a degree or other formal award.

COURSE SUBJECT AREAS OFFERED OUTSIDE OF DEGREE PROGRAMS

Undergraduate—accounting and computer science; anthropology; area, ethnic, cultural, and gender studies related; biological and physical sciences; biology; business administration, management and operations; business, management, and marketing related; computer and information sciences; health services/allied health/health sciences; mathematics; natural sciences; physics; public health; social work.

DRAKE UNIVERSITY
Des Moines, Iowa
Distance Learning Program
http://www.drake.edu

Drake University was founded in 1881. It is accredited by North Central Association of Colleges and Schools. It first offered distance learning courses in 1997. In fall 2007, there were 6,000 students enrolled in distance learning courses. Institutionally administered financial aid is available to distance learners.

Services Distance learners have accessibility to academic advising, bookstore, campus computer network, e-mail services, library services.

Contact Mr. Charles Sengstock, Director of Extension Education, Drake University, School of Education, 3206 University Avenue, Des Moines, IA 50311. Telephone: 515-271-2184. E-mail: charles.sengstrock@drake.edu.

DEGREES AND AWARDS
Programs offered do not lead to a degree or other formal award.

COURSE SUBJECT AREAS OFFERED OUTSIDE OF DEGREE PROGRAMS

Undergraduate—accounting and related services; biochemistry, biophysics and molecular biology; business administration, management and operations; business/commerce; business/managerial economics; communication and journalism related; communication and media; computer and information sciences; creative writing; economics; education; education related; English; fine and studio art; health professions related; history; human resources management; information science/studies; international relations and affairs; journalism; legal research and advanced professional studies; liberal arts and sciences, general studies and humanities; management information systems; management sciences and quantitative methods; marketing; mathematics and computer science; peace studies and conflict resolution; pharmacy, pharmaceutical sciences, and administration; political science and government; psychology; psychology related; public relations, advertising, and applied communication related; social sciences related; special education; visual and performing arts related.

Graduate—accounting and computer science; business administration, management and operations; business/commerce; economics; education; finance and financial management services; health professions related; health services/allied health/health sciences; history; human resources management; information science/studies; insurance; journalism; music; peace studies and conflict resolution; pharmacy, pharmaceutical sciences, and administration; political science and government; psychology; public administration; public administration and social service professions related; public health; public relations, advertising, and applied communication related; rehabilitation and therapeutic professions.

DREW UNIVERSITY
Madison, New Jersey
http://www.drew.edu/theo.aspx

Drew University was founded in 1867. It is accredited by Middle States Association of Colleges and Schools. It first offered distance learning courses in 1998. In fall 2007, there were 70 students enrolled in distance learning courses. Institutionally administered financial aid is available to distance learners.

Services Distance learners have accessibility to academic advising, bookstore, campus computer network, e-mail services, library services.

Contact Dr. Carl Savage, Interim Director, Doctor of Ministry Program, Drew University, 36 Madison Avenue, 12 CAMPUS, Madison, NJ 07940. Telephone: 973-408-3630. Fax: 973-408-3178. E-mail: csavage@drew. edu.

DEGREES AND AWARDS
Programs offered do not lead to a degree or other formal award.

COURSE SUBJECT AREAS OFFERED OUTSIDE OF DEGREE PROGRAMS
Graduate—theological and ministerial studies.
Non-credit—theological and ministerial studies.

DREXEL UNIVERSITY
Philadelphia, Pennsylvania
E-Learning
http://www.drexel.com/petersons
Drexel University was founded in 1891. It is accredited by Middle States Association of Colleges and Schools. It first offered distance learning courses in 1997. In fall 2007, there were 3,500 students enrolled in distance learning courses. Institutionally administered financial aid is available to distance learners.
Services Distance learners have accessibility to academic advising, bookstore, career placement assistance, e-mail services, library services, tutoring.
Contact Drexel University Online, Drexel University, One Drexel Plaza, 3001 Market Street, Suite 300, Philadelphia, PA 19104. Telephone: 866-440-1949. Fax: 215-895-0525. E-mail: info@drexel.com.

DEGREES AND AWARDS
BS Communication; Communications and Applied Technology; Computing and Security Technology; Education; General Studies–Individualized Studies; General Studies, Business minor; Health Services Administration; Professional Studies; Psychology
BSN Nursing–RN to BSN
Certificate Clinical Trials Research; Complementary and Integrative Therapies; Contemporary Nursing Faculty; Education–Graduate Intern Teaching Certificate; Education–Post-Bachelor's Teaching Certificate; Epidemiology and Biostatistics; Healthcare Informatics; Instructional Technology Specialist; Medical Billing and Coding; Nursing Leadership in Health Systems Management; Nursing–Innovation and Intra/Entrepreneurship in Advanced Nursing Practice; Principal's Certification; Retail Leadership; Teaching English as a Second Language (TESL); Toxicology and Industrial Hygiene
CAGS Information Science and Technology
Graduate Certificate Engineering Management
MBA Business Administration
MHS Physicians Assistant Studies
MS Clinical Research Organization and Management; Computer Science; Educational Administration–Collaborative Leadership; Electrical Engineering; Engineering Management; Global and International Education; Higher Education; Human Resource Development; Information Systems; Learning Technologies; Library and Information Science; Math Learning and Teaching; Science of Instruction; Software Engineering; Sport Management; Teaching, Learning, and Curriculum
MSN Acute Care Nurse Practitioner; Adult Psychiatric Mental Health Nurse Practitioner; Clinical Trials Research; Contemporary Nursing Faculty; Nursing Leadership in Health Systems Management; Nursing–Innovation and Intra/Entrepreneurship in Advanced Nursing Practice; Nursing–Women's Health Nurse Practitioner; Nursing–Women's Health completion program for Nurse Practitioners

COURSE SUBJECT AREAS OFFERED OUTSIDE OF DEGREE PROGRAMS
Undergraduate—apparel and textiles; business administration, management and operations; business/commerce; business, management, and marketing related; communications technologies and support services related; computer and information sciences; computer science; finance and financial management services; health professions related; health services/allied health/health sciences; marketing; nursing; psychology; sales, merchandising, and related marketing operations (general).

Graduate—alternative and complementary medical support services; alternative and complementary medicine and medical systems; business administration, management and operations; business/commerce; business/corporate communications; business, management, and marketing related; clinical/medical laboratory science and allied professions; computer and information sciences; computer and information sciences and support services related; computer engineering; computer engineering technologies; computer science; curriculum and instruction; education; educational administration and supervision; educational assessment, evaluation, and research; educational/instructional media design; education related; education (specific levels and methods); education (specific subject areas); electrical and electronic engineering technologies; electrical, electronics and communications engineering; engineering; engineering/industrial management; engineering related; engineering-related fields; engineering-related technologies; engineering science; engineering technologies related; engineering technology; English as a second/foreign language (teaching); English as a second language; entrepreneurial and small business operations; finance and financial management services; health professions related; information science/studies; international and comparative education; international/global studies; library science; library science related; management information systems; marketing; nursing; pharmacology and toxicology; public health; sales, merchandising, and related marketing operations (general); sales, merchandising, and related marketing operations (specialized); science technologies related; statistics; teaching assistants/aides.

See full description on page 378.

DREXEL UNIVERSITY
Philadelphia, Pennsylvania
LeBow College of Business
http://mbaonline.lebow.drexel.edu
Drexel University was founded in 1891. It is accredited by Middle States Association of Colleges and Schools. It first offered distance learning courses in 1998. In fall 2007, there were 214 students enrolled in distance learning courses. Institutionally administered financial aid is available to distance learners.
Services Distance learners have accessibility to academic advising, bookstore, campus computer network, career placement assistance, e-mail services, library services.
Contact Mr. John Adamski, Director, Graduate Admissions, Drexel University, 207 Matheson Hall, 3141 Chestnut Street, Philadelphia, PA 19104. Telephone: 215-895-0562. Fax: 215-895-1012. E-mail: mba@drexel.edu.

DEGREES AND AWARDS
MBA Business; Pharmaceutical Management

COURSE SUBJECT AREAS OFFERED OUTSIDE OF DEGREE PROGRAMS
Undergraduate—accounting and related services; business administration, management and operations; business/commerce; business/corporate communications; business/managerial economics; management sciences and quantitative methods; marketing; sales, merchandising, and related marketing operations (general); taxation.

Graduate—accounting and related services; business administration, management and operations; business, management, and marketing related; business/managerial economics; computer/information technology administration and management; entrepreneurial and small business operations; finance and financial management services; international business; management sciences and quantitative methods; marketing; operations research.

DUKE UNIVERSITY
Durham, North Carolina
Nicholas School of the Environment and Earth Sciences
http://www.nicholas.duke.edu/del

Duke University was founded in 1838. It is accredited by Southern Association of Colleges and Schools. It first offered distance learning courses in 2004. In fall 2007, there were 23 students enrolled in distance learning courses. Institutionally administered financial aid is available to distance learners.

Services Distance learners have accessibility to academic advising, bookstore, campus computer network, career placement assistance, e-mail services, library services.

Contact Director, Duke Environmental Leadership Program, Duke University, Nicholas School of the Environment and Earth Sciences, Box 90328, Durham, NC 27708-0328. Telephone: 919-613-8082. Fax: 919-613-9002. E-mail: del@nicholas.duke.edu.

DEGREES AND AWARDS
MEM Duke Environmental Leadership Master of Environmental Management

See full description on page 380.

DUQUESNE UNIVERSITY
Pittsburgh, Pennsylvania
Center for Distance Learning
http://www.distancelearning.duq.edu/

Duquesne University was founded in 1878. It is accredited by Middle States Association of Colleges and Schools. It first offered distance learning courses in 1996. In fall 2007, there were 2,800 students enrolled in distance learning courses. Institutionally administered financial aid is available to distance learners.

Services Distance learners have accessibility to academic advising, bookstore, campus computer network, career placement assistance, e-mail services, library services, tutoring.

Contact Ruth Newberry, Director, Educational Technology, Duquesne University, Rockwell Hall, 600 Forbes Avenue, Pittsburgh, PA 15282. Telephone: 412-396-1813. Fax: 412-396-5144. E-mail: edtech@duq.edu.

DEGREES AND AWARDS
BS Degree completion; Humane Leadership
BSN Nursing–RN to BSN/MSN
Certificate Nursing–Post-BSN
Graduate Certificate Nursing–Post-Masters; Organizational Leadership in Animal Advocacy
MA Leadership and Liberal Studies
MEM Environmental Science and Management
MS Community Leadership; Leadership and Business Ethics; Leadership and Information Technology–Masters of Leadership and Information Technology; Music Education–Masters in Music Education; Sports Leadership
MSN Nursing
PhD Nursing–Doctor of Nursing Practice; Nursing

COURSE SUBJECT AREAS OFFERED OUTSIDE OF DEGREE PROGRAMS
Undergraduate—accounting and computer science; business administration, management and operations; business, management, and marketing related; communication and media; computer and information sciences; fine and studio art; philosophy; philosophy and religious studies related; theological and ministerial studies; theology and religious vocations related.
Graduate—accounting and computer science; business administration, management and operations; communication and media; community health services; community organization and advocacy; computer and information sciences and support services related; computer/information technology administration and management; computer software and media applications; curriculum and instruction; education; educational/instructional media design; management information systems; music; nursing; pastoral counseling and specialized ministries; philosophy and

religious studies related; public administration; public policy analysis; technology education/industrial arts.
Non-credit—animal sciences; computer and information sciences; legal support services.

EARLHAM SCHOOL OF RELIGION
Richmond, Indiana
http://esr.earlham.edu

Earlham School of Religion was founded in 1960. It first offered distance learning courses in 2001. In fall 2007, there were 82 students enrolled in distance learning courses. Institutionally administered financial aid is available to distance learners.

Services Distance learners have accessibility to academic advising, bookstore, campus computer network, e-mail services, library services.

Contact Ms. Susan G. Axtell, Director of Recruitment and Admissions, Earlham School of Religion, 228 College Avenue, Richmond, IN 47374. Telephone: 800-432-1377. Fax: 765-983-1688. E-mail: axtelsu@earlham.edu.

DEGREES AND AWARDS
MA ESR Access
MDiv ESR Access

COURSE SUBJECT AREAS OFFERED OUTSIDE OF DEGREE PROGRAMS
Graduate—biblical and other theological languages and literatures; biblical studies; creative writing; pastoral counseling and specialized ministries; peace studies and conflict resolution; religious education; religious studies; theological and ministerial studies; theology and religious vocations related.

EAST ARKANSAS COMMUNITY COLLEGE
Forrest City, Arkansas
http://www.eacc.edu

East Arkansas Community College was founded in 1974. It is accredited by North Central Association of Colleges and Schools. It first offered distance learning courses in 2000. In fall 2007, there were 640 students enrolled in distance learning courses. Institutionally administered financial aid is available to distance learners.

Services Distance learners have accessibility to academic advising, bookstore, campus computer network, e-mail services, library services.

Contact Jacqueline Perkins, Distance Learning Coordinator, East Arkansas Community College, 1700 Newcastle Road, Forrest City, AR 72335. Telephone: 870-633-4480 Ext. 362. Fax: 870-633-7222. E-mail: jperkins@eacc.edu.

DEGREES AND AWARDS
Programs offered do not lead to a degree or other formal award.

COURSE SUBJECT AREAS OFFERED OUTSIDE OF DEGREE PROGRAMS
Undergraduate—accounting and computer science; business/managerial economics; computer software and media applications; criminal justice and corrections; education (specific levels and methods); English composition; geography and cartography; health and physical education/fitness; health services/allied health/health sciences; history; languages (Romance languages); legal professions and studies related; manufacturing engineering; mathematics; mathematics and statistics related.

EAST CAROLINA UNIVERSITY
Greenville, North Carolina
Division of Continuing Studies
http://www.options.ecu.edu

East Carolina University was founded in 1907. It is accredited by Southern Association of Colleges and Schools. It first offered distance learning courses in 1947. In fall 2007, there were 5,644 students enrolled in distance learning courses. Institutionally administered financial aid is available to distance learners.

Services Distance learners have accessibility to academic advising, bookstore, campus computer network, e-mail services, library services.

Contact Jennifer Baysden, Distance Education Program Coordinator, East Carolina University, Self Help Center, Greenville, NC 27858. Telephone: 800-328-9275. E-mail: options@ecu.edu.

DEGREES AND AWARDS

BS Communication/Public Relations/Journalism concentration; Education–Birth-Kindergarten Education; Health Information Management; Health Services Management; Hospitality Management; Hospitality Management; Industrial Technology–Bioprocess Manufacturing; Industrial Technology–Industrial Distribution and Logistics; Industrial Technology–Industrial Supervision; Industrial Technology–Information and Computer Technology; Industrial Technology–Manufacturing Systems; Information Technologies

BSBA Business Administration

BSN Nursing–RN to BSN

Graduate Certificate Assistive Technology; Communication–Professional Communication; Community College Teaching; Computer Network Professional; Distance Instruction; Health Care Management; Information Assurance; Lean Six Sigma; Multicultural Literature; Performance Improvement; Security Studies; Substance Abuse/Addiction Counseling; Technology Facilitator; Virtual Reality in Education and Training; Website Developer

MA English–Professional and Technical Communication concentration; Health Education; Multicultural and Transnational Literatures emphasis; Psychology, general

MAE Art Education; Business Education; Health/Teacher Education; Science Teacher Education; Special Education

MAEd Birth–Kindergarten Education

MBA Business Administration

MCM Construction Management

MLS Library Science

MM Music Education

MS Criminal Justice; Instructional Technology; Nutrition; Occupational Safety; Software Engineering; Speech Language and Auditory Pathology; Technology Systems–Computer Networking Management; Technology Systems–Digital Communications; Technology Systems–Distribution and Logistics; Technology Systems–Information Security; Technology Systems–Manufacturing; Technology Systems–Performance Improvement; Technology Systems–Quality Systems; Vocational Education–Information Technologies

MSE Instructional Technology

MSEH Environmental Health

MSN Adult Nurse Practitioner; Neonatal Nurse Practitioner; Nurse Midwifery; Nursing Education; Nursing Leadership; Nursing–Clinical Nurse Specialist; Nursing–Family Nurse Practitioner

COURSE SUBJECT AREAS OFFERED OUTSIDE OF DEGREE PROGRAMS

Undergraduate—bilingual, multilingual, and multicultural education; biology; business administration, management and operations; business/commerce; business/corporate communications; business, management, and marketing related; business operations support and assistant services; chemistry; communication and journalism related; communication and media; computer and information sciences; computer and information sciences and support services related; computer/information technology administration and management; curriculum and instruction; data entry/microcomputer applications; data processing; education; educational assessment, evaluation, and research; educational psychology; education (specific subject areas); engineering technology; hospitality administration; human development, family studies, and related services; industrial production technologies; information science/studies; journalism; management information systems; manufacturing engineering; nursing; philosophy; philosophy and religious studies related; sales, merchandising, and related marketing operations (specialized); technology education/industrial arts.

Graduate—accounting and related services; building/construction finishing, management, and inspection; business administration, management and operations; business/commerce; business, management, and marketing related; communication disorders sciences and services; computer and information sciences; computer/information technology administration and management; computer science; computer software and media applications; computer systems networking and telecommunica-

tions; construction management; criminal justice and corrections; criminology; data processing; education; educational assessment, evaluation, and research; educational/instructional media design; educational psychology; engineering technologies related; English; fine and studio art; foods, nutrition, and related services; industrial production technologies; library science; nursing; nutrition sciences; psychology; psychology related; quality control and safety technologies; rehabilitation and therapeutic professions; special education; technical and business writing; technology education/industrial arts.

See full description on page 382.

EAST CENTRAL COMMUNITY COLLEGE
Decatur, Mississippi
Adult and Continuing Education
http://www.eccc.edu

East Central Community College was founded in 1928. It is accredited by Southern Association of Colleges and Schools. It first offered distance learning courses in 2000. In fall 2007, there were 456 students enrolled in distance learning courses. Institutionally administered financial aid is available to distance learners.

Services Distance learners have accessibility to academic advising, bookstore, campus computer network, e-mail services, library services, tutoring.

Contact Dr. Chris C. Jenkins, Dean of Distance Learning Education, East Central Community College, PO Box 129, Decatur, MS 39327. Telephone: 601-635-6322. Fax: 601-635-4011. E-mail: cjenkins@eccc.edu.

DEGREES AND AWARDS
Programs offered do not lead to a degree or other formal award.

COURSE SUBJECT AREAS OFFERED OUTSIDE OF DEGREE PROGRAMS

Undergraduate—accounting and computer science; allied health and medical assisting services; American literature (United States and Canadian); biblical studies; biological and physical sciences; business administration, management and operations; chemistry; computer and information sciences; developmental and child psychology; economics; education; English; English composition; history; mathematics; music; nursing; physical sciences; psychology; sociology.

EASTERN ILLINOIS UNIVERSITY
Charleston, Illinois
School of Continuing Education
http://www.eiu.edu/~adulted

Eastern Illinois University was founded in 1895. It is accredited by North Central Association of Colleges and Schools. It first offered distance learning courses in 1994. In fall 2007, there were 1,300 students enrolled in distance learning courses. Institutionally administered financial aid is available to distance learners.

Services Distance learners have accessibility to academic advising, bookstore, campus computer network, career placement assistance, e-mail services, library services.

Contact Dr. L. Kaye Woodward, Director, Bachelor of Arts in General Studies Program, Eastern Illinois University, 600 Lincoln Avenue, Charleston, IL 61920. Telephone: 217-581-5618. Fax: 217-581-7076. E-mail: bgsba@www.eiu.edu.

DEGREES AND AWARDS
BA General Studies

COURSE SUBJECT AREAS OFFERED OUTSIDE OF DEGREE PROGRAMS

Undergraduate—accounting and computer science; astronomy and astrophysics; biological and biomedical sciences related; biological and physical sciences; biology; education; education (specific subject areas); family and consumer economics; human development, family studies, and related services; industrial production technologies; mathematics and statistics related; psychology; social sciences related.

Graduate—accounting and related services; building/construction finishing, management, and inspection; business administration, management and operations; computer and information sciences; educational administration and supervision; family and consumer economics; human development, family studies, and related services; marketing.
Non-credit—legal support services.

EASTERN IOWA COMMUNITY COLLEGE DISTRICT
Davenport, Iowa
http://www.eicc.edu

Eastern Iowa Community College District is accredited by North Central Association of Colleges and Schools. It first offered distance learning courses in 2000. In fall 2007, there were 1,798 students enrolled in distance learning courses. Institutionally administered financial aid is available to distance learners.
Services Distance learners have accessibility to academic advising, bookstore, career placement assistance, library services, tutoring.
Contact Dr. Jeff Larson, Dean of EICCD E-learning Enterprise, Eastern Iowa Community College District, 326 West Third Street, Davenport, IA 52801. Telephone: 563-336-5237. E-mail: jlarson@eicc.edu.

DEGREES AND AWARDS
AA Liberal Arts
AAS Cancer Information Management; Health Information Technology; Health, Safety, and Environmental Technology; Information Technology
AS Liberal Arts

COURSE SUBJECT AREAS OFFERED OUTSIDE OF DEGREE PROGRAMS
Non-credit—accounting and computer science; communications technology; computer and information sciences; computer and information sciences and support services related; computer/information technology administration and management; computer programming; computer science; computer software and media applications; computer systems networking and telecommunications; data entry/microcomputer applications; mathematics; mathematics and computer science.

EASTERN KENTUCKY UNIVERSITY
Richmond, Kentucky
Continuing Education and Outreach
http://www.eku.edu/onlinelearning/

Eastern Kentucky University was founded in 1906. It is accredited by Southern Association of Colleges and Schools. It first offered distance learning courses in 1995. In fall 2007, there were 4,500 students enrolled in distance learning courses. Institutionally administered financial aid is available to distance learners.
Services Distance learners have accessibility to academic advising, bookstore, campus computer network, career placement assistance, e-mail services, library services, tutoring.
Contact William St. Pierre, System Director for Credit Programs, Eastern Kentucky University, 202 Perkins Building, 521 Lancaster Avenue, Richmond, KY 40475. Telephone: 859-622-8342. Fax: 859-622-6205. E-mail: bill.stpierre@eku.edu.

DEGREES AND AWARDS
BS Corrections and Juvenile Justice; Fire and Safety Engineering Technology
MS Corrections and Juvenile Justice; Loss Prevention and Safety

COURSE SUBJECT AREAS OFFERED OUTSIDE OF DEGREE PROGRAMS
Undergraduate—accounting and computer science; anthropology; biology; curriculum and instruction; English composition; fine and studio art; geography and cartography; health professions related; history; journalism; marketing; mathematics and statistics related; nursing; philosophy and religious studies related; political science and government; radio, television, and digital communication; social work.

Graduate—business administration, management and operations; counseling psychology; curriculum and instruction; educational administration and supervision; library science; nursing; special education.

EASTERN MENNONITE UNIVERSITY
Harrisonburg, Virginia
Eastern Mennonite Seminary
http://www.emu.edu/seminary/distancelearning/

Eastern Mennonite University was founded in 1917. It is accredited by Southern Association of Colleges and Schools. It first offered distance learning courses in 1997. In fall 2007, there were 20 students enrolled in distance learning courses. Institutionally administered financial aid is available to distance learners.
Services Distance learners have accessibility to academic advising, bookstore, campus computer network, career placement assistance, e-mail services, library services.
Contact Don Yoder, Director of Online Studies, Eastern Mennonite University, 1200 Park Road, Harrisonburg, VA 22802-2462. Telephone: 540-432-4257. Fax: 540-432-4598. E-mail: semadmiss@emu.edu.

DEGREES AND AWARDS
Programs offered do not lead to a degree or other formal award.

COURSE SUBJECT AREAS OFFERED OUTSIDE OF DEGREE PROGRAMS
Graduate—biblical studies; pastoral counseling and specialized ministries; peace studies and conflict resolution; philosophy; philosophy and religious studies related; religious studies; theological and ministerial studies.

EASTERN MICHIGAN UNIVERSITY
Ypsilanti, Michigan
Distance Education
http://www.ce.emich.edu

Eastern Michigan University was founded in 1849. It is accredited by North Central Association of Colleges and Schools. It first offered distance learning courses in 1997. In fall 2007, there were 2,818 students enrolled in distance learning courses. Institutionally administered financial aid is available to distance learners.
Services Distance learners have accessibility to academic advising, bookstore, campus computer network, career placement assistance, e-mail services, library services, tutoring.
Contact Jody Cebina, Assistant Director, Distance Education, Eastern Michigan University, Continuing Education, 101 Boone Hall, Ypsilanti, MI 48197. Telephone: 734-487-1081. Fax: 734-487-6695. E-mail: distance.education@emich.edu.

DEGREES AND AWARDS
BS Dietetics; Technology Management (degree completion)
Graduate Certificate Educational Media and Technology; Geographic Information Systems; Human Resource Management
MS Earth Science Education; Educational Media and Technology; Engineering; Human Nutrition; Integrated Marketing Communications; Quality

COURSE SUBJECT AREAS OFFERED OUTSIDE OF DEGREE PROGRAMS
Undergraduate—applied mathematics; Army J.R.O.T.C/R.O.T.C; biological and physical sciences; biology; biotechnology; business administration, management and operations; business/commerce; business/corporate communications; business, management, and marketing related; cell biology and anatomical sciences; chemistry; communication and journalism related; communication and media; computer systems networking and telecommunications; dietetics and clinical nutrition services; dramatic/theater arts and stagecraft; education; educational administration and supervision; educational assessment, evaluation, and research; education (specific subject areas); English; English composition; entrepreneurial and small business operations; ethnic, cultural minority, and gender studies; finance and financial management services; fine and studio art; food science and technology; foods, nutrition, and

related services; genetics; geography and cartography; history; hospitality administration; human resources management; legal professions and studies related; legal research and advanced professional studies; legal studies (non-professional general, undergraduate); legal support services; liberal arts and sciences, general studies and humanities; marketing; mathematics; military studies; nursing; nutrition sciences; philosophy; philosophy and religious studies related; political science and government; psychology; sales, merchandising, and related marketing operations (general); sales, merchandising, and related marketing operations (specialized); social sciences; sociology; special education; technology education/industrial arts.

Graduate—accounting and computer science; accounting and related services; biomathematics and bioinformatics; business administration, management and operations; business/commerce; business/corporate communications; business, management, and marketing related; computer software and media applications; dietetics and clinical nutrition services; education; educational administration and supervision; educational assessment, evaluation, and research; educational/instructional media design; educational psychology; education related; education (specific levels and methods); education (specific subject areas); engineering; engineering/industrial management; engineering related; engineering science; engineering technologies related; ethnic, cultural minority, and gender studies; food science and technology; foods, nutrition, and related services; geography and cartography; geological and earth sciences/geosciences; human resources management; languages (Germanic); legal research and advanced professional studies; marketing; mathematics; mathematics and statistics related; nursing; psychology related; quality control and safety technologies; sales, merchandising, and related marketing operations (general); school psychology; statistics; technology education/industrial arts.

Non-credit—accounting and related services; education; education related; human resources management.

See full description on page 384.

EASTERN OREGON UNIVERSITY
La Grande, Oregon
Division of Distance Education
http://www.eou.edu/dde/

Eastern Oregon University was founded in 1929. It is accredited by Northwest Commission on Colleges and Universities. It first offered distance learning courses in 1978. In fall 2007, there were 1,800 students enrolled in distance learning courses. Institutionally administered financial aid is available to distance learners.
Services Distance learners have accessibility to academic advising, bookstore, campus computer network, career placement assistance, e-mail services, library services, tutoring.
Contact Mary Koza, Career and Advising Services, Eastern Oregon University, Career and Advising Services, One University Boulevard, La Grande, OR 97850-2899. Telephone: 800-544-2195. Fax: 541-962-3378. E-mail: mkoza@eou.edu.

DEGREES AND AWARDS
BA English Literature; Physical Activity and Health; Psychology

BS Business Administration; Business and Economics; Fire Services Administration; Liberal Studies; Philosophy, Politics, and Economics; Physical Activity and Health; Psychology

COURSE SUBJECT AREAS OFFERED OUTSIDE OF DEGREE PROGRAMS

Undergraduate—accounting and related services; agricultural business and management; anthropology; biology; botany/plant biology; business/commerce; chemistry; computer science; criminology; dramatic/theater arts and stagecraft; economics; English; English language and literature related; geography and cartography; health and physical education/fitness; music; philosophy; physics; political science and government; psychology.

EASTERN UNIVERSITY
St. Davids, Pennsylvania
http://www.eastern.edu

Eastern University was founded in 1952. It is accredited by Middle States Association of Colleges and Schools. It first offered distance learning courses in 2000. In fall 2007, there were 841 students enrolled in distance learning courses. Institutionally administered financial aid is available to distance learners.
Services Distance learners have accessibility to academic advising, bookstore, campus computer network, career placement assistance, e-mail services, library services, tutoring.
Contact Kate Fuerst, Associate Registrar, Accelerated and Online Programs, Eastern University, 1300 Eagle Road, St. Davids, PA 19087-3696. Telephone: 610-341-4392 Ext. Fax: 610-341-1707 Ext. E-mail: kfuerst@eastern.edu.

DEGREES AND AWARDS
MA Organizational Leadership
PhD Organizational Leadership

COURSE SUBJECT AREAS OFFERED OUTSIDE OF DEGREE PROGRAMS
Undergraduate—biblical studies.
Non-credit—biblical studies.

EASTERN WASHINGTON UNIVERSITY
Cheney, Washington
Division for International and Educational Outreach
http://www.ewu.edu/dieo

Eastern Washington University was founded in 1882. It is accredited by Northwest Commission on Colleges and Universities. It first offered distance learning courses in 1970. In fall 2007, there were 600 students enrolled in distance learning courses. Institutionally administered financial aid is available to distance learners.
Services Distance learners have accessibility to academic advising, bookstore, campus computer network, e-mail services, library services.
Contact Michele Opsal, Program Coordinator, Eastern Washington University, 300 Senior Hall, Cheney, WA 99004-2442. Telephone: 800-924-6606. Fax: 509-359-6257. E-mail: gothedistance@ewu.edu.

DEGREES AND AWARDS
Programs offered do not lead to a degree or other formal award.

COURSE SUBJECT AREAS OFFERED OUTSIDE OF DEGREE PROGRAMS
Undergraduate—accounting and related services; business/commerce; communication and media; creative writing; education; English; ethnic, cultural minority, and gender studies; fine and studio art; foods, nutrition, and related services; geography and cartography; health and physical education/fitness; history; human resources management; languages (Germanic); philosophy; psychology related; social psychology; social work; sociology.
Graduate—social work.
Non-credit—allied health diagnostic, intervention, and treatment professions; business administration, management and operations; business/commerce; business/corporate communications; business, management, and marketing related; education; health and physical education/fitness; human resources management; international business; languages (foreign languages related); social work; technical and business writing.

EASTERN WEST VIRGINIA COMMUNITY AND TECHNICAL COLLEGE
Moorefield, West Virginia
http://www.eastern.wvnet.edu

Eastern West Virginia Community and Technical College was founded in 1999. It is accredited by North Central Association of Colleges and Schools. It first offered distance learning courses in 2001. In fall 2007, there were 300 students enrolled in distance learning courses. Institutionally administered financial aid is available to distance learners.
Services Distance learners have accessibility to academic advising, bookstore, library services, tutoring.

Contact Laurel Godlove, Academic Services Program Coordinator, Eastern West Virginia Community and Technical College, 1929 State Road 55, Moorefield, WV 26836. Telephone: 304-434-8000. Fax: 304-434-7000. E-mail: lgodlove@eastern.wvnet.edu.

DEGREES AND AWARDS
Programs offered do not lead to a degree or other formal award.

COURSE SUBJECT AREAS OFFERED OUTSIDE OF DEGREE PROGRAMS
Undergraduate—accounting and computer science; business, management, and marketing related; business operations support and assistant services; computer and information sciences; economics; English; history; liberal arts and sciences, general studies and humanities; marketing; music; political science and government; psychology; sociology; statistics.

EASTERN WYOMING COLLEGE
Torrington, Wyoming
Outreach
http://ewc.wy.edu
Eastern Wyoming College was founded in 1948. It is accredited by North Central Association of Colleges and Schools. It first offered distance learning courses in 1990. In fall 2007, there were 289 students enrolled in distance learning courses. Institutionally administered financial aid is available to distance learners.
Services Distance learners have accessibility to academic advising, bookstore, e-mail services, library services, tutoring.
Contact Aaron Bahmer, Instructional Technologist, Eastern Wyoming College, 3200 West C Street, Torrington, WY 82240. Telephone: 307-532-8284. Fax: 307-532-8229. E-mail: aaron.bahmer@ewc.wy.edu.

DEGREES AND AWARDS
AA Criminal Justice; Interdisciplinary Studies
AAS Business Administration
AS Interdisciplinary Studies

COURSE SUBJECT AREAS OFFERED OUTSIDE OF DEGREE PROGRAMS
Undergraduate—accounting and related services; biology; business administration, management and operations; business/commerce; computer and information sciences; computer software and media applications; criminal justice and corrections; economics; English; English composition; geological and earth sciences/geosciences; health and physical education/fitness; physiological psychology/psychobiology; political science and government; sociology; zoology/animal biology.

EAST GEORGIA COLLEGE
Swainsboro, Georgia
http://www.ega.edu
East Georgia College was founded in 1973. It is accredited by Southern Association of Colleges and Schools. It first offered distance learning courses in 1997. In fall 2007, there were 148 students enrolled in distance learning courses. Institutionally administered financial aid is available to distance learners.
Contact Ms. Priscilla Adams, Director, Continuing Education, East Georgia College, 131 College Circle, Swainsboro, GA 30401. Telephone: 478-289-2120. Fax: 478-289-2057. E-mail: pmadams@ega.edu.

DEGREES AND AWARDS
Programs offered do not lead to a degree or other formal award.

COURSE SUBJECT AREAS OFFERED OUTSIDE OF DEGREE PROGRAMS
Non-credit—health and medical administrative services.

EAST LOS ANGELES COLLEGE
Monterey Park, California
http://www.elac.edu
East Los Angeles College was founded in 1945. It is accredited by Western Association of Schools and Colleges. It first offered distance learning courses in 1998. In fall 2007, there were 1,400 students enrolled in distance learning courses. Institutionally administered financial aid is available to distance learners.
Services Distance learners have accessibility to academic advising, bookstore, e-mail services, library services.
Contact Dr. Wendy Bass, Distance Education Coordinator, East Los Angeles College, 1301 Avenida Cesar Chavez, Monterey Park, CA 91754. Telephone: 323-415-5313. E-mail: basskew@elac.edu.

DEGREES AND AWARDS
Programs offered do not lead to a degree or other formal award.

COURSE SUBJECT AREAS OFFERED OUTSIDE OF DEGREE PROGRAMS
Undergraduate—accounting and related services; business operations support and assistant services; computer and information sciences; family and consumer economics; fine and studio art; foods, nutrition, and related services; health and physical education/fitness; history; liberal arts and sciences, general studies and humanities; management information systems; mathematics; philosophy; psychology; speech and rhetoric; visual and performing arts.

EAST TENNESSEE STATE UNIVERSITY
Johnson City, Tennessee
Office of Distance Education
http://online.etsu.edu
East Tennessee State University was founded in 1911. It is accredited by Southern Association of Colleges and Schools. It first offered distance learning courses in 1990. In fall 2007, there were 12,000 students enrolled in distance learning courses. Institutionally administered financial aid is available to distance learners.
Services Distance learners have accessibility to academic advising, bookstore, campus computer network, career placement assistance, e-mail services, library services, tutoring.
Contact Pat Westington, Internet Program Support Coordinator, East Tennessee State University, Box 70427, Johnson City, TN 37614-0427. Telephone: 423-439-8613. Fax: 423-439-8564. E-mail: westingt@etsu.edu.

DEGREES AND AWARDS
BGS General Studies–Bachelor of General Studies
BS Allied Health Leadership–BS completion program; Applied Science–Bachelor of Applied Science; Dental Hygiene–BS completion program
MA Liberal Studies
MBA/MPA Public Administration
MCP/MPH Master of Public Health

COURSE SUBJECT AREAS OFFERED OUTSIDE OF DEGREE PROGRAMS
Undergraduate—accounting and related services; allied health diagnostic, intervention, and treatment professions; communications technology; comparative literature; criminal justice and corrections; curriculum and instruction; developmental and child psychology; education; educational psychology; education related; English; English composition; geography and cartography; history; liberal arts and sciences, general studies and humanities; psychology; sales, merchandising, and related marketing operations (general); special education; statistics; technical and business writing.
Graduate—business administration, management and operations; city/urban, community and regional planning; curriculum and instruction; education; educational assessment, evaluation, and research; educational/instructional media design; education related; liberal arts and sciences, general studies and humanities; museum studies; public health; religious studies.

Non-credit—allied health and medical assisting services; alternative and complementary medical support services; behavioral sciences; business administration, management and operations; business, management, and marketing related; communication and journalism related; computer and information sciences; computer and information sciences and support services related; computer programming; computer software and media applications; computer systems analysis; computer systems networking and telecommunications; creative writing; culinary arts and related services; entrepreneurial and small business operations; legal support services; liberal arts and sciences, general studies and humanities; marketing; sales, merchandising, and related marketing operations (general).

EDGECOMBE COMMUNITY COLLEGE
Tarboro, North Carolina
http://www.edgecombe.edu

Edgecombe Community College was founded in 1968. It is accredited by Southern Association of Colleges and Schools. It first offered distance learning courses in 1991. In fall 2007, there were 917 students enrolled in distance learning courses. Institutionally administered financial aid is available to distance learners.

Services Distance learners have accessibility to academic advising, bookstore, campus computer network, career placement assistance, e-mail services, library services, tutoring.

Contact Mr. Richard Greene, Distance Learning Director, Edgecombe Community College, 225 Tarboro Street, Rocky Mount, NC 27801. Telephone: 252-823-5166 Ext. 340. Fax: 252-985-2212. E-mail: greener@edgecombe.edu.

DEGREES AND AWARDS
AAS Health Information Technology

COURSE SUBJECT AREAS OFFERED OUTSIDE OF DEGREE PROGRAMS
Undergraduate—accounting and related services; business administration, management and operations; business/commerce; business/corporate communications; business, management, and marketing related; computer and information sciences; computer and information sciences and support services related; computer/information technology administration and management; computer programming; computer software and media applications; computer systems analysis; computer systems networking and telecommunications; data entry/microcomputer applications; education (specific subject areas); English composition; ethnic, cultural minority, and gender studies; health and medical administrative services; health/medical preparatory programs; history; human development, family studies, and related services; management information systems; psychology; sociology; technical and business writing.
Non-credit—accounting and related services; area, ethnic, cultural, and gender studies related; business administration, management and operations; business/commerce; business/corporate communications; business, management, and marketing related; business/managerial economics; business operations support and assistant services; communication and media; community health services; computer and information sciences; computer and information sciences and support services related; computer/information technology administration and management; computer programming; computer science; computer software and media applications; data entry/microcomputer applications; English; English as a second language; health and medical administrative services; management information systems; sales, merchandising, and related marketing operations (specialized).

EDISON STATE COMMUNITY COLLEGE
Piqua, Ohio
http://www.edisonohio.edu/

Edison State Community College was founded in 1973. It is accredited by North Central Association of Colleges and Schools. It first offered distance learning courses in 1987. In fall 2007, there were 675 students enrolled in distance learning courses. Institutionally administered financial aid is available to distance learners.

Services Distance learners have accessibility to academic advising, bookstore, career placement assistance, e-mail services, library services, tutoring.

Contact Cecelia Green, Coordinator of Distance Learning, Edison State Community College, 1973 Edison Drive, Piqua, OH 45356. Telephone: 937-778-8600 Ext. 7883. E-mail: cgreen@edisonohio.edu.

DEGREES AND AWARDS
AA General degree
AAB Medical Office Assistant

COURSE SUBJECT AREAS OFFERED OUTSIDE OF DEGREE PROGRAMS
Undergraduate—accounting and related services; anthropology; biology; business administration, management and operations; business/commerce; business/corporate communications; business operations support and assistant services; cell biology and anatomical sciences; chemistry; computer and information sciences; computer engineering; computer/information technology administration and management; computer programming; computer science; computer software and media applications; computer systems analysis; computer systems networking and telecommunications; criminal justice and corrections; design and applied arts; dramatic/theater arts and stagecraft; ecology, evolution, and population biology; economics; engineering design; engineering/industrial management; English composition; fine and studio art; geography and cartography; history; human development, family studies, and related services; human resources management; industrial production technologies; management information systems; marketing; mathematics; mathematics and computer science; nursing; philosophy; philosophy and religious studies related; physics; psychology; psychology related; public relations, advertising, and applied communication related; religious studies; sociology; speech and rhetoric; statistics.
Non-credit—accounting and related services; business administration, management and operations; business/commerce; business operations support and assistant services; computer and information sciences; computer/information technology administration and management; computer software and media applications; human resources management.

ELAINE P. NUNEZ COMMUNITY COLLEGE
Chalmette, Louisiana
http://www.nunez.edu

Elaine P. Nunez Community College was founded in 1992. It is accredited by Southern Association of Colleges and Schools. It first offered distance learning courses in 1998. In fall 2007, there were 313 students enrolled in distance learning courses. Institutionally administered financial aid is available to distance learners.

Services Distance learners have accessibility to library services.

Contact Mr. Ron Chapman, E-Learning Coordinator, Elaine P. Nunez Community College, 3710 Paris Road, Chalmette, LA 70043. Telephone: 504-278-7485. E-mail: rchapman@nunez.edu.

DEGREES AND AWARDS
Programs offered do not lead to a degree or other formal award.

COURSE SUBJECT AREAS OFFERED OUTSIDE OF DEGREE PROGRAMS
Undergraduate—business/commerce; computer and information sciences and support services related; education related; English composition; health and medical administrative services; history; industrial production technologies; psychology; sociology.

ELGIN COMMUNITY COLLEGE
Elgin, Illinois
http://www.elgin.edu

Elgin Community College was founded in 1949. It is accredited by North Central Association of Colleges and Schools. It first offered distance learning courses in 1980. In fall 2007, there were 1,500 students enrolled in distance learning courses. Institutionally administered financial aid is available to distance learners.

Services Distance learners have accessibility to academic advising, bookstore, campus computer network, e-mail services, library services, tutoring.

Contact Billie B. Barnett, Distance Learning Operations Coordinator, Elgin Community College, 1700 Spartan Drive, Elgin, IL 60123. Telephone: 847-214-7945. Fax: 847-608-5479. E-mail: bbarnett@elgin.edu.

DEGREES AND AWARDS
Programs offered do not lead to a degree or other formal award.

COURSE SUBJECT AREAS OFFERED OUTSIDE OF DEGREE PROGRAMS
Undergraduate—accounting and related services; allied health and medical assisting services; anthropology; business, management, and marketing related; computer and information sciences; computer/information technology administration and management; data entry/microcomputer applications; education related; English; English composition; geological and earth sciences/geosciences; health professions related; human services; legal studies (non-professional general, undergraduate); liberal arts and sciences, general studies and humanities; marketing; mathematics; music; psychology.

ELIZABETH CITY STATE UNIVERSITY
Elizabeth City, North Carolina
http://www.ecsu.edu
Elizabeth City State University was founded in 1891. It is accredited by Southern Association of Colleges and Schools. It first offered distance learning courses in 1998. In fall 2007, there were 400 students enrolled in distance learning courses. Institutionally administered financial aid is available to distance learners.
Services Distance learners have accessibility to academic advising, bookstore, campus computer network, career placement assistance, e-mail services, library services, tutoring.
Contact Dr. Kimberley N. Stevenson, Director of Distance and Continuing Education, Elizabeth City State University, 1704 Weeksville Road, 208 Information Technology Center, Elizabeth City, NC 27909. Telephone: 252-335-3699. Fax: 252-335-3426. E-mail: knstevenson@mail.ecsu.edu.

DEGREES AND AWARDS
Programs offered do not lead to a degree or other formal award.

COURSE SUBJECT AREAS OFFERED OUTSIDE OF DEGREE PROGRAMS
Undergraduate—accounting and related services; air transportation; biology; business administration, management and operations; business/commerce; business/corporate communications; business, management, and marketing related; business/managerial economics; chemistry; criminal justice and corrections; education; educational/instructional media design; educational psychology; education (specific subject areas); English composition; health and physical education/fitness; history; human development, family studies, and related services; human resources management; management sciences and quantitative methods; music; psychology; public administration; public policy analysis; sales, merchandising, and related marketing operations (general); sociology; special education; statistics; taxation.
Graduate—education; educational administration and supervision.

ELIZABETHTOWN COLLEGE
Elizabethtown, Pennsylvania
Center for Continuing Education and Distance Learning
http://www.etowndegrees.com
Elizabethtown College was founded in 1899. It is accredited by Middle States Association of Colleges and Schools. It first offered distance learning courses in 2001. In fall 2007, there were 150 students enrolled in distance learning courses. Institutionally administered financial aid is available to distance learners.
Services Distance learners have accessibility to academic advising, bookstore, campus computer network, e-mail services, library services.

Contact Dr. John Kokolus, Dean of Continuing Education and Distance Learning, Elizabethtown College, 1 Alpha Drive, Elizabethtown, PA 17022. Telephone: 717-361-1291. Fax: 717-361-1466. E-mail: kokolusj@etown.edu.

DEGREES AND AWARDS
Programs offered do not lead to a degree or other formal award.

COURSE SUBJECT AREAS OFFERED OUTSIDE OF DEGREE PROGRAMS
Undergraduate—accounting and computer science; accounting and related services; American literature (United States and Canadian); area, ethnic, cultural, and gender studies related; business administration, management and operations; business/commerce; business/corporate communications; communication and journalism related; communication and media; English; history; human resources management; medieval and Renaissance studies.

ELIZABETHTOWN COMMUNITY AND TECHNICAL COLLEGE
Elizabethtown, Kentucky
Distance Learning Program
http://www.elizabethtowncc.com
Elizabethtown Community and Technical College was founded in 1964. It is accredited by Southern Association of Colleges and Schools. It first offered distance learning courses in 1985. In fall 2007, there were 500 students enrolled in distance learning courses. Institutionally administered financial aid is available to distance learners.
Services Distance learners have accessibility to academic advising, bookstore, career placement assistance, e-mail services, library services.
Contact Dr. Dale Buckles, Dean of Student Affairs, Elizabethtown Community and Technical College, 600 College Street Road, Elizabethtown, KY 42701. Telephone: 270-769-2371 Ext. 4231. Fax: 270-769-0736. E-mail: dale.buckles@kctcs.edu.

DEGREES AND AWARDS
Programs offered do not lead to a degree or other formal award.

COURSE SUBJECT AREAS OFFERED OUTSIDE OF DEGREE PROGRAMS
Undergraduate—business/commerce; communication and media; criminology; English composition; foods, nutrition, and related services; history; management sciences and quantitative methods; nursing; social psychology.

ELLSWORTH COMMUNITY COLLEGE
Iowa Falls, Iowa
Iowa Valley Continuing Education
http://www.iavalley.edu
Ellsworth Community College was founded in 1890. It is accredited by North Central Association of Colleges and Schools. It first offered distance learning courses in 1999. In fall 2007, there were 440 students enrolled in distance learning courses. Institutionally administered financial aid is available to distance learners.
Services Distance learners have accessibility to bookstore, campus computer network, e-mail services, library services.
Contact Dr. Chris Russell, Chief Academic Officer, Ellsworth Community College, 1100 College Avenue, Iowa Falls, IA 50126. Telephone: 641-648-8504. E-mail: chris.russell@iavalley.edu.

DEGREES AND AWARDS
Programs offered do not lead to a degree or other formal award.

COURSE SUBJECT AREAS OFFERED OUTSIDE OF DEGREE PROGRAMS
Undergraduate—accounting and computer science; business/commerce; health professions related.

EMBRY-RIDDLE AERONAUTICAL UNIVERSITY
Daytona Beach, Florida
Distance Learning
http://www.erau.edu/db/degrees/mbaa/
Embry-Riddle Aeronautical University was founded in 1926. It is accredited by Southern Association of Colleges and Schools. It first offered distance learning courses in 2003. In fall 2007, there were 55 students enrolled in distance learning courses. Institutionally administered financial aid is available to distance learners.
Services Distance learners have accessibility to academic advising, bookstore, career placement assistance, e-mail services, library services.
Contact Director of International and Graduate Admissions, Embry-Riddle Aeronautical University, 600 South Clyde Morris Boulevard, Daytona Beach, FL 32114. Telephone: 386-226-7178. Fax: 386-226-7070. E-mail: graduate.admissions@erau.edu.

DEGREES AND AWARDS

MBA Business Administration in Aviation

COURSE SUBJECT AREAS OFFERED OUTSIDE OF DEGREE PROGRAMS

Undergraduate—aerospace, aeronautical and astronautical engineering; business administration, management and operations; business/managerial economics; English composition; finance and financial management services; legal studies (non-professional general, undergraduate); management sciences and quantitative methods; marketing; mathematics and statistics related; statistics.

Graduate—business administration, management and operations; management information systems; management sciences and quantitative methods.

Non-credit—air transportation.

EMBRY-RIDDLE AERONAUTICAL UNIVERSITY
Daytona Beach, Florida
Worldwide Online
http://www.erau.edu/ec/dleo/index.html
Embry-Riddle Aeronautical University was founded in 1926. It is accredited by Southern Association of Colleges and Schools. It first offered distance learning courses in 1983. In fall 2007, there were 2,335 students enrolled in distance learning courses. Institutionally administered financial aid is available to distance learners.
Services Distance learners have accessibility to academic advising, bookstore, career placement assistance, library services.
Contact Mrs. Linda Dammer, Associate Dean of Worldwide Online Administration, Embry-Riddle Aeronautical University, 600 South Clyde Morris Boulevard, Daytona Beach, FL 32114-3900. Telephone: 386-226-6397. Fax: 386-226-7627. E-mail: dleo.student.recruiter@erau.edu.

DEGREES AND AWARDS

AS Aircraft Maintenance; Professional Aeronautics; Technical Management
BS Aviation Maintenance Management; Professional Aeronautics; Technical Management
MAS Aeronautical Science
MS Management

COURSE SUBJECT AREAS OFFERED OUTSIDE OF DEGREE PROGRAMS

Undergraduate—applied mathematics; business/commerce; computer science; economics; English; legal studies (non-professional general, undergraduate); social sciences; statistics; technical and business writing.
Graduate—air transportation; business administration, management and operations; business/commerce; psychology.
Non-credit—air transportation.

EMORY UNIVERSITY
Atlanta, Georgia
Rollins School of Public Health
http://www.sph.emory.edu/CMPH/index.php
Emory University was founded in 1836. It is accredited by Southern Association of Colleges and Schools. It first offered distance learning courses in 1997. In fall 2007, there were 150 students enrolled in distance learning courses. Institutionally administered financial aid is available to distance learners.
Services Distance learners have accessibility to academic advising, bookstore, campus computer network, career placement assistance, e-mail services, library services.
Contact Ms. Essie Mills Reynolds, Business Analyst, Emory University, 1518 Clifton Road, RSPH, Office 152, Atlanta, GA 30322. Telephone: 404-727-8711. Fax: 404-727-3996. E-mail: emills@sph.emory.edu.

DEGREES AND AWARDS

MPH Public Health–Career Master of Public Health program

COURSE SUBJECT AREAS OFFERED OUTSIDE OF DEGREE PROGRAMS

Graduate—public health.

ENDICOTT COLLEGE
Beverly, Massachusetts
http://www.endicott.edu/gps
Endicott College was founded in 1939. It is accredited by New England Association of Schools and Colleges. It first offered distance learning courses in 2003. In fall 2007, there were 250 students enrolled in distance learning courses. Institutionally administered financial aid is available to distance learners.
Services Distance learners have accessibility to academic advising, bookstore, campus computer network, career placement assistance, e-mail services, library services, tutoring.
Contact Dr. Mary Huegel, Dean of School of Graduate and Professional Studies, Endicott College, 376 Hale Street, Beverly, MA 01915. Telephone: 978-232-2084. Fax: 978-232-3000. E-mail: mhuegel@endicott.edu.

DEGREES AND AWARDS
Programs offered do not lead to a degree or other formal award.

COURSE SUBJECT AREAS OFFERED OUTSIDE OF DEGREE PROGRAMS

Undergraduate—business administration, management and operations; business/commerce; business, management, and marketing related; education; English; human development, family studies, and related services; industrial production technologies; management information systems; management sciences and quantitative methods; natural sciences; nutrition sciences; psychology; social sciences.
Graduate—business/commerce; education.
Non-credit—business/commerce.

ERIE COMMUNITY COLLEGE
Buffalo, New York
http://www.ecc.edu/
Erie Community College was founded in 1971. It is accredited by Middle States Association of Colleges and Schools. It first offered distance learning courses in 1992. In fall 2007, there were 573 students enrolled in distance learning courses. Institutionally administered financial aid is available to distance learners.
Services Distance learners have accessibility to academic advising, bookstore, campus computer network, career placement assistance, e-mail services, library services, tutoring.
Contact Ms. Martha Dixon, Assistant Academic Dean, Distance Learning, Erie Community College, 4041 Southwestern Boulevard, Orchard Park, NY 14127. Telephone: 716-851-1939. Fax: 716-851-1629. E-mail: dixon@ecc.edu.

DEGREES AND AWARDS
AA Liberal Arts and Science/Humanities and Social Science
AAS Business–Business Administration; Business–Office Management; Telecommunications Technology–Verizon
AS Business–Business Administration (transfer option)
Certificate Computer Applications for the Office

COURSE SUBJECT AREAS OFFERED OUTSIDE OF DEGREE PROGRAMS
Undergraduate—accounting and related services; anthropology; archeology; biological and biomedical sciences related; business administration, management and operations; business/commerce; business/corporate communications; chemistry; clinical/medical laboratory science and allied professions; computer/information technology administration and management; computer science; computer software and media applications; computer systems analysis; creative writing; criminal justice and corrections; culinary arts and related services; data entry/microcomputer applications; developmental and child psychology; dietetics and clinical nutrition services; dramatic/theater arts and stagecraft; economics; education; English; English composition; English language and literature related; entrepreneurial and small business operations; finance and financial management services; fine and studio art; geography and cartography; health and medical administrative services; health and physical education/fitness; history; hospitality administration; human resources management; journalism; languages (Romance languages); legal professions and studies related; liberal arts and sciences, general studies and humanities; marketing; mathematics; music; natural resources conservation and research; nutrition sciences; personality psychology; philosophy; physiology, pathology and related sciences; political science and government; psychology; religious studies; sales, merchandising, and related marketing operations (general); science, technology and society; social psychology; social sciences related; sociology; statistics; technical and business writing.

ERIE COMMUNITY COLLEGE, NORTH CAMPUS
Williamsville, New York
http://www.ecc.edu/
Erie Community College, North Campus was founded in 1946. It is accredited by Middle States Association of Colleges and Schools. It first offered distance learning courses in 1990. In fall 2007, there were 1,486 students enrolled in distance learning courses. Institutionally administered financial aid is available to distance learners.
Services Distance learners have accessibility to academic advising, bookstore, campus computer network, career placement assistance, e-mail services, library services, tutoring.
Contact Ms. Martha Dixon, Assistant Academic Dean, Distance Learning, Erie Community College, North Campus, 4041 Southwestern Boulevard, Orchard Park, NY 14127. Telephone: 716-851-1939. Fax: 716-851-1629. E-mail: dixon@ecc.edu.

DEGREES AND AWARDS
AA Liberal Arts and Science/Humanities and Social Science
AAS Business–Business Administration; Business–Office Management; Telecomunications Techology–Verizon
AS Business–Business Administration (transfer option)
Certificate Computer Applications for the Office

COURSE SUBJECT AREAS OFFERED OUTSIDE OF DEGREE PROGRAMS
Undergraduate—accounting and related services; anthropology; archeology; biological and biomedical sciences related; business administration, management and operations; business/commerce; business/corporate communications; chemistry; clinical/medical laboratory science and allied professions; computer/information technology administration and management; computer science; computer software and media applications; computer systems analysis; creative writing; criminal justice and corrections; culinary arts and related services; data entry/microcomputer applications; developmental and child psychology; dietetics and clinical nutrition services; dramatic/theater arts and stagecraft; economics; education; English; English composition; English language and literature related; entrepreneurial and small business operations; finance and financial management services; fine and studio art; geography and cartography;

health and medical administrative services; health and physical education/fitness; history; hospitality administration; human resources management; journalism; languages (Romance languages); legal professions and studies related; liberal arts and sciences, general studies and humanities; marketing; mathematics; music; natural resources conservation and research; nutrition sciences; personality psychology; philosophy; physiology, pathology and related sciences; political science and government; psychology; religious studies; sales, merchandising, and related marketing operations (general); science, technology and society; social psychology; social sciences related; sociology; statistics; technical and business writing.

ERIE COMMUNITY COLLEGE, SOUTH CAMPUS
Orchard Park, New York
http://www.ecc.edu/
Erie Community College, South Campus was founded in 1974. It is accredited by Middle States Association of Colleges and Schools. It first offered distance learning courses in 1991. In fall 2007, there were 718 students enrolled in distance learning courses. Institutionally administered financial aid is available to distance learners.
Services Distance learners have accessibility to academic advising, bookstore, campus computer network, career placement assistance, e-mail services, library services, tutoring.
Contact Ms. Martha Dixon, Assistant Academic Dean, Distance Learning, Erie Community College, South Campus, 4041 Southwestern Boulevard, Orchard Park, NY 14127. Telephone: 716-851-1939. Fax: 716-851-1629. E-mail: dixon@ecc.edu.

DEGREES AND AWARDS
AA Liberal Arts and Science/Humanities and Social Science
AAS Business–Business Administration; Business–Office Management; Telecommunications Technology–Verizon
AS Business–Business Administration (transfer option)
Certificate Computer Applications for the Office

COURSE SUBJECT AREAS OFFERED OUTSIDE OF DEGREE PROGRAMS
Undergraduate—accounting and related services; anthropology; archeology; biological and biomedical sciences related; business administration, management and operations; business/commerce; business/corporate communications; chemistry; clinical/medical laboratory science and allied professions; computer/information technology administration and management; computer science; computer software and media applications; computer systems analysis; creative writing; criminal justice and corrections; culinary arts and related services; data entry/microcomputer applications; developmental and child psychology; dietetics and clinical nutrition services; dramatic/theater arts and stagecraft; economics; education; English; English composition; English language and literature related; entrepreneurial and small business operations; finance and financial management services; fine and studio art; geography and cartography; health and medical administrative services; health and physical education/fitness; history; hospitality administration; human resources management; journalism; languages (Romance languages); legal professions and studies related; liberal arts and sciences, general studies and humanities; marketing; mathematics; music; natural resources conservation and research; nutrition sciences; personality psychology; philosophy; physiology, pathology and related sciences; political science and government; psychology; religious studies; sales, merchandising, and related marketing operations (general); science, technology and society; social psychology; social sciences related; sociology; statistics; technical and business writing.

ERIKSON INSTITUTE
Chicago, Illinois
http://www.erikson.edu/programs.
asp?file=infantstudiesonline
Erikson Institute was founded in 1966. It is accredited by North Central Association of Colleges and Schools. It first offered distance learning courses in 2001. In fall 2007, there were 15 students enrolled in distance learning courses. Institutionally administered financial aid is available to distance learners.
Services Distance learners have accessibility to academic advising, bookstore, campus computer network, e-mail services, library services.

Contact Ms. Valerie Williams, Associate Director, Admissions and Multicultural Student Affairs, Erikson Institute, 420 North Wabash Avenue, 6th Floor, Chicago, IL 60611. Telephone: 312-893-7142. Fax: 312-755-0928. E-mail: vwilliams@erikson.edu.

DEGREES AND AWARDS

Programs offered do not lead to a degree or other formal award.

COURSE SUBJECT AREAS OFFERED OUTSIDE OF DEGREE PROGRAMS

Non-credit—human development, family studies, and related services.

EUGENE BIBLE COLLEGE
Eugene, Oregon
External Studies Department
http://www.ebc.edu
Eugene Bible College was founded in 1925. It is accredited by Association for Biblical Higher Education. It first offered distance learning courses in 1987. In fall 2007, there were 46 students enrolled in distance learning courses. Institutionally administered financial aid is available to distance learners.
Services Distance learners have accessibility to academic advising, bookstore, e-mail services.
Contact Mrs. Bettie S. Delury, Director of External Studies, Eugene Bible College, 2155 Bailey Hill Road, Eugene, OR 97405. Telephone: 541-485-1780 Ext. 3200. Fax: 541-762-2301. E-mail: distance-ed@ebc.edu.

DEGREES AND AWARDS

Programs offered do not lead to a degree or other formal award.

COURSE SUBJECT AREAS OFFERED OUTSIDE OF DEGREE PROGRAMS

Undergraduate—applied mathematics; biblical and other theological languages and literatures; biblical studies; biological and physical sciences; biology; education; educational psychology; English literature (British and Commonwealth); history; intercultural/multicultural and diversity studies; languages (Modern Greek); mathematics; missionary studies and missiology; music; pastoral counseling and specialized ministries; physical sciences; religious education; religious/sacred music; religious studies; school psychology; sociology; theological and ministerial studies.

EUGENIO MARÍA DE HOSTOS COMMUNITY COLLEGE OF THE CITY UNIVERSITY OF NEW YORK
Bronx, New York
http://www.hostos.cuny.edu/oaa/insttech.htm
Eugenio María de Hostos Community College of the City University of New York was founded in 1968. It is accredited by Middle States Association of Colleges and Schools. It first offered distance learning courses in 1999. In fall 2007, there were 700 students enrolled in distance learning courses. Institutionally administered financial aid is available to distance learners.
Services Distance learners have accessibility to campus computer network, e-mail services, library services.
Contact Dr. Loreto Porte, EdD, Director of Instructional Technology, Eugenio María de Hostos Community College of the City University of New York, 500 Grand Concourse, Bronx, NY 10451. Telephone: 718-518-6673. E-mail: lporte@hostos.cuny.edu.

DEGREES AND AWARDS

AAS Early Childhood Education
CCCPE Information Systems

COURSE SUBJECT AREAS OFFERED OUTSIDE OF DEGREE PROGRAMS

Undergraduate—accounting and related services; biological and physical sciences; business/commerce; computer programming; dental support

services and allied professions; English; health professions related; information science/studies; public administration; social sciences; visual and performing arts.

EVEREST COLLEGE
Phoenix, Arizona
http://cci.edu
Everest College was founded in 1982. It is accredited by Accrediting Council for Independent Colleges and Schools. It first offered distance learning courses in 2002. In fall 2007, there were 1,200 students enrolled in distance learning courses. Institutionally administered financial aid is available to distance learners.
Services Distance learners have accessibility to academic advising, bookstore, campus computer network, career placement assistance, e-mail services, library services, tutoring.
Contact Jim Askins, Director of Admissions, Everest College, 10400 North 25th Avenue, Suite 190, Phoenix, AZ 85021. Telephone: 602-942-4141 Ext. 2704. Fax: 602-943-0960. E-mail: jaskins@cci.edu.

DEGREES AND AWARDS

Programs offered do not lead to a degree or other formal award.

COURSE SUBJECT AREAS OFFERED OUTSIDE OF DEGREE PROGRAMS

Undergraduate—accounting and related services; business administration, management and operations; business operations support and assistant services; criminology; nursing.

EVERETT COMMUNITY COLLEGE
Everett, Washington
Library/Media/Arts and Distance Learning
http://www.everettcc.edu/elearning
Everett Community College was founded in 1941. It is accredited by Northwest Commission on Colleges and Universities. It first offered distance learning courses in 1997. In fall 2007, there were 1,800 students enrolled in distance learning courses. Institutionally administered financial aid is available to distance learners.
Services Distance learners have accessibility to academic advising, bookstore, e-mail services, library services, tutoring.
Contact Sara J. Frizelle, Director of eLearning, Everett Community College, 2000 Tower Street, Everett, WA 98201. Telephone: 425-388-9585. Fax: 425-259-8257. E-mail: elearning@everettcc.edu.

DEGREES AND AWARDS

AAS Direct Transfer
AGS General Studies

COURSE SUBJECT AREAS OFFERED OUTSIDE OF DEGREE PROGRAMS

Undergraduate—accounting and related services; allied health and medical assisting services; American literature (United States and Canadian); anthropology; applied mathematics; area, ethnic, cultural, and gender studies related; biology; business administration, management and operations; business/commerce; communication and journalism related; computer and information sciences; criminal justice and corrections; criminology; economics; English composition; film/video and photographic arts; geography and cartography; graphic communications; health professions related; history; human development, family studies, and related services; journalism; liberal arts and sciences, general studies and humanities; library science related; mathematics; music; nutrition sciences; philosophy; physical sciences; psychology; psychology related; science technologies related; science, technology and society; social sciences; sociology; visual and performing arts.

EVERGREEN VALLEY COLLEGE
San Jose, California
Telecourse Program
http://www.evc.edu

Evergreen Valley College was founded in 1975. It is accredited by Western Association of Schools and Colleges. It first offered distance learning courses in 1981. In fall 2007, there were 800 students enrolled in distance learning courses. Institutionally administered financial aid is available to distance learners.

Services Distance learners have accessibility to library services, tutoring.

Contact Janice Tomisaka, Program Specialist, Evergreen Valley College, 3095 Yerba Buena Road, San Jose, CA 95135-1598. Telephone: 408-270-6422. Fax: 408-532-1858. E-mail: jan.tomisaka@evc.edu.

DEGREES AND AWARDS
Programs offered do not lead to a degree or other formal award.

COURSE SUBJECT AREAS OFFERED OUTSIDE OF DEGREE PROGRAMS

Undergraduate—anthropology; astronomy and astrophysics; business/commerce; computer and information sciences; English composition; history; languages (Romance languages); library science related; mathematics; music; political science and government; psychology; sociology.

EXCELSIOR COLLEGE
Albany, New York
Learning Services
http://www.excelsior.edu

Excelsior College was founded in 1970. It is accredited by Middle States Association of Colleges and Schools. It first offered distance learning courses in 1970. In fall 2007, there were 34,653 students enrolled in distance learning courses. Institutionally administered financial aid is available to distance learners.

Services Distance learners have accessibility to academic advising, bookstore, career placement assistance, library services, tutoring.

Contact Dana Offerman, PhD, Provost and Chief Academic Officer, Excelsior College, 7 Columbia Circle, Albany, NY 12203. Telephone: 518-464-8500. Fax: 518-464-8700. E-mail: dofferman@excelsior.edu.

DEGREES AND AWARDS
AA Liberal Arts
AAS Administrative/Management Studies; Aviation Studies; Nursing; Technical Studies
AD Occupational Studies in Aviation Studies
AS Business; Computer Software; Electronics Technology; Liberal Arts; Nuclear Technology; Nursing; Science; Technology
BA Liberal Arts; Liberal Studies
BS Accounting NYS CPA track; Accounting; Business, general; Computer Technology; Criminal Justice; Electronics Engineering Technology; Finance; Global Business; Health Sciences; Hospitality Management; Information Technology; Management Information Systems; Management of Human Resources; Marketing; Nuclear Engineering Technology; Operations Management; Risk Management and Insurance; Science
BSN Nursing
BST Technology
MA Liberal Studies
MBA Business
MS Nursing

COURSE SUBJECT AREAS OFFERED OUTSIDE OF DEGREE PROGRAMS

Undergraduate—accounting and computer science; American literature (United States and Canadian); behavioral sciences; biology; business administration, management and operations; business, management, and marketing related; computer and information sciences; computer software and media applications; criminal justice and corrections; English; English composition; health/medical preparatory programs; history; international/global studies; liberal arts and sciences, general studies and humanities; management information systems; mathematics; nuclear engineering technology; psychology.

Graduate—business administration, management and operations; health/medical preparatory programs; liberal arts and sciences, general studies and humanities; nursing.

See full description on page 386.

FAIRFIELD UNIVERSITY
Fairfield, Connecticut
http://www.fairfield.edu/x19806.html

Fairfield University was founded in 1942. It is accredited by New England Association of Schools and Colleges. It first offered distance learning courses in 2002. In fall 2007, there were 200 students enrolled in distance learning courses. Institutionally administered financial aid is available to distance learners.

Services Distance learners have accessibility to academic advising, bookstore, campus computer network, e-mail services, library services, tutoring.

Contact Neil Landino, Assistant Dean, Advising, Fairfield University, University College, North Benson Road, Fairfield, CT 06824. Telephone: 203-254-4000 Ext. 2622. Fax: 203-254-4106. E-mail: nlandino@mail.fairfield.edu.

DEGREES AND AWARDS
AA General degree
BPS Professional Studies

FERRIS STATE UNIVERSITY
Big Rapids, Michigan
http://www.ferris.edu/

Ferris State University was founded in 1884. It is accredited by North Central Association of Colleges and Schools. It first offered distance learning courses in 1991. In fall 2007, there were 60 students enrolled in distance learning courses. Institutionally administered financial aid is available to distance learners.

Services Distance learners have accessibility to academic advising, bookstore, campus computer network, career placement assistance, e-mail services, library services, tutoring.

Contact Mr. Steve Cox, Producer and Director, Ferris State University, 1010 Campus Drive, FLITE 460C, Big Rapids, MI 49307. Telephone: 231-591-2721. Fax: 231-591-2785. E-mail: coxs@ferris.edu.

DEGREES AND AWARDS
Programs offered do not lead to a degree or other formal award.

COURSE SUBJECT AREAS OFFERED OUTSIDE OF DEGREE PROGRAMS

Undergraduate—biological and physical sciences; English as a second language; mathematics and statistics related; ophthalmic and optometric support services and allied professions.

Graduate—ophthalmic and optometric support services and allied professions.

FIELDING GRADUATE UNIVERSITY
Santa Barbara, California
http://www.fielding.edu/

Fielding Graduate University was founded in 1974. It is accredited by Western Association of Schools and Colleges. It first offered distance learning courses in 1974. In fall 2007, there were 1,500 students enrolled in distance learning courses. Institutionally administered financial aid is available to distance learners.

Services Distance learners have accessibility to academic advising, bookstore, e-mail services, library services.

Contact Kathy Belway, Admissions Assistant, Fielding Graduate University, 2112 Santa Barbara Street, Santa Barbara, CA 93105-3538. Telephone: 800-340-1099. Fax: 805-687-9793. E-mail: admission@fielding.edu.

DEGREES AND AWARDS

Certificate Evidence Based Coaching; Integral Studies; Organization Management and Development; Respecialization in Clinical Psychology; Teaching in the Virtual Classroom
MA Organization Management and Development
EdD Educational Leadership and Change
PhD Clinical Psychology; Human and Organizational Development; Media Psychology

COURSE SUBJECT AREAS OFFERED OUTSIDE OF DEGREE PROGRAMS

Non-credit—business administration, management and operations.

FINGER LAKES COMMUNITY COLLEGE
Canandaigua, New York
http://www.flcc.edu

Finger Lakes Community College was founded in 1965. It is accredited by Middle States Association of Colleges and Schools. It first offered distance learning courses in 1970. In fall 2007, there were 507 students enrolled in distance learning courses. Institutionally administered financial aid is available to distance learners.
Services Distance learners have accessibility to academic advising, bookstore, campus computer network, career placement assistance, e-mail services, library services.
Contact Ms. Bonnie Ritts, Director of Admissions, Finger Lakes Community College, 4355 Lakeshore Drive, Canandaigua, NY 14424. Telephone: 585-394-3500 Ext. 7278. Fax: 585-394-5005. E-mail: admissions@flcc.edu.

DEGREES AND AWARDS
AAS Electronic Commerce

COURSE SUBJECT AREAS OFFERED OUTSIDE OF DEGREE PROGRAMS

Undergraduate—accounting and computer science; biology; business/commerce; business/corporate communications; communication and journalism related; computer and information sciences; computer/information technology administration and management; computer programming; criminal justice and corrections; economics; education; health and physical education/fitness; history; legal studies (non-professional general, undergraduate); liberal arts and sciences, general studies and humanities; marketing; mathematics and statistics related; nursing; philosophy; psychology; sales, merchandising, and related marketing operations (specialized); sociology.
Non-credit—computer software and media applications.

FITCHBURG STATE COLLEGE
Fitchburg, Massachusetts
Division of Graduate and Continuing Education
http://www.fsc.edu/

Fitchburg State College was founded in 1894. It is accredited by New England Association of Schools and Colleges. It first offered distance learning courses in 1989. In fall 2007, there were 300 students enrolled in distance learning courses. Institutionally administered financial aid is available to distance learners.
Services Distance learners have accessibility to academic advising, bookstore, campus computer network, career placement assistance, e-mail services, library services, tutoring.
Contact Michael B. Leamy, EdD, Distance Education Coordinator, Fitchburg State College, 160 Pearl Street, Fitchburg, MA 01420. Telephone: 978-665-4783. Fax: 978-665-3658. E-mail: mleamy1@fsc.edu.

DEGREES AND AWARDS
MBA Business Administration
MEd Elementary Education; Secondary Education
MSN Nursing–Master of Science in Forensic Nursing

COURSE SUBJECT AREAS OFFERED OUTSIDE OF DEGREE PROGRAMS

Undergraduate—accounting and computer science; behavioral sciences; biological and physical sciences; business administration, management and operations; communication and media; computer science; education; education related; English; mathematics; nursing; school psychology; social sciences; sociology.
Graduate—behavioral sciences; business administration, management and operations; communication and media; education; educational administration and supervision; education related; nursing; social sciences.

FIVE TOWNS COLLEGE
Dix Hills, New York

Five Towns College was founded in 1972. It is accredited by Middle States Association of Colleges and Schools. It first offered distance learning courses in 2002. In fall 2007, there were 500 students enrolled in distance learning courses.
Contact Mr. Jerry Cohen, Dean of Enrollment, Five Towns College, 305 North Service Road, Dix Hills, NY 11746. Telephone: 631-424-7000 Ext. 2121. Fax: 631-656-2172. E-mail: jcohen@ftc.edu.

DEGREES AND AWARDS
Programs offered do not lead to a degree or other formal award.

COURSE SUBJECT AREAS OFFERED OUTSIDE OF DEGREE PROGRAMS

Undergraduate—liberal arts and sciences, general studies and humanities.

FLATHEAD VALLEY COMMUNITY COLLEGE
Kalispell, Montana
Education Services
http://www.fvcc.edu

Flathead Valley Community College was founded in 1967. It is accredited by Northwest Commission on Colleges and Universities. It first offered distance learning courses in 1992. In fall 2007, there were 318 students enrolled in distance learning courses. Institutionally administered financial aid is available to distance learners.
Services Distance learners have accessibility to academic advising, bookstore, e-mail services, library services.
Contact Faith Hodges, Director of Enrollment Planning and Research, Flathead Valley Community College, 777 Grandview Drive, Kalispell, MT 59901. Telephone: 406-756-3812. Fax: 406-756-3815. E-mail: fhodges@fvcc.edu.

DEGREES AND AWARDS
Programs offered do not lead to a degree or other formal award.

COURSE SUBJECT AREAS OFFERED OUTSIDE OF DEGREE PROGRAMS

Undergraduate—accounting and related services; allied health and medical assisting services; anthropology; biological and physical sciences; business administration, management and operations; computer software and media applications; curriculum and instruction; education (specific subject areas); English; English composition; film/video and photographic arts; geological and earth sciences/geosciences; gerontology; heating, air conditioning, ventilation and refrigeration maintenance technology; human services; languages (foreign languages related); nursing; political science and government; psychology; real estate; sociology; speech and rhetoric.
Non-credit—accounting and computer science; business/commerce; computer/information technology administration and management; computer programming; computer software and media applications; entrepreneurial and small business operations; film/video and photographic arts; legal studies (non-professional general, undergraduate).

FLORIDA GULF COAST UNIVERSITY
Fort Myers, Florida
Enrollment Services
http://www.fgcu.edu

Florida Gulf Coast University was founded in 1991. It is accredited by Southern Association of Colleges and Schools. It first offered distance learning courses in 1997. In fall 2007, there were 3,963 students enrolled in distance learning courses. Institutionally administered financial aid is available to distance learners.

Services Distance learners have accessibility to academic advising, bookstore, campus computer network, career placement assistance, e-mail services, library services, tutoring.

Contact Marc Laviolette, Admissions Director, Florida Gulf Coast University, 10501 FGCU Boulevard South, Fort Myers, FL 33965-6565. Telephone: 239-590-7878. Fax: 239-590-7894. E-mail: admissions@fgcu.edu.

DEGREES AND AWARDS

BS Criminal Justice; Health Science; Legal Studies
MBA Business Administration
MPA Public Administration
MS Geriatric Recreational Therapy; Health Science

COURSE SUBJECT AREAS OFFERED OUTSIDE OF DEGREE PROGRAMS

Undergraduate—accounting and related services; computer science; criminal justice and corrections; educational administration and supervision; education related; environmental/environmental health engineering; finance and financial management services; gerontology; health and medical administrative services; health services/allied health/health sciences; history; human services; information science/studies; management sciences and quantitative methods; marketing; mathematics; nursing; psychology; public administration.
Graduate—education related; legal professions and studies related; public administration.

FLORIDA INSTITUTE OF TECHNOLOGY
Melbourne, Florida
University Alliance–Distance Learning
http://dl.fit.edu

Florida Institute of Technology was founded in 1958. It is accredited by Southern Association of Colleges and Schools. It first offered distance learning courses in 1995. In fall 2007, there were 689 students enrolled in distance learning courses. Institutionally administered financial aid is available to distance learners.

Services Distance learners have accessibility to academic advising, bookstore, career placement assistance, e-mail services, library services.

Contact Mr. Brian Ehrlich, Director, Online Program Administration, Florida Institute of Technology, 150 West University Boulevard, Melbourne, FL 32901. Telephone: 321-422-5137. Fax: 321-574-1498. E-mail: behrlich@fit.edu.

DEGREES AND AWARDS

AA Business Administration; Liberal Arts
BA Accounting; Business Administration; Criminal Justice
BS Computer Information Systems
MBA Business Administration
MS Information Technology

FLORIDA INSTITUTE OF TECHNOLOGY
Melbourne, Florida
University College–Distance Learning Division–Virtual Campus
http://uc.fit.edu/dl

Florida Institute of Technology was founded in 1958. It is accredited by Southern Association of Colleges and Schools. It first offered distance learning courses in 1995. In fall 2007, there were 689 students enrolled in distance learning courses. Institutionally administered financial aid is available to distance learners.

Services Distance learners have accessibility to academic advising, bookstore, career placement assistance, e-mail services, library services.

Contact Ms. Penny Vassar, Senior Resident Administrator, Florida Institute of Technology, 150 West University Boulevard, Melbourne, FL 32901. Telephone: 888-225-2239. Fax: 864-226-2258. E-mail: pvassar@fit.edu.

DEGREES AND AWARDS

MPA Public Administration
MS Acquisition and Contract Management; Human Resources Management; Information Technology; Logistics Management; Management; Material Acquisition Management; Operations Research; Project Management; Systems Management
PMBA Business Administration–Professional Master of Business Administration

COURSE SUBJECT AREAS OFFERED OUTSIDE OF DEGREE PROGRAMS

Graduate—accounting and related services; business administration, management and operations; business/commerce; business/managerial economics; engineering/industrial management; human resources management; information science/studies; management sciences and quantitative methods; marketing; systems engineering; systems science and theory.
Non-credit—behavioral sciences; psychology related.

See full description on page 388.

FLORIDA STATE UNIVERSITY
Tallahassee, Florida
Office for Distributed and Distance Learning
http://learningforlife.fsu.edu/online

Florida State University was founded in 1851. It is accredited by Southern Association of Colleges and Schools. It first offered distance learning courses in 1987. In fall 2007, there were 3,179 students enrolled in distance learning courses. Institutionally administered financial aid is available to distance learners.

Services Distance learners have accessibility to academic advising, bookstore, campus computer network, career placement assistance, e-mail services, library services, tutoring.

Contact Student Support Services, Florida State University, Academic and Professional Program Services, C3500 University Center, Tallahassee, FL 32306-2550. Telephone: 877-357-8283. Fax: 850-644-5803. E-mail: inquiries@campus.fsu.edu.

DEGREES AND AWARDS

BS Interdisciplinary Social Science; Software Engineering
BSN Nursing–RN to BSN
MBA Business Administration
MS Criminology, Criminal Justice Studies major; Educational Leadership/Administration; Information Studies; Instructional Systems–Open and Distance Learning major; Instructional Systems–Performance Improvement and Human Resource Development major; Management Information Systems; Mathematics Education; Physical Education; Risk Management/Insurance; Science Education; Special Education; Speech Language Pathology
MSN Nurse Educator
MSW Social Work

COURSE SUBJECT AREAS OFFERED OUTSIDE OF DEGREE PROGRAMS

Undergraduate—classical and ancient studies; economics; geography and cartography; music; political science and government; public administration; sociology; urban studies/affairs.
Graduate—computer and information sciences; educational/instructional media design; human resources management; information science/studies; library science related; nursing; social work; special education.
Non-credit—building/construction finishing, management, and inspection; computer/information technology administration and management; computer software and media applications; finance and financial management services.

FLORIDA TECH UNIVERSITY ONLINE
Tampa, Florida
http://www.floridatechonline.com
Florida Tech University Online first offered distance learning courses in 2004. In fall 2007, there were 1,000 students enrolled in distance learning courses. Institutionally administered financial aid is available to distance learners.
Services Distance learners have accessibility to academic advising, bookstore, campus computer network, e-mail services, library services, tutoring.
Contact Mr. Jimmy Lynch, Director of Enrollment, Florida Tech University Online, 9417 Princess Palm Avenue, Tampa, FL 33619. Telephone: 888-352-8324. E-mail: jimmy-lynch@universityalliance.com.

DEGREES AND AWARDS
AA Business Administration; Liberal Arts
BA Accounting; Business Administration, Accounting specialization; Business Administration, Computer Information Systems specialization; Business Administration, Healthcare Management specialization; Business Administration, Management specialization; Business Administration, Marketing specialization; Criminal Justice
BS Computer Information Systems
MBA Accounting and Finance specialization; Healthcare specialization; Management specialization; Marketing specialization
MSIT Information Technology

FONTBONNE UNIVERSITY
St. Louis, Missouri
http://www.fontbonne.edu/
Fontbonne University was founded in 1917. It is accredited by North Central Association of Colleges and Schools. It first offered distance learning courses in 2000. In fall 2007, there were 625 students enrolled in distance learning courses. Institutionally administered financial aid is available to distance learners.
Services Distance learners have accessibility to academic advising, bookstore, campus computer network, e-mail services, library services, tutoring.
Contact Ms. Ame Mead, Director, Online Programs, Fontbonne University, 6800 Wydown Boulevard, St. Louis, MO 63105-3098. Telephone: 314-889-4514. Fax: 314-719-3601. E-mail: amead@fontbonne.edu.

DEGREES AND AWARDS
MS Computer Education

COURSE SUBJECT AREAS OFFERED OUTSIDE OF DEGREE PROGRAMS
Undergraduate—business administration, management and operations; communication and media; computer software and media applications; economics; English composition; housing and human environments; mathematics; philosophy; psychology; religious studies.
Graduate—business administration, management and operations; communication disorders sciences and services; computer software and media applications; education.

FOOTHILL COLLEGE
Los Altos Hills, California
Foothill Global Access
http://www.foothillglobalaccess.org
Foothill College was founded in 1958. It is accredited by Western Association of Schools and Colleges. It first offered distance learning courses in 1970. In fall 2007, there were 4,500 students enrolled in distance learning courses. Institutionally administered financial aid is available to distance learners.
Services Distance learners have accessibility to academic advising, bookstore, campus computer network, career placement assistance, e-mail services, library services, tutoring.

Contact Helen Kikoshima, Administrative Assistant, Foothill Global Access, Foothill College, 12345 El Monte Road, Los Altos Hills, CA 94022. Telephone: 650-949-7446. E-mail: kikoshimahelen@fhda.edu.

DEGREES AND AWARDS
AA Economics; General Studies/Social Science; History; Psychology

COURSE SUBJECT AREAS OFFERED OUTSIDE OF DEGREE PROGRAMS
Undergraduate—accounting and related services; anthropology; archeology; area, ethnic, cultural, and gender studies related; business administration, management and operations; communications technology; comparative literature; computer and information sciences; data entry/microcomputer applications; dramatic/theater arts and stagecraft; economics; English as a second language; English composition; film/video and photographic arts; finance and financial management services; fine and studio art; history; library science; linguistic, comparative, and related language studies; music; psychology; radio, television, and digital communication; social sciences; sociology.

FORT HAYS STATE UNIVERSITY
Hays, Kansas
Virtual College
http://www.fhsu.edu/virtualcollege
Fort Hays State University was founded in 1902. It is accredited by North Central Association of Colleges and Schools. It first offered distance learning courses in 1987. In fall 2007, there were 5,155 students enrolled in distance learning courses. Institutionally administered financial aid is available to distance learners.
Services Distance learners have accessibility to academic advising, bookstore, campus computer network, career placement assistance, e-mail services, library services, tutoring.
Contact Kevin Splichal, Student Success Coordinator, Fort Hays State University, 600 Park Street, Hays, KS 67601-4099. Telephone: 800-628-FHSU. Fax: 785-628-4037. E-mail: klsplichal@fhsu.edu.

DEGREES AND AWARDS
AGS General Studies
BA Sociology
BBA Business Communication; Management Information Systems; Management–Human Resources concentration; Management; Marketing
BGS General Studies; Military specialties
BS Early Childhood Unified; Elementary Education; Information Networking and Telecommunications (Computer Networking and Telecommunications concentration); Information Networking and Telecommunications (Web Development concentration); Justice Studies; Organizational Leadership; Technology Leadership
BSN Nursing–RN to BSN
Certificate Business Information Systems; Community Development; E-Commerce Web Development; Geographic Information Systems (GIS); Grant Proposal Writing and Program Evaluation; Human Resource Management; Internetworking; Leadership; Life Issues; Management; Post-Masters Nursing Administration; Post-Masters Nursing Education; Web Development
Certification Addictions Counseling Certification program; Computer Science–Cisco Certified Network Associate Preparation, Military; Computer Science–Cisco Certified Network Associate Preparation, accelerated; English Speakers of Other Languages Endorsement
Endorsement Library Media Specialist; Reading Specialist
Graduate Certificate Advanced Business; Business; Organizational Leadership
MBA Leadership
MLS Liberal Studies
MS Education; Educational Administration; Health and Human Performance; Instructional Technology; Special Education
MSN Family Nurse Practitioner track; Nursing Administration; Nursing Education

COURSE SUBJECT AREAS OFFERED OUTSIDE OF DEGREE PROGRAMS

Undergraduate—accounting and computer science; biological and physical sciences; business administration, management and operations; communication and journalism related; communication disorders sciences and services; computer and information sciences; criminal justice and corrections; economics; educational administration and supervision; education related; English; geological and earth sciences/geosciences; health and physical education/fitness; history; information science/studies; languages (foreign languages related); liberal arts and sciences, general studies and humanities; marketing; mathematics and computer science; multi-/interdisciplinary studies related; music; nursing; philosophy; physics; political science and government; psychology; sociology; special education; technology education/industrial arts.

Graduate—education related; education (specific subject areas); health and physical education/fitness; liberal arts and sciences, general studies and humanities; multi-/interdisciplinary studies related; nursing; special education.

Non-credit—accounting and computer science; accounting and related services; business administration, management and operations; communication and journalism related; economics; family psychology; management information systems; sales, merchandising, and related marketing operations (general).

FORT VALLEY STATE UNIVERSITY
Fort Valley, Georgia
http://www.fvsu.edu/

Fort Valley State University was founded in 1895. It is accredited by Southern Association of Colleges and Schools. It first offered distance learning courses in 1998. In fall 2007, there were 396 students enrolled in distance learning courses. Institutionally administered financial aid is available to distance learners.

Services Distance learners have accessibility to e-mail services, library services.

Contact Amanda Glover, Distance and Distributed Learning Coordinator, Fort Valley State University, 1005 State University Drive, Information Technology, Fort Valley, GA 31030. Telephone: 478-825-6228. E-mail: gloverа@fvsu.edu.

DEGREES AND AWARDS
Programs offered do not lead to a degree or other formal award.

COURSE SUBJECT AREAS OFFERED OUTSIDE OF DEGREE PROGRAMS

Undergraduate—accounting and computer science; accounting and related services; agricultural and food products processing; agricultural/biological engineering and bioengineering; agricultural business and management; animal sciences; behavioral sciences; biology; business, management, and marketing related; business/managerial economics; chemistry; communication and media; computer and information sciences; computer science; criminal justice and corrections; curriculum and instruction; dramatic/theater arts and stagecraft; electrical and electronic engineering technologies; health and physical education/fitness; history; international relations and affairs; languages (foreign languages related); liberal arts and sciences, general studies and humanities; marketing; mathematics; military technologies; political science and government; psychology; social work; sociology.

Graduate—animal sciences; environmental/environmental health engineering; mental and social health services and allied professions.

FOX VALLEY TECHNICAL COLLEGE
Appleton, Wisconsin
http://www.fvtc.edu

Fox Valley Technical College was founded in 1967. It is accredited by North Central Association of Colleges and Schools. It first offered distance learning courses in 1991. In fall 2007, there were 6,014 students enrolled in distance learning courses. Institutionally administered financial aid is available to distance learners.

Services Distance learners have accessibility to bookstore, e-mail services, library services.

Contact Ms. Marge E. Jeffers, Director, Instructional Development and Delivery, Fox Valley Technical College, 1825 North Bluemound, PO Box 2277, Appleton, WI 54912-2277. Telephone: 920-831-4397. Fax: 920-735-5618. E-mail: jeffersm@fvtc.edu.

DEGREES AND AWARDS
Programs offered do not lead to a degree or other formal award.

COURSE SUBJECT AREAS OFFERED OUTSIDE OF DEGREE PROGRAMS

Undergraduate—accounting and computer science; allied health and medical assisting services; applied mathematics; building/construction finishing, management, and inspection; business administration, management and operations; cell biology and anatomical sciences; chemistry; communication and journalism related; computer and information sciences; construction trades; criminal justice and corrections; economics; fire protection; marketing; nursing; psychology; social sciences.

FRAMINGHAM STATE COLLEGE
Framingham, Massachusetts
Division of Academic Technology and Distance Learning
http://www.academicsonline.org/

Framingham State College was founded in 1839. It is accredited by New England Association of Schools and Colleges. It first offered distance learning courses in 1998. In fall 2007, there were 655 students enrolled in distance learning courses. Institutionally administered financial aid is available to distance learners.

Services Distance learners have accessibility to academic advising, bookstore, campus computer network, e-mail services, library services, tutoring.

Contact Ms. Robin Robinson, Director of Distance Learning, Framingham State College, 100 State Street, PO Box 9101, Framingham, MA 01701-9101. Telephone: 508-626-4688. E-mail: atde@frc.mass.edu.

DEGREES AND AWARDS
MEd Curriculum and Instructional Technology

COURSE SUBJECT AREAS OFFERED OUTSIDE OF DEGREE PROGRAMS

Undergraduate—anthropology; biology; business administration, management and operations; computer science; economics; English; foods, nutrition, and related services; geological and earth sciences/geosciences; history; mathematics; music; political science and government; psychology; sociology.

Graduate—business administration, management and operations; business, management, and marketing related; education; education (specific subject areas); finance and financial management services; foods, nutrition, and related services; special education.

FRANCISCAN UNIVERSITY OF STEUBENVILLE
Steubenville, Ohio
Distance Learning
http://www.franciscan.edu/distancelearning

Franciscan University of Steubenville was founded in 1946. It is accredited by North Central Association of Colleges and Schools. It first offered distance learning courses in 1995. In fall 2007, there were 300 students enrolled in distance learning courses. Institutionally administered financial aid is available to distance learners.

Services Distance learners have accessibility to academic advising, bookstore, e-mail services, library services.

Contact Ms. Virginia Garrison, Coordinator, Franciscan University of Steubenville, Distance Learning, 1235 University Boulevard, Steubenville, OH 43952. Telephone: 800-466-8336. Fax: 740-284-7037. E-mail: distance@franciscan.edu.

DEGREES AND AWARDS
MA Theology

COURSE SUBJECT AREAS OFFERED OUTSIDE OF DEGREE PROGRAMS

Undergraduate—philosophy; theological and ministerial studies.
Graduate—theological and ministerial studies.
Non-credit—philosophy; theological and ministerial studies.

FRANKLIN PIERCE UNIVERSITY
Rindge, New Hampshire
http://www.fpconline.net

Franklin Pierce University was founded in 1962. It is accredited by New England Association of Schools and Colleges. It first offered distance learning courses in 2004. Institutionally administered financial aid is available to distance learners.

Services Distance learners have accessibility to academic advising, bookstore, campus computer network, career placement assistance, e-mail services, library services, tutoring.

Contact Online Programs, Franklin Pierce University, 40 University Drive, Rindge, NH 03461. Telephone: 603-899-4000.

DEGREES AND AWARDS

AA Criminal Justice; General Studies; Human Services; Management; Marketing

BA Criminal Justice

BS Computer Information Technology; General Studies; Human Services; Management; Marketing

Certificate Accounting; Human Services; Management; Marketing; Paralegal

Graduate Certificate Emerging Network Technologies; Health Practice Management; Human Resource Management; eCommerce

MBA Health Practice Management; Human Resource Management; Leadership

MS Information Technology Management

FRANKLIN UNIVERSITY
Columbus, Ohio
Technical and Non-Campus-Based Programs
http://www.franklin.edu

Franklin University was founded in 1902. It is accredited by North Central Association of Colleges and Schools. It first offered distance learning courses in 1996. In fall 2007, there were 4,203 students enrolled in distance learning courses. Institutionally administered financial aid is available to distance learners.

Services Distance learners have accessibility to academic advising, bookstore, campus computer network, career placement assistance, e-mail services, library services, tutoring.

Contact Admissions, Franklin University, 201 South Grant Avenue, Columbus, OH 43215. Telephone: 614-797-4700. Fax: 614-797-4799. E-mail: info@franklin.edu.

DEGREES AND AWARDS

AS Accounting; Business Administration; Computer Science; Financial Management; Forensic Accounting; Information Technology

BS Accounting; Applied Management; Business Administration; Business Forensics; Computer Science; Financial Management; Forensic Accounting; Health Care Management; Human Resource Management; Information Technology; Management Information Sciences; Management; Marketing; Public Safety Management; Web Development; eMarketing

MBA Business Administration–Online MBA

COURSE SUBJECT AREAS OFFERED OUTSIDE OF DEGREE PROGRAMS

Undergraduate—accounting and related services; business administration, management and operations; communication and media; computer science; economics; finance and financial management services; health and medical administrative services; human resources management; information science/studies; marketing; mathematics and computer science; statistics.

Graduate—business administration, management and operations.

See full description on page 390.

FRANK PHILLIPS COLLEGE
Borger, Texas
http://www.fpctx.edu

Frank Phillips College was founded in 1948. It is accredited by Southern Association of Colleges and Schools. It first offered distance learning courses in 1986. In fall 2007, there were 300 students enrolled in distance learning courses. Institutionally administered financial aid is available to distance learners.

Services Distance learners have accessibility to academic advising, bookstore, career placement assistance, e-mail services, library services.

Contact Ms. Kim Ward, Coordinator of Extended Education, Frank Phillips College, 1301 Roosevelt, Borger, TX 79007. Telephone: 806-457-4200 Ext. 775. Fax: 806-457-4231. E-mail: kward@fpctx.edu.

DEGREES AND AWARDS
Programs offered do not lead to a degree or other formal award.

COURSE SUBJECT AREAS OFFERED OUTSIDE OF DEGREE PROGRAMS

Undergraduate—accounting and related services; biology; developmental and child psychology; economics; English composition; history; marketing; mathematics and computer science; mathematics and statistics related; political science and government; social psychology; social sciences; speech and rhetoric.

Non-credit—allied health and medical assisting services; computer software and media applications; health professions related.

FULTON-MONTGOMERY COMMUNITY COLLEGE
Johnstown, New York
http://fmcc.suny.edu/

Fulton-Montgomery Community College was founded in 1964. It is accredited by Middle States Association of Colleges and Schools. It first offered distance learning courses in 2002. In fall 2007, there were 70 students enrolled in distance learning courses. Institutionally administered financial aid is available to distance learners.

Contact Mr. Reid J. Smalley, Director of Continuing Education and Workforce Development, Fulton-Montgomery Community College, 2805 State Highway 67, Johnstown, NY 12095. Telephone: 518-762-4651 Ext. 8102. Fax: 518-762-4334. E-mail: reid.smalley@fmcc.suny.edu.

DEGREES AND AWARDS
Programs offered do not lead to a degree or other formal award.

COURSE SUBJECT AREAS OFFERED OUTSIDE OF DEGREE PROGRAMS

Non-credit—accounting and related services; business administration, management and operations; business/commerce; business, management, and marketing related; computer software and media applications; computer systems networking and telecommunications; education related; entrepreneurial and small business operations; health professions related; languages (foreign languages related).

GADSDEN STATE COMMUNITY COLLEGE
Gadsden, Alabama
Distance Learning
http://www.gadsdenstate.edu/dl/

Gadsden State Community College was founded in 1965. It is accredited by Southern Association of Colleges and Schools. It first offered distance learning courses in 1978. In fall 2007, there were 1,481 students enrolled in distance learning courses. Institutionally administered financial aid is available to distance learners.

Services Distance learners have accessibility to academic advising, bookstore, campus computer network, career placement assistance, e-mail services, library services.

Contact Ms. Sara W. Brenizer, Associate Dean, Distance Learning, Gadsden State Community College, PO Box 227, 1001 Wallace Drive, 240 B Inzer Hall, Gadsden, AL 35902. Telephone: 256-439-6833. Fax: 256-549-8466. E-mail: sbrenizer@gadsdenstate.edu.

DEGREES AND AWARDS

AGS General Studies

AS Business Administration

COURSE SUBJECT AREAS OFFERED OUTSIDE OF DEGREE PROGRAMS

Undergraduate—accounting and computer science; biology; business administration, management and operations; business/managerial economics; chemistry; computer science; cosmetology and related personal grooming services; economics; education related; English; health and physical education/fitness; health services/allied health/health sciences; history; mathematics; music; nursing; nutrition sciences; philosophy; political science and government; psychology; sociology; speech and rhetoric.

GALVESTON COLLEGE

Galveston, Texas

Distance Education

http://www.gc.edu/gc/Distance_Education.asp

Galveston College was founded in 1967. It is accredited by Southern Association of Colleges and Schools. It first offered distance learning courses in 1987. In fall 2007, there were 400 students enrolled in distance learning courses. Institutionally administered financial aid is available to distance learners.

Services Distance learners have accessibility to academic advising, bookstore, career placement assistance, library services, tutoring.

Contact Mrs. Jenni Willis-Opalenik, Coordinator of Distance Learning, Galveston College, 4015 Avenue Q, R-110, Galveston, TX 77550. Telephone: 409-944-1243. Fax: 409-944-1521. E-mail: jopaleni@gc.edu.

DEGREES AND AWARDS

Programs offered do not lead to a degree or other formal award.

COURSE SUBJECT AREAS OFFERED OUTSIDE OF DEGREE PROGRAMS

Undergraduate—accounting and computer science; accounting and related services; allied health and medical assisting services; allied health diagnostic, intervention, and treatment professions; American literature (United States and Canadian); anthropology; behavioral sciences; biology; business administration, management and operations; business/corporate communications; business operations support and assistant services; chemistry; communication and journalism related; communications technologies and support services related; community health services; computer and information sciences; computer and information sciences and support services related; computer/information technology administration and management; computer programming; computer science; computer software and media applications; computer systems networking and telecommunications; criminal justice and corrections; culinary arts and related services; developmental and child psychology; economics; education; English; English composition; English literature (British and Commonwealth); food science and technology; foods, nutrition, and related services; geography and cartography; health and physical education/fitness; health professions related; health services/allied health/health sciences; history; hospitality administration; information science/studies; journalism; liberal arts and sciences, general studies and humanities; management information systems; marketing; mathematics; music; nuclear and industrial radiologic technologies; nursing; philosophy and religious studies related; political science and government; psychology; social sciences; sociology; speech and rhetoric; statistics.

Non-credit—accounting and computer science; accounting and related services; business, management, and marketing related; computer/information technology administration and management; computer programming; family and consumer sciences/human sciences related; foods, nutrition, and related services; hospitality administration; legal studies (non-professional general, undergraduate); real estate.

GARRETT COLLEGE

McHenry, Maryland

Garrett Communiversity

http://www.garrettcollege.edu

Garrett College was founded in 1966. It is accredited by Middle States Association of Colleges and Schools. It first offered distance learning courses in 1994. In fall 2007, there were 50 students enrolled in distance learning courses. Institutionally administered financial aid is available to distance learners.

Services Distance learners have accessibility to academic advising, bookstore, campus computer network, e-mail services, library services.

Contact Ms. Lisa Bernard, Coordinator of Distance Learning, Garrett College, 687 Mosser Road, McHenry, MD 21541. Telephone: 301-387-3155. Fax: 301-387-3055. E-mail: dlearn@garrettcollege.edu.

DEGREES AND AWARDS

AGS General Studies

COURSE SUBJECT AREAS OFFERED OUTSIDE OF DEGREE PROGRAMS

Undergraduate—English composition.

Non-credit—social work.

GATEWAY COMMUNITY COLLEGE

New Haven, Connecticut

http://www.gwcc.commnet.edu/

Gateway Community College was founded in 1992. It is accredited by New England Association of Schools and Colleges. It first offered distance learning courses in 1999. In fall 2007, there were 412 students enrolled in distance learning courses. Institutionally administered financial aid is available to distance learners.

Services Distance learners have accessibility to academic advising, career placement assistance, e-mail services, library services, tutoring.

Contact Ms. Kim Shea, Director of Admissions, Gateway Community College, 60 Sargent Drive, New Haven, CT 06511. Telephone: 203-285-2011. Fax: 203-285-2018. E-mail: kshea@gwcc.commnet.edu.

DEGREES AND AWARDS

Programs offered do not lead to a degree or other formal award.

COURSE SUBJECT AREAS OFFERED OUTSIDE OF DEGREE PROGRAMS

Undergraduate—business/commerce; health/medical preparatory programs; microbiological sciences and immunology; philosophy; political science and government; social sciences.

GATEWAY TECHNICAL COLLEGE

Kenosha, Wisconsin

http://www.gtc.edu

Gateway Technical College was founded in 1911. It is accredited by North Central Association of Colleges and Schools. It first offered distance learning courses in 1941. In fall 2007, there were 1,140 students enrolled in distance learning courses. Institutionally administered financial aid is available to distance learners.

Services Distance learners have accessibility to academic advising, bookstore, campus computer network, career placement assistance, e-mail services, library services, tutoring.

Contact Jeff Robshaw, Vice President, Learning Innovation, Gateway Technical College, Kenosha, WI 53144. Telephone: 262-564-3676. E-mail: robshawj@gtc.edu.

DEGREES AND AWARDS

AAS Accounting; Instructional Assistant; Supervisory Managment; Technical Communications

COURSE SUBJECT AREAS OFFERED OUTSIDE OF DEGREE PROGRAMS

Undergraduate—accounting and related services; allied health and medical assisting services; business, management, and marketing related;

computer science; education related; mathematics; nursing; plant sciences; psychology; sociology; teaching assistants/aides.

GENESEE COMMUNITY COLLEGE
Batavia, New York
Information Technology and Distance Learning
http://www.genesee.edu/DL

Genesee Community College was founded in 1966. It is accredited by Middle States Association of Colleges and Schools. It first offered distance learning courses in 1987. In fall 2007, there were 1,260 students enrolled in distance learning courses. Institutionally administered financial aid is available to distance learners.

Services Distance learners have accessibility to academic advising, bookstore, campus computer network, career placement assistance, e-mail services, library services, tutoring.

Contact Ms. Judith M. Littlejohn, Academic Support/Distance Learning Advisor, Genesee Community College, 1 College Road, Batavia, NY 14020-9704. Telephone: 585-343-0055 Ext. 6158. Fax: 585-343-0433. E-mail: jmlittlejohn@genesee.edu.

DEGREES AND AWARDS

AAS Business Administration; Criminal Justice; Entrepreneurship

AS Business Administration; Criminal Justice; Economic Crime Investigation; General Studies; Teacher Education Transfer

COURSE SUBJECT AREAS OFFERED OUTSIDE OF DEGREE PROGRAMS

Undergraduate—accounting and related services; anthropology; business/commerce; business, management, and marketing related; computer and information sciences; creative writing; criminal justice and corrections; developmental and child psychology; economics; education; education related; English composition; English language and literature related; gerontology; history; hospitality administration; marketing; mathematics; mathematics and statistics related; music; political science and government; psychology; psychology related; sales, merchandising, and related marketing operations (general); social sciences; sociology; statistics.

See full description on page 392.

GEORGE C. WALLACE COMMUNITY COLLEGE
Dothan, Alabama
http://wallace.edu

George C. Wallace Community College was founded in 1949. It is accredited by Southern Association of Colleges and Schools. It first offered distance learning courses in 2001. In fall 2007, there were 1,000 students enrolled in distance learning courses. Institutionally administered financial aid is available to distance learners.

Services Distance learners have accessibility to academic advising, career placement assistance, e-mail services, library services.

Contact Mr. David Cruz-Wells, Distance Education Technology Specialist, George C. Wallace Community College, 1141 Wallace Drive, Dothan, AL 36303. Telephone: 334-556-2255. E-mail: dcruzwells@wallace.edu.

DEGREES AND AWARDS

Programs offered do not lead to a degree or other formal award.

COURSE SUBJECT AREAS OFFERED OUTSIDE OF DEGREE PROGRAMS

Undergraduate—accounting and related services; biological and physical sciences; biology; business administration, management and operations; business/commerce; chemistry; computer and information sciences; data entry/microcomputer applications; economics; English composition; English literature (British and Commonwealth); fine and studio art; history; mathematics; physical sciences; psychology.

GEORGE FOX UNIVERSITY
Newberg, Oregon

George Fox University was founded in 1891. It is accredited by Northwest Commission on Colleges and Universities. It first offered distance learning courses in 2004. In fall 2007, there were 302 students enrolled in distance learning courses.

Services Distance learners have accessibility to academic advising, bookstore, e-mail services, library services.

Contact Admissions, George Fox University, Newberg, OR 97132. E-mail: admissions@georgefox.edu.

DEGREES AND AWARDS

Programs offered do not lead to a degree or other formal award.

COURSE SUBJECT AREAS OFFERED OUTSIDE OF DEGREE PROGRAMS

Graduate—business administration, management and operations; educational administration and supervision; educational assessment, evaluation, and research; pastoral counseling and specialized ministries.

GEORGE MASON UNIVERSITY
Fairfax, Virginia
http://www.gmu.edu/

George Mason University was founded in 1957. It is accredited by Southern Association of Colleges and Schools. It first offered distance learning courses in 1990. In fall 2007, there were 898 students enrolled in distance learning courses. Institutionally administered financial aid is available to distance learners.

Services Distance learners have accessibility to academic advising, bookstore, campus computer network, career placement assistance, e-mail services, library services.

Contact Miss Cheryl Choy, Special Assistant for Distance and Technical Education, Office of the Provost, George Mason University, 4400 University Drive, MSN 1D6, Fairfax, VA 22030. E-mail: cchoy@gmu.edu.

DEGREES AND AWARDS

Graduate Certificate Computer Networking; E-Learning; Nonprofit Management; Quality Improvement and Outcomes Management
MA Transportation Policy, Operations, and Logistics
MSCS Computer Science
MSN Nursing Administration

COURSE SUBJECT AREAS OFFERED OUTSIDE OF DEGREE PROGRAMS

Undergraduate—computer science; English composition; geography and cartography.
Graduate—biological and biomedical sciences related; business, management, and marketing related; computer science; computer systems networking and telecommunications; health professions related; nursing; public administration and social service professions related.

THE GEORGE WASHINGTON UNIVERSITY
Washington, District of Columbia
Graduate School of Political Management

The George Washington University was founded in 1821. It is accredited by Middle States Association of Colleges and Schools.

Contact Graduate School of Political Management, The George Washington University, 2121 Eye Street NW, Washington, DC 20052. Telephone: 202-994-1000.

DEGREES AND AWARDS

MPS Political Management; Strategic Public Relations

THE GEORGE WASHINGTON UNIVERSITY
Washington, District of Columbia
http://nearyou.gwu.edu/

The George Washington University was founded in 1821. It is accredited by Middle States Association of Colleges and Schools. Institutionally administered financial aid is available to distance learners.

Contact GW Near You, The George Washington University, 2029 K Street NW, Washington, DC 20006. Telephone: 202-994-1000. E-mail: nearyou@gwu.edu.

DEGREES AND AWARDS

Certificate Event Management; International Public Health–Community Oriented Primary Care option; Records Management
AMTA Accelerated Master of Tourism Administration
MA Educational Technology Leadership
MBA/MHSA Clinical Health Sciences; Clinical Management and Leadership; Clinical Research Administration; Emergency Health Services
MPS Law Firm Management
MS Health Science; Project Management

GEORGIA COLLEGE & STATE UNIVERSITY
Milledgeville, Georgia
http://www.gcsu.edu/

Georgia College & State University was founded in 1889. It is accredited by Southern Association of Colleges and Schools. It first offered distance learning courses in 1995. In fall 2007, there were 299 students enrolled in distance learning courses. Institutionally administered financial aid is available to distance learners.
Services Distance learners have accessibility to campus computer network, career placement assistance, e-mail services, library services.
Contact Ms. Maryllis Wolfgang, Director of Graduate Admissions, Georgia College & State University, Campus Box 107, Milledgeville, GA 31061. Telephone: 478-445-1184. Fax: 478-445-1336. E-mail: lis.wolfgang@gcsu.edu.

DEGREES AND AWARDS

MBA Web MBA
MMT Music Therapy

COURSE SUBJECT AREAS OFFERED OUTSIDE OF DEGREE PROGRAMS

Undergraduate—health professions related.
Graduate—education; health professions related; management information systems; nursing.

GEORGIA HIGHLANDS COLLEGE
Rome, Georgia
Department of Extended Learning
http://www.georgiahighlands.edu/extendedlearning/

Georgia Highlands College was founded in 1970. It is accredited by Southern Association of Colleges and Schools. It first offered distance learning courses in 1977. In fall 2007, there were 653 students enrolled in distance learning courses. Institutionally administered financial aid is available to distance learners.
Services Distance learners have accessibility to academic advising, bookstore, campus computer network, e-mail services, library services, tutoring.
Contact Jeff Brown, Director of Extended Learning, Georgia Highlands College, Heritage Hall Campus, 415 East Third Avenue, Rome, GA 30161. Telephone: 706-802-5300. Fax: 706-295-6732. E-mail: jbrown@highlands.edu.

DEGREES AND AWARDS

Programs offered do not lead to a degree or other formal award.

COURSE SUBJECT AREAS OFFERED OUTSIDE OF DEGREE PROGRAMS

Undergraduate—allied health and medical assisting services; biology; developmental and child psychology; economics; English; English composition; English language and literature related; health and physical education/fitness; history; mathematics; nursing; psychology.

GEORGIA INSTITUTE OF TECHNOLOGY
Atlanta, Georgia
Center for Distance Learning
http://www.dlpe.gatech.edu/dl/

Georgia Institute of Technology was founded in 1885. It is accredited by Southern Association of Colleges and Schools. It first offered distance learning courses in 1977. In fall 2007, there were 1,000 students enrolled in distance learning courses. Institutionally administered financial aid is available to distance learners.
Services Distance learners have accessibility to academic advising, bookstore, campus computer network, e-mail services, library services.

Contact Ms. Tanya Krawiec, Student Support Services Manager, Georgia Institute of Technology, 84 5th Street NW, Room 013, Atlanta, GA 30308-1031. Telephone: 404-894-3378. Fax: 404-894-8924. E-mail: tanya.krawiec@dlpe.gatech.edu.

DEGREES AND AWARDS

MS Aerospace Engineering; Computational Science and Engineering (CSE); Electrical Engineering; Environmental Engineering; Industrial and Systems Engineering; Mechanical Engineering; Medical Physics; Operations Research

COURSE SUBJECT AREAS OFFERED OUTSIDE OF DEGREE PROGRAMS

Graduate—aerospace, aeronautical and astronautical engineering; applied mathematics; architectural engineering; architecture related; biomedical/medical engineering; building/construction finishing, management, and inspection; civil engineering; computer and information sciences; computer engineering; computer engineering technologies; computer science; computer systems analysis; engineering design; engineering/industrial management; environmental/environmental health engineering; mathematics; mechanical engineering.
Non-credit—aerospace, aeronautical and astronautical engineering; civil engineering; computer engineering; environmental/environmental health engineering; mathematics; mechanical engineering.
See full description on page 394.

GEORGIA STATE UNIVERSITY
Atlanta, Georgia
Division of Distance and Distributed Learning
http://www.gsu.edu/uets

Georgia State University was founded in 1913. It is accredited by Southern Association of Colleges and Schools. It first offered distance learning courses in 1996. In fall 2007, there were 20,000 students enrolled in distance learning courses. Institutionally administered financial aid is available to distance learners.
Services Distance learners have accessibility to academic advising, bookstore, campus computer network, career placement assistance, e-mail services, library services, tutoring.
Contact Project Manager, Georgia State University, PO Box 3994, Atlanta, GA 30302. E-mail: pchristopher@gsu.edu.

DEGREES AND AWARDS

Programs offered do not lead to a degree or other formal award.

COURSE SUBJECT AREAS OFFERED OUTSIDE OF DEGREE PROGRAMS

Undergraduate—American literature (United States and Canadian); area, ethnic, cultural, and gender studies related; biology; chemistry; communication and journalism related; computer and information sciences; computer science; criminal justice and corrections; economics; English; ethnic, cultural minority, and gender studies; geological and earth sciences/geosciences; gerontology; history; international business; journalism; languages (Germanic); languages (Romance languages); marketing; mathematics; nursing; nutrition sciences; philosophy; physics; psychology; public administration; public health; real estate; social sciences; social work; sociology; statistics.
Graduate—accounting and related services; business/commerce; economics; educational/instructional media design; information science/studies; nursing.

GLENVILLE STATE COLLEGE
Glenville, West Virginia
http://www.glenville.edu/

Glenville State College was founded in 1872. It is accredited by North Central Association of Colleges and Schools. It first offered distance learning courses in 1997. In fall 2007, there were 219 students enrolled in distance learning courses. Institutionally administered financial aid is available to distance learners.
Services Distance learners have accessibility to academic advising, bookstore, campus computer network, career placement assistance, e-mail services, library services, tutoring.

Contact Dr. Kathy Butler, Provost and Senior Vice President, Glenville State College, 200 High Street, Glenville, WV 26351. Telephone: 304-462-4100. Fax: 304-462-8619. E-mail: kathy.butler@glenville.edu.

DEGREES AND AWARDS
Programs offered do not lead to a degree or other formal award.

COURSE SUBJECT AREAS OFFERED OUTSIDE OF DEGREE PROGRAMS

Undergraduate—business, management, and marketing related; computer software and media applications; criminal justice and corrections; economics; education (specific subject areas); English; history; mathematics and statistics related; political science and government.

GLOBAL UNIVERSITY
Springfield, Missouri
http://www.globaluniversity.edu/

Global University was founded in 1948. It is accredited by Distance Education and Training Council. It first offered distance learning courses in 1948. In fall 2007, there were 5,300 students enrolled in distance learning courses. Institutionally administered financial aid is available to distance learners.

Services Distance learners have accessibility to academic advising, e-mail services, library services.

Contact Rev. Todd Waggoner, Director of Enrollment and International Student Services, Global University, 1211 South Glenstone Avenue, Springfield, MO 65804. Telephone: 417-862-9533 Ext. 2335. Fax: 417-863-9621. E-mail: twaggoner@globaluniversity.edu.

DEGREES AND AWARDS
AA Bible/Theology; Church Ministries; Religious Studies
BA Bible and Theology; Missions; Religious Education
Diploma Ministry; Theology
MA Biblical Studies–Broad Field Plan; Biblical Studies–New Testament concentration; Ministerial Studies–Broad Field Plan; Ministerial Studies–Education concentration; Ministerial Studies–Leadership concentration; Ministerial Studies–Missions concentration
MDiv Divinity

COURSE SUBJECT AREAS OFFERED OUTSIDE OF DEGREE PROGRAMS

Non-credit—biblical and other theological languages and literatures; biblical studies; business administration, management and operations; languages (foreign languages related); missionary studies and missiology; music; pastoral counseling and specialized ministries; philosophy and religious studies related; religious education; religious/sacred music; religious studies; theological and ministerial studies; theology and religious vocations related.

GOLDEN GATE UNIVERSITY
San Francisco, California
CyberCampus
http://www.ggu.edu/cybercampus

Golden Gate University was founded in 1901. It is accredited by Western Association of Schools and Colleges. It first offered distance learning courses in 1997. In fall 2007, there were 1,221 students enrolled in distance learning courses.

Services Distance learners have accessibility to academic advising, bookstore, e-mail services.

Contact Enrollment Counselor, Golden Gate University, 536 Mission Street, San Francisco, CA 94105. Telephone: 888-448-3381. E-mail: admissions@ggu.edu.

DEGREES AND AWARDS
BA Management
BBA Accounting; Business Administration; Human Resources Management; Information Technology; Public Administration

Certificate Accounting (Undergraduate); Database Technology and Management (Undergraduate); Human Resource Management; Information Technology; Public Administration

Graduate Certificate Accounting; Estate Planning; Finance; Financial Planning; Human Resource Management; Information Technology; Integrated Marketing Communications; International Taxation; Marketing; Operations and Supply Chain Management; Public Relations; Taxation

MBA Accounting; Business Administration; Finance; Human Resource Management; Information Technology; International Business; Management; Marketing; Operations and Supply Chain Management; Public Administration

MBA/M Acc Accounting

MPA Executive Master of Public Administration

MS Finance–Corporate Finance concentration; Finance; Financial Planning and Taxation; Financial Planning; Human Resource Management; Information Technology; Integrated Marketing Communications; Marketing; Taxation

COURSE SUBJECT AREAS OFFERED OUTSIDE OF DEGREE PROGRAMS

Undergraduate—accounting and related services; business, management, and marketing related; communication and media; economics; English composition; English language and literature related; finance and financial management services; information science/studies; marketing; mathematics; philosophy.

Graduate—accounting and related services; business, management, and marketing related; economics; English composition; finance and financial management services; information science/studies; marketing; mathematics; taxation.

GOLDEN WEST COLLEGE
Huntington Beach, California
http://www.onlinegwc.org

Golden West College was founded in 1966. It is accredited by Western Association of Schools and Colleges. It first offered distance learning courses in 1999. In fall 2007, there were 9,521 students enrolled in distance learning courses. Institutionally administered financial aid is available to distance learners.

Services Distance learners have accessibility to academic advising, bookstore, library services, tutoring.

Contact Help Desk, Golden West College. Telephone: 714-895-8389. E-mail: helpdesk@onlinegwc.org.

DEGREES AND AWARDS
AA Criminal Justice

COURSE SUBJECT AREAS OFFERED OUTSIDE OF DEGREE PROGRAMS

Undergraduate—accounting and computer science; accounting and related services; anthropology; archeology; behavioral sciences; bilingual, multilingual, and multicultural education; biological and physical sciences; biology; biopsychology; business administration, management and operations; business/commerce; business, management, and marketing related; computer and information sciences; computer programming; computer science; computer software and media applications; criminal justice and corrections; criminology; developmental and child psychology; English; English composition; history; languages (Romance languages); library science; linguistic, comparative, and related language studies; marketing; mathematics; mathematics and computer science; philosophy; political science and government; psychology; real estate; social sciences; sociology.

GONZAGA UNIVERSITY
Spokane, Washington
School of Professional Studies
http://www.gonzaga.edu/

Gonzaga University was founded in 1887. It is accredited by Northwest Commission on Colleges and Universities. It first offered distance learning courses in 1995. In fall 2007, there were 900 students enrolled in distance learning courses. Institutionally administered financial aid is available to distance learners.

Services Distance learners have accessibility to academic advising, bookstore, campus computer network, career placement assistance, e-mail services, library services, tutoring.

Contact Distance Learning Programs, Gonzaga University, East 502 Boone, Spokane, WA 99258. Telephone: 866-295-3105.

DEGREES AND AWARDS

MA Communication and Leadership Studies; Organizational Leadership
MS Nursing

COURSE SUBJECT AREAS OFFERED OUTSIDE OF DEGREE PROGRAMS

Undergraduate—social sciences.
Graduate—communication and media; nursing; social sciences.

GORDON-CONWELL THEOLOGICAL SEMINARY
South Hamilton, Massachusetts
Independent Studies Program
http://www.gordonconwell.edu/ockenga/semlink/

Gordon-Conwell Theological Seminary was founded in 1884. It is accredited by New England Association of Schools and Colleges. It first offered distance learning courses in 1986. In fall 2007, there were 1,250 students enrolled in distance learning courses.

Services Distance learners have accessibility to academic advising, bookstore, career placement assistance, library services.

Contact Mr. Craig F. Bridges, Semlink Assistant Director, Gordon-Conwell Theological Seminary, 130 Essex Street, South Hamilton, MA 01982. Telephone: 978-646-4144. Fax: 978-646-4565. E-mail: semlink @gcts.edu.

DEGREES AND AWARDS

Programs offered do not lead to a degree or other formal award.

COURSE SUBJECT AREAS OFFERED OUTSIDE OF DEGREE PROGRAMS

Graduate—biblical and other theological languages and literatures; biblical studies; developmental and child psychology; pastoral counseling and specialized ministries; philosophy and religious studies related; religious education; religious studies; theological and ministerial studies; theology and religious vocations related.
Non-credit—biblical and other theological languages and literatures; biblical studies; developmental and child psychology; pastoral counseling and specialized ministries; philosophy and religious studies related; religious education; religious studies; theological and ministerial studies; theology and religious vocations related.

GOUCHER COLLEGE
Baltimore, Maryland
Center for Graduate and Professional Studies
http://www.goucher.edu

Goucher College was founded in 1885. It is accredited by Middle States Association of Colleges and Schools. It first offered distance learning courses in 1995. In fall 2007, there were 220 students enrolled in distance learning courses. Institutionally administered financial aid is available to distance learners.

Services Distance learners have accessibility to academic advising, bookstore, campus computer network, e-mail services, library services.
Contact Ms. Megan Cornett, Director of Student Services, Goucher College, Welch Center for Graduate and Professional Studies, 1021

Dulaney Valley Road, Baltimore, MD 21204. Telephone: 410-337-6200. Fax: 410-337-6085. E-mail: mcornett@goucher.edu.

DEGREES AND AWARDS

MA Arts Administration; Historic Preservation
MFA Creative Nonfiction

COURSE SUBJECT AREAS OFFERED OUTSIDE OF DEGREE PROGRAMS

Graduate—education.

GOVERNORS STATE UNIVERSITY
University Park, Illinois
Center for Extended Learning and Communications Services
http://www.govst.edu

Governors State University was founded in 1969. It is accredited by North Central Association of Colleges and Schools. It first offered distance learning courses in 1981. In fall 2007, there were 1,221 students enrolled in distance learning courses. Institutionally administered financial aid is available to distance learners.

Services Distance learners have accessibility to academic advising, bookstore, e-mail services, library services, tutoring.
Contact Veronica Williams, Director of School of Extended Learning, Governors State University, 1 University Parkway, University Park, IL 60466. Telephone: 708-534-4099. Fax: 708-534-8458. E-mail: v-williams@govst.edu.

DEGREES AND AWARDS

BA Interdisciplinary Studies

COURSE SUBJECT AREAS OFFERED OUTSIDE OF DEGREE PROGRAMS

Undergraduate—accounting and related services; anthropology; communication and media; developmental and child psychology; English composition; fine and studio art; geography and cartography; marketing; psychology; social work; sociology.
Graduate—anthropology; developmental and child psychology; fine and studio art; social work; sociology.
Non-credit—communication and media; criminal justice and corrections; education; educational assessment, evaluation, and research; education related; health professions related.

GRACE COLLEGE
Winona Lake, Indiana
http://gts.grace.edu/distance-education.htm

Grace College was founded in 1948. It is accredited by North Central Association of Colleges and Schools. It first offered distance learning courses in 1999. In fall 2007, there were 64 students enrolled in distance learning courses. Institutionally administered financial aid is available to distance learners.

Services Distance learners have accessibility to academic advising, bookstore, campus computer network, career placement assistance, e-mail services, library services.
Contact Mrs. Deea N. Breeden, Distance Education, Grace College, 200 Seminary Drive, Winona Lake, IN 46590. Telephone: 800-544-7223 Ext. 6437. Fax: 574-372-5113. E-mail: breededn@grace.edu.

DEGREES AND AWARDS

MA Local Church Ministry

GRACELAND UNIVERSITY
Lamoni, Iowa
Distance Learning
http://www.graceland.edu

Graceland University was founded in 1895. It is accredited by North Central Association of Colleges and Schools. It first offered distance learning courses in 1988. In fall 2007, there were 755 students enrolled in distance learning courses. Institutionally administered financial aid is available to distance learners.

Services Distance learners have accessibility to academic advising, bookstore, campus computer network, e-mail services, library services, tutoring.

Contact Paul Binnicker, Director of Operations, Graceland University, 1401 West Truman Road, Independence, MO 64050. Telephone: 800-833-0524. Fax: 816-833-2990. E-mail: binnicke@graceland.edu.

DEGREES AND AWARDS

BA Health Care Management
BSN Nursing
MEd Collaborative Learning and Teaching; Quality Schools; Technology Integration
MSN Family Nurse Practitioner; Nurse Educator
PMC Family Nurse Practitioner; Nurse Educator

COURSE SUBJECT AREAS OFFERED OUTSIDE OF DEGREE PROGRAMS

Undergraduate—accounting and related services; behavioral sciences; biochemistry, biophysics and molecular biology; biology; business administration, management and operations; chemistry; comparative literature; computer and information sciences; developmental and child psychology; dramatic/theater arts and stagecraft; English composition; history; industrial and organizational psychology; information science/studies; marketing; microbiological sciences and immunology; nursing; psychology; sociology; speech and rhetoric; statistics.
Graduate—education.

GRAND RAPIDS COMMUNITY COLLEGE
Grand Rapids, Michigan
Distance Learning Committee
http://www.grcc.edu

Grand Rapids Community College was founded in 1914. It is accredited by North Central Association of Colleges and Schools. It first offered distance learning courses in 1982. In fall 2007, there were 3,000 students enrolled in distance learning courses. Institutionally administered financial aid is available to distance learners.
Services Distance learners have accessibility to academic advising, bookstore, campus computer network, career placement assistance, e-mail services, library services, tutoring.
Contact Garret Brand, Director of Distance Learning and Instructional Technologies, Grand Rapids Community College, 143 Bostwick NE, Grand Rapids, MI 49503. Telephone: 616-234-4308. E-mail: gbrand@grcc.edu.

DEGREES AND AWARDS
Programs offered do not lead to a degree or other formal award.

COURSE SUBJECT AREAS OFFERED OUTSIDE OF DEGREE PROGRAMS

Undergraduate—anthropology; applied mathematics; architecture; astronomy and astrophysics; behavioral sciences; business administration, management and operations; business/commerce; business/corporate communications; business, management, and marketing related; communication and journalism related; computer/information technology administration and management; computer systems networking and telecommunications; criminal justice and corrections; criminology; developmental and child psychology; economics; English; English composition; film/video and photographic arts; geography and cartography; history; mathematics and statistics related; philosophy; political science and government; psychology; social psychology; sociology; statistics; technology education/industrial arts; visual and performing arts.
Non-credit—applied mathematics; business/corporate communications; communication and journalism related; computer software and media applications; English as a second language; quality control and safety technologies.

GRAND RAPIDS THEOLOGICAL SEMINARY OF CORNERSTONE UNIVERSITY
Grand Rapids, Michigan
http://grts.cornerstone.edu/

Grand Rapids Theological Seminary of Cornerstone University was founded in 1945. It is accredited by North Central Association of Colleges and Schools. It first offered distance learning courses in 1969. Institutionally administered financial aid is available to distance learners.
Services Distance learners have accessibility to academic advising, bookstore, career placement assistance, e-mail services, library services.

Contact Tara Kram, Director of Admissions, Grand Rapids Theological Seminary of Cornerstone University, 1001 East Beltline Avenue NE, Grand Rapids, MI 49525. Telephone: 800-697-1133. Fax: 616-254-1623. E-mail: grts@cornerstone.edu.

DEGREES AND AWARDS
Programs offered do not lead to a degree or other formal award.

COURSE SUBJECT AREAS OFFERED OUTSIDE OF DEGREE PROGRAMS

Graduate—biblical and other theological languages and literatures; biblical studies; counseling psychology; intercultural/multicultural and diversity studies; languages (foreign languages related); missionary studies and missiology; multi-/interdisciplinary studies related; pastoral counseling and specialized ministries; religious education; religious studies; theological and ministerial studies; theology and religious vocations related; urban studies/affairs.
Non-credit—biblical and other theological languages and literatures; biblical studies; religious studies; theological and ministerial studies; theology and religious vocations related.

GRAND VIEW COLLEGE
Des Moines, Iowa
Camp Dodge Campus
http://www.gvc.edu

Grand View College was founded in 1896. It is accredited by North Central Association of Colleges and Schools. It first offered distance learning courses in 1994. Institutionally administered financial aid is available to distance learners.
Services Distance learners have accessibility to academic advising, bookstore, campus computer network, career placement assistance, e-mail services, library services.
Contact Director of Camp Dodge Campus, Grand View College, 1200 Grandview Avenue, Des Moines, IA 50316. Telephone: 515-245-4546. Fax: 515-252-4753.

DEGREES AND AWARDS
Programs offered do not lead to a degree or other formal award.

COURSE SUBJECT AREAS OFFERED OUTSIDE OF DEGREE PROGRAMS

Undergraduate—business, management, and marketing related; business/managerial economics; criminal justice and corrections; criminology; English; English composition; history; psychology; social psychology; sociology; speech and rhetoric.

GRANITE STATE COLLEGE
Concord, New Hampshire
http://www.granite.edu

Granite State College was founded in 1972. It is accredited by New England Association of Schools and Colleges. It first offered distance learning courses in 1999. In fall 2007, there were 617 students enrolled in distance learning courses. Institutionally administered financial aid is available to distance learners.
Services Distance learners have accessibility to academic advising, bookstore, e-mail services, library services, tutoring.
Contact Ms. Jane Williamson, Call Center Coordinator, Granite State College, 8 Old Suncook Road, Concord, NH 03301. Telephone: 888-228-3000. Fax: 603-513-1389. E-mail: jane.williamson@granite.edu.

DEGREES AND AWARDS

AA General Studies
AS Behavioral Science; Business
BA Self-Design
BS Applied Technology, Allied Health Services option; Applied Technology, Education and Training option; Applied Technology, Management option; Business Management; Criminal Justice; Criminal Justice, Administration option; Self-Design

COURSE SUBJECT AREAS OFFERED OUTSIDE OF DEGREE PROGRAMS

Undergraduate—behavioral sciences; business administration, management and operations; business, management, and marketing related; communication and media; computer/information technology administration and management; computer programming; criminal justice and corrections; education (specific levels and methods); finance and financial management services; health and medical administrative services; history; human development, family studies, and related services; human resources management; liberal arts and sciences, general studies and humanities; management information systems; management sciences and quantitative methods; mathematics; multi-/interdisciplinary studies related; psychology related; social sciences.

Graduate—education (specific subject areas); special education.

Non-credit—computer software and media applications.

GRANTHAM UNIVERSITY
Kansas City, Missouri
http://www.grantham.edu/

Grantham University was founded in 1951. It is accredited by Distance Education and Training Council. It first offered distance learning courses in 1990. Institutionally administered financial aid is available to distance learners.

Services Distance learners have accessibility to academic advising, bookstore, career placement assistance, library services, tutoring.

Contact Ms. DeAnn Wandler, Director of Admissions, Grantham University, 7200 NW 86th Street, Kansas City, MO 64153. Telephone: 800-955-2527. Fax: 816-595-5757. E-mail: admissions@grantham.edu.

DEGREES AND AWARDS

AA Business Management

AS Business Administration; Computer Engineering Technology; Computer Science; Criminal Justice–Computer Science; Criminal Justice–Homeland Security; Criminal Justice; Electronics Engineering Technology; General Studies; Interdisciplinary Studies

BS Business Administration; Business Management; Computer Engineering Technology; Computer Science; Criminal Justice–Computer Science; Criminal Justice–Homeland Security; Criminal Justice; Electronics Engineering Technology; General Studies; Interdisciplinary Studies

MBA Business Administration; Information Management; Project Management

MS Information Management Technology; Information Management–Project Management; Information Technology

COURSE SUBJECT AREAS OFFERED OUTSIDE OF DEGREE PROGRAMS

Undergraduate—accounting and related services; business administration, management and operations; business/commerce; business, management, and marketing related; business/managerial economics; chemistry; computer and information sciences; computer engineering; computer engineering technologies; computer/information technology administration and management; computer programming; computer science; computer software and media applications; computer systems analysis; computer systems networking and telecommunications; criminal justice and corrections; data entry/microcomputer applications; economics; electrical and electronic engineering technologies; electrical, electronics and communications engineering; engineering; English composition; finance and financial management services; history; human resources management; information science/studies; legal studies (non-professional general, undergraduate); management information systems; marketing; mathematics; mathematics and computer science; mathematics and statistics related; physics; psychology; psychology related; sales, merchandising, and related marketing operations (general); sociology; technical and business writing.

Graduate—accounting and related services; business/managerial economics; communications technology; finance and financial management services; management information systems; marketing; systems engineering.

See full description on page 396.

GRATZ COLLEGE
Melrose Park, Pennsylvania
http://www.gratz.edu

Gratz College was founded in 1895. It is accredited by Middle States Association of Colleges and Schools. It first offered distance learning courses in 2000. In fall 2007, there were 110 students enrolled in distance learning courses. Institutionally administered financial aid is available to distance learners.

Services Distance learners have accessibility to academic advising, e-mail services, library services.

Contact Ms. Ronni D. Ticker, Director, Online and Distance Learning, Gratz College, 7605 Old York Road, Melrose Park, PA 19027. Telephone: 215-635-7300 Ext. 115. Fax: 215-635-7399. E-mail: online@gratz.edu.

DEGREES AND AWARDS

BA Jewish Studies

CAGS Holocaust Studies; Jewish Early Childhood Education; Jewish Education; Jewish Music; Jewish Non-Profit Management; Jewish Studies

MA Jewish Education; Jewish Studies

GREENFIELD COMMUNITY COLLEGE
Greenfield, Massachusetts
http://www.gcc.mass.edu/

Greenfield Community College was founded in 1962. It is accredited by New England Association of Schools and Colleges. It first offered distance learning courses in 2002. In fall 2007, there were 45 students enrolled in distance learning courses. Institutionally administered financial aid is available to distance learners.

Services Distance learners have accessibility to campus computer network, e-mail services, library services.

Contact Michelle M. Barthelemy, Coordinator of Distance Learning/Instructional Technology, Greenfield Community College, One College Drive, Center for Teaching and Learning, Greenfield, MA 01301. E-mail: online@gcc.mass.edu.

DEGREES AND AWARDS

Programs offered do not lead to a degree or other formal award.

COURSE SUBJECT AREAS OFFERED OUTSIDE OF DEGREE PROGRAMS

Undergraduate—anthropology; biological and physical sciences; computer/information technology administration and management; education; English composition; history; mathematics; psychology; sociology.

GREEN MOUNTAIN COLLEGE
Poultney, Vermont
http://www.greenmtn.edu/graduate_studies/index.asp

Green Mountain College was founded in 1834. It is accredited by New England Association of Schools and Colleges. It first offered distance learning courses in 2006. In fall 2007, there were 57 students enrolled in distance learning courses. Institutionally administered financial aid is available to distance learners.

Services Distance learners have accessibility to academic advising, bookstore, campus computer network, career placement assistance, e-mail services, library services, tutoring.

Contact Dr. Sandra Bartholomew, Dean of Enrollment Management, Green Mountain College, Admissions, One Brennan Circle, Poultney, VT 05764. Telephone: 802-287-8220. Fax: 802-287-8099. E-mail: bartholomews@greenmtn.edu.

DEGREES AND AWARDS

MBA Non-Profit Organization Management; Sustainable Business Practices

MS Environmental Studies in Conservation Biology; Self-Designed concentration; Writing and Communications concentration

GREENVILLE TECHNICAL COLLEGE
Greenville, South Carolina
Distance Learning
http://www.college-online.com
Greenville Technical College was founded in 1962. It is accredited by Southern Association of Colleges and Schools. It first offered distance learning courses in 1990. In fall 2007, there were 3,550 students enrolled in distance learning courses. Institutionally administered financial aid is available to distance learners.
Services Distance learners have accessibility to academic advising, bookstore, campus computer network, career placement assistance, e-mail services, library services, tutoring.
Contact Mr. Christopher Satterfield, Advisor, Online and Non-Traditional, Greenville Technical College, PO Box 5616, Greenville, SC 29606-5616. Telephone: 864-250-8393. Fax: 864-250-8085. E-mail: chris.satterfield @gvltec.edu.

DEGREES AND AWARDS
Programs offered do not lead to a degree or other formal award.

COURSE SUBJECT AREAS OFFERED OUTSIDE OF DEGREE PROGRAMS
Undergraduate—accounting and computer science; American literature (United States and Canadian); astronomy and astrophysics; business, management, and marketing related; computer programming; economics; English composition; English language and literature related; fine and studio art; history; human services; languages (foreign languages related); marketing; mathematics; music; philosophy and religious studies related; physics; political science and government; psychology; sociology.

GULF COAST COMMUNITY COLLEGE
Panama City, Florida
http://de.gulfcoast.edu/
Gulf Coast Community College was founded in 1957. It is accredited by Southern Association of Colleges and Schools. It first offered distance learning courses in 1994. Institutionally administered financial aid is available to distance learners.
Services Distance learners have accessibility to academic advising, bookstore, campus computer network, e-mail services, library services.
Contact Mrs. Cindy L. Coggeshall, Senior Administrative Assistant, E-Learning, Gulf Coast Community College, 5230 West U.S. Highway 98, Panama City, FL 32401. Telephone: 850-769-1551 Ext. 5807. Fax: 850-873-3592. E-mail: ccoggeshall@gulfcoast.edu.

DEGREES AND AWARDS
AA General Studies; General degree

COURSE SUBJECT AREAS OFFERED OUTSIDE OF DEGREE PROGRAMS
Undergraduate—biological and physical sciences; chemistry; dental support services and allied professions; developmental and child psychology; economics; English composition; fire protection; health/medical preparatory programs; history; mathematics; music; nursing; physical sciences; psychology; social sciences; sociology; statistics.

HAGERSTOWN COMMUNITY COLLEGE
Hagerstown, Maryland
http://www.hagerstowncc.edu/
Hagerstown Community College was founded in 1946. It is accredited by Middle States Association of Colleges and Schools. It first offered distance learning courses in 1998. In fall 2007, there were 189 students enrolled in distance learning courses. Institutionally administered financial aid is available to distance learners.
Services Distance learners have accessibility to bookstore, library services.
Contact Angela Kelley, Test Center Administrator, Hagerstown Community College, Continuing Education, 11400 Robinwood Drive, Hag-

erstown, MD 21742. Telephone: 301-790-2800 Ext. 553. Fax: 301-733-4229. E-mail: kelleya@hagerstowncc.edu.

DEGREES AND AWARDS
Programs offered do not lead to a degree or other formal award.

COURSE SUBJECT AREAS OFFERED OUTSIDE OF DEGREE PROGRAMS
Non-credit—accounting and related services; allied health and medical assisting services; business, management, and marketing related; computer programming; computer software and media applications; computer systems networking and telecommunications; culinary arts and related services; publishing.

HALIFAX COMMUNITY COLLEGE
Weldon, North Carolina
Distance Learning
http://www.halifaxcc.edu
Halifax Community College was founded in 1967. It is accredited by Southern Association of Colleges and Schools. It first offered distance learning courses in 1999. In fall 2007, there were 1,247 students enrolled in distance learning courses. Institutionally administered financial aid is available to distance learners.
Services Distance learners have accessibility to academic advising, bookstore, e-mail services, library services, tutoring.
Contact Beth Gray-Robertson, Director of Distance Learning, Halifax Community College, PO Drawer 809, Weldon, NC 27890. Telephone: 252-536-7299. Fax: 252-536-6347. E-mail: robertsonb@halifaxcc.edu.

DEGREES AND AWARDS
Programs offered do not lead to a degree or other formal award.

COURSE SUBJECT AREAS OFFERED OUTSIDE OF DEGREE PROGRAMS
Undergraduate—accounting and related services; business/commerce; communication and media; computer and information sciences and support services related; computer science; developmental and child psychology; economics; education; English composition; English literature (British and Commonwealth); fine and studio art; mathematics; religious studies; teaching assistants/aides.
Non-credit—business administration, management and operations; computer software and media applications; computer systems networking and telecommunications; data entry/microcomputer applications; education (specific levels and methods).

HAMLINE UNIVERSITY
St. Paul, Minnesota
http://www.hamline.edu/
Hamline University was founded in 1854. It is accredited by North Central Association of Colleges and Schools. It first offered distance learning courses in 1998. In fall 2007, there were 124 students enrolled in distance learning courses. Institutionally administered financial aid is available to distance learners.
Services Distance learners have accessibility to campus computer network, career placement assistance, e-mail services, library services.
Contact Annette McNamara, Program Administrator, Hamline University, 1536 Hewitt Avenue, A1720, St. Paul, MN 55104-1284. Telephone: 651-523-2175. Fax: 651-523-2489. E-mail: amcnamara@gw. hamline.edu.

DEGREES AND AWARDS
Programs offered do not lead to a degree or other formal award.

COURSE SUBJECT AREAS OFFERED OUTSIDE OF DEGREE PROGRAMS
Undergraduate—history.
Graduate—bilingual, multilingual, and multicultural education; education; educational/instructional media design; education related; education (specific levels and methods); education (specific subject areas);

English as a second/foreign language (teaching); English as a second language; mathematics; public administration and social service professions related; special education.

Non-credit—education; educational administration and supervision; educational/instructional media design; education related; education (specific subject areas); English as a second/foreign language (teaching); English as a second language; political science and government; public administration; public administration and social service professions related.

HARFORD COMMUNITY COLLEGE
Bel Air, Maryland
http://www.harford.edu/Online/
Harford Community College was founded in 1957. It is accredited by Middle States Association of Colleges and Schools. It first offered distance learning courses in 1999. In fall 2007, there were 1,250 students enrolled in distance learning courses. Institutionally administered financial aid is available to distance learners.
Services Distance learners have accessibility to academic advising, bookstore, campus computer network, career placement assistance, e-mail services, library services, tutoring.
Contact Christel Vonderscheer, Director of E-Learning, Harford Community College, 401 Thomas Run Road, Bel Air, MD 21015. Telephone: 410-836-4145. Fax: 410-836-4481. E-mail: cvonders@harford.edu.

DEGREES AND AWARDS
AA General Studies
AS Business Administration

COURSE SUBJECT AREAS OFFERED OUTSIDE OF DEGREE PROGRAMS
Undergraduate—biology; educational psychology; English; English composition; English literature (British and Commonwealth); mathematics; psychology; social sciences related.
Non-credit—computer and information sciences; computer programming; computer systems networking and telecommunications; real estate.

HARRISBURG AREA COMMUNITY COLLEGE
Harrisburg, Pennsylvania
Distance Education Office
http://www.hacc.edu/VirtualCampus
Harrisburg Area Community College was founded in 1964. It is accredited by Middle States Association of Colleges and Schools. It first offered distance learning courses in 1987. In fall 2007, there were 3,600 students enrolled in distance learning courses. Institutionally administered financial aid is available to distance learners.
Services Distance learners have accessibility to academic advising, bookstore, career placement assistance, library services, tutoring.
Contact Mr. Robert Karas, Counselor, Harrisburg Area Community College, 1 HACC Drive, Harrisburg, PA 17110. Telephone: 717-780-2613. Fax: 717-780-1925. E-mail: rdkaras@hacc.edu.

DEGREES AND AWARDS
AA Business Administration

COURSE SUBJECT AREAS OFFERED OUTSIDE OF DEGREE PROGRAMS
Undergraduate—accounting and related services; allied health and medical assisting services; American literature (United States and Canadian); anthropology; applied mathematics; astronomy and astrophysics; biological and physical sciences; business administration, management and operations; business/commerce; business, management, and marketing related; business/managerial economics; computer programming; computer science; computer software and media applications; criminal justice and corrections; developmental and child psychology; economics; education; engineering; English; English composition; English literature (British and Commonwealth); environmental/environmental health engineering; foods, nutrition, and related services; geography and cartography; geological and earth sciences/geosciences; history; information science/studies; library science related; marketing; mathematics;

mathematics and computer science; microbiological sciences and immunology; nursing; philosophy; physical sciences; psychology; public health; sociology; statistics; technical and business writing.

HARRIS-STOWE STATE UNIVERSITY
St. Louis, Missouri
http://www.hssu.edu/
Harris-Stowe State University was founded in 1857. It is accredited by North Central Association of Colleges and Schools.
Contact Office of Admissions, Harris-Stowe State University, 3026 Laclede Ave., Saint Louis, MO 63103. Telephone: 314-340-3300. E-mail: admissions@hssu.edu.

DEGREES AND AWARDS
Programs offered do not lead to a degree or other formal award.

COURSE SUBJECT AREAS OFFERED OUTSIDE OF DEGREE PROGRAMS
Undergraduate—health and medical administrative services; philosophy.

HAWKEYE COMMUNITY COLLEGE
Waterloo, Iowa
Department of Academic Telecommunications
http://www.hawkeyecollege.edu/distancelearning
Hawkeye Community College was founded in 1966. It is accredited by North Central Association of Colleges and Schools. It first offered distance learning courses in 1993. In fall 2007, there were 1,200 students enrolled in distance learning courses. Institutionally administered financial aid is available to distance learners.
Services Distance learners have accessibility to academic advising, bookstore, campus computer network, career placement assistance, e-mail services, library services.
Contact Ms. Dawn L. Fratzke, Distance Learning Coordinator/Region VII ICN Regional Scheduler, Hawkeye Community College, 1501 East Orange Road, Tama Hall, Room 112A, Waterloo, IA 50704. Telephone: 319-296-4022. Fax: 319-296-4018. E-mail: dfratzke@hawkeyecollege.edu.

DEGREES AND AWARDS
Programs offered do not lead to a degree or other formal award.

HAYWOOD COMMUNITY COLLEGE
Clyde, North Carolina
http://www.haywood.edu
Haywood Community College was founded in 1964. It is accredited by Southern Association of Colleges and Schools. It first offered distance learning courses in 1992. In fall 2007, there were 900 students enrolled in distance learning courses. Institutionally administered financial aid is available to distance learners.
Services Distance learners have accessibility to academic advising, bookstore, career placement assistance, e-mail services, library services, tutoring.
Contact Debbie Rowland, Coordinator of Admissions, Haywood Community College, 185 Freedlander Drive, Clyde, NC 28716. Telephone: 828-627-4646. Fax: 828-627-4513. E-mail: drowland@haywood.edu.

DEGREES AND AWARDS
AAS Business Administration; Criminal Justice Technology; Early Childhood Associate–Special Education; Early Childhood Associate–Teacher Associate; Early Childhood Education

COURSE SUBJECT AREAS OFFERED OUTSIDE OF DEGREE PROGRAMS
Undergraduate—accounting and related services; animal sciences; anthropology; applied horticulture/horticultural business services; behavioral sciences; business administration, management and operations; business/commerce; computer and information sciences; computer engi-

neering technologies; computer/information technology administration and management; computer programming; computer science; computer software and media applications; computer systems analysis; computer systems networking and telecommunications; construction engineering; construction management; construction trades; construction trades related; cosmetology and related personal grooming services; criminal justice and corrections; criminology; data entry/microcomputer applications; developmental and child psychology; economics; education; education related; engineering; engineering/industrial management; engineering technologies related; English; English composition; English language and literature related; entrepreneurial and small business operations; finance and financial management services; fine and studio art; forestry; health and physical education/fitness; history; human development, family studies, and related services; information science/studies; liberal arts and sciences, general studies and humanities; management information systems; mathematics; mathematics and computer science; music; natural resources and conservation related; natural resources conservation and research; natural resources management and policy; natural sciences; parks, recreation and leisure; parks, recreation and leisure facilities management; parks, recreation, and leisure related; plant sciences; political science and government; psychology; religious studies; social sciences; social sciences related; sociology; soil sciences; teaching assistants/aides; technical and business writing; wildlife and wildlands science and management.

HEBREW COLLEGE
Newton Centre, Massachusetts
http://www.hebrewcollege.edu/online

Hebrew College was founded in 1921. It is accredited by New England Association of Schools and Colleges. It first offered distance learning courses in 1995. In fall 2007, there were 150 students enrolled in distance learning courses. Institutionally administered financial aid is available to distance learners.

Services Distance learners have accessibility to academic advising, bookstore, campus computer network, career placement assistance, library services, tutoring.

Contact Kate Nachman, Director of Admissions, Hebrew College, 160 Herrick Road, Newton Centre, MA 02459. Telephone: 617-559-8610. Fax: 617-559-8601. E-mail: knachman@hebrewcollege.edu.

DEGREES AND AWARDS
MA Jewish Studies
MEd Master of Jewish Education

COURSE SUBJECT AREAS OFFERED OUTSIDE OF DEGREE PROGRAMS

Undergraduate—biblical and other theological languages and literatures; biblical studies; education related; ethnic, cultural minority, and gender studies; languages (Middle/Near Eastern and Semitic); linguistic, comparative, and related language studies; philosophy and religious studies related; religious studies.

Graduate—biblical and other theological languages and literatures; biblical studies; education related; ethnic, cultural minority, and gender studies; languages (Middle/Near Eastern and Semitic); linguistic, comparative, and related language studies; philosophy and religious studies related; religious studies.

Non-credit—biblical and other theological languages and literatures; biblical studies; education related; ethnic, cultural minority, and gender studies; languages (Middle/Near Eastern and Semitic); linguistic, comparative, and related language studies; philosophy and religious studies related; religious studies.

HENDERSON COMMUNITY COLLEGE
Henderson, Kentucky
http://www.hencc.kctcs.edu

Henderson Community College was founded in 1963. It is accredited by Southern Association of Colleges and Schools. It first offered distance learning courses in 1985. In fall 2007, there were 1,000 students enrolled in distance learning courses. Institutionally administered financial aid is available to distance learners.

Services Distance learners have accessibility to academic advising, bookstore, campus computer network, e-mail services, library services.

Contact Lisa Jackson, Distance Learning Coordinator, Henderson Community College, 2660 South Green Street, Henderson, KY 42420. Telephone: 270-831-9678. Fax: 270-831-9675. E-mail: lisa.jackson@kctcs.edu.

DEGREES AND AWARDS
Programs offered do not lead to a degree or other formal award.

COURSE SUBJECT AREAS OFFERED OUTSIDE OF DEGREE PROGRAMS

Undergraduate—agriculture; biology; botany/plant biology; business administration, management and operations; business, management, and marketing related; business/managerial economics; communication and journalism related; computer and information sciences; English; history; library science; mathematics; music; physics; psychology.

HENRY FORD COMMUNITY COLLEGE
Dearborn, Michigan
http://www.hfcc.edu

Henry Ford Community College was founded in 1938. It is accredited by North Central Association of Colleges and Schools. It first offered distance learning courses in 2004. Institutionally administered financial aid is available to distance learners.

Services Distance learners have accessibility to bookstore, e-mail services, library services.

Contact Dr. Vivian Beaty, Director of Instructional Technology, Henry Ford Community College, Instructional Technology, 5101 Evergreen Road, Dearborn, MI 48128-1495. Telephone: 313-845-9663 Ext. 3. Fax: 313-845-9844. E-mail: vbeaty@hfcc.edu.

DEGREES AND AWARDS
AA Religious Studies
AGS General Education Studies

COURSE SUBJECT AREAS OFFERED OUTSIDE OF DEGREE PROGRAMS

Undergraduate—anthropology; applied mathematics; astronomy and astrophysics; cell biology and anatomical sciences; computer and information sciences; computer software and media applications; criminal justice and corrections; educational/instructional media design; English; English composition; history; housing and human environments; journalism; languages (Middle/Near Eastern and Semitic); liberal arts and sciences, general studies and humanities; mathematics; mathematics and statistics related; natural sciences; nutrition sciences; political science and government; precision metal working; psychology; religious studies; science, technology and society; social sciences; sociology; statistics; technical and business writing.

HERITAGE CHRISTIAN UNIVERSITY
Florence, Alabama
Distance Learning
http://www.hcu.edu/

Heritage Christian University was founded in 1971. It is accredited by Association for Biblical Higher Education. It first offered distance learning courses in 1992. In fall 2007, there were 27 students enrolled in distance learning courses. Institutionally administered financial aid is available to distance learners.

Services Distance learners have accessibility to academic advising, bookstore, career placement assistance, e-mail services, library services, tutoring.

Contact Shay Bingham, Admissions Assistant, Heritage Christian University, PO Box HCU, Florence, AL 35630. Telephone: 800-367-3565 Ext. 223. Fax: 256-766-9289. E-mail: sbingham@hcu.edu.

DEGREES AND AWARDS
Programs offered do not lead to a degree or other formal award.

COURSE SUBJECT AREAS OFFERED OUTSIDE OF DEGREE PROGRAMS

Undergraduate—biblical and other theological languages and literatures; biblical studies.

Graduate—biblical and other theological languages and literatures; biblical studies.

Non-credit—biblical and other theological languages and literatures; biblical studies.

HERITAGE COLLEGE
Denver, Colorado
http://www.heritage-education.com/

Heritage College was founded in 1986. It is accredited by Accrediting Commission of Career Schools and Colleges of Technology. It first offered distance learning courses in 2002. In fall 2007, there were 150 students enrolled in distance learning courses. Institutionally administered financial aid is available to distance learners.

Services Distance learners have accessibility to academic advising, campus computer network, e-mail services, library services, tutoring.

Contact Ms. Heidi McDonald, Director of Admissions, Heritage College, 12 Lakeside Lane, Denver, CO 80212. Telephone: 303-477-7240 Ext. 10140. Fax: 303-477-7276. E-mail: heidim@heritage-education.com.

DEGREES AND AWARDS

AGS Structured Learning

COURSE SUBJECT AREAS OFFERED OUTSIDE OF DEGREE PROGRAMS

Undergraduate—health services/allied health/health sciences.
Non-credit—health services/allied health/health sciences.

HERKIMER COUNTY COMMUNITY COLLEGE
Herkimer, New York
Internet Academy
http://www.ia.herkimer.edu

Herkimer County Community College was founded in 1966. It is accredited by Middle States Association of Colleges and Schools. It first offered distance learning courses in 1997. In fall 2007, there were 2,060 students enrolled in distance learning courses. Institutionally administered financial aid is available to distance learners.

Services Distance learners have accessibility to academic advising, bookstore, career placement assistance, e-mail services, library services, tutoring.

Contact Ms. Linda C. Lamb, Associate Dean of Continuing Education/Internet Academy, Herkimer County Community College, 100 Reservoir Road, Herkimer, NY 13550. Telephone: 315-866-0300 Ext. 8422. Fax: 315-866-0402. E-mail: lamblc@herkimer.edu.

DEGREES AND AWARDS

AA Liberal Arts and Sciences–General Studies; Liberal Arts and Sciences–Humanities; Liberal Arts and Sciences–Social Science

AAS Business Administration; Business–Accounting; Business–Health Services Management Technology; Business–Human Resource Management; Business–Marketing; Business–Small Business Management; Criminal Justice; Human Services; Paralegal; Travel and Tourism–Hospitality and Events Management

AS Business Administration; Business–Accounting; Business–Business Administration; Criminal Justice; Criminal Justice–Cybersecurity; Criminal Justice–Economic Crime; Health Services Management

Certificate Corrections; Medical Coder/Transcriptionist; Small Business Management; Teaching Assistant

COURSE SUBJECT AREAS OFFERED OUTSIDE OF DEGREE PROGRAMS

Undergraduate—accounting and related services; biology; business administration, management and operations; business/commerce; business/corporate communications; computer and information sciences; computer software and media applications; computer systems networking and telecommunications; criminal justice and corrections; developmental and child psychology; English; entrepreneurial and small business operations; human resources management; human services; liberal arts and sciences, general studies and humanities; mathematics and computer science; psychology; sales, merchandising, and related marketing operations (specialized).

HIBBING COMMUNITY COLLEGE
Hibbing, Minnesota
http://www.hibbing.edu

Hibbing Community College was founded in 1916. It is accredited by North Central Association of Colleges and Schools. It first offered distance learning courses in 2003. In fall 2007, there were 600 students enrolled in distance learning courses. Institutionally administered financial aid is available to distance learners.

Services Distance learners have accessibility to academic advising, bookstore, campus computer network, career placement assistance, e-mail services, library services, tutoring.

Contact Mr. Michael Raich, Dean of Acadmic Affairs, Hibbing Community College, 1515 East 25th Street, Hibbing, MN 55746-3300. Telephone: 218-262-7000. Fax: 218-262-6717. E-mail: michaelraich@hibbing.edu.

DEGREES AND AWARDS

AA General degree; Medical Lab Tech

COURSE SUBJECT AREAS OFFERED OUTSIDE OF DEGREE PROGRAMS

Undergraduate—accounting and related services; anthropology; area, ethnic, cultural, and gender studies related; biological and physical sciences; business administration, management and operations; business, management, and marketing related; chemistry; clinical/medical laboratory science and allied professions; computer and information sciences; computer programming; computer science; computer software and media applications; criminal justice and corrections; culinary arts and related services; data entry/microcomputer applications; economics; English composition; fine and studio art; foods, nutrition, and related services; health/medical preparatory programs; history; information science/studies; intercultural/multicultural and diversity studies; liberal arts and sciences, general studies and humanities; mathematics; multi-/interdisciplinary studies related; music; philosophy; political science and government; psychology; social sciences; sociology.

Non-credit—accounting and related services; computer and information sciences; computer software and media applications; real estate.

HILLSBOROUGH COMMUNITY COLLEGE
Tampa, Florida
Distance Learning Office
http://www.hccfl.edu/distance-learning.apx

Hillsborough Community College was founded in 1968. It is accredited by Southern Association of Colleges and Schools. It first offered distance learning courses in 1971. In fall 2007, there were 4,500 students enrolled in distance learning courses. Institutionally administered financial aid is available to distance learners.

Services Distance learners have accessibility to academic advising, bookstore, career placement assistance, e-mail services, library services, tutoring.

Contact Melissa Zucal, Distance Learning Manager, Hillsborough Community College, 39 Columbia, Suite 714, Tampa, FL 33606. Telephone: 813-259-6531. Fax: 813-259-6536. E-mail: mzucal@hccfl.edu.

DEGREES AND AWARDS

Programs offered do not lead to a degree or other formal award.

COURSE SUBJECT AREAS OFFERED OUTSIDE OF DEGREE PROGRAMS

Undergraduate—American literature (United States and Canadian); American Sign Language (ASL); applied mathematics; astronomy and astrophysics; biology; business administration, management and operations; business/commerce; communication and media; computer and

information sciences; computer/information technology administration and management; computer programming; computer science; computer software and media applications; creative writing; criminal justice and corrections; developmental and child psychology; economics; English; English composition; finance and financial management services; fire protection; foods, nutrition, and related services; geological and earth sciences/geosciences; geological/geophysical engineering; health professions related; human development, family studies, and related services; legal studies (non-professional general, undergraduate); marketing; nutrition sciences; ophthalmic and optometric support services and allied professions; political science and government; psychology; sociology.
Non-credit—accounting and related services; crafts, folk art and artisanry; languages (Romance languages).

HOBE SOUND BIBLE COLLEGE
Hobe Sound, Florida
Department of External Studies
http://www.hsbc.edu

Hobe Sound Bible College was founded in 1960. It is accredited by Association for Biblical Higher Education. It first offered distance learning courses in 1993. In fall 2007, there were 70 students enrolled in distance learning courses. Institutionally administered financial aid is available to distance learners.

Services Distance learners have accessibility to academic advising, e-mail services, library services.

Contact Mr. Dalbert N. Walker, Dean of Adult Distributed Education, Hobe Sound Bible College, PO Box 1065, Hobe Sound, FL 33475. Telephone: 772-546-5534 Ext. 1014. Fax: 772-545-1422. E-mail: dalbertwalker@hsbc.edu.

DEGREES AND AWARDS
BA Christian Studies, general

COURSE SUBJECT AREAS OFFERED OUTSIDE OF DEGREE PROGRAMS
Undergraduate—biblical studies; missionary studies and missiology; pastoral counseling and specialized ministries; philosophy and religious studies related.
Non-credit—biblical studies; education; missionary studies and missiology; pastoral counseling and specialized ministries; philosophy and religious studies related.

HOCKING COLLEGE
Nelsonville, Ohio
Instructional Development
http://online.hocking.edu/

Hocking College was founded in 1968. It is accredited by North Central Association of Colleges and Schools. It first offered distance learning courses in 1995. In fall 2007, there were 560 students enrolled in distance learning courses. Institutionally administered financial aid is available to distance learners.

Services Distance learners have accessibility to academic advising, campus computer network, e-mail services, library services.

Contact Mrs. Joni Tornwall, Online Learning Coordinator, Hocking College, JL 256, 3301 Hocking Parkway, Nelsonville, OH 45764. Telephone: 740-753-7116. E-mail: tornwall_j@hocking.edu.

DEGREES AND AWARDS
Programs offered do not lead to a degree or other formal award.

COURSE SUBJECT AREAS OFFERED OUTSIDE OF DEGREE PROGRAMS
Undergraduate—accounting and computer science; allied health and medical assisting services; cell biology and anatomical sciences; communication and media; creative writing; economics; English; English composition; health/medical preparatory programs; hospitality administration; liberal arts and sciences, general studies and humanities; mathematics; psychology; social sciences; speech and rhetoric; technical and business writing; visual and performing arts related.

HODGES UNIVERSITY
Naples, Florida
http://www.hodges.edu/admissions/distanceEducation

Hodges University was founded in 1990. It is accredited by Southern Association of Colleges and Schools. It first offered distance learning courses in 1995. In fall 2007, there were 601 students enrolled in distance learning courses. Institutionally administered financial aid is available to distance learners.

Services Distance learners have accessibility to academic advising, bookstore, campus computer network, career placement assistance, e-mail services, library services, tutoring.

Contact Ms. Jane Trembath, Director of Distance Admissions, Hodges University, 2655 Northbrooke Drive, Naples, FL 34119. Telephone: 866-684-6689. Fax: 866-684-6064. E-mail: jtrembath@hodges.edu.

DEGREES AND AWARDS
AS Health Information Technology; Interdisciplinary Studies; Paralegal Studies
BS Criminal Justice; Information Systems Management; Interdisciplinary Studies; Management
MBA Business Administration
MISM Information Systems Management
MPA Public Administration
MPS Professional Studies
MS Criminal Justice
MSM Management

HOFSTRA UNIVERSITY
Hempstead, New York
http://www.hofstra.edu/Academics/dl/index.html

Hofstra University was founded in 1935. It is accredited by Middle States Association of Colleges and Schools. It first offered distance learning courses in 2002. In fall 2007, there were 250 students enrolled in distance learning courses. Institutionally administered financial aid is available to distance learners.

Services Distance learners have accessibility to academic advising, bookstore, e-mail services, library services.

Contact Mr. Ron Chalmers, Senior Instructional Designer, Hofstra University, 203 McEwen Hall, 125 Hofstra University, Hempstead, NY 11549-1000. Telephone: 516-463-4532. E-mail: fcsrac@hofstra.edu.

DEGREES AND AWARDS
MS Computer Science

COURSE SUBJECT AREAS OFFERED OUTSIDE OF DEGREE PROGRAMS
Undergraduate—American literature (United States and Canadian); anthropology; audiovisual communications technologies; biology; computer and information sciences; computer programming; computer software and media applications; computer systems analysis; computer systems networking and telecommunications; curriculum and instruction; education; English; health professions related; history; liberal arts and sciences, general studies and humanities; sales, merchandising, and related marketing operations (general); special education.
Graduate—computer and information sciences; special education.

HOLY APOSTLES COLLEGE AND SEMINARY
Cromwell, Connecticut
http://www.holyapostles.edu

Holy Apostles College and Seminary was founded in 1956. It is accredited by New England Association of Schools and Colleges. It first offered distance learning courses in 1998. In fall 2007, there were 130 students enrolled in distance learning courses. Institutionally administered financial aid is available to distance learners.

Services Distance learners have accessibility to academic advising, library services, tutoring.

Contact Mr. Robert Mish, Distance Learning Coordinator, Holy Apostles College and Seminary, 33 Prospect Hill Road, Cromwell, CT 06416. Telephone: 860-632-3015. Fax: 860-632-3075. E-mail: distancelearn@ holyapostles.edu.

DEGREES AND AWARDS

MA Philosophy; Theology

COURSE SUBJECT AREAS OFFERED OUTSIDE OF DEGREE PROGRAMS

Graduate—philosophy and religious studies related.

HOLY NAMES UNIVERSITY
Oakland, California
http://www.hnu.edu

Holy Names University was founded in 1868. It is accredited by Western Association of Schools and Colleges. It first offered distance learning courses in 1995. In fall 2007, there were 73 students enrolled in distance learning courses. Institutionally administered financial aid is available to distance learners.

Services Distance learners have accessibility to academic advising, bookstore, e-mail services, library services.

Contact Lisamarie Gibson, Adult and Graduate Recruiter, Holy Names University, 3500 Mountain Boulevard, Oakland, CA 94619-1699. Telephone: 510-436-1351. Fax: 510-436-1325. E-mail: admissions@hnu.edu.

DEGREES AND AWARDS

BSN Nursing–Accelerated RN to BSN

HOLYOKE COMMUNITY COLLEGE
Holyoke, Massachusetts
http://webtide.hccdl.org

Holyoke Community College was founded in 1946. It is accredited by New England Association of Schools and Colleges. It first offered distance learning courses in 1999. In fall 2007, there were 1,324 students enrolled in distance learning courses. Institutionally administered financial aid is available to distance learners.

Services Distance learners have accessibility to academic advising, bookstore, career placement assistance, e-mail services, library services, tutoring.

Contact Dean Gloria A. DeFillipo, Dean of Distance Education, Holyoke Community College, 303 Homestead Avenue, Holyoke, MA 01040. Telephone: 413-552-2236. Fax: 413-552-2045. E-mail: gdefillipo@hcc.mass.edu.

DEGREES AND AWARDS

Programs offered do not lead to a degree or other formal award.

COURSE SUBJECT AREAS OFFERED OUTSIDE OF DEGREE PROGRAMS

Undergraduate—accounting and computer science; applied mathematics; business administration, management and operations; business, management, and marketing related; communication and media; computer science; creative writing; criminal justice and corrections; criminology; data entry/microcomputer applications; economics; English language and literature related; history; hospitality administration; human resources management; human services; mathematics; music; nutrition sciences; political science and government; psychology; sociology; special education; statistics.

HONOLULU COMMUNITY COLLEGE
Honolulu, Hawaii
Distance Learning
http://honolulu.hawaii.edu/distance

Honolulu Community College was founded in 1920. It is accredited by Western Association of Schools and Colleges. It first offered distance learning courses in 1991. In fall 2007, there were 1,000 students enrolled in distance learning courses. Institutionally administered financial aid is available to distance learners.

Services Distance learners have accessibility to academic advising, bookstore, campus computer network, career placement assistance, e-mail services, library services.

Contact Janice T. Petersen, Distance Learning Coordinator, Honolulu Community College, 874 Dillingham Boulevard, Honolulu, HI 96817. Telephone: 808-845-9437. Fax: 808-847-9679. E-mail: janp@hcc.hawaii.edu.

DEGREES AND AWARDS

Programs offered do not lead to a degree or other formal award.

COURSE SUBJECT AREAS OFFERED OUTSIDE OF DEGREE PROGRAMS

Undergraduate—anthropology; architectural engineering technology; astronomy and astrophysics; chemistry; education (specific levels and methods); English; English composition; fire protection; food science and technology; foods, nutrition, and related services; geological and earth sciences/geosciences; history; liberal arts and sciences, general studies and humanities; microbiological sciences and immunology; philosophy; philosophy and religious studies related; physical sciences; political science and government; psychology; social sciences related; speech and rhetoric.

HOPE INTERNATIONAL UNIVERSITY
Fullerton, California
Distance Learning Department
http://www.hiu.edu

Hope International University was founded in 1928. It is accredited by Western Association of Schools and Colleges. It first offered distance learning courses in 1994. In fall 2007, there were 260 students enrolled in distance learning courses. Institutionally administered financial aid is available to distance learners.

Services Distance learners have accessibility to academic advising, bookstore, career placement assistance, e-mail services, library services.

Contact Teresa Smith, Director of Admissions, Graduate and Adult Programs, Hope International University, 2500 East Nutwood Avenue, Fullerton, CA 92831. Telephone: 714-879-3901 Ext. 7371. Fax: 714-681-7450. E-mail: spsadmissions@hiu.edu.

DEGREES AND AWARDS

AA Biblical Studies; Christian Ministry; General Education

BS Christian Ministry; Human Development; Intercultural Studies; Management

Certificate Biblical Studies

Graduate Certificate Christian Leadership; Church Planting; Intercultural Studies; International Development; Worship

MA Ministry

MBA Educational Administration; Executive Ministry; International Development; Management; Nonprofit Management

MEd Education

MSM Educational Administration; Executive Ministry; International Development

COURSE SUBJECT AREAS OFFERED OUTSIDE OF DEGREE PROGRAMS

Undergraduate—anthropology; behavioral sciences; biblical studies; business, management, and marketing related; economics; history; human development, family studies, and related services; intercultural/multicultural and diversity studies; liberal arts and sciences, general studies and humanities; philosophy; psychology; religious studies; sociology.

Graduate—agricultural business and management; biblical studies; business administration, management and operations; education; music; psychology; religious studies; theological and ministerial studies; urban studies/affairs.

Non-credit—biblical studies; ethnic, cultural minority, and gender studies; history; psychology; religious studies.

HOPKINSVILLE COMMUNITY COLLEGE
Hopkinsville, Kentucky
http://www.hopkinsville.kctcs.edu/DistanceLearning/index.htm

Hopkinsville Community College was founded in 1965. It is accredited by Southern Association of Colleges and Schools. It first offered distance learning courses in 2000. In fall 2007, there were 2,698 students enrolled in distance learning courses. Institutionally administered financial aid is available to distance learners.

Services Distance learners have accessibility to academic advising, bookstore, campus computer network, career placement assistance, e-mail services, library services, tutoring.

Contact Dr. Lance Roland Angell, Dean, Institutional Effectiveness, Hopkinsville Community College, ADM 212, 720 North Drive, PO Box 2100, Hopkinsville, KY 42241-2100. Telephone: 270-707-3709. Fax: 270-885-5755. E-mail: lance.angell@kctcs.edu.

DEGREES AND AWARDS
Programs offered do not lead to a degree or other formal award.

COURSE SUBJECT AREAS OFFERED OUTSIDE OF DEGREE PROGRAMS
Undergraduate—accounting and related services; astronomy and astrophysics; biological and physical sciences; business administration, management and operations; business operations support and assistant services; chemistry; communication and media; computer and information sciences; economics; engineering-related technologies; English; fine and studio art; geography and cartography; health and physical education/fitness; history; mathematics; music; nursing; philosophy; physics; psychology; religious studies; sociology; statistics.
Non-credit—accounting and related services; business, management, and marketing related; business operations support and assistant services; communication and media; computer and information sciences; criminal justice and corrections; culinary arts and related services; education; English; English as a second/foreign language (teaching); English as a second language; English composition; fine and studio art; human resources management; manufacturing engineering; mathematics; music; nursing; psychology; real estate.

HORIZON COLLEGE & SEMINARY
Saskatoon, Saskatchewan, Canada
http://www.horizon.edu

Horizon College & Seminary was founded in 1930. It is provincially chartered. It first offered distance learning courses in 1995. In fall 2007, there were 27 students enrolled in distance learning courses. Institutionally administered financial aid is available to distance learners.

Services Distance learners have accessibility to academic advising, bookstore, campus computer network, e-mail services, tutoring.

Contact Deborah McConkey, Assistant Registrar, Horizon College & Seminary, 1303 Jackson Avenue, Saskatoon, SK S7H 2M9, Canada. Telephone: 306-374-6655. Fax: 306-373-6968. E-mail: admissions@horizon.edu.

DEGREES AND AWARDS
Programs offered do not lead to a degree or other formal award.

COURSE SUBJECT AREAS OFFERED OUTSIDE OF DEGREE PROGRAMS
Undergraduate—biblical and other theological languages and literatures; biblical studies; psychology; theological and ministerial studies.
Graduate—biblical studies; theological and ministerial studies.

HOUSTON COMMUNITY COLLEGE SYSTEM
Houston, Texas
Distance Education Department
http://www.distance.hccs.edu

Houston Community College System was founded in 1971. It is accredited by Southern Association of Colleges and Schools. It first offered distance learning courses in 1985. In fall 2007, there were 8,139 students enrolled in distance learning courses. Institutionally administered financial aid is available to distance learners.

Services Distance learners have accessibility to academic advising, bookstore, e-mail services, library services, tutoring.

Contact Eva Gonzalez, Distance Education Associate, Houston Community College System, 3100 Main Street, MC 1740, Houston, TX 77002. Telephone: 713-718-5152. Fax: 713-718-5388. E-mail: eva.gonzalez@hccs.edu.

DEGREES AND AWARDS
Programs offered do not lead to a degree or other formal award.

COURSE SUBJECT AREAS OFFERED OUTSIDE OF DEGREE PROGRAMS
Undergraduate—accounting and related services; American literature (United States and Canadian); anthropology; astronomy and astrophysics; biology; business administration, management and operations; chemistry; community health services; computer/information technology administration and management; computer science; criminology; developmental and child psychology; economics; English composition; English literature (British and Commonwealth); film/video and photographic arts; fine and studio art; fire protection; foods, nutrition, and related services; geography and cartography; history; human development, family studies, and related services; human resources management; human services; languages (Romance languages); management information systems; marketing; mathematics; mathematics and statistics related; philosophy; physical sciences; political science and government; psychology; real estate; social psychology; sociology.

HUNTINGTON COLLEGE OF HEALTH SCIENCES
Knoxville, Tennessee
http://www.hchs.edu

Huntington College of Health Sciences was founded in 1984. It is accredited by Distance Education and Training Council. It first offered distance learning courses in 1985. In fall 2007, there were 600 students enrolled in distance learning courses. Institutionally administered financial aid is available to distance learners.

Services Distance learners have accessibility to bookstore, e-mail services.

Contact Cheryl Freeman, Director/Registrar, Huntington College of Health Sciences, 1204 D Kenesaw Avenue, Knoxville, TN 37919. Telephone: 800-290-4226. Fax: 865-524-8339. E-mail: studentservices@hchs.edu.

DEGREES AND AWARDS
AS Nutrition
BAS Bachelor of Health Sciences
MS Nutrition–Master of Science of Nutrition

COURSE SUBJECT AREAS OFFERED OUTSIDE OF DEGREE PROGRAMS
Undergraduate—biochemistry, biophysics and molecular biology; biological and physical sciences; biology; cell biology and anatomical sciences; chemistry; developmental and child psychology; English; foods, nutrition, and related services; marketing; mathematics; nutrition sciences; physiology, pathology and related sciences; psychology.
Graduate—chemistry; foods, nutrition, and related services; health professions related; nutrition sciences.
Non-credit—foods, nutrition, and related services; health professions related.

IIA COLLEGE
Phoenix, Arizona
http://www.iia-online.com

IIA College was founded in 1979. It is accredited by Accrediting Council for Independent Colleges and Schools. It first offered distance learning courses in 2000. Institutionally administered financial aid is available to distance learners.

Services Distance learners have accessibility to academic advising, bookstore, campus computer network, career placement assistance, e-mail services, library services, tutoring.

Contact IIA Online Programs, IIA College, 2111 East Highland, Suite 400, Phoenix, AZ 85016. Telephone: 602-644-7000.

DEGREES AND AWARDS

AA Accounting; Business; Health Technology Management, Medical Assistant specialization; Health Technology Management, Patient Care Technician specialization; Justice Administration; Nursing; Paralegal Studies
BA Management

ILISAGVIK COLLEGE
Barrow, Alaska
http://www.ilisagvik.cc
Ilisagvik College was founded in 1995. It is accredited by Northwest Commission on Colleges and Universities. It first offered distance learning courses in 2001. In fall 2007, there were 60 students enrolled in distance learning courses. Institutionally administered financial aid is available to distance learners.
Services Distance learners have accessibility to academic advising, bookstore, campus computer network, career placement assistance, e-mail services, library services, tutoring.
Contact Mr. Rob Carrillo, Distance Education Coordinator, Ilisagvik College, PO Box 749, Barrow, AK 99723. Telephone: 907-852-1706. Fax: 907-852-1739. E-mail: rob.carrillo@ilisagvik.cc.

DEGREES AND AWARDS
Programs offered do not lead to a degree or other formal award.

COURSE SUBJECT AREAS OFFERED OUTSIDE OF DEGREE PROGRAMS
Undergraduate—allied health and medical assisting services; business administration, management and operations; computer software and media applications; English composition; science, technology and society.

ILLINOIS EASTERN COMMUNITY COLLEGES, FRONTIER COMMUNITY COLLEGE
Fairfield, Illinois
http://www.iecc.edu/fcc
Illinois Eastern Community Colleges, Frontier Community College was founded in 1976. It is accredited by North Central Association of Colleges and Schools. It first offered distance learning courses in 1994. In fall 2007, there were 85 students enrolled in distance learning courses. Institutionally administered financial aid is available to distance learners.
Services Distance learners have accessibility to academic advising, bookstore, campus computer network, career placement assistance, e-mail services, library services, tutoring.
Contact Ms. Blenda Demaret, Interim Dean, Illinois Eastern Community Colleges, Frontier Community College, 2 Frontier Drive, Fairfield, IL 62837. Telephone: 618-842-3711 Ext. 4007. Fax: 618-842-6340. E-mail: demaretb@iecc.edu.

DEGREES AND AWARDS
AAS Administrative Information Tech; Transfer degree
AGS General Studies
AS Transfer degree

COURSE SUBJECT AREAS OFFERED OUTSIDE OF DEGREE PROGRAMS
Undergraduate—business/commerce; foods, nutrition, and related services; health and physical education/fitness; marketing; nutrition sciences.

ILLINOIS EASTERN COMMUNITY COLLEGES, LINCOLN TRAIL COLLEGE
Robinson, Illinois
http://www.iecc.edu/ltc
Illinois Eastern Community Colleges, Lincoln Trail College was founded in 1969. It is accredited by North Central Association of Colleges and Schools. It first offered distance learning courses in 1994. In fall 2007, there were 341 students enrolled in distance learning courses. Institutionally administered financial aid is available to distance learners.
Services Distance learners have accessibility to academic advising, bookstore, campus computer network, career placement assistance, e-mail services, library services, tutoring.

Contact Ms. Penny Quinn, Dean of Instruction, Illinois Eastern Community Colleges, Lincoln Trail College, 11220 State Highway 1, Robinson, IL 62454. Telephone: 618-544-7423. E-mail: quinnp@iecc.edu.

DEGREES AND AWARDS
AAS Administrative Information Tech; Transfer degree
AGS General Studies
AS Transfer degree

COURSE SUBJECT AREAS OFFERED OUTSIDE OF DEGREE PROGRAMS
Undergraduate—accounting and computer science; astronomy and astrophysics; business/commerce; computer software and media applications; computer systems networking and telecommunications; English composition; geography and cartography; health professions related; mathematics; psychology; psychology related.

ILLINOIS EASTERN COMMUNITY COLLEGES, OLNEY CENTRAL COLLEGE
Olney, Illinois
http://www.iecc.edu/occ
Illinois Eastern Community Colleges, Olney Central College was founded in 1962. It is accredited by North Central Association of Colleges and Schools. It first offered distance learning courses in 1994. In fall 2007, there were 469 students enrolled in distance learning courses. Institutionally administered financial aid is available to distance learners.
Services Distance learners have accessibility to academic advising, bookstore, campus computer network, career placement assistance, e-mail services, library services, tutoring.
Contact Ms. Lisa Benson, Dean of Instruction, Illinois Eastern Community Colleges, Olney Central College, 305 North West Street, Olney, IL 62450. Telephone: 618-395-7777 Ext. 2002. Fax: 618-395-5212. E-mail: bensonl@iecc.edu.

DEGREES AND AWARDS
AAS Accounting and Computing; Administrative Information Tech; Medical Office Assistant; Transfer degree
AGS General Studies
AS Transfer degree

COURSE SUBJECT AREAS OFFERED OUTSIDE OF DEGREE PROGRAMS
Undergraduate—accounting and related services; business/commerce; communication and media; computer and information sciences; economics; English composition; liberal arts and sciences, general studies and humanities; mathematics; psychology; social sciences.

ILLINOIS EASTERN COMMUNITY COLLEGES, WABASH VALLEY COLLEGE
Mount Carmel, Illinois
http://www.iecc.edu/wvc
Illinois Eastern Community Colleges, Wabash Valley College was founded in 1960. It is accredited by North Central Association of Colleges and Schools. It first offered distance learning courses in 1994. In fall 2007, there were 228 students enrolled in distance learning courses. Institutionally administered financial aid is available to distance learners.
Services Distance learners have accessibility to academic advising, bookstore, campus computer network, career placement assistance, e-mail services, library services, tutoring.
Contact Theresa Marcotte, Dean of Instruction, Illinois Eastern Community Colleges, Wabash Valley College, 2200 College Drive, Mount Carmel, IL 62863. Telephone: 618-363-8641. E-mail: marcottet@iecc.edu.

DEGREES AND AWARDS
AAS Administrative Information Tech; Transfer degree
AGS General Studies
AS Transfer degree

COURSE SUBJECT AREAS OFFERED OUTSIDE OF DEGREE PROGRAMS

Undergraduate—accounting and related services; business/commerce; chemistry; history; human resources management; liberal arts and sciences, general studies and humanities; mathematics; mathematics and statistics related; psychology; statistics.

ILLINOIS STATE UNIVERSITY
Normal, Illinois
Extended University
http://www.exu.ilstu.edu
Illinois State University was founded in 1857. It is accredited by North Central Association of Colleges and Schools. It first offered distance learning courses in 1994. In fall 2007, there were 940 students enrolled in distance learning courses. Institutionally administered financial aid is available to distance learners.
Services Distance learners have accessibility to academic advising, bookstore, campus computer network, career placement assistance, e-mail services, library services.
Contact Susan Deason, Associate Director, Extended University, Illinois State University, Campus Box 4090, Normal, IL 61790. Telephone: 309-438-5288. Fax: 309-438-5069. E-mail: sdeason@ilstu.edu.

DEGREES AND AWARDS
BSN Nursing
Certification Visual Impairment and Blindness
MSN Gerontological Nurse Practicioner
PhD Nursing

COURSE SUBJECT AREAS OFFERED OUTSIDE OF DEGREE PROGRAMS
Undergraduate—agriculture; chemistry; communication disorders sciences and services; education related; English; English as a second language; health professions related; history; intercultural/multicultural and diversity studies; languages (foreign languages related); library science related; linguistic, comparative, and related language studies; marketing; mathematics; nursing; technology education/industrial arts.
Graduate—curriculum and instruction; educational administration and supervision; linguistic, comparative, and related language studies; nursing; special education; technology education/industrial arts.

IMMACULATA UNIVERSITY
Immaculata, Pennsylvania
http://www.immaculata.edu/
Immaculata University was founded in 1920. It is accredited by Middle States Association of Colleges and Schools. It first offered distance learning courses in 1999. In fall 2007, there were 2,100 students enrolled in distance learning courses. Institutionally administered financial aid is available to distance learners.
Services Distance learners have accessibility to academic advising, bookstore, campus computer network, career placement assistance, e-mail services, library services, tutoring.
Contact Mr. Kenneth P. Morlino, Director of Online Programs, Immaculata University, Box 300, 1145 King Road, Immaculata, PA 19345-0300. Telephone: 610-647-4400 Ext. 3085. Fax: 610-647-0215. E-mail: kmorlino@immaculata.edu.

DEGREES AND AWARDS
BA Financial Management; Health Care Management; Human Performance Management; Organization Dynamics; Organization Dynamics; Organization Dynamics

COURSE SUBJECT AREAS OFFERED OUTSIDE OF DEGREE PROGRAMS
Undergraduate—biblical and other theological languages and literatures; biological and biomedical sciences related; biological and physical sciences; biology; business administration, management and operations; business/managerial economics; computer and information sciences; computer and information sciences and support services related; computer/

information technology administration and management; computer science; computer software and media applications; computer systems analysis; English composition; family and consumer economics; family and consumer sciences/human sciences; foods, nutrition, and related services; history; human resources management; psychology; religious studies; sociology.
Graduate—counseling psychology; education related; human development, family studies, and related services; statistics.

INDEPENDENCE UNIVERSITY
Salt Lake City, Utah
http://www.independence.edu
Independence University was founded in 1978. It is accredited by Accrediting Commission of Career Schools and Colleges of Technology. It first offered distance learning courses in 1978. In fall 2007, there were 2,000 students enrolled in distance learning courses. Institutionally administered financial aid is available to distance learners.
Services Distance learners have accessibility to academic advising, campus computer network, e-mail services, library services, tutoring.
Contact Enrollment Advisors, Independence University, 5295 South Commerce Drive, Suite G-50, Salt Lake City, UT 84107. Telephone: 800-972-5149. Fax: 801-263-0345. E-mail: info@independence.edu.

DEGREES AND AWARDS
AS Allied Health; Business in General Business; Business; Early Childhood Education; Respiratory Therapy
BS Business, general; Health Services Management; Respiratory Care
BSN Nursing–Bachelors of Science in Nursing
MBA Business Administration; Health Care
MPH Public Health
MS Health Care Administration; Health Services Community Health; Health Services Wellness Promotion; Nursing Administration; Nursing Community Health; Nursing Gerontology; Nursing Wellness; Nursing

COURSE SUBJECT AREAS OFFERED OUTSIDE OF DEGREE PROGRAMS
Undergraduate—business, management, and marketing related.
Graduate—community health services; gerontology; health psychology.

INDIANA STATE UNIVERSITY
Terre Haute, Indiana
Office of Distance Support Services
http://www.indstate.edu/distance
Indiana State University was founded in 1865. It is accredited by North Central Association of Colleges and Schools. It first offered distance learning courses in 1969. In fall 2007, there were 2,000 students enrolled in distance learning courses. Institutionally administered financial aid is available to distance learners.
Services Distance learners have accessibility to academic advising, bookstore, campus computer network, career placement assistance, e-mail services, library services.
Contact Distance Support Services, Indiana State University, Erickson Hall, Room 122, Terre Haute, IN 47809. Telephone: 888-237-8080. Fax: 812-237-8023. E-mail: studentservices@indstate.edu.

DEGREES AND AWARDS
AS General Aviation Flight Technology
BS Business Administration; Career and Technical Education; Criminology and Criminal Justice; Electronics Technology; Human Resource Development; Insurance and Risk Management; Mechanical Engineering Technology; Nursing–LPN-BS; Nursing–RN to BS; Technology Management
Certificate Corrections; Law Enforcement; Private Security and Loss Prevention
License Driver Education Instructor; Middle/Secondary Teaching; School Administration; Visual Impairment; Vocational Business Education
Graduate Certificate Human Resource Development; Public Administration; Public Personnel Administration; School Library Media Services; Teaching English as a Second or Foreign Language

MA Criminology and Criminal Justice
MPA Public Administration
MS Criminology and Criminal Justice; Electronics and Computer Technology; Health and Safety (Occupational Safety Management specialization); Human Resource Development; Nursing–Family Nurse Practitioner specialization; Nursing–Nursing Administration specialization; Nursing–Nursing Education specialization; Student Affairs and Higher Education
PhD Technology Management

COURSE SUBJECT AREAS OFFERED OUTSIDE OF DEGREE PROGRAMS

Undergraduate—accounting and computer science; accounting and related services; aerospace, aeronautical and astronautical engineering; biological and physical sciences; biology; botany/plant biology; business administration, management and operations; business/commerce; business, management, and marketing related; business operations support and assistant services; chemistry; community health services; computer programming; computer science; construction engineering technology; construction management; criminal justice and corrections; criminology; curriculum and instruction; drafting/design engineering technologies; economics; education; education related; electrical and electronic engineering technologies; engineering-related technologies; English; English composition; finance and financial management services; geography and cartography; health and physical education/fitness; history; human resources management; human services; insurance; library science related; management information systems; marketing; mathematics; mathematics and computer science; mathematics and statistics related; mechanical engineering related technologies; music; nursing; personality psychology; psychology; sociology; technical and business writing; technology education/industrial arts.
Graduate—bilingual, multilingual, and multicultural education; counseling psychology; criminal justice and corrections; criminology; curriculum and instruction; developmental and child psychology; education; educational administration and supervision; educational assessment, evaluation, and research; educational/instructional media design; educational psychology; education related; education (specific levels and methods); education (specific subject areas); electrical and electronic engineering technologies; electrical, electronics and communications engineering; electromechanical and instrumentation and maintenance technologies; English as a second/foreign language (teaching); English as a second language; finance and financial management services; human resources management; industrial and organizational psychology; library science related; nursing; public administration; public administration and social service professions related; school psychology; special education; student counseling and personnel services.

See full description on page 398.

INDIANA TECH
Fort Wayne, Indiana
Independent Study
http://www.indianatech.edu
Indiana Tech was founded in 1930. It is accredited by North Central Association of Colleges and Schools. It first offered distance learning courses in 1982. In fall 2007, there were 390 students enrolled in distance learning courses. Institutionally administered financial aid is available to distance learners.
Services Distance learners have accessibility to academic advising, bookstore, campus computer network, e-mail services.
Contact Mrs. Alisa Scagnoli, Academic Resource Specialist, Indiana Tech, 1600 East Washington Boulevard, Fort Wayne, IN 46803. Telephone: 800-937-2448 Ext. 2242. Fax: 260-422-5561. E-mail: amscagnoli@indianatech.edu.

DEGREES AND AWARDS

AS Business Administration; General Studies
BS Business Administration
BSBA Human Resources; Management; Marketing

COURSE SUBJECT AREAS OFFERED OUTSIDE OF DEGREE PROGRAMS

Undergraduate—accounting and related services; business administration, management and operations; business/commerce; computer and information sciences; English composition; mathematics; psychology; social sciences.

INDIANA UNIVERSITY OF PENNSYLVANIA
Indiana, Pennsylvania
School of Continuing Education
http://www.iup.edu/continuing-ed/
Indiana University of Pennsylvania was founded in 1875. It is accredited by Middle States Association of Colleges and Schools. It first offered distance learning courses in 1990. In fall 2007, there were 1,050 students enrolled in distance learning courses. Institutionally administered financial aid is available to distance learners.
Services Distance learners have accessibility to academic advising, bookstore, campus computer network, career placement assistance, e-mail services, library services.
Contact Mr. Nicholas Kolb, Dean, College of Continuing Education, Indiana University of Pennsylvania, Sutton Hall, Room 209, Indiana, PA 15705. Telephone: 724-357-2209. E-mail: nicholas.kolb@iup.edu.

DEGREES AND AWARDS

Certification Physics (WINPC)
Graduate Certificate Safety Sciences
MA Criminology
MS Safety Science

COURSE SUBJECT AREAS OFFERED OUTSIDE OF DEGREE PROGRAMS

Undergraduate—accounting and related services; anthropology; business, management, and marketing related; finance and financial management services; foods, nutrition, and related services; hospitality administration; information science/studies; management information systems; marketing; mathematics; physics; political science and government; psychology.
Graduate—business, management, and marketing related; criminal justice and corrections; criminology; engineering-related fields; foods, nutrition, and related services; liberal arts and sciences, general studies and humanities; political science and government.

INDIANA UNIVERSITY–PURDUE UNIVERSITY FORT WAYNE
Fort Wayne, Indiana
http://www.ipfw.edu/dlearning
Indiana University–Purdue University Fort Wayne was founded in 1917. It is accredited by North Central Association of Colleges and Schools. It first offered distance learning courses in 1996. In fall 2007, there were 2,948 students enrolled in distance learning courses. Institutionally administered financial aid is available to distance learners.
Services Distance learners have accessibility to bookstore, campus computer network, e-mail services, library services.
Contact Deborah Hein, Program Assistant, Indiana University–Purdue University Fort Wayne, 2101 East Coliseum Boulevard, Fort Wayne, IN 46805. Telephone: 260-481-6111. Fax: 260-481-6949. E-mail: dlearn@ipfw.edu.

DEGREES AND AWARDS

BGS Associate of Arts and Bachelor of General Studies

COURSE SUBJECT AREAS OFFERED OUTSIDE OF DEGREE PROGRAMS

Undergraduate—accounting and related services; biology; business/commerce; communication and media; comparative literature; computer science; economics; education; engineering/industrial management; English composition; history; journalism; mathematics; nursing; philosophy; political science and government; psychology; sociology.

Graduate—business administration, management and operations; educational administration and supervision; nursing.
Non-credit—business/corporate communications; business, management, and marketing related; business operations support and assistant services; computer software and media applications; computer systems networking and telecommunications.

INDIANA UNIVERSITY SYSTEM
Bloomington, Indiana
School of Continuing Studies
http://scs.indiana.edu
Indiana University System is accredited by North Central Association of Colleges and Schools. It first offered distance learning courses in 1995. In fall 2007, there were 4,000 students enrolled in distance learning courses. Institutionally administered financial aid is available to distance learners.
Services Distance learners have accessibility to academic advising, bookstore, campus computer network, e-mail services, library services.
Contact Peer Advisor, Indiana University System, Owen Hall 001, 790 East Kirkwood Avenue, Bloomington, IN 47405-7101. Telephone: 800-334-1011. Fax: 812-855-8680. E-mail: scs@indiana.edu.

DEGREES AND AWARDS
AA General Studies
BGS General Studies Degree program
Certificate Accounting–Healthcare Accounting and Financial Management; Distance Education
MS Adult Education

COURSE SUBJECT AREAS OFFERED OUTSIDE OF DEGREE PROGRAMS
Undergraduate—liberal arts and sciences, general studies and humanities.
Graduate—education related.
Non-credit—accounting and related services; education (specific levels and methods); taxation.
See full description on page 400.

INDIANA WESLEYAN UNIVERSITY
Marion, Indiana
Center for Distributed Learning
http://www.IWUonline.com
Indiana Wesleyan University was founded in 1920. It is accredited by North Central Association of Colleges and Schools. It first offered distance learning courses in 1996. In fall 2007, there were 4,595 students enrolled in distance learning courses. Institutionally administered financial aid is available to distance learners.
Services Distance learners have accessibility to academic advising, e-mail services, library services.
Contact Mr. Jeff Whetzel, Online Enrollment Services, Indiana Wesleyan University, 1900 West 50th Street, Marion, IN 46953. Telephone: 888-IWU-2day. Fax: 765-677-2973. E-mail: info@iwuonline.com.

DEGREES AND AWARDS
AS Accounting; Business; Criminal Justice; General Studies
BS Accounting (Bachelor completion); Business Information Systems (Bachelor completion); Criminal Justice (Bachelor completion); General Studies; Management (Bachelor completion); Nursing–RN to BS completion
BSBA Business Administration (Bachelor completion)
Certificate Communication; Communications; Criminal Justice; Human Services; Religious Studies
License Exceptional Needs with Mild Interventions (Special Ed)
MA Ministry (Ministerial Leadership and Youth Ministry concentrations)
MBA Business Administration
MEd Education
MSM Management
MSN Nursing Education and Nursing Administration majors

COURSE SUBJECT AREAS OFFERED OUTSIDE OF DEGREE PROGRAMS
Undergraduate—biblical and other theological languages and literatures; biblical studies; communication and media; computer and information sciences; computer software and media applications; criminal justice and corrections; English composition; fine and studio art; history; liberal arts and sciences, general studies and humanities; mathematics; music; philosophy and religious studies related; psychology.
Graduate—educational psychology.

INDIAN RIVER COMMUNITY COLLEGE
Fort Pierce, Florida
Distance Learning
http://www.ircc.edu/portal/layout_web1.
aspx?PortalPageID=142
Indian River Community College was founded in 1960. It is accredited by Southern Association of Colleges and Schools. It first offered distance learning courses in 1995. In fall 2007, there were 2,708 students enrolled in distance learning courses. Institutionally administered financial aid is available to distance learners.
Services Distance learners have accessibility to academic advising, bookstore, campus computer network, career placement assistance, e-mail services, library services, tutoring.
Contact Dr. Henri Sue Bynum, Vice President of Academic Affairs, Indian River Community College, 3209 Virginia Avenue, Fort Pierce, FL 34981-5596. Telephone: 772-462-7215. Fax: 772-462-4796. E-mail: hbynum@ircc.edu.

DEGREES AND AWARDS
Programs offered do not lead to a degree or other formal award.

COURSE SUBJECT AREAS OFFERED OUTSIDE OF DEGREE PROGRAMS
Undergraduate—accounting and related services; allied health and medical assisting services; anthropology; biology; business/commerce; business, management, and marketing related; business/managerial economics; communication and journalism related; computer and information sciences; computer and information sciences and support services related; computer programming; computer science; computer software and media applications; criminal justice and corrections; philosophy; philosophy and religious studies related; physical sciences; physics; sociology; special education; teaching assistants/aides; technical and business writing.
Non-credit—insurance; real estate.

INSTITUTE FOR CHRISTIAN STUDIES
Toronto, Ontario, Canada
http://www.icscanada.edu
Institute for Christian Studies was founded in 1967. It is provincially chartered. It first offered distance learning courses in 1990. In fall 2007, there were 19 students enrolled in distance learning courses. Institutionally administered financial aid is available to distance learners.
Services Distance learners have accessibility to academic advising, bookstore, e-mail services, library services.
Contact Ms. Robbin Burry, Registrar, Academic and Student Services Officer, Institute for Christian Studies, 229 College Street, 2nd Floor, Toronto, ON M5T 1R4, Canada. Telephone: 888-326-5347 Ext. 234. Fax: 416-979-2331 Ext. 234. E-mail: registrar@icscanada.edu.

DEGREES AND AWARDS
M Phil Master of Worldview Studies in Education

COURSE SUBJECT AREAS OFFERED OUTSIDE OF DEGREE PROGRAMS
Graduate—education related; philosophy; philosophy and religious studies related; political science and government; theological and ministerial studies.

IONA COLLEGE
New Rochelle, New York
http://www.iona.edu

Iona College was founded in 1940. It is accredited by Middle States Association of Colleges and Schools. It first offered distance learning courses in 1999. In fall 2007, there were 310 students enrolled in distance learning courses. Institutionally administered financial aid is available to distance learners.

Services Distance learners have accessibility to academic advising, bookstore, campus computer network, career placement assistance, e-mail services, library services, tutoring.

Contact Mr. Kevin Cavanagh, Assistant Vice President for College Admissions, Iona College, Admissions, 715 North Avenue, New Rochelle, NY 10801. Telephone: 914-633-2502. Fax: 914-633-2642. E-mail: kcavanagh@iona.edu.

DEGREES AND AWARDS
Programs offered do not lead to a degree or other formal award.

COURSE SUBJECT AREAS OFFERED OUTSIDE OF DEGREE PROGRAMS
Undergraduate—business administration, management and operations; business/corporate communications; business, management, and marketing related; business operations support and assistant services; cognitive psychology and psycholinguistics; communication and journalism related; communication and media; computer and information sciences and support services related; computer programming; computer software and media applications; economics; entrepreneurial and small business operations; family psychology; finance and financial management services; health and medical administrative services; health professions related; health services/allied health/health sciences; international business; legal studies (non-professional general, undergraduate); liberal arts and sciences, general studies and humanities; management information systems; marketing; philosophy; philosophy and religious studies related; psychology; science, technology and society; social work.
Graduate—business administration, management and operations; business/commerce; business/corporate communications; business, management, and marketing related; communication and journalism related; communications technologies and support services related; computer systems analysis; computer systems networking and telecommunications; education; educational administration and supervision; educational assessment, evaluation, and research; educational/instructional media design; education (specific levels and methods); education (specific subject areas); finance and financial management services; health and medical administrative services; health professions related; health services/allied health/health sciences; human resources management; information science/studies; international business; journalism; languages (Romance languages); legal professions and studies related; management information systems; marketing; psychology; public relations, advertising, and applied communication related.

IVY TECH COMMUNITY COLLEGE–BLOOMINGTON
Bloomington, Indiana
http://www.bloomington.ivytech.edu/

Ivy Tech Community College–Bloomington was founded in 2001. It is accredited by North Central Association of Colleges and Schools. In fall 2007, there were 1,355 students enrolled in distance learning courses. Institutionally administered financial aid is available to distance learners.

Services Distance learners have accessibility to academic advising, bookstore, campus computer network, career placement assistance, e-mail services, library services.

Contact Beth Pless, Director of Enrollment Services, Ivy Tech Community College–Bloomington, 200 Daniels Way, Bloomington, IN 47404-0393. Telephone: 812-330-6161. Fax: 812-330-6200. E-mail: bpless@ivytech.edu.

DEGREES AND AWARDS
AAS Accounting; Business Administration; Computer Information Systems; Design Technology; Early Childhood Education; Human Services; Office Administration; Paralegal

AS Computer Information Systems; Criminal Justice; General Studies; Human Services; Library Assistant; Paralegal

COURSE SUBJECT AREAS OFFERED OUTSIDE OF DEGREE PROGRAMS
Undergraduate—business administration, management and operations; business operations support and assistant services; criminal justice and corrections; mathematics.

IVY TECH COMMUNITY COLLEGE–CENTRAL INDIANA
Indianapolis, Indiana
http://www.ivytech.edu/indianapolis/

Ivy Tech Community College–Central Indiana was founded in 1963. It is accredited by North Central Association of Colleges and Schools. It first offered distance learning courses in 1995. In fall 2007, there were 2,694 students enrolled in distance learning courses. Institutionally administered financial aid is available to distance learners.

Services Distance learners have accessibility to academic advising, bookstore, campus computer network, career placement assistance, e-mail services, library services.

Contact Tracy Funk, Director of Admissions, Ivy Tech Community College–Central Indiana, 50 West Fall Creek Parkway North Drive, Indianapolis, IN 46208-4777. Telephone: 317-921-4371. Fax: 317-921-4753. E-mail: tfunk@ivytech.edu.

DEGREES AND AWARDS
AAS Accounting; Business Administration; Computer Information Systems; Design Technology; Early Childhood Education; Human Services; Office Administration; Paralegal

AS Computer Information Systems; Criminal Justice; General Studies; Human Services; Library Assistant; Paralegal

COURSE SUBJECT AREAS OFFERED OUTSIDE OF DEGREE PROGRAMS
Undergraduate—business operations support and assistant services; criminal justice and corrections; mathematics.

IVY TECH COMMUNITY COLLEGE–COLUMBUS
Columbus, Indiana
http://www.ivytech.edu/columbus/

Ivy Tech Community College–Columbus was founded in 1963. It is accredited by North Central Association of Colleges and Schools. It first offered distance learning courses in 1995. In fall 2007, there were 1,056 students enrolled in distance learning courses. Institutionally administered financial aid is available to distance learners.

Services Distance learners have accessibility to academic advising, bookstore, campus computer network, career placement assistance, e-mail services, library services.

Contact Neil S. Bagadiong, Director of Admissions/Assistant to the Dean of Student Affairs, Ivy Tech Community College–Columbus, 4475 Central Avenue, Columbus, IN 47203-1868. Telephone: 812-374-5129 Ext. Fax: 812-372-0311. E-mail: nbagadio@ivytech.edu.

DEGREES AND AWARDS
AAS Accounting; Business Administration; Computer Information Systems; Design Technology; Early Childhood Education; Human Services; Office Administration; Paralegal

AS Computer Information Systems; Criminal Justice; General Studies; Human Services; Library Assistant; Paralegal

COURSE SUBJECT AREAS OFFERED OUTSIDE OF DEGREE PROGRAMS
Undergraduate—business administration, management and operations; business operations support and assistant services; mathematics.

IVY TECH COMMUNITY COLLEGE–EAST CENTRAL
Muncie, Indiana
http://www.ivytech.edu/eastcentral/

Ivy Tech Community College–East Central was founded in 1968. It is accredited by North Central Association of Colleges and Schools. It first offered distance learning courses in 1995. In fall 2007, there were 1,585 students enrolled in distance learning courses. Institutionally administered financial aid is available to distance learners.

Services Distance learners have accessibility to academic advising, bookstore, campus computer network, career placement assistance, e-mail services, library services.

Contact Corey A. Sharp, Director of Enrollment Management, Ivy Tech Community College–East Central, 4301 South Cowan Road, Muncie, IN 47302-9448. Telephone: 765-289-2291. Fax: 765-289-2292. E-mail: csharp@ivytech.edu.

DEGREES AND AWARDS

AAS Accounting; Business Administration; Computer Information Systems; Design Technolgy; Early Childhood Education; Human Services; Office Administration; Paralegal Studies
AS Computer Information Systems; Criminal Justice; General Studies; Human Services; Library Technical Assistant; Paralegal Studies

COURSE SUBJECT AREAS OFFERED OUTSIDE OF DEGREE PROGRAMS

Undergraduate—business administration, management and operations; business operations support and assistant services; criminal justice and corrections; mathematics; psychology.

IVY TECH COMMUNITY COLLEGE–KOKOMO
Kokomo, Indiana
http://www.ivytech.edu/kokomo/

Ivy Tech Community College–Kokomo was founded in 1968. It is accredited by North Central Association of Colleges and Schools. It first offered distance learning courses in 1995. In fall 2007, there were 624 students enrolled in distance learning courses. Institutionally administered financial aid is available to distance learners.

Services Distance learners have accessibility to academic advising, bookstore, campus computer network, career placement assistance, e-mail services, library services.

Contact Suzanne Dillman, Director of Admissions, Ivy Tech Community College–Kokomo, 1815 East Morgan Street, Kokomo, IN 46903-1373. Telephone: 765-459-0561 Ext. 318. Fax: 765-454-5111. E-mail: sdillman@ivytech.edu.

DEGREES AND AWARDS

AAS Accounting; Business Administration; Computer Information Systems; Design Technology; Early Childhood Education; Human Services; Office Administration; Paralegal Studies
AS Computer Information Systems; Criminal Justice; General Studies; Human Services; Library Technical Assistant; Paralegal

COURSE SUBJECT AREAS OFFERED OUTSIDE OF DEGREE PROGRAMS

Undergraduate—criminal justice and corrections; English composition; history; quality control and safety technologies.

IVY TECH COMMUNITY COLLEGE–LAFAYETTE
Lafayette, Indiana
http://www.laf.ivytech.edu/

Ivy Tech Community College–Lafayette was founded in 1968. It is accredited by North Central Association of Colleges and Schools. It first offered distance learning courses in 1995. In fall 2007, there were 1,071 students enrolled in distance learning courses. Institutionally administered financial aid is available to distance learners.

Services Distance learners have accessibility to academic advising, bookstore, campus computer network, career placement assistance, e-mail services, library services.

Contact Ivan Hernandez, Director of Admissions, Ivy Tech Community College–Lafayette, 3101 South Creasy Lane, Lafayette, IN 47903. Telephone: 765-269-5253. E-mail: ihernand@ivytech.edu.

DEGREES AND AWARDS

AAS Accounting; Business Administration; Computer Information Systems; Design Technology; Early Childhood Education; Human Services; Office Administration; Paralegal Studies
AS Computer Information Systems; Criminal Justice; General Studies; Human Services; Library Technical Assistant; Paralegal Studies

IVY TECH COMMUNITY COLLEGE–NORTH CENTRAL
South Bend, Indiana
Instructional Technology
http://www.ivytech.edu/southbend/

Ivy Tech Community College–North Central was founded in 1968. It is accredited by North Central Association of Colleges and Schools. It first offered distance learning courses in 1989. In fall 2007, there were 1,480 students enrolled in distance learning courses. Institutionally administered financial aid is available to distance learners.

Services Distance learners have accessibility to academic advising, bookstore, campus computer network, career placement assistance, e-mail services, library services.

Contact Janice Austin, Director of Admissions, Ivy Tech Community College–North Central, 220 Dean Johnson Boulevard, South Bend, IN 46601. Telephone: 574-289-7001. Fax: 574-236-7177. E-mail: jaustin@ivytech.edu.

DEGREES AND AWARDS

AAS Accounting; Business Administration; Computer Information Systems; Design Technology; Early Childhood Education; Human Services; Office Administration; Paralegal Studies
AS Computer Information Systems; Criminal Justice; General Studies; Human Services; Library Technical Assistant; Paralegal Studies

COURSE SUBJECT AREAS OFFERED OUTSIDE OF DEGREE PROGRAMS

Undergraduate—biology; economics; English composition; philosophy; political science and government; psychology; sales, merchandising, and related marketing operations (general); sociology; visual and performing arts related.

IVY TECH COMMUNITY COLLEGE–NORTHEAST
Fort Wayne, Indiana
http://www.ivytech.edu/fortwayne/

Ivy Tech Community College–Northeast was founded in 1969. It is accredited by North Central Association of Colleges and Schools. It first offered distance learning courses in 1995. In fall 2007, there were 1,277 students enrolled in distance learning courses. Institutionally administered financial aid is available to distance learners.

Services Distance learners have accessibility to academic advising, bookstore, campus computer network, career placement assistance, e-mail services, library services.

Contact Steve Scheer, Director of Admissions, Ivy Tech Community College–Northeast, 3800 North Anthony Boulevard, Fort Wayne, IN 46805-1489. Telephone: 260-480-4221. Fax: 260-480-4177. E-mail: sscheer@ivytech.edu.

DEGREES AND AWARDS

AAS Accounting; Business Administration; Computer Information Systems; Design Technology; Early Childhood Education; Human Services; Office Administration; Paralegal Studies
AS Computer Information Systems; Criminal Justice; General Studies; General Studies; Human Services; Library Technical Assistant; Paralegal Studies

COURSE SUBJECT AREAS OFFERED OUTSIDE OF DEGREE PROGRAMS

Undergraduate—construction engineering technology; fire protection.

IVY TECH COMMUNITY COLLEGE–NORTHWEST
Gary, Indiana
http://www.nwi.ivytech.edu/

Ivy Tech Community College–Northwest was founded in 1963. It is accredited by North Central Association of Colleges and Schools. It first offered distance learning courses in 1995. In fall 2007, there were 1,114 students enrolled in distance learning courses. Institutionally administered financial aid is available to distance learners.
Services Distance learners have accessibility to academic advising, bookstore, campus computer network, career placement assistance, e-mail services, library services.
Contact Keith Howard, Vice Chancellor for Student Affairs, Ivy Tech Community College–Northwest, 1440 East 35th Avenue, Gary, IN 46409-1499. Telephone: 219-981-1111 Ext. 273. Fax: 219-981-4452. E-mail: khoward@ivytech.edu.

DEGREES AND AWARDS

AAS Accounting; Business Administration; Computer Information Systems; Design Technology; Early Childhood Education; Human Services; Office Administration; Paralegal Studies

AS Computer Information Systems; Criminal Justice; General Studies; Human Services; Library Technical Assistant; Paralegal Studies

COURSE SUBJECT AREAS OFFERED OUTSIDE OF DEGREE PROGRAMS

Undergraduate—accounting and related services; business administration, management and operations; business operations support and assistant services; economics; English composition; fire protection; history; hospitality administration; marketing; mathematics; nursing; physical sciences; psychology; sociology.

IVY TECH COMMUNITY COLLEGE–SOUTHEAST
Madison, Indiana
http://www.ivytech.edu/southeast/

Ivy Tech Community College–Southeast was founded in 1963. It is accredited by North Central Association of Colleges and Schools. It first offered distance learning courses in 1995. In fall 2007, there were 741 students enrolled in distance learning courses. Institutionally administered financial aid is available to distance learners.
Services Distance learners have accessibility to academic advising, bookstore, campus computer network, career placement assistance, e-mail services, library services.
Contact Cindy Hutcherson, Assistant Director of Admissions and Career Counselor, Ivy Tech Community College–Southeast, 590 Ivy Tech Drive, Madison, IN 47250-1881. Telephone: 812-265-2580. Fax: 812-265-4028. E-mail: chutcher@ivytech.edu.

DEGREES AND AWARDS

AAS Accounting; Business Administration; Computer Information Systems; Design Technology; Early Childhood Education; Human Services; Office Administration; Paralegal

AS Computer Information Systems; Criminal Justice; General Studies; Human Services; Library Assistant; Paralegal

COURSE SUBJECT AREAS OFFERED OUTSIDE OF DEGREE PROGRAMS

Undergraduate—business administration, management and operations; business operations support and assistant services; criminal justice and corrections.

IVY TECH COMMUNITY COLLEGE–SOUTHERN INDIANA
Sellersburg, Indiana
http://www.ivytech.edu/sellersburg/

Ivy Tech Community College–Southern Indiana was founded in 1968. It is accredited by North Central Association of Colleges and Schools. It first offered distance learning courses in 1995. In fall 2007, there were 727 students enrolled in distance learning courses. Institutionally administered financial aid is available to distance learners.
Services Distance learners have accessibility to academic advising, bookstore, campus computer network, career placement assistance, e-mail services, library services.
Contact Pat Fawcett, Assistant Dean of Enrollment Services, Ivy Tech Community College–Southern Indiana, 8204 Highway 311, Sellersburg, IN 47172-1897. Telephone: 812-246-3301 Ext. 4128. Fax: 812-246-9905. E-mail: pfawcett@ivytech.edu.

DEGREES AND AWARDS

AAS Accounting; Business Administration; Computer Information Systems; Design Technology; Early Childhood Education; Human Services; Office Administration; Paralegal

AS Computer Information Systems; Criminal Justice; General Studies; Human Services; Library Assistant; Paralegal

COURSE SUBJECT AREAS OFFERED OUTSIDE OF DEGREE PROGRAMS

Undergraduate—business administration, management and operations; business operations support and assistant services; criminal justice and corrections; mathematics; sociology.

IVY TECH COMMUNITY COLLEGE–SOUTHWEST
Evansville, Indiana
http://www.ivytech.edu/evansville/

Ivy Tech Community College–Southwest was founded in 1963. It is accredited by North Central Association of Colleges and Schools. It first offered distance learning courses in 1995. In fall 2007, there were 969 students enrolled in distance learning courses. Institutionally administered financial aid is available to distance learners.
Services Distance learners have accessibility to academic advising, bookstore, campus computer network, career placement assistance, e-mail services, library services.
Contact Denise Johnson-Kincaid, Inteirm Director of Admissions, Ivy Tech Community College–Southwest, 3501 First Avenue, Evansville, IN 47710-3398. Telephone: 812-429-1430. Fax: 812-246-9905 Ext. E-mail: ajohnson@ivytech.edu.

DEGREES AND AWARDS

AAS Accounting; Business Administration; Computer Information Systems; Design Technology; Early Childhood Education; Human Services; Office Administration; Paralegal

AS Computer Information Systems; Criminal Justice; General Studies; Human Services; Library Assistant; Paralegal

COURSE SUBJECT AREAS OFFERED OUTSIDE OF DEGREE PROGRAMS

Undergraduate—business administration, management and operations; business operations support and assistant services; criminal justice and corrections; mathematics.

IVY TECH COMMUNITY COLLEGE–WABASH VALLEY
Terre Haute, Indiana
http://goivytech.net/

Ivy Tech Community College–Wabash Valley was founded in 1966. It is accredited by North Central Association of Colleges and Schools. It first offered distance learning courses in 1995. In fall 2007, there were 1,694 students enrolled in distance learning courses. Institutionally administered financial aid is available to distance learners.
Services Distance learners have accessibility to academic advising, bookstore, campus computer network, career placement assistance, e-mail services, library services.

Contact Michael Fisher, Director of Admissions, Ivy Tech Community College–Wabash Valley, 7999 US Highway 41, Terre Haute, IN 47802-4898. Telephone: 812-298-2300. Fax: 812-299-5723. E-mail: mfisher@ivytech.edu.

DEGREES AND AWARDS

AAS Accounting; Business Administration; Computer Information Systems; Design Technology; Early Childhood Education; Human Services; Office Administration; Paralegal

AS Computer Information Systems; Criminal Justice; General Studies; Human Services; Library Assistant; Paralegal

COURSE SUBJECT AREAS OFFERED OUTSIDE OF DEGREE PROGRAMS

Undergraduate—biology; business administration, management and operations; business operations support and assistant services; mathematics; psychology.

IVY TECH COMMUNITY COLLEGE–WHITEWATER
Richmond, Indiana
http://www.ivytech.edu/richmond/

Ivy Tech Community College–Whitewater was founded in 1963. It is accredited by North Central Association of Colleges and Schools. It first offered distance learning courses in 1995. In fall 2007, there were 1,099 students enrolled in distance learning courses. Institutionally administered financial aid is available to distance learners.
Services Distance learners have accessibility to academic advising, bookstore, career placement assistance, e-mail services, library services, tutoring.
Contact Christine Rethlake, Director of Admissions, Ivy Tech Community College–Whitewater, 2325 Chester Boulevard, Richmond, IN 47374-1298. Telephone: 765-966-2656 Ext. 1212. Fax: 765-962-8741. E-mail: crethlake@ivytech.edu.

DEGREES AND AWARDS

AAS Accounting; Business Administration; Computer Information Systems; Design Technology; Early Childhood Education; Human Services; Office Administration; Paralegal

AS Computer Information Systems; Criminal Justice; General Studies; Human Services; Library Assistant; Paralegal

COURSE SUBJECT AREAS OFFERED OUTSIDE OF DEGREE PROGRAMS

Undergraduate—business administration, management and operations; business operations support and assistant services; criminal justice and corrections; mathematics; psychology.

JACKSON STATE UNIVERSITY
Jackson, Mississippi
http://www.jsums.edu/~dl

Jackson State University was founded in 1877. It is accredited by Southern Association of Colleges and Schools. It first offered distance learning courses in 1998. In fall 2007, there were 1,196 students enrolled in distance learning courses. Institutionally administered financial aid is available to distance learners.
Services Distance learners have accessibility to academic advising, campus computer network, career placement assistance, e-mail services, library services.
Contact Dr. Edelia J. Carthan, Assistant Director, Distance Learning, Jackson State University, JSU Box 17199, Jackson, MS 39217. Telephone: 601-979-2244. Fax: 601-979-8246. E-mail: edelia.j.carthan@jsums.edu.

DEGREES AND AWARDS

Programs offered do not lead to a degree or other formal award.

COURSE SUBJECT AREAS OFFERED OUTSIDE OF DEGREE PROGRAMS

Undergraduate—biology; chemistry; computer programming; data entry/microcomputer applications; education; educational psychology; health and physical education/fitness; history; liberal arts and sciences, general studies and humanities; mathematics; music; social sciences; social work; sociology; special education.
Graduate—communication disorders sciences and services; counseling psychology; education; educational administration and supervision; special education.

JACKSONVILLE STATE UNIVERSITY
Jacksonville, Alabama
Department of Distance Education
http://myjsuonline.com

Jacksonville State University was founded in 1883. It is accredited by Southern Association of Colleges and Schools. It first offered distance learning courses in 1994. In fall 2007, there were 2,899 students enrolled in distance learning courses. Institutionally administered financial aid is available to distance learners.
Services Distance learners have accessibility to academic advising, bookstore, career placement assistance, e-mail services, library services.
Contact Ms. Gina Glass, Secretary to the Associate Vice President of Distance Education, Jacksonville State University, Office of Distance Education, 700 Pelham Road North, Jacksonville, AL 36265-1602. Telephone: 256-782-8172. Fax: 256-782-8128. E-mail: gglass@jsu.edu.

DEGREES AND AWARDS

BS Emergency Management (Homeland Security minor); Emergency Management (Public Safety Communications minor); Family and Consumer Sciences, Child Development concentration
BSN Nursing–STEP Nursing program
Certificate Spatial Analysis and Management
CAGS Nursing Education
Graduate Certificate Emergency Management
MBA Business Administration
MEd Physical Education
MPA Athletic Administration; Emergency Management; Spatial Analysis and Management concentration
MS Computer Systems and Software Design; Emergency Management; Manufacturing Systems Technology
MSN Nursing

COURSE SUBJECT AREAS OFFERED OUTSIDE OF DEGREE PROGRAMS

Undergraduate—accounting and computer science; accounting and related services; American literature (United States and Canadian); anthropology; applied mathematics; atmospheric sciences and meteorology; behavioral sciences; biological and biomedical sciences related; biological and physical sciences; biology; biopsychology; business administration, management and operations; business/commerce; business/corporate communications; business, management, and marketing related; business/managerial economics; chemistry; clinical psychology; community health services; computer and information sciences; computer and information sciences and support services related; computer/information technology administration and management; computer programming; computer science; computer software and media applications; computer systems analysis; computer systems networking and telecommunications; criminal justice and corrections; criminology; curriculum and instruction; data processing; developmental and child psychology; economics; education; educational administration and supervision; educational assessment, evaluation, and research; educational/instructional media design; educational psychology; education related; education (specific levels and methods); education (specific subject areas); engineering; English; English composition; English language and literature related; English literature (British and Commonwealth); environmental control technologies; family and consumer economics; family and consumer sciences/human sciences; family and consumer sciences/human sciences business services; family and consumer sciences/human sciences related; finance and financial management services; foods, nutrition, and related services; genetics; geography and cartography; geological and earth sciences/geosciences; gerontology; geropsychology; health and physical education/fitness; health professions related; history; human development, family studies, and related services; information science/studies; international business; languages (foreign languages related); liberal arts and sciences, general studies and humanities; management information systems; management sciences and quantitative methods; marketing; mathematics; mathematics and computer science; mathematics and statistics related; medical basic sciences; music; neuroscience; nursing; nutrition sciences; physical sciences; physics; political science and government; psychology; psychology related; psychopharmacology; public administration; public administration and social service professions related; quality control and safety technologies; sales, merchandising, and related marketing operations (general); sales, merchandising, and related marketing operations (specialized); school psychology; science, technology and society; security and protective services related; social and philosophical foundations of education; social psychology; social sciences; social work; sociology; special education; statistics; student counseling and personnel services; technology education/industrial arts.

Graduate—accounting and computer science; accounting and related services; behavioral sciences; biology; business administration, management and operations; business/commerce; business/corporate communications; business, management, and marketing related; business/managerial economics; chemistry; clinical psychology; computer and information sciences; computer and information sciences and support services related; computer engineering; computer/information technology administration and management; computer programming; computer science; computer software and media applications; computer systems analysis; computer systems networking and telecommunications; criminal justice and corrections; criminology; curriculum and instruction; developmental and child psychology; economics; education; educational administration and supervision; educational assessment, evaluation, and research; educational/instructional media design; educational psychology; education related; education (specific levels and methods); education (specific subject areas); environmental control technologies; family and consumer sciences/human sciences related; finance and financial management services; fire protection; geography and cartography; geological and earth sciences/geosciences; health and physical education/fitness; health professions related; health psychology; human development, family studies, and related services; human resources management; information science/studies; liberal arts and sciences, general studies and humanities; management information systems; management sciences and quantitative methods; marketing; mathematics and computer science; medical basic sciences; neuroscience; nursing; pharmacology and toxicology; physical sciences; political science and government; psychology; psychology related; psychopharmacology; public administration; public administration and social service professions related; quality control and safety technologies; sales, merchandising, and related marketing operations (general); sales, merchandising, and related marketing operations (specialized); school psychology; science, technology and society; security and protective services related; social and philosophical foundations of education; social sciences; social work; sociology; special education; statistics.

JAMES A. RHODES STATE COLLEGE
Lima, Ohio
http://www.rhodesstate.edu
James A. Rhodes State College was founded in 1971. It is accredited by North Central Association of Colleges and Schools. It first offered distance learning courses in 1991. In fall 2007, there were 843 students enrolled in distance learning courses. Institutionally administered financial aid is available to distance learners.
Services Distance learners have accessibility to academic advising, bookstore, campus computer network, career placement assistance, e-mail services, library services, tutoring.
Contact Chad Teman, Admissions, James A. Rhodes State College, 4240 Campus Drive, Lima, OH 45804. Telephone: 419-995-8010. Fax: 419-995-8098. E-mail: teman.c@rhodesstate.edu.

DEGREES AND AWARDS
AAB Business Administration

AAS Corrections; Emergency Medical Services program; Industrial Engineering Technology

COURSE SUBJECT AREAS OFFERED OUTSIDE OF DEGREE PROGRAMS
Undergraduate—accounting and related services; allied health and medical assisting services; American Sign Language (ASL); business/commerce; business operations support and assistant services; civil engineering technology; communication and media; computer programming; computer software and media applications; construction trades related; criminal justice and corrections; dental support services and allied professions; education (specific levels and methods); electrical/electronics maintenance and repair technology; engineering technologies related; finance and financial management services; geography and cartography; health/medical preparatory programs; human services; legal studies (non-professional general, undergraduate); liberal arts and sciences, general studies and humanities; mathematics and statistics related; nursing; physiology, pathology and related sciences; psychology related; quality control and safety technologies; sales, merchandising, and related marketing operations (general); sales, merchandising, and related marketing operations (specialized); social sciences related.

JAMES MADISON UNIVERSITY
Harrisonburg, Virginia
Distance Learning Center, Office of Continuing Education
http://jmuonline.jmu.edu
James Madison University was founded in 1908. It is accredited by Southern Association of Colleges and Schools. It first offered distance learning courses in 1996. In fall 2007, there were 784 students enrolled in distance learning courses. Institutionally administered financial aid is available to distance learners.
Services Distance learners have accessibility to academic advising, bookstore, campus computer network, career placement assistance, e-mail services, library services.
Contact Dr. Jim Mazoue, Distance Learning Coordinator, Distributed and Distance Learning, James Madison University, 5321 East Campus Library, MSC 4602, Harrisonburg, VA 22807. Telephone: 540-568-2591. Fax: 540-568-6734. E-mail: mazouejg@jmu.edu.

DEGREES AND AWARDS
MBA Information Security
MCC Information Security

COURSE SUBJECT AREAS OFFERED OUTSIDE OF DEGREE PROGRAMS
Undergraduate—accounting and related services; biology; business/commerce; communication and media; communications technology; education (specific levels and methods); English; English composition; health and physical education/fitness; health professions related; history; human resources management; linguistic, comparative, and related language studies; nutrition sciences; philosophy; psychology; sociology; statistics; technical and business writing.
Graduate—business administration, management and operations; computer science; special education.
Non-credit—allied health diagnostic, intervention, and treatment professions; American literature (United States and Canadian); applied mathematics; archeology; architecture; astronomy and astrophysics; biological and biomedical sciences related; biological and physical sciences; building/construction finishing, management, and inspection; business/commerce; business/corporate communications; business, management, and marketing related; communication and journalism related; communication disorders sciences and services; computer programming; computer science; computer systems networking and telecommunications; construction engineering technology; construction trades related; cosmetology and related personal grooming services; counseling psychology; crafts, folk art and artisanry; creative writing; criminal justice and corrections; culinary arts and related services; data entry/microcomputer applications; education; education (specific levels and methods); English; English as a second language; English composition; entrepreneurial and small business operations; family and consumer sciences/human sciences; film/video and photographic arts; fine and studio art; fire protection; foods, nutrition,

and related services; forestry; geography and cartography; geological and earth sciences/geosciences; health aides/attendants/orderlies; health and physical education/fitness; health/medical preparatory programs; history; human resources management; human services; information science/ studies; international business; journalism; landscape architecture; languages (Germanic); languages (Romance languages); liberal arts and sciences, general studies and humanities; library assistant; linguistic, comparative, and related language studies; management sciences and quantitative methods; marketing; mathematics and computer science; museum studies; music; natural resources and conservation related; nursing; parks, recreation, and leisure related; physical sciences; physical sciences related; physics; plant sciences; political science and government; precision systems maintenance and repair technologies; public administration; public health; public relations, advertising, and applied communication related; quality control and safety technologies; radio, television, and digital communication; real estate; sales, merchandising, and related marketing operations (general); sales, merchandising, and related marketing operations (specialized); social sciences; special education; speech and rhetoric; student counseling and personnel services; systems engineering; taxation; transportation and materials moving related; urban studies/affairs; visual and performing arts.

JAMESTOWN COMMUNITY COLLEGE
Jamestown, New York
Distance Education
http://www.sunyjcc.edu/online
Jamestown Community College was founded in 1950. It is accredited by Middle States Association of Colleges and Schools. It first offered distance learning courses in 1995. In fall 2007, there were 700 students enrolled in distance learning courses. Institutionally administered financial aid is available to distance learners.

Services Distance learners have accessibility to academic advising, bookstore, campus computer network, career placement assistance, e-mail services, library services, tutoring.

Contact Admissions Office, Jamestown Community College, 525 Falconer Street, PO Box 20, Jamestown, NY 14702-0020. Telephone: 800-388-8557 Ext. 1001. Fax: 716-338-1450. E-mail: admissions@ mail.sunyjcc.edu.

DEGREES AND AWARDS

AA Individual Studies

AAS Computer Information Systems; Individual Studies; Information Technology

AS Computer Science; Individual Studies

CCCPE Individual Studies; Information Technology; Psychology of the Workplace

COURSE SUBJECT AREAS OFFERED OUTSIDE OF DEGREE PROGRAMS

Non-credit—accounting and related services; business administration, management and operations; business/commerce; business/corporate communications; business, management, and marketing related; business operations support and assistant services; communication and media; computer and information sciences; computer and information sciences and support services related; computer software and media applications; computer systems networking and telecommunications; creative writing; English composition; entrepreneurial and small business operations; finance and financial management services; food science and technology; health and medical administrative services; human resources management; human services; journalism; liberal arts and sciences, general studies and humanities; linguistic, comparative, and related language studies; marketing; psychology related; real estate; sociology.

JEFFERSON COLLEGE
Hillsboro, Missouri
Learning Resources
http://www.jeffco.edu/
Jefferson College was founded in 1963. It is accredited by North Central Association of Colleges and Schools. It first offered distance learning courses in 1984. In fall 2007, there were 734 students enrolled in distance learning courses. Institutionally administered financial aid is available to distance learners.

Services Distance learners have accessibility to academic advising, bookstore, campus computer network, career placement assistance, e-mail services, library services.

Contact Mr. Allan A. Wamsley, Director of Instructional Support Center, Jefferson College, 1000 Viking Drive, Hillsboro, MO 63050. Telephone: 636-797-3000 Ext. 342. Fax: 636-789-5801. E-mail: awamsley@jeffco. edu.

DEGREES AND AWARDS

Programs offered do not lead to a degree or other formal award.

COURSE SUBJECT AREAS OFFERED OUTSIDE OF DEGREE PROGRAMS

Undergraduate—biological and physical sciences; biology; business/ commerce; chemistry; computer software and media applications; criminal justice and corrections; economics; education; English composition; geography and cartography; health and physical education/fitness; history; mathematics; music; philosophy; physics; psychology; social sciences; sociology; speech and rhetoric; visual and performing arts.

JEFFERSON COLLEGE OF HEALTH SCIENCES
Roanoke, Virginia
http://www.jchs.edu/
Jefferson College of Health Sciences was founded in 1982. It is accredited by Southern Association of Colleges and Schools. It first offered distance learning courses in 1999. In fall 2007, there were 400 students enrolled in distance learning courses. Institutionally administered financial aid is available to distance learners.

Services Distance learners have accessibility to academic advising, bookstore, e-mail services, library services.

Contact Bridget Moore, Dean, Technology Services, Jefferson College of Health Sciences, PO Box 13186, Roanoke, VA 24031. Telephone: 540-224-4676. Fax: 540-985-8512. E-mail: bhmoore@jchs.edu.

DEGREES AND AWARDS

BS Healthcare Management
BSN Nursing–RN to BSN

COURSE SUBJECT AREAS OFFERED OUTSIDE OF DEGREE PROGRAMS

Undergraduate—allied health diagnostic, intervention, and treatment professions; business administration, management and operations; community health services; computer software and media applications; English composition; foods, nutrition, and related services; gerontology; health and medical administrative services; health and physical education/ fitness; health/medical preparatory programs; health professions related; human resources management; nursing; philosophy; psychology; public health; rehabilitation and therapeutic professions; sociology; statistics; technical and business writing.

Graduate—nursing; philosophy.

Non-credit—allied health diagnostic, intervention, and treatment professions; nursing.

JEFFERSON COMMUNITY COLLEGE
Watertown, New York
Division of Continuing Education
http://www.sunyjefferson.edu

Jefferson Community College was founded in 1961. It is accredited by Middle States Association of Colleges and Schools. It first offered distance learning courses in 1995. In fall 2007, there were 1,000 students enrolled in distance learning courses. Institutionally administered financial aid is available to distance learners.

Services Distance learners have accessibility to academic advising, bookstore, career placement assistance, e-mail services, library services, tutoring.

Contact MaKeever Clarke, Distance Learning Coordinator, Jefferson Community College, 1220 Coffeen Street, Watertown, NY 13601. Telephone: 315-786-6527. Fax: 315-786-0158. E-mail: mclarke@sunyjefferson.edu.

DEGREES AND AWARDS

AA Individual Studies; Liberal Arts–Humanities and Social Science

AAS Individual Studies

AS Business Administration; Criminal Justice; Individual Studies

COURSE SUBJECT AREAS OFFERED OUTSIDE OF DEGREE PROGRAMS

Undergraduate—business administration, management and operations; business, management, and marketing related; economics; English composition; history; mathematics and statistics related; psychology; sociology; technical and business writing.

JEFFERSON COMMUNITY COLLEGE
Steubenville, Ohio

Jefferson Community College was founded in 1966. It is accredited by North Central Association of Colleges and Schools. It first offered distance learning courses in 2001. In fall 2007, there were 470 students enrolled in distance learning courses. Institutionally administered financial aid is available to distance learners.

Services Distance learners have accessibility to academic advising, bookstore, library services.

Contact Ms. Kimberly Patterson, Online and Transfer Coordinator, Jefferson Community College, 4000 Sunset Boulevard, Steubenville, OH 43952. Telephone: 740-264-5591 Ext. 112. Fax: 740-266-2706. E-mail: kpatterson@jcc.edu.

DEGREES AND AWARDS

Programs offered do not lead to a degree or other formal award.

COURSE SUBJECT AREAS OFFERED OUTSIDE OF DEGREE PROGRAMS

Undergraduate—accounting and related services; American literature (United States and Canadian); behavioral sciences; biology; business administration, management and operations; business/commerce; business/corporate communications; business, management, and marketing related; communication and journalism related; communication and media; comparative literature; computer and information sciences; creative writing; criminal justice and corrections; criminology; developmental and child psychology; dramatic/theater arts and stagecraft; economics; education; educational psychology; English; English composition; English language and literature related; English literature (British and Commonwealth); foods, nutrition, and related services; geography and cartography; health services/allied health/health sciences; history; human resources management; journalism; marketing; mathematics; mathematics and statistics related; personality psychology; philosophy; political science and government; psychology; social psychology; social sciences; sociology; statistics.

JOHN A. LOGAN COLLEGE
Carterville, Illinois
Learning Resources
http://www.jalc.edu

John A. Logan College was founded in 1967. It is accredited by North Central Association of Colleges and Schools. It first offered distance learning courses in 1979. In fall 2007, there were 1,015 students enrolled in distance learning courses. Institutionally administered financial aid is available to distance learners.

Services Distance learners have accessibility to academic advising, campus computer network, career placement assistance, library services, tutoring.

Contact Robert Fester, Advisor and Counselor, John A. Logan College, 700 Logan College Road, Carterville, IL 62918. Telephone: 618-985-2828 Ext. 8385. E-mail: bobfester@jalc.edu.

DEGREES AND AWARDS

Programs offered do not lead to a degree or other formal award.

COURSE SUBJECT AREAS OFFERED OUTSIDE OF DEGREE PROGRAMS

Undergraduate—accounting and computer science; accounting and related services; allied health diagnostic, intervention, and treatment professions; American Sign Language (ASL); biology; business administration, management and operations; business/commerce; business, management, and marketing related; computer and information sciences; creative writing; data processing; dental support services and allied professions; design and applied arts; dramatic/theater arts and stagecraft; education; English; English composition; English language and literature related; film/video and photographic arts; fine and studio art; history; hospitality administration; liberal arts and sciences, general studies and humanities; marketing; mathematics; mathematics and computer science; physics; political science and government; psychology; psychology related; religious studies; speech and rhetoric; technology education/industrial arts; visual and performing arts.

THE JOHNS HOPKINS UNIVERSITY
Baltimore, Maryland
Bloomberg School of Public Health
http://distance.jhsph.edu

The Johns Hopkins University was founded in 1876. It is accredited by Middle States Association of Colleges and Schools. It first offered distance learning courses in 1997. In fall 2007, there were 600 students enrolled in distance learning courses. Institutionally administered financial aid is available to distance learners.

Services Distance learners have accessibility to academic advising, bookstore, campus computer network, career placement assistance, e-mail services, library services, tutoring.

Contact Mr. David Earle, Academic Administrator, The Johns Hopkins University, 615 North Wolfe Street, Room W1015, Baltimore, MD 21205. Telephone: 410-955-1291. E-mail: dearle@jhsph.edu.

DEGREES AND AWARDS

MPH Part-time/Internet-based Master of Public Health

JOHNSON BIBLE COLLEGE
Knoxville, Tennessee
Distance Learning Office
http://www.jbc.edu/mastersnt/

Johnson Bible College was founded in 1893. It is accredited by Association for Biblical Higher Education. It first offered distance learning courses in 1988. In fall 2007, there were 79 students enrolled in distance learning courses. Institutionally administered financial aid is available to distance learners.

Services Distance learners have accessibility to academic advising, bookstore, campus computer network, e-mail services, library services.

Contact Dr. John C. Ketchen, Director of Distance Learning, Johnson Bible College, 7900 Johnson Drive, Knoxville, TN 37998. Telephone: 865-251-2254. Fax: 865-251-2285. E-mail: mketchen@jbc.edu.

DEGREES AND AWARDS
MA New Testament

COURSE SUBJECT AREAS OFFERED OUTSIDE OF DEGREE PROGRAMS
Undergraduate—biblical studies.
Graduate—biblical studies.

JOHNSON COUNTY COMMUNITY COLLEGE
Overland Park, Kansas
http://www.jccc.edu
Johnson County Community College was founded in 1967. It is accredited by North Central Association of Colleges and Schools. It first offered distance learning courses in 1975. In fall 2007, there were 4,000 students enrolled in distance learning courses. Institutionally administered financial aid is available to distance learners.
Services Distance learners have accessibility to academic advising, bookstore, campus computer network, career placement assistance, e-mail services, library services, tutoring.
Contact Dr. Ed Lovitt, Distance Learning Coordinator, Johnson County Community College, 12345 College Boulevard, Overland Park, KS 66210-1299. Telephone: 913-469-8500 Ext. 3975. E-mail: elovitt@jccc.edu.

DEGREES AND AWARDS
AA Multidisciplinary Study
AGS General Studies
Certificate Certified Medication Aide Update; Certified Nurse Aide

COURSE SUBJECT AREAS OFFERED OUTSIDE OF DEGREE PROGRAMS
Undergraduate—accounting and related services; anthropology; biology; chemistry; computer software and media applications; computer systems networking and telecommunications; economics; English composition; English literature (British and Commonwealth); history; legal support services; marketing; mathematics; psychology; sociology; speech and rhetoric; technical and business writing.
Non-credit—computer software and media applications; health and medical administrative services; health/medical preparatory programs; real estate.

JOHNSON STATE COLLEGE
Johnson, Vermont
External Degree Program
http://www.jsc.edu
Johnson State College was founded in 1828. It is accredited by New England Association of Schools and Colleges. It first offered distance learning courses in 1998. In fall 2007, there were 250 students enrolled in distance learning courses. Institutionally administered financial aid is available to distance learners.
Services Distance learners have accessibility to academic advising, bookstore, career placement assistance, e-mail services, library services.
Contact Ms. Rhonda Osgood, Staff Assistant, EDP, Johnson State College, External Degree Program, 337 College Hill, Johnson, VT 05656. Telephone: 802-635-1290. E-mail: rhonda.osgood@jsc.edu.

DEGREES AND AWARDS
Programs offered do not lead to a degree or other formal award.

COURSE SUBJECT AREAS OFFERED OUTSIDE OF DEGREE PROGRAMS
Undergraduate—behavioral sciences; biology; biopsychology; business administration, management and operations; educational psychology; English; history; marketing; psychology; religious studies; special education.

JOHN WOOD COMMUNITY COLLEGE
Quincy, Illinois
Alternative and Distance Learning Center
http://www.jwcc.edu/instruct/JWCC_Online.asp
John Wood Community College was founded in 1974. It is accredited by North Central Association of Colleges and Schools. It first offered distance learning courses in 1987. In fall 2007, there were 800 students enrolled in distance learning courses. Institutionally administered financial aid is available to distance learners.
Services Distance learners have accessibility to academic advising, bookstore, campus computer network, career placement assistance, e-mail services, library services, tutoring.
Contact Ms. Bonnie Scranton, Dean of Enrollment Services, John Wood Community College, 1301 South 48th Street, Quincy, IL 62305. Telephone: 217-224-6500 Ext. 4336. Fax: 217-224-4208. E-mail: bscranton@jwcc.edu.

DEGREES AND AWARDS
Programs offered do not lead to a degree or other formal award.

COURSE SUBJECT AREAS OFFERED OUTSIDE OF DEGREE PROGRAMS
Undergraduate—accounting and related services; anthropology; Army J.R.O.T.C/R.O.T.C; astronomy and astrophysics; business administration, management and operations; business/commerce; cell biology and anatomical sciences; computer and information sciences; computer software and media applications; criminal justice and corrections; data entry/microcomputer applications; developmental and child psychology; ecology, evolution, and population biology; economics; English composition; fine and studio art; health and physical education/fitness; history; languages (Romance languages); liberal arts and sciences, general studies and humanities; mathematics; military studies; music; philosophy; philosophy and religious studies related; physical sciences; physics; plant sciences; political science and government; psychology; religious studies; security and protective services related; social psychology; social sciences; sociology; special education; statistics.

JONES INTERNATIONAL UNIVERSITY
Centennial, Colorado
http://www.jiu.edu
Jones International University was founded in 1995. It is accredited by North Central Association of Colleges and Schools. It first offered distance learning courses in 1995. In fall 2007, there were 1,200 students enrolled in distance learning courses. Institutionally administered financial aid is available to distance learners.
Services Distance learners have accessibility to academic advising, bookstore, e-mail services, library services.
Contact Admission Counselor, Jones International University, 9697 East Mineral Avenue, Centennial, CO 80112. Telephone: 800-811-5663. Fax: 303-799-0966. E-mail: info@international.edu.

DEGREES AND AWARDS
AA Business Administration
AS Digital Media
BA Business Communication
BBA Business Administration
MA Business Communication
MBA Business Administration
MEd Adult Education and Leadership; Education–K-12 Educators and Administration
DBA Business Administration
EdD K-12 Education Leadership

COURSE SUBJECT AREAS OFFERED OUTSIDE OF DEGREE PROGRAMS
Undergraduate—business administration, management and operations; business/corporate communications; communications technology; computer/information technology administration and management; computer software and media applications; computer systems networking and telecommunications; entrepreneurial and small business operations; human

resources management; international business; multi-/interdisciplinary studies related; technical and business writing.

Graduate—business/corporate communications; business, management, and marketing related; communication and journalism related; computer software and media applications; computer systems networking and telecommunications; educational/instructional media design; education related; entrepreneurial and small business operations; international business; library science related; multi-/interdisciplinary studies related; peace studies and conflict resolution; public relations, advertising, and applied communication related.

J. SARGEANT REYNOLDS COMMUNITY COLLEGE
Richmond, Virginia
Division of Instructional Technologies and Distance Education
http://www.reynolds.edu

J. Sargeant Reynolds Community College was founded in 1972. It is accredited by Southern Association of Colleges and Schools. It first offered distance learning courses in 1980. In fall 2007, there were 2,173 students enrolled in distance learning courses. Institutionally administered financial aid is available to distance learners.

Services Distance learners have accessibility to academic advising, bookstore, campus computer network, e-mail services, library services, tutoring.

Contact M.R. Macbeth, Coordinator of Center for Distance Learning, J. Sargeant Reynolds Community College, Center for Distance Learning, PO Box 85622, Richmond, VA 23285-5622. Telephone: 804-523-5612. Fax: 804-371-3822. E-mail: distance-ed@reynolds.edu.

DEGREES AND AWARDS
AAS Early Childhood Development; Marketing; Respiratory Therapy
AS Business Administration

COURSE SUBJECT AREAS OFFERED OUTSIDE OF DEGREE PROGRAMS
Undergraduate—accounting and related services; American literature (United States and Canadian); biology; business administration, management and operations; business, management, and marketing related; business operations support and assistant services; chemistry; computer science; computer software and media applications; criminal justice and corrections; developmental and child psychology; economics; education; English composition; food science and technology; health and physical education/fitness; history; human development, family studies, and related services; information science/studies; linguistic, comparative, and related language studies; marketing; mathematics; nursing; philosophy; political science and government; psychology; social sciences related; sociology; speech and rhetoric.

JUDSON COLLEGE
Marion, Alabama
Distance Learning Program
http://www.judson.edu

Judson College was founded in 1838. It is accredited by Southern Association of Colleges and Schools. It first offered distance learning courses in 1976. In fall 2007, there were 100 students enrolled in distance learning courses. Institutionally administered financial aid is available to distance learners.

Services Distance learners have accessibility to academic advising, bookstore, campus computer network, career placement assistance, e-mail services, library services.

Contact Mr. Bradley A. Moore, Director of Distance Learning, Judson College, 302 Bibb Street, Marion, AL 36756. Telephone: 800-447-9472 Ext. 5169. Fax: 334-683-5169. E-mail: bmoore3@judson.edu.

DEGREES AND AWARDS
BA Business; Criminal Justice; Education–Secondary Education; English; History; Music; Psychology; Religious Studies
BMin Ministry Studies
BS Business; Criminal Justice; Education; Psychology

COURSE SUBJECT AREAS OFFERED OUTSIDE OF DEGREE PROGRAMS
Undergraduate—behavioral sciences; biblical studies; bioethics/medical ethics; biological and physical sciences; business administration, management and operations; creative writing; criminal justice and corrections; developmental and child psychology; ecology, evolution, and population biology; economics; education; education (specific levels and methods); education (specific subject areas); English; English composition; English literature (British and Commonwealth); history; music; philosophy and religious studies related; political science and government; psychology; social sciences; sociology.

JUDSON UNIVERSITY
Elgin, Illinois
Division of Continuing Education
http://www.judsonu.edu

Judson University was founded in 1963. It is accredited by North Central Association of Colleges and Schools. It first offered distance learning courses in 1998. In fall 2007, there were 230 students enrolled in distance learning courses. Institutionally administered financial aid is available to distance learners.

Services Distance learners have accessibility to academic advising, bookstore, campus computer network, career placement assistance, e-mail services, library services, tutoring.

Contact Robert Lindahl, Student Specialist for Customized Learning Center, Judson University, 1151 North State Street, Elgin, IL 60123. Telephone: 847-628-1547. Fax: 847-628-1513. E-mail: rlindahl@judsonu.edu.

DEGREES AND AWARDS
BA Management and Leadership

COURSE SUBJECT AREAS OFFERED OUTSIDE OF DEGREE PROGRAMS
Undergraduate—astronomy and astrophysics; biblical studies; communication and media; computer software and media applications; criminal justice and corrections; English; English composition; environmental control technologies; fine and studio art; history; liberal arts and sciences, general studies and humanities; mathematics; political science and government; psychology; public relations, advertising, and applied communication related; sociology; technical and business writing.

KANSAS STATE UNIVERSITY
Manhattan, Kansas
Division of Continuing Education, Continuing Learning
http://www.dce.k-state.edu/distance/

Kansas State University was founded in 1863. It is accredited by North Central Association of Colleges and Schools. It first offered distance learning courses in 1971. In fall 2007, there were 7,000 students enrolled in distance learning courses. Institutionally administered financial aid is available to distance learners.

Services Distance learners have accessibility to academic advising, bookstore, campus computer network, career placement assistance, e-mail services, library services.

Contact Ron Jackson, Program Coordinator, Kansas State University, Division of Continuing Education, 224 College Court Building, Manhattan, KS 66506. Telephone: 785-532-2523. Fax: 785-532-5637. E-mail: rdj7@k-state.edu.

DEGREES AND AWARDS
BS Animal Science and Industry; Business, general; Dietetics; Early Childhood Education; Elementary Education; Food Science and Industry; Interdisciplinary Social Sciences; Technology Management
Certificate of Completion Family Development Credential
Certificate Food Science; Occupational Health Psychology; Personal Financial Planning
Endorsement ESL Endorsement in Elementary and Secondary Education
CAGS Business Administration

CCCPE Conflict Resolution; Conflict Resolution

Graduate Certificate Academic Advising; Applied Statistics; Educational Computing, Design, and Online Learning/Classroom Technology; Food Safety and Defense; Food Science; Gerontology; Organizational Leadership; Public Administration; Youth Development

MS Academic Advising; Adult and Continuing Education; Agribusiness; Chemical Engineering; Civil Engineering; Community Development; Educational Administration; Educational Computing, Design, and Online Learning/Classroom Technology; Electrical Engineering; Engineering Management; Food Science and Industry; Gerontology; Industrial/Organizational Psychology; Mechanical Engineering; Merchandising; Personal Financial Planning; Software Engineering; Youth Development

COURSE SUBJECT AREAS OFFERED OUTSIDE OF DEGREE PROGRAMS

Undergraduate—accounting and computer science; accounting and related services; agricultural and domestic animal services; agricultural and food products processing; agricultural business and management; agricultural production; agriculture; agriculture and agriculture operations related; animal sciences; applied horticulture/horticultural business services; area, ethnic, cultural, and gender studies related; behavioral sciences; biochemistry, biophysics and molecular biology; biological and physical sciences; business administration, management and operations; business/commerce; business, management, and marketing related; chemistry; computer and information sciences; developmental and child psychology; dietetics and clinical nutrition services; English; ethnic, cultural minority, and gender studies; family and consumer sciences/human sciences; family and consumer sciences/human sciences related; finance and financial management services; food science and technology; foods, nutrition, and related services; geography and cartography; history; human development, family studies, and related services; information science/studies; management information systems; marketing; music; natural resources and conservation related; natural resources conservation and research; natural resources management and policy; natural sciences; nutrition sciences; physical sciences; physical sciences related; political science and government; psychology; social psychology; social sciences; social sciences related; sociology; statistics.

Graduate—agricultural and food products processing; agricultural business and management; agricultural public services; agriculture; agriculture and agriculture operations related; animal sciences; apparel and textiles; chemical engineering; civil engineering; community health services; community organization and advocacy; community psychology; computer engineering; computer science; computer software and media applications; electrical, electronics and communications engineering; engineering; engineering/industrial management; engineering related; engineering science; family and consumer sciences/human sciences; family and consumer sciences/human sciences related; family psychology; finance and financial management services; gerontology; human resources management; industrial and organizational psychology; mechanical engineering; mechanical engineering related technologies; plant sciences; psychology; quality control and safety technologies.

Non-credit—agricultural and food products processing; agriculture; education; educational administration and supervision; educational assessment, evaluation, and research; educational psychology; education related; education (specific levels and methods); education (specific subject areas); family and consumer economics; family and consumer sciences/human sciences; family and consumer sciences/human sciences related; family psychology; finance and financial management services; food science and technology; foods, nutrition, and related services; social sciences related; work and family studies.

See full description on page 402.

KAPLAN UNIVERSITY ONLINE
Fort Lauderdale, Florida
http://www.kaplan.edu/

Kaplan University Online first offered distance learning courses in 1999. In fall 2007, there were 39,000 students enrolled in distance learning courses. Institutionally administered financial aid is available to distance learners.

Services Distance learners have accessibility to academic advising, bookstore, career placement assistance, e-mail services, library services, tutoring.

Contact Information, Kaplan University Online, 6301 Kaplan University Ave, Fort Lauderdale, FL 33309. Telephone: 866-527-5268. E-mail: infoku@kaplan.edu.

DEGREES AND AWARDS

AAS Accounting; Business Administration/Management; Computer Information Systems; Criminal Justice; Global Travel and Hospitality Management; Medical Assisting; Medical Office Management; Medical Transcription; Nursing; Paralegal Studies

AS Interdisciplinary Studies

BS Accounting; Business; Communication; Criminal Justice; Health Science; Health and Wellness; Information Technology; Legal Studies; Nutrition Science; Paralegal Studies; Psychology

BSN Nursing

Certificate Corrections; Crime Scene Technician; Information Assurance; Information Technology Pathway; Internet and Website Development; Introduction to Computer Programming Language; Legal Secretary; Pathway to Paralegal (Post-baccalaureate); Private Security Management; Private Security; Professional Development for Teachers (Postbaccalaureate); Teacher Intern (Postbaccalaureate)

MAT Teaching

MBA Business Administration

MS Criminal Justice; Information Technology; Legal Studies; Management

MSE Education; Higher Education

MSN Nursing

COURSE SUBJECT AREAS OFFERED OUTSIDE OF DEGREE PROGRAMS

Non-credit—business administration, management and operations; business/managerial economics; computer and information sciences; computer/information technology administration and management; computer systems networking and telecommunications; finance and financial management services; health professions related; health services/allied health/health sciences; nursing.

KASKASKIA COLLEGE
Centralia, Illinois
http://www.kaskaskia.edu

Kaskaskia College was founded in 1966. It is accredited by North Central Association of Colleges and Schools. It first offered distance learning courses in 1993. In fall 2007, there were 1,200 students enrolled in distance learning courses. Institutionally administered financial aid is available to distance learners.

Services Distance learners have accessibility to academic advising, bookstore, campus computer network, career placement assistance, e-mail services, library services, tutoring.

Contact Ms. Joyce Pryor, Online Student Support Specialist, Kaskaskia College, 27210 College Road, Centralia, IL 62801. Telephone: 618-545-3240. Fax: 618-532-1990. E-mail: jpryor@kaskaskia.edu.

DEGREES AND AWARDS

AAS Accounting

COURSE SUBJECT AREAS OFFERED OUTSIDE OF DEGREE PROGRAMS

Undergraduate—accounting and related services; biological and physical sciences; business administration, management and operations; business operations support and assistant services; computer and information sciences; computer software and media applications; developmental and child psychology; dramatic/theater arts and stagecraft; English; English composition; fine and studio art; geography and cartography; history; mathematics; music; psychology; speech and rhetoric; statistics.

KAUAI COMMUNITY COLLEGE
Lihue, Hawaii
University Center-Kauai
http://kauai.hawaii.edu

Kauai Community College was founded in 1965. It is accredited by Western Association of Schools and Colleges. It first offered distance learning courses in 1988. In fall 2007, there were 145 students enrolled in distance learning courses. Institutionally administered financial aid is available to distance learners.

Services Distance learners have accessibility to academic advising, bookstore, e-mail services, library services.

Contact Ms. Pua Larson, Educational Specialist, Kauai Community College, 3-1901 Kaumualii Highway, Lihue, HI 96766-9500. Telephone: 808-245-8330. Fax: 808-245-8232. E-mail: marlapua@hawaii.edu.

DEGREES AND AWARDS
Programs offered do not lead to a degree or other formal award.

COURSE SUBJECT AREAS OFFERED OUTSIDE OF DEGREE PROGRAMS

Undergraduate—accounting and related services; business administration, management and operations; nursing; psychology; social sciences.

Graduate—accounting and related services; education (specific subject areas); library science; social work.

KEAN UNIVERSITY
Union, New Jersey
http://www.kean.edu/

Kean University was founded in 1855. It is accredited by Middle States Association of Colleges and Schools. It first offered distance learning courses in 1998. In fall 2007, there were 915 students enrolled in distance learning courses. Institutionally administered financial aid is available to distance learners.

Services Distance learners have accessibility to bookstore, campus computer network, e-mail services, library services.

Contact Dr. Michael Searson, Executive Director, Center for External Education and Development, Kean University, 1000 Morris Avenue, Union, NJ 07083. Telephone: 908-737-7147. Fax: 908-737-7007. E-mail: msearson@kean.edu.

DEGREES AND AWARDS
Programs offered do not lead to a degree or other formal award.

COURSE SUBJECT AREAS OFFERED OUTSIDE OF DEGREE PROGRAMS

Undergraduate—accounting and related services; biology; criminal justice and corrections; economics; education (specific levels and methods); education (specific subject areas); finance and financial management services; fine and studio art; history; international business; liberal arts and sciences, general studies and humanities; marketing; parks, recreation and leisure facilities management; political science and government; psychology; sociology.

Graduate—accounting and related services; educational administration and supervision; education (specific levels and methods); special education.

Non-credit—accounting and related services; business administration, management and operations; business, management, and marketing related; communication and journalism related; computer and information sciences; computer programming; computer software and media applications; creative writing; education; English as a second language; family and consumer sciences/human sciences; film/video and photographic arts; finance and financial management services; fine and studio art; health and physical education/fitness; health professions related; languages (Romance languages); legal professions and studies related; mathematics; music; parks, recreation and leisure; personal and culinary services related; technical and business writing; visual and performing arts; work and family studies.

KEISER UNIVERSITY
Fort Lauderdale, Florida
http://online.keiseruniversity.edu

Keiser University was founded in 1977. It is accredited by Accrediting Bureau of Health Education Schools. It first offered distance learning courses in 1999. In fall 2007, there were 2,500 students enrolled in distance learning courses. Institutionally administered financial aid is available to distance learners.

Services Distance learners have accessibility to academic advising, bookstore, campus computer network, career placement assistance, e-mail services, library services, tutoring.

Contact Admissions Counselor, Keiser University, 1900 West Commercial Boulevard, Fort Lauderdale, FL 33309. Telephone: 888-453-4737. Fax: 954-351-4040. E-mail: admissions@keiseruniversity.edu.

DEGREES AND AWARDS

AA Accounting; Criminal Justice; Health Service Administration; Homeland Security; Homeland Security; Information Technology; Paralegal Studies

AS Computer Networking and Security Management; Fire Science; Medical Assisting

BA Accounting; Business Administration–en espanol (in the Spanish language); Business Administration–offered in the Spanish language; Business Administration; Criminal Justice; Health Services Administration; Homeland Security; Legal Studies

BS Health Sciences; Information Technology Management; Information Technology Management; Management of Information Systems

BSN Nursing–RN to BSN

MA Criminal Justice

MBA Business Administration

MEd Education

See full description on page 404.

KENTUCKY STATE UNIVERSITY
Frankfort, Kentucky
KSU Distance Learning
http://www.kysu.edu

Kentucky State University was founded in 1886. It is accredited by Southern Association of Colleges and Schools. It first offered distance learning courses in 1997. In fall 2007, there were 1,000 students enrolled in distance learning courses. Institutionally administered financial aid is available to distance learners.

Services Distance learners have accessibility to academic advising, e-mail services, library services.

Contact Ms. Jennifer Miles, Coordinator of Online Programs, Kentucky State University, 400 East Main Street, Academic Services Building, 507, Frankfort, KY 40601. Telephone: 502-597-7023. Fax: 502-597-5046. E-mail: jennifer.miles@kysu.edu.

DEGREES AND AWARDS

Programs offered do not lead to a degree or other formal award.

COURSE SUBJECT AREAS OFFERED OUTSIDE OF DEGREE PROGRAMS

Undergraduate—accounting and related services; biological and physical sciences; business administration, management and operations; computer and information sciences; computer programming; computer science; drafting/design engineering technologies; economics; English; English composition; linguistic, comparative, and related language studies; management information systems; music; psychology; public administration and social service professions related; sales, merchandising, and related marketing operations (general); social work; sociology; speech and rhetoric.

Graduate—biological and physical sciences; public administration and social service professions related; special education.

KETTERING UNIVERSITY
Flint, Michigan
Graduate School
http://kettering.edu/graduate
Kettering University was founded in 1919. It is accredited by North Central Association of Colleges and Schools. It first offered distance learning courses in 1982. In fall 2007, there were 700 students enrolled in distance learning courses. Institutionally administered financial aid is available to distance learners.
Services Distance learners have accessibility to academic advising, bookstore, campus computer network, e-mail services, library services.
Contact Joanne Allen, Publications Coordinator, Kettering University, 1700 West Third Avenue, Flint, MI 48504-4898. Telephone: 866-584-7237 Ext. 5. Fax: 810-762-9935. E-mail: gradoff@kettering.edu.

DEGREES AND AWARDS
MBA General Concentration; I.T. Concentration; Manufacturing Engineering (Industrial and Manufacturing Engineering concentration); Mechanical Design (ME concentration); Power Electronics and Machine Drives (EE Concentration); Systems Engineering (Industrial and Manufacturing Engineering concentration); Wireless Communications (EE Concentration)
MS Information Technology; Manufacturing Management; Manufacturing Operations; Operations Management
MSE Engineering–Electrical and Computer Engineering concentration; Engineering–Manufacturing Engineering concentration; Engineering–Mechanical Design concentration
MSEM Engineering Management

COURSE SUBJECT AREAS OFFERED OUTSIDE OF DEGREE PROGRAMS
Non-credit—business administration, management and operations; business, management, and marketing related; computer/information technology administration and management; electrical, electronics and communications engineering; engineering; engineering design; engineering related; engineering-related fields; industrial engineering; management information systems; management sciences and quantitative methods; manufacturing engineering; mathematics and statistics related; mechanical engineering; quality control and safety technologies.

See full description on page 406.

KIRTLAND COMMUNITY COLLEGE
Roscommon, Michigan
http://eservices.kirtland.edu/elearning
Kirtland Community College was founded in 1966. It is accredited by North Central Association of Colleges and Schools. It first offered distance learning courses in 1996. In fall 2007, there were 108 students enrolled in distance learning courses. Institutionally administered financial aid is available to distance learners.
Services Distance learners have accessibility to academic advising, bookstore, e-mail services, library services, tutoring.
Contact Ms. Kerry L. Lashley, eLearning Coordinator, Kirtland Community College, 10775 North St. Helen Road, Roscommon, MI 48653. Telephone: 989-275-5000 Ext. 499. Fax: 989-275-8510. E-mail: lashleyk@kirtland.edu.

DEGREES AND AWARDS
AAB General Business
Certificate Bookkeeping; Entrepreneurship

COURSE SUBJECT AREAS OFFERED OUTSIDE OF DEGREE PROGRAMS
Undergraduate—accounting and related services; allied health and medical assisting services; biology; business administration, management and operations; business/commerce; business, management, and marketing related; business operations support and assistant services; creative writing; English composition; psychology; sales, merchandising, and related marketing operations (specialized).

KNOWLEDGE SYSTEMS INSTITUTE
Skokie, Illinois
http://distancelearning.ksi.edu/
Knowledge Systems Institute was founded in 1978. It is accredited by North Central Association of Colleges and Schools. It first offered distance learning courses in 2007. In fall 2007, there were 11 students enrolled in distance learning courses. Institutionally administered financial aid is available to distance learners.
Services Distance learners have accessibility to academic advising, bookstore, campus computer network, career placement assistance, e-mail services, library services, tutoring.
Contact Ms. Jerilyn Tinio, Office Manager, Knowledge Systems Institute, 3420 Main Street, Skokie, IL 60076. Telephone: 847-679-3135. Fax: 847-679-3166. E-mail: office@ksi.edu.

DEGREES AND AWARDS
MS Computer and Information Sciences

COURSE SUBJECT AREAS OFFERED OUTSIDE OF DEGREE PROGRAMS
Graduate—computer and information sciences; computer engineering; computer engineering technologies; computer/information technology administration and management; computer programming; computer science; computer software and media applications.

LABETTE COMMUNITY COLLEGE
Parsons, Kansas
http://www.labette.edu
Labette Community College was founded in 1923. It is accredited by North Central Association of Colleges and Schools. It first offered distance learning courses in 1985. In fall 2007, there were 1,147 students enrolled in distance learning courses. Institutionally administered financial aid is available to distance learners.
Services Distanee learners have accessibility to academic advising, bookstore, campus computer network, library services, tutoring.
Contact Ms. Elizabeth Ann Walker, Outreach Director, Labette Community College, 200 South 14th Street, Parsons, KS 67357. Telephone: 620-820-1221. Fax: 620-421-4481. E-mail: elizabethw@labette.edu.

DEGREES AND AWARDS
AAS Financial Services
AGS General Studies

COURSE SUBJECT AREAS OFFERED OUTSIDE OF DEGREE PROGRAMS
Undergraduate—allied health diagnostic, intervention, and treatment professions; business/managerial economics; communication and media; computer programming; computer science; computer software and media applications; computer systems networking and telecommunications; criminology; developmental and child psychology; English composition; finance and financial management services; fine and studio art; genetics; geography and cartography; health and physical education/fitness; health/medical preparatory programs; history; human resources management; liberal arts and sciences, general studies and humanities; management information systems; mathematics; mathematics and statistics related; music; physical sciences; political science and government; psychology; sociology; speech and rhetoric.

LACKAWANNA COLLEGE
Scranton, Pennsylvania
Distance Learning Center
http://www.lackawanna.edu
Lackawanna College was founded in 1894. It is accredited by Middle States Association of Colleges and Schools. It first offered distance learning courses in 1994. In fall 2007, there were 613 students enrolled in distance learning courses. Institutionally administered financial aid is available to distance learners.
Services Distance learners have accessibility to academic advising, bookstore, career placement assistance, e-mail services, library services.

Contact Mr. Griffith R. Lewis, Senior Director, MIS, Lackawanna College, 501 Vine Street, Scranton, PA 18509. Telephone: 570-961-7853. Fax: 570-961-7877. E-mail: lewisg@lackawanna.edu.

DEGREES AND AWARDS
Programs offered do not lead to a degree or other formal award.

COURSE SUBJECT AREAS OFFERED OUTSIDE OF DEGREE PROGRAMS
Undergraduate—accounting and computer science; audiovisual communications technologies; behavioral sciences; business administration, management and operations; communication and journalism related; communication and media; economics; education; English; English composition; history; human services; mathematics; psychology; public administration; social sciences; sociology; statistics.

LAKELAND COLLEGE
Sheboygan, Wisconsin
Lakeland College Online
http://www.lakeland.edu/online
Lakeland College was founded in 1862. It is accredited by North Central Association of Colleges and Schools. It first offered distance learning courses in 1997. In fall 2007, there were 800 students enrolled in distance learning courses. Institutionally administered financial aid is available to distance learners.
Services Distance learners have accessibility to academic advising, bookstore, campus computer network, e-mail services, library services, tutoring.
Contact Cindy Thill, Academic Counselor, Lakeland College, PO Box 359, Sheboygan, WI 53082-0359. Telephone: 800-569-2166 Ext. 1268. Fax: 920-565-1268. E-mail: thillcr@lakeland.edu.

DEGREES AND AWARDS
BA Accounting; Business Administration; Computer Science; Criminal Justice; Marketing
MBA Business Administration

COURSE SUBJECT AREAS OFFERED OUTSIDE OF DEGREE PROGRAMS
Undergraduate—accounting and related services; business/commerce; computer science; sales, merchandising, and related marketing operations (general).
Graduate—business administration, management and operations.

LAKELAND COMMUNITY COLLEGE
Kirtland, Ohio
Instructional Technology
http://www.lakelandcc.edu/dl
Lakeland Community College was founded in 1967. It is accredited by North Central Association of Colleges and Schools. It first offered distance learning courses in 2000. In fall 2007, there were 1,500 students enrolled in distance learning courses. Institutionally administered financial aid is available to distance learners.
Services Distance learners have accessibility to academic advising, bookstore, campus computer network, career placement assistance, e-mail services, library services, tutoring.
Contact Mr. Corrie Bergeron, Instructional Designer, Lakeland Community College, 7700 Clocktower Drive, Kirtland, OH 44094-5198. Telephone: 440-525-7232. E-mail: cbergeron@lakelandcc.edu.

DEGREES AND AWARDS
AA General degree

COURSE SUBJECT AREAS OFFERED OUTSIDE OF DEGREE PROGRAMS
Undergraduate—accounting and related services; applied mathematics; biology; computer and information sciences; economics; entrepreneurial and small business operations; film/video and photographic arts; fine and

studio art; geography and cartography; health and physical education/fitness; history; marketing; sociology; statistics.
Non-credit—accounting and related services; applied horticulture/horticultural business services; business/corporate communications; business, management, and marketing related; business/managerial economics; business operations support and assistant services; communication and journalism related; communication and media; communication disorders sciences and services; communications technology; community health services; community organization and advocacy; computer and information sciences; computer and information sciences and support services related; computer engineering; computer/information technology administration and management; computer programming; data entry/microcomputer applications; data processing; engineering related; entrepreneurial and small business operations; environmental control technologies; environmental/environmental health engineering; family and consumer economics; film/video and photographic arts; finance and financial management services; fine and studio art; gerontology; health and physical education/fitness; health professions related; heating, air conditioning, ventilation and refrigeration maintenance technology; historic preservation and conservation; history; hospitality administration; human development, family studies, and related services; languages (South Asian); management information systems; management sciences and quantitative methods; public relations, advertising, and applied communication related; quality control and safety technologies; real estate; sales, merchandising, and related marketing operations (general); sales, merchandising, and related marketing operations (specialized); soil sciences; special education; taxation; veterinary biomedical and clinical sciences; wildlife and wildlands science and management.

LAKE REGION STATE COLLEGE
Devils Lake, North Dakota
http://www.lrsc.nodak.edu
Lake Region State College was founded in 1941. It is accredited by North Central Association of Colleges and Schools. It first offered distance learning courses in 1980. In fall 2007, there were 425 students enrolled in distance learning courses. Institutionally administered financial aid is available to distance learners.
Services Distance learners have accessibility to academic advising, bookstore, career placement assistance, e-mail services, library services, tutoring.
Contact Daniel J. Driessen, Director of Continuing Education, Lake Region State College, 1801 College Drive North, Devils Lake, ND 58301. Telephone: 701-662-1508. E-mail: daniel.driessen@lrsc.nodak.edu.

DEGREES AND AWARDS
AA Accounting and Business Administration; Liberal Arts
AAS Early Childhood Associate; Legal Assistant (Paralegal); Marketing/Management; Paraeducator; Speech Language Pathology Assistant

COURSE SUBJECT AREAS OFFERED OUTSIDE OF DEGREE PROGRAMS
Undergraduate—accounting and computer science; accounting and related services; biological and biomedical sciences related; biology; business administration, management and operations; chemistry; health and physical education/fitness; history; mathematics; psychology; sales, merchandising, and related marketing operations (specialized); social work.

LAKE-SUMTER COMMUNITY COLLEGE
Leesburg, Florida
http://www.lscc.edu
Lake-Sumter Community College was founded in 1962. It is accredited by Southern Association of Colleges and Schools. It first offered distance learning courses in 1986. In fall 2007, there were 1,600 students enrolled in distance learning courses. Institutionally administered financial aid is available to distance learners.
Services Distance learners have accessibility to academic advising, library services, tutoring.

Contact Ms. Becky Fudge, Senior Staff Assistant, Lake-Sumter Community College, 9501 Highway 441, Leesburg, FL 34788. Telephone: 352-365-3665. E-mail: admissinquiry@lscc.edu.

DEGREES AND AWARDS
Programs offered do not lead to a degree or other formal award.

COURSE SUBJECT AREAS OFFERED OUTSIDE OF DEGREE PROGRAMS
Undergraduate—business administration, management and operations; business/commerce; business/corporate communications; business, management, and marketing related; computer software and media applications; economics; education; English composition; English language and literature related; foods, nutrition, and related services; health and medical administrative services; health/medical preparatory programs; library science; nursing; physical sciences; psychology; psychology related.

LAKE SUPERIOR COLLEGE
Duluth, Minnesota
http://www.lsc.edu/connect/
Lake Superior College was founded in 1995. It is accredited by North Central Association of Colleges and Schools. It first offered distance learning courses in 1997. In fall 2007, there were 2,000 students enrolled in distance learning courses. Institutionally administered financial aid is available to distance learners.
Services Distance learners have accessibility to academic advising, bookstore, campus computer network, career placement assistance, e-mail services, library services, tutoring.
Contact Melissa Leno, Enrollment Services Specialist, Lake Superior College, 2101 Trinity Road, Duluth, MN 55811. Telephone: 218-733-5903. E-mail: m.leno@lsc.edu.

DEGREES AND AWARDS
AA Liberal Education
AAS Accountant; Paralegal Studies
AS Accountant; Business Administration; Paralegal Studies
Certificate Bookkeeping–Professional Bookkeeper; Hemodialysis Patient Care Technician; Microcomputer Office Specialist

COURSE SUBJECT AREAS OFFERED OUTSIDE OF DEGREE PROGRAMS
Undergraduate—accounting and related services; anthropology; astronomy and astrophysics; biological and physical sciences; business/commerce; business/corporate communications; business operations support and assistant services; communication and media; computer and information sciences; computer software and media applications; economics; English composition; fine and studio art; geography and cartography; geological and earth sciences/geosciences; health/medical preparatory programs; health professions related; history; liberal arts and sciences, general studies and humanities; mathematics; philosophy and religious studies related; physical sciences; political science and government; psychology; sociology; technical and business writing.

LAMAR STATE COLLEGE–PORT ARTHUR
Port Arthur, Texas
Academic Division
http://www.lamarpa.edu/
Lamar State College–Port Arthur was founded in 1909. It is accredited by Southern Association of Colleges and Schools. It first offered distance learning courses in 1996. In fall 2007, there were 600 students enrolled in distance learning courses. Institutionally administered financial aid is available to distance learners.
Services Distance learners have accessibility to academic advising, campus computer network, e-mail services, library services.
Contact Dr. Charles Gongre, Dean of Academic Programs, Lamar State College–Port Arthur, PO Box 310, Port Arthur, TX 77641. Telephone: 409-984-6229. Fax: 409-984-6000. E-mail: charles.gongre@lamarpa.edu.

DEGREES AND AWARDS
Programs offered do not lead to a degree or other formal award.

COURSE SUBJECT AREAS OFFERED OUTSIDE OF DEGREE PROGRAMS
Undergraduate—astronomy and astrophysics; biblical and other theological languages and literatures; business administration, management and operations; computer and information sciences; computer programming; computer science; computer software and media applications; computer systems networking and telecommunications; data entry/microcomputer applications; economics; English composition; foods, nutrition, and related services; health professions related; mathematics; philosophy; philosophy and religious studies related; psychology.
Non-credit—allied health and medical assisting services; allied health diagnostic, intervention, and treatment professions; alternative and complementary medical support services; alternative and complementary medicine and medical systems; American literature (United States and Canadian); business administration, management and operations; business/commerce; business, management, and marketing related; business/managerial economics; business operations support and assistant services; computer and information sciences; computer/information technology administration and management; computer programming; computer science; computer software and media applications; computer systems analysis; computer systems networking and telecommunications; creative writing; data entry/microcomputer applications; data processing; entrepreneurial and small business operations; finance and financial management services; health aides/attendants/orderlies; human resources management; information science/studies; management information systems; marketing; public relations, advertising, and applied communication related; sales, merchandising, and related marketing operations (general); sales, merchandising, and related marketing operations (specialized); technical and business writing.

LAREDO COMMUNITY COLLEGE
Laredo, Texas
http://www.laredo.edu/dl
Laredo Community College was founded in 1946. It is accredited by Southern Association of Colleges and Schools. It first offered distance learning courses in 1998. In fall 2007, there were 950 students enrolled in distance learning courses. Institutionally administered financial aid is available to distance learners.
Services Distance learners have accessibility to bookstore, library services, tutoring.
Contact Ms. Perla Canales, Technology Coordinator, Laredo Community College, West End Washington Street, Laredo, TX 78040. Telephone: 956-721-5368. Fax: 956-721-5873. E-mail: pcanales@laredo.edu.

DEGREES AND AWARDS
Programs offered do not lead to a degree or other formal award.

COURSE SUBJECT AREAS OFFERED OUTSIDE OF DEGREE PROGRAMS
Undergraduate—accounting and related services; allied health and medical assisting services; American literature (United States and Canadian); applied mathematics; biological and biomedical sciences related; biological and physical sciences; biology; business administration, management and operations; business/corporate communications; business, management, and marketing related; computer and information sciences; computer science; computer software and media applications; criminal justice and corrections; dance; economics; education; English; English composition; English literature (British and Commonwealth); fine and studio art; geography and cartography; health and physical education/fitness; history; languages (foreign languages related); mathematics; mathematics and computer science; medical basic sciences; music; psychology; real estate; social sciences; social sciences related; sociology; speech and rhetoric; technical and business writing.

LA SIERRA UNIVERSITY
Riverside, California
http://www.lasierra.edu/digital

La Sierra University was founded in 1922. It is accredited by Western Association of Schools and Colleges. It first offered distance learning courses in 1999. In fall 2007, there were 100 students enrolled in distance learning courses. Institutionally administered financial aid is available to distance learners.

Services Distance learners have accessibility to academic advising, bookstore, campus computer network, e-mail services, library services, tutoring.

Contact Sandra S. Green, EdD, Director of Digit@1 Le@rning, La Sierra University, 4500 Riverwalk Parkway, Riverside, CA 92515. Telephone: 951-785-2984. Fax: 951-785-2316. E-mail: sgreen@lasierra.edu.

DEGREES AND AWARDS
MA Curriculum and Instruction–Educational Technology
MAT Teaching

COURSE SUBJECT AREAS OFFERED OUTSIDE OF DEGREE PROGRAMS
Undergraduate—education (specific levels and methods); education (specific subject areas).
Graduate—educational/instructional media design; education related; education (specific levels and methods); education (specific subject areas).
Non-credit—special education.

LAURENTIAN UNIVERSITY
Sudbury, Ontario, Canada
Centre for Continuing Education
http://cce.laurentian.ca

Laurentian University was founded in 1960. It is provincially chartered. It first offered distance learning courses in 1972. In fall 2007, there were 8,000 students enrolled in distance learning courses. Institutionally administered financial aid is available to distance learners.

Services Distance learners have accessibility to academic advising, bookstore, campus computer network, career placement assistance, e-mail services, library services, tutoring.

Contact Mr. Jean Dennie, Program Manager/Academic Advisor, Laurentian University, 935 Ramsey Lake Road, Sudbury, ON P3E 2C6, Canada. Telephone: 705-675-1151 Ext. 3942. Fax: 705-675-4897. E-mail: jdennie@laurentian.ca.

DEGREES AND AWARDS
BA Etudes francaises (en developpement); Folklore et Ethnologie de l'amerique Francaise; Gerontology; History (in development); Law and Justice; Native Studies (Honours); Native Studies; Psychologie; Psychology; Religious Studies; Sciences Religieuses; Sociology; Women's Studies
BS Liberal Science
BSN Nursing–BSN for Registered Nurses
BSW Service Social (en franþais); Social Work–Native Human Services
Certificate Family Life Studies and Human Sexuality; Folklore et Ethnologie de l'amerique Francaise; Gerontology; Law and Justice; Women's Studies

LAWRENCE TECHNOLOGICAL UNIVERSITY
Southfield, Michigan
http://www.ltu.edu/ltuonline/

Lawrence Technological University was founded in 1932. It is accredited by North Central Association of Colleges and Schools. It first offered distance learning courses in 1998. In fall 2007, there were 350 students enrolled in distance learning courses. Institutionally administered financial aid is available to distance learners.

Services Distance learners have accessibility to academic advising, bookstore, campus computer network, career placement assistance, e-mail services, library services, tutoring.

Contact Dr. Alan McCord, Executive Director, LTU Online, Lawrence Technological University, 21000 West Ten Mile Road, Southfield, MI 48075. Telephone: 248-204-2380. Fax: 248-204-2389. E-mail: ltuonline @ltu.edu.

DEGREES AND AWARDS
BS Information Technology
CCCPE Architecture Management; Non-Profit Management and Leadership; Project Management
MBA Business Administration
MEM Master of Engineering Management

COURSE SUBJECT AREAS OFFERED OUTSIDE OF DEGREE PROGRAMS
Undergraduate—business administration, management and operations; computer/information technology administration and management; human resources management; mathematics and statistics related.
Graduate—architecture related; business administration, management and operations; computer/information technology administration and management; educational/instructional media design; engineering; finance and financial management services; human resources management; information science/studies; international business; management information systems; marketing.

LEHIGH CARBON COMMUNITY COLLEGE
Schnecksville, Pennsylvania
Office of Distance Learning
http://www.lccc.edu/distance-learning/

Lehigh Carbon Community College was founded in 1967. It is accredited by Middle States Association of Colleges and Schools. It first offered distance learning courses in 1995. In fall 2007, there were 2,600 students enrolled in distance learning courses. Institutionally administered financial aid is available to distance learners.

Services Distance learners have accessibility to academic advising, bookstore, e-mail services, library services, tutoring.

Contact Beverly J. Benfer, Director of Distance Learning and Instructional Technology, Lehigh Carbon Community College, 4750 Orchard Road, Schnecksville, PA 18078. Telephone: 610-799-1591. Fax: 610-799-1159. E-mail: bbenfer@lccc.edu.

DEGREES AND AWARDS
AA Business Administration; Education; Liberal Arts
AAS Business Management; Early Childhood Education
Certification Business Management
Specialized diploma Business Management; Early Childhood Education; Health Care Coding

COURSE SUBJECT AREAS OFFERED OUTSIDE OF DEGREE PROGRAMS
Undergraduate—accounting and related services; American literature (United States and Canadian); astronomy and astrophysics; biology; business administration, management and operations; business, management, and marketing related; business operations support and assistant services; computer and information sciences; computer science; criminal justice and corrections; curriculum and instruction; developmental and child psychology; economics; education; educational administration and supervision; educational psychology; education related; education (specific levels and methods); education (specific subject areas); English; English as a second/foreign language (teaching); English composition; English language and literature related; English literature (British and Commonwealth); finance and financial management services; geography and cartography; health and medical administrative services; health and physical education/fitness; health professions related; history; human development, family studies, and related services; human resources management; industrial and organizational psychology; liberal arts and sciences, general studies and humanities; marketing; mathematics; mathematics and statistics related; multi-/interdisciplinary studies related; music; philosophy; physics; political science and government; psychology; psychology related; school psychology; social sciences; social sciences related; sociology; special education; speech and rhetoric; statistics; technical and business writing.

LEHIGH UNIVERSITY
Bethlehem, Pennsylvania
Office of Distance Learning
http://www.distance.lehigh.edu

Lehigh University was founded in 1865. It is accredited by Middle States Association of Colleges and Schools. It first offered distance learning courses in 1992. In fall 2007, there were 700 students enrolled in distance learning courses. Institutionally administered financial aid is available to distance learners.

Services Distance learners have accessibility to academic advising, bookstore, campus computer network, career placement assistance, e-mail services, library services, tutoring.

Contact Lisa Moughan, Marketing Coordinator, Lehigh University, 436 Brodhead Avenue, Bethlehem, PA 18015. Telephone: 610-758-4372. Fax: 610-758-4190. E-mail: lim2@lehigh.edu.

DEGREES AND AWARDS
Certificate Project Management; Supply Chain Management
Graduate Certificate Regulatory Affairs
MBA Business Administration
ME Chemical Engineering; Polymer Science and Engineering
MME Mechanical Engineering (MS or MEng)
MS Chemistry; Manufacturing Systems Engineering; Molecular Biology; Polymer Science and Engineering; Quality Engineering
MSIS Information and Systems Engineering (MS or MEng)

COURSE SUBJECT AREAS OFFERED OUTSIDE OF DEGREE PROGRAMS
Graduate—biological and physical sciences; business administration, management and operations; cell biology and anatomical sciences; chemical engineering; chemistry; polymer/plastics engineering.
Non-credit—business administration, management and operations; business/corporate communications; chemical engineering; chemistry; engineering/industrial management; polymer/plastics engineering.

LETOURNEAU UNIVERSITY
Longview, Texas
Adult Education Degree Programs
http://www.letu.edu/

LeTourneau University was founded in 1946. It is accredited by Southern Association of Colleges and Schools. It first offered distance learning courses in 1999. Institutionally administered financial aid is available to distance learners.

Services Distance learners have accessibility to academic advising, bookstore, campus computer network, career placement assistance, e-mail services, library services, tutoring.

Contact Adult Education Degree Programs, LeTourneau University, PO Box 7668, Longview, TX 75607-7668. Telephone: 866-430-5388.

DEGREES AND AWARDS
BBA Online BBA
BS Psychology
MBA Educational Leadership; Finance; Human Resource Management; International Business; Management; Marketing

LEWIS-CLARK STATE COLLEGE
Lewiston, Idaho
Distance Learning
http://www.lcsc.edu/dl

Lewis-Clark State College was founded in 1893. It is accredited by Northwest Commission on Colleges and Universities. It first offered distance learning courses in 1995. In fall 2007, there were 1,015 students enrolled in distance learning courses. Institutionally administered financial aid is available to distance learners.

Services Distance learners have accessibility to academic advising, bookstore, campus computer network, career placement assistance, e-mail services, library services.

Contact Carolyn D. Quintero, Coordinator, Faculty/Student Services, Lewis-Clark State College, 500 Eighth Avenue, Lewiston, ID 83501. Telephone: 208-792-2148. Fax: 208-792-2444. E-mail: cdquintero@lcsc.edu.

DEGREES AND AWARDS
Programs offered do not lead to a degree or other formal award.

COURSE SUBJECT AREAS OFFERED OUTSIDE OF DEGREE PROGRAMS
Undergraduate—accounting and computer science; business administration, management and operations; business operations support and assistant services; communication and media; computer and information sciences; economics; education; English composition; history; human development, family studies, and related services; liberal arts and sciences, general studies and humanities; management information systems; mathematics and statistics related; natural sciences; nursing; philosophy; political science and government; psychology; social sciences.

LIBERTY UNIVERSITY
Lynchburg, Virginia
Distance Learning Program
http://www.liberty.edu/distancelearning

Liberty University was founded in 1971. It is accredited by Southern Association of Colleges and Schools. It first offered distance learning courses in 1985. In fall 2007, there were 18,223 students enrolled in distance learning courses. Institutionally administered financial aid is available to distance learners.

Services Distance learners have accessibility to academic advising, bookstore, campus computer network, career placement assistance, e-mail services, library services, tutoring.

Contact Mrs. Leslee Rapp, Director of Admissions, Liberty University, 1971 University Boulevard, Lynchburg, VA 24502-2269. Telephone: 800-424-9595. Fax: 800-628-7977. E-mail: dlpadmissions@liberty.edu.

DEGREES AND AWARDS
AA Accounting; Business; Criminal Justice; General Studies; Management Information Systems; Psychology; Religion
BS Accounting; Business; Criminal Justice; Management Information Systems; Multidisciplinary Studies–Education concentration; Multidisciplinary Studies; Psychology; Religion
BSN Nursing–RN to BSN
MA Christian Leadership; Evangelism and Church Planting; Human Services; Marriage and Family Therapy; Pastoral Counseling; Professional Counseling; Theological Studies; Worship Studies
MAR Religion
MAT Teaching
MBA Business Administration
MDiv Divinity
MEd Education
MS Accounting
MSM Management
MSN Nursing
DMin Ministry
EdD Education
PhD Counseling

COURSE SUBJECT AREAS OFFERED OUTSIDE OF DEGREE PROGRAMS
Undergraduate—accounting and related services; biblical and other theological languages and literatures; biblical studies; biology; business/commerce; business/corporate communications; business, management, and marketing related; business/managerial economics; clinical child psychology; communication and media; computer/information technology administration and management; criminal justice and corrections; developmental and child psychology; economics; education; educational psychology; English composition; gerontology; history; marketing; philosophy; psychology; religious studies; social psychology; social sciences; taxation; theology and religious vocations related.
Graduate—accounting and related services; biblical studies; business administration, management and operations; business, management, and

marketing related; counseling psychology; curriculum and instruction; educational administration and supervision; educational assessment, evaluation, and research; educational/instructional media design; educational psychology; education related; education (specific levels and methods); education (specific subject areas); English; family and consumer sciences/human sciences; psychology; religious studies; school psychology; special education; theological and ministerial studies; theology and religious vocations related.

LIFE PACIFIC COLLEGE
San Dimas, California
School of Distance Learning
http://www.lifepacific.edu/distance

Life Pacific College was founded in 1923. It is accredited by Association for Biblical Higher Education. It first offered distance learning courses in 1941. In fall 2007, there were 400 students enrolled in distance learning courses. Institutionally administered financial aid is available to distance learners.
Services Distance learners have accessibility to academic advising, bookstore, career placement assistance, library services.
Contact Brian Tomhave, Director, Life Pacific College, 1100 West Covina Boulevard, San Dimas, CA 91773. Telephone: 877-851-0900. Fax: 909-706-3099. E-mail: distance@lifepacific.edu.

DEGREES AND AWARDS
AA Biblical Studies
BA Ministry and Leadership degree completion program

COURSE SUBJECT AREAS OFFERED OUTSIDE OF DEGREE PROGRAMS
Undergraduate—biblical studies; philosophy and religious studies related; theological and ministerial studies.
Non-credit—biblical and other theological languages and literatures; biblical studies; religious studies.

LIMESTONE COLLEGE
Gaffney, South Carolina
The Block Program
http://www.limestonevirtualcampus.net

Limestone College was founded in 1845. It is accredited by Southern Association of Colleges and Schools. It first offered distance learning courses in 1997. In fall 2007, there were 1,834 students enrolled in distance learning courses. Institutionally administered financial aid is available to distance learners.
Services Distance learners have accessibility to academic advising, bookstore, campus computer network, career placement assistance, e-mail services, library services, tutoring.
Contact Mrs. Katie Phillips, Academic Advisor/Vocational Rehabilitation Coordinator, Limestone College, Extended Campus, 1115 College Drive, Gaffney, SC 29340-3799. Telephone: 864-488-4597. Fax: 864-488-4595. E-mail: kphillips@limestone.edu.

DEGREES AND AWARDS
AA Business Administration; Computer Science Internet Management; Computer Science Management Information Systems; Computer Science Programming; Liberal Studies
BA Criminal Justice; Human Resource Development; Liberal Studies; Psychology
BS Business Administration–Accounting; Business Administration–Computer Programming; Business Administration–Computer Software Applications; Business Administration–General Business; Business Administration–Management; Computer Science Information Technology; Computer Science Internet Management–Database; Computer Science Internet Management–E-commerce; Computer Science Internet Management–Operations Management; Computer Science Internet Management–Web Development; Computer Science Internet Management, general; Computer Science Programming; Computer Science, Computer and Information Systems Security; Liberal Studies

COURSE SUBJECT AREAS OFFERED OUTSIDE OF DEGREE PROGRAMS
Undergraduate—accounting and related services; American literature (United States and Canadian); astronomy and astrophysics; biblical studies; biology; business administration, management and operations; business/commerce; business/corporate communications; comparative literature; computer and information sciences; computer and information sciences and support services related; computer/information technology administration and management; computer programming; computer science; computer software and media applications; computer systems analysis; computer systems networking and telecommunications; creative writing; criminal justice and corrections; data entry/microcomputer applications; data processing; dramatic/theater arts and stagecraft; economics; education (specific levels and methods); English; English composition; English language and literature related; finance and financial management services; geography and cartography; gerontology; history; human resources management; human services; information science/studies; international business; legal studies (non-professional general, undergraduate); management information systems; management sciences and quantitative methods; marketing; mathematics; music; philosophy; political science and government; psychology; psychology related; religious studies; sales, merchandising, and related marketing operations (general); social psychology; social work; sociology; statistics; technical and business writing.

LINCOLN CHRISTIAN COLLEGE
Lincoln, Illinois
Distance Learning
http://www.lccs.edu

Lincoln Christian College was founded in 1944. It is accredited by Association for Biblical Higher Education. It first offered distance learning courses in 1993. In fall 2007, there were 250 students enrolled in distance learning courses. Institutionally administered financial aid is available to distance learners.
Services Distance learners have accessibility to academic advising, bookstore, campus computer network, e-mail services, library services.
Contact Admissions, Lincoln Christian College, 100 Campus View Drive, Lincoln, IL 62656. Telephone: 217-732-3168 Ext. 2315. E-mail: coladmis@lccs.edu.

DEGREES AND AWARDS
Programs offered do not lead to a degree or other formal award.

COURSE SUBJECT AREAS OFFERED OUTSIDE OF DEGREE PROGRAMS
Undergraduate—biblical and other theological languages and literatures; biblical studies; education (specific levels and methods); English as a second/foreign language (teaching); languages (Middle/Near Eastern and Semitic); religious studies; theological and ministerial studies; theology and religious vocations related.
Graduate—biblical and other theological languages and literatures; biblical studies; English as a second/foreign language (teaching); languages (Middle/Near Eastern and Semitic); religious studies; theological and ministerial studies.
Non-credit—biblical and other theological languages and literatures; biblical studies; education (specific levels and methods); languages (Middle/Near Eastern and Semitic); religious studies; theological and ministerial studies.

LINN-BENTON COMMUNITY COLLEGE
Albany, Oregon
Media Services
http://www.linnbenton.edu

Linn-Benton Community College was founded in 1966. It is accredited by Northwest Commission on Colleges and Universities. It first offered distance learning courses in 1979. In fall 2007, there were 854 students enrolled in distance learning courses. Institutionally administered financial aid is available to distance learners.
Services Distance learners have accessibility to academic advising, bookstore, career placement assistance, e-mail services, library services.

Contact Christine Baker, Outreach Coordinator, Linn-Benton Community College, Admissions and Records, 6500 Pacific Boulevard SW, Albany, OR 97321. Telephone: 541-917-4811. Fax: 541-917-4868. E-mail: admissions@linnbenton.edu.

DEGREES AND AWARDS
Programs offered do not lead to a degree or other formal award.

COURSE SUBJECT AREAS OFFERED OUTSIDE OF DEGREE PROGRAMS
Undergraduate—American literature (United States and Canadian); animal sciences; anthropology; applied mathematics; astronomy and astrophysics; business administration, management and operations; business/commerce; business/managerial economics; computer software and media applications; creative writing; criminal justice and corrections; dental support services and allied professions; economics; education; English; health and medical administrative services; health and physical education/fitness; history; human development, family studies, and related services; journalism; liberal arts and sciences, general studies and humanities; mathematics; public relations, advertising, and applied communication related; religious studies; technical and business writing.
Non-credit—English as a second language; mathematics; personal and culinary services related.

LIPSCOMB UNIVERSITY
Nashville, Tennessee
http://www.lipscomb.edu/
Lipscomb University was founded in 1891. It is accredited by Southern Association of Colleges and Schools. It first offered distance learning courses in 1999. In fall 2007, there were 80 students enrolled in distance learning courses. Institutionally administered financial aid is available to distance learners.
Services Distance learners have accessibility to bookstore, campus computer network, career placement assistance, e-mail services, library services.
Contact Mr. Al Austelle, Director of the Center for Instructional Technology, Lipscomb University, One University Park Drive, Nashville, TN 37204-3951. Telephone: 615-966-5703. Fax: 615-966-6559. E-mail: al.austelle@lipscomb.edu.

DEGREES AND AWARDS
Programs offered do not lead to a degree or other formal award.

COURSE SUBJECT AREAS OFFERED OUTSIDE OF DEGREE PROGRAMS
Undergraduate—biblical studies; English.
Graduate—biblical studies; business administration, management and operations.

LOCK HAVEN UNIVERSITY OF PENNSYLVANIA
Lock Haven, Pennsylvania
http://ecampus.lhup.edu/
Lock Haven University of Pennsylvania was founded in 1870. It is accredited by Middle States Association of Colleges and Schools. It first offered distance learning courses in 1995. In fall 2007, there were 500 students enrolled in distance learning courses. Institutionally administered financial aid is available to distance learners.
Services Distance learners have accessibility to academic advising, bookstore, campus computer network, e-mail services, library services.
Contact Carlos R. Morales, PhD, Executive Director of eCampus and Learning Technologies, Lock Haven University of Pennsylvania, Court House Annex, Lock Haven, PA 17745. Telephone: 570-484-2404. Fax: 570-484-2981. E-mail: cmorales@lhup.edu.

DEGREES AND AWARDS
MEd Alternative Education; Teaching and Learning
MHS Physician Assistant
MLA Liberal Arts

COURSE SUBJECT AREAS OFFERED OUTSIDE OF DEGREE PROGRAMS
Undergraduate—applied mathematics; bioethics/medical ethics; comparative literature; computer programming; criminology; education; English composition; fine and studio art; foods, nutrition, and related services; geography and cartography; health and physical education/fitness; health/medical preparatory programs; history; music; political science and government; psychology; sociology.
Graduate—education; health professions related; liberal arts and sciences, general studies and humanities.
Non-credit—allied health and medical assisting services; business/commerce; computer and information sciences and support services related; construction trades; education; legal professions and studies related.
See full description on page 408.

LOMA LINDA UNIVERSITY
Loma Linda, California
http://www.llu.edu/
Loma Linda University was founded in 1905. It is accredited by Western Association of Schools and Colleges. It first offered distance learning courses in 1996. In fall 2007, there were 700 students enrolled in distance learning courses. Institutionally administered financial aid is available to distance learners.
Services Distance learners have accessibility to academic advising, bookstore, e-mail services, library services.
Contact Prof. Rafael Molina, Director of Office of Distance Learning, Loma Linda University, Nichol Hall 1510, Loma Linda, CA 92350. Telephone: 909-558-7762. Fax: 909-558-5937. E-mail: rvmolina@llu.edu.

DEGREES AND AWARDS
Programs offered do not lead to a degree or other formal award.

COURSE SUBJECT AREAS OFFERED OUTSIDE OF DEGREE PROGRAMS
Undergraduate—clinical/medical laboratory science and allied professions; health professions related.
Graduate—health and medical administrative services; health professions related; medical clinical sciences/graduate medical studies; philosophy and religious studies related; psychology; social sciences.

LONG BEACH CITY COLLEGE
Long Beach, California
http://de.lbcc.edu
Long Beach City College was founded in 1927. It is accredited by Western Association of Schools and Colleges. It first offered distance learning courses in 1980. In fall 2007, there were 4,290 students enrolled in distance learning courses. Institutionally administered financial aid is available to distance learners.
Services Distance learners have accessibility to academic advising, bookstore, career placement assistance, library services, tutoring.
Contact Ms. Wendi Lopez, Distance Learning Program Specialist, Long Beach City College, 4901 East Carson Street, Long Beach, CA 90808. Telephone: 562-938-4025. Fax: 562-938-4814. E-mail: wlopez@lbcc.edu.

DEGREES AND AWARDS
Programs offered do not lead to a degree or other formal award.

COURSE SUBJECT AREAS OFFERED OUTSIDE OF DEGREE PROGRAMS
Undergraduate—accounting and related services; anthropology; astronomy and astrophysics; biology; business administration, management and operations; clinical child psychology; computer and information sciences; computer programming; computer science; computer software and media applications; computer systems networking and telecommunications; creative writing; dance; design and applied arts; developmental and child psychology; drafting/design engineering technologies; economics; electrical/electronics maintenance and repair technology; English; English

as a second language; English composition; film/video and photographic arts; foods, nutrition, and related services; geography and cartography; health/medical preparatory programs; history; human development, family studies, and related services; international business; liberal arts and sciences, general studies and humanities; library science; marketing; mathematics; mathematics and statistics related; music; nursing; nutrition sciences; pharmacy, pharmaceutical sciences, and administration; philosophy; political science and government; psychology; radio, television, and digital communication; real estate; social psychology; social sciences; sociology; statistics.

LOS ANGELES HARBOR COLLEGE
Wilmington, California
Distance Education Programs
http://www.lahc.edu/classes/online.html

Los Angeles Harbor College was founded in 1949. It is accredited by Western Association of Schools and Colleges. It first offered distance learning courses in 1996. In fall 2007, there were 1,200 students enrolled in distance learning courses. Institutionally administered financial aid is available to distance learners.

Services Distance learners have accessibility to bookstore, campus computer network, e-mail services, library services.

Contact Dr. Robert Richards, Associate Dean, Research and Planning, Los Angeles Harbor College, 1111 Figueroa Place, Wilmington, CA 90744. Telephone: 310-233-4044. Fax: 310-233-4661. E-mail: richarr@lahc.edu.

DEGREES AND AWARDS
Programs offered do not lead to a degree or other formal award.

COURSE SUBJECT AREAS OFFERED OUTSIDE OF DEGREE PROGRAMS

Undergraduate—accounting and related services; business/commerce; computer and information sciences; computer programming; criminal justice and corrections; criminology; economics; English; English composition; English language and literature related; nursing; political science and government; psychology; sociology.

LOS ANGELES TRADE-TECHNICAL COLLEGE
Los Angeles, California
http://www.lattc.edu/lattc/on_line_classes.htm

Los Angeles Trade-Technical College was founded in 1925. It is accredited by Western Association of Schools and Colleges. It first offered distance learning courses in 1986. In fall 2007, there were 300 students enrolled in distance learning courses. Institutionally administered financial aid is available to distance learners.

Services Distance learners have accessibility to academic advising, bookstore, campus computer network, e-mail services, library services.

Contact Linda Delzeit-McIntyre, Director, Los Angeles Trade-Technical College, 400 West Washington Boulevard, Los Angeles, CA 90015. Telephone: 213-763-3733. Fax: 213-406-1237. E-mail: delzeil@lattc.edu.

DEGREES AND AWARDS
Programs offered do not lead to a degree or other formal award.

COURSE SUBJECT AREAS OFFERED OUTSIDE OF DEGREE PROGRAMS

Undergraduate—accounting and computer science; anthropology; astronomy and astrophysics; business, management, and marketing related; computer software and media applications; construction trades; criminal justice and corrections; developmental and child psychology; English; English composition; English language and literature related; family psychology; film/video and photographic arts; geography and cartography; health and physical education/fitness; heating, air conditioning, ventilation and refrigeration maintenance technology; history; human development, family studies, and related services; legal professions and studies related; liberal arts and sciences, general studies and humanities; marketing; mathematics; mathematics and statistics related; nutrition

sciences; philosophy; political science and government; psychology; public relations, advertising, and applied communication related; real estate; sales, merchandising, and related marketing operations (general); sociology; statistics.

LOUISIANA STATE UNIVERSITY AND AGRICULTURAL AND MECHANICAL COLLEGE
Baton Rouge, Louisiana
Division of Continuing Education, Extended Learning and Independent Study
http://www.outreach.lsu.edu/

Louisiana State University and Agricultural and Mechanical College was founded in 1860. It is accredited by Southern Association of Colleges and Schools. It first offered distance learning courses in 1984. Institutionally administered financial aid is available to distance learners.

Services Distance learners have accessibility to academic advising, bookstore, campus computer network, career placement assistance, e-mail services, library services.

Contact Ms. Stacey P. Vessel, Coordinator, Extended Learning, Louisiana State University and Agricultural and Mechanical College, 1225 Pleasant Hall, Baton Rouge, LA 70803. Telephone: 225-578-7031. Fax: 225-578-7470. E-mail: svessel@outreach.lsu.edu.

DEGREES AND AWARDS
Programs offered do not lead to a degree or other formal award.

COURSE SUBJECT AREAS OFFERED OUTSIDE OF DEGREE PROGRAMS

Undergraduate—accounting and related services; American literature (United States and Canadian); anthropology; area, ethnic, cultural, and gender studies related; biological and physical sciences; business, management, and marketing related; communication and journalism related; computer and information sciences; economics; education; English composition; English language and literature related; English literature (British and Commonwealth); ethnic, cultural minority, and gender studies; family and consumer economics; geography and cartography; geological and earth sciences/geosciences; health and physical education/fitness; information science/studies; journalism; languages (foreign languages related); library science; mathematics; military studies; music; philosophy and religious studies related; physical sciences; social sciences related; social work; speech and rhetoric.

Graduate—agriculture and agriculture operations related; civil engineering; environmental/environmental health engineering; human resources management.

LOUISIANA STATE UNIVERSITY AND AGRICULTURAL AND MECHANICAL COLLEGE
Baton Rouge, Louisiana
Independent Study
http://www.outreach.lsu.edu/idl

Louisiana State University and Agricultural and Mechanical College was founded in 1860. It is accredited by Southern Association of Colleges and Schools. It first offered distance learning courses in 1941. In fall 2007, there were 9,000 students enrolled in distance learning courses. Institutionally administered financial aid is available to distance learners.

Services Distance learners have accessibility to bookstore, e-mail services, library services.

Contact Vivian Cupples, Learner Services Coordinator, Louisiana State University and Agricultural and Mechanical College, Independent and Distance Learning, 1225 Pleasant Hall, Baton Rouge, LA 70803. Telephone: 800-234-5046. Fax: 225-578-3090. E-mail: iservices@outreach.lsu.edu.

DEGREES AND AWARDS
Programs offered do not lead to a degree or other formal award.

COURSE SUBJECT AREAS OFFERED OUTSIDE OF DEGREE PROGRAMS

Undergraduate—accounting and related services; anthropology; biology; business administration, management and operations; cell biology and

anatomical sciences; communication and media; community health services; comparative literature; criminology; curriculum and instruction; developmental and child psychology; dramatic/theater arts and stagecraft; ecology, evolution, and population biology; economics; educational assessment, evaluation, and research; educational psychology; education (specific levels and methods); English; English composition; English language and literature related; English literature (British and Commonwealth); ethnic, cultural minority, and gender studies; finance and financial management services; fine and studio art; geography and cartography; geological and earth sciences/geosciences; health and physical education/fitness; history; journalism; languages (classics and classical); languages (Germanic); languages (Romance languages); legal studies (non-professional general, undergraduate); library science related; linguistic, comparative, and related language studies; management information systems; management sciences and quantitative methods; marketing; mathematics; mathematics and statistics related; mechanical engineering; military studies; music; philosophy; philosophy and religious studies related; physical sciences; physics; physiology, pathology and related sciences; political science and government; psychology; psychology related; school psychology; social sciences; social sciences related; sociology; speech and rhetoric; statistics; technical and business writing.
Non-credit—biology; English composition; mathematics.

LOYOLA UNIVERSITY NEW ORLEANS
New Orleans, Louisiana
Off-Campus Learning Program
http://citycollege.loyno.edu/oclp/index.html
Loyola University New Orleans was founded in 1912. It is accredited by Southern Association of Colleges and Schools. It first offered distance learning courses in 1991. Institutionally administered financial aid is available to distance learners.
Services Distance learners have accessibility to academic advising, bookstore, campus computer network, career placement assistance, e-mail services, library services, tutoring.
Contact Off-Campus Learning Program, Loyola University New Orleans, New Orleans, LA 70118. Telephone: 504-865-3250.

DEGREES AND AWARDS
BSN Nursing–RN to BSN
MSN Health Care Systems Management

LURLEEN B. WALLACE COMMUNITY COLLEGE
Andalusia, Alabama
http://www.lbwcc.edu/cms/page.aspx?pageid=228
Lurleen B. Wallace Community College was founded in 1969. It is accredited by Southern Association of Colleges and Schools. It first offered distance learning courses in 2001. In fall 2007, there were 300 students enrolled in distance learning courses. Institutionally administered financial aid is available to distance learners.
Services Distance learners have accessibility to academic advising, bookstore, campus computer network, career placement assistance, library services, tutoring.
Contact Mr. James G. Aplin, Associate Dean of Instructional and Information Technology, Lurleen B. Wallace Community College, PO Box 1418, Andalusia, AL 36420. Telephone: 334-881-2227. Fax: 334-881-2300. E-mail: jgaplin@lbwcc.edu.

DEGREES AND AWARDS
Programs offered do not lead to a degree or other formal award.

COURSE SUBJECT AREAS OFFERED OUTSIDE OF DEGREE PROGRAMS
Undergraduate—accounting and computer science; biology; business, management, and marketing related; computer software and media applications; economics; English; fine and studio art; history; mathematics; music; physical sciences; psychology; sociology.

LUZERNE COUNTY COMMUNITY COLLEGE
Nanticoke, Pennsylvania
Telecollege
http://www.luzerne.edu/
Luzerne County Community College was founded in 1966. It is accredited by Middle States Association of Colleges and Schools. It first offered distance learning courses in 1981. In fall 2007, there were 12,000 students enrolled in distance learning courses. Institutionally administered financial aid is available to distance learners.
Services Distance learners have accessibility to bookstore, career placement assistance, e-mail services, library services.
Contact Mr. Barry E. Cipala, Director of the Distance Learning Center, Luzerne County Community College, 1333 South Prospect Street, Nanticoke, PA 18634. Telephone: 570-740-0559 Ext. 559. Fax: 570-740-0295. E-mail: bcipala@luzerne.edu.

DEGREES AND AWARDS
AS General Studies

COURSE SUBJECT AREAS OFFERED OUTSIDE OF DEGREE PROGRAMS
Undergraduate—accounting and related services; business administration, management and operations; computer and information sciences; liberal arts and sciences, general studies and humanities.
Non-credit—computer software and media applications.

LYNN UNIVERSITY
Boca Raton, Florida
The Institute for Distance Learning
http://www.lynn.edu/distancelearning
Lynn University was founded in 1962. It is accredited by Southern Association of Colleges and Schools. It first offered distance learning courses in 1998. In fall 2007, there were 1,000 students enrolled in distance learning courses. Institutionally administered financial aid is available to distance learners.
Services Distance learners have accessibility to academic advising, bookstore, campus computer network, career placement assistance, e-mail services, library services, tutoring.
Contact Ms. Ioulia Nikiforova-Bohannan, Assistant Director of Admissions, Lynn University, 3601 North Military Trail, Boca Raton, FL 33431. Telephone: 561-237-7803. Fax: 561-237-7100. E-mail: inikiforova@lynn.edu.

DEGREES AND AWARDS
BS Business Administration; Criminal Justice; Psychology
Certification Emergency and Disaster Management
Graduate Certificate Emergency and Disaster Management
MBA Aviation Management; Financial Valuation and Investment Management; Hospitality Management; International Business; Marketing; Mass Communication and Media Management; Sports and Athletics Administration
MEd Educational Leadership, Higher Education Administration specialization; Educational Leadership, School Administration specialization; Educational Leadership, School Administration with ESOL endorsement specialization
MS Criminal Justice Administration; Emergency Planning and Administration

See full description on page 410.

MACON STATE COLLEGE
Macon, Georgia
Office of Distance Learning
http://www.maconstate.edu
Macon State College was founded in 1968. It is accredited by Southern Association of Colleges and Schools. It first offered distance learning courses in 1997. In fall 2007, there were 1,568 students enrolled in distance learning courses. Institutionally administered financial aid is available to distance learners.
Services Distance learners have accessibility to academic advising, bookstore, career placement assistance, e-mail services, library services, tutoring.

Contact Admissions Office, Macon State College, Macon, GA 31206. Telephone: 478-471-2800. E-mail: mscinfo@maconstate.edu.

DEGREES AND AWARDS
Programs offered do not lead to a degree or other formal award.

COURSE SUBJECT AREAS OFFERED OUTSIDE OF DEGREE PROGRAMS
Undergraduate—accounting and computer science; accounting and related services; applied mathematics; business/commerce; business/corporate communications; comparative literature; computer and information sciences; computer/information technology administration and management; computer programming; computer software and media applications; computer systems analysis; computer systems networking and telecommunications; education; English; English composition; graphic communications; health and medical administrative services; health services/allied health/health sciences; history; mathematics; mathematics and computer science; mathematics and statistics related; nursing; psychology; statistics.

MALONE COLLEGE
Canton, Ohio
Malone College Online Learning
http://www.malone.edu/online
Malone College was founded in 1892. It is accredited by North Central Association of Colleges and Schools. It first offered distance learning courses in 1999. In fall 2007, there were 450 students enrolled in distance learning courses. Institutionally administered financial aid is available to distance learners.
Services Distance learners have accessibility to academic advising, bookstore, career placement assistance, e-mail services, library services.
Contact Sharon Purvis, Online Coordinator, Malone College, 515 25th Street NW, Canton, OH 44709. Telephone: 330-471-8423. Fax: 330-471-8570. E-mail: distancelearning@malone.edu.

DEGREES AND AWARDS
BA Business Management

COURSE SUBJECT AREAS OFFERED OUTSIDE OF DEGREE PROGRAMS
Undergraduate—biblical studies; biology; business administration, management and operations; business/commerce; communication and journalism related; communication and media; developmental and child psychology; educational/instructional media design; English composition; English literature (British and Commonwealth); fine and studio art; health and physical education/fitness; history; human development, family studies, and related services; liberal arts and sciences, general studies and humanities; philosophy; political science and government; psychology; social sciences related; sociology.
Graduate—biblical studies; counseling psychology.

MANATEE COMMUNITY COLLEGE
Bradenton, Florida
Distance Education
http://www.mccfl.edu/
Manatee Community College was founded in 1957. It is accredited by Southern Association of Colleges and Schools. It first offered distance learning courses in 1973. In fall 2007, there were 1,300 students enrolled in distance learning courses. Institutionally administered financial aid is available to distance learners.
Services Distance learners have accessibility to bookstore, campus computer network, e-mail services, library services.
Contact Ms. Nancy H. Edwards, Director of eLearning, Manatee Community College, 5840 26th Street West, Bradenton, FL 34207. Telephone: 941-752-5645. Fax: 941-727-2058. E-mail: edwardn@mccfl.edu.

DEGREES AND AWARDS
Programs offered do not lead to a degree or other formal award.

COURSE SUBJECT AREAS OFFERED OUTSIDE OF DEGREE PROGRAMS
Undergraduate—accounting and related services; American literature (United States and Canadian); anthropology; applied mathematics; biology; business administration, management and operations; business/commerce; business, management, and marketing related; business/managerial economics; computer and information sciences; developmental and child psychology; English composition; history; legal support services; management information systems; marketing; mathematics and statistics related; philosophy and religious studies related; sales, merchandising, and related marketing operations (specialized); sociology.

MANHATTAN SCHOOL OF MUSIC
New York, New York
http://www.msmnyc.edu/special/distancelearning/
Manhattan School of Music was founded in 1917. It is accredited by Middle States Association of Colleges and Schools. It first offered distance learning courses in 1996. In fall 2007, there were 1,700 students enrolled in distance learning courses. Institutionally administered financial aid is available to distance learners.
Contact Juliana Han, Distance Learning Program Coordinator, Manhattan School of Music, 120 Claremont Avenue, New York, NY 10027. Telephone: 212-749-2802 Ext. 4488. Fax: 212-749-0562. E-mail: jhan@msmnyc.edu.

DEGREES AND AWARDS
Programs offered do not lead to a degree or other formal award.

COURSE SUBJECT AREAS OFFERED OUTSIDE OF DEGREE PROGRAMS
Undergraduate—education related; music; visual and performing arts.
Graduate—education related; music; visual and performing arts.
Non-credit—music; visual and performing arts.

MANOR COLLEGE
Jenkintown, Pennsylvania
http://www.manor.edu/
Manor College was founded in 1947. It is accredited by Middle States Association of Colleges and Schools. It first offered distance learning courses in 1998. In fall 2007, there were 131 students enrolled in distance learning courses. Institutionally administered financial aid is available to distance learners.
Services Distance learners have accessibility to academic advising, campus computer network, e-mail services, library services.
Contact Sally Mydlowec, Executive Vice President and Dean of Academic Affairs, Manor College, 700 Fox Chase Road, Jenkintown, PA 19046. Telephone: 215-885-2360 Ext. 243. Fax: 215-576-6564. E-mail: smydlowec@manor.edu.

DEGREES AND AWARDS
Programs offered do not lead to a degree or other formal award.

COURSE SUBJECT AREAS OFFERED OUTSIDE OF DEGREE PROGRAMS
Undergraduate—animal sciences; business administration, management and operations; business/commerce; computer and information sciences; legal studies (non-professional general, undergraduate); marketing; psychology; religious studies; sociology.

MANSFIELD UNIVERSITY OF PENNSYLVANIA
Mansfield, Pennsylvania
Center for Lifelong Learning
http://cll.mansfield.edu
Mansfield University of Pennsylvania was founded in 1857. It is accredited by Middle States Association of Colleges and Schools. It first offered distance learning courses in 1995. In fall 2007, there were 1,147 students enrolled in distance learning courses. Institutionally administered financial aid is available to distance learners.
Services Distance learners have accessibility to academic advising, bookstore, campus computer network, career placement assistance, e-mail services, library services, tutoring.

Contact Brian Barden, Director of Enrollment Management, Mansfield University of Pennsylvania, Alumni Hall, Mansfield, PA 16933. Telephone: 570-662-4813. Fax: 570-662-4121. E-mail: bbarden@mansfield.edu.

DEGREES AND AWARDS
BA Art History
BSN Nursing–RN to BSN
MEd Art Education
MSE Library and Information Technologies–School Library and Information Technologies
MSN Nursing Education

COURSE SUBJECT AREAS OFFERED OUTSIDE OF DEGREE PROGRAMS
Undergraduate—accounting and related services; business administration, management and operations; communication and journalism related; computer and information sciences; criminal justice and corrections; economics; education; English; English language and literature related; history; mathematics; music; nursing; nutrition sciences; psychology; sociology.
Graduate—education; library science; nursing.

MARANATHA BAPTIST BIBLE COLLEGE
Watertown, Wisconsin
http://www.mbbc.edu/
Maranatha Baptist Bible College was founded in 1968. It is accredited by North Central Association of Colleges and Schools. It first offered distance learning courses in 2001. In fall 2007, there were 50 students enrolled in distance learning courses. Institutionally administered financial aid is available to distance learners.
Services Distance learners have accessibility to academic advising, campus computer network, e-mail services.
Contact Mr. Steven D. Carlson, Associate Registrar, Maranatha Baptist Bible College, 745 West Main Street, Watertown, WI 53094. Telephone: 920-206-2344. Fax: 920-261-9109. E-mail: scarlson@mbbc.edu.

DEGREES AND AWARDS
Programs offered do not lead to a degree or other formal award.

COURSE SUBJECT AREAS OFFERED OUTSIDE OF DEGREE PROGRAMS
Undergraduate—American literature (United States and Canadian); astronomy and astrophysics; biblical studies; educational/instructional media design.
Graduate—biblical studies; pastoral counseling and specialized ministries; religious studies.

MARIAN COLLEGE OF FOND DU LAC
Fond du Lac, Wisconsin
http://www.mariancollege.edu/
Marian College of Fond du Lac was founded in 1936. It is accredited by North Central Association of Colleges and Schools. It first offered distance learning courses in 2000. In fall 2007, there were 336 students enrolled in distance learning courses. Institutionally administered financial aid is available to distance learners.
Services Distance learners have accessibility to academic advising, bookstore, campus computer network, career placement assistance, e-mail services, library services.
Contact Ms. Cheryl Teichmiller, Registrar, Marian College of Fond du Lac, 45 South National Avenue, Fond du Lac, WI 54935. Telephone: 800-262-7426 Ext. 7618. Fax: 920-926-6708. E-mail: cteichmiller@mariancollege.edu.

DEGREES AND AWARDS
Programs offered do not lead to a degree or other formal award.

COURSE SUBJECT AREAS OFFERED OUTSIDE OF DEGREE PROGRAMS
Undergraduate—biology; business administration, management and operations; criminal justice and corrections; education; history; languages (Romance languages); philosophy; sociology.
Graduate—curriculum and instruction; education.

MARION TECHNICAL COLLEGE
Marion, Ohio
http://www.mtc.edu
Marion Technical College was founded in 1971. It is accredited by North Central Association of Colleges and Schools. It first offered distance learning courses in 1995. In fall 2007, there were 330 students enrolled in distance learning courses. Institutionally administered financial aid is available to distance learners.
Services Distance learners have accessibility to academic advising, campus computer network, career placement assistance, e-mail services, library services.
Contact Vicky Wood, Dean of Business and Instructional Technologies, Marion Technical College, 1467 Mount Vernon Avenue, Marion, OH 43302. Telephone: 740-389-4636 Ext. 265. Fax: 740-389-6136. E-mail: woodv@mtc.edu.

DEGREES AND AWARDS
Programs offered do not lead to a degree or other formal award.

COURSE SUBJECT AREAS OFFERED OUTSIDE OF DEGREE PROGRAMS
Undergraduate—business operations support and assistant services; clinical/medical laboratory science and allied professions; computer software and media applications; English composition; legal studies (non-professional general, undergraduate); management information systems; mathematics; mathematics and computer science; psychology.

MARIST COLLEGE
Poughkeepsie, New York
School of Management
http://www.marist.edu/management
Marist College was founded in 1929. It is accredited by Middle States Association of Colleges and Schools. It first offered distance learning courses in 1998. In fall 2007, there were 250 students enrolled in distance learning courses. Institutionally administered financial aid is available to distance learners.
Services Distance learners have accessibility to academic advising, bookstore, campus computer network, career placement assistance, e-mail services, library services.
Contact Kelly Holmes, Director of Admission, Marist College, School of Graduate and Continuing Education, Poughkeepsie, NY 12601. Telephone: 845-575-3800. Fax: 845-575-3166. E-mail: graduate@marist.edu.

DEGREES AND AWARDS
MBA Business Administration
MPA Public Administration

COURSE SUBJECT AREAS OFFERED OUTSIDE OF DEGREE PROGRAMS
Undergraduate—accounting and related services; business, management, and marketing related; economics; finance and financial management services; legal studies (non-professional general, undergraduate); statistics.
Graduate—accounting and related services; business administration, management and operations; business, management, and marketing related; business/managerial economics; finance and financial management services; international business; management sciences and quantitative methods; marketing.

MARIST COLLEGE
Poughkeepsie, New York
School of Communication and the Arts
http://www.marist.edu/commarts/macommunication/

Marist College was founded in 1929. It is accredited by Middle States Association of Colleges and Schools. It first offered distance learning courses in 2004. In fall 2007, there were 60 students enrolled in distance learning courses. Institutionally administered financial aid is available to distance learners.

Services Distance learners have accessibility to academic advising, bookstore, campus computer network, e-mail services, library services.

Contact Dr. Mary S. Alexander, Director of the MA Program in Communication, Marist College, School of Communication and the Arts, 3399 North Road, Poughkeepsie, NY 12601-1387. Telephone: 845-575-3000 Ext. 2732. E-mail: missy.alexander@marist.edu.

DEGREES AND AWARDS
MA Communication–Organizational Communication and Leadership

COURSE SUBJECT AREAS OFFERED OUTSIDE OF DEGREE PROGRAMS

Undergraduate—communication and media; journalism; liberal arts and sciences, general studies and humanities.

Graduate—business administration, management and operations; communication and media; information science/studies; public administration.

MARQUETTE UNIVERSITY
Milwaukee, Wisconsin
http://www.marquette.edu/online

Marquette University was founded in 1881. It is accredited by North Central Association of Colleges and Schools. It first offered distance learning courses in 1997. In fall 2007, there were 75 students enrolled in distance learning courses. Institutionally administered financial aid is available to distance learners.

Services Distance learners have accessibility to academic advising, bookstore, campus computer network, e-mail services, library services.

Contact Heidi Schweizer, Director of Center for Electronic Learning, Marquette University, PO Box 1881, Schroeder Health Complex 199E, School of Education, Milwaukee, WI 53201. Telephone: 414-288-8811. Fax: 414-288-3945. E-mail: heidi.schweizer@marquette.edu.

DEGREES AND AWARDS
Programs offered do not lead to a degree or other formal award.

COURSE SUBJECT AREAS OFFERED OUTSIDE OF DEGREE PROGRAMS

Undergraduate—education; nursing.
Graduate—education; nursing.
Non-credit—education.

MARSHALLTOWN COMMUNITY COLLEGE
Marshalltown, Iowa
http://www.iavalley.edu

Marshalltown Community College was founded in 1927. It is accredited by North Central Association of Colleges and Schools. It first offered distance learning courses in 1998. In fall 2007, there were 808 students enrolled in distance learning courses. Institutionally administered financial aid is available to distance learners.

Services Distance learners have accessibility to academic advising, bookstore, campus computer network, e-mail services, library services.

Contact Dr. Chris A. Russell, Chief Academic Officer, Marshalltown Community College, 3700 South Center Street, Marshalltown, IA 50158. Telephone: 641-844-5716. E-mail: chris.russell@iavalley.edu.

DEGREES AND AWARDS
AA General degree

COURSE SUBJECT AREAS OFFERED OUTSIDE OF DEGREE PROGRAMS

Undergraduate—accounting and computer science; allied health and medical assisting services; business/commerce.

Non-credit—allied health and medical assisting services.

MARSHALL UNIVERSITY
Huntington, West Virginia
Distributed Education Technology
http://www.marshall.edu/muonline

Marshall University was founded in 1837. It is accredited by North Central Association of Colleges and Schools. It first offered distance learning courses in 1986. In fall 2007, there were 6,274 students enrolled in distance learning courses. Institutionally administered financial aid is available to distance learners.

Services Distance learners have accessibility to academic advising, bookstore, campus computer network, career placement assistance, e-mail services, library services, tutoring.

Contact Crystal Stewart, Program Specialist, Marshall University, One John Marshall Drive, Drinko Library 313A, Huntington, WV 25755-2140. Telephone: 304-696-2970. Fax: 304-696-3229. E-mail: stewar14@marshall.edu.

DEGREES AND AWARDS
AGS General Studies
BA Regents Bachelor of Arts degree
Certification Public Library Technology (PLT)
MEd Elementary or Secondary Education

COURSE SUBJECT AREAS OFFERED OUTSIDE OF DEGREE PROGRAMS

Undergraduate—accounting and related services; business administration, management and operations; business/managerial economics; chemistry; communication and journalism related; communication and media; computer and information sciences; computer and information sciences and support services related; computer engineering; developmental and child psychology; economics; English composition; geography and cartography; history; journalism; library science; management information systems; marketing; mathematics; mathematics and computer science; mathematics and statistics related; nursing; philosophy; psychology; social work; sociology; statistics; visual and performing arts.

Graduate—accounting and related services; computer and information sciences; marketing; social work; sociology; technology education/industrial arts; visual and performing arts.

MARYMOUNT UNIVERSITY
Arlington, Virginia
http://www.marymount.edu

Marymount University was founded in 1950. It is accredited by Southern Association of Colleges and Schools. It first offered distance learning courses in 1999. Institutionally administered financial aid is available to distance learners.

Services Distance learners have accessibility to academic advising, bookstore, campus computer network, career placement assistance, e-mail services, library services, tutoring.

Contact Ms. Francesca Reed, Director, Graduate Admissions, Marymount University, 2807 North Glebe Road, Arlington, VA 22207. Telephone: 703-284-5901. Fax: 703-527-3815. E-mail: francesca.reed@marymount.edu.

DEGREES AND AWARDS
BSN Nursing–RN to BSN
MEd Catholic School Leadership

COURSE SUBJECT AREAS OFFERED OUTSIDE OF DEGREE PROGRAMS

Undergraduate—nursing.

Graduate—business administration, management and operations; business/commerce; business, management, and marketing related; computer science; education; information science/studies.

MASSACHUSETTS COLLEGE OF ART AND DESIGN
Boston, Massachusetts
Graduate and Continuing Education
http://www.massartplus.org

Massachusetts College of Art and Design was founded in 1873. It is accredited by New England Association of Schools and Colleges. It first offered distance learning courses in 2005. In fall 2007, there were 50 students enrolled in distance learning courses. Institutionally administered financial aid is available to distance learners.

Services Distance learners have accessibility to academic advising, bookstore, campus computer network, e-mail services, library services.

Contact Joe Doucette, Advisor, Massachusetts College of Art and Design, 621 Huntington Avenue, Boston, MA 02115. Telephone: 617-879-7165. Fax: 617-879-7171. E-mail: joe.doucette@massart.edu.

DEGREES AND AWARDS
Programs offered do not lead to a degree or other formal award.

COURSE SUBJECT AREAS OFFERED OUTSIDE OF DEGREE PROGRAMS
Undergraduate—architectural history and criticism; architecture; area, ethnic, cultural, and gender studies related; design and applied arts; visual and performing arts.
Graduate—visual and performing arts.

MASSACHUSETTS COLLEGE OF LIBERAL ARTS
North Adams, Massachusetts
http://www.mcla.edu/

Massachusetts College of Liberal Arts was founded in 1894. It is accredited by New England Association of Schools and Colleges. In fall 2007, there were 38 students enrolled in distance learning courses. Institutionally administered financial aid is available to distance learners.

Contact Ms. Melissa James, Office Manager, Massachusetts College of Liberal Arts, 375 Church Street, North Adams, MA 01247. Telephone: 413-662-5543. Fax: 413-662-5104. E-mail: m.james@mcla.edu.

DEGREES AND AWARDS
Programs offered do not lead to a degree or other formal award.

COURSE SUBJECT AREAS OFFERED OUTSIDE OF DEGREE PROGRAMS
Undergraduate—business administration, management and operations; computer science; English composition; philosophy.
Graduate—education; educational/instructional media design.

MASSASOIT COMMUNITY COLLEGE
Brockton, Massachusetts
http://www.massasoit.mass.edu/acad_depts/dist_learn/dist_learn.cfm

Massasoit Community College was founded in 1966. It is accredited by New England Association of Schools and Colleges. It first offered distance learning courses in 1998. In fall 2007, there were 1,800 students enrolled in distance learning courses. Institutionally administered financial aid is available to distance learners.

Services Distance learners have accessibility to bookstore, campus computer network, e-mail services, library services, tutoring.

Contact Candy Center, Dean of e-Learning and Non-Traditional Programs, Massasoit Community College, 1 Massasoit Boulevard, Brockton, MA 02302. Telephone: 508-588-9100 Ext. 1615. Fax: 508-427-1250. E-mail: ccenter@massasoit.mass.edu.

DEGREES AND AWARDS
Programs offered do not lead to a degree or other formal award.

COURSE SUBJECT AREAS OFFERED OUTSIDE OF DEGREE PROGRAMS
Undergraduate—accounting and related services; anthropology; biological and physical sciences; business administration, management and operations; business/commerce; business/corporate communications; chemistry; computer and information sciences; computer software and media applications; film/video and photographic arts; geography and cartography; history; human development, family studies, and related services; international business; mathematics; music; philosophy; physical sciences; psychology; psychology related; sales, merchandising, and related marketing operations (specialized); sociology; speech and rhetoric; statistics.
Non-credit—business/commerce; communication and media; computer and information sciences; computer software and media applications; creative writing; gerontology; health professions related; human resources management; journalism; peace studies and conflict resolution; precision systems maintenance and repair technologies; sales, merchandising, and related marketing operations (general); sales, merchandising, and related marketing operations (specialized); social sciences; taxation.

MASTER'S COLLEGE AND SEMINARY
Toronto, Ontario, Canada
http://www.mcs.edu/

Master's College and Seminary was founded in 1939. It is provincially chartered. It first offered distance learning courses in 1996. In fall 2007, there were 210 students enrolled in distance learning courses. Institutionally administered financial aid is available to distance learners.

Services Distance learners have accessibility to academic advising, bookstore, e-mail services, library services.

Contact Rev. Luc Lombardi, Dean of College Operations, Master's College and Seminary, 3080 Yonge Street, Box 70, Suite 3040, Toronto, ON M4N 3N1, Canada. Telephone: 800-295-6368 Ext. 224. E-mail: luciano.lombardi@mcs.edu.

DEGREES AND AWARDS
Programs offered do not lead to a degree or other formal award.

COURSE SUBJECT AREAS OFFERED OUTSIDE OF DEGREE PROGRAMS
Undergraduate—biblical and other theological languages and literatures; biblical studies; counseling psychology; pastoral counseling and specialized ministries; philosophy and religious studies related; religious education; religious studies; theological and ministerial studies; theology and religious vocations related.

MAYVILLE STATE UNIVERSITY
Mayville, North Dakota
Enrollment Services Office
http://www.mayvillestate.edu

Mayville State University was founded in 1889. It is accredited by North Central Association of Colleges and Schools. It first offered distance learning courses in 1999. In fall 2007, there were 284 students enrolled in distance learning courses. Institutionally administered financial aid is available to distance learners.

Services Distance learners have accessibility to academic advising, bookstore, campus computer network, career placement assistance, e-mail services, library services.

Contact Mr. Robert Bertsch, Director of Admissions and Extended Learning, Mayville State University, 330 Third Street NE, Mayville, ND 58257. Telephone: 701-788-4631. Fax: 701-788-4748. E-mail: r_bertsch@mayvillestate.edu.

DEGREES AND AWARDS
AA Early Childhood Education Associate
BA Early Childhood Education
BEd Elementary Education
BS Business Administration (Bachelor of Applied Science); Business Administration; Computer Information Systems (Bachelor of Applied Science)

COURSE SUBJECT AREAS OFFERED OUTSIDE OF DEGREE PROGRAMS

Undergraduate—accounting and related services; biology; business administration, management and operations; chemistry; education; English composition; human development, family studies, and related services; library science.

MCDOWELL TECHNICAL COMMUNITY COLLEGE
Marion, North Carolina
Educational Programs
http://www.mcdowelltech.edu/
McDowell Technical Community College was founded in 1964. It is accredited by Southern Association of Colleges and Schools. It first offered distance learning courses in 1991. In fall 2007, there were 411 students enrolled in distance learning courses. Institutionally administered financial aid is available to distance learners.
Services Distance learners have accessibility to academic advising, campus computer network, e-mail services, library services, tutoring.
Contact Mr. Donald Glen Ford, Director of Distance Education, McDowell Technical Community College, 54 College Drive, Marion, NC 28752-9724. Telephone: 828-652-0651. Fax: 828-659-1077. E-mail: donf@mcdowelltech.edu.

DEGREES AND AWARDS
Programs offered do not lead to a degree or other formal award.

COURSE SUBJECT AREAS OFFERED OUTSIDE OF DEGREE PROGRAMS

Undergraduate—accounting and related services; allied health and medical assisting services; business administration, management and operations; business/commerce; computer systems networking and tele-communications; education; education (specific levels and methods); English language and literature related; information science/studies; liberal arts and sciences, general studies and humanities; mathematics and statistics related; psychology related; social sciences.

MCMURRY UNIVERSITY
Abilene, Texas
http://www.mcm.edu
McMurry University was founded in 1923. It is accredited by Southern Association of Colleges and Schools. It first offered distance learning courses in 2000. In fall 2007, there were 102 students enrolled in distance learning courses. Institutionally administered financial aid is available to distance learners.
Services Distance learners have accessibility to academic advising, bookstore, e-mail services, library services.
Contact Mrs. Vicki Dunnam, Online Educational Design Support Specialist, McMurry University, Box 207, McMurry Station, Abilene, TX 79697. Telephone: 325-793-4987. E-mail: dunnam.vicki@mcm.edu.

DEGREES AND AWARDS
Programs offered do not lead to a degree or other formal award.

COURSE SUBJECT AREAS OFFERED OUTSIDE OF DEGREE PROGRAMS
Undergraduate—biblical studies; biochemistry, biophysics and molecular biology; biology; business administration, management and operations; business/managerial economics; chemistry; computer/information technology administration and management; curriculum and instruction; dramatic/theater arts and stagecraft; educational psychology; education (specific levels and methods); English; English composition; history; languages (foreign languages related); management information systems; mathematics; psychology; religious studies.

MEDICAL COLLEGE OF WISCONSIN
Milwaukee, Wisconsin
Master of Public Health Degree Programs
http://www.mcw.edu/mph
Medical College of Wisconsin was founded in 1913. It is accredited by North Central Association of Colleges and Schools. It first offered distance learning courses in 1986. In fall 2007, there were 137 students enrolled in distance learning courses. Institutionally administered financial aid is available to distance learners.
Services Distance learners have accessibility to academic advising, bookstore, campus computer network, career placement assistance, e-mail services, library services.
Contact Beverly Carlson, Program Coordinator, MPH Degree Program, Medical College of Wisconsin, Department of Population Health, 8701 Watertown Plank Road, Milwaukee, WI 53226. Telephone: 414-456-4510. Fax: 414-456-6520. E-mail: mph@mcw.edu.

DEGREES AND AWARDS
Graduate Certificate Public Health
MPH Occupational Health; Public and Community Health

COURSE SUBJECT AREAS OFFERED OUTSIDE OF DEGREE PROGRAMS
Graduate—accounting and related services; behavioral sciences; bioethics/medical ethics; community health services; community organization and advocacy; educational assessment, evaluation, and research; environmental/environmental health engineering; health and medical administrative services; health/medical preparatory programs; health professions related; public health.

MEMORIAL UNIVERSITY OF NEWFOUNDLAND
St. John's, Newfoundland and Labrador, Canada
Distance Education and Learning Technologies
http://www.distance.mun.ca
Memorial University of Newfoundland was founded in 1925. It is provincially chartered. It first offered distance learning courses in 1969. In fall 2007, there were 4,776 students enrolled in distance learning courses. Institutionally administered financial aid is available to distance learners.
Services Distance learners have accessibility to academic advising, bookstore, e-mail services, library services.
Contact Clyde Hillier, Manager, Client Relations, Memorial University of Newfoundland, G.A. Hickman Building, ED-2000, St. John's, NF A1B 3X8, Canada. Telephone: 709-737-8700. Fax: 709-737-4070. E-mail: distance@mun.ca.

DEGREES AND AWARDS
BBA Business Administration
BN Nursing–Post-RN
BS Maritime Studies–Bachelor of Maritime Studies (BMS); Technology–Bachelor Technology (BTech)
Certificate Business Administration; Career Development; Criminology; Library Studies; Newfoundland Studies; Public Administration
Diploma Business Administration
MEd Counseling Psychology; Curriculum Teaching and Learning Studies; Educational Leadership Studies; Information Technology; Postsecondary Studies
MN Nursing
MSW Social Work

COURSE SUBJECT AREAS OFFERED OUTSIDE OF DEGREE PROGRAMS
Undergraduate—anthropology; biology; business administration, management and operations; computer science; economics; education; education related; engineering; English; library science; mathematics; nursing; philosophy; political science and government; psychology; religious studies; social work; sociology; statistics.
Graduate—criminology; education related; library science; nursing; social work.

MERCER COUNTY COMMUNITY COLLEGE
Trenton, New Jersey
http://www.mccc.edu/

Mercer County Community College was founded in 1966. It is accredited by Middle States Association of Colleges and Schools. It first offered distance learning courses in 1998. In fall 2007, there were 1,863 students enrolled in distance learning courses. Institutionally administered financial aid is available to distance learners.

Services Distance learners have accessibility to academic advising, bookstore, career placement assistance, e-mail services, library services, tutoring.

Contact Michael Sullivan, Coordinator, Mercer County Community College, 1200 Old Trenton Road, Trenton, NJ 08690. Telephone: 609-570-3315 Ext. 3315. E-mail: sullivam@mccc.edu.

DEGREES AND AWARDS
Programs offered do not lead to a degree or other formal award.

COURSE SUBJECT AREAS OFFERED OUTSIDE OF DEGREE PROGRAMS

Undergraduate—accounting and related services; anthropology; business/commerce; computer and information sciences; computer software and media applications; economics; English composition; health and physical education/fitness; history; mathematics; philosophy; psychology related; sociology.

Non-credit—computer/information technology administration and management; computer systems networking and telecommunications; finance and financial management services; technical and business writing.

MERCY COLLEGE
Dobbs Ferry, New York
Mercy Online
http://www.mercy.edu/mercyonline/

Mercy College was founded in 1951. It is accredited by Middle States Association of Colleges and Schools. It first offered distance learning courses in 1990. In fall 2007, there were 1,800 students enrolled in distance learning courses. Institutionally administered financial aid is available to distance learners.

Services Distance learners have accessibility to academic advising, bookstore, campus computer network, career placement assistance, e-mail services, library services, tutoring.

Contact Mr. John DiElsi, Dean, Mercy Online, Mercy College, 555 Broadway, Dobbs Ferry, NY 10522. Telephone: 914-674-7527. Fax: 914-674-7479. E-mail: jdielsi@mercy.edu.

DEGREES AND AWARDS
AA Liberal Arts and Sciences
AAS Business
AS Accounting; Liberal Arts and Sciences
BA Behavioral Science; English; History; Psychology
BS Behavioral Science; Business Administration; Computer Information Systems; Computer Science; Criminal Justice; English; Health Science; History; Information Assurance and Security; Mathematics; Nursing; Organizational Management; Psychology; Spanish
MA English Literature
MBA Business Administration
MPA Health Services Management
MS Counseling; Health Services Management; Human Resource Management; Information Assurance and Security; Internet Business Systems; Nursing Education; Organizational Leadership; Psychology
MSN Nursing Administration

COURSE SUBJECT AREAS OFFERED OUTSIDE OF DEGREE PROGRAMS

Undergraduate—accounting and related services; area, ethnic, cultural, and gender studies related; biological and physical sciences; biology; business administration, management and operations; business/commerce; communications technology; community organization and advocacy; comparative literature; computer and information sciences; computer science; creative writing; criminal justice and corrections; curriculum and instruction; developmental and child psychology; economics; education; educational administration and supervision; educational psychology; English; English composition; English literature (British and Commonwealth); environmental/environmental health engineering; fine and studio art; health professions related; health services/allied health/health sciences; history; human services; international business; languages (foreign languages related); legal studies (non-professional general, undergraduate); liberal arts and sciences, general studies and humanities; management information systems; management sciences and quantitative methods; marketing; mathematics and statistics related; nursing; public administration and social service professions related; public health; social psychology; sociology; statistics.

Graduate—American literature (United States and Canadian); business administration, management and operations; business/commerce; business/corporate communications; business, management, and marketing related; business/managerial economics; community health services; comparative literature; computer and information sciences; computer and information sciences and support services related; computer/information technology administration and management; computer science; computer software and media applications; computer systems analysis; counseling psychology; English; English language and literature related; English literature (British and Commonwealth); health services/allied health/health sciences; human services; management information systems; management sciences and quantitative methods; marketing; peace studies and conflict resolution; psychology; psychology related; sales, merchandising, and related marketing operations (specialized); social sciences related.

MESA COMMUNITY COLLEGE
Mesa, Arizona
http://www.mc.maricopa.edu/distance/

Mesa Community College was founded in 1965. It is accredited by North Central Association of Colleges and Schools. It first offered distance learning courses in 1998. In fall 2007, there were 4,500 students enrolled in distance learning courses. Institutionally administered financial aid is available to distance learners.

Services Distance learners have accessibility to academic advising, bookstore, campus computer network, career placement assistance, e-mail services, library services, tutoring.

Contact Alicia Barnett, Distance Learning Advisor, Mesa Community College, 1833 West Southern Avenue, Mesa, AZ 85202. Telephone: 480-461-7924. E-mail: mcconline@mcmail.maricopa.edu.

DEGREES AND AWARDS
Programs offered do not lead to a degree or other formal award.

COURSE SUBJECT AREAS OFFERED OUTSIDE OF DEGREE PROGRAMS

Undergraduate—biology; business administration, management and operations; communication and media; computer/information technology administration and management; computer programming; computer science; computer software and media applications; creative writing; criminal justice and corrections; economics; English; English composition; family and consumer sciences/human sciences related; foods, nutrition, and related services; health/medical preparatory programs; health professions related; history; linguistic, comparative, and related language studies; mathematics; nursing; physiological psychology/psychobiology; political science and government; religious studies; school psychology; technical and business writing.

MESA STATE COLLEGE
Grand Junction, Colorado
Continuing Education Center
http://www.mesastate.edu/online

Mesa State College was founded in 1925. It is accredited by North Central Association of Colleges and Schools. It first offered distance learning courses in 1996. In fall 2007, there were 632 students enrolled in distance learning courses. Institutionally administered financial aid is available to distance learners.

Services Distance learners have accessibility to academic advising, bookstore, campus computer network, career placement assistance, e-mail services, library services, tutoring.

Contact Rance Larsen, Director of Admissions, Mesa State College, 1100 North Avenue, Grand Junction, CO 81501. Telephone: 800-982-6372. Fax: 970-248-1464. E-mail: admissions@mesastate.edu.

DEGREES AND AWARDS
Programs offered do not lead to a degree or other formal award.

COURSE SUBJECT AREAS OFFERED OUTSIDE OF DEGREE PROGRAMS
Undergraduate—biology; dance; education; English; fine and studio art; health and physical education/fitness; history; management sciences and quantitative methods; nursing; political science and government; psychology; public administration; sociology; speech and rhetoric; visual and performing arts.
Graduate—education.

METROPOLITAN STATE UNIVERSITY
St. Paul, Minnesota
http://www.metrostate.edu
Metropolitan State University was founded in 1971. It is accredited by North Central Association of Colleges and Schools. It first offered distance learning courses in 1994. In fall 2007, there were 1,018 students enrolled in distance learning courses. Institutionally administered financial aid is available to distance learners.
Services Distance learners have accessibility to academic advising, bookstore, career placement assistance, e-mail services, library services, tutoring.
Contact Ms. Monir Johnson, Director of Admissions, Metropolitan State University, 700 East 7th Street, St. Paul, MN 55106. Telephone: 651-793-1303. Fax: 651-793-1310. E-mail: monir.johnson@metrostate.edu.

DEGREES AND AWARDS
BA Individualized Studies
BAS Organizational Administration
BS Business Administration; Management; Marketing
Certificate Nursing–Continence Care Nurse; Nursing–Ostomy Care Nurse; Nursing–Wound Care Nurse; Nursing–Wound Ostomy Continence Nurse
MBA Business Administration
MS Public and Non-Profit Management–Master of Public and Non-Profit Management
MSN Nursing
DNP Nursing Practice

COURSE SUBJECT AREAS OFFERED OUTSIDE OF DEGREE PROGRAMS
Undergraduate—accounting and related services; anthropology; business administration, management and operations; communication and journalism related; criminal justice and corrections; dramatic/theater arts and stagecraft; economics; English composition; English language and literature related; finance and financial management services; history; hospitality administration; human resources management; human services; information science/studies; international business; legal studies (non-professional general, undergraduate); management information systems; marketing; mathematics; multi-/interdisciplinary studies related; music; nursing; philosophy; physics; political science and government; psychology; public administration; statistics.
Graduate—business administration, management and operations; criminal justice and corrections; economics; management information systems; marketing; nursing; public administration.

MGH INSTITUTE OF HEALTH PROFESSIONS
Boston, Massachusetts
http://www.mghihp.edu
MGH Institute of Health Professions was founded in 1977. It is accredited by New England Association of Schools and Colleges. It first offered distance learning courses in 2000. In fall 2007, there were 320 students enrolled in distance learning courses. Institutionally administered financial aid is available to distance learners.
Services Distance learners have accessibility to academic advising, bookstore, campus computer network, e-mail services, library services, tutoring.

Contact Ms. Maureen R. Judd, Director of Admissions, MGH Institute of Health Professions, 36 1st Avenue, Boston, MA 02129-4557. Telephone: 617-726-6069. Fax: 617-726-8010. E-mail: mjudd@mghihp.edu.

DEGREES AND AWARDS
Certificate Medical Imaging post-Baccalaureate certificate
Graduate Certificate Clinical Investigation
MS Clinical Investigations
DPT Physical Therapy–Transitional Doctor of Physical Therapy

COURSE SUBJECT AREAS OFFERED OUTSIDE OF DEGREE PROGRAMS
Graduate—communication disorders sciences and services; health professions related; nursing.

MIAMI DADE COLLEGE
Miami, Florida
Virtual College
http://virtual.mdc.edu
Miami Dade College was founded in 1960. It is accredited by Southern Association of Colleges and Schools. It first offered distance learning courses in 1997. In fall 2007, there were 5,756 students enrolled in distance learning courses. Institutionally administered financial aid is available to distance learners.
Services Distance learners have accessibility to academic advising, bookstore, e-mail services, library services.
Contact Lloyd Hollingsworth, Student Services Coordinator, Miami Dade College, 300 NE 2nd Avenue, Miami, FL 33132-2297. Telephone: 305-237-3873. Fax: 305-237-3863. E-mail: lholling@mdc.edu.

DEGREES AND AWARDS
AA Pre-Bachelor of Arts
AS Business Administration

COURSE SUBJECT AREAS OFFERED OUTSIDE OF DEGREE PROGRAMS
Undergraduate—accounting and related services; American literature (United States and Canadian); atmospheric sciences and meteorology; biblical studies; biological and biomedical sciences related; biological and physical sciences; biology; business administration, management and operations; computer and information sciences; economics; education; English; English composition; health and medical administrative services; human development, family studies, and related services; international relations and affairs; liberal arts and sciences, general studies and humanities; library science related; management sciences and quantitative methods; marketing; mathematics; nursing; philosophy and religious studies related; physical sciences related; political science and government; psychology; religious studies; social sciences; speech and rhetoric; statistics; taxation.
Non-credit—health professions related.

MICHIGAN STATE UNIVERSITY
East Lansing, Michigan
Educational Technology Programs
http://edutech.msu.edu
Michigan State University was founded in 1855. It is accredited by American Academy for Liberal Education. It first offered distance learning courses in 2000. In fall 2007, there were 30 students enrolled in distance learning courses. Institutionally administered financial aid is available to distance learners.
Services Distance learners have accessibility to academic advising, bookstore, career placement assistance, e-mail services, library services, tutoring.
Contact Mrs. Brook Thompson, Administrative Assistant, Michigan State University, 444 Erickson Hall, East Lansing, MI 48824. Telephone: 517-432-9259. Fax: 517-353-6393. E-mail: brookt@msu.edu.

DEGREES AND AWARDS
MAE Educational Technology

COURSE SUBJECT AREAS OFFERED OUTSIDE OF DEGREE PROGRAMS
Graduate—education; educational/instructional media design; educational psychology; education related.

MICHIGAN STATE UNIVERSITY
East Lansing, Michigan
Outreach Instructional Programs
http://www.online-contined.msu.edu
Michigan State University was founded in 1855. It is accredited by American Academy for Liberal Education. It first offered distance learning courses in 1992. In fall 2007, there were 10,856 students enrolled in distance learning courses. Institutionally administered financial aid is available to distance learners.
Services Distance learners have accessibility to academic advising, bookstore, e-mail services, library services.
Contact Jerry Rhead, Director, Strategy and Advisory Services, Michigan State University, 51 Kellogg Center, Harrison Road, East Lansing, MI 48824. Telephone: 517-432-1950. Fax: 517-432-1327. E-mail: rhead@ msu.edu.

DEGREES AND AWARDS
Certificate of Achievement Chemical Engineering Continuing Education/ Bridging Program
Certificate of Completion Coaching Education; Judicial Administration Graduate specialization
Certificate Educational Technology; Homeland Security Studies; International Food Law; Molecular Laboratory Diagnostics; School Social Work Competency Series; Security Management Graduate specialization; Watershed Management; Youth Development Specialist; Youth Program Management and Evaluation
MA Education; Educational Technology; Youth Development
MS Criminal Justice; Food Safety; Packaging; Physics
PhD Physics

COURSE SUBJECT AREAS OFFERED OUTSIDE OF DEGREE PROGRAMS
Undergraduate—chemical engineering; computer and information sciences; computer systems networking and telecommunications; economics; food science and technology; geography and cartography; mathematics; social sciences; technology education/industrial arts.
Graduate—chemical engineering; clinical/medical laboratory science and allied professions; community organization and advocacy; computer systems networking and telecommunications; criminal justice and corrections; education; educational administration and supervision; educational psychology; engineering related; entrepreneurial and small business operations; nursing; social work.
Non-credit—chemical engineering; community organization and advocacy; computer and information sciences; social work.

MICHIGAN TECHNOLOGICAL UNIVERSITY
Houghton, Michigan
Sponsored Educational Programs
http://techonline.mtu.edu
Michigan Technological University was founded in 1885. It is accredited by North Central Association of Colleges and Schools. It first offered distance learning courses in 1984. In fall 2007, there were 192 students enrolled in distance learning courses. Institutionally administered financial aid is available to distance learners.
Services Distance learners have accessibility to academic advising, bookstore, campus computer network, e-mail services, library services.
Contact Ms. Patricia A. Lins, Director, Educational Technology/Online Learning, Michigan Technological University, Educational Technology/

Online Learning, 1400 Townsend Drive, Houghton, MI 49931. Telephone: 906-487-2925. Fax: 906-487-2787. E-mail: plins@mtu.edu.

DEGREES AND AWARDS
MS Electrical Engineering; Mechanical Engineering
MSE Earth Systems Science
PhD Mechanical Engineering

COURSE SUBJECT AREAS OFFERED OUTSIDE OF DEGREE PROGRAMS
Undergraduate—astronomy and astrophysics; biological and biomedical sciences related; chemical engineering; computer and information sciences; electrical, electronics and communications engineering; mathematics; mechanical engineering; physics.
Graduate—electrical, electronics and communications engineering; mechanical engineering.
Non-credit—astronomy and astrophysics; physics.

MIDDLE GEORGIA COLLEGE
Cochran, Georgia
Office of Continuing Education
http://www.mgc.edu/mgconline
Middle Georgia College was founded in 1884. It is accredited by Southern Association of Colleges and Schools. It first offered distance learning courses in 1998. In fall 2007, there were 340 students enrolled in distance learning courses. Institutionally administered financial aid is available to distance learners.
Services Distance learners have accessibility to academic advising, bookstore, campus computer network, e-mail services, library services, tutoring.
Contact Mr. Darryl J. Hancock, Director of Distance Learning and Professional Development, Middle Georgia College, 1100 Second Street SE, Cochran, GA 31014. Telephone: 478-934-3505. E-mail: dhancock @mgc.edu.

DEGREES AND AWARDS
AS Business Administration

MIDDLESEX COMMUNITY COLLEGE
Middletown, Connecticut
http://www.mxctc.commnet.edu/distance
Middlesex Community College was founded in 1966. It is accredited by New England Association of Schools and Colleges. It first offered distance learning courses in 1999. In fall 2007, there were 720 students enrolled in distance learning courses. Institutionally administered financial aid is available to distance learners.
Services Distance learners have accessibility to academic advising, bookstore, campus computer network, e-mail services, library services, tutoring.
Contact Dr. Yi Guan-Raczkowski, Director of Distance Learning, Middlesex Community College, 100 Training Hill Road, Middletown, CT 06457. Telephone: 860-343-5783. E-mail: yguan@mxcc.commnet. edu.

DEGREES AND AWARDS
Programs offered do not lead to a degree or other formal award.

COURSE SUBJECT AREAS OFFERED OUTSIDE OF DEGREE PROGRAMS
Undergraduate—accounting and computer science; anthropology; astronomy and astrophysics; biology; business administration, management and operations; business, management, and marketing related; communication and journalism related; communication and media; computer and information sciences; developmental and child psychology; economics; education; history; mathematics; philosophy; psychology; sociology.

MIDDLESEX COMMUNITY COLLEGE
Bedford, Massachusetts
http://www.middlesex.mass.edu/online

Middlesex Community College was founded in 1970. It is accredited by New England Association of Schools and Colleges. It first offered distance learning courses in 1996. In fall 2007, there were 2,400 students enrolled in distance learning courses. Institutionally administered financial aid is available to distance learners.

Services Distance learners have accessibility to academic advising, bookstore, campus computer network, e-mail services, library services, tutoring.

Contact Sanford A. Arbogast, Instructional Technology Analyst, Middlesex Community College, Academic Resources Building, Springs Road, Bedford, MA 01730. Telephone: 781-280-3739. Fax: 781-280-3771. E-mail: arbogasts@middlesex.mass.edu.

DEGREES AND AWARDS

AA Liberal Arts and Sciences

AAS Liberal Studies

ABA Accounting; Business Administration Career; Hospitality Management; Small Business Administration

AS Business Administration transfer; Criminal Justice–Administration option; Criminal Justice–Law Enforcement option; Fire Protection; Psychology

Certificate Liberal Studies; Small Business Management; Web Publishing

COURSE SUBJECT AREAS OFFERED OUTSIDE OF DEGREE PROGRAMS

Undergraduate—accounting and related services; anthropology; area, ethnic, cultural, and gender studies related; behavioral sciences; biological and biomedical sciences related; biological and physical sciences; biology; business administration, management and operations; business/commerce; business/corporate communications; business, management, and marketing related; business/managerial economics; clinical child psychology; communication and journalism related; communication and media; communications technology; community health services; community psychology; comparative literature; computer and information sciences; computer and information sciences and support services related; computer programming; computer science; computer software and media applications; creative writing; criminal justice and corrections; criminology; data entry/microcomputer applications; dental support services and allied professions; developmental and child psychology; economics; education; educational psychology; English; English composition; English language and literature related; English literature (British and Commonwealth); ethnic, cultural minority, and gender studies; family psychology; fine and studio art; fire protection; foods, nutrition, and related services; geography and cartography; history; hospitality administration; human resources management; human services; journalism; languages (foreign languages related); legal professions and studies related; legal studies (non-professional general, undergraduate); liberal arts and sciences, general studies and humanities; linguistic, comparative, and related language studies; marketing; mathematics; mathematics and computer science; mathematics and statistics related; museum studies; natural sciences; philosophy; philosophy and religious studies related; physical sciences; political science and government; psychology; psychology related; public health; public relations, advertising, and applied communication related; publishing; radio, television, and digital communication; social psychology; social sciences; social sciences related; sociology; statistics; taxation; technical and business writing.

Non-credit—business administration, management and operations; business/commerce; computer software and media applications; computer systems analysis; creative writing; finance and financial management services; fine and studio art; gerontology; technical and business writing.

MIDDLE TENNESSEE STATE UNIVERSITY
Murfreesboro, Tennessee
College of Continuing Education and Distance Learning
http://www.mtsu.edu/learn

Middle Tennessee State University was founded in 1911. It is accredited by Southern Association of Colleges and Schools. It first offered distance learning courses in 1994. In fall 2007, there were 6,058 students enrolled in distance learning courses. Institutionally administered financial aid is available to distance learners.

Services Distance learners have accessibility to academic advising, bookstore, campus computer network, e-mail services, library services, tutoring.

Contact Dr. Dianna Rust, Director, Academic Outreach and Distance Learning, Middle Tennessee State University, 1301 East Main Street, MTSU Box X109, Murfreesboro, TN 37132. Telephone: 615-898-5611. Fax: 615-896-7925. E-mail: drust@mtsu.edu.

DEGREES AND AWARDS

BS Liberal Studies; Professional Studies, Information Technology concentration; Professional Studies, Organizational Leadership concentration

BSN Nursing

MEd Teaching and Learning, advanced studies

MPS Professional Studies, Strategic Leadership concentration

MSN Nursing

COURSE SUBJECT AREAS OFFERED OUTSIDE OF DEGREE PROGRAMS

Undergraduate—accounting and related services; aerospace, aeronautical and astronautical engineering; agricultural business and management; American literature (United States and Canadian); area, ethnic, cultural, and gender studies related; astronomy and astrophysics; business administration, management and operations; business/corporate communications; communication and media; criminal justice and corrections; economics; education; educational psychology; English; English composition; food science and technology; geological and earth sciences/geosciences; health and physical education/fitness; human resources management; journalism; liberal arts and sciences, general studies and humanities; mathematics; nursing; political science and government; radio, television, and digital communication; sales, merchandising, and related marketing operations (general); social sciences; social work; sociology.

Graduate—aerospace, aeronautical and astronautical engineering; economics; educational assessment, evaluation, and research; marketing; mathematics; nursing.

Non-credit—allied health and medical assisting services; area, ethnic, cultural, and gender studies related; bilingual, multilingual, and multicultural education; business administration, management and operations; business/commerce; business/corporate communications; business, management, and marketing related; business/managerial economics; city/urban, community and regional planning; computer and information sciences; computer/information technology administration and management; computer programming; computer science; computer software and media applications; computer systems networking and telecommunications; crafts, folk art and artisanry; culinary arts and related services; engineering/industrial management; English as a second language; fine and studio art; human resources management; industrial and organizational psychology; linguistic, comparative, and related language studies; management information systems; nursing; real estate; sales, merchandising, and related marketing operations (specialized).

MIDSTATE COLLEGE
Peoria, Illinois
http://www.midstate.edu/

Midstate College was founded in 1888. It is accredited by North Central Association of Colleges and Schools. It first offered distance learning courses in 1999. In fall 2007, there were 233 students enrolled in distance learning courses. Institutionally administered financial aid is available to distance learners.

Services Distance learners have accessibility to academic advising, bookstore, career placement assistance, e-mail services, library services, tutoring.

Contact Ms. Jessica Hancock, Director of Admissions, Midstate College, 411 West Northmoor Road, Peoria, IL 61614. Telephone: 309-692-4092 Ext. 1090. Fax: 309-692-3893. E-mail: admissions@midstate.edu.

DEGREES AND AWARDS
BBA Business Administration

COURSE SUBJECT AREAS OFFERED OUTSIDE OF DEGREE PROGRAMS
Undergraduate—accounting and related services; allied health and medical assisting services; applied mathematics; business, management, and marketing related; computer and information sciences; computer software and media applications; English composition; psychology.

MIDWAY COLLEGE
Midway, Kentucky
http://www.midway.edu/
Midway College was founded in 1847. It is accredited by Southern Association of Colleges and Schools. It first offered distance learning courses in 2003. In fall 2007, there were 328 students enrolled in distance learning courses. Institutionally administered financial aid is available to distance learners.
Services Distance learners have accessibility to academic advising, bookstore, e-mail services, library services.
Contact Patti Kirk, Admissions Counselor/Recruiter, Midway College, 512 East Stephens Street, Midway, KY 40347. Telephone: 800-952-4122. E-mail: midwayonlinecollege@midway.edu.

DEGREES AND AWARDS
Programs offered do not lead to a degree or other formal award.

COURSE SUBJECT AREAS OFFERED OUTSIDE OF DEGREE PROGRAMS
Undergraduate—accounting and related services; biological and physical sciences; computer science; economics; education related; finance and financial management services; geography and cartography; mathematics; music; psychology; religious studies.

MIDWESTERN BAPTIST THEOLOGICAL SEMINARY
Kansas City, Missouri
http://www.mbts.edu/
Midwestern Baptist Theological Seminary was founded in 1957. It is accredited by North Central Association of Colleges and Schools. It first offered distance learning courses in 2001. In fall 2007, there were 50 students enrolled in distance learning courses. Institutionally administered financial aid is available to distance learners.
Services Distance learners have accessibility to academic advising, bookstore, career placement assistance, library services.
Contact Rob Friebel, Director of Recruitment, Midwestern Baptist Theological Seminary, 5001 North Oak Trafficway, Kansas City, MO 64118. Telephone: 816-414-3733. E-mail: rfriebel@mbts.edu.

DEGREES AND AWARDS
MDiv Master of Divinity

MIDWESTERN STATE UNIVERSITY
Wichita Falls, Texas
http://www.mwsu.edu/
Midwestern State University was founded in 1922. It is accredited by Southern Association of Colleges and Schools. It first offered distance learning courses in 1972. In fall 2007, there were 850 students enrolled in distance learning courses. Institutionally administered financial aid is available to distance learners.
Services Distance learners have accessibility to academic advising, bookstore, campus computer network, career placement assistance, e-mail services, library services.

Contact Dr. Pamela Morgan, Director of Extended Education, Midwestern State University, 3410 Taft Boulevard, Wichita Falls, TX 76308-2099. Telephone: 940-397-4785. Fax: 940-397-4868. E-mail: pamela.morgan@mwsu.edu.

DEGREES AND AWARDS
BAA Arts and Science–Applied Arts and Sciences
BSRS Radiologic Sciences
MAE Educational Leadership
MS Radiologic Sciences (Education or Administration major)

COURSE SUBJECT AREAS OFFERED OUTSIDE OF DEGREE PROGRAMS
Undergraduate—business/commerce; business/corporate communications; communication and media; computer and information sciences; criminal justice and corrections; education; geography and cartography; health professions related; liberal arts and sciences, general studies and humanities; political science and government; psychology related; public administration; sociology.
Graduate—education related; health professions related; nursing.

MIDWIVES COLLEGE OF UTAH
Orem, Utah
http://www.midwifery.edu
Midwives College of Utah was founded in 1980. It is accredited by Midwifery Education Accreditation Council. It first offered distance learning courses in 1980. In fall 2007, there were 125 students enrolled in distance learning courses. Institutionally administered financial aid is available to distance learners.
Services Distance learners have accessibility to academic advising, bookstore, campus computer network, e-mail services, library services, tutoring.
Contact Cindy Winward, Administrative Assistant, Midwives College of Utah, 1174 East 2700 South, Suite 8, Salt Lake City, UT 84106. Telephone: 866-680-2756. Fax: 866-207-2024. E-mail: office@midwifery.edu.

DEGREES AND AWARDS
Programs offered do not lead to a degree or other formal award.

COURSE SUBJECT AREAS OFFERED OUTSIDE OF DEGREE PROGRAMS
Undergraduate—education.
Graduate—education.
Non-credit—education.

MILLERSVILLE UNIVERSITY OF PENNSYLVANIA
Millersville, Pennsylvania
MU Online
http://www.millersville.edu/~muonline/
Millersville University of Pennsylvania was founded in 1855. It is accredited by Middle States Association of Colleges and Schools. It first offered distance learning courses in 1998. In fall 2007, there were 867 students enrolled in distance learning courses. Institutionally administered financial aid is available to distance learners.
Services Distance learners have accessibility to academic advising, bookstore, campus computer network, career placement assistance, e-mail services, library services.
Contact Stephen J. Anspacher, Director of Distance Learning and Off-Campus Programs, Millersville University of Pennsylvania, PO Box 1002, Millersville, PA 17551. Telephone: 717-871-2457. Fax: 717-871-2022. E-mail: stephen.anspacher@millersville.edu.

DEGREES AND AWARDS
MS Emergency Management

COURSE SUBJECT AREAS OFFERED OUTSIDE OF DEGREE PROGRAMS

Undergraduate—atmospheric sciences and meteorology; business administration, management and operations; chemistry; communication and media; economics; education; education (specific subject areas); English composition; health and physical education/fitness; linguistic, comparative, and related language studies; music; nursing; psychology; sociology; special education.

Graduate—business administration, management and operations; education; education (specific subject areas); English composition; health and physical education/fitness; linguistic, comparative, and related language studies; nursing; special education; technology education/industrial arts.

MILWAUKEE SCHOOL OF ENGINEERING
Milwaukee, Wisconsin
MSOE-TV
http://www.msoe.edu/admiss

Milwaukee School of Engineering was founded in 1903. It is accredited by North Central Association of Colleges and Schools. It first offered distance learning courses in 1989. In fall 2007, there were 126 students enrolled in distance learning courses. Institutionally administered financial aid is available to distance learners.

Services Distance learners have accessibility to academic advising, bookstore, campus computer network, career placement assistance, e-mail services, library services.

Contact Ms. Mary Nielsen, Registrar, Milwaukee School of Engineering, 1025 North Broadway, Milwaukee, WI 53202-3109. Telephone: 414-277-7216. Fax: 414-277-6914. E-mail: nielsen@msoe.edu.

DEGREES AND AWARDS
Programs offered do not lead to a degree or other formal award.

COURSE SUBJECT AREAS OFFERED OUTSIDE OF DEGREE PROGRAMS

Undergraduate—business, management, and marketing related; computer and information sciences; management information systems.
Graduate—business administration, management and operations.

MINNEAPOLIS COLLEGE OF ART AND DESIGN
Minneapolis, Minnesota
MCAD Distance Learning
http://online.mcad.edu

Minneapolis College of Art and Design was founded in 1886. It is accredited by North Central Association of Colleges and Schools. It first offered distance learning courses in 1995. In fall 2007, there were 150 students enrolled in distance learning courses. Institutionally administered financial aid is available to distance learners.

Services Distance learners have accessibility to academic advising, bookstore, campus computer network, library services, tutoring.

Contact Rebecca J. Alm, Director of Online Learning, Minneapolis College of Art and Design, 2501 Stevens Avenue, Minneapolis, MN 55404. Telephone: 612-874-3658. Fax: 612-874-3704. E-mail: rebecca_alm@mcad.edu.

DEGREES AND AWARDS
Programs offered do not lead to a degree or other formal award.

COURSE SUBJECT AREAS OFFERED OUTSIDE OF DEGREE PROGRAMS

Undergraduate—design and applied arts; film/video and photographic arts; fine and studio art; visual and performing arts related.
Graduate—design and applied arts; film/video and photographic arts; fine and studio art; visual and performing arts related.
Non-credit—design and applied arts; film/video and photographic arts; fine and studio art; visual and performing arts related.

MINNESOTA SCHOOL OF BUSINESS–RICHFIELD
Richfield, Minnesota
http://www.msbcollege.edu

Minnesota School of Business–Richfield was founded in 1877. It is accredited by Accrediting Council for Independent Colleges and Schools. It first offered distance learning courses in 2000. In fall 2007, there were 990 students enrolled in distance learning courses. Institutionally administered financial aid is available to distance learners.

Services Distance learners have accessibility to academic advising, campus computer network, career placement assistance, e-mail services, library services, tutoring.

Contact Jennifer Foss-Wille, Online Director of Admissions, Minnesota School of Business–Richfield, 1401 West 76th Street, Suite 500, Richfield, MN 55423. Telephone: 877-609-8889. E-mail: jfoss-wille@msbcollege.edu.

DEGREES AND AWARDS

AAS Accounting and Tax Specialist; Business Administration; Cosmetology Business; Information Technology; Management Accounting; Paralegal; Transportation Business

BS Accounting; Business Administration; Business Management; Health Care Management; Information Technology; Paralegal

MBA Business Administration

COURSE SUBJECT AREAS OFFERED OUTSIDE OF DEGREE PROGRAMS

Undergraduate—accounting and related services; animal sciences; biology; business administration, management and operations; communication and media; computer science; entrepreneurial and small business operations; health and medical administrative services; international business; legal professions and studies related; legal studies (non-professional general, undergraduate); liberal arts and sciences, general studies and humanities; mathematics; taxation; technical and business writing; veterinary biomedical and clinical sciences.

Graduate—business administration, management and operations.

MINNESOTA STATE COMMUNITY AND TECHNICAL COLLEGE–FERGUS FALLS
Fergus Falls, Minnesota
http://www.distance.minnesota.edu

Minnesota State Community and Technical College–Fergus Falls was founded in 1960. It is accredited by North Central Association of Colleges and Schools. It first offered distance learning courses in 1995. In fall 2007, there were 2,000 students enrolled in distance learning courses. Institutionally administered financial aid is available to distance learners.

Services Distance learners have accessibility to academic advising, bookstore, e-mail services, library services, tutoring.

Contact Minnesota Online Support Center, Minnesota State Community and Technical College–Fergus Falls, 150 2nd Street SW, Suite B, Box 309, Perham, MN 56573. Telephone: 800-456-8519. Fax: 218-347-6214. E-mail: distancemn@custhelp.com.

DEGREES AND AWARDS

AA Liberal Arts and Sciences

AAS Computer Help Desk Technician; Computer Programming; Computer and Network Technology; Health Information Technology; Human Resources; Legal Administrative Assistant; Medical Administrative Assistant; Paralegal; Pharmacy Technology; Radiologic Technology

AS Human Resources

Certificate CISCO Networking; Computer Support Essentials; Computer and Network Technology; Medical Transcription; Web Development

Diploma Legal Secretary Technology; Medical Coding and Insurance; Medical Office Assistant; Pharmacy Technology

MINOT STATE UNIVERSITY
Minot, North Dakota
Continuing Education
http://www.minotstateu.edu/online
Minot State University was founded in 1913. It is accredited by North Central Association of Colleges and Schools. It first offered distance learning courses in 1991. In fall 2007, there were 1,147 students enrolled in distance learning courses. Institutionally administered financial aid is available to distance learners.
Services Distance learners have accessibility to academic advising, bookstore, campus computer network, career placement assistance, e-mail services, library services, tutoring.
Contact Jolina Miller, Online Program Coordinator, Minot State University, Center for Extended Learning, 500 University Avenue West, Minot, ND 58707. Telephone: 701-858-3430. Fax: 701-858-4343. E-mail: online@minotstateu.edu.

DEGREES AND AWARDS

AS Developmental Disabilities
BGS General Studies
BS Management Information Systems; Management; Virtual Business
BSAST Applied Business Information Technology; Applied Management
BSN Nursing for Registered Nurses
Certificate Developmental Disabilities
CAGS Knowledge Management
CCCPE Application Software Specialist; Web Development
MS Information Systems; Management

COURSE SUBJECT AREAS OFFERED OUTSIDE OF DEGREE PROGRAMS

Undergraduate—accounting and related services; American literature (United States and Canadian); anthropology; computer programming; computer science; creative writing; criminal justice and corrections; economics; education; education (specific levels and methods); English; English composition; English literature (British and Commonwealth); entrepreneurial and small business operations; health services/allied health/health sciences; history; human resources management; information science/studies; management information systems; marketing; mathematics; nursing; philosophy; psychology; psychology related; psychopharmacology; sociology; special education; statistics; technical and business writing.
Graduate—business administration, management and operations; management information systems; special education.

MINOT STATE UNIVERSITY–BOTTINEAU CAMPUS
Bottineau, North Dakota
http://www.misu-b.nodak.edu
Minot State University–Bottineau Campus was founded in 1906. It is accredited by North Central Association of Colleges and Schools. It first offered distance learning courses in 2000. In fall 2007, there were 201 students enrolled in distance learning courses. Institutionally administered financial aid is available to distance learners.
Services Distance learners have accessibility to academic advising, bookstore, e-mail services, library services.
Contact Kayla O'Toole, Distance Education Coordinator, Minot State University–Bottineau Campus, 105 Simrall Boulevard, Bottineau, ND 58318. Telephone: 888-918-5623. E-mail: kayla.otoole@misu.nodak.edu.

DEGREES AND AWARDS

AA Liberal Arts
AAS Accounting Technician; Administrative Assistant; Advertising and Marketing; Caregiver Services–Adult; Caregiver Services–Child; Medical Assistant; Medical Secretary; Paraeducation; Recreation Management
Certificate of Completion Basic Grounds Work Skills; Medical Coding; Medical Transcription; Recreation Management
Certificate Paraeducation

Diploma Advertising and Marketing; Bookkeeping; Greenhouse Technology; Landscape Technology; Medical Assistant; Medical Coding; Medical Transcription; Reception Services; Urban Forestry Technology

COURSE SUBJECT AREAS OFFERED OUTSIDE OF DEGREE PROGRAMS

Undergraduate—accounting and related services; allied health and medical assisting services; applied horticulture/horticultural business services; biological and biomedical sciences related; business administration, management and operations; business, management, and marketing related; business operations support and assistant services; education related; forestry; gerontology; health and medical administrative services; health and physical education/fitness; health professions related; health services/allied health/health sciences; liberal arts and sciences, general studies and humanities; marketing; medical basic sciences; parks, recreation and leisure; parks, recreation and leisure facilities management; parks, recreation, and leisure related; plant sciences; teaching assistants/aides.

MISERICORDIA UNIVERSITY
Dallas, Pennsylvania
http://www.misericordia.edu
Misericordia University was founded in 1924. It is accredited by Middle States Association of Colleges and Schools. It first offered distance learning courses in 1994. In fall 2007, there were 375 students enrolled in distance learning courses. Institutionally administered financial aid is available to distance learners.
Services Distance learners have accessibility to academic advising, bookstore, campus computer network, career placement assistance, e-mail services, library services, tutoring.
Contact Ms. Larree Brown, Assistant Director, Recruitment and Admissions, Misericordia University, Center for Adult and Continuing Education, 301 Lake Street, Dallas, PA 18612. Telephone: 570-674-6451. Fax: 570-674-6232. E-mail: lbrown@misericordia.edu.

DEGREES AND AWARDS

MBA/MA Organizational Management
OTD Occupational Therapy

COURSE SUBJECT AREAS OFFERED OUTSIDE OF DEGREE PROGRAMS

Undergraduate—accounting and computer science; allied health diagnostic, intervention, and treatment professions; applied mathematics; business administration, management and operations; business, management, and marketing related; developmental and child psychology; health and medical administrative services; history; human resources management; human services; international business; nursing; philosophy; political science and government; psychology related; religious studies; social sciences; sociology; statistics.

MISSISSIPPI DELTA COMMUNITY COLLEGE
Moorhead, Mississippi
http://www.msdelta.edu/distancelearning/index.html
Mississippi Delta Community College was founded in 1926. It is accredited by Southern Association of Colleges and Schools. It first offered distance learning courses in 2000. In fall 2007, there were 600 students enrolled in distance learning courses. Institutionally administered financial aid is available to distance learners.
Services Distance learners have accessibility to academic advising, bookstore, campus computer network, e-mail services, library services.
Contact Mrs. Jackie Bailey-Hall, Distance Learning Coordinator, Mississippi Delta Community College, PO Box 668, Moorhead, MS 38761. Telephone: 662-246-6319. Fax: 662-246-6296. E-mail: jbailey@msdelta.edu.

DEGREES AND AWARDS

Programs offered do not lead to a degree or other formal award.

COURSE SUBJECT AREAS OFFERED OUTSIDE OF DEGREE PROGRAMS

Undergraduate—accounting and computer science; behavioral sciences; biological and physical sciences; business/commerce; chemistry; criminal justice and corrections; economics; English; English composition; family and consumer sciences/human sciences; health and physical education/fitness; history; mathematics; music; physical sciences; political science and government; psychology; social sciences; sociology; speech and rhetoric.

MISSISSIPPI STATE UNIVERSITY
Mississippi State, Mississippi
Division of Continuing Education
http://www.distance.msstate.edu

Mississippi State University was founded in 1878. It is accredited by Southern Association of Colleges and Schools. It first offered distance learning courses in 1987. In fall 2007, there were 1,700 students enrolled in distance learning courses. Institutionally administered financial aid is available to distance learners.

Services Distance learners have accessibility to academic advising, bookstore, campus computer network, career placement assistance, e-mail services, library services.

Contact Dr. Laura A. Crittenden, Manager, Office of Academic Outreach, Mississippi State University, Division of Academic Outreach and Continuing Education, 1 Barr Avenue, PO Box 5247, Mississippi State, MS 39762-5247. Telephone: 662-325-2677. Fax: 662-325-0930. E-mail: lcrittenden@aoce.msstate.edu.

DEGREES AND AWARDS

BS Elementary Education; Geosciences; Interdisciplinary Studies

Certificate Geosciences, Broadcast Meteorology; Geosciences, Operational Meteorology; Geospatial and Remote Sensing

Graduate Certificate Business Administration; Economics of Development; Geospatial and Remote Sensing; Vision Specialist

MA Interdisciplinary Sciences

MAT Community College Leadership

MBA Business Administration; Project Management

MS Food Science, Nutrition, and Health Promotion; General Biology–Teachers in Biology; Geosciences, Teachers in Geoscience; Industrial Engineering; Master of Engineering; Public Policy Administration; Workforce Education Leadership

PhD Community College Leadership; Engineering, Industrial Engineering concentration

COURSE SUBJECT AREAS OFFERED OUTSIDE OF DEGREE PROGRAMS

Undergraduate—accounting and computer science; accounting and related services; biological and physical sciences; biology; communication and journalism related; communication and media; computer and information sciences; computer science; counseling psychology; curriculum and instruction; developmental and child psychology; educational/instructional media design; educational psychology; education related; education (specific levels and methods); education (specific subject areas); fine and studio art; forestry; geological and earth sciences/geosciences; human development, family studies, and related services; insurance; landscape architecture; mathematics; multi-/interdisciplinary studies related; physical sciences related; physics; special education; statistics; technology education/industrial arts; zoology/animal biology.

Graduate—agriculture; business administration, management and operations; business/commerce; business/managerial economics; chemical engineering; civil engineering; computer engineering; computer science; counseling psychology; curriculum and instruction; educational administration and supervision; educational assessment, evaluation, and research; educational/instructional media design; educational psychology; education (specific subject areas); electrical, electronics and communications engineering; engineering; engineering technologies related; health professions related; public administration.

MISSISSIPPI UNIVERSITY FOR WOMEN
Columbus, Mississippi
Continuing Education
http://www.muw.edu/

Mississippi University for Women was founded in 1884. It is accredited by Southern Association of Colleges and Schools. It first offered distance learning courses in 1994. In fall 2007, there were 38 students enrolled in distance learning courses. Institutionally administered financial aid is available to distance learners.

Services Distance learners have accessibility to academic advising, bookstore, career placement assistance, e-mail services, library services.

Contact Kathy McShane, Coordinator, Mississippi University for Women, Advanced Placement Option, 1918 Briar Ridge Road, Tupelo, MS 38804. Telephone: 662-844-0284. Fax: 662-844-1927. E-mail: kmshane@muw.edu.

DEGREES AND AWARDS

BSN Nursing

COURSE SUBJECT AREAS OFFERED OUTSIDE OF DEGREE PROGRAMS

Undergraduate—American literature (United States and Canadian); nursing.

MISSOURI STATE UNIVERSITY
Springfield, Missouri
College of Continuing Education and the Extended University
http://ec.missouristate.edu

Missouri State University was founded in 1905. It is accredited by North Central Association of Colleges and Schools. It first offered distance learning courses in 1974. In fall 2007, there were 4,000 students enrolled in distance learning courses. Institutionally administered financial aid is available to distance learners.

Services Distance learners have accessibility to academic advising, bookstore, campus computer network, career placement assistance, e-mail services, library services.

Contact Darren Young, Technical Support Specialist, Missouri State University, The Extended Campus, Academic Outreach and Distance Learning, 901 South National, Springfield, MO 65897. Telephone: 888-767-8444. Fax: 417-836-6111. E-mail: darrenyoung@missouristate.edu.

DEGREES AND AWARDS

BA Bachelor of Applied Science in Technology Management (two-year completion)

BS Elementary Education; General Business (completion degree)

Certificate Manufacturing Management

Certification Education–Missouri Visual Impairment Personnel Preparation program

Graduate Certificate Instructional Technology Specialist; Project Management; Sports Management

MBA Business Administration foundation courses; Business Administration

MS Administrative Studies; Computer Information Systems; Elementary Education; Project Management

MSW Social Work

PMC Nurse Educator

COURSE SUBJECT AREAS OFFERED OUTSIDE OF DEGREE PROGRAMS

Undergraduate—accounting and related services; agricultural and domestic animal services; agricultural business and management; anthropology; apparel and textiles; astronomy and astrophysics; chemistry; communication and journalism related; computer and information sciences; creative writing; developmental and child psychology; economics; English language and literature related; film/video and photographic arts; finance and financial management services; health and physical education/fitness; history; human development, family studies, and related services; industrial production technologies; marketing; mathematics and statistics related; music; nursing; physics; political science and government; religious studies; social work; sociology; special education.

Graduate—accounting and related services; agricultural and domestic animal services; communication and media; computer and information sciences; counseling psychology; criminal justice and corrections; curriculum and instruction; economics; education; educational administration and supervision; education (specific levels and methods); education (specific subject areas); finance and financial management services; health and physical education/fitness; history; industrial production technologies; legal research and advanced professional studies; library science; marketing; nursing; political science and government; psychology; religious studies; sales, merchandising, and related marketing operations (specialized); social work; taxation.

Non-credit—information science/studies; management information systems; mental and social health services and allied professions.

MISSOURI STATE UNIVERSITY–WEST PLAINS
West Plains, Missouri
http://ce.missouristate.edu/outreach/

Missouri State University–West Plains was founded in 1963. It is accredited by North Central Association of Colleges and Schools. It first offered distance learning courses in 1998. In fall 2007, there were 200 students enrolled in distance learning courses. Institutionally administered financial aid is available to distance learners.

Services Distance learners have accessibility to academic advising, bookstore, campus computer network, career placement assistance, e-mail services, library services, tutoring.

Contact Ms. Deanna M. Smith, Academic Outreach Coordinator, Missouri State University–West Plains, 128 Garfield, West Plains, MO 65791. Telephone: 417-255-7931. Fax: 417-255-7933. E-mail: deannasmith@missouristate.edu.

DEGREES AND AWARDS
BAS General Agriculture; Technology Management
BS Elementary Education; General Business; Nursing
MBA Business Administration
MS Educational Administration; Elementary Education

COURSE SUBJECT AREAS OFFERED OUTSIDE OF DEGREE PROGRAMS
Undergraduate—agriculture; American Sign Language (ASL); computer/information technology administration and management; computer science; counseling psychology.
Graduate—counseling psychology.

MISSOURI UNIVERSITY OF SCIENCE AND TECHNOLOGY
Rolla, Missouri
Extended Programs
http://dce.mst.edu

Missouri University of Science and Technology was founded in 1870. It is accredited by North Central Association of Colleges and Schools. It first offered distance learning courses in 1985. In fall 2007, there were 500 students enrolled in distance learning courses. Institutionally administered financial aid is available to distance learners.

Services Distance learners have accessibility to academic advising, bookstore, campus computer network, career placement assistance, e-mail services, library services.

Contact Ms. Sue Turner, Director, Distance and Continuing Education, Missouri University of Science and Technology, 216 University Center, Rolla, MO 65409. Telephone: 573-341-4132. Fax: 573-341-4992. E-mail: suet@mst.edu.

DEGREES AND AWARDS
MBA Business Administration
MEG Geotechnics
MEngr Manufacturing Engineering; Mining Engineering
MS IST Information Science and Technology
MS Systems Engineering

MSCE Civil Engineering
MSCS Computer Science
MSE Engineering Management; Environmental Engineering
MSME Mechanical Engineering

COURSE SUBJECT AREAS OFFERED OUTSIDE OF DEGREE PROGRAMS
Graduate—business administration, management and operations; business, management, and marketing related; civil engineering; civil engineering technology; computer and information sciences; computer science; electrical and electronic engineering technologies; electrical, electronics and communications engineering; engineering; engineering/industrial management; engineering mechanics; engineering science; manufacturing engineering; mechanical engineering; systems engineering.
Non-credit—aerospace, aeronautical and astronautical engineering; chemistry; civil engineering; computer and information sciences; computer science; electrical and electronic engineering technologies; engineering; engineering/industrial management; engineering related; engineering-related fields; environmental/environmental health engineering; geological and earth sciences/geosciences; materials engineering; surveying engineering; systems engineering; transportation and materials moving related.

MITCHELL TECHNICAL INSTITUTE
Mitchell, South Dakota
http://www.mitchelltech.edu

Mitchell Technical Institute was founded in 1968. It is accredited by North Central Association of Colleges and Schools. It first offered distance learning courses in 1994. In fall 2007, there were 150 students enrolled in distance learning courses. Institutionally administered financial aid is available to distance learners.

Services Distance learners have accessibility to academic advising, career placement assistance, e-mail services.

Contact John J. Heemstra, Telecommunications Coordinator, Mitchell Technical Institute, 821 North Capital, Mitchell, SD 57301. Telephone: 605-995-3065. Fax: 605-995-3067. E-mail: john.heemstra@mitchelltech.edu.

DEGREES AND AWARDS
Programs offered do not lead to a degree or other formal award.

COURSE SUBJECT AREAS OFFERED OUTSIDE OF DEGREE PROGRAMS
Undergraduate—accounting and computer science; business, management, and marketing related; computer and information sciences; computer software and media applications; curriculum and instruction; engineering-related technologies; health services/allied health/health sciences.
Non-credit—agricultural business and management; business, management, and marketing related; business operations support and assistant services; computer and information sciences; computer software and media applications; data entry/microcomputer applications; entrepreneurial and small business operations; health professions related; heating, air conditioning, ventilation and refrigeration maintenance technology; quality control and safety technologies.

MOBERLY AREA COMMUNITY COLLEGE
Moberly, Missouri
http://www.macc.edu/

Moberly Area Community College was founded in 1927. It is accredited by North Central Association of Colleges and Schools. It first offered distance learning courses in 1995. In fall 2007, there were 722 students enrolled in distance learning courses. Institutionally administered financial aid is available to distance learners.

Services Distance learners have accessibility to academic advising, bookstore, campus computer network, career placement assistance, e-mail services, library services, tutoring.

Contact Dr. James Grant, Dean of Student Services, Moberly Area Community College, 101 College Avenue, Moberly, MO 65270. Telephone: 660-263-4110 Ext. 239. Fax: 660-263-2406. E-mail: jamesg@macc.edu.

DEGREES AND AWARDS

AAS Computer Information Technology

COURSE SUBJECT AREAS OFFERED OUTSIDE OF DEGREE PROGRAMS

Undergraduate—accounting and related services; biology; business administration, management and operations; computer science; electrical and electronic engineering technologies; English; fine and studio art; geography and cartography; history; human development, family studies, and related services; mathematics; psychology; social sciences related; sociology; speech and rhetoric.

MONMOUTH UNIVERSITY
West Long Branch, New Jersey
http://www.monmouth.edu/

Monmouth University was founded in 1933. It is accredited by Middle States Association of Colleges and Schools. It first offered distance learning courses in 1998. In fall 2007, there were 76 students enrolled in distance learning courses. Institutionally administered financial aid is available to distance learners.

Services Distance learners have accessibility to academic advising, bookstore, campus computer network, career placement assistance, e-mail services, library services.

Contact Robert D. McCaig, EdD, Vice President for Enrollment Management, Monmouth University, 400 Cedar Avenue, West Long Branch, NJ 07764-1898. Telephone: 732-571-3413. Fax: 732-263-5101. E-mail: rmccaig@monmouth.edu.

DEGREES AND AWARDS

Programs offered do not lead to a degree or other formal award.

COURSE SUBJECT AREAS OFFERED OUTSIDE OF DEGREE PROGRAMS

Undergraduate—anthropology; communication and media; education; health services/allied health/health sciences; philosophy.
Graduate—communication and media; criminal justice and corrections; education; nursing.

MONROE COMMUNITY COLLEGE
Rochester, New York
http://www.monroecc.edu/

Monroe Community College was founded in 1961. It is accredited by Middle States Association of Colleges and Schools. It first offered distance learning courses in 1997. In fall 2007, there were 2,235 students enrolled in distance learning courses. Institutionally administered financial aid is available to distance learners.

Services Distance learners have accessibility to academic advising, bookstore, campus computer network, career placement assistance, e-mail services, library services.

Contact Elizabeth Ripton, Director, Registration and Records, Monroe Community College, 1000 East Henrietta Road, Rochester, NY 14623-5780. Telephone: 585-292-2300. E-mail: eripton@monroecc.edu.

DEGREES AND AWARDS

AAS Criminal Justice
AS Business Administration; Liberal Arts; Physical Education Studies
Certificate of Completion Coaching–New York State Coaching certification
Certificate Dental Assisting

COURSE SUBJECT AREAS OFFERED OUTSIDE OF DEGREE PROGRAMS

Undergraduate—accounting and related services; American literature (United States and Canadian); biology; business/commerce; communi-

cation and media; criminal justice and corrections; dental support services and allied professions; English composition; liberal arts and sciences, general studies and humanities; mathematics; psychology; public relations, advertising, and applied communication related; social sciences.

MONROE COUNTY COMMUNITY COLLEGE
Monroe, Michigan
http://www.monroeccc.edu

Monroe County Community College was founded in 1964. It is accredited by North Central Association of Colleges and Schools. It first offered distance learning courses in 2000. In fall 2007, there were 600 students enrolled in distance learning courses. Institutionally administered financial aid is available to distance learners.

Services Distance learners have accessibility to academic advising, bookstore, campus computer network, career placement assistance, e-mail services, library services, tutoring.

Contact Mr. Mark Hall, Director of Admissions and Guidance Services, Monroe County Community College, 1555 South Raisinville Road, Monroe, MI 48161. Telephone: 734-384-4261. Fax: 734-242-9711. E-mail: mhall@monroeccc.edu.

DEGREES AND AWARDS

Programs offered do not lead to a degree or other formal award.

COURSE SUBJECT AREAS OFFERED OUTSIDE OF DEGREE PROGRAMS

Undergraduate—business/commerce; computer and information sciences; computer software and media applications; economics; English composition; mathematics; nursing; political science and government; psychology; technical and business writing; work and family studies.

MONTANA TECH OF THE UNIVERSITY OF MONTANA
Butte, Montana
Office of Extended Studies
http://www.mtech.edu

Montana Tech of The University of Montana was founded in 1895. It is accredited by Northwest Commission on Colleges and Universities. It first offered distance learning courses in 1996. In fall 2007, there were 500 students enrolled in distance learning courses. Institutionally administered financial aid is available to distance learners.

Services Distance learners have accessibility to academic advising, bookstore, campus computer network, career placement assistance, e-mail services, library services.

Contact Ms. Laura Riddle, Inquiry Processing Specialist, Montana Tech of The University of Montana, 1300 West Park Street, Butte, MT 59701-8997. Telephone: 406-496-4791. Fax: 406-496-4710. E-mail: lriddle@mtech.edu.

DEGREES AND AWARDS

MPM Project Engineering and Management
MS Industrial Hygiene

COURSE SUBJECT AREAS OFFERED OUTSIDE OF DEGREE PROGRAMS

Undergraduate—business/commerce; computer software and media applications; English composition; health professions related; mathematics; nursing; philosophy; psychology; sociology; technical and business writing.
Graduate—engineering/industrial management; health professions related; public health.

MONTCALM COMMUNITY COLLEGE
Sidney, Michigan
http://www.montcalm.edu/

Montcalm Community College was founded in 1965. It is accredited by North Central Association of Colleges and Schools. It first offered distance learning courses in 2002. In fall 2007, there were 684 students enrolled in distance learning courses. Institutionally administered financial aid is available to distance learners.

Services Distance learners have accessibility to academic advising, bookstore, career placement assistance, library services.

Contact Debra Alexander, Director of Admissions, Montcalm Community College, 2800 College Drive, Sidney, MI 48885-9723. Telephone: 989-328-1250. Fax: 989-328-2950. E-mail: admissions@montcalm.edu.

DEGREES AND AWARDS
Programs offered do not lead to a degree or other formal award.

COURSE SUBJECT AREAS OFFERED OUTSIDE OF DEGREE PROGRAMS
Undergraduate—accounting and related services; biology; business administration, management and operations; business/commerce; computer programming; criminal justice and corrections; data entry/microcomputer applications; economics; English; international business; psychology.
Non-credit—accounting and related services; business administration, management and operations; computer and information sciences; health professions related.

MONTGOMERY COMMUNITY COLLEGE
Troy, North Carolina
http://www.montgomery.edu
Montgomery Community College was founded in 1967. It is accredited by Southern Association of Colleges and Schools. It first offered distance learning courses in 2000. In fall 2007, there were 350 students enrolled in distance learning courses. Institutionally administered financial aid is available to distance learners.
Services Distance learners have accessibility to academic advising, bookstore, campus computer network, career placement assistance, library services, tutoring.
Contact Dean Thomas M. Sargent, Dean of Education Technology, Montgomery Community College, 1011 Page Street, Troy, NC 27371. Telephone: 910-576-6222 Ext. 217. Fax: 910-576-2176. E-mail: sargentt@montgomery.edu.

DEGREES AND AWARDS
AAB Business Administration
AAS Criminal Justice

COURSE SUBJECT AREAS OFFERED OUTSIDE OF DEGREE PROGRAMS
Undergraduate—accounting and related services; allied health and medical assisting services; American literature (United States and Canadian); business administration, management and operations; business/commerce; business/managerial economics; business operations support and assistant services; computer and information sciences; computer software and media applications; criminal justice and corrections; English; English composition; human resources management; liberal arts and sciences, general studies and humanities; medical basic sciences; psychology; religious education; sociology; technical and business writing.
Non-credit—allied health and medical assisting services; biblical studies; business administration, management and operations; business/corporate communications; computer and information sciences; computer software and media applications; English; English composition.

MONTGOMERY COUNTY COMMUNITY COLLEGE
Blue Bell, Pennsylvania
Learning Resources Unit
http://www.mc3.edu/elearning/
Montgomery County Community College was founded in 1964. It is accredited by Middle States Association of Colleges and Schools. It first offered distance learning courses in 1992. In fall 2007, there were 753 students enrolled in distance learning courses. Institutionally administered financial aid is available to distance learners.
Services Distance learners have accessibility to academic advising, bookstore, campus computer network, career placement assistance, e-mail services, library services, tutoring.

Contact Dr. Doreen M. Fisher, Director of e-Learning, Montgomery County Community College, 340 DeKalb Pike, 257 College Hall, Blue Bell, PA 19422. Telephone: 215-641-6589. Fax: 215-619-7167. E-mail: dfisher@mc3.edu.

DEGREES AND AWARDS
AA Elementary Education; Secondary Education; Social Science
AAS Computer Apps/Office Procedures; Criminal Justice; Early Childhood Education; Management
AGS General Studies
AS Accounting; Business Administration–International option; Business Administration; Computer Science; Liberal Studies; Management Information Systems
Certificate Business Management; International Studies

COURSE SUBJECT AREAS OFFERED OUTSIDE OF DEGREE PROGRAMS
Undergraduate—accounting and related services; anthropology; astronomy and astrophysics; biology; business administration, management and operations; business/commerce; computer and information sciences; computer programming; computer science; computer software and media applications; criminology; dental support services and allied professions; developmental and child psychology; economics; education; English composition; English literature (British and Commonwealth); geography and cartography; geological and earth sciences/geosciences; health professions related; history; liberal arts and sciences, general studies and humanities; marketing; mathematics; nursing; nutrition sciences; philosophy; psychology; social psychology; sociology; statistics; technical and business writing.
Non-credit—accounting and related services; business operations support and assistant services; English as a second language; health and medical administrative services; health professions related; technology education/industrial arts.

MOORPARK COLLEGE
Moorpark, California
http://www.moorparkcollege.edu
Moorpark College was founded in 1967. It is accredited by Western Association of Schools and Colleges. It first offered distance learning courses in 1978. In fall 2007, there were 500 students enrolled in distance learning courses. Institutionally administered financial aid is available to distance learners.
Services Distance learners have accessibility to academic advising, library services, tutoring.
Contact Richard Torres, Outreach Coordinator, Moorpark College, 7075 Campus Road, Moorpark, CA 93021. Telephone: 805-378-1400. E-mail: mcoutreach@vcccd.edu.

DEGREES AND AWARDS
Programs offered do not lead to a degree or other formal award.

COURSE SUBJECT AREAS OFFERED OUTSIDE OF DEGREE PROGRAMS
Undergraduate—allied health and medical assisting services; allied health diagnostic, intervention, and treatment professions; anthropology; area, ethnic, cultural, and gender studies related; behavioral sciences; business/commerce; business, management, and marketing related; classical and ancient studies; communication and journalism related; communication and media; computer and information sciences; education related; English; English composition; ethnic, cultural minority, and gender studies; languages (classics and classical); languages (foreign languages related); languages (Romance languages); mathematics; nursing; philosophy; psychology; sociology.

MOTLOW STATE COMMUNITY COLLEGE
Tullahoma, Tennessee
Academic Affairs
http://www.mscc.edu

Motlow State Community College was founded in 1969. It is accredited by Southern Association of Colleges and Schools. It first offered distance learning courses in 1996. In fall 2007, there were 375 students enrolled in distance learning courses. Institutionally administered financial aid is available to distance learners.

Services Distance learners have accessibility to academic advising, bookstore, campus computer network, career placement assistance, e-mail services, library services, tutoring.

Contact Ms. Brenda Lewis, Interim Vice President for Academic Affairs, Motlow State Community College, PO Box 8500, Lynchburg, TN 37352-8500. Telephone: 931-393-1696. Fax: 931-393-1681. E-mail: blewis@mscc.edu.

DEGREES AND AWARDS

AAS Business Technology; Nursing; Web Technology

COURSE SUBJECT AREAS OFFERED OUTSIDE OF DEGREE PROGRAMS

Undergraduate—computer and information sciences; economics; management information systems; mathematics; statistics.

MOUNTAIN EMPIRE COMMUNITY COLLEGE
Big Stone Gap, Virginia
Office of Continuing and Distance Education
http://www.me.vccs.edu/distance/index.html

Mountain Empire Community College was founded in 1972. It is accredited by Southern Association of Colleges and Schools. It first offered distance learning courses in 1979. In fall 2007, there were 900 students enrolled in distance learning courses. Institutionally administered financial aid is available to distance learners.

Services Distance learners have accessibility to academic advising, bookstore, campus computer network, career placement assistance, e-mail services, library services, tutoring.

Contact Susan Kennedy, Coordinator of Distance Education, Mountain Empire Community College, 3441 Mountain Empire Road, Big Stone Gap, VA 24219. Telephone: 276-523-7488. Fax: 276-523-7486. E-mail: skennedy@me.vccs.edu.

DEGREES AND AWARDS

AAS Accounting; Administrative Support Technology Medical Office Specialist; Administrative Support Technology; Business Administration; Correctional Services; General Studies; Liberal Arts; Water/Wastewater specialization

Certificate Career Studies Certificate–Accounting; Career Studies Certificate–Child Development; Career Studies Certificate–Computer Software Specialist; Career Studies Certificate–Geographical Information Systems; Career Studies Certificate–Health Information Technology; Career Studies Certificate–Legal Office Assisting; Career Studies Certificate–Medical Records Clerk; Career Studies Certificate–Medical Transcriptionist; Career Studies Certificate–Office Automation Specialist; Career Studies Certificate–Personal Computing for Home and Office; Career Studies Certificate–Polysomnography; Career Studies Certificate–Wastewater Plant Operator; Career Studies Certificate–Water Plant Operator; Career Studies Certificate–Word Processing; Clerical Assistant

COURSE SUBJECT AREAS OFFERED OUTSIDE OF DEGREE PROGRAMS

Undergraduate—accounting and related services; astronomy and astrophysics; atmospheric sciences and meteorology; biology; business/commerce; communication and media; computer and information sciences; criminal justice and corrections; criminology; developmental and child psychology; economics; English composition; fine and studio art; geological and earth sciences/geosciences; health and physical education/fitness; history; human development, family studies, and related services; languages (Romance languages); legal studies (non-professional general,

undergraduate); linguistic, comparative, and related language studies; marketing; mathematics; music; psychology; religious studies; sociology; speech and rhetoric.

MOUNTAIN STATE UNIVERSITY
Beckley, West Virginia
Online Programs
http://www.distancelearning.mountainstate.edu

Mountain State University was founded in 1933. It is accredited by North Central Association of Colleges and Schools. Institutionally administered financial aid is available to distance learners.

Services Distance learners have accessibility to academic advising, bookstore, campus computer network, e-mail services.

Contact Tockie Wynn, Enrollment Advisor, Mountain State University, Off-Site Admissions Center, 2145 MetroCenter Boulevard, Suite 400, Orlando, FL 32835-7632. Telephone: 866-312-9595.

DEGREES AND AWARDS

BS Criminal Justice Administration
MS Strategic Leadership

MOUNTAIN VIEW COLLEGE
Dallas, Texas
http://www.mvc.dcccd.edu/

Mountain View College was founded in 1970. It is accredited by Southern Association of Colleges and Schools. It first offered distance learning courses in 1972. In fall 2007, there were 1,000 students enrolled in distance learning courses. Institutionally administered financial aid is available to distance learners.

Services Distance learners have accessibility to academic advising, bookstore, e-mail services, library services.

Contact Dean Glenda Hall, Registrar, Mountain View College, Dallas, TX 75211. E-mail: ghall@dcccd.edu.

DEGREES AND AWARDS

AA Arts and Sciences

COURSE SUBJECT AREAS OFFERED OUTSIDE OF DEGREE PROGRAMS

Undergraduate—accounting and related services; computer and information sciences and support services related.

Non-credit—computer and information sciences and support services related.

MOUNT ALLISON UNIVERSITY
Sackville, New Brunswick, Canada
Continuing and Distance Education
http://www.mta.ca/conted/index.html

Mount Allison University was founded in 1839. It is provincially chartered. It first offered distance learning courses in 1965. In fall 2007, there were 117 students enrolled in distance learning courses. Institutionally administered financial aid is available to distance learners.

Services Distance learners have accessibility to academic advising, bookstore, campus computer network, e-mail services, library services, tutoring.

Contact Ms. Heather Patterson, Director, Mount Allison University, Continuous Learning, 62 York Street, Sackville, NB E4L 1E2, Canada. Telephone: 506-364-2266. Fax: 506-364-2272. E-mail: hpatters@mta.ca.

DEGREES AND AWARDS

Programs offered do not lead to a degree or other formal award.

MT. HOOD COMMUNITY COLLEGE
Gresham, Oregon
http://online.mhcc.edu

Mt. Hood Community College was founded in 1966. It is accredited by Northwest Commission on Colleges and Universities. It first offered distance learning courses in 1998. In fall 2007, there were 1,000 students enrolled in distance learning courses. Institutionally administered financial aid is available to distance learners.

Services Distance learners have accessibility to academic advising, bookstore, campus computer network, e-mail services, library services, tutoring.

Contact Ms. Catherine Vogt, Program Coordinator, Mt. Hood Community College, 26000 SE Stark Street, Gresham, OR 97030. Telephone: 503-491-6995. Fax: 503-491-6064. E-mail: cat.vogt@mhcc.edu.

DEGREES AND AWARDS
Programs offered do not lead to a degree or other formal award.

COURSE SUBJECT AREAS OFFERED OUTSIDE OF DEGREE PROGRAMS

Undergraduate—accounting and computer science; accounting and related services; allied health and medical assisting services; American literature (United States and Canadian); anthropology; applied mathematics; biology; business administration, management and operations; business operations support and assistant services; chemistry; computer and information sciences; computer software and media applications; creative writing; economics; English composition; health and medical administrative services; psychology; technical and business writing; visual and performing arts.

MOUNT OLIVE COLLEGE
Mount Olive, North Carolina
http://www.moc.edu

Mount Olive College was founded in 1951. It is accredited by Southern Association of Colleges and Schools. It first offered distance learning courses in 2003. In fall 2007, there were 350 students enrolled in distance learning courses. Institutionally administered financial aid is available to distance learners.

Services Distance learners have accessibility to bookstore, e-mail services.

Contact Mrs. Julia K. Pacilli, Manager of Enrollment Information, Mount Olive College, Office of Admissions, 634 Henderson Street, Mount Olive, NC 28365. Telephone: 919-658-7795 Ext. 1204. Fax: 919-658-9816. E-mail: jpacilli@moc.edu.

DEGREES AND AWARDS
BS Criminal Justice and Criminology

COURSE SUBJECT AREAS OFFERED OUTSIDE OF DEGREE PROGRAMS

Undergraduate—accounting and computer science; American literature (United States and Canadian); biblical studies; biology; business administration, management and operations; criminal justice and corrections; criminology; developmental and child psychology; economics; education; English composition; English language and literature related; English literature (British and Commonwealth); health and physical education/fitness; history; liberal arts and sciences, general studies and humanities; management information systems; mathematics; music; parks, recreation, and leisure related; psychology; religious studies; sociology.

MT. SAN ANTONIO COLLEGE
Walnut, California
Distance Learning
http://www.mtsac.edu/instruction/distlearn

Mt. San Antonio College was founded in 1946. It is accredited by Western Association of Schools and Colleges. It first offered distance learning courses in 1993. In fall 2007, there were 2,108 students enrolled in distance learning courses. Institutionally administered financial aid is available to distance learners.

Services Distance learners have accessibility to academic advising, bookstore, campus computer network, e-mail services, library services, tutoring.

Contact Kerry C. Stern, Dean, Mt. San Antonio College, Learning Resources, 1100 North Grand Avenue, Walnut, CA 91789. Telephone: 909-594-5611 Ext. 5658. Fax: 909-468-3992. E-mail: kstern@mtsac.edu.

DEGREES AND AWARDS
Programs offered do not lead to a degree or other formal award.

COURSE SUBJECT AREAS OFFERED OUTSIDE OF DEGREE PROGRAMS

Undergraduate—accounting and related services; alternative and complementary medical support services; anthropology; biology; business administration, management and operations; chemistry; computer and information sciences; creative writing; economics; English as a second language; English composition; family and consumer sciences/human sciences; hospitality administration; journalism; legal studies (nonprofessional general, undergraduate); philosophy; psychology; real estate; religious studies; sales, merchandising, and related marketing operations (specialized); sociology.

Non-credit—computer software and media applications.

MOUNT WACHUSETT COMMUNITY COLLEGE
Gardner, Massachusetts
Division of Continuing Education
http://www.mwcc.edu

Mount Wachusett Community College was founded in 1963. It is accredited by New England Association of Schools and Colleges. It first offered distance learning courses in 1994. In fall 2007, there were 1,263 students enrolled in distance learning courses. Institutionally administered financial aid is available to distance learners.

Services Distance learners have accessibility to academic advising, bookstore, campus computer network, career placement assistance, e-mail services, library services, tutoring.

Contact Ms. Debora Brennan, Distance Learning Administrative Assistant, Mount Wachusett Community College, 444 Green Street, Gardner, MA 01440. Telephone: 978-630-9275. Fax: 978-630-9537. E-mail: dbrennan@mwcc.mass.edu.

DEGREES AND AWARDS
AS Business Administration; Computer Information Systems; General Studies; Human Services; Liberal Studies; Paralegal Studies

COURSE SUBJECT AREAS OFFERED OUTSIDE OF DEGREE PROGRAMS

Undergraduate—biology; business administration, management and operations; communication and journalism related; computer programming; computer software and media applications; criminal justice and corrections; criminology; economics; English composition; film/video and photographic arts; history; human development, family studies, and related services; human resources management; human services; journalism; legal professions and studies related; management information systems; marketing; mathematics; mathematics and statistics related; mental and social health services and allied professions; nursing; political science and government; psychology; social sciences; sociology; statistics.

Non-credit—business operations support and assistant services; computer software and media applications; forestry.

MURRAY STATE COLLEGE
Tishomingo, Oklahoma
http://www.mscok.edu

Murray State College was founded in 1908. It is accredited by North Central Association of Colleges and Schools. It first offered distance learning courses in 1996. In fall 2007, there were 1,128 students enrolled in distance learning courses. Institutionally administered financial aid is available to distance learners.

Services Distance learners have accessibility to academic advising, bookstore, campus computer network, career placement assistance, e-mail services, library services, tutoring.

Contact Mrs. Priscilla Ann Washington, Distance Learning Coordinator, Murray State College, One Murray Campus, Tishomingo, OK 73460. Telephone: 580-371-2371 Ext. 123. Fax: 580-371-9844. E-mail: pwashington@mscok.edu.

DEGREES AND AWARDS

Programs offered do not lead to a degree or other formal award.

COURSE SUBJECT AREAS OFFERED OUTSIDE OF DEGREE PROGRAMS

Undergraduate—accounting and computer science; allied health and medical assisting services; American literature (United States and Canadian); applied mathematics; behavioral sciences; biological and physical sciences; biology; business administration, management and operations; business/corporate communications; computer software and media applications; criminal justice and corrections; economics; English literature (British and Commonwealth); finance and financial management services; history; marketing; mathematics; music; physical sciences; political science and government.

MURRAY STATE UNIVERSITY
Murray, Kentucky
Continuing Education
http://ceao.murraystate.edu

Murray State University was founded in 1922. It is accredited by Southern Association of Colleges and Schools. It first offered distance learning courses in 1990. In fall 2007, there were 5,300 students enrolled in distance learning courses. Institutionally administered financial aid is available to distance learners.

Services Distance learners have accessibility to academic advising, bookstore, campus computer network, e-mail services, library services.

Contact Crystal Riley, Coordinator of Distance Learning, Murray State University, 303 Sparks Hall, CEAO, Murray, KY 42071-0009. Telephone: 800-669-7654. Fax: 270-809-3593. E-mail: crystal.riley@murraystate.edu.

DEGREES AND AWARDS

BBA Business–Bachelor of Science in Business

BGS Independent Studies–Bachelor of Independent Studies/General Studies

BS Telecommunications Systems Management

Endorsement English as a Second Language; Gifted and Talented

COURSE SUBJECT AREAS OFFERED OUTSIDE OF DEGREE PROGRAMS

Undergraduate—agricultural business and management; agriculture; agriculture and agriculture operations related; animal sciences; anthropology; business administration, management and operations; business/commerce; communication disorders sciences and services; computer and information sciences; computer programming; computer science; computer systems networking and telecommunications; education; English composition; geography and cartography; geological and earth sciences/geosciences; graphic communications; history; human development, family studies, and related services; journalism; legal studies (non-professional general, undergraduate); mathematics and statistics related; music; nursing; philosophy; philosophy and religious studies related; public relations, advertising, and applied communication related; radio, television, and digital communication; social sciences; social sciences related; social work; sociology.

Graduate—bilingual, multilingual, and multicultural education; communication disorders sciences and services; computer systems networking and telecommunications; educational administration and supervision; English as a second/foreign language (teaching); English as a second language; human services; marketing; nursing; quality control and safety technologies; special education.

MYERS UNIVERSITY
Cleveland, Ohio
COOL Program (College Options On-Line)
http://www.myers.edu/online

Myers University was founded in 1848. It is accredited by North Central Association of Colleges and Schools. It first offered distance learning courses in 1976. In fall 2007, there were 414 students enrolled in distance learning courses. Institutionally administered financial aid is available to distance learners.

Services Distance learners have accessibility to academic advising, bookstore, campus computer network, career placement assistance, e-mail services, library services, tutoring.

Contact Ms. Brooke A. Scharlott, Vice President of Academic Affairs, Myers University, 3921 Chester Avenue, Cleveland, OH 44114. Telephone: 216-432-8941. E-mail: bscharlott@myers.edu.

DEGREES AND AWARDS

BS Criminal Justice Administration; Health Services Management; Information Technology

BSBA Accounting; Corporate Management; Finance; Forensic Accounting; Human Resource Management; Industrial Management; Management Information Systems; Marketing; Small Business Entrepreneurship

COURSE SUBJECT AREAS OFFERED OUTSIDE OF DEGREE PROGRAMS

Undergraduate—accounting and related services; American literature (United States and Canadian); applied mathematics; business administration, management and operations; business/commerce; business/corporate communications; business, management, and marketing related; business/managerial economics; communication and media; computer and information sciences; computer and information sciences and support services related; computer engineering; computer/information technology administration and management; computer programming; computer science; computer software and media applications; computer systems analysis; computer systems networking and telecommunications; criminal justice and corrections; criminology; data entry/microcomputer applications; economics; English composition; entrepreneurial and small business operations; finance and financial management services; geography and cartography; history; human resources management; information science/studies; international business; legal studies (non-professional general, undergraduate); management information systems; management sciences and quantitative methods; marketing; mathematics; military studies; political science and government; psychology; public administration; public relations, advertising, and applied communication related; sales, merchandising, and related marketing operations (specialized); sociology.

Graduate—business administration, management and operations; business/commerce.

NAROPA UNIVERSITY
Boulder, Colorado
Outreach Office
http://www.naropa.edu/distancelearning

Naropa University was founded in 1974. It is accredited by North Central Association of Colleges and Schools. It first offered distance learning courses in 1999. In fall 2007, there were 200 students enrolled in distance learning courses. Institutionally administered financial aid is available to distance learners.

Services Distance learners have accessibility to academic advising, bookstore, career placement assistance, e-mail services, library services.

Contact Jirka Hladis, Director of Distance Learning Curriculum Development, Naropa University, 2130 Arapahoe Avenue, Boulder, CO 80302. Telephone: 303-245-4702. E-mail: jirka@naropa.edu.

DEGREES AND AWARDS

MA Contemplative Education; Transpersonal Psychology; Transpersonal Psychology, Ecopsychology concentration

MFA Creative Writing

COURSE SUBJECT AREAS OFFERED OUTSIDE OF DEGREE PROGRAMS

Undergraduate—area, ethnic, cultural, and gender studies related; clinical psychology; community psychology; comparative literature; counseling psychology; creative writing; developmental and child psychology; ethnic, cultural minority, and gender studies; experimental psychology; liberal arts and sciences, general studies and humanities; multi-/interdisciplinary studies related; philosophy and religious studies related; psychology; religious studies.

Graduate—area, ethnic, cultural, and gender studies related; education; English; languages (East Asian); liberal arts and sciences, general studies and humanities; multi-/interdisciplinary studies related; psychology related; religious education.

Non-credit—area, ethnic, cultural, and gender studies related; area studies; creative writing; education; educational psychology; education related; ethnic, cultural minority, and gender studies; human development, family studies, and related services; philosophy; philosophy and religious studies related; psychology; psychology related; religious education; religious/sacred music; religious studies; theological and ministerial studies; theology and religious vocations related.

See full description on page 412.

NASHVILLE STATE TECHNICAL COMMUNITY COLLEGE
Nashville, Tennessee
http://www.nscc.edu
Nashville State Technical Community College was founded in 1970. It is accredited by Southern Association of Colleges and Schools. It first offered distance learning courses in 1998. In fall 2007, there were 4,700 students enrolled in distance learning courses. Institutionally administered financial aid is available to distance learners.
Services Distance learners have accessibility to academic advising, bookstore, career placement assistance, library services, tutoring.
Contact Doug Jameson, Coordinator of Distance Education, Nashville State Technical Community College, 120 White Bridge Road, Nashville, TN 37209. Telephone: 615-353-3461. Fax: 615-353-3774. E-mail: doug.jameson@nscc.edu.

DEGREES AND AWARDS
AA General Studies
AAS Applied Science; General degree

COURSE SUBJECT AREAS OFFERED OUTSIDE OF DEGREE PROGRAMS
Undergraduate—education (specific subject areas); entrepreneurial and small business operations; nursing; special education.
Non-credit—business operations support and assistant services.

NASSAU COMMUNITY COLLEGE
Garden City, New York
College of the Air
http://www.ncc.edu
Nassau Community College was founded in 1959. It is accredited by Middle States Association of Colleges and Schools. It first offered distance learning courses in 1991. In fall 2007, there were 1,800 students enrolled in distance learning courses. Institutionally administered financial aid is available to distance learners.
Services Distance learners have accessibility to academic advising, bookstore, campus computer network, e-mail services, library services.
Contact Prof. Arthur L. Friedman, EdD, Coordinator, Distance Education, Nassau Community College, One Education Drive, Garden City, NY 11530-6793. Telephone: 516-572-7883. Fax: 516-572-0690. E-mail: friedma@ncc.edu.

DEGREES AND AWARDS
Programs offered do not lead to a degree or other formal award.

COURSE SUBJECT AREAS OFFERED OUTSIDE OF DEGREE PROGRAMS

Undergraduate—accounting and related services; anthropology; apparel and textiles; astronomy and astrophysics; atmospheric sciences and meteorology; behavioral sciences; biology; business administration, management and operations; business/commerce; computer and information sciences; developmental and child psychology; economics; English composition; English language and literature related; entrepreneurial and small business operations; foods, nutrition, and related services; geological and earth sciences/geosciences; health and physical education/fitness; history; languages (Romance languages); legal studies (non-professional general, undergraduate); marketing; mathematics; mathematics and statistics related; music; nutrition sciences; physical sciences related; psychology; psychology related; sociology; statistics.
Non-credit—English; mathematics.

NATIONAL UNIVERSITY
La Jolla, California
NU Online
http://www.nu.edu
National University was founded in 1971. It is accredited by Western Association of Schools and Colleges. It first offered distance learning courses in 1994. In fall 2007, there were 18,759 students enrolled in distance learning courses. Institutionally administered financial aid is available to distance learners.
Services Distance learners have accessibility to academic advising, bookstore, campus computer network, career placement assistance, e-mail services, library services, tutoring.
Contact Mr. James Wilson, Associate Regional Dean, Online, National University, 4121 Camino del Rio South, San Diego, CA 92108. Telephone: 800-NAT-UNIV Ext. 7288. Fax: 858-563 7211. E-mail: jwilson@nu.edu.

DEGREES AND AWARDS
AA General Studies–Associate of Arts; Health Care Administration
BA Arabic Studies; Early Childhood Development; English–Single Subject Preparation in English; English; Global Studies; History; Management; Marketing; Psychology; Sociology
BBA Business Administration
BS Accountancy; Allied Health; Computer Science; Construction Engineering; Criminal Justice Administration; Financial Management; Information Systems; Information Technology Management; Nursing; Organizational Behavior; Software Engineering
Certificate Early Childhood Special Education
Certification Administrative Services Certificate; Education–Level I Education Specialist Credential: Mild/Mod; Education–TED Multiple or Single Subject Teaching Credential
EMBA Executive Master of Business Administration (Spanish version)
Graduate Certificate Supply Chain Management
MA English; Human Behavior; Human Resource Management and Organizational Development; Management
MAT Teaching
MBA Business Administration; Business Administration
MBA/MHA Master of Health Care Administration
MEd Cross Cultural Teaching
MFA Creative Writing; Digital Cinema
MPA Public Administration
MS Computer Science; Educational Administration and Administrative Services; Educational Technology; Educational and Instructional Technology; Electronic Business; Engineering Management; Forensic Sciences–Master of Forensic Sciences; Homeland Security and Safety Engineering; Information Systems; Organizational Leadership; Special Education and Level I Specialist Credential Mild/Moderate; Technology Management

COURSE SUBJECT AREAS OFFERED OUTSIDE OF DEGREE PROGRAMS
Undergraduate—accounting and related services; allied health and medical assisting services; biological and physical sciences; building/construction finishing, management, and inspection; business administration, management and operations; business/commerce; communications

technology; computer software and media applications; construction engineering technology; counseling psychology; criminal justice and corrections; developmental and child psychology; education; English; history; information science/studies; international/global studies; management sciences and quantitative methods; nursing; psychology; public administration.

Graduate—accounting and related services; business administration, management and operations; business/commerce; computer and information sciences; computer programming; computer science; computer software and media applications; computer systems analysis; counseling psychology; creative writing; criminology; education; educational administration and supervision; educational/instructional media design; education (specific subject areas); human resources management; public administration; special education; technology education/industrial arts.

NAUGATUCK VALLEY COMMUNITY COLLEGE
Waterbury, Connecticut
http://www.nvcc.commnet.edu
Naugatuck Valley Community College was founded in 1992. It is accredited by New England Association of Schools and Colleges. It first offered distance learning courses in 1998. In fall 2007, there were 984 students enrolled in distance learning courses. Institutionally administered financial aid is available to distance learners.
Services Distance learners have accessibility to academic advising, bookstore, campus computer network, career placement assistance, e-mail services, library services, tutoring.
Contact Ms. Stacey L. Williams, Director of Distance Learning, Naugatuck Valley Community College, 750 Chase Parkway, Waterbury, CT 06708. Telephone: 203-575-8182. E-mail: swilliams@nvcc.commnet.edu.

DEGREES AND AWARDS
Programs offered do not lead to a degree or other formal award.

COURSE SUBJECT AREAS OFFERED OUTSIDE OF DEGREE PROGRAMS
Undergraduate—accounting and related services; American literature (United States and Canadian); applied horticulture/horticultural business services; applied mathematics; astronomy and astrophysics; behavioral sciences; biology; business administration, management and operations; business, management, and marketing related; business/managerial economics; business operations support and assistant services; communication and journalism related; communication and media; computer and information sciences; computer science; computer systems networking and telecommunications; creative writing; criminal justice and corrections; culinary arts and related services; developmental and child psychology; economics; English; English composition; English language and literature related; fine and studio art; health professions related; hospitality administration; human development, family studies, and related services; insurance; legal research and advanced professional studies; legal studies (non-professional general, undergraduate); liberal arts and sciences, general studies and humanities; mathematics; music; nursing; nutrition sciences; philosophy; psychology; real estate; sales, merchandising, and related marketing operations (specialized); social work; sociology; statistics; vehicle maintenance and repair technologies; visual and performing arts related.
Non-credit—accounting and related services; crafts, folk art and artisanry; dance; data entry/microcomputer applications; data processing; English as a second language; health and physical education/fitness; health/medical preparatory programs; real estate.

NEBRASKA CHRISTIAN COLLEGE
Papillon, Nebraska
http://www.nechristian.edu
Nebraska Christian College was founded in 1944. It is accredited by Association for Biblical Higher Education. It first offered distance learning courses in 2000. In fall 2007, there were 50 students enrolled in distance learning courses. Institutionally administered financial aid is available to distance learners.
Services Distance learners have accessibility to academic advising, e-mail services, library services.

Contact Dr. M. Shane Wood, Chief Academic Officer, Nebraska Christian College, 12550 South 114th Street, Papillion, NE 68046. Telephone: 402-935-9400. Fax: 402-935-9500. E-mail: swood@nechristian.edu.

DEGREES AND AWARDS
Programs offered do not lead to a degree or other formal award.

COURSE SUBJECT AREAS OFFERED OUTSIDE OF DEGREE PROGRAMS
Undergraduate—missionary studies and missiology; theological and ministerial studies; theology and religious vocations related.

NEUMANN COLLEGE
Aston, Pennsylvania
neumannonline.org
http://www.neumann.edu/academics/online.asp
Neumann College was founded in 1965. It is accredited by Middle States Association of Colleges and Schools. It first offered distance learning courses in 1998. In fall 2007, there were 300 students enrolled in distance learning courses. Institutionally administered financial aid is available to distance learners.
Services Distance learners have accessibility to academic advising, bookstore, campus computer network, career placement assistance, e-mail services, library services, tutoring.
Contact Dr. Patricia Szymurski, Dean, Division of Continuing Adult and Professional Studies, Neumann College, One Neumann Drive, Aston, PA 19014-1298. Telephone: 610-558-5530. Fax: 610-361-5490. E-mail: szymurst@neumann.edu.

DEGREES AND AWARDS
AA Liberal Studies
MS Management Science

COURSE SUBJECT AREAS OFFERED OUTSIDE OF DEGREE PROGRAMS
Undergraduate—criminology; English; English literature (British and Commonwealth); human resources management; mathematics and statistics related; psychology; religious studies; technical and business writing.
Graduate—management information systems; management sciences and quantitative methods; nursing.

NEW ENGLAND COLLEGE
Henniker, New Hampshire
New England College was founded in 1946. It is accredited by New England Association of Schools and Colleges. It first offered distance learning courses in 2004. Institutionally administered financial aid is available to distance learners.
Contact Graduate and Professional Studies, New England College, 24 Bridge Street, Henniker, NH 03242. Telephone: 603-428-2000.

DEGREES AND AWARDS
BS Healthcare Administration
MA Public Policy
MSM Banking and Financial Management; Operations Management; Real Estate Management; Strategic Leadership
MSMM Marketing Management

NEW ENGLAND INSTITUTE OF TECHNOLOGY
Warwick, Rhode Island
http://blackboard.neit.edu
New England Institute of Technology was founded in 1940. It is accredited by New England Association of Schools and Colleges. It first offered distance learning courses in 1996. In fall 2007, there were 138 students enrolled in distance learning courses. Institutionally administered financial aid is available to distance learners.
Services Distance learners have accessibility to academic advising, bookstore, campus computer network, career placement assistance, e-mail services, library services, tutoring.

Contact Mr. Michael Caruso, Admissions Officer, New England Institute of Technology, 2500 Post Road, Warwick, RI 02886. Telephone: 401-739-5000 Ext. 3411. E-mail: mcaruso@neit.edu.

DEGREES AND AWARDS

AS Computer Technology; Information Technology; Surgical Technology

COURSE SUBJECT AREAS OFFERED OUTSIDE OF DEGREE PROGRAMS

Undergraduate—English composition; mathematics; physics; physiology, pathology and related sciences; psychology; sociology.

NEW JERSEY CITY UNIVERSITY
Jersey City, New Jersey
Continuing Education
http://newlearning.njcu.edu

New Jersey City University was founded in 1927. It is accredited by Middle States Association of Colleges and Schools. It first offered distance learning courses in 1997. In fall 2007, there were 1,932 students enrolled in distance learning courses. Institutionally administered financial aid is available to distance learners.

Services Distance learners have accessibility to bookstore, e-mail services, library services.

Contact Marie A. Fosello, Director of Online Learning, New Jersey City University, 2039 Kennedy Boulevard, Jersey City, NJ 07305-1597. Telephone: 201-200-3449. Fax: 201-200-2188. E-mail: conted@njcu.edu.

DEGREES AND AWARDS

MA Educational Technology
MS Accounting

COURSE SUBJECT AREAS OFFERED OUTSIDE OF DEGREE PROGRAMS

Undergraduate—accounting and related services; business/commerce; criminal justice and corrections; economics; international relations and affairs; mathematics; physics; political science and government; public health.
Graduate—accounting and related services; business administration, management and operations; criminology; educational administration and supervision; educational/instructional media design; public health; special education.

NEW JERSEY INSTITUTE OF TECHNOLOGY
Newark, New Jersey
Continuing Professional Education
http://cpe.njit.edu/

New Jersey Institute of Technology was founded in 1881. It is accredited by Middle States Association of Colleges and Schools. It first offered distance learning courses in 1985. In fall 2007, there were 900 students enrolled in distance learning courses. Institutionally administered financial aid is available to distance learners.

Services Distance learners have accessibility to academic advising, bookstore, campus computer network, career placement assistance, e-mail services, library services, tutoring.

Contact Ellen Schreihoffer, Director of Extended Learning Delivery, New Jersey Institute of Technology, University Heights, Newark, NJ 07102. Telephone: 973-596-6093. Fax: 973-596-3288. E-mail: el@njit.edu.

DEGREES AND AWARDS

BA Information Systems
BS Business; Computer Science; Information Systems; Information Technology
Certificate Essentials of Business Application Design; Essentials of Information Security; Essentials of Information Systems Management; Essentials of Web Application Development
Graduate Certificate Applied Statistical Methods; Biostatistics Essentials; Business & Computing; Business and Information Systems Imple-

mentation; Construction Management; Construction Management; Data Mining; Emergency Management; Environmental Sustainability; Finance for Managers; Information Assurance; Information Management for Managers; International Commerce; Internet Applications Development; Management Essentials; Management of Technology; Network Security and Information Assurance; Pharmaceutical Management; Pharmaceutical Manufacturing; Pharmaceutical Technology; Pharmaceuticalá Management; Power Systems Engineering; Practice of Technical Communications; Project Management; Sustainable Design; Telecommunications Networking; Venture and Innovation Management
MS Applied Mathematics; Applied Statistics; Architectural Studies; Computer Science; Engineering Management; Environmental Sciences; Information Systems; Management; Pharmaceutical Engineering; Professional and Technical Communications; Transportation

COURSE SUBJECT AREAS OFFERED OUTSIDE OF DEGREE PROGRAMS

Undergraduate—accounting and computer science; business/commerce; computer and information sciences; computer science; computer systems networking and telecommunications; information science/studies; management information systems.

Graduate—accounting and computer science; business administration, management and operations; business, management, and marketing related; communication and journalism related; computer/information technology administration and management; computer science; computer systems networking and telecommunications; engineering technologies related; information science/studies; management information systems; management sciences and quantitative methods; pharmacy, pharmaceutical sciences, and administration; statistics; technical and business writing.

NEW MEXICO HIGHLANDS UNIVERSITY
Las Vegas, New Mexico
http://www.nmhu.edu/

New Mexico Highlands University was founded in 1893. It is accredited by North Central Association of Colleges and Schools. It first offered distance learning courses in 1996. In fall 2007, there were 600 students enrolled in distance learning courses. Institutionally administered financial aid is available to distance learners.

Services Distance learners have accessibility to academic advising, bookstore, campus computer network, e-mail services, library services, tutoring.

Contact Miss Evonne Roybal-Tafoya, Director of Educational Outreach Services, New Mexico Highlands University, Educational Outreach Services, Box 9000, Las Vegas, NM 87701. Telephone: 505-454-3271. Fax: 505-454-3066. E-mail: roybal_ej@nmhu.edu.

DEGREES AND AWARDS

Programs offered do not lead to a degree or other formal award.

COURSE SUBJECT AREAS OFFERED OUTSIDE OF DEGREE PROGRAMS

Undergraduate—accounting and related services; bilingual, multilingual, and multicultural education; business administration, management and operations; business/commerce; business, management, and marketing related; business/managerial economics; computer science; criminology; curriculum and instruction; economics; education; educational administration and supervision; education related; health and physical education/fitness; management information systems; management sciences and quantitative methods; social work; special education.

Graduate—accounting and related services; bilingual, multilingual, and multicultural education; business administration, management and operations; business/commerce; business, management, and marketing related; business/managerial economics; curriculum and instruction; education; educational administration and supervision; education related; education (specific subject areas); English as a second/foreign language (teaching); health and physical education/fitness; management information systems; special education.

NEW MEXICO INSTITUTE OF MINING AND TECHNOLOGY
Socorro, New Mexico
Distance Education Department
http://distance.nmt.edu

New Mexico Institute of Mining and Technology was founded in 1889. It is accredited by North Central Association of Colleges and Schools. It first offered distance learning courses in 2000. In fall 2007, there were 130 students enrolled in distance learning courses. Institutionally administered financial aid is available to distance learners.

Services Distance learners have accessibility to academic advising, bookstore, campus computer network, career placement assistance, e-mail services, library services, tutoring.

Contact Mrs. Wendi Rae Carrillo, Student and Faculty Support Specialist, New Mexico Institute of Mining and Technology, 801 Leroy Place, Socorro, NM 87801. Telephone: 575-835-6908. Fax: 575-835-5541. E-mail: wcarrillo@admin.nmt.edu.

DEGREES AND AWARDS

Programs offered do not lead to a degree or other formal award.

COURSE SUBJECT AREAS OFFERED OUTSIDE OF DEGREE PROGRAMS

Undergraduate—aerospace, aeronautical and astronautical engineering; management information systems.

Graduate—aerospace, aeronautical and astronautical engineering; computer science; education (specific subject areas); engineering mechanics; environmental/environmental health engineering; management sciences and quantitative methods; materials engineering; mathematics; mechanical engineering; petroleum engineering.

NEW MEXICO JUNIOR COLLEGE
Hobbs, New Mexico
http://www.nmjc.edu

New Mexico Junior College was founded in 1965. It is accredited by North Central Association of Colleges and Schools. It first offered distance learning courses in 2001. In fall 2007, there were 1,150 students enrolled in distance learning courses. Institutionally administered financial aid is available to distance learners.

Services Distance learners have accessibility to academic advising, bookstore, campus computer network, career placement assistance, e-mail services, library services, tutoring.

Contact Mr. Jeff McCool, Dean of Training and Outreach, New Mexico Junior College, 5317 Lovington Highway, Hobbs, NM 88240. Telephone: 575-492-4711. Fax: 575-492-4727. E-mail: jmccool@nmjc.edu.

DEGREES AND AWARDS

Programs offered do not lead to a degree or other formal award.

COURSE SUBJECT AREAS OFFERED OUTSIDE OF DEGREE PROGRAMS

Undergraduate—accounting and computer science; allied health and medical assisting services; American literature (United States and Canadian); biblical and other theological languages and literatures; biology; business administration, management and operations; communication and journalism related; communication and media; computer software and media applications; criminal justice and corrections; design and applied arts; economics; education related; English composition; geological and earth sciences/geosciences; history; mathematics; mathematics and statistics related; nuclear and industrial radiologic technologies; psychology; social sciences; sociology.

Non-credit—building/construction finishing, management, and inspection; business/corporate communications; business, management, and marketing related; dance; entrepreneurial and small business operations; languages (foreign languages related).

NEW MEXICO STATE UNIVERSITY
Las Cruces, New Mexico
Office of Distance Education and Weekend College
http://distance.nmsu.edu

New Mexico State University was founded in 1888. It is accredited by North Central Association of Colleges and Schools. It first offered distance learning courses in 1989. In fall 2007, there were 4,037 students enrolled in distance learning courses. Institutionally administered financial aid is available to distance learners.

Services Distance learners have accessibility to academic advising, bookstore, campus computer network, career placement assistance, e-mail services, library services.

Contact Dr. Roberta Derlin, Associate Vice President for Student Success/ Associate Dean, College of Extended Learning, New Mexico State University, Box 30001, MSC 3CEL, Las Cruces, NM 88003. Telephone: 575-646-5095. Fax: 575-646-2044. E-mail: rderlin@nmsu.edu.

DEGREES AND AWARDS

BA Health and Social Services; Sociology
BBA General Business; Marketing
BCJ Criminal Justice
BS Elementary Education; Hotel, Restaurant, and Tourism Management; Information and Communication Technology
BSN Nursing
Certificate Online Teaching and Learning; Systems Engineering
Endorsement Information Technology Coordinator; Reading
License Educational Administrative Licensure; Elementary Licensure (post-BA); School Counseling Licensure; Special Education Alternative licensure
MA Agricultural and Extension Educator; Education; Educational Administration; Sociology
MAT Teaching of Science
MCJ Criminal Justice
MS Industrial Engineering
MSN Psychiatric-Mental Health
MSW Social Work
EdD Educational Administration (Educational Leadership)
PhD Curriculum and Instruction-Learning Technologies emphasis; Nursing

COURSE SUBJECT AREAS OFFERED OUTSIDE OF DEGREE PROGRAMS

Undergraduate—business administration, management and operations; business/commerce; community health services; computer/information technology administration and management; criminal justice and corrections; foods, nutrition, and related services; human services; mathematics; sociology.

Graduate—criminal justice and corrections; education related; industrial engineering; manufacturing engineering; mechanical engineering; nursing; nutrition sciences; sociology; special education.

NEW RIVER COMMUNITY COLLEGE
Dublin, Virginia
Distance Education and Off-Campus Services
http://de.nr.edu

New River Community College was founded in 1969. It is accredited by Southern Association of Colleges and Schools. It first offered distance learning courses in 1980. In fall 2007, there were 1,616 students enrolled in distance learning courses. Institutionally administered financial aid is available to distance learners.

Services Distance learners have accessibility to academic advising, bookstore, e-mail services, library services.

Contact Diane Viers, Media Specialist, New River Community College, PO Box 1127, 5251 College Drive, Dublin, VA 24084. Telephone: 540-674-3600 Ext. 4341. Fax: 540-674-3626. E-mail: nrvierb@nr.edu.

DEGREES AND AWARDS

AAS Education; General Studies

COURSE SUBJECT AREAS OFFERED OUTSIDE OF DEGREE PROGRAMS

Undergraduate—accounting and related services; American literature (United States and Canadian); American Sign Language (ASL); biological and physical sciences; biology; business, management, and marketing related; chemistry; computer science; criminal justice and corrections; developmental and child psychology; economics; educational psychology; English; English composition; entrepreneurial and small business operations; finance and financial management services; history; marketing; mathematics; music; psychology; sociology; statistics.

THE NEW SCHOOL: A UNIVERSITY
New York, New York
The New School Online–Bachelor's Program
http://adultba.newschool.edu

The New School: A University was founded in 1919. It is accredited by Middle States Association of Colleges and Schools. It first offered distance learning courses in 1994. Institutionally administered financial aid is available to distance learners.
Services Distance learners have accessibility to academic advising, bookstore, campus computer network, e-mail services, library services.
Contact Mr. David Norris, Director of Admission, The New School: A University, 66 West 12th Street, Room 401, New York, NY 10011. Telephone: 212-229-5630. Fax: 212-989-3887. E-mail: norrisd@ newschool.edu.

DEGREES AND AWARDS
BA Liberal Arts

COURSE SUBJECT AREAS OFFERED OUTSIDE OF DEGREE PROGRAMS

Undergraduate—communication and journalism related; communication and media; creative writing; liberal arts and sciences, general studies and humanities.
Non-credit—communication and journalism related; communication and media; creative writing; liberal arts and sciences, general studies and humanities.
See full description on page 414.

THE NEW SCHOOL: A UNIVERSITY
New York, New York
The New School Online–TESOL
http://www.newschool.edu/matesol/

The New School: A University was founded in 1919. It is accredited by Middle States Association of Colleges and Schools. It first offered distance learning courses in 1994. Institutionally administered financial aid is available to distance learners.
Services Distance learners have accessibility to academic advising, bookstore, campus computer network, e-mail services, library services.
Contact Ms. Gerianne Brusati, Associate Dean of Admissions, The New School: A University, 66 West 12th Street, Room 401, New York, NY 10011. Telephone: 212-229-5630. Fax: 212-989-3887. E-mail: brusatig @newschool.edu.

DEGREES AND AWARDS
MA Teaching English to Speakers of Other Languages
See full description on page 416.

THE NEW SCHOOL: A UNIVERSITY
New York, New York
The New School Online–Master of Arts in Media Studies Program
http://www.newschool.edu/mmp/

The New School: A University was founded in 1919. It is accredited by Middle States Association of Colleges and Schools. It first offered distance learning courses in 1994. Institutionally administered financial aid is available to distance learners.
Services Distance learners have accessibility to academic advising, bookstore, campus computer network, e-mail services, library services.

Contact Ms. Gerianne Brusati, Associate Dean for Admissions, The New School: A University, 66 West 12th Street, Room 401, New York, NY 10011. Telephone: 212-229-5630. Fax: 212-989-3887. E-mail: brusatig @newschool.edu.

DEGREES AND AWARDS
Graduate Certificate Media Management
MA Media Studies
See full description on page 418.

NEW YORK INSTITUTE OF TECHNOLOGY
Old Westbury, New York
On-Line Campus
http://www.nyit.edu

New York Institute of Technology was founded in 1955. It is accredited by Middle States Association of Colleges and Schools. It first offered distance learning courses in 1984. In fall 2007, there were 2,416 students enrolled in distance learning courses. Institutionally administered financial aid is available to distance learners.
Services Distance learners have accessibility to academic advising, bookstore, campus computer network, career placement assistance, e-mail services, library services.
Contact Ms. Kathleen Lyons, Assistant Director of Admissions, New York Institute of Technology, Carleton Avenue, PO Box 9029, Central Islip, NY 11729-9029. Telephone: 631-348-3200. Fax: 631-348-0912. E-mail: klyons@nyit.edu.

DEGREES AND AWARDS
BA Interdisciplinary Studies
BPS Hospitality Management; Interdisciplinary Studies
BS Business Administration; Community Mental Health; Criminal Justice; Interdisciplinary Studies; Psychology; Sociology
MBA Business
MS Energy Management

COURSE SUBJECT AREAS OFFERED OUTSIDE OF DEGREE PROGRAMS

Undergraduate—accounting and related services; anthropology; biology; business administration, management and operations; business, management, and marketing related; communication and media; creative writing; criminal justice and corrections; design and applied arts; economics; English; English composition; English language and literature related; environmental control technologies; finance and financial management services; journalism; legal studies (non-professional general, undergraduate); marketing; mechanical engineering; philosophy; philosophy and religious studies related; political science and government; social psychology; social work; sociology; speech and rhetoric; statistics.
Graduate—accounting and related services; business administration, management and operations; educational/instructional media design; management information systems; marketing.
Non-credit—computer and information sciences; computer and information sciences and support services related; computer/information technology administration and management; computer software and media applications; culinary arts and related services.

NICHOLS COLLEGE
Dudley, Massachusetts
Nichols College was founded in 1815. It is accredited by New England Association of Schools and Colleges.
Contact Online Programs, Nichols College, 124 Center Road, Dudley, MA 01571. Telephone: 508-213-1560.

DEGREES AND AWARDS
BSBA General Business
MBA Sport Management; Traditional MBA
MOL Organizational Leadership

NIPISSING UNIVERSITY
North Bay, Ontario, Canada
Centre for Continuing Education
http://www.nipissingu.ca/cce

Nipissing University was founded in 1992. It is provincially chartered. It first offered distance learning courses in 1997. In fall 2007, there were 450 students enrolled in distance learning courses. Institutionally administered financial aid is available to distance learners.

Services Distance learners have accessibility to academic advising, e-mail services, library services, tutoring.

Contact Emily Rostoks, Continuing Education Generalist, Nipissing University, 100 College Drive, Box 5002, North Bay, ON P1B 8L7, Canada. Telephone: 705-474-3450 Ext. 4343. Fax: 705-475-0264. E-mail: cce@nipissingu.ca.

DEGREES AND AWARDS
BComm Financial Services

COURSE SUBJECT AREAS OFFERED OUTSIDE OF DEGREE PROGRAMS
Undergraduate—accounting and related services; business administration, management and operations; business/commerce; business, management, and marketing related; economics; finance and financial management services; human resources management; international business; management sciences and quantitative methods; marketing.

NORTHAMPTON COUNTY AREA COMMUNITY COLLEGE
Bethlehem, Pennsylvania
Online Learning
http://www.northampton.edu

Northampton County Area Community College was founded in 1967. It is accredited by Middle States Association of Colleges and Schools. It first offered distance learning courses in 1998. In fall 2007, there were 4,000 students enrolled in distance learning courses. Institutionally administered financial aid is available to distance learners.

Services Distance learners have accessibility to academic advising, bookstore, campus computer network, career placement assistance, e-mail services, library services, tutoring.

Contact Ms. Lealan M. Zaccone, Assistant Director of Online Learning, Northampton County Area Community College, Kopecek Hall Room 230, 3835 Green Pond Road, Bethlehem, PA 18020. Telephone: 610-861-4154. Fax: 610-332-6595. E-mail: lzaccone@northampton.edu.

DEGREES AND AWARDS
AA Business Administration; Criminal Justice; General Studies; Individualized Transfer Studies; Liberal Arts; Social Work; Social Work; Sports Management
AAS Accounting; Early Childhood Education
AS Business Management
Specialized diploma Child Care–Family Child Care; Child Care–School Age Child Care; Early Childhood Education–Home-based Early Childhood Education; Library Technical Services

COURSE SUBJECT AREAS OFFERED OUTSIDE OF DEGREE PROGRAMS
Undergraduate—accounting and related services; allied health and medical assisting services; anthropology; applied mathematics; astronomy and astrophysics; behavioral sciences; biological and biomedical sciences related; biological and physical sciences; biology; business administration, management and operations; business/commerce; business/corporate communications; business, management, and marketing related; business/managerial economics; chemistry; clinical child psychology; clinical psychology; communication and journalism related; communication and media; communications technologies and support services related; computer and information sciences; computer and information sciences and support services related; computer science; computer software and media applications; counseling psychology; creative writing; criminal justice and corrections; data entry/microcomputer applications; developmental and child psychology; dietetics and clinical nutrition services;

economics; education; educational administration and supervision; educational psychology; education related; education (specific levels and methods); education (specific subject areas); electrical/electronics maintenance and repair technology; electromechanical and instrumentation and maintenance technologies; engineering/industrial management; engineering physics; engineering-related technologies; English; English as a second/foreign language (teaching); English as a second language; English composition; English language and literature related; English literature (British and Commonwealth); entrepreneurial and small business operations; experimental psychology; foods, nutrition, and related services; geography and cartography; geological and earth sciences/geosciences; health and physical education/fitness; history; human development, family studies, and related services; journalism; library assistant; marketing; mathematics; mathematics and statistics related; music; nursing; philosophy; psychology; sales, merchandising, and related marketing operations (general); social and philosophical foundations of education; social sciences; social sciences related; social work; sociology; special education; statistics; teaching assistants/aides.
Non-credit—education related; nursing.

NORTH ARKANSAS COLLEGE
Harrison, Arkansas
Articulated Programs and Distance Learning
http://www.northark.edu/

North Arkansas College was founded in 1974. It is accredited by North Central Association of Colleges and Schools. It first offered distance learning courses in 1988. In fall 2007, there were 600 students enrolled in distance learning courses. Institutionally administered financial aid is available to distance learners.

Services Distance learners have accessibility to bookstore, campus computer network, e-mail services, library services.

Contact Mr. John P. Walsh, Director of Distance Education, North Arkansas College, 1515 Pioneer Drive, Harrison, AR 72601. Telephone: 870-391-3308. Fax: 870-391-3250. E-mail: jwalsh@northark.edu.

DEGREES AND AWARDS
Programs offered do not lead to a degree or other formal award.

COURSE SUBJECT AREAS OFFERED OUTSIDE OF DEGREE PROGRAMS
Undergraduate—accounting and related services; agricultural business and management; agricultural production; anthropology; biological and physical sciences; business/corporate communications; computer/information technology administration and management; economics; education related; English composition; fine and studio art; history; human resources management; management information systems; mathematics; nursing; psychology; social sciences related; technical and business writing.
Non-credit—computer and information sciences and support services related; computer/information technology administration and management; computer software and media applications.

NORTH CAROLINA STATE UNIVERSITY
Raleigh, North Carolina
Distance Education
http://distance.ncsu.edu

North Carolina State University was founded in 1887. It is accredited by Southern Association of Colleges and Schools. It first offered distance learning courses in 1976. In fall 2007, there were 4,462 students enrolled in distance learning courses. Institutionally administered financial aid is available to distance learners.

Services Distance learners have accessibility to academic advising, bookstore, campus computer network, career placement assistance, e-mail services, library services, tutoring.

Contact Melissa M. Williford, Director, Distance Education Administrative Services, North Carolina State University, Campus Box 7292, DELTA, Venture IV, Raleigh, NC 27695-7292. Telephone: 919-515-9030. Fax: 919-515-6668. E-mail: melissa_williford@ncsu.edu.

DEGREES AND AWARDS

BA Leadership in the Public Sector

Certificate Computer Programming; HACCP/Food Safety Managers

Graduate Certificate Biological and Agricultural Engineering; Community College Teaching; Geographic Information Systems; Horticulture Science

MBAE Biological and Agricultural Engineering

MCE Chemical Engineering; Civil Engineering

MCS Computer Science

ME Engineering Online

MEd Curriculum and Instruction; Training and Development

MFHD Masters of Science in Human Development and Family Studies, Family Life and Parent Education concentration

MS Wood and Paper Science

MSAE Aerospace Engineering

MSE Agricultural Teacher Education

MSME Mechanical Engineering

MT Textiles Off-Campus programs (TOP)

COURSE SUBJECT AREAS OFFERED OUTSIDE OF DEGREE PROGRAMS

Undergraduate—accounting and related services; agricultural and domestic animal services; agricultural and food products processing; agricultural production; agriculture; American literature (United States and Canadian); animal sciences; anthropology; apparel and textiles; biological and physical sciences; business/commerce; business, management, and marketing related; chemistry; computer programming; educational psychology; education (specific subject areas); English; English as a second/foreign language (teaching); English composition; forestry; genetics; health and physical education/fitness; history; languages (Modern Greek); languages (Romance languages); languages (South Asian); mathematics; multi-/interdisciplinary studies related; music; nutrition sciences; parks, recreation and leisure facilities management; philosophy; physics; political science and government; psychology; soil sciences; technical and business writing; textile sciences and engineering; zoology/animal biology.

Graduate—agricultural and food products processing; agriculture; agriculture and agriculture operations related; biological and physical sciences; chemical engineering; civil engineering; computer engineering; curriculum and instruction; educational administration and supervision; education (specific subject areas); engineering; information science/studies; textile sciences and engineering.

NORTH CENTRAL MISSOURI COLLEGE
Trenton, Missouri
http://www.ncmissouri.edu

North Central Missouri College was founded in 1925. It is accredited by North Central Association of Colleges and Schools. It first offered distance learning courses in 1998. In fall 2007, there were 8 students enrolled in distance learning courses. Institutionally administered financial aid is available to distance learners.

Services Distance learners have accessibility to campus computer network, e-mail services, library services.

Contact Mrs. Linda L. Brown, Registrar, North Central Missouri College, Trenton, MO 64683. Telephone: 660-359-3948 Ext. 1205. E-mail: lbrown@mail.ncmissouri.edu.

DEGREES AND AWARDS
Programs offered do not lead to a degree or other formal award.

COURSE SUBJECT AREAS OFFERED OUTSIDE OF DEGREE PROGRAMS
Undergraduate—English composition; mathematics.

NORTH CENTRAL STATE COLLEGE
Mansfield, Ohio
http://www.ncstatecollege.edu

North Central State College was founded in 1961. It is accredited by North Central Association of Colleges and Schools. It first offered distance learning courses in 1994. In fall 2007, there were 329 students enrolled in distance learning courses. Institutionally administered financial aid is available to distance learners.

Services Distance learners have accessibility to academic advising, bookstore, campus computer network, e-mail services, library services, tutoring.

Contact Gina Kamwithi, Chair, Community Education Department, North Central State College, Community Education Department, 2441 Kenwood Cirlce, Mansfield, OH 44901. Telephone: 419-755-4711. Fax: 419-755-5674. E-mail: dl@ncstatecollege.edu.

DEGREES AND AWARDS
Programs offered do not lead to a degree or other formal award.

COURSE SUBJECT AREAS OFFERED OUTSIDE OF DEGREE PROGRAMS
Undergraduate—accounting and computer science; allied health and medical assisting services; behavioral sciences; biological and physical sciences; business administration, management and operations; business/corporate communications; English literature (British and Commonwealth); international business.

NORTH CENTRAL TEXAS COLLEGE
Gainesville, Texas
http://www.nctc.edu

North Central Texas College was founded in 1924. It is accredited by Southern Association of Colleges and Schools. It first offered distance learning courses in 1999. In fall 2007, there were 1,457 students enrolled in distance learning courses. Institutionally administered financial aid is available to distance learners.

Services Distance learners have accessibility to academic advising, bookstore, library services, tutoring.

Contact Debbie J. Huffman, Director of e-Learning, North Central Texas College, 1525 West California Street, Gainesville, TX 76240. Telephone: 940-668-7731 Ext. 4475. Fax: 940-668-6490. E-mail: dhuffman@nctc.edu.

DEGREES AND AWARDS
Programs offered do not lead to a degree or other formal award.

COURSE SUBJECT AREAS OFFERED OUTSIDE OF DEGREE PROGRAMS
Undergraduate—agricultural business and management; American literature (United States and Canadian); biology; business administration, management and operations; business, management, and marketing related; business operations support and assistant services; computer and information sciences; computer/information technology administration and management; computer software and media applications; computer systems networking and telecommunications; criminal justice and corrections; criminology; dance; data entry/microcomputer applications; developmental and child psychology; economics; education; English; English composition; English language and literature related; English literature (British and Commonwealth); fine and studio art; history; mathematics; music; nutrition sciences; political science and government; psychology; sociology; speech and rhetoric.

NORTHCENTRAL UNIVERSITY
Prescott Valley, Arizona
MBA Program
http://www.ncu.edu

Northcentral University is accredited by North Central Association of Colleges and Schools. It first offered distance learning courses in 1996. In fall 2007, there were 5,879 students enrolled in distance learning courses. Institutionally administered financial aid is available to distance learners.

Services Distance learners have accessibility to academic advising, bookstore, campus computer network, e-mail services, library services.

Contact Mr. Brent Passey, Director of Admissions, Northcentral University, 10000 East University Drive, Prescott Valley, AZ 86314. Telephone: 866-776-0331. Fax: 928-541-7817. E-mail: info@ncu.edu.

DEGREES AND AWARDS

BA Business Administration; Psychology

MA Psychology

MBA Business Administration

MEd Education

DBA Business Administration

EdD Education

PhD Business Administration; Education; Psychology–Marriage and Family Therapy specialization; Psychology

COURSE SUBJECT AREAS OFFERED OUTSIDE OF DEGREE PROGRAMS

Undergraduate—business administration, management and operations; computer/information technology administration and management; education related; psychology.

Graduate—business administration, management and operations; computer and information sciences and support services related; criminal justice and corrections; education; engineering/industrial management; family psychology; finance and financial management services; human resources management; industrial and organizational psychology; international business; psychology related; public administration.

NORTH DAKOTA STATE COLLEGE OF SCIENCE
Wahpeton, North Dakota
http://www.ndscs.edu/

North Dakota State College of Science was founded in 1903. It is accredited by North Central Association of Colleges and Schools. It first offered distance learning courses in 1968. In fall 2007, there were 942 students enrolled in distance learning courses. Institutionally administered financial aid is available to distance learners.

Services Distance learners have accessibility to academic advising, bookstore, career placement assistance, e-mail services, library services, tutoring.

Contact Ms. Margaret Wall, Dean of Extended Learning, North Dakota State College of Science, 800 Sixth Street North, Wahpeton, ND 58076-0002. Telephone: 701-671-2430. Fax: 701-671-2416. E-mail: margaret.wall@ndscs.edu.

DEGREES AND AWARDS

AAS Administrative Assistant; Architectural Drafting and Estimating Technology; Business Management–eBusiness emphasis; Civil Engineering and Surveying Technology; Health Information Technician; Pharmacy Technician

AS Nursing–Practical Nursing

Certificate Computer Information Systems–Web Design; HIT–Medical Coding; Medical Transcription

COURSE SUBJECT AREAS OFFERED OUTSIDE OF DEGREE PROGRAMS

Undergraduate—accounting and related services; allied health and medical assisting services; applied mathematics; biology; business administration, management and operations; business, management, and marketing related; chemistry; civil engineering technology; computer and information sciences; computer and information sciences and support services related; computer/information technology administration and management; computer programming; developmental and child psychology; drafting/design engineering technologies; economics; English; English composition; foods, nutrition, and related services; health and medical administrative services; health and physical education/fitness; health professions related; history; marketing; mathematics; microbiological sciences and immunology; psychology; psychology related; social sciences; sociology; technical and business writing.

NORTH DAKOTA STATE UNIVERSITY
Fargo, North Dakota
Division of Distance and Continuing Education
http://www.ndsu.edu/dce

North Dakota State University was founded in 1890. It is accredited by North Central Association of Colleges and Schools. It first offered distance learning courses in 1998. Institutionally administered financial aid is available to distance learners.

Services Distance learners have accessibility to academic advising, bookstore, career placement assistance, e-mail services, library services, tutoring.

Contact Karen Murie, Distance Learning Coordinator, North Dakota State University, PO Box 5819, University Station, Fargo, ND 58105. Telephone: 701-231-7015. Fax: 701-231-7016. E-mail: karen.murie@ndsu.edu.

DEGREES AND AWARDS

BS Sociology

BSN LPN/RN to BSN

BUS University Studies

CAGS Family Financial Planning; Food Protection; Gerontology; Merchandising; Software Engineering

MS Communication; Community Development; Construction Management; Dietetics; Family Financial Planning; Family and Consumer Science Education; Gerontology; Merchandising

COURSE SUBJECT AREAS OFFERED OUTSIDE OF DEGREE PROGRAMS

Undergraduate—applied mathematics; clinical psychology; communication and media; computer and information sciences; data entry/microcomputer applications; developmental and child psychology; education; foods, nutrition, and related services; hospitality administration; human development, family studies, and related services; mathematics.

Graduate—clinical psychology; communication and media; computer engineering; curriculum and instruction; education; educational administration and supervision; educational/instructional media design; education (specific levels and methods); family and consumer economics; human development, family studies, and related services; psychology; special education.

Non-credit—aerospace, aeronautical and astronautical engineering; allied health and medical assisting services; business/commerce; business operations support and assistant services; clinical psychology; computer and information sciences; computer programming; computer science; computer software and media applications; data entry/microcomputer applications; human development, family studies, and related services.

See full description on page 420.

NORTHEAST ALABAMA COMMUNITY COLLEGE
Rainsville, Alabama
http://www.nacc.edu

Northeast Alabama Community College was founded in 1963. It is accredited by Southern Association of Colleges and Schools. It first offered distance learning courses in 2000. In fall 2007, there were 853 students enrolled in distance learning courses. Institutionally administered financial aid is available to distance learners.

Services Distance learners have accessibility to academic advising, bookstore, campus computer network, career placement assistance, e-mail services, library services, tutoring.

Contact Mrs. Judith Lea, Blackboard Administrator, Northeast Alabama Community College, 138 AL Highway 35, Rainsville, AL 35986. Telephone: 256-228-6001 Ext. 309. Fax: 256-228-6992. E-mail: leaj@nacc.edu.

DEGREES AND AWARDS

Programs offered do not lead to a degree or other formal award.

COURSE SUBJECT AREAS OFFERED OUTSIDE OF DEGREE PROGRAMS

Undergraduate—accounting and computer science; American literature (United States and Canadian); behavioral sciences; biology; business administration, management and operations; chemistry; computer science; criminal justice and corrections; data processing; economics; English composition; English literature (British and Commonwealth); mathematics; music; psychology; sociology.

NORTHEASTERN ILLINOIS UNIVERSITY
Chicago, Illinois
http://www.neiu.edu/

Northeastern Illinois University was founded in 1961. It is accredited by North Central Association of Colleges and Schools. It first offered distance learning courses in 2000. In fall 2007, there were 100 students enrolled in distance learning courses. Institutionally administered financial aid is available to distance learners.

Services Distance learners have accessibility to campus computer network, e-mail services, library services.

Contact Mr. Bradley F. Baker, Dean of Libraries/Learning Resources, Northeastern Illinois University, 5500 North St. Louis Avenue, Chicago, IL 60625. Telephone: 773-442-4466. Fax: 773-442-4531. E-mail: b-baker@neiu.edu.

DEGREES AND AWARDS
Programs offered do not lead to a degree or other formal award.

COURSE SUBJECT AREAS OFFERED OUTSIDE OF DEGREE PROGRAMS

Undergraduate—business administration, management and operations; educational/instructional media design; fine and studio art; geological and earth sciences/geosciences; mathematics; music; psychology; social work.
Graduate—educational administration and supervision; education (specific subject areas); gerontology.

NORTHEASTERN UNIVERSITY
Boston, Massachusetts
Distance Learning Center
http://www.spcs.neu.edu/online/

Northeastern University was founded in 1898. It is accredited by New England Association of Schools and Colleges. It first offered distance learning courses in 1984. In fall 2007, there were 1,700 students enrolled in distance learning courses. Institutionally administered financial aid is available to distance learners.

Services Distance learners have accessibility to academic advising, bookstore, campus computer network, career placement assistance, e-mail services, library services, tutoring.

Contact Denise Weir, Director, Distance Learning, Northeastern University, 360 Huntington Avenue, 263 RY, Boston, MA 02115. Telephone: 617-373-7563. E-mail: d.weir@neu.edu.

DEGREES AND AWARDS
AS Accounting; Arts and Sciences; Business Administration; Finance; Human Resources Management; Management Information Systems; Marketing; Marketing
BS English; Environmental Studies; Finance and Accounting Management; History; Human Services; Information Technology; Leadership; Liberal Arts with Business minor; Liberal Studies; Management; Organizational Communications; Political Science; Psychology; Public Affairs; Sociology; Technical Communications
Certification Business English
Graduate Certificate Forensic Accounting; Higher Education Administration; Information Security Management; International Regulatory Affairs; Interpreter Education Master Mentor; Leadership; Network Security Management; Nonprofit Management; Pharmacogenetics Essentials; Project Management; Vaccines–Technologies, Trends, and Bioterrorism
MEd K-12 Specialization
MPS Informatics
MS Applied Nutrition; Interpreter Pedagogy; Leadership; Regulatory Affairs for Drugs, Biologics, and Medical Devices; Respiratory Care Leadership
MSEE Electrical and Computer Engineering

MSIS Information Systems

COURSE SUBJECT AREAS OFFERED OUTSIDE OF DEGREE PROGRAMS

Undergraduate—accounting and related services; business administration, management and operations; computer programming; finance and financial management services; health services/allied health/health sciences; human resources management; legal studies (non-professional general, undergraduate); legal support services; technical and business writing.

NORTHEAST IOWA COMMUNITY COLLEGE
Calmar, Iowa
http://www.nicc.edu

Northeast Iowa Community College was founded in 1966. It is accredited by North Central Association of Colleges and Schools. It first offered distance learning courses in 1993. In fall 2007, there were 2,420 students enrolled in distance learning courses. Institutionally administered financial aid is available to distance learners.

Services Distance learners have accessibility to academic advising, bookstore, campus computer network, career placement assistance, e-mail services, library services.

Contact Mari Eitel, Secretary, Distance Learning, Northeast Iowa Community College, Highway 150 South, PO Box 400, Calmar, IA 52132. Telephone: 563-562-3263 Ext. 374. Fax: 563-562-4362. E-mail: eitelm @nicc.edu.

DEGREES AND AWARDS
AA Business Administration; Criminal Justice; General degree
AAS Agriculture Business; Business Specialist; Health Information Technology
Certification Institutional Food Service Supervisor
Diploma Medical Transcriptionist

COURSE SUBJECT AREAS OFFERED OUTSIDE OF DEGREE PROGRAMS

Undergraduate—accounting and computer science; accounting and related services; agricultural business and management; applied mathematics; biological and physical sciences; biology; chemistry; cognitive psychology and psycholinguistics; communication and media; cosmetology and related personal grooming services; developmental and child psychology; English composition; English literature (British and Commonwealth); history; human resources management; management information systems; marketing; nutrition sciences; religious studies; statistics.

NORTHEAST STATE TECHNICAL COMMUNITY COLLEGE
Blountville, Tennessee
Evening and Distance Education
http://northeaststate.edu

Northeast State Technical Community College was founded in 1966. It is accredited by Southern Association of Colleges and Schools. It first offered distance learning courses in 1996. In fall 2007, there were 3,200 students enrolled in distance learning courses. Institutionally administered financial aid is available to distance learners.

Services Distance learners have accessibility to academic advising, bookstore, campus computer network, career placement assistance, e-mail services, library services.

Contact Mr. James M. Ramey, Coordinator of Distance Education Programs and Services, Northeast State Technical Community College, PO Box 246, Blountville, TN 37617. Telephone: 423-354-2497. Fax: 423-323-0224. E-mail: jmramey@northeaststate.edu.

DEGREES AND AWARDS
AAS Business

COURSE SUBJECT AREAS OFFERED OUTSIDE OF DEGREE PROGRAMS

Undergraduate—accounting and related services; astronomy and astrophysics; biological and physical sciences; business administration, management and operations; chemistry; computer and information sciences; economics; education; English; English composition; history; mathematics; music; political science and government; psychology; social sciences; speech and rhetoric.

NORTHERN STATE UNIVERSITY
Aberdeen, South Dakota
Continuing Education
http://www.northern.edu

Northern State University was founded in 1901. It is accredited by North Central Association of Colleges and Schools. It first offered distance learning courses in 1994. In fall 2007, there were 274 students enrolled in distance learning courses. Institutionally administered financial aid is available to distance learners.
Services Distance learners have accessibility to academic advising, bookstore, campus computer network, career placement assistance, e-mail services, library services, tutoring.
Contact Peggy Hallstrom, Registrar, Northern State University, 1200 South Jay Street, Aberdeen, SD 57401-7198. Telephone: 605-626-2012. Fax: 605-626-2587. E-mail: hallstrp@northern.edu.

DEGREES AND AWARDS
Programs offered do not lead to a degree or other formal award.

COURSE SUBJECT AREAS OFFERED OUTSIDE OF DEGREE PROGRAMS
Undergraduate—biological and physical sciences; business/commerce; computer and information sciences; criminology; dramatic/theater arts and stagecraft; economics; educational psychology; English; English composition; health and physical education/fitness; languages (Germanic); library science; linguistic, comparative, and related language studies; mathematics; mathematics and statistics related; music; sociology.
Graduate—education; educational psychology.

NORTHERN VIRGINIA COMMUNITY COLLEGE
Annandale, Virginia
Extended Learning Institute
http://eli.nvcc.edu

Northern Virginia Community College was founded in 1965. It is accredited by Southern Association of Colleges and Schools. It first offered distance learning courses in 1975. In fall 2007, there were 6,500 students enrolled in distance learning courses. Institutionally administered financial aid is available to distance learners.
Services Distance learners have accessibility to academic advising, bookstore, campus computer network, e-mail services, library services, tutoring.
Contact Jayne Townend, Admissions and Registration, Northern Virginia Community College, 8333 Little River Turnpike, Annandale, VA 22003-3796. Telephone: 703-323-3347. Fax: 703-323-3392. E-mail: elicoursespecialists@nvcc.edu.

DEGREES AND AWARDS
AA Liberal Arts
AAS Business Administration–Administrative Support Technology specialization; Business Management–Public Management specialization; Business Management
AS Accounting; Business Administration; General Studies; Information Technology; Social Sciences

COURSE SUBJECT AREAS OFFERED OUTSIDE OF DEGREE PROGRAMS
Undergraduate—biology; business administration, management and operations; business, management, and marketing related; chemistry; communication and journalism related; computer and information sciences; criminal justice and corrections; economics; education; engineering; English; English as a second language; health services/allied health/health sciences; history; languages (East Asian); languages (Middle/Near Eastern and Semitic); languages (Romance languages);

legal professions and studies related; mathematics; nursing; philosophy; physics; psychology; religious studies; sociology; speech and rhetoric.

NORTH FLORIDA COMMUNITY COLLEGE
Madison, Florida
http://www.nfcc.edu

North Florida Community College was founded in 1958. It is accredited by Southern Association of Colleges and Schools. It first offered distance learning courses in 2000. In fall 2007, there were 800 students enrolled in distance learning courses. Institutionally administered financial aid is available to distance learners.
Services Distance learners have accessibility to campus computer network, e-mail services, library services.
Contact Dr. Sharon Erle, Chief Academic Officer, North Florida Community College, 325 Turner Davis Drive, Madison, FL 32340. Telephone: 850-973-1603. E-mail: erles@nfcc.edu.

DEGREES AND AWARDS
Programs offered do not lead to a degree or other formal award.

COURSE SUBJECT AREAS OFFERED OUTSIDE OF DEGREE PROGRAMS
Undergraduate—accounting and computer science; business, management, and marketing related; computer software and media applications; educational/instructional media design; education related; English composition; English language and literature related; human development, family studies, and related services; nutrition sciences; psychology; social sciences; sociology.

NORTH IOWA AREA COMMUNITY COLLEGE
Mason City, Iowa
http://www.niacc.edu

North Iowa Area Community College was founded in 1918. It is accredited by North Central Association of Colleges and Schools. It first offered distance learning courses in 1989. In fall 2007, there were 575 students enrolled in distance learning courses. Institutionally administered financial aid is available to distance learners.
Services Distance learners have accessibility to academic advising, bookstore, e-mail services, library services.
Contact Ms. Michelle Petznic, Registrar, North Iowa Area Community College, 500 College Drive, Mason City, IA 50401. Telephone: 641-422-4205. Fax: 641-422-4112. E-mail: petznmic@niacc.edu.

DEGREES AND AWARDS
AA Pre-Baccalaureate

COURSE SUBJECT AREAS OFFERED OUTSIDE OF DEGREE PROGRAMS
Undergraduate—accounting and related services; applied mathematics; biology; business/commerce; business, management, and marketing related; chemistry; economics; English composition; geography and cartography; history; human resources management; mathematics; philosophy; psychology; speech and rhetoric; statistics; visual and performing arts.
Non-credit—computer software and media applications; human development, family studies, and related services; nursing; public health.

NORTH LAKE COLLEGE
Irving, Texas
http://www.northlakecollege.edu

North Lake College was founded in 1977. It is accredited by Southern Association of Colleges and Schools. It first offered distance learning courses in 2000. In fall 2007, there were 2,168 students enrolled in distance learning courses. Institutionally administered financial aid is available to distance learners.
Services Distance learners have accessibility to academic advising, bookstore, campus computer network, career placement assistance, e-mail services, library services, tutoring.

Contact Ms. Shirley Thompson, Professor, North Lake College, Irving, TX 75052. E-mail: sthompson@dcccd.edu.

DEGREES AND AWARDS
AAS Mortgage Banking; Real Estate

COURSE SUBJECT AREAS OFFERED OUTSIDE OF DEGREE PROGRAMS

Undergraduate—accounting and related services; bilingual, multilingual, and multicultural education; biological and physical sciences; biology; business/commerce; business, management, and marketing related; chemistry; communications technology; computer and information sciences; computer programming; computer systems networking and telecommunications; economics; education; English; English as a second language; English composition; history; human development, family studies, and related services; languages (Romance languages); mathematics; music; philosophy; physics; political science and government; psychology; real estate; sociology; statistics; transportation and materials moving related.

NORTHLAND COMMUNITY AND TECHNICAL COLLEGE–THIEF RIVER FALLS
Thief River Falls, Minnesota
http://www.distance.minnesota.edu

Northland Community and Technical College–Thief River Falls was founded in 1965. It is accredited by North Central Association of Colleges and Schools. It first offered distance learning courses in 1996. In fall 2007, there were 1,350 students enrolled in distance learning courses. Institutionally administered financial aid is available to distance learners.
Services Distance learners have accessibility to academic advising, bookstore, career placement assistance, e-mail services, library services, tutoring.
Contact Minnesota Online Support Center, Northland Community and Technical College–Thief River Falls, 150 2nd Avenue SW, Suite B, Box 309, Perham, MN 56573. Telephone: 800-456-8519. Fax: 218-347-6217. E-mail: distancemn@custhellp.com.

DEGREES AND AWARDS
AA Liberal Arts and Sciences
AAS Practical Nursing

COURSE SUBJECT AREAS OFFERED OUTSIDE OF DEGREE PROGRAMS

Undergraduate—accounting and related services; biology; business administration, management and operations; business/commerce; business operations support and assistant services; communication and media; computer and information sciences; mathematics; nursing.

NORTH PARK UNIVERSITY
Chicago, Illinois
http://www.northpark.edu/

North Park University was founded in 1891. It is accredited by North Central Association of Colleges and Schools. It first offered distance learning courses in 1999. In fall 2007, there were 200 students enrolled in distance learning courses. Institutionally administered financial aid is available to distance learners.
Services Distance learners have accessibility to bookstore, campus computer network, e-mail services, library services.
Contact Ms. Allyson Dickie, Associate Dean of Distributed Learning, North Park University, 3225 West Foster Avenue, Chicago, IL 60625. Telephone: 773-244-6287. E-mail: dickiea@northpark.edu.

DEGREES AND AWARDS
MM Not-for-Profit Management

COURSE SUBJECT AREAS OFFERED OUTSIDE OF DEGREE PROGRAMS
Graduate—theological and ministerial studies.
Non-credit—theological and ministerial studies.

NORTH SEATTLE COMMUNITY COLLEGE
Seattle, Washington
Distance Learning Office
http://www.virtualcollege.org

North Seattle Community College was founded in 1970. It is accredited by Northwest Commission on Colleges and Universities. It first offered distance learning courses in 1994. In fall 2007, there were 1,136 students enrolled in distance learning courses. Institutionally administered financial aid is available to distance learners.
Services Distance learners have accessibility to academic advising, bookstore, campus computer network, career placement assistance, e-mail services, library services, tutoring.
Contact Carol Howe, Program Coordinator, North Seattle Community College, 9600 College Way North, LB2237, Seattle, WA 98103. Telephone: 206-527-3738. Fax: 206-985-3984. E-mail: distance@sccd.ctc.edu.

DEGREES AND AWARDS
AA General Studies

COURSE SUBJECT AREAS OFFERED OUTSIDE OF DEGREE PROGRAMS

Undergraduate—accounting and related services; anthropology; astronomy and astrophysics; biological and physical sciences; business/commerce; communication and media; computer programming; computer software and media applications; computer systems networking and telecommunications; economics; English composition; film/video and photographic arts; geological and earth sciences/geosciences; human development, family studies, and related services; journalism; library science related; mathematics; music; philosophy; psychology.

NORTHWEST ARKANSAS COMMUNITY COLLEGE
Bentonville, Arkansas
Northwest Arkansas Distance Education
http://www.nwacc.edu/disted

NorthWest Arkansas Community College was founded in 1989. It is accredited by North Central Association of Colleges and Schools. It first offered distance learning courses in 1997. In fall 2007, there were 1,639 students enrolled in distance learning courses. Institutionally administered financial aid is available to distance learners.
Services Distance learners have accessibility to academic advising, bookstore, career placement assistance, e-mail services, library services, tutoring.
Contact Mr. Clint Brooks, Director of Distance Learning, NorthWest Arkansas Community College, BH 2413, One College Drive, Bentonville, AR 72712. Telephone: 479-619-4382. Fax: 479-619-4383. E-mail: cbrooks@nwacc.edu.

DEGREES AND AWARDS
AA Transfer degree
AAS Environmental and Regulatory Science

COURSE SUBJECT AREAS OFFERED OUTSIDE OF DEGREE PROGRAMS
Undergraduate—accounting and related services; agricultural and food products processing; agriculture; allied health diagnostic, intervention, and treatment professions; apparel and textiles; applied mathematics; behavioral sciences; biology; business administration, management and operations; business/corporate communications; business, management, and marketing related; business operations support and assistant services; chemistry; communication and media; computer and information sciences; computer and information sciences and support services related; computer/information technology administration and management; computer programming; computer software and media applications; computer systems networking and telecommunications; creative writing; criminal justice and corrections; developmental and child psychology; economics; English; English composition; English language and literature related; entrepreneurial and small business operations; fine and studio art; fire protection; food science and technology; foods, nutrition, and related services; geography and cartography; geological and earth

sciences/geosciences; health and physical education/fitness; health professions related; health services/allied health/health sciences; history; hospitality administration; international business; legal studies (non-professional general, undergraduate); liberal arts and sciences, general studies and humanities; mathematics; medical basic sciences; music; nutrition sciences; personal and culinary services related; philosophy; political science and government; psychology; psychology related; social sciences; social sciences related; sociology; speech and rhetoric.

Non-credit—English composition; mathematics.

NORTHWESTERN CONNECTICUT COMMUNITY COLLEGE
Winsted, Connecticut
http://www.nwcc.commnet.edu/

Northwestern Connecticut Community College was founded in 1965. It is accredited by New England Association of Schools and Colleges. It first offered distance learning courses in 1997. In fall 2007, there were 300 students enrolled in distance learning courses. Institutionally administered financial aid is available to distance learners.

Services Distance learners have accessibility to academic advising, bookstore, e-mail services, library services, tutoring.

Contact Beverly J. King, Director, Education Technology/Distance Learning, Northwestern Connecticut Community College, Park Place East, Winsted, CT 06098. Telephone: 860-738-6323. E-mail: bking@nwcc.commnet.edu.

DEGREES AND AWARDS
Programs offered do not lead to a degree or other formal award.

COURSE SUBJECT AREAS OFFERED OUTSIDE OF DEGREE PROGRAMS
Undergraduate—allied health and medical assisting services; biological and physical sciences; business, management, and marketing related; computer and information sciences; English as a second/foreign language (teaching); English composition; geography and cartography; history; mathematics; philosophy; psychology; science, technology and society; sociology.

Non-credit—computer and information sciences; computer software and media applications; technical and business writing.

NORTHWESTERN MICHIGAN COLLEGE
Traverse City, Michigan
Distance Education Services
http://www.nmc.edu/flo/

Northwestern Michigan College was founded in 1951. It is accredited by North Central Association of Colleges and Schools. It first offered distance learning courses in 1982. In fall 2007, there were 1,460 students enrolled in distance learning courses. Institutionally administered financial aid is available to distance learners.

Services Distance learners have accessibility to academic advising, bookstore, campus computer network, career placement assistance, e-mail services, library services, tutoring.

Contact Janet Oliver, Director, Northwestern Michigan College, Educational Media Technologies, 1701 East Front Street, Traverse City, MI 49686. Telephone: 231-995-1076. Fax: 231-995-1080. E-mail: joliver@nmc.edu.

DEGREES AND AWARDS
AAS Business Administration; Education, general transfer
AD Nursing
AGS Associate in General Studies (AGS)
Certificate Office Applications Specialist

COURSE SUBJECT AREAS OFFERED OUTSIDE OF DEGREE PROGRAMS
Undergraduate—accounting and related services; anthropology; biology; business administration, management and operations; business/corporate communications; business, management, and marketing related; chemistry; computer and information sciences; computer and information

sciences and support services related; computer programming; computer software and media applications; computer systems networking and telecommunications; creative writing; criminal justice and corrections; economics; English composition; English language and literature related; history; legal studies (non-professional general, undergraduate); mathematics and statistics related; music; nursing; pharmacology and toxicology; philosophy; physics; psychology; psychology related; sociology; statistics; technical and business writing.

NORTHWESTERN OKLAHOMA STATE UNIVERSITY
Alva, Oklahoma
http://www.nwalva.edu/

Northwestern Oklahoma State University was founded in 1897. It is accredited by North Central Association of Colleges and Schools. It first offered distance learning courses in 2004. In fall 2007, there were 923 students enrolled in distance learning courses. Institutionally administered financial aid is available to distance learners.

Services Distance learners have accessibility to bookstore, campus computer network, e-mail services, library services.

Contact Dr. Nancy J. Knous, Coordinator of Distance Learning, Northwestern Oklahoma State University, 709 Oklahoma Boulevard, Alva, OK 73717. Telephone: 580-327-8443. Fax: 580-327-8431. E-mail: njknous@nwosu.edu.

DEGREES AND AWARDS
Programs offered do not lead to a degree or other formal award.

COURSE SUBJECT AREAS OFFERED OUTSIDE OF DEGREE PROGRAMS
Undergraduate—accounting and computer science; accounting and related services; business administration, management and operations; business/commerce; business/corporate communications; communication and media; criminal justice and corrections; curriculum and instruction; education; English; English literature (British and Commonwealth); history; public relations, advertising, and applied communication related; social psychology; sociology.

Graduate—bilingual, multilingual, and multicultural education; business administration, management and operations; educational administration and supervision; education related.

NORTHWESTERN STATE UNIVERSITY OF LOUISIANA
Natchitoches, Louisiana
http://www.nsula.edu/ece

Northwestern State University of Louisiana was founded in 1884. It is accredited by Southern Association of Colleges and Schools. It first offered distance learning courses in 1998. In fall 2007, there were 4,508 students enrolled in distance learning courses. Institutionally administered financial aid is available to distance learners.

Services Distance learners have accessibility to academic advising, bookstore, campus computer network, career placement assistance, e-mail services, library services, tutoring.

Contact Dr. Darlene Williams, Vice President for Technology, Research, and Economic Development, Northwestern State University of Louisiana, Electronic and Continuing Education, 100 Dodd Hall, Natchitoches, LA 71497. Telephone: 318-357-6355. Fax: 318-357-5573. E-mail: darlene@nsula.edu.

DEGREES AND AWARDS
AA Criminal Justice
ABA Business Administration
AD Office Administration
AGS General Studies
BA Criminal Justice
BGS General Studies
BS Psychology
BSN Nursing–RN to BSN
BSRS Radiologic Science

Certification Mild/Moderate Special Education; School Media Specialist
Advanced Graduate Diploma Educational Leadership and Instruction
MA Adult Education; Art
MAE Educational Technology
MSE Health and Human Performance

COURSE SUBJECT AREAS OFFERED OUTSIDE OF DEGREE PROGRAMS

Undergraduate—accounting and related services; biological and physical sciences; business administration, management and operations; business, management, and marketing related; chemistry; communication and journalism related; computer and information sciences; computer software and media applications; creative writing; criminal justice and corrections; economics; educational/instructional media design; education related; education (specific levels and methods); English; English composition; family and consumer sciences/human sciences; finance and financial management services; fine and studio art; health and physical education/ fitness; history; journalism; library science related; marketing; mathematics; nursing; physical sciences; psychology; social work; technical and business writing; zoology/animal biology.
Graduate—educational administration and supervision; educational assessment, evaluation, and research; educational/instructional media design; educational psychology; education related; psychology; special education.

NORTHWEST MISSOURI STATE UNIVERSITY
Maryville, Missouri
Center for Information Technology in Education
http://www.NorthwestOnline.org
Northwest Missouri State University was founded in 1905. It is accredited by North Central Association of Colleges and Schools. It first offered distance learning courses in 1999. In fall 2007, there were 1,100 students enrolled in distance learning courses. Institutionally administered financial aid is available to distance learners.
Services Distance learners have accessibility to academic advising, bookstore, campus computer network, career placement assistance, e-mail services, library services.
Contact Dr. Roger Von Holzen, Director of Center for Information Technology in Education, Northwest Missouri State University, OL 246, Maryville, MO 64468. Telephone: 660-562-1532. Fax: 660-562-1049. E-mail: rvh@nwmissouri.edu.

DEGREES AND AWARDS
BS Accounting; Business Management; Management Information Systems; Office Information Systems
MS Applied Computer Science; Geographic Information Science
MSE Special Education; Teaching–Instructional Technology

COURSE SUBJECT AREAS OFFERED OUTSIDE OF DEGREE PROGRAMS

Undergraduate—communication and media; computer and information sciences; dramatic/theater arts and stagecraft; geography and cartography; history; linguistic, comparative, and related language studies; mathematics; music; philosophy; political science and government; psychology.
Graduate—computer and information sciences; education; educational/ instructional media design; geography and cartography; special education.
Non-credit—educational/instructional media design; geography and cartography.

NORTHWEST TECHNICAL COLLEGE
Bemidji, Minnesota
http://www.distance.minnesota.edu
Northwest Technical College was founded in 1993. It is accredited by North Central Association of Colleges and Schools. It first offered distance learning courses in 1995. In fall 2007, there were 650 students enrolled in distance learning courses. Institutionally administered financial aid is available to distance learners.
Services Distance learners have accessibility to academic advising, bookstore, career placement assistance, e-mail services, library services, tutoring.

Contact Minnesota Online Support Center, Northwest Technical College, 150 2nd Avenue SW, Suite B, Box 309, Perham, MN 56573. Telephone: 800-456-8519. Fax: 218-347-6214. E-mail: distancemn@custhellp. com.

DEGREES AND AWARDS
AAS Accounting; Administrative Assistant; Individualized Occupational Preparation; Medical Administrative Secretary Technology; Medical Practices Office Manager; Sales, Marketing, and Management; Supervisory Management
AS Nursing
Certificate General Business; Individualized Occupational Preparation; Management; Marketing; Medical Coding; Medical Insurance; Medical Transcription; Sales; Supervisory Leadership Essentials
Diploma Accounting Clerk; Administrative Support; Individualized Occupational Preparation; Medical Office Technology; Medical Secretary Technology; Sales and Marketing; Supervisory Leadership

COURSE SUBJECT AREAS OFFERED OUTSIDE OF DEGREE PROGRAMS

Undergraduate—accounting and related services; allied health and medical assisting services; applied mathematics; behavioral sciences; biological and physical sciences; business administration, management and operations; business, management, and marketing related; chemistry; English composition; health and medical administrative services; marketing; nursing.

NORTHWOOD UNIVERSITY
Midland, Michigan
University College
http://www.northwood.edu/adults/onlinedegrees/
Northwood University was founded in 1959. It is accredited by North Central Association of Colleges and Schools. It first offered distance learning courses in 1965. In fall 2007, there were 575 students enrolled in distance learning courses. Institutionally administered financial aid is available to distance learners.
Services Distance learners have accessibility to academic advising, bookstore, campus computer network, career placement assistance, e-mail services, library services, tutoring.
Contact Kimberly G. Leach, Program Center Manager, Northwood University, 4000 Whiting Drive, Midland, MI 48640. Telephone: 800-445-5873. Fax: 989-837-4457. E-mail: leachk@northwood.edu.

DEGREES AND AWARDS
Programs offered do not lead to a degree or other formal award.

COURSE SUBJECT AREAS OFFERED OUTSIDE OF DEGREE PROGRAMS

Undergraduate—business, management, and marketing related.

NORTHWOOD UNIVERSITY, TEXAS CAMPUS
Cedar Hill, Texas
http://www.northwood.edu/
Northwood University, Texas Campus was founded in 1966. It is accredited by North Central Association of Colleges and Schools. It first offered distance learning courses in 2000. In fall 2007, there were 275 students enrolled in distance learning courses. Institutionally administered financial aid is available to distance learners.
Services Distance learners have accessibility to academic advising, bookstore, campus computer network, career placement assistance, e-mail services, library services.
Contact Ms. Kim G. Leach, Program Center Manager, Northwood University, Texas Campus, 4000 Whiting Drive, Midland, MI 48640. Telephone: 800-445-5873. Fax: 989-837-4840. E-mail: leachk@ northwood.edu.

DEGREES AND AWARDS
Programs offered do not lead to a degree or other formal award.

COURSE SUBJECT AREAS OFFERED OUTSIDE OF DEGREE PROGRAMS

Undergraduate—accounting and related services; business administration, management and operations; business, management, and marketing related; business/managerial economics; economics; English composition; human resources management; marketing; psychology related.

NOVA SCOTIA AGRICULTURAL COLLEGE
Truro, Nova Scotia, Canada
Center for Continuing and Distance Education
http://www.nsac.ca/cde

Nova Scotia Agricultural College was founded in 1905. It is provincially chartered. It first offered distance learning courses in 1996. In fall 2007, there were 45 students enrolled in distance learning courses. Institutionally administered financial aid is available to distance learners.

Services Distance learners have accessibility to academic advising, bookstore, e-mail services, library services.

Contact Mrs. Pamela Doyle, Administrative Assistant, Nova Scotia Agricultural College, PO Box 550, 23 Sheep Hill Lane, Truro, NS B2N 5E3, Canada. Telephone: 902-893-6666. Fax: 902-895-5528. E-mail: cde@nsac.ca.

DEGREES AND AWARDS

Programs offered do not lead to a degree or other formal award.

COURSE SUBJECT AREAS OFFERED OUTSIDE OF DEGREE PROGRAMS

Undergraduate—agricultural business and management; agricultural production; agriculture; animal sciences; plant sciences.

Non-credit—agriculture; animal sciences; plant sciences.

NOVA SOUTHEASTERN UNIVERSITY
Fort Lauderdale, Florida
Fischler School of Education and Human Services

Nova Southeastern University was founded in 1964. It is accredited by Southern Association of Colleges and Schools.

Contact Online Programs, Nova Southeastern University, 1750 NE 167th Street, North Miami Beach, FL 33162. Telephone: 800-986-3223.

DEGREES AND AWARDS

BS Education, Child Development concentration; Elementary Education with ESOL endorsement; Elementary Education; Exceptional Student Education; Exceptional Student Education with ESOL endorsement; Pre-Kindergarten/Primary Education (Age 3–Grade 3); Secondary Education–Biology; Secondary Education–Mathematics

MS Education–Athletic Administration; Education–Charter School Education and Leadership; Education–Cognitive and Behavioral Disabilities; Education–Computer Science Education; Education–Early Literacy and Reading Education; Education–Educational Media; Education–Elementary Education; Education–English Education; Education–Exceptional Student Education; Education–Gifted Education; Education–Interdisciplinary Arts; Education–Mathematics Education; Education–Prekindergarten and Primary Education; Education–Reading Education; Education–Science Education; Education–Social Studies Education; Education–Spanish Language Education; Education–Teaching English as a Foreign Language; Education–Teaching English to Speakers of Other Languages (TESOL); Instructional Technology and Distance Education

EdD Education–Health Care Education; Education–Higher Education; Education–Human Services Administration; Education–Instructional Leadership; Education–Instructional Technology and Distance Education; Education–Organizational Leadership; Education–Special Education; Education–Speech-Language Pathology; Educational Leadership

NOVA SOUTHEASTERN UNIVERSITY
Fort Lauderdale, Florida
Graduate School of Computer and Information Sciences
http://www.nova.edu/scis

Nova Southeastern University was founded in 1964. It is accredited by Southern Association of Colleges and Schools. It first offered distance learning courses in 1983. In fall 2007, there were 1,200 students enrolled in distance learning courses. Institutionally administered financial aid is available to distance learners.

Services Distance learners have accessibility to academic advising, bookstore, campus computer network, career placement assistance, e-mail services, library services.

Contact Program Counselor, Nova Southeastern University, Recruitment Office, Carl DeSantis Building, 4th Floor, 3301 College Avenue, Fort Lauderdale, FL 33314. Telephone: 800-986-2247. Fax: 954-262-3915. E-mail: scisinfo@nova.edu.

DEGREES AND AWARDS

MS Computer Information Systems; Computer Science; Computing Technology in Education; Information Security; Management Information Systems

PhD Computer Information Systems; Computer Science; Computing Technology in Education; Information Systems

COURSE SUBJECT AREAS OFFERED OUTSIDE OF DEGREE PROGRAMS

Graduate—computer and information sciences; computer and information sciences and support services related; computer/information technology administration and management; computer programming; computer science; computer software and media applications; computer systems analysis; computer systems networking and telecommunications; educational/instructional media design; education related; management information systems; medical illustration and informatics; systems science and theory; technology education/industrial arts.

See full description on page 422.

NOVA SOUTHEASTERN UNIVERSITY
Fort Lauderdale, Florida
H. Wayne Huizenga School of Business and Entrepreneurship
http://www.nova.edu/business

Nova Southeastern University was founded in 1964. It is accredited by Southern Association of Colleges and Schools. It first offered distance learning courses in 1973. In fall 2007, there were 830 students enrolled in distance learning courses. Institutionally administered financial aid is available to distance learners.

Services Distance learners have accessibility to academic advising, bookstore, campus computer network, career placement assistance, e-mail services, library services, tutoring.

Contact Karen Golberg, Assistant Director of Recruitment, Nova Southeastern University, Carl DeSantis Building, 3301 College Avenue, Fort Lauderdale-Davie, FL 33314-7796. Telephone: 800-672-7223 Ext. 25039. Fax: 954-262-5039. E-mail: karen@nsu.nova.edu.

DEGREES AND AWARDS
BSBA Business Administration
MBA Business Administration; Finance
MBA/M Acc Accounting
MBA/MIA International Business Administration–Master of International Business Administration
MBOL Leadership
MPA Public Administration
MSHRM Human Resource Management
MT Taxation–Master of Taxation

COURSE SUBJECT AREAS OFFERED OUTSIDE OF DEGREE PROGRAMS

Graduate—accounting and computer science; human resources management; international business; management information systems; marketing.

NYACK COLLEGE
Nyack, New York
http://www.nyackcollege.edu/

Nyack College was founded in 1882. It is accredited by Middle States Association of Colleges and Schools. It first offered distance learning courses in 1999. In fall 2007, there were 60 students enrolled in distance learning courses.

Services Distance learners have accessibility to academic advising, bookstore, career placement assistance, e-mail services, library services.

Contact Office of Admissions, Nyack College, 350 North Highland Ave, Nyack, NY 10960. Telephone: 845-358-1710 Ext. 4459. E-mail: enroll @nyack.edu.

DEGREES AND AWARDS
Programs offered do not lead to a degree or other formal award.

COURSE SUBJECT AREAS OFFERED OUTSIDE OF DEGREE PROGRAMS

Undergraduate—communication and media; political science and government; psychology; religious studies.

THE OHIO STATE UNIVERSITY
Columbus, Ohio
Technology Enhanced Learning and Research (TELR)
http://telr.osu.edu

The Ohio State University was founded in 1870. It is accredited by North Central Association of Colleges and Schools. It first offered distance learning courses in 1995. In fall 2007, there were 2,952 students enrolled in distance learning courses. Institutionally administered financial aid is available to distance learners.

Services Distance learners have accessibility to academic advising, bookstore, campus computer network, e-mail services, library services, tutoring.

Contact Dr. Joanne E. Dehoney, EdD, Interim Executive Director for e-Learning, The Ohio State University, Technology Enhanced Learning and Research, 1971 Neil Avenue, BSE 480, Columbus, OH 43210. Telephone: 614-247-6819. Fax: 614-292-7081. E-mail: dehoney.1@ osu.edu.

DEGREES AND AWARDS
EMBA Business Administration
MSE Welding Engineering
PharmD NonTraditional PharmD

COURSE SUBJECT AREAS OFFERED OUTSIDE OF DEGREE PROGRAMS

Undergraduate—business/commerce; engineering related; family and consumer economics; forestry; linguistic, comparative, and related language studies; plant sciences; political science and government; social work; visual and performing arts related.

Graduate—business administration, management and operations; educational administration and supervision; education related; engineering related; mechanical engineering; nuclear engineering; nursing; plant sciences; social work.

Non-credit—gerontology; mental and social health services and allied professions; special education.

OKALOOSA-WALTON COLLEGE
Niceville, Florida
Distance Learning
http://www.owc.edu

Okaloosa-Walton College was founded in 1963. It is accredited by Southern Association of Colleges and Schools. It first offered distance learning courses in 1994. In fall 2007, there were 2,866 students enrolled in distance learning courses. Institutionally administered financial aid is available to distance learners.

Services Distance learners have accessibility to academic advising, bookstore, campus computer network, career placement assistance, e-mail services, library services, tutoring.

Contact Mr. Mike Van Dyke, Manager, Learning Technologies, Okaloosa-Walton College, 100 College Boulevard, Niceville, FL 32578-1295. Telephone: 850-729-6448. Fax: 850-729-5295. E-mail: vandykem@ owc.edu.

DEGREES AND AWARDS
Programs offered do not lead to a degree or other formal award.

COURSE SUBJECT AREAS OFFERED OUTSIDE OF DEGREE PROGRAMS

Undergraduate—accounting and computer science; accounting and related services; allied health and medical assisting services; allied health diagnostic, intervention, and treatment professions; alternative and complementary medical support services; anthropology; applied mathematics; behavioral sciences; bilingual, multilingual, and multicultural education; biological and physical sciences; biology; business administration, management and operations; business/commerce; business/corporate communications; business, management, and marketing related; business/ managerial economics; cell biology and anatomical sciences; chemistry; classical and ancient studies; communications technology; computer and information sciences; computer programming; computer science; computer software and media applications; computer systems networking and telecommunications; criminal justice and corrections; criminology; dental support services and allied professions; economics; educational psychology; English composition; health/medical preparatory programs; health professions related; health services/allied health/health sciences; history; languages (foreign languages related); liberal arts and sciences, general studies and humanities; mathematics; mathematics and statistics related; medical basic sciences; nursing; philosophy; physical sciences; physical sciences related; political science and government; psychology; psychology related; public relations, advertising, and applied communication related; quality control and safety technologies; religious studies; sales, merchandising, and related marketing operations (general); social sciences; sociology; statistics; technology education/industrial arts.

OKEFENOKEE TECHNICAL COLLEGE
Waycross, Georgia
http://www.okefenokeetech.edu

Okefenokee Technical College is accredited by Council on Occupational Education. It first offered distance learning courses in 1999. In fall 2007, there were 350 students enrolled in distance learning courses. Institutionally administered financial aid is available to distance learners.

Services Distance learners have accessibility to academic advising, bookstore, e-mail services, library services, tutoring.

Contact Amanda G. Morris, Coordinator of Distance Education and Web Master, Okefenokee Technical College, 1701 Carswell Avenue, Waycross, GA 31503. Telephone: 912-287-5851. Fax: 912-287-4865. E-mail: amorris@okefenokeetech.edu.

DEGREES AND AWARDS
Programs offered do not lead to a degree or other formal award.

COURSE SUBJECT AREAS OFFERED OUTSIDE OF DEGREE PROGRAMS

Undergraduate—allied health and medical assisting services; business, management, and marketing related; computer and information sciences.
Graduate—allied health and medical assisting services; business, management, and marketing related; computer and information sciences.
Non-credit—allied health and medical assisting services; business, management, and marketing related; computer and information sciences.

OKLAHOMA PANHANDLE STATE UNIVERSITY
Goodwell, Oklahoma
http://www.opsu.edu/

Oklahoma Panhandle State University was founded in 1909. It is accredited by North Central Association of Colleges and Schools. It first offered distance learning courses in 1992. In fall 2007, there were 493 students enrolled in distance learning courses. Institutionally administered financial aid is available to distance learners.

Services Distance learners have accessibility to academic advising, bookstore, campus computer network, e-mail services, library services.

Contact Bobby Jenkins, Registrar, Oklahoma Panhandle State University, PO Box 430, Goodwell, OK 73939. Telephone: 580-349-1376. E-mail: bjenkins@opsu.edu.

DEGREES AND AWARDS
Programs offered do not lead to a degree or other formal award.

COURSE SUBJECT AREAS OFFERED OUTSIDE OF DEGREE PROGRAMS
Undergraduate—accounting and computer science; accounting and related services; behavioral sciences; biological and physical sciences; biology; business administration, management and operations; business, management, and marketing related; chemistry; computer and information sciences; economics; English; English language and literature related; history; mathematics; music; natural sciences; nursing; physical sciences; political science and government; psychology; social sciences; sociology; speech and rhetoric.

OKLAHOMA STATE UNIVERSITY
Stillwater, Oklahoma
Distance Learning
http://is.okstate.edu
Oklahoma State University was founded in 1890. It is accredited by North Central Association of Colleges and Schools. It first offered distance learning courses in 1945. In fall 2007, there were 2,000 students enrolled in distance learning courses. Institutionally administered financial aid is available to distance learners.
Services Distance learners have accessibility to academic advising, bookstore, campus computer network, library services.
Contact Jenny England, Administrative Support Specialist, Oklahoma State University, 309 Wes Watkins Center, Stillwater, OK 74078. Telephone: 405-744-6390. Fax: 405-744-3420. E-mail: ics-inf@okstate.edu.

DEGREES AND AWARDS
Programs offered do not lead to a degree or other formal award.

COURSE SUBJECT AREAS OFFERED OUTSIDE OF DEGREE PROGRAMS
Undergraduate—accounting and related services; American literature (United States and Canadian); animal sciences; anthropology; applied horticulture/horticultural business services; business administration, management and operations; business/corporate communications; communication disorders sciences and services; counseling psychology; creative writing; economics; education related; electrical, electronics and communications engineering; English composition; English literature (British and Commonwealth); finance and financial management services; fire protection; foods, nutrition, and related services; geography and cartography; geological and earth sciences/geosciences; health and physical education/fitness; history; journalism; languages (Germanic); languages (Romance languages); legal studies (non-professional general, undergraduate); management information systems; marketing; mathematics and statistics related; political science and government; psychology; sales, merchandising, and related marketing operations (general); sociology; statistics; technical and business writing.
Non-credit—fire protection.

OLD DOMINION UNIVERSITY
Norfolk, Virginia
Office of Distance Learning and Extended Education
http://www.dl.odu.edu
Old Dominion University was founded in 1930. It is accredited by Southern Association of Colleges and Schools. It first offered distance learning courses in 1984. In fall 2007, there were 3,000 students enrolled in distance learning courses. Institutionally administered financial aid is available to distance learners.
Services Distance learners have accessibility to academic advising, bookstore, campus computer network, career placement assistance, e-mail services, library services.

Contact Mrs. Anita Wiggins Bailey, Enrollment Services Specialist, Old Dominion University, Gornto TELETECHNET Center, Norfolk, VA 23529. Telephone: 800-968-2638. Fax: 757-683-5492. E-mail: awiggins@odu.edu.

DEGREES AND AWARDS
BA Criminal Justice
BHS Health Sciences
BS Computer Science; Criminal Justice; Education–Teacher Preparation; Human Services; Occupational and Technical Studies
BSBA Accounting, Finance, Information Systems, Marketing; Management
BSET Civil Engineering Technology; Electrical Engineering Technology; Engineering Technology, general; Mechanical Engineering Technology
BSN Nursing
MEM Engineering Management
MS Community Health; Education–Pre-K through 6; Occupational and Technical Studies; Special Education
MSN Nursing–Nurse Leader and Nurse Educator options
PhD Community College Leadership; Occupation and Technical Studies

COURSE SUBJECT AREAS OFFERED OUTSIDE OF DEGREE PROGRAMS
Undergraduate—accounting and related services; business/corporate communications; business/managerial economics; communication and media; community health services; computer science; criminal justice and corrections; education related; engineering technologies related; finance and financial management services; industrial and organizational psychology; management information systems; management sciences and quantitative methods; marketing; philosophy; social psychology; sociology.
Graduate—accounting and related services; aerospace, aeronautical and astronautical engineering; education related; environmental/environmental health engineering; finance and financial management services; management information systems; marketing; mechanical engineering.

ORANGE COAST COLLEGE
Costa Mesa, California
http://www.orangecoastcollege.com
Orange Coast College was founded in 1947. It is accredited by Western Association of Schools and Colleges. It first offered distance learning courses in 1998. In fall 2007, there were 3,721 students enrolled in distance learning courses. Institutionally administered financial aid is available to distance learners.
Services Distance learners have accessibility to academic advising, bookstore, e-mail services, library services.
Contact Ms. Kristin Clark, Dean of Enrollment Services, Orange Coast College, 2701 Fairview Road, Costa Mesa, CA 92626. Telephone: 714-432-0202. E-mail: kclark@mail.occ.cccd.edu.

DEGREES AND AWARDS
AA Real Estate

COURSE SUBJECT AREAS OFFERED OUTSIDE OF DEGREE PROGRAMS
Undergraduate—accounting and related services; allied health and medical assisting services; anthropology; biology; business, management, and marketing related; business operations support and assistant services; computer and information sciences; computer/information technology administration and management; computer programming; computer software and media applications; drafting/design engineering technologies; economics; English composition; food science and technology; foods, nutrition, and related services; health and medical administrative services; hospitality administration; human development, family studies, and related services; music; real estate; sales, merchandising, and related marketing operations (specialized).

OREGON INSTITUTE OF TECHNOLOGY
Klamath Falls, Oregon
http://www.oit.edu/dist

Oregon Institute of Technology was founded in 1947. It is accredited by Northwest Commission on Colleges and Universities. It first offered distance learning courses in 1997. In fall 2007, there were 715 students enrolled in distance learning courses. Institutionally administered financial aid is available to distance learners.

Services Distance learners have accessibility to academic advising, bookstore, campus computer network, career placement assistance, e-mail services, library services, tutoring.

Contact Barb DeKalb, Director of Distance Education, Oregon Institute of Technology, 3201 Campus Drive, Klamath Falls, OR 97601. Telephone: 541-885-1142. Fax: 541-885-1139. E-mail: barb.dekalb@oit.edu.

DEGREES AND AWARDS
AAS Polysomnographic Technology
BS Allied Health Management; Dental Hygiene–Dental Hygiene degree completion; Information Technology Online; Operations Management; Radiological Science–Radiological Science degree completion; Respiratory Care; Ultrasound–degree completion in Ultrasound, Echocardiography option; Ultrasound–degree completion in Ultrasound, Vascular Technology option
Certificate of Completion Polysomnographic Technology

COURSE SUBJECT AREAS OFFERED OUTSIDE OF DEGREE PROGRAMS
Undergraduate—accounting and related services; allied health diagnostic, intervention, and treatment professions; anthropology; business administration, management and operations; business/commerce; computer and information sciences; computer/information technology administration and management; dental support services and allied professions; economics; engineering/industrial management; human development, family studies, and related services; management information systems; mathematics; psychology; social sciences; technical and business writing.

OREGON STATE UNIVERSITY
Corvallis, Oregon
Extended Campus
http://ecampus.oregonstate.edu

Oregon State University was founded in 1868. It is accredited by Northwest Commission on Colleges and Universities. It first offered distance learning courses in 1986. In fall 2007, there were 2,800 students enrolled in distance learning courses. Institutionally administered financial aid is available to distance learners.

Services Distance learners have accessibility to academic advising, bookstore, campus computer network, career placement assistance, e-mail services, library services, tutoring.

Contact Ecampus Student Services Center, Oregon State University, OSU Extended Campus, 4943 The Valley Library, Corvallis, OR 97331-4504. Telephone: 800-667-1465. Fax: 541-737-2734. E-mail: ecampus@oregonstate.edu.

DEGREES AND AWARDS
BA Liberal Studies
BS Agriculture, general; Environmental Sciences; Liberal Studies; Natural Resources
Certificate of Completion Management and Human Resource Skills for Pharmacists
Certificate Geographic Information Sciences
Endorsement ESOL/Bilingual Education
License Continuing Teaching Licensure
Graduate Certificate Health Management and Policy; Sustainable Natural Resources; Sustainable Natural Resources
MAT Early Childhood/Elementary Education
MEd Adult Education; Education
MHP Radiation Health Physics
MS Radiation Health Physics
EdD Community College Leadership concentration

PhD Community College Leadership concentration; Counseling

COURSE SUBJECT AREAS OFFERED OUTSIDE OF DEGREE PROGRAMS
Undergraduate—agricultural business and management; agriculture; agriculture and agriculture operations related; American literature (United States and Canadian); anthropology; area, ethnic, cultural, and gender studies related; atmospheric sciences and meteorology; botany/plant biology; business/commerce; business/corporate communications; chemistry; communication and media; creative writing; ecology, evolution, and population biology; economics; education; education related; English; English composition; ethnic, cultural minority, and gender studies; fishing and fisheries sciences and management; forestry; geological and earth sciences/geosciences; health and medical administrative services; health services/allied health/health sciences; history; liberal arts and sciences, general studies and humanities; mathematics and statistics related; natural resources and conservation related; natural resources conservation and research; natural resources management and policy; philosophy; philosophy and religious studies related; plant sciences; political science and government; psychology; sales, merchandising, and related marketing operations (general); science, technology and society; social sciences related; sociology; soil sciences; statistics; technical and business writing; wildlife and wildlands science and management.
Graduate—counseling psychology; education; educational administration and supervision; education related; education (specific levels and methods); education (specific subject areas); English as a second/foreign language (teaching); English as a second language; environmental/environmental health engineering; foods, nutrition, and related services; geography and cartography; geological and earth sciences/geosciences; health and medical administrative services; health professions related; natural resources conservation and research; natural resources management and policy; nuclear and industrial radiologic technologies; public health.
Non-credit—business, management, and marketing related; communication and media; computer software and media applications; English; English as a second language; family and consumer economics; film/video and photographic arts; fine and studio art; health and medical administrative services; human resources management; languages (Romance languages); linguistic, comparative, and related language studies; pharmacology and toxicology; pharmacy, pharmaceutical sciences, and administration; psychology; sales, merchandising, and related marketing operations (specialized).

See full description on page 424.

OTTAWA UNIVERSITY
Ottawa, Kansas
Kansas City Campus
http://www.ottawa.edu

Ottawa University was founded in 1865. It is accredited by North Central Association of Colleges and Schools. It first offered distance learning courses in 1976. In fall 2007, there were 600 students enrolled in distance learning courses. Institutionally administered financial aid is available to distance learners.

Services Distance learners have accessibility to academic advising, bookstore, e-mail services, library services.

Contact Karen Adams, Enrollment Manager, Ottawa University, 20 Corporate Woods, 10865 Grandview Drive, Overland Park, KS 66210. Telephone: 888-404-6852. Fax: 913-451-0806. E-mail: adamsk@ottawa.edu.

DEGREES AND AWARDS
BA Management of Health Services
MA Human Resources
MBA Business Administration

COURSE SUBJECT AREAS OFFERED OUTSIDE OF DEGREE PROGRAMS
Undergraduate—health and medical administrative services.

OUACHITA TECHNICAL COLLEGE
Malvern, Arkansas
http://www.otcweb.edu
Ouachita Technical College was founded in 1972. It is accredited by North Central Association of Colleges and Schools. It first offered distance learning courses in 1998. In fall 2007, there were 543 students enrolled in distance learning courses. Institutionally administered financial aid is available to distance learners.
Services Distance learners have accessibility to academic advising, bookstore, campus computer network, career placement assistance, e-mail services, library services, tutoring.
Contact Mr. Tony Hunnicutt, Distance Learning Coordinator, Ouachita Technical College, One College Circle, Malvern, AR 72104. Telephone: 501-337-5000 Ext. 1106. Fax: 501-337-9382. E-mail: thunnicutt@otcweb.edu.

DEGREES AND AWARDS
AA Education, general
AAS Criminal Justice

COURSE SUBJECT AREAS OFFERED OUTSIDE OF DEGREE PROGRAMS
Undergraduate—behavioral sciences; biological and physical sciences; biology; business administration, management and operations; computer and information sciences; computer software and media applications; computer systems networking and telecommunications; criminal justice and corrections; English composition; history; human resources management; liberal arts and sciences, general studies and humanities; mathematics; philosophy; political science and government; psychology; social sciences; sociology.

OXNARD COLLEGE
Oxnard, California
http://www.oxnardcollege.edu
Oxnard College was founded in 1975. It is accredited by Western Association of Schools and Colleges. It first offered distance learning courses in 1997. In fall 2007, there were 196 students enrolled in distance learning courses. Institutionally administered financial aid is available to distance learners.
Services Distance learners have accessibility to academic advising, bookstore, e-mail services, library services.
Contact Mr. Jaime Casillas, Dean of Economic Development and Innovation, Oxnard College, 4000 South Rose Avenue, Oxnard, CA 93033. Telephone: 805-986-5888. Fax: 805-986-5988. E-mail: jcasillas@vcccd.edu.

DEGREES AND AWARDS
Programs offered do not lead to a degree or other formal award.

COURSE SUBJECT AREAS OFFERED OUTSIDE OF DEGREE PROGRAMS
Undergraduate—accounting and related services; American literature (United States and Canadian); anthropology; applied mathematics; area, ethnic, cultural, and gender studies related; area studies; astronomy and astrophysics; bilingual, multilingual, and multicultural education; biological and biomedical sciences related; biology; botany/plant biology; business administration, management and operations; business/commerce; business/corporate communications; business, management, and marketing related; business operations support and assistant services; chemistry; clinical psychology; communication and media; computer and information sciences; computer engineering; computer/information technology administration and management; computer programming; computer science; computer software and media applications; computer systems analysis; computer systems networking and telecommunications; creative writing; criminal justice and corrections; culinary arts and related services; data entry/microcomputer applications; dental support services and allied professions; developmental and child psychology; dramatic/theater arts and stagecraft; economics; education; English; English as a second language; English composition; environmental control technologies; film/video and photographic arts; fine and studio art; fire protection; geological and earth sciences/geosciences; heating, air conditioning, ventilation and refrigeration maintenance technology; history; human development, family studies, and related services; human services; international business; languages (foreign languages related); legal studies (non-professional general, undergraduate); library science related; marketing; mathematics; mechanic and repair technologies related; microbiological sciences and immunology; music; philosophy; physical sciences; physics; political science and government; psychology; public health; public relations, advertising, and applied communication related; radio, television, and digital communication; sales, merchandising, and related marketing operations (specialized); social psychology; sociology; special education; speech and rhetoric; taxation; technical and business writing.

PACE UNIVERSITY
New York, New York
Online Pace
http://www.online.pace.edu
Pace University was founded in 1906. It is accredited by Middle States Association of Colleges and Schools. It first offered distance learning courses in 1997. In fall 2007, there were 1,460 students enrolled in distance learning courses. Institutionally administered financial aid is available to distance learners.
Services Distance learners have accessibility to academic advising, bookstore, campus computer network, career placement assistance, e-mail services, library services, tutoring.
Contact Ms. Christine Moloughney, Coordinator of Online Support Services, Pace University, One Pace Plaza, New York, NY 10038. Telephone: 212-346-1471. E-mail: cmoloughney@pace.edu.

DEGREES AND AWARDS
AS Applied Information Technology, Telecommunications degree
BS Communication Studies–Professional Communication Studies; Professional Technology Studies; Telecommunications
Graduate Certificate Business Aspects of Publishing; Internet Technologies; Internet Technology; Telecommunications
MBA Business Administration–e.MBA
MS Internet Technology for E-Commerce; Publishing
DPS Computing

COURSE SUBJECT AREAS OFFERED OUTSIDE OF DEGREE PROGRAMS
Undergraduate—accounting and related services; American literature (United States and Canadian); anthropology; bilingual, multilingual, and multicultural education; biological and physical sciences; biology; business administration, management and operations; business/commerce; chemistry; communication and journalism related; communication and media; community organization and advocacy; comparative literature; computer and information sciences and support services related; computer programming; computer science; computer software and media applications; computer systems networking and telecommunications; criminal justice and corrections; criminology; economics; education; education (specific subject areas); English; English composition; ethnic, cultural minority, and gender studies; finance and financial management services; fine and studio art; history; information science/studies; international business; languages (foreign languages related); legal studies (non-professional general, undergraduate); linguistic, comparative, and related language studies; marketing; mathematics; mathematics and statistics related; multi-/interdisciplinary studies related; nursing; physical sciences; political science and government; psychology; science, technology and society; social sciences; sociology; statistics; technical and business writing; visual and performing arts.
Graduate—bilingual, multilingual, and multicultural education; business administration, management and operations; business/commerce; community health services; community organization and advocacy; computer and information sciences; computer and information sciences and support services related; computer/information technology administration and management; computer programming; computer software and media applications; computer systems analysis; computer systems networking and telecommunications; curriculum and instruction; education; educational administration and supervision; educational assessment, evaluation, and research; educational/instructional media design; education

related; health and medical administrative services; health/medical preparatory programs; information science/studies; management information systems; marketing; nursing; public administration; publishing; student counseling and personnel services.

Non-credit—business/commerce; computer and information sciences; education; liberal arts and sciences, general studies and humanities; nursing; personal and culinary services related.

PACIFIC OAKS COLLEGE
Pasadena, California
Distance Learning
http://www.pacificoaks.edu

Pacific Oaks College was founded in 1945. It is accredited by Western Association of Schools and Colleges. It first offered distance learning courses in 1996. In fall 2007, there were 177 students enrolled in distance learning courses. Institutionally administered financial aid is available to distance learners.

Services Distance learners have accessibility to academic advising, bookstore, library services.

Contact Amy Peterson, Admissions Coordinator, Pacific Oaks College, 5 Westmoreland Place, Pasadena, CA 91103. Telephone: 626-397-1349. E-mail: admissions@pacificoaks.edu.

DEGREES AND AWARDS
BA Human Development
MA Human Development

COURSE SUBJECT AREAS OFFERED OUTSIDE OF DEGREE PROGRAMS

Undergraduate—education (specific levels and methods); human development, family studies, and related services.
Graduate—education (specific levels and methods); human development, family studies, and related services.

PACIFIC UNION COLLEGE
Angwin, California
http://www.puc.edu/

Pacific Union College was founded in 1882. It is accredited by Western Association of Schools and Colleges. It first offered distance learning courses in 2001. In fall 2007, there were 32 students enrolled in distance learning courses. Institutionally administered financial aid is available to distance learners.

Services Distance learners have accessibility to academic advising, bookstore, campus computer network, e-mail services, library services, tutoring.

Contact Nancy Lecourt, PhD, Academic Dean, Pacific Union College, One Angwin Avenue, Angwin, CA 94508. Telephone: 707-965-6234. E-mail: nlecourt@puc.edu.

DEGREES AND AWARDS
Programs offered do not lead to a degree or other formal award.

COURSE SUBJECT AREAS OFFERED OUTSIDE OF DEGREE PROGRAMS

Undergraduate—health and physical education/fitness; mathematics; nursing; religious studies.

PALM BEACH COMMUNITY COLLEGE
Lake Worth, Florida
http://www.pbcc.edu/dl

Palm Beach Community College was founded in 1933. It is accredited by Southern Association of Colleges and Schools. It first offered distance learning courses in 1997. In fall 2007, there were 6,624 students enrolled in distance learning courses. Institutionally administered financial aid is available to distance learners.

Services Distance learners have accessibility to academic advising, bookstore, career placement assistance, e-mail services, library services.

Contact Ms. Anne Guiler, Distance Learning Coordinator, Palm Beach Community College, 4200 Congress Avenue, Lake Worth, FL 33461. Telephone: 561-868-4088. E-mail: guilera@pbcc.edu.

DEGREES AND AWARDS
AA General Studies

COURSE SUBJECT AREAS OFFERED OUTSIDE OF DEGREE PROGRAMS

Undergraduate—accounting and related services; anthropology; astronomy and astrophysics; biological and physical sciences; business/commerce; chemistry; communication and media; computer and information sciences; developmental and child psychology; economics; education; electrical and electronic engineering technologies.

PALOMAR COLLEGE
San Marcos, California
Educational Television
http://www.palomar.edu/pctv

Palomar College was founded in 1946. It is accredited by Western Association of Schools and Colleges. It first offered distance learning courses in 1975. In fall 2007, there were 5,734 students enrolled in distance learning courses. Institutionally administered financial aid is available to distance learners.

Services Distance learners have accessibility to academic advising, bookstore, campus computer network, career placement assistance, e-mail services, library services, tutoring.

Contact Ms. Marlene deLeon, Staff Assistant, Palomar College, 1140 West Mission Road, San Marcos, CA 92069. Telephone: 760-744-1150 Ext. 3055. Fax: 760-761-3519. E-mail: mdeleon@palomar.edu.

DEGREES AND AWARDS
Programs offered do not lead to a degree or other formal award.

COURSE SUBJECT AREAS OFFERED OUTSIDE OF DEGREE PROGRAMS

Undergraduate—accounting and computer science; accounting and related services; American Sign Language (ASL); anthropology; archeology; area, ethnic, cultural, and gender studies related; behavioral sciences; bilingual, multilingual, and multicultural education; biochemistry, biophysics and molecular biology; biological and physical sciences; biology; botany/plant biology; business administration, management and operations; business/commerce; business, management, and marketing related; business/managerial economics; business operations support and assistant services; cell biology and anatomical sciences; chemistry; communication and journalism related; communication and media; communications technologies and support services related; computer and information sciences; computer and information sciences and support services related; computer/information technology administration and management; computer programming; computer science; computer software and media applications; computer systems analysis; computer systems networking and telecommunications; counseling psychology; criminal justice and corrections; data entry/microcomputer applications; developmental and child psychology; ecology, evolution, and population biology; economics; educational/instructional media design; English; English composition; entrepreneurial and small business operations; ethnic, cultural minority, and gender studies; family and consumer economics; family and consumer sciences/human sciences; family and consumer sciences/human sciences business services; family and consumer sciences/human sciences related; family psychology; finance and financial management services; fine and studio art; fire protection; foods, nutrition, and related services; geography and cartography; geological and earth sciences/geosciences; geological/geophysical engineering; graphic communications; health and physical education/fitness; history; human development, family studies, and related services; information science/studies; insurance; international business; journalism; languages (American Indian/Native American); languages (foreign languages related); languages (Iranian/Persian); languages (Romance languages); legal professions and studies related; legal research and advanced professional studies; legal studies (non-professional general, undergraduate); legal support services; liberal arts and sciences, general studies and humanities; library assistant; library science; library science related; marketing; mathematics; mathematics and statistics related; music; natural sciences; nutrition sciences; personality psychology; philosophy; philosophy and religious studies related; plant sciences; political science and government; psychology; psychology related; public administration; radio, television, and digital communication; real estate; religious studies; sales, merchandising, and related marketing operations (general); social psychology; social sciences; social sciences related; sociology; statistics; visual and performing arts; work and family studies.

PAMLICO COMMUNITY COLLEGE
Grantsboro, North Carolina
http://www.pamlicocc.edu/

Pamlico Community College was founded in 1963. It is accredited by Southern Association of Colleges and Schools. It first offered distance learning courses in 1999. In fall 2007, there were 200 students enrolled in distance learning courses. Institutionally administered financial aid is available to distance learners.

Services Distance learners have accessibility to academic advising, campus computer network, career placement assistance, e-mail services, library services, tutoring.

Contact Ms. Kathleen Mayo, Distance Learning Coordinator, Pamlico Community College, PO Box 185, Grantsboro, NC 28529. Telephone: 252-249-1851 Ext. 3012. Fax: 252-249-2377. E-mail: kmayo@pamlicocc.edu.

DEGREES AND AWARDS
Programs offered do not lead to a degree or other formal award.

COURSE SUBJECT AREAS OFFERED OUTSIDE OF DEGREE PROGRAMS
Undergraduate—accounting and computer science; accounting and related services; allied health and medical assisting services; American literature (United States and Canadian); applied mathematics; behavioral sciences; biological and physical sciences; biology; business administration, management and operations; business/commerce; business, management, and marketing related; business/managerial economics; chemistry; communications technology; computer and information sciences; computer/information technology administration and management; computer programming; computer software and media applications; computer systems networking and telecommunications; cosmetology and related personal grooming services; criminal justice and corrections; criminology; education; education (specific levels and methods); electrical and electronic engineering technologies; English; English as a second language; English composition; English language and literature related; fire protection; health aides/attendants/orderlies; health and medical administrative services; health services/allied health/health sciences; history; masonry; mathematics; mathematics and computer science; mathematics and statistics related; psychology.

PARKLAND COLLEGE
Champaign, Illinois
Distance Education
http://online.parkland.edu

Parkland College was founded in 1967. It is accredited by North Central Association of Colleges and Schools. It first offered distance learning courses in 1988. In fall 2007, there were 2,605 students enrolled in distance learning courses. Institutionally administered financial aid is available to distance learners.

Services Distance learners have accessibility to academic advising, bookstore, campus computer network, career placement assistance, e-mail services, library services, tutoring.

Contact Brett Coup, Director, Distance and Virtual Learning, Parkland College, 2400 West Bradley Avenue, Champaign, IL 61821. Telephone: 217-353-2639. E-mail: bcoup@parkland.edu.

DEGREES AND AWARDS
AA Early Childhood Education, Elementary Education, Secondary Education, Special Education, and Mass Communication (Integrated) con-

centrations; History, Liberal Arts and Sciences, Mass Communications (Advertising/Public Relations; Journalism), Political Science, and Psychology concentrations
AAS Business Management
AGS General Studies
AS Business Administration and Business Education concentrations
Certificate Independent Business Management

COURSE SUBJECT AREAS OFFERED OUTSIDE OF DEGREE PROGRAMS
Undergraduate—accounting and related services; agricultural business and management; anthropology; astronomy and astrophysics; biology; cell biology and anatomical sciences; chemistry; communication and media; computer and information sciences; computer programming; computer software and media applications; developmental and child psychology; dramatic/theater arts and stagecraft; economics; English composition; fine and studio art; health and physical education/fitness; history; journalism; legal studies (non-professional general, undergraduate); marketing; mathematics and statistics related; music; philosophy; physics; political science and government; psychology; social psychology; social sciences related; sociology; speech and rhetoric; statistics.

PARK UNIVERSITY
Parkville, Missouri
School for Extended Learning
http://www.park.edu/online

Park University was founded in 1875. It is accredited by North Central Association of Colleges and Schools. It first offered distance learning courses in 1996. In fall 2007, there were 5,500 students enrolled in distance learning courses. Institutionally administered financial aid is available to distance learners.

Services Distance learners have accessibility to academic advising, bookstore, campus computer network, career placement assistance, e-mail services, library services, tutoring.

Contact Ms. Nancy Eastman, Associate Dean, Enrollment Services, Park University, Park Student Success Center, 8700 NW River Park Drive, Parkville, MO 64152-3795. Telephone: 816-584-2526. Fax: 816-584-2150. E-mail: pssc@park.edu.

DEGREES AND AWARDS
BS Criminal Justice Administration; Management; Management; Management/Computer Information Systems; Management/Human Resources; Management/Marketing; Social Psychology
MBA Business Administration; Health Care/Health Services Management; International Business
MEd Education, general; Law–School Law; Multi-Cultural Education; Teaching At-Risk Students
MPA Disaster and Emergency Management; Government–Business Relations; Nonprofit and Community Services Management; Public Management

COURSE SUBJECT AREAS OFFERED OUTSIDE OF DEGREE PROGRAMS
Undergraduate—accounting and related services; American literature (United States and Canadian); area, ethnic, cultural, and gender studies related; biblical studies; biology; business administration, management and operations; business/commerce; business/corporate communications; business, management, and marketing related; communication and journalism related; communication and media; computer and information sciences; computer programming; creative writing; criminal justice and corrections; criminology; economics; education related; English; English composition; finance and financial management services; geography and cartography; geological and earth sciences/geosciences; health and medical administrative services; history; human resources management; management information systems; marketing; mathematics; philosophy and religious studies related; political science and government; psychology; sales, merchandising, and related marketing operations (general); social psychology; statistics.
Graduate—business administration, management and operations; business, management, and marketing related; computer and information sciences;

education; educational administration and supervision; international business; public administration; public administration and social service professions related.

See full description on page 426.

PASCO-HERNANDO COMMUNITY COLLEGE
New Port Richey, Florida
http://www.phcc.edu
Pasco-Hernando Community College was founded in 1972. It is accredited by Southern Association of Colleges and Schools. It first offered distance learning courses in 1993. In fall 2007, there were 4,308 students enrolled in distance learning courses. Institutionally administered financial aid is available to distance learners.
Services Distance learners have accessibility to academic advising, bookstore, campus computer network, e-mail services, library services.
Contact Adm. Cheryl Sandoe, Assistant Dean of Academic Technology, Pasco-Hernando Community College, 10230 Ridge Road, New Port Richey, FL 34654-5199. Telephone: 727-816-3367. Fax: 727-816-3300. E-mail: sandoec@phcc.edu.

DEGREES AND AWARDS
Programs offered do not lead to a degree or other formal award.

COURSE SUBJECT AREAS OFFERED OUTSIDE OF DEGREE PROGRAMS
Undergraduate—allied health and medical assisting services; biology; business administration, management and operations; business/commerce; business, management, and marketing related; computer and information sciences; computer/information technology administration and management; computer programming; computer software and media applications; computer systems networking and telecommunications; educational administration and supervision; educational/instructional media design; education related; education (specific levels and methods); English composition; English literature (British and Commonwealth); health and physical education/fitness; history; legal support services; mathematics; mathematics and statistics related; nutrition sciences; physical sciences; political science and government; psychology; religious studies; social sciences related; sociology; speech and rhetoric.
Non-credit—business/corporate communications; computer and information sciences; computer programming; computer software and media applications; education; education related; education (specific subject areas); English; family and consumer economics; health and medical administrative services; health professions related; health services/allied health/health sciences; insurance; legal studies (non-professional general, undergraduate); personal and culinary services related; real estate; sales, merchandising, and related marketing operations (general); sales, merchandising, and related marketing operations (specialized); technical and business writing.

PASSAIC COUNTY COMMUNITY COLLEGE
Paterson, New Jersey
http://www.pccc.edu
Passaic County Community College was founded in 1968. It is accredited by Middle States Association of Colleges and Schools. It first offered distance learning courses in 1998. In fall 2007, there were 825 students enrolled in distance learning courses. Institutionally administered financial aid is available to distance learners.
Services Distance learners have accessibility to academic advising, bookstore, e-mail services, library services, tutoring.
Contact Mr. Randy Jenkins, Director of Online Learning, Passaic County Community College, 1 College Boulevard, Paterson, NJ 07505-1179. Telephone: 973-684-5790. Fax: 973-684-5413. E-mail: rjenkins@pccc.edu.

DEGREES AND AWARDS
AA Humanities option
AAS Health Information Technology

COURSE SUBJECT AREAS OFFERED OUTSIDE OF DEGREE PROGRAMS
Undergraduate—business/commerce; communication and media; computer and information sciences; criminal justice and corrections; English; fire protection; health professions related; history; mathematics and statistics related; physical sciences; psychology; sociology; statistics.

PATRICK HENRY COLLEGE
Purcellville, Virginia
http://www.phc.edu/distancelearning
Patrick Henry College was founded in 1999. It is accredited by American Academy for Liberal Education. It first offered distance learning courses in 2001. In fall 2007, there were 130 students enrolled in distance learning courses. Institutionally administered financial aid is available to distance learners.
Services Distance learners have accessibility to academic advising, bookstore, e-mail services, library services, tutoring.
Contact Mr. Daniel Burns, Admissions Counselor for Distance Learning, Patrick Henry College, One Patrick Henry Circle, Purcellville, VA 20132. Telephone: 540-338-1776. Fax: 540-338-9808. E-mail: dpburns@phc.edu.

DEGREES AND AWARDS
Programs offered do not lead to a degree or other formal award.

COURSE SUBJECT AREAS OFFERED OUTSIDE OF DEGREE PROGRAMS
Undergraduate—biblical studies; biology; economics; English composition; history; languages (classics and classical); legal studies (non-professional general, undergraduate); liberal arts and sciences, general studies and humanities; music; philosophy; philosophy and religious studies related; political science and government; public policy analysis.

PATRICK HENRY COMMUNITY COLLEGE
Martinsville, Virginia
Learning Resource Center
http://www.ph.vccs.edu
Patrick Henry Community College was founded in 1962. It is accredited by Southern Association of Colleges and Schools. It first offered distance learning courses in 1981. In fall 2007, there were 1,800 students enrolled in distance learning courses. Institutionally administered financial aid is available to distance learners.
Services Distance learners have accessibility to academic advising, bookstore, campus computer network, career placement assistance, e-mail services, library services, tutoring.
Contact Mark Nelson, Distance Learning Webmaster, Patrick Henry Community College, PO Box 5311, Martinsville, VA 24115. Telephone: 276-656-0275. Fax: 276-656-0353. E-mail: mnelson@ph.vccs.edu.

DEGREES AND AWARDS
AAS General Studies; Information Systems Technology
AS Business Administration
Certificate Career Studies–Allied Health; Career Studies–Management Assistant; Career Studies–Medical Transcriptionist; Career Studies–Office Assisting; Career Studies–Wellness; Clerical Studies

COURSE SUBJECT AREAS OFFERED OUTSIDE OF DEGREE PROGRAMS
Undergraduate—accounting and related services; biological and physical sciences; business administration, management and operations; communication and media; computer/information technology administration and management; computer systems networking and telecommunications; developmental and child psychology; economics; English composition; English literature (British and Commonwealth); fine and studio art; health and physical education/fitness; history; management information systems; mathematics; psychology; religious studies; sociology.

PEIRCE COLLEGE
Philadelphia, Pennsylvania
Peirce College Non-Traditional Education
http://www.peirce.edu

Peirce College was founded in 1865. It is accredited by Middle States Association of Colleges and Schools. It first offered distance learning courses in 1997. In fall 2007, there were 1,799 students enrolled in distance learning courses. Institutionally administered financial aid is available to distance learners.

Services Distance learners have accessibility to academic advising, bookstore, career placement assistance, library services, tutoring.

Contact Ms. Nadine M. Maher, Dean, Enrollment Management, Peirce College, 1420 Pine Street, Philadelphia, PA 19102. Telephone: 888-467-3472 Ext. 9214. Fax: 215-670-9366. E-mail: info@peirce.edu.

DEGREES AND AWARDS

AS Business Administration–Accounting concentration; Business Administration–Business Law concentration; Business Administration–Entrepreneurship/Small Business Management concentration; Business Administration–Human Resource Management concentration; Business Administration–Management concentration; Business Administration–Marketing concentration; Information Technology–Desktop Applications for Business concentration; Information Technology–Network Security concentration; Information Technology–Networking concentration; Information Technology–Programming Application and Development concentration; Information Technology–Technology Management concentration; Paralegal Studies
BS Business Administration–Accounting concentration; Business Administration–Business Law concentration; Business Administration–Entrepreneurship/Small Business Management concentration; Business Administration–Human Resource Management concentration; Business Administration–Management concentration; Business Administration–Marketing concentration; Business Administration–Real Estate Management concentration; Information Technology–Desktop Applications for Business concentration; Information Technology–Information Security concentration; Information Technology–Network Security concentration; Information Technology–Networking concentration; Information Technology–Programming and Application Development concentration; Information Technology–Technology Management concentration; Paralegal Studies
Certificate Business Administration–Business Law concentration; Certified Information Systems Security Professional (CISSP); Information Technology–.NET Technology concentration; Information Technology–Help Desk Technician concentration; Information Technology–Windows Network Operating System concentration; Paralegal Studies

COURSE SUBJECT AREAS OFFERED OUTSIDE OF DEGREE PROGRAMS

Undergraduate—economics; English; English composition; history; liberal arts and sciences, general studies and humanities; mathematics and statistics related; psychology; sociology.

See full description on page 428.

PELLISSIPPI STATE TECHNICAL COMMUNITY COLLEGE
Knoxville, Tennessee
Educational Technology Services
http://www.pstcc.edu/ets

Pellissippi State Technical Community College was founded in 1974. It is accredited by Southern Association of Colleges and Schools. It first offered distance learning courses in 1991. In fall 2007, there were 1,700 students enrolled in distance learning courses. Institutionally administered financial aid is available to distance learners.

Services Distance learners have accessibility to academic advising, bookstore, campus computer network, career placement assistance, e-mail services, library services, tutoring.

Contact Dr. Dennis Adams, Dean of Instructional Services, Pellissippi State Technical Community College, 10915 Hardin Valley Road, Knoxville, TN 37933. Telephone: 865-694-6593. E-mail: dadams@pstcc.edu.

DEGREES AND AWARDS
AAS Web Technology

COURSE SUBJECT AREAS OFFERED OUTSIDE OF DEGREE PROGRAMS

Undergraduate—accounting and related services; American literature (United States and Canadian); anthropology; archeology; behavioral sciences; biology; business administration, management and operations; business/commerce; business, management, and marketing related; communication and media; computer and information sciences; computer software and media applications; English composition; history; human resources management; marketing; mathematics and statistics related; philosophy and religious studies related; physics; psychology; public relations, advertising, and applied communication related; sociology; speech and rhetoric; statistics; visual and performing arts related.

PENINSULA COLLEGE
Port Angeles, Washington
http://pc.ctc.edu/

Peninsula College was founded in 1961. It is accredited by Northwest Commission on Colleges and Universities. It first offered distance learning courses in 1994. In fall 2007, there were 2,161 students enrolled in distance learning courses. Institutionally administered financial aid is available to distance learners.

Services Distance learners have accessibility to academic advising, bookstore, career placement assistance, library services, tutoring.

Contact Vicki Sievert, Distance/eLearning Coordinator, Peninsula College, 1502 East Lauridsen Boulevard, Port Angeles, WA 98362. Telephone: 360-417-6272. Fax: 360-417-6295. E-mail: vickis@pcadmin.ctc.edu.

DEGREES AND AWARDS
AA Liberal Arts
AAS Criminal Justice

COURSE SUBJECT AREAS OFFERED OUTSIDE OF DEGREE PROGRAMS

Undergraduate—accounting and related services; allied health and medical assisting services; American literature (United States and Canadian); anthropology; astronomy and astrophysics; biblical and other theological languages and literatures; biochemistry, biophysics and molecular biology; biological and physical sciences; business administration, management and operations; business/commerce; business, management, and marketing related; chemistry; communication and journalism related; computer and information sciences; computer software and media applications; criminal justice and corrections; dental support services and allied professions; developmental and child psychology; economics; education; English composition; English literature (British and Commonwealth); entrepreneurial and small business operations; family psychology; geological and earth sciences/geosciences; health and physical education/fitness; health professions related; history; human development, family studies, and related services; information science/studies; journalism; liberal arts and sciences, general studies and humanities; mathematics; mathematics and computer science; mathematics and statistics related; music; natural sciences; nursing; nutrition sciences; pharmacology and toxicology; philosophy; physical sciences; political science and government; psychology; social sciences; sociology.

PENN STATE UNIVERSITY PARK
State College, Pennsylvania
Department of Distance Education/World Campus
http://www.worldcampus.psu.edu

Penn State University Park was founded in 1855. It is accredited by Middle States Association of Colleges and Schools. It first offered distance learning courses in 1998. In fall 2007, there were 6,000 students enrolled in distance learning courses. Institutionally administered financial aid is available to distance learners.

Services Distance learners have accessibility to academic advising, bookstore, campus computer network, e-mail services, library services.

Contact Adult Learner Enrollment Services, Penn State University Park, 128 Outreach Building, 100 Innovation Boulevard, University Park, PA 16802. Telephone: 800-252-3592. Fax: 814-865-3290. E-mail: psuwd@psu.edu.

DEGREES AND AWARDS

AA Letters, Arts, and Sciences
AS Business Administration; Hotel, Restaurant, and Institutional Management; Human Development and Family Studies; Information Sciences and Technology
BA Law and Society; Letters, Arts, and Sciences; Psychology
BS Criminal Justice; Organizational Leadership; Psychology; Turfgrass Science
BSN Nursing–RN to BSN
Certificate Adult Development and Aging Services; Children, Youth, and Family Services; Family Literacy; Hospitality Management; Hotel, Restaurant, and Institutional Management; Information Science and Technology; Labor Studies and Industrial Relations; Nursing Management; Organizational Communication; Turfgrass Management; Turfgrass Management, advanced; Weather Forecasting
Certification Special Education Supervisory Certificate
Graduate Certificate Applied Behavior Analysis for Special Education; Applied Statistics; Autism; Bioterrorism Preparedness; Children's Literature; Community and Economic Development; Disaster Preparedness; Distance Education; Educational Technology Integration; Family Literacy; Geographic Information Systems; Geospatial Intelligence; Institutional Research; Project Management; Reading Instruction for Special Education (RISE); Supply Chain and Information Systems
MA Geographic Information Systems
MBA i-MBA
ME Systems Engineering
MEd Adult Education; Curriculum and Instruction–Children's Literature; Earth Sciences; Instructional Systems–Educational Technology
MPM Project Management
MPS Community and Economic Development; Community and Economic Development; Human Resources and Employment Relations; Supply Chain Management
MS/MPH Homeland Security in Public Health Preparedness

See full description on page 430.

PENNSYLVANIA COLLEGE OF TECHNOLOGY
Williamsport, Pennsylvania
http://www.pct.edu/away
Pennsylvania College of Technology was founded in 1965. It is accredited by Middle States Association of Colleges and Schools. It first offered distance learning courses in 1996. In fall 2007, there were 493 students enrolled in distance learning courses. Institutionally administered financial aid is available to distance learners.
Services Distance learners have accessibility to academic advising, bookstore, campus computer network, career placement assistance, e-mail services, library services, tutoring.
Contact Paula Neal, Distance Learning Services Assistant, Pennsylvania College of Technology, One College Avenue, DIF #50, Williamsport, PA 17701. Telephone: 570-320-8019. Fax: 570-321-5559. E-mail: distancelearning@pct.edu.

DEGREES AND AWARDS

BS Applied Health Studies; Automotive Technology Management; Dental Hygiene; Technology Management
BSN Nursing

COURSE SUBJECT AREAS OFFERED OUTSIDE OF DEGREE PROGRAMS

Undergraduate—accounting and related services; architecture; biological and biomedical sciences related; biology; building/construction finishing, management, and inspection; business/commerce; business/corporate communications; chemistry; computer and information sciences; construction engineering technology; dental support services and allied professions; English language and literature related; environmental/environmental health engineering; finance and financial management

services; fine and studio art; geological and earth sciences/geosciences; health professions related; history; international business; marketing; mathematics; nursing; philosophy and religious studies related; statistics.
See full description on page 432.

PENNSYLVANIA HIGHLANDS COMMUNITY COLLEGE
Johnstown, Pennsylvania
Pennsylvania Highlands Community College was founded in 1994. It is accredited by Middle States Association of Colleges and Schools. In fall 2007, there were 326 students enrolled in distance learning courses.
Contact Mr. Meryl Rutz, Director of Advising, Pennsylvania Highlands Community College, 101 Community College Way, Johnstown, PA 15904. Telephone: 814-262-6433. E-mail: mrutz@pennhighlands.edu.

DEGREES AND AWARDS
Programs offered do not lead to a degree or other formal award.

COURSE SUBJECT AREAS OFFERED OUTSIDE OF DEGREE PROGRAMS

Undergraduate—anthropology; astronomy and astrophysics; English composition; health and physical education/fitness; human resources management; mathematics; psychology; sociology.

PHILADELPHIA UNIVERSITY
Philadelphia, Pennsylvania
http://www.philau.edu/
Philadelphia University was founded in 1884. It is accredited by Middle States Association of Colleges and Schools. It first offered distance learning courses in 1998. In fall 2007, there were 147 students enrolled in distance learning courses. Institutionally administered financial aid is available to distance learners.
Services Distance learners have accessibility to academic advising, bookstore, campus computer network, career placement assistance, e-mail services, library services, tutoring.
Contact Mr. Jack Klett, Director of Graduate Admissions, Philadelphia University, School House Lane and Henry Avenue, Philadelphia, PA 19144. Telephone: 215-951-2943. E-mail: gradadms@philau.edu.

DEGREES AND AWARDS
Certificate Nurse-Midwifery
MBA Textile and Apparel Marketing
MS Disaster Medicine and Management; Midwifery

COURSE SUBJECT AREAS OFFERED OUTSIDE OF DEGREE PROGRAMS

Undergraduate—accounting and related services; business administration, management and operations; economics; finance and financial management services; legal studies (non-professional general, undergraduate); management information systems; management sciences and quantitative methods; marketing; operations research; statistics.
Graduate—accounting and related services; apparel and textiles; finance and financial management services; international business; management information systems; management sciences and quantitative methods; marketing; statistics.

PIEDMONT COMMUNITY COLLEGE
Roxboro, North Carolina
http://www.piedmont.cc.edu
Piedmont Community College was founded in 1970. It is accredited by Southern Association of Colleges and Schools. It first offered distance learning courses in 1989. In fall 2007, there were 721 students enrolled in distance learning courses. Institutionally administered financial aid is available to distance learners.
Services Distance learners have accessibility to academic advising, bookstore, campus computer network, career placement assistance, e-mail services, library services, tutoring.

Contact Libbie McPhaul-Moore, Distance Education Coordinator/Instructor, Piedmont Community College, PO Box 1197, Roxboro, NC 27573. Telephone: 336-599-1181 Ext. 2445. Fax: 336-599-9146. E-mail: mcphaul@piedmontcc.edu.

DEGREES AND AWARDS

AA University Transfer
AAS Business Administration; Information Systems; Web Technologoes
Certificate Accounting; Business Administration; Information Systems; Marketing
Diploma Business Administration; Information Systems

COURSE SUBJECT AREAS OFFERED OUTSIDE OF DEGREE PROGRAMS

Undergraduate—biology; business operations support and assistant services; communication and media; computer programming; creative writing; English; English composition; entrepreneurial and small business operations; fine and studio art; health and physical education/fitness; history; human development, family studies, and related services; human services; mathematics and statistics related; psychology; social work; sociology; technical and business writing.

PIEDMONT TECHNICAL COLLEGE
Greenwood, South Carolina
Division of Instructional Technology
http://www.ptc.edu/dl

Piedmont Technical College was founded in 1966. It is accredited by Southern Association of Colleges and Schools. It first offered distance learning courses in 1995. In fall 2007, there were 2,500 students enrolled in distance learning courses. Institutionally administered financial aid is available to distance learners.

Services Distance learners have accessibility to academic advising, bookstore, campus computer network, career placement assistance, e-mail services, library services, tutoring.

Contact Dr. Daniel D. Koenig, Associate Vice President for Institutional Support and Technology, Piedmont Technical College, 620 North Emerald Road, PO Box 1467, Greenwood, SC 29648. Telephone: 864-941-8446. Fax: 864-941-8703. E-mail: koenig.d@ptc.edu.

DEGREES AND AWARDS

AA Liberal Arts
AAS Associate in Industrial Technology, Major in Industrial Electronics Technology
AD Business–Associate in Business, General Business major; Business–Associate in Business, Office Systems Technology major

COURSE SUBJECT AREAS OFFERED OUTSIDE OF DEGREE PROGRAMS

Undergraduate—American literature (United States and Canadian); biology; business administration, management and operations; business/commerce; cell biology and anatomical sciences; chemistry; communication and media; computer science; design and applied arts; English composition; English literature (British and Commonwealth); fine and studio art; history; languages (Romance languages); legal studies (non-professional general, undergraduate); management information systems; mathematics and statistics related; music; philosophy and religious studies related; plant sciences; political science and government; psychology; sociology; speech and rhetoric; statistics.

PIKES PEAK COMMUNITY COLLEGE
Colorado Springs, Colorado
Learning Technologies
http://www.ppcc.edu

Pikes Peak Community College was founded in 1968. It is accredited by North Central Association of Colleges and Schools. It first offered distance learning courses in 1978. In fall 2007, there were 2,500 students enrolled in distance learning courses. Institutionally administered financial aid is available to distance learners.

Services Distance learners have accessibility to academic advising, bookstore, campus computer network, e-mail services, library services, tutoring.

Contact Julie Witherow, Director of Distance Education, Pikes Peak Community College, 5675 South Academy Boulevard, Colorado Springs, CO 80906-5498. Telephone: 719-502-3049. Fax: 719-540-7532. E-mail: witherow@ppcc.edu.

DEGREES AND AWARDS

AAS Fire Science Technology

COURSE SUBJECT AREAS OFFERED OUTSIDE OF DEGREE PROGRAMS

Undergraduate—accounting and related services; American literature (United States and Canadian); anthropology; astronomy and astrophysics; biological and physical sciences; business administration, management and operations; business/commerce; business/corporate communications; business/managerial economics; business operations support and assistant services; computer and information sciences and support services related; computer programming; computer science; computer software and media applications; computer systems networking and telecommunications; criminal justice and corrections; criminology; design and applied arts; dramatic/theater arts and stagecraft; economics; English; English composition; fire protection; geography and cartography; history; journalism; marketing; natural resources and conservation related; natural resources conservation and research; political science and government; psychology; radio, television, and digital communication; social psychology; sociology; technical and business writing.

PINE TECHNICAL COLLEGE
Pine City, Minnesota
Distance Education Center
http://www.pinetech.edu

Pine Technical College was founded in 1965. It is accredited by North Central Association of Colleges and Schools. It first offered distance learning courses in 1985. In fall 2007, there were 200 students enrolled in distance learning courses. Institutionally administered financial aid is available to distance learners.

Services Distance learners have accessibility to academic advising, bookstore, campus computer network, e-mail services, library services, tutoring.

Contact Nancy Mach, Dean of Student Services, Pine Technical College, 900 4th Street SE, Pine City, MN 55063. Telephone: 320-629-5173. Fax: 320-629-5101. E-mail: machn@pinetech.edu.

DEGREES AND AWARDS

Programs offered do not lead to a degree or other formal award.

COURSE SUBJECT AREAS OFFERED OUTSIDE OF DEGREE PROGRAMS

Undergraduate—accounting and related services; American Sign Language (ASL); business, management, and marketing related; education (specific levels and methods); health professions related; mathematics; public administration and social service professions related.
Non-credit—health professions related.

PITTSBURGH TECHNICAL INSTITUTE
Oakdale, Pennsylvania
http://www.pti.edu/adult-division/index.html

Pittsburgh Technical Institute was founded in 1946. It is accredited by Middle States Association of Colleges and Schools. It first offered distance learning courses in 2001. In fall 2007, there were 75 students enrolled in distance learning courses. Institutionally administered financial aid is available to distance learners.

Services Distance learners have accessibility to academic advising, bookstore, campus computer network, career placement assistance, e-mail services, library services, tutoring.

Contact Jeff Leedstrom, Director of Adult Enrollment, Pittsburgh Technical Institute, 1111 McKee Road, Oakdale, PA 15071. Telephone: 412-809-5100. Fax: 412-809-5351. E-mail: leedstrom.jeff@pti.edu.

DEGREES AND AWARDS
Programs offered do not lead to a degree or other formal award.

COURSE SUBJECT AREAS OFFERED OUTSIDE OF DEGREE PROGRAMS
Undergraduate—business administration, management and operations; computer/information technology administration and management; drafting/design engineering technologies; electrical, electronics and communications engineering; health professions related.

PLYMOUTH STATE UNIVERSITY
Plymouth, New Hampshire
http://www.plymouth.edu/online/

Plymouth State University was founded in 1871. It is accredited by New England Association of Schools and Colleges. It first offered distance learning courses in 2000. In fall 2007, there were 372 students enrolled in distance learning courses. Institutionally administered financial aid is available to distance learners.

Services Distance learners have accessibility to academic advising, bookstore, campus computer network, e-mail services, library services, tutoring.

Contact Ms. Stacey L. Curdie, Director of Online Education, Plymouth State University, MSC 47B, 17 High Street, Plymouth, NH 03264. Telephone: 603-535-2813. E-mail: scurdie@plymouth.edu.

DEGREES AND AWARDS
Programs offered do not lead to a degree or other formal award.

COURSE SUBJECT AREAS OFFERED OUTSIDE OF DEGREE PROGRAMS
Undergraduate—bilingual, multilingual, and multicultural education; business administration, management and operations; business/corporate communications; communication and media; computer software and media applications; criminal justice and corrections; criminology; English; English as a second/foreign language (teaching); English composition; geography and cartography; human resources management; linguistic, comparative, and related language studies; music; social psychology.
Graduate—business/commerce; business/corporate communications; business, management, and marketing related; computer and information sciences; education; educational assessment, evaluation, and research; special education.
Non-credit—accounting and computer science; allied health and medical assisting services; animal sciences; business administration, management and operations; business/commerce; business/corporate communications; business, management, and marketing related; business operations support and assistant services; computer software and media applications; computer systems analysis; computer systems networking and telecommunications; film/video and photographic arts; finance and financial management services; graphic communications; health professions related; veterinary biomedical and clinical sciences.

PORTLAND COMMUNITY COLLEGE
Portland, Oregon
Distance Learning Department
http://www.distance.pcc.edu

Portland Community College was founded in 1961. It is accredited by Northwest Commission on Colleges and Universities. It first offered distance learning courses in 1981. In fall 2007, there were 5,732 students enrolled in distance learning courses. Institutionally administered financial aid is available to distance learners.

Services Distance learners have accessibility to academic advising, bookstore, career placement assistance, e-mail services, library services.

Contact Dennis Hitchcox, Programming Coordinator, Distance Education, Portland Community College, PO Box 19000, Portland, OR 97280-0990. Telephone: 503-977-4655. Fax: 503-977-4858. E-mail: dhitchco@pcc.edu.

DEGREES AND AWARDS
Programs offered do not lead to a degree or other formal award.

COURSE SUBJECT AREAS OFFERED OUTSIDE OF DEGREE PROGRAMS
Undergraduate—accounting and related services; aerospace, aeronautical and astronautical engineering; allied health and medical assisting services; anthropology; biology; business administration, management and operations; business, management, and marketing related; business operations support and assistant services; computer and information sciences; computer and information sciences and support services related; computer science; computer software and media applications; dental support services and allied professions; developmental and child psychology; economics; education; English composition; fire protection; foods, nutrition, and related services; geography and cartography; health and physical education/fitness; health professions related; history; human development, family studies, and related services; marketing; mathematics; mathematics and statistics related; music; nursing; physical sciences related; psychology; real estate; social sciences; sociology; statistics; technical and business writing.
Non-credit—computer/information technology administration and management; computer programming; computer software and media applications; computer systems networking and telecommunications; creative writing; education related; health professions related; languages (foreign languages related); legal professions and studies related; pharmacy, pharmaceutical sciences, and administration; psychology related.

PRAIRIE VIEW A&M UNIVERSITY
Prairie View, Texas
Office of Distance Learning
http://dl.pvamu.edu

Prairie View A&M University was founded in 1878. It is accredited by Southern Association of Colleges and Schools. It first offered distance learning courses in 1992. In fall 2007, there were 948 students enrolled in distance learning courses. Institutionally administered financial aid is available to distance learners.

Services Distance learners have accessibility to bookstore, campus computer network, e-mail services, library services.

Contact Dr. John R. Williams, Director, Office of Distance Learning, Prairie View A&M University, PO Box 519, MS 1210, Prairie View, TX 77446. Telephone: 936-261-3283. Fax: 936-261-3289. E-mail: jrwilliams@pvamu.edu.

DEGREES AND AWARDS
MBA General Business Administration

COURSE SUBJECT AREAS OFFERED OUTSIDE OF DEGREE PROGRAMS
Undergraduate—accounting and computer science; architecture; business, management, and marketing related; communication and journalism related; computer engineering technologies; economics; English language and literature related; finance and financial management services; history; information science/studies; languages (foreign languages related); materials engineering; nursing.
Graduate—computer/information technology administration and management; criminal justice and corrections; economics; education; ethnic, cultural minority, and gender studies; finance and financial management services; management information systems; marketing; nursing; psychology.

PRATT COMMUNITY COLLEGE
Pratt, Kansas
http://www.prattcc.edu

Pratt Community College was founded in 1938. It is accredited by North Central Association of Colleges and Schools. It first offered distance learning courses in 1999. In fall 2007, there were 350 students enrolled in distance learning courses. Institutionally administered financial aid is available to distance learners.

Services Distance learners have accessibility to academic advising, bookstore, campus computer network, career placement assistance, e-mail services, library services, tutoring.

Contact Pam Dietz, Dean of Academic Instruction, Pratt Community College, 348 NE SR 61, Pratt, KS 67124. Telephone: 620-672-9800 Ext. 238. Fax: 620-672-5288. E-mail: pamd@prattcc.edu.

DEGREES AND AWARDS
Programs offered do not lead to a degree or other formal award.

COURSE SUBJECT AREAS OFFERED OUTSIDE OF DEGREE PROGRAMS

Undergraduate—accounting and related services; American literature (United States and Canadian); biology; business administration, management and operations; chemistry; communication and media; criminology; economics; education; geography and cartography; history; liberal arts and sciences, general studies and humanities; mathematics; music; political science and government; psychology; social sciences related; sociology.

PRESCOTT COLLEGE
Prescott, Arizona
http://www.prescott.edu/

Prescott College was founded in 1966. It is accredited by North Central Association of Colleges and Schools. It first offered distance learning courses in 1978. In fall 2007, there were 600 students enrolled in distance learning courses. Institutionally administered financial aid is available to distance learners.
Services Distance learners have accessibility to academic advising, bookstore, career placement assistance, e-mail services, library services, tutoring.
Contact Melanie Lefever, Assistant Director of Admissions, Prescott College, Admissions, 220 Grove Avenue, Prescott, AZ 86301. Telephone: 877-350-2100 Ext. 2106. Fax: 928-776-5242. E-mail: admissions@prescott.edu.

DEGREES AND AWARDS
BA Adventure Education; Art; Business; Communications; Computer Information Systems; Counseling Psychology/Human Services; Creative Writing; Criminal Justice; Cultural and Regional Studies; Education; Elementary Education; Environmental Studies; History; Humanities; Journalism; Management; Music; Natural Resources and Conservation; Political Science; Special Education; Sustainable Community Development; Theater
Certification Teacher Certification
MA Adventure Education; Alternative Energy Systems; Anthropology; Art History; Art Therapy; Arts Management; Bilingual Education; Counseling and Psychology; Counseling–School Guidance Counseling; Cultural Studies; Ecology; Education; Educational Administration; Environmental Education; Environmental Education; Environmental Studies; Equine Assisted Mental Health; Film and Cinema Studies; Fire Science; Foreign Languages; Gay and Lesbian Studies; Gender Studies; Higher Education Administration; Humanities; Land Use Planning; Mental Health Counseling; Museum Studies; Natural Resources and Conservation; Peace Studies; Philosophy; Photography; Playwriting and Screenwriting; Religious Studies; Sustainability Education; Sustainable Community Development; Wetlands Management; Wildlife Management
PhD Education–Sustainability Education

COURSE SUBJECT AREAS OFFERED OUTSIDE OF DEGREE PROGRAMS

Undergraduate—accounting and related services; bilingual, multilingual, and multicultural education; business administration, management and operations; communication and media; community organization and advocacy; counseling psychology; creative writing; education; English; ethnic, cultural minority, and gender studies; history; human development, family studies, and related services; human services; liberal arts and sciences, general studies and humanities; natural resources conservation and research; parks, recreation and leisure; philosophy and religious studies related; psychology; visual and performing arts; wildlife and wildlands science and management.
Graduate—area, ethnic, cultural, and gender studies related; city/urban, community and regional planning; clinical psychology; communication and media; community organization and advocacy; creative writing;

education; ethnic, cultural minority, and gender studies; history; human development, family studies, and related services; human services; movement and mind-body therapies; natural resources and conservation related; natural resources management and policy; parks, recreation and leisure facilities management; peace studies and conflict resolution; philosophy and religious studies related; psychology; visual and performing arts; wildlife and wildlands science and management.

See full description on page 434.

PRESENTATION COLLEGE
Aberdeen, South Dakota
http://www.presentation.edu/

Presentation College was founded in 1951. It is accredited by North Central Association of Colleges and Schools. It first offered distance learning courses in 1994. In fall 2007, there were 449 students enrolled in distance learning courses. Institutionally administered financial aid is available to distance learners.
Services Distance learners have accessibility to academic advising, bookstore, campus computer network, career placement assistance, e-mail services, library services, tutoring.
Contact JoEllen Lindner, Vice President for Enrollment and Student Retention Services, Presentation College, 1500 North Main Street, Aberdeen, SD 57401. Telephone: 605-229-8492. Fax: 605-229-8425. E-mail: joellen.lindner@presentation.edu.

DEGREES AND AWARDS
AS Medical Office Administration; Surgical Technology completion program
BS Business Completion; Nursing–AD-LPN to BSN Nursing completion; Nursing–LPN Certificate to BSN Nursing completion; Nursing–RN to BSN completion; Radiologic Technology completion program
Certificate Medical Transcription

COURSE SUBJECT AREAS OFFERED OUTSIDE OF DEGREE PROGRAMS

Undergraduate—American Sign Language (ASL); English composition; mathematics; psychology; statistics.

PROVIDENCE COLLEGE AND THEOLOGICAL SEMINARY
Otterburne, Manitoba, Canada
Department of Continuing Education
http://prov.ca

Providence College and Theological Seminary was founded in 1925. It is provincially chartered. It first offered distance learning courses in 1975. In fall 2007, there were 100 students enrolled in distance learning courses. Institutionally administered financial aid is available to distance learners.
Services Distance learners have accessibility to academic advising, bookstore, campus computer network, career placement assistance, e-mail services, library services.
Contact Mr. Adrian Enns, Director of College Admissions, Providence College and Theological Seminary, 10 College Crescent, Otterburne, MB R0A 1G0, Canada. Telephone: 204-433-7488. Fax: 204-433-7158. E-mail: info@prov.ca.

DEGREES AND AWARDS
Programs offered do not lead to a degree or other formal award.

COURSE SUBJECT AREAS OFFERED OUTSIDE OF DEGREE PROGRAMS

Undergraduate—biblical and other theological languages and literatures; biblical studies; communication and media; theological and ministerial studies; theology and religious vocations related.
Graduate—area, ethnic, cultural, and gender studies related; biblical and other theological languages and literatures; biblical studies; business operations support and assistant services; counseling psychology; education related; missionary studies and missiology; pastoral counseling and specialized ministries; religious studies; theological and ministerial studies; theology and religious vocations related.

Non-credit—area, ethnic, cultural, and gender studies related; biblical and other theological languages and literatures; biblical studies; counseling psychology; education related; human resources management; missionary studies and missiology; pastoral counseling and specialized ministries; religious/sacred music; theological and ministerial studies; theology and religious vocations related.

PULASKI TECHNICAL COLLEGE
North Little Rock, Arkansas
http://www.pulaskitech.edu

Pulaski Technical College was founded in 1945. It is accredited by North Central Association of Colleges and Schools. It first offered distance learning courses in 1999. In fall 2007, there were 2,985 students enrolled in distance learning courses. Institutionally administered financial aid is available to distance learners.

Services Distance learners have accessibility to bookstore, campus computer network, e-mail services, library services, tutoring.

Contact Mr. Jason Green, Distance Learning Director, Pulaski Technical College, 3000 West Scenic Drive, North Little Rock, AR 72118. Telephone: 501-812-2716. Fax: 501-771-2844. E-mail: jkgreen@pulaskitech.edu.

DEGREES AND AWARDS
AA General Education

COURSE SUBJECT AREAS OFFERED OUTSIDE OF DEGREE PROGRAMS

Undergraduate—accounting and computer science; accounting and related services; allied health and medical assisting services; American literature (United States and Canadian); anthropology; applied mathematics; biology; business administration, management and operations; business/commerce; business operations support and assistant services; computer and information sciences; computer systems networking and telecommunications; data entry/microcomputer applications; data processing; economics; education; education related; English; English composition; family and consumer economics; health and medical administrative services; history; languages (foreign languages related); legal professions and studies related; legal studies (non-professional general, undergraduate); liberal arts and sciences, general studies and humanities; mathematics; mathematics and computer science; natural sciences; philosophy; physical sciences; political science and government; psychology; religious studies; social sciences; sociology; speech and rhetoric; visual and performing arts.

Non-credit—languages (Romance languages).

QUEEN'S UNIVERSITY AT KINGSTON
Kingston, Ontario, Canada
Continuing and Distance Studies
http://www.queensu.ca/cds

Queen's University at Kingston was founded in 1841. It is provincially chartered. It first offered distance learning courses in 1941. In fall 2007, there were 2,500 students enrolled in distance learning courses. Institutionally administered financial aid is available to distance learners.

Services Distance learners have accessibility to academic advising, bookstore, campus computer network, career placement assistance, e-mail services, library services, tutoring.

Contact Wilma Fernetich, Distance Education Advisor, Queen's University at Kingston, Kingston, ON K7L 2N6, Canada. Telephone: 613-533-6000 Ext. 77770. Fax: 613-533-6805. E-mail: fernetic@post.queensu.ca.

DEGREES AND AWARDS
Programs offered do not lead to a degree or other formal award.

COURSE SUBJECT AREAS OFFERED OUTSIDE OF DEGREE PROGRAMS

Undergraduate—biology; business/commerce; classical and ancient studies; cognitive science; creative writing; dramatic/theater arts and stagecraft; economics; English composition; English literature (British

and Commonwealth); ethnic, cultural minority, and gender studies; geography and cartography; history; languages (Germanic); nutrition sciences; pharmacology and toxicology; philosophy; psychology; religious studies; social psychology; sociology; statistics.

QUINEBAUG VALLEY COMMUNITY COLLEGE
Danielson, Connecticut
http://www.qvcc.commnet.edu/

Quinebaug Valley Community College was founded in 1971. It is accredited by New England Association of Schools and Colleges. It first offered distance learning courses in 1998. In fall 2007, there were 334 students enrolled in distance learning courses. Institutionally administered financial aid is available to distance learners.

Services Distance learners have accessibility to academic advising, library services, tutoring.

Contact Dr. Toni T. Moumouris, Enrollment and Transition Counselor, Quinebaug Valley Community College, 742 Upper Maple Street, Danielson, CT 06239. Telephone: 860-412-7208. Fax: 860-412-7222. E-mail: tmoumouris@qvcc.commnet.edu.

DEGREES AND AWARDS
Certificate Health Information Management Technology

COURSE SUBJECT AREAS OFFERED OUTSIDE OF DEGREE PROGRAMS

Undergraduate—anthropology; biological and physical sciences; business, management, and marketing related; education; engineering; English language and literature related; health and medical administrative services; history; human services; liberal arts and sciences, general studies and humanities; materials science; nutrition sciences; political science and government; polymer/plastics engineering; sociology.

Non-credit—accounting and computer science; allied health and medical assisting services; building/construction finishing, management, and inspection; business/corporate communications; computer software and media applications; engineering-related fields; health and medical administrative services; legal professions and studies related; real estate; sales, merchandising, and related marketing operations (general); technology education/industrial arts.

QUINNIPIAC UNIVERSITY
Hamden, Connecticut
http://www.quinnipiac.edu/quonline

Quinnipiac University was founded in 1929. It is accredited by New England Association of Schools and Colleges. It first offered distance learning courses in 2001. Institutionally administered financial aid is available to distance learners.

Services Distance learners have accessibility to academic advising, bookstore, campus computer network, career placement assistance, e-mail services, library services, tutoring.

Contact Online Programs, Quinnipiac University, 275 Mount Carmel Avenue, Hamden, CT 06518. Telephone: 203-582-8200.

DEGREES AND AWARDS
BS Organizational Leadership
MS Higher Education Leadership Professional focus; Human Resource Leadership Professional focus; Information Technology Leadership Professional focus; Insurance Leadership Professional focus; Organizational Leadership, general degree

RANDOLPH COMMUNITY COLLEGE
Asheboro, North Carolina
Virtual Campus
http://www.virtualrandolph.org

Randolph Community College was founded in 1962. It is accredited by Southern Association of Colleges and Schools. It first offered distance learning courses in 1998. In fall 2007, there were 1,500 students enrolled in distance learning courses. Institutionally administered financial aid is available to distance learners.

Services Distance learners have accessibility to academic advising, bookstore, e-mail services, library services, tutoring.

Contact Crystal J. Kingrey, Assistant to the Director of Distance Education, Randolph Community College, 629 Industrial Park Avenue, PO Box 1009, Asheboro, NC 27205. Telephone: 336-633-0263. Fax: 336-629-4695. E-mail: cjkingrey@randolph.edu.

DEGREES AND AWARDS

AA College Transfer

AAS Accounting; Business Administration; Criminal Justice; Information Systems; Office Systems Technology

COURSE SUBJECT AREAS OFFERED OUTSIDE OF DEGREE PROGRAMS

Undergraduate—accounting and related services; computer and information sciences; computer software and media applications; criminal justice and corrections; economics; education (specific subject areas); English composition; ethnic, cultural minority, and gender studies; finance and financial management services; history; human development, family studies, and related services; human services; languages (foreign languages related); legal studies (non-professional general, undergraduate); marketing; mathematics; music; philosophy and religious studies related; psychology; sociology.

Non-credit—accounting and related services; allied health and medical assisting services; allied health diagnostic, intervention, and treatment professions; biology; business operations support and assistant services; clinical/medical laboratory science and allied professions; computer and information sciences; computer software and media applications; creative writing; gerontology; human services; languages (foreign languages related); legal support services; medical basic sciences; pharmacy, pharmaceutical sciences, and administration.

RAPPAHANNOCK COMMUNITY COLLEGE
Glenns, Virginia
Flexible Learning Opportunities (FLO)
http://www.rappahannock.edu

Rappahannock Community College was founded in 1970. It is accredited by Southern Association of Colleges and Schools. It first offered distance learning courses in 1995. In fall 2007, there were 1,200 students enrolled in distance learning courses. Institutionally administered financial aid is available to distance learners.

Services Distance learners have accessibility to academic advising, bookstore, campus computer network, career placement assistance, e-mail services, library services, tutoring.

Contact Kristy Walker, Assistant for Distance Learning and Technology, Rappahannock Community College, 52 Campus Drive, Warsaw, VA 22572. Telephone: 804-333-6786. Fax: 804-333-6784. E-mail: kwalker @rappahannock.edu.

DEGREES AND AWARDS

AAS General Studies

Certificate Administrative Support; Bookkeeping/Accounting

COURSE SUBJECT AREAS OFFERED OUTSIDE OF DEGREE PROGRAMS

Undergraduate—accounting and related services; allied health and medical assisting services; American literature (United States and Canadian); business administration, management and operations; business/corporate communications; community health services; criminal justice and corrections; English composition; fine and studio art; health and physical education/fitness; history; mathematics; psychology; religious studies; sociology.

Non-credit—real estate.

READING AREA COMMUNITY COLLEGE
Reading, Pennsylvania
http://www.racc.edu

Reading Area Community College was founded in 1971. It is accredited by Middle States Association of Colleges and Schools. It first offered distance learning courses in 1986. In fall 2007, there were 500 students enrolled in distance learning courses. Institutionally administered financial aid is available to distance learners.

Services Distance learners have accessibility to academic advising, bookstore, campus computer network, e-mail services, library services.

Contact Ms. Mary Ellen G. Heckman, Assistant Dean of Library Services and Learning Resources, Reading Area Community College, 10 South Second Street, PO Box 1706, Reading, PA 19603. Telephone: 610-372-4721 Ext. 5061. E-mail: mheckman@racc.edu.

DEGREES AND AWARDS

AGS General Studies

COURSE SUBJECT AREAS OFFERED OUTSIDE OF DEGREE PROGRAMS

Undergraduate—accounting and related services; anthropology; biological and biomedical sciences related; business administration, management and operations; business/commerce; computer and information sciences; developmental and child psychology; economics; English composition; human development, family studies, and related services; languages (Romance languages); mathematics; psychology; sociology.

RED ROCKS COMMUNITY COLLEGE
Lakewood, Colorado
Learning and Resource Center
http://www.rrcc.edu/online

Red Rocks Community College was founded in 1969. It is accredited by North Central Association of Colleges and Schools. It first offered distance learning courses in 1980. In fall 2007, there were 1,600 students enrolled in distance learning courses. Institutionally administered financial aid is available to distance learners.

Services Distance learners have accessibility to academic advising, bookstore, e-mail services, library services.

Contact Rebecca Woulfe, eLearning Director, Red Rocks Community College, 13300 West 6th Avenue, Lakewood, CO 80228. Telephone: 303-914-6444. Fax: 303-914-6716. E-mail: rebecca.woulfe@rrcc.edu.

DEGREES AND AWARDS

AAS Building Code Enforcement; Business; Construction Technology–Construction Electrician emphasis; Construction Technology–Power Technology emphasis; Emergency Management and Planning; Fire Science Management

COURSE SUBJECT AREAS OFFERED OUTSIDE OF DEGREE PROGRAMS

Undergraduate—accounting and related services; anthropology; applied mathematics; astronomy and astrophysics; building/construction finishing, management, and inspection; communication disorders sciences and services; computer and information sciences; computer programming; computer science; computer software and media applications; computer systems analysis; computer systems networking and telecommunications; criminal justice and corrections; data processing; design and applied arts; developmental and child psychology; education related; English as a second language; English composition; fine and studio art; fire protection; geography and cartography; history; mathematics; music; social psychology; sociology; visual and performing arts related.

REGENT COLLEGE
Vancouver, British Columbia, Canada
http://www.regent-college.edu/academics/cstudies/

Regent College was founded in 1968. It is provincially chartered. It first offered distance learning courses in 1998. In fall 2007, there were 375 students enrolled in distance learning courses. Institutionally administered financial aid is available to distance learners.

Services Distance learners have accessibility to academic advising, bookstore, library services, tutoring.

Contact Doug Hills, Administrative Assistant, Regent College, 5800 University Boulevard, Vancouver, BC V6T 2E4, Canada. Telephone: 604-224-3245. Fax: 604-224-3097. E-mail: continuingstudies@regent-college.edu.

DEGREES AND AWARDS

Programs offered do not lead to a degree or other formal award.

COURSE SUBJECT AREAS OFFERED OUTSIDE OF DEGREE PROGRAMS
Undergraduate—biblical studies.
Graduate—biblical studies; theological and ministerial studies; theology and religious vocations related.
Non-credit—biblical studies.

REGENT UNIVERSITY
Virginia Beach, Virginia
Distance Education
http://www.regent.edu
Regent University was founded in 1977. It is accredited by Southern Association of Colleges and Schools. It first offered distance learning courses in 1989. In fall 2007, there were 3,122 students enrolled in distance learning courses. Institutionally administered financial aid is available to distance learners.
Services Distance learners have accessibility to academic advising, bookstore, campus computer network, career placement assistance, e-mail services, library services, tutoring.
Contact Mr. Jerrod Fishback, Central Enrollment Management, Regent University, 1000 Regent University Drive, SC 218, Virginia Beach, VA 23464. Telephone: 800-373-5504. Fax: 757-226-4381. E-mail: admissions@regent.edu.

DEGREES AND AWARDS
AA Business; Christian Studies; General Studies; Psychology
BA Animation; Cinema-Television; Communications; English; English; Journalism; Religious Studies; Theatre
BS Global Business; Interdisciplinary Studies; Organizational Leadership and Management; Political Science; Psychology
Certificate TESOL
CAGS Education; Leadership
Graduate Certificate Leadership; Strategic Foresight
MA Biblical Studies; Cinema Arts; Communication Studies; Government; Human Services Counseling; Journalism; Organizational Leadership; Practical Theology; Strategic Foresight; Television Arts; Theater Arts
MBA Business Administration
MDiv Practical Theology
MEd Christian School Program; Cross-Categorical Special Education; Educational Leadership; Individualized Degree program; Student Affairs; TESOL
DMin Ministry–Leadership and Renewal
DSL Strategic Leadership
EdD Education Doctorate
PhD Communication; Counseling Education and Supervision; Organizational Leadership; Renewal Studies

COURSE SUBJECT AREAS OFFERED OUTSIDE OF DEGREE PROGRAMS
Undergraduate—business administration, management and operations; business/commerce; business, management, and marketing related; communication and journalism related; communication and media; communications technology; education; English; film/video and photographic arts; history; international business; mathematics; natural sciences; physical sciences; political science and government; psychology; social sciences; theological and ministerial studies; theology and religious vocations related; visual and performing arts.
Graduate—accounting and related services; biblical studies; business administration, management and operations; business/commerce; business, management, and marketing related; communication and journalism related; communication and media; communications technology; counseling psychology; education; English as a second language; international business; pastoral counseling and specialized ministries; political science and government; psychology; public administration; public policy analysis; theological and ministerial studies; theology and religious vocations related; visual and performing arts.
Non-credit—accounting and related services; business administration, management and operations; business/commerce; business, management, and marketing related; communication and journalism related; education;

educational administration and supervision; education related; English as a second language; film/video and photographic arts; human resources management; international business; international/global studies; international relations and affairs; pastoral counseling and specialized ministries; public policy analysis; religious education; religious studies; theology and religious vocations related; visual and performing arts.

REGIS UNIVERSITY
Denver, Colorado
School for Professional Studies and Distance Learning
http://www.regisuniversityonline.org
Regis University was founded in 1877. It is accredited by North Central Association of Colleges and Schools. It first offered distance learning courses in 1992. In fall 2007, there were 5,157 students enrolled in distance learning courses. Institutionally administered financial aid is available to distance learners.
Services Distance learners have accessibility to academic advising, bookstore, campus computer network, career placement assistance, e-mail services, library services, tutoring.
Contact Denise Copeland, Administrative Coordinator of CPS Distance Education, Regis University, Adult Learning Center, Mail Code K-18, 3333 Regis Boulevard, Denver, CO 80221. Telephone: 303-964-3651. Fax: 303-964-5436. E-mail: dcopelan@regis.edu.

DEGREES AND AWARDS
BS Business Administration; Computer Information Systems; Computer Networking; Computer Science; Finance; Marketing; Public Administration
BSN Nursing–RN to BSN
Certificate of Completion Computer Networking; Computer Programming–Java Programming; Computer Programming–UNIX (Solaris); Irish Studies; Management Information Systems
Certificate Public Administration
Graduate Certificate Database Technologies (MSCIT); E-Commerce Engineering (MSCIT); Executive International Management (MSM); Executive Leadership (MSM); Humane and Environmental Studies (MNM); Leadership (MNM); Management of Technology (MSCIT); Networking Technologies (MSCIT); Object-Oriented Technologies (MSCIT); Program Management (MNM); Project Management–Executive Project Management (MSM); Resource Development (MNM); Strategic Business Management (MSM)
MBA Business Administration
MEd Education
MS Computer Information Technology; Nonprofit Management
MSM Management

COURSE SUBJECT AREAS OFFERED OUTSIDE OF DEGREE PROGRAMS
Undergraduate—accounting and related services; business administration, management and operations; business/managerial economics; communication and media; computer/information technology administration and management; computer programming; computer science; computer systems networking and telecommunications; finance and financial management services; history; information science/studies; marketing; philosophy and religious studies related; public administration; religious studies; sales, merchandising, and related marketing operations (general); social psychology; sociology; statistics.
Graduate—accounting and related services; anthropology; business/corporate communications; business, management, and marketing related; business/managerial economics; computer and information sciences; computer and information sciences and support services related; computer/information technology administration and management; computer programming; computer science; computer systems networking and telecommunications; curriculum and instruction; educational administration and supervision; education related; education (specific levels and methods); finance and financial management services; international business; management information systems; management sciences and quantitative methods; marketing; philosophy and religious studies related; public administration; public administration and social service professions related.

REND LAKE COLLEGE
Ina, Illinois
Learning Resource Center
http://www.rlc.edu

Rend Lake College was founded in 1967. It is accredited by North Central Association of Colleges and Schools. It first offered distance learning courses in 1995. In fall 2007, there were 900 students enrolled in distance learning courses. Institutionally administered financial aid is available to distance learners.

Services Distance learners have accessibility to academic advising, bookstore, campus computer network, career placement assistance, e-mail services, library services, tutoring.

Contact Krystal N. Prusacki, Distance Learning and Media Technology Specialist, Rend Lake College, 468 North Ken Gray Parkway, Ina, IL 62846. Telephone: 618-437-5321 Ext. 1299. Fax: 618-437-5677. E-mail: prusackik@rlc.edu.

DEGREES AND AWARDS
Programs offered do not lead to a degree or other formal award.

COURSE SUBJECT AREAS OFFERED OUTSIDE OF DEGREE PROGRAMS

Undergraduate—agriculture; anthropology; biology; business/commerce; business/corporate communications; clinical child psychology; computer science; criminal justice and corrections; English; English composition; geological and earth sciences/geosciences; health and physical education/fitness; health services/allied health/health sciences; history; liberal arts and sciences, general studies and humanities; mathematics; microbiological sciences and immunology; music; nursing; nutrition sciences; philosophy and religious studies related; plant sciences; political science and government; psychology; real estate; religious studies; social sciences; sociology; speech and rhetoric; work and family studies.

Non-credit—accounting and related services; business administration, management and operations; business/commerce; business operations support and assistant services; computer software and media applications; entrepreneurial and small business operations; human resources management; languages (foreign languages related); sales, merchandising, and related marketing operations (general).

THE RICHARD STOCKTON COLLEGE OF NEW JERSEY
Pomona, New Jersey
Office of Distance Education
http://www.stockton.edu

The Richard Stockton College of New Jersey was founded in 1969. It is accredited by Middle States Association of Colleges and Schools. It first offered distance learning courses in 1996. In fall 2007, there were 1,800 students enrolled in distance learning courses. Institutionally administered financial aid is available to distance learners.

Services Distance learners have accessibility to campus computer network, e-mail services, library services.

Contact Dennis Fotia, Distance Education Coordinator, The Richard Stockton College of New Jersey, PO Box 195, Pomona, NJ 08240-0195. Telephone: 609-652-4580. Fax: 609-626-5562. E-mail: dennis.fotia@stockton.edu.

DEGREES AND AWARDS
Programs offered do not lead to a degree or other formal award.

COURSE SUBJECT AREAS OFFERED OUTSIDE OF DEGREE PROGRAMS

Undergraduate—allied health and medical assisting services; anthropology; applied mathematics; business administration, management and operations; English composition; ethnic, cultural minority, and gender studies; film/video and photographic arts; gerontology; health professions related; journalism; liberal arts and sciences, general studies and humanities; marketing; nursing; psychology; sociology.

Graduate—allied health and medical assisting services; business, management, and marketing related; information science/studies; nursing.

RICHLAND COMMUNITY COLLEGE
Decatur, Illinois
Lifelong Learning Division

Richland Community College was founded in 1971. It is accredited by North Central Association of Colleges and Schools. It first offered distance learning courses in 1994. In fall 2007, there were 400 students enrolled in distance learning courses. Institutionally administered financial aid is available to distance learners.

Services Distance learners have accessibility to academic advising, campus computer network, career placement assistance, e-mail services, library services.

Contact Ms. Catherine L. Sebok, Director, Recruitment and Outreach Services, Richland Community College, One College Park, Decatur, IL 62521. Telephone: 217-875-7200 Ext. 558. Fax: 217-875-7783. E-mail: csebok@richland.cc.edu.

DEGREES AND AWARDS
Programs offered do not lead to a degree or other formal award.

COURSE SUBJECT AREAS OFFERED OUTSIDE OF DEGREE PROGRAMS

Undergraduate—accounting and related services; business/corporate communications; computer software and media applications; creative writing; developmental and child psychology; English composition; fine and studio art; history; psychology; social psychology; sociology.

RICHMOND COMMUNITY COLLEGE
Hamlet, North Carolina

Richmond Community College was founded in 1964. It is accredited by Southern Association of Colleges and Schools. It first offered distance learning courses in 2005. In fall 2007, there were 500 students enrolled in distance learning courses. Institutionally administered financial aid is available to distance learners.

Contact Ms. Sharon Goodman, Director of Counseling, Richmond Community College, PO Box 1189, Hamlet, NC 28345. Telephone: 910-400-1734. Fax: 910-582-7102. E-mail: sharong@richmondcc.edu.

DEGREES AND AWARDS
Programs offered do not lead to a degree or other formal award.

COURSE SUBJECT AREAS OFFERED OUTSIDE OF DEGREE PROGRAMS

Undergraduate—accounting and computer science; business administration, management and operations; business/managerial economics; computer science; criminal justice and corrections; economics; English; psychology; sociology.

Non-credit—business operations support and assistant services.

RIVERSIDE COMMUNITY COLLEGE DISTRICT
Riverside, California
Open Campus
http://www.opencampus.com

Riverside Community College District was founded in 1916. It is accredited by Western Association of Schools and Colleges. It first offered distance learning courses in 1982. In fall 2007, there were 10,000 students enrolled in distance learning courses. Institutionally administered financial aid is available to distance learners.

Services Distance learners have accessibility to academic advising, bookstore, campus computer network, career placement assistance, e-mail services, library services.

Contact Col. Glen Brady, Director, Distance Education, Riverside Community College District, Open Campus, 4800 Magnolia Avenue, Riverside, CA 92506-1299. Telephone: 951-222-8561. Fax: 951-328-3596. E-mail: glen.brady@rcc.edu.

DEGREES AND AWARDS
Programs offered do not lead to a degree or other formal award.

COURSE SUBJECT AREAS OFFERED OUTSIDE OF DEGREE PROGRAMS

Undergraduate—accounting and related services; American Sign Language (ASL); anthropology; architectural history and criticism; architecture; astronomy and astrophysics; business administration, management and operations; business/commerce; communication and media; computer and information sciences; computer science; computer systems networking and telecommunications; criminology; economics; English; film/video and photographic arts; geography and cartography; graphic communications; history; hospitality administration; human resources management; languages (foreign languages related); legal support services; library science; linguistic, comparative, and related language studies; marketing; mathematics; music; nursing; nutrition sciences; philosophy; political science and government; psychology; radio, television, and digital communication; real estate; religious studies; sociology; transportation and materials moving related; visual and performing arts; work and family studies.

Non-credit—business administration, management and operations; computer and information sciences; computer programming; computer software and media applications; creative writing; economics; graphic communications; health professions related; linguistic, comparative, and related language studies.

ROCHESTER INSTITUTE OF TECHNOLOGY
Rochester, New York
Graduate Enrollment Services
http://www.rit.edu/online

Rochester Institute of Technology was founded in 1829. It is accredited by Middle States Association of Colleges and Schools. It first offered distance learning courses in 1979. In fall 2007, there were 4,000 students enrolled in distance learning courses. Institutionally administered financial aid is available to distance learners.

Services Distance learners have accessibility to academic advising, bookstore, campus computer network, career placement assistance, e-mail services, library services.

Contact Ms. Diane Ellison, Director, Office of Part-time and Graduate Enrollment Services, Rochester Institute of Technology, Bausch & Lomb Center, Room 1241, 58 Lomb Memorial Drive, Rochester, NY 14623. Telephone: 585-475-2229. Fax: 585-475-7164. E-mail: distance@rit.edu.

DEGREES AND AWARDS

BS Arts and Science–Applied Arts and Science; Electrical/Mechanical Engineering Technology; Safety Technology; Telecommunications Engineering Technology
Certificate Disaster and Emergency Management; E-business; Health Systems Administration; Industrial Environmental Management; International Logistics and Transportation Management; Public Relations Communications–Professional Writing; Quality Implementation; Quality Management, basic; Safety and Health Technology; Structural Design; Technical Communication, basic; Technical Communications, advanced; Telecommunications–Data Communications; Telecommunications–Network Management; Telecommunications–Voice Communications
Graduate Certificate Digital Print and Publishing; Elements of Health Care Leadership; Health Information Resources; Health Systems Finance; Learning and Knowledge Management Systems; Project Management; Senior Living Management; Statistical Methods for Product and Process Improvement; Statistical Quality; Technical Information Design
MEngr Microelectronics Manufacturing Engineering
MS Applied Statistics; Environmental Health and Safety Management; Facility Management; Health Systems Administration; Imaging Science; Learning and Knowledge Management Systems; Networking and Systems Administration; Print Media; Professional Studies; Software Development and Management; Telecommunications Engineering Technology

COURSE SUBJECT AREAS OFFERED OUTSIDE OF DEGREE PROGRAMS

Undergraduate—anthropology; business administration, management and operations; chemistry; civil engineering technology; communication and media; engineering mechanics; English composition; mechanical engineering; political science and government; psychology; sociology.

Graduate—business administration, management and operations; environmental/environmental health engineering; hospitality administration; statistics.

ROCKLAND COMMUNITY COLLEGE
Suffern, New York
Telecourse and Distance Learning Department
http://www.sunyrockland.edu/virtualrcc

Rockland Community College was founded in 1959. It is accredited by Middle States Association of Colleges and Schools. It first offered distance learning courses in 1985. In fall 2007, there were 800 students enrolled in distance learning courses. Institutionally administered financial aid is available to distance learners.

Services Distance learners have accessibility to academic advising, bookstore, campus computer network, career placement assistance, e-mail services, library services.

Contact Mr. Rick Echevarria, Administrative Assistant, Rockland Community College, 145 College Road, Room 8300, Suffern, NY 10901. Telephone: 845-574-4713. E-mail: rechevar@sunyrockland.edu.

DEGREES AND AWARDS

Programs offered do not lead to a degree or other formal award.

COURSE SUBJECT AREAS OFFERED OUTSIDE OF DEGREE PROGRAMS

Undergraduate—anthropology; biology; business/commerce; chemistry; computer science; economics; English; English composition; finance and financial management services; fine and studio art; geography and cartography; health/medical preparatory programs; health professions related; history; liberal arts and sciences, general studies and humanities; marketing; mathematics; medical basic sciences; nursing; philosophy; physical sciences; political science and government; psychology; social sciences related.

Graduate—economics; statistics.

Non-credit—nursing.

ROGER WILLIAMS UNIVERSITY
Bristol, Rhode Island
School of Continuing Studies
http://scs.rwu.edu

Roger Williams University was founded in 1956. It is accredited by New England Association of Schools and Colleges. It first offered distance learning courses in 1974. In fall 2007, there were 234 students enrolled in distance learning courses. Institutionally administered financial aid is available to distance learners.

Services Distance learners have accessibility to academic advising, bookstore, campus computer network, career placement assistance, e-mail services, library services.

Contact John Stout, Dean, School of Continuing Studies, Roger Williams University, 150 Washington Street, Providence, RI 02903. Telephone: 401-254-3530. Fax: 401-254-3560. E-mail: jstout@rwu.edu.

DEGREES AND AWARDS

Programs offered do not lead to a degree or other formal award.

COURSE SUBJECT AREAS OFFERED OUTSIDE OF DEGREE PROGRAMS

Undergraduate—criminal justice and corrections; criminology; finance and financial management services; health and medical administrative services; health services/allied health/health sciences; history; industrial production technologies; legal studies (non-professional general, undergraduate); physical sciences related; public administration; public administration and social service professions related; sociology.

ROOSEVELT UNIVERSITY
Chicago, Illinois
Distance Learning
http://www.roosevelt.edu/ruonline

Roosevelt University was founded in 1945. It is accredited by North Central Association of Colleges and Schools. It first offered distance learning courses in 2001. In fall 2007, there were 1,000 students enrolled in distance learning courses. Institutionally administered financial aid is available to distance learners.

Services Distance learners have accessibility to academic advising, bookstore, campus computer network, career placement assistance, e-mail services, library services, tutoring.

Contact Ms. Linda Gunden, Program Coordinator, Admission and Advising, Roosevelt University, 430 South Michigan Avenue, Chicago, IL 60605. Telephone: 312-341-2610. Fax: 312-341-2601. E-mail: lgunden@roosevelt.edu.

DEGREES AND AWARDS
BGS Psychology
BPS Criminal Justice Leadership; Organizational Leadership
Certificate Criminal Justice Leadership; Geographic Information Systems; Organizational Leadership
Graduate Certificate E-Learning; Instructional Design; Online Teaching; Performance Consulting; Training and Development
MA Teacher Leadership; Training and Development

COURSE SUBJECT AREAS OFFERED OUTSIDE OF DEGREE PROGRAMS
Undergraduate—accounting and related services; biological and biomedical sciences related; business administration, management and operations; business/corporate communications; computer science; criminal justice and corrections; curriculum and instruction; education; educational/instructional media design; education related; education (specific levels and methods); education (specific subject areas); English composition; hospitality administration; intercultural/multicultural and diversity studies; legal studies (non-professional general, undergraduate); liberal arts and sciences, general studies and humanities; multi-/interdisciplinary studies related; personality psychology; physical sciences; psychology; social sciences; sociology; statistics; visual and performing arts.
Graduate—business/corporate communications; communications technology; education; educational administration and supervision; educational/instructional media design; education related; hospitality administration; legal professions and studies related.
Non-credit—legal professions and studies related.

See full description on page 436.

ROSALIND FRANKLIN UNIVERSITY OF MEDICINE AND SCIENCE
North Chicago, Illinois
http://www.rosalindfranklin.edu

Rosalind Franklin University of Medicine and Science was founded in 1912. It is accredited by North Central Association of Colleges and Schools. It first offered distance learning courses in 1993. In fall 2007, there were 146 students enrolled in distance learning courses. Institutionally administered financial aid is available to distance learners.

Services Distance learners have accessibility to academic advising, bookstore, campus computer network, e-mail services, library services, tutoring.

Contact Ms. Laura Nelson, Administrative Assistant, Rosalind Franklin University of Medicine and Science, 3333 Green Bay Road, North Chicago, IL 60064-3095. Telephone: 847-578-3310. Fax: 847-578-8623. E-mail: laura.nelson@rosalindfranklin.edu.

DEGREES AND AWARDS
CAGS Healthcare Administration and Management; Women's Health
MS Clinical Laboratory Sciences (advanced and categorical); Clinical Laboratory Sciences (entry-level); Clinical Nutrition/Nutrition Education; Healthcare Administration and Management; Women's Health
DPT Physical Therapy–Post-Professional Doctor of Physical Therapy
PhD Interprofessional Healthcare Studies

ROSE STATE COLLEGE
Midwest City, Oklahoma
Academic Affairs
http://www.rose.edu/dl/

Rose State College was founded in 1968. It is accredited by North Central Association of Colleges and Schools. It first offered distance learning courses in 1972. In fall 2007, there were 2,299 students enrolled in distance learning courses. Institutionally administered financial aid is available to distance learners.

Services Distance learners have accessibility to academic advising, bookstore, campus computer network, career placement assistance, e-mail services, library services, tutoring.

Contact Chris Meyer, Director of Distance Learning, Rose State College, Learning Resources Center, 6420 SE 15th Street, Midwest City, OK 73110. Telephone: 405-733-7913. E-mail: cmeyer@rose.edu.

DEGREES AND AWARDS
AA Business; English; History; Liberal Arts; Social Sciences
AAS E-commerce and Webmaster Technology; Library Technical Assistant

COURSE SUBJECT AREAS OFFERED OUTSIDE OF DEGREE PROGRAMS
Undergraduate—accounting and computer science; accounting and related services; allied health and medical assisting services; allied health diagnostic, intervention, and treatment professions; alternative and complementary medical support services; alternative and complementary medicine and medical systems; American literature (United States and Canadian); apparel and textiles; audiovisual communications technologies; biology; business administration, management and operations; business/commerce; business/corporate communications; business, management, and marketing related; business/managerial economics; communication and journalism related; computer/information technology administration and management; computer programming; computer science; computer software and media applications; computer systems analysis; computer systems networking and telecommunications; creative writing; criminal justice and corrections; developmental and child psychology; economics; English; English composition; English language and literature related; English literature (British and Commonwealth); foods, nutrition, and related services; geography and cartography; geological and earth sciences/geosciences; geological/geophysical engineering; graphic communications; health and physical education/fitness; health/medical preparatory programs; health professions related; health services/allied health/health sciences; history; information science/studies; legal professions and studies related; legal research and advanced professional studies; legal studies (non-professional general, undergraduate); liberal arts and sciences, general studies and humanities; library assistant; library science; library science related; marketing; mathematics; nursing; philosophy; philosophy and religious studies related; physical sciences; physical sciences related; political science and government; psychology; psychology related; social psychology; social sciences; social sciences related; sociology.
Non-credit—health and physical education/fitness.

RUSH UNIVERSITY
Chicago, Illinois
http://www.rushu.rush.edu/nursing

Rush University was founded in 1969. It is accredited by North Central Association of Colleges and Schools. It first offered distance learning courses in 1998. In fall 2007, there were 100 students enrolled in distance learning courses. Institutionally administered financial aid is available to distance learners.

Services Distance learners have accessibility to campus computer network, e-mail services, library services.

Contact Ms. Hicela C. Woods, Director, Rush University, College Admission Services, 600 South Paulina, Suite 440, Chicago, IL 60612. Telephone: 312-942-7100. Fax: 312-942-2219. E-mail: hicela_castruita@rush.edu.

DEGREES AND AWARDS
CCCPE Specialist in Blood Bank Certificate
Graduate Certificate Healthcare Ethics

MSN Nursing

PhD Nursing

SACRAMENTO CITY COLLEGE
Sacramento, California
Distance/Online Education
http://www.scc.losrios.edu/de
Sacramento City College was founded in 1916. It is accredited by Western Association of Schools and Colleges. It first offered distance learning courses in 1986. In fall 2007, there were 5,611 students enrolled in distance learning courses. Institutionally administered financial aid is available to distance learners.

Services Distance learners have accessibility to academic advising, bookstore, campus computer network, e-mail services, library services, tutoring.

Contact Jim Hill, Program Support Specialist, Sacramento City College, Learning Resources Division, 3835 Freeport Boulevard, Sacramento, CA 95822. Telephone: 916-558-2146. E-mail: hillj@scc.losrios.edu.

DEGREES AND AWARDS
Programs offered do not lead to a degree or other formal award.

COURSE SUBJECT AREAS OFFERED OUTSIDE OF DEGREE PROGRAMS
Undergraduate—accounting and computer science; accounting and related services; allied health and medical assisting services; allied health diagnostic, intervention, and treatment professions; alternative and complementary medical support services; anthropology; applied mathematics; area, ethnic, cultural, and gender studies related; astronomy and astrophysics; audiovisual communications technologies; bilingual, multilingual, and multicultural education; biological and biomedical sciences related; biological and physical sciences; biology; business administration, management and operations; business/commerce; business/corporate communications; business, management, and marketing related; business/managerial economics; business operations support and assistant services; chemistry; clinical/medical laboratory science and allied professions; clinical psychology; cognitive psychology and psycholinguistics; communication and journalism related; communication and media; communications technologies and support services related; communications technology; computer and information sciences; computer and information sciences and support services related; computer/information technology administration and management; computer programming; computer science; computer software and media applications; computer systems analysis; computer systems networking and telecommunications; creative writing; data entry/microcomputer applications; dental support services and allied professions; design and applied arts; dramatic/theater arts and stagecraft; electrical/electronics maintenance and repair technology; electromechanical and instrumentation and maintenance technologies; English; English as a second language; English composition; ethnic, cultural minority, and gender studies; family and consumer economics; family and consumer sciences/human sciences; family and consumer sciences/human sciences business services; finance and financial management services; foods, nutrition, and related services; geography and cartography; geological and earth sciences/geosciences; gerontology; graphic communications; health professions related; health services/allied health/health sciences; heating, air conditioning, ventilation and refrigeration maintenance technology; history; journalism; library assistant; library science; library science related; mathematics; mathematics and computer science; mathematics and statistics related; nursing; nutrition sciences; philosophy; philosophy and religious studies related; physical sciences; physiology, pathology and related sciences; political science and government; psychology; psychology related; public policy analysis; real estate; social sciences; sociology; statistics; transportation and materials moving related.

SACRED HEART UNIVERSITY
Fairfield, Connecticut
University College/ Continuing Education
http://onlinelearning.sacredheart.edu
Sacred Heart University was founded in 1963. It is accredited by New England Association of Schools and Colleges. It first offered distance learning courses in 1997. In fall 2007, there were 600 students enrolled in distance learning courses. Institutionally administered financial aid is available to distance learners.

Services Distance learners have accessibility to academic advising, bookstore, campus computer network, career placement assistance, e-mail services, library services, tutoring.

Contact David M. Demers, PhD, Director, Instructional Technology, Sacred Heart University, 5151 Park Avenue, Fairfield, CT 06825. Telephone: 203-365-7613. Fax: 203-365-7695. E-mail: demersd@sacredheart.edu.

DEGREES AND AWARDS
BSN Nursing
MSHA Geriatric Rehabilitation and Wellness
MSN Nursing–Patient Care Services Administration–Family Nurse Practitioner

COURSE SUBJECT AREAS OFFERED OUTSIDE OF DEGREE PROGRAMS
Undergraduate—biological and physical sciences; business administration, management and operations; chemistry; communication and media; computer and information sciences; computer science; English composition; English language and literature related; fine and studio art; health professions related; history; international business; languages (foreign languages related); liberal arts and sciences, general studies and humanities; linguistic, comparative, and related language studies; marketing; music; philosophy; philosophy and religious studies related; physical sciences; political science and government; religious education; religious studies; social sciences related.
Graduate—accounting and related services; business administration, management and operations; computer science; economics; education; finance and financial management services; gerontology; health professions related; marketing; mathematics; nursing.

SADDLEBACK COLLEGE
Mission Viejo, California
Office of Instruction
http://www.saddleback.edu
Saddleback College was founded in 1967. It is accredited by Western Association of Schools and Colleges. It first offered distance learning courses in 1975. In fall 2007, there were 4,000 students enrolled in distance learning courses. Institutionally administered financial aid is available to distance learners.

Services Distance learners have accessibility to academic advising, bookstore, campus computer network, career placement assistance, e-mail services, library services.

Contact Ms. Sheri L. Nelson, Senior Administrative Assistant, Saddleback College, AGB 117, 28000 Marguerite Parkway, Mission Viejo, CA 92692. Telephone: 949-582-4515. Fax: 949-347-0438. E-mail: snelson@saddleback.edu.

DEGREES AND AWARDS
Programs offered do not lead to a degree or other formal award.

COURSE SUBJECT AREAS OFFERED OUTSIDE OF DEGREE PROGRAMS
Undergraduate—accounting and computer science; accounting and related services; American Sign Language (ASL); anthropology; business, management, and marketing related; business/managerial economics; communication and journalism related; computer science; developmental and child psychology; educational administration and supervision; English; geography and cartography; gerontology; health/medical preparatory programs; history; human development, family studies, and related services; international business; journalism; library science related; man-

agement information systems; marketing; mathematics; music; nursing; physics; political science and government; radio, television, and digital communication; real estate; sales, merchandising, and related marketing operations (general); sales, merchandising, and related marketing operations (specialized); social sciences related; sociology.

ST. AMBROSE UNIVERSITY
Davenport, Iowa
http://www.sau.edu/

St. Ambrose University was founded in 1882. It is accredited by North Central Association of Colleges and Schools. It first offered distance learning courses in 1990. In fall 2007, there were 190 students enrolled in distance learning courses. Institutionally administered financial aid is available to distance learners.

Services Distance learners have accessibility to academic advising, bookstore, campus computer network, career placement assistance, e-mail services, library services.

Contact Ms. Meg F. Halligan, Director of Admissions, St. Ambrose University, 518 West Locust Street, Davenport, IA 52803-2898. Telephone: 563-333-6311. Fax: 563-333-6321. E-mail: halliganmegf@sau.edu.

DEGREES AND AWARDS
Programs offered do not lead to a degree or other formal award.

COURSE SUBJECT AREAS OFFERED OUTSIDE OF DEGREE PROGRAMS

Undergraduate—business administration, management and operations; economics; education (specific subject areas); finance and financial management services; mathematics; philosophy; psychology.

Graduate—business administration, management and operations; education (specific subject areas); pastoral counseling and specialized ministries; special education; statistics.

SAINT CHARLES COMMUNITY COLLEGE
St. Peters, Missouri
Distance Learning
http://www.stchas.edu/distance/

Saint Charles Community College was founded in 1986. It is accredited by North Central Association of Colleges and Schools. It first offered distance learning courses in 1992. In fall 2007, there were 1,072 students enrolled in distance learning courses. Institutionally administered financial aid is available to distance learners.

Services Distance learners have accessibility to academic advising, bookstore, career placement assistance, library services, tutoring.

Contact Dr. Stephanie D. Tolson, Dean of Learning Resources, Saint Charles Community College, Learning Resource Center, 4601 Mid Rivers Mall Drive, Cottleville, MO 63376. Telephone: 636-922-8512. Fax: 636-922-8434. E-mail: stolson@stchas.edu.

DEGREES AND AWARDS
Programs offered do not lead to a degree or other formal award.

COURSE SUBJECT AREAS OFFERED OUTSIDE OF DEGREE PROGRAMS

Undergraduate—accounting and computer science; allied health and medical assisting services; anthropology; biology; business/commerce; criminal justice and corrections; economics; English; geography and cartography; health and physical education/fitness; history; mathematics; music; nursing; political science and government; psychology; sociology.

Non-credit—computer software and media applications; English as a second language; entrepreneurial and small business operations; finance and financial management services; human resources management; insurance; marketing.

ST. CLAIR COUNTY COMMUNITY COLLEGE
Port Huron, Michigan
http://www.SC4.edu/onlinelearning

St. Clair County Community College was founded in 1923. It is accredited by North Central Association of Colleges and Schools. It first offered distance learning courses in 2000. In fall 2007, there were 720 students enrolled in distance learning courses. Institutionally administered financial aid is available to distance learners.

Services Distance learners have accessibility to academic advising, bookstore, career placement assistance, e-mail services, library services, tutoring.

Contact Linda Davis, Dean of eLearning, Instructional Technology and Assessment, St. Clair County Community College, 323 Erie Street, PO Box 5015, Port Huron, MI 48061-5015. Telephone: 810-989-5765. E-mail: ldavis@sc4.edu.

DEGREES AND AWARDS
AA General degree
AD AAS Nursing, Health Care Provider to RN Articulation; Business (transfer program); General Education

COURSE SUBJECT AREAS OFFERED OUTSIDE OF DEGREE PROGRAMS

Undergraduate—accounting and related services; astronomy and astrophysics; business administration, management and operations; business/corporate communications; chemistry; communication and journalism related; computer and information sciences; creative writing; economics; education (specific levels and methods); electrical and electronic engineering technologies; English composition; geography and cartography; history; mathematics; nursing; political science and government; psychology; social sciences; sociology; speech and rhetoric; statistics.

ST. CLOUD STATE UNIVERSITY
St. Cloud, Minnesota
Center for Continuing Studies
http://www.stcloudstate.edu/continuingstudies

St. Cloud State University was founded in 1869. It is accredited by North Central Association of Colleges and Schools. It first offered distance learning courses in 1975. In fall 2007, there were 3,200 students enrolled in distance learning courses. Institutionally administered financial aid is available to distance learners.

Services Distance learners have accessibility to academic advising, bookstore, campus computer network, career placement assistance, e-mail services, library services, tutoring.

Contact Dr. Patricia Aceves, Director of Distributed Learning, St. Cloud State University, 720 4th Avenue South, St. Cloud, MN 56301. Telephone: 320-308-3081. Fax: 320-308-5041. E-mail: paceves@stcloudstate.edu.

DEGREES AND AWARDS
AA Liberal Arts
BA Criminal Justice Studies
BGS Community Psychology; Self-Designed
BS Special Education
BSAST Aviation Maintenance Management
MA Teaching English as a Second Language
MBA Business Administration
MS Behavior Analysis; Criminal Justice Studies; Educational Administration; Environmental and Technological Studies; Higher Education Administration; Information Media

COURSE SUBJECT AREAS OFFERED OUTSIDE OF DEGREE PROGRAMS

Undergraduate—aerospace, aeronautical and astronautical engineering; American literature (United States and Canadian); anthropology; astronomy and astrophysics; biology; botany/plant biology; chemistry; communication and media; counseling psychology; creative writing; criminal justice and corrections; economics; educational administration and supervision; English; English as a second language; English composition; environmental/environmental health engineering; history; management information systems; mathematics; philosophy; physics; psychology; social sciences related; sociology; special education; speech and rhetoric; statistics.

Graduate—behavioral sciences; community psychology; criminal justice and corrections; English as a second language; psychology related; statistics.

ST. EDWARD'S UNIVERSITY
Austin, Texas
New College
http://www.stedwards.edu

St. Edward's University was founded in 1885. It is accredited by Southern Association of Colleges and Schools. It first offered distance learning courses in 1994. In fall 2007, there were 300 students enrolled in distance learning courses. Institutionally administered financial aid is available to distance learners.

Services Distance learners have accessibility to academic advising, bookstore, campus computer network, career placement assistance, e-mail services, library services, tutoring.

Contact Ms. Bridget Sowinski, Coordinator, Center for Academic Progress, St. Edward's University, Center for Academic Progress, 3001 South Congress Avenue, Austin, TX 78704-6489. Telephone: 512-428-0161. Fax: 512-428-1032. E-mail: bridgets@stedwards.edu.

DEGREES AND AWARDS
Programs offered do not lead to a degree or other formal award.

COURSE SUBJECT AREAS OFFERED OUTSIDE OF DEGREE PROGRAMS

Undergraduate—accounting and related services; anthropology; business administration, management and operations; business/corporate communications; business, management, and marketing related; business/managerial economics; communication and media; computer systems analysis; criminal justice and corrections; economics; education; English; history; human resources management; philosophy; public administration; sales, merchandising, and related marketing operations (general); social sciences related; statistics.

Graduate—accounting and related services; business administration, management and operations; business/corporate communications; business/managerial economics; computer/information technology administration and management; computer systems analysis; counseling psychology; entrepreneurial and small business operations; human resources management; human services; liberal arts and sciences, general studies and humanities; marketing; peace studies and conflict resolution; public relations, advertising, and applied communication related; sales, merchandising, and related marketing operations (general); sales, merchandising, and related marketing operations (specialized).

Non-credit—business administration, management and operations; computer/information technology administration and management; computer systems analysis.

SAINT FRANCIS MEDICAL CENTER COLLEGE OF NURSING
Peoria, Illinois
http://www.sfmccon.edu

Saint Francis Medical Center College of Nursing was founded in 1986. It is accredited by North Central Association of Colleges and Schools. It first offered distance learning courses in 2001. In fall 2007, there were 105 students enrolled in distance learning courses. Institutionally administered financial aid is available to distance learners.

Services Distance learners have accessibility to academic advising, campus computer network, e-mail services, library services.

Contact Dr. Janice F. Boundy, Associate Dean, Graduate Program/Professor, Saint Francis Medical Center College of Nursing, 511 NE Greenleaf Street, Peoria, IL 61603. Telephone: 309-655-2230. Fax: 309-624-8973. E-mail: janice.f.boundy@osfhealthcare.org.

DEGREES AND AWARDS
MSN Nursing

COURSE SUBJECT AREAS OFFERED OUTSIDE OF DEGREE PROGRAMS
Undergraduate—nursing.
Graduate—nursing.

SAINT FRANCIS UNIVERSITY
Loretto, Pennsylvania
Academic Affairs
http://www.francis.edu

Saint Francis University was founded in 1847. It is accredited by Middle States Association of Colleges and Schools. It first offered distance learning courses in 1995. In fall 2007, there were 150 students enrolled in distance learning courses. Institutionally administered financial aid is available to distance learners.

Services Distance learners have accessibility to academic advising, bookstore, campus computer network, career placement assistance, e-mail services, library services, tutoring.

Contact Dr. Peter Skoner, Associate Vice President for Academic Affairs, Saint Francis University, 313 Scotus Hall, PO Box 600, Loretto, PA 15940. Telephone: 814-472-3085. Fax: 814-472-3365. E-mail: pskoner @francis.edu.

DEGREES AND AWARDS
MMS Medicine

COURSE SUBJECT AREAS OFFERED OUTSIDE OF DEGREE PROGRAMS

Undergraduate—accounting and computer science; American literature (United States and Canadian); behavioral sciences; biblical and other theological languages and literatures; biblical studies; bioethics/medical ethics; biological and physical sciences; biology; business administration, management and operations; business/commerce; business/corporate communications; business, management, and marketing related; business/managerial economics; business operations support and assistant services; computer and information sciences; computer and information sciences and support services related; English language and literature related; English literature (British and Commonwealth); history; information science/studies; management information systems; philosophy; philosophy and religious studies related; physical sciences; physical sciences related; psychology; religious studies; social work; sociology.

Graduate—bioethics/medical ethics; business administration, management and operations; business/commerce; business/corporate communications; business, management, and marketing related; business/managerial economics.

ST. JOHN'S UNIVERSITY
Queens, New York
The School of Education
http://www.stjohns.edu/distancelearning

St. John's University was founded in 1870. It is accredited by Middle States Association of Colleges and Schools. It first offered distance learning courses in 1994. In fall 2007, there were 394 students enrolled in distance learning courses. Institutionally administered financial aid is available to distance learners.

Services Distance learners have accessibility to academic advising, bookstore, campus computer network, career placement assistance, e-mail services, library services, tutoring.

Contact Kelly K. Ronayne, Assistant Dean, St. John's University, 8000 Utopia Parkway, Sullivan Hall, SB 9, Queens, NY 11439. Telephone: 718-990-2304. Fax: 718-990-2343. E-mail: graded@stjohns.edu.

DEGREES AND AWARDS

MS Ed School Building Leader in Educational Administration and Supervision; Teaching Children with Disabilities in Childhood Education

PMC School District Leader Professional Diploma

COURSE SUBJECT AREAS OFFERED OUTSIDE OF DEGREE PROGRAMS

Graduate—education; educational administration and supervision; educational assessment, evaluation, and research; educational/instructional media design; education related; education (specific levels and methods); education (specific subject areas); library science.

ST. JOHN'S UNIVERSITY
Queens, New York
http://www.stjohns.edu/distancelearning

St. John's University was founded in 1870. It is accredited by Middle States Association of Colleges and Schools. It first offered distance learning courses in 1994. In fall 2007, there were 1,250 students enrolled in distance learning courses. Institutionally administered financial aid is available to distance learners.

Services Distance learners have accessibility to academic advising, bookstore, campus computer network, career placement assistance, e-mail services, library services, tutoring.

Contact Dr. Jeffery E. Olson, Associate Provost, Online Learning and Services, St. John's University, 8000 Utopia Parkway, Queens, NY 11439. Telephone: 718-990-5705. Fax: 718-990-5689. E-mail: distancelearning@stjohns.edu.

DEGREES AND AWARDS

AA Liberal Studies
AS Business; Criminal Justice
BA Liberal Studies
BS Administrative Studies; Criminal Justice
MA Liberal Studies
MS Ed School Building Leader in Educational Administration and Supervision; Teaching Children with Disabilities in Childhood Education
PMC School District Leader Professional Diploma

COURSE SUBJECT AREAS OFFERED OUTSIDE OF DEGREE PROGRAMS

Undergraduate—accounting and related services; business administration, management and operations; communication and journalism related; computer science; criminal justice and corrections; economics; education; English; history; languages (Romance languages); legal studies (non-professional general, undergraduate); marketing; mathematics; pharmacy, pharmaceutical sciences, and administration; philosophy; physics; political science and government; science technologies related; sociology; theology and religious vocations related.

Graduate—business, management, and marketing related; criminal justice and corrections; economics; education; educational administration and supervision; educational assessment, evaluation, and research; educational/instructional media design; education related; education (specific levels and methods); education (specific subject areas); liberal arts and sciences, general studies and humanities; library science.

ST. JOSEPH'S COLLEGE, LONG ISLAND CAMPUS
Patchogue, New York
http://www. sjcny.edu/omop

St. Joseph's College, Long Island Campus was founded in 1916. It is accredited by Middle States Association of Colleges and Schools. It first offered distance learning courses in 1999. In fall 2007, there were 350 students enrolled in distance learning courses. Institutionally administered financial aid is available to distance learners.

Services Distance learners have accessibility to academic advising, bookstore, career placement assistance, e-mail services, library services, tutoring.

Contact Ms. Shannon M. O'Neill, Assistant to the Dean, St. Joseph's College, Long Island Campus, 155 West Roe Boulevard, Patchogue, NY 11772. Telephone: 631-447-3260. Fax: 631-447-5192. E-mail: smoneill@sjcny.edu.

DEGREES AND AWARDS

BS Organizational Management
Certificate Human Resources; Leadership and Supervision

COURSE SUBJECT AREAS OFFERED OUTSIDE OF DEGREE PROGRAMS

Undergraduate—biology; English; history; psychology; social sciences.
Graduate—business administration, management and operations; human resources management.

ST. JOSEPH'S COLLEGE, NEW YORK
Brooklyn, New York
http://www.sjcny.edu/omop

St. Joseph's College, New York was founded in 1916. It is accredited by Middle States Association of Colleges and Schools. It first offered distance learning courses in 1999. In fall 2007, there were 350 students enrolled in distance learning courses. Institutionally administered financial aid is available to distance learners.

Services Distance learners have accessibility to academic advising, bookstore, career placement assistance, e-mail services, library services, tutoring.

Contact Ms. Shannon M. O'Neill, Assistant to the Dean, St. Joseph's College, New York, 155 West Roe Boulevard, Patchogue, NY 11772. Telephone: 631-447-3260. Fax: 631-447-5192. E-mail: smoneill@sjcny.edu.

DEGREES AND AWARDS

BS Organizational Management
Certificate Human Resources; Leadership and Supervision

COURSE SUBJECT AREAS OFFERED OUTSIDE OF DEGREE PROGRAMS

Undergraduate—biology; English; history; psychology; social sciences.
Graduate—business administration, management and operations; human resources management.

SAINT JOSEPH'S COLLEGE OF MAINE
Standish, Maine
Graduate & Professional Studies
http://www.sjcme.edu/gps

Saint Joseph's College of Maine was founded in 1912. It is accredited by New England Association of Schools and Colleges. It first offered distance learning courses in 1976. In fall 2007, there were 4,000 students enrolled in distance learning courses. Institutionally administered financial aid is available to distance learners.

Services Distance learners have accessibility to academic advising, bookstore, campus computer network, career placement assistance, e-mail services, library services, tutoring.

Contact Lynne Robinson, Director of Admissions, Saint Joseph's College of Maine, 278 Whites Bridge Road, Standish, ME 04084-5263. Telephone: 800-752-4723. Fax: 207-892-7480. E-mail: info@sjcme.edu.

DEGREES AND AWARDS

AS Adult Education and Training; Business Administration; Criminal Justice; General Studies; Human Services; Information Technology Management; Management; Psychology
BA Adult Religious Education
BLS Christian Tradition
BS General Studies; Health Care Administration; Long-Term Care Administration; Radiological Sciences
BSBA Business Administration
BSN Nursing
BSPA Professional Arts
Certificate Adult Education and Training; Business Administration; Christian Tradition; Health Care Management; Health Care Management, advanced; Information Technology Management; Long-Term Care Administration; Long-Term Care Administration, advanced; Professional Studies
Graduate Certificate Nursing Administration and Leadership; Nursing and Healthcare Education
MBA Quality Leadership
MBA/MSN Health Services Administration and Nursing Dual degree

MHSA Health Services Administration
MSE Education
MSN Nursing

COURSE SUBJECT AREAS OFFERED OUTSIDE OF DEGREE PROGRAMS

Undergraduate—accounting and related services; biblical studies; business administration, management and operations; communication and media; computer/information technology administration and management; criminology; developmental and child psychology; educational assessment, evaluation, and research; education (specific subject areas); English composition; health and medical administrative services; human services; industrial and organizational psychology; marketing; multi-/interdisciplinary studies related; nursing; pastoral counseling and specialized ministries; philosophy and religious studies related; religious education; social psychology; sociology.

Graduate—accounting and related services; business administration, management and operations; business/corporate communications; business, management, and marketing related; business/managerial economics; curriculum and instruction; educational administration and supervision; educational assessment, evaluation, and research; education (specific subject areas); entrepreneurial and small business operations; health and medical administrative services; management sciences and quantitative methods; marketing; nursing; public administration; sales, merchandising, and related marketing operations (specialized).

Non-credit—biblical studies; pastoral counseling and specialized ministries; religious studies.

See full description on page 438.

SAINT JOSEPH'S UNIVERSITY
Philadelphia, Pennsylvania
http://www.sju.edu/

Saint Joseph's University was founded in 1851. It is accredited by Middle States Association of Colleges and Schools. It first offered distance learning courses in 2001. Institutionally administered financial aid is available to distance learners.
Services Distance learners have accessibility to e-mail services, library services.
Contact University Contact Information, Saint Joseph's University, 5600 City Avenue, Philadelphia, PA 19131-1395. Telephone: 610-660-1000.

DEGREES AND AWARDS
Certificate Online Accelerated Teacher Certification Program (OATCERT)
MS Business Intelligence; Instructional Technology

SAINT LEO UNIVERSITY
Saint Leo, Florida
Center for Distance Learning
http://info.saintleo.edu/COL

Saint Leo University was founded in 1889. It is accredited by Southern Association of Colleges and Schools. It first offered distance learning courses in 1998. In fall 2007, there were 9,222 students enrolled in distance learning courses. Institutionally administered financial aid is available to distance learners.
Services Distance learners have accessibility to academic advising, bookstore, campus computer network, career placement assistance, e-mail services, library services, tutoring.
Contact Admissions Coordinator, Saint Leo University, Center for Online Learning, MC 2260, PO Box 6665, Saint Leo, FL 33574-6665. Telephone: 888-875-8265. Fax: 352-588-4793. E-mail: colslu@greenwoodhall.com.

DEGREES AND AWARDS
AA Liberal Arts
AAB Business Administration
BA Accounting; Business Administration, Accounting concentration; Business Administration, Health Services Management concentration; Business Administration, Management concentration; Criminal Justice
BS Computer Information Systems

CAGS Criminal Justice Management; Exceptional Student Education; Information Security Management; Reading

MAT Teaching

MBA Accounting concentration; Criminal Justice concentration; General track; Health Care Administration concentration; Human Resources Administration concentration; Information Security Management concentration; Sport Business concentration

MEd Educational Leadership; Exceptional Student Education concentration; Exceptional and Secondary Education–Middle Grades English; Exceptional and Secondary Education–Middle Grades Mathematics; Exceptional and Secondary Education–Middle Grades Science; Exceptional and Secondary Education–Middle Grades Social Studies; Instructional Leadership concentration; Reading concentration

MS Criminal Justice; Criminal Justice, Critical Incident Management concentration; Instructional Design

COURSE SUBJECT AREAS OFFERED OUTSIDE OF DEGREE PROGRAMS

Undergraduate—accounting and related services; biological and biomedical sciences related; business administration, management and operations; business/corporate communications; computer and information sciences; computer and information sciences and support services related; computer programming; computer software and media applications; computer systems analysis; computer systems networking and telecommunications; criminal justice and corrections; criminology; English; English composition; fine and studio art; human resources management; liberal arts and sciences, general studies and humanities; management sciences and quantitative methods; marketing; mathematics; philosophy; philosophy and religious studies related; physical sciences; psychology; public administration; social sciences related; taxation.

ST. LOUIS COMMUNITY COLLEGE SYSTEM
St. Louis, Missouri
Telelearning Services
http://stlcc.edu/distance

St. Louis Community College System is accredited by North Central Association of Colleges and Schools. It first offered distance learning courses in 1973. In fall 2007, there were 6,814 students enrolled in distance learning courses. Institutionally administered financial aid is available to distance learners.
Services Distance learners have accessibility to academic advising, bookstore, e-mail services, library services.
Contact Daniel A. Bain, PhD, Director of Telelearning Services, St. Louis Community College System, Telelearning Services Department, 300 South Broadway, St. Louis, MO 63102. Telephone: 314-539-5056. Fax: 314-539-5125. E-mail: dbain@stlcc.edu.

DEGREES AND AWARDS
Programs offered do not lead to a degree or other formal award.

COURSE SUBJECT AREAS OFFERED OUTSIDE OF DEGREE PROGRAMS

Undergraduate—accounting and computer science; American literature (United States and Canadian); biological and physical sciences; communication and journalism related; computer and information sciences; computer and information sciences and support services related; computer software and media applications; data entry/microcomputer applications; funeral service and mortuary science; history; languages (Romance languages); marketing; mathematics; sociology.

Non-credit—business administration, management and operations; business/commerce; business, management, and marketing related; management information systems.

See full description on page 440.

SAINT LOUIS UNIVERSITY
St. Louis, Missouri
School of Nursing
http://www.slu.edu/colleges/NR

Saint Louis University was founded in 1818. It is accredited by North Central Association of Colleges and Schools. It first offered distance learning courses in 1997. In fall 2007, there were 311 students enrolled in distance learning courses. Institutionally administered financial aid is available to distance learners.

Services Distance learners have accessibility to academic advising, bookstore, campus computer network, career placement assistance, e-mail services, library services, tutoring.

Contact Scott Ragsdale, Recruitment Specialist, Saint Louis University, 3525 Caroline Street, St. Louis, MO 63104-1099. Telephone: 314-977-8995. Fax: 314-977-8949. E-mail: slunurse@slu.edu.

DEGREES AND AWARDS
MSN Nursing
PMC Nursing
PhD Nursing

SAINT MARY-OF-THE-WOODS COLLEGE
Saint Mary-of-the-Woods, Indiana
Distance & Graduate Programs
http://www.smwc.edu

Saint Mary-of-the-Woods College was founded in 1840. It is accredited by North Central Association of Colleges and Schools. It first offered distance learning courses in 1974. In fall 2007, there were 1,200 students enrolled in distance learning courses. Institutionally administered financial aid is available to distance learners.

Services Distance learners have accessibility to academic advising, career placement assistance, e-mail services.

Contact Mrs. Jill Blunk, Director of Distance and Graduate Admission, Saint Mary-of-the-Woods College, Saint Mary-of-the-Woods, IN 47876. E-mail: wedadms@smwc.edu.

DEGREES AND AWARDS
AD General Program
BA General Program
MAMT Music Therapy
MEd Education

COURSE SUBJECT AREAS OFFERED OUTSIDE OF DEGREE PROGRAMS
Undergraduate—accounting and related services; business administration, management and operations; clinical psychology; computer and information sciences; creative writing; education; English; history; human resources management; human services; journalism; marketing; mathematics; political science and government; psychology; social sciences; social sciences related; special education; theology and religious vocations related.
Graduate—business, management, and marketing related; education; environmental design; rehabilitation and therapeutic professions; theology and religious vocations related.

SAINT MARY-OF-THE-WOODS COLLEGE
Saint Mary-of-the-Woods, Indiana
Woods External Degree Program
http://www.smwc.edu/cgi-bin/site.pl

Saint Mary-of-the-Woods College was founded in 1840. It is accredited by North Central Association of Colleges and Schools. It first offered distance learning courses in 1973. In fall 2007, there were 1,300 students enrolled in distance learning courses. Institutionally administered financial aid is available to distance learners.

Services Distance learners have accessibility to academic advising, bookstore, career placement assistance, e-mail services, library services, tutoring.

Contact Sara Lindsey, Associate Director of Admission, Saint Mary-of-the-Woods College, Office of Distance and Graduate Admission, 122 Guerin Hall, Saint Mary-of-the-Woods, IN 47876. Telephone: 800-499-0373. Fax: 812-535-5010. E-mail: wedadms@smwc.edu.

DEGREES AND AWARDS
AA Humanities; Paralegal Studies
AS Accounting; Business, general; Early Childhood/Child Development
BA Creative Writing; Criminal Justice; English; History and Political Studies; Humanities; Journalism; Mathematics; Paralegal Studies; Professional Writing; Social Science/History; Theology
BS Accounting Information Systems; Accounting; Business Administration; Computer Information Systems; Digital Media Communication; Education–Kindergarten-Elementary Education; Education–Middle School/High School Special Education; Education–Preschool-Grade 3 Education/Mild Intervention; Human Resource Management; Human Services; Marketing; Psychology; Secondary Education–English; Secondary Education–Mathematics; Secondary Education–Social Studies
Certificate Paralegal Studies
MA Art Therapy; Earth Literacy; Music Therapy; Pastoral Theology
MEd Education
MLD Leadership Development

COURSE SUBJECT AREAS OFFERED OUTSIDE OF DEGREE PROGRAMS
Undergraduate—accounting and related services; business administration, management and operations; business/commerce; computer and information sciences; creative writing; education; education related; education (specific levels and methods); education (specific subject areas); history; human resources management; human services; journalism; liberal arts and sciences, general studies and humanities; marketing; mathematics; political science and government; psychology; social sciences related; special education; technical and business writing; theology and religious vocations related.
Graduate—business administration, management and operations; business, management, and marketing related; education; education related; music; natural resources and conservation related; psychology related; theological and ministerial studies; theology and religious vocations related.

ST. MARY'S UNIVERSITY
San Antonio, Texas
Graduate School
http://www.stmarytx.edu

St. Mary's University was founded in 1852. It is accredited by Southern Association of Colleges and Schools. It first offered distance learning courses in 1997. In fall 2007, there were 63 students enrolled in distance learning courses. Institutionally administered financial aid is available to distance learners.

Services Distance learners have accessibility to academic advising, bookstore, campus computer network, career placement assistance, e-mail services, library services.

Contact Dr. Henry Flores, Dean of the Graduate School, St. Mary's University, One Camino Santa Maria, Box 43, San Antonio, TX 78228. Telephone: 210-436-3101. Fax: 210-431-2220. E-mail: hflores@stmarytx.edu.

DEGREES AND AWARDS
MA Community Counseling; International Relations

COURSE SUBJECT AREAS OFFERED OUTSIDE OF DEGREE PROGRAMS
Non-credit—accounting and computer science; accounting and related services.

ST. PETERSBURG THEOLOGICAL SEMINARY
St. Petersburg, Florida

St. Petersburg Theological Seminary was founded in 1983. It is accredited by Transnational Association of Christian Colleges and Schools. It first offered distance learning courses in 2007.

Services Distance learners have accessibility to academic advising.

Contact Dr. Amy Mormino, Director of Online Learning, St. Petersburg Theological Seminary, 10830 Navajo Drive, St. Petersburg, FL 33706-3116. Telephone: 727-399-0276. Fax: 727-399-1324. E-mail: registrar @sptseminary.edu.

DEGREES AND AWARDS
MD/M Div Master of Divinity

COURSE SUBJECT AREAS OFFERED OUTSIDE OF DEGREE PROGRAMS
Undergraduate—religious education; religious studies.
Graduate—religious education; religious studies.
Non-credit—religious education; religious studies.

SAM HOUSTON STATE UNIVERSITY
Huntsville, Texas
Correspondence Course Division
http://cor.shsu.edu
Sam Houston State University was founded in 1879. It is accredited by Southern Association of Colleges and Schools. It first offered distance learning courses in 1953. In fall 2007, there were 1,200 students enrolled in distance learning courses. Institutionally administered financial aid is available to distance learners.
Services Distance learners have accessibility to bookstore, e-mail services, library services.
Contact Gail M. Wright, Correspondence Course Coordinator, Sam Houston State University, Box 2536, Huntsville, TX 77341-2536. Telephone: 936-294-1003. Fax: 936-294-3703. E-mail: cor_gmw@shsu.edu.

DEGREES AND AWARDS
Programs offered do not lead to a degree or other formal award.

COURSE SUBJECT AREAS OFFERED OUTSIDE OF DEGREE PROGRAMS
Undergraduate—agricultural business and management; anthropology; business, management, and marketing related; chemistry; creative writing; economics; English; family and consumer economics; film/video and photographic arts; finance and financial management services; food science and technology; foods, nutrition, and related services; geological and earth sciences/geosciences; gerontology; health professions related; history; legal studies (non-professional general, undergraduate); marketing; mathematics and statistics related; nutrition sciences; philosophy; political science and government; psychology; sociology; statistics.

SAMUEL MERRITT COLLEGE
Oakland, California
Academic Affairs
http://www.samuelmerritt.edu
Samuel Merritt College was founded in 1909. It is accredited by Western Association of Schools and Colleges. It first offered distance learning courses in 2001. In fall 2007, there were 28 students enrolled in distance learning courses. Institutionally administered financial aid is available to distance learners.
Services Distance learners have accessibility to academic advising, bookstore, campus computer network, e-mail services, library services, tutoring.
Contact Mr. John Garten-Shuman, Vice President of Enrollment Services, Samuel Merritt College, Bechtel Hall, 450 30th Street, Oakland, CA 94609. Telephone: 800-607-6377. Fax: 510-869-6525. E-mail: jgartens@samuelmerritt.edu.

DEGREES AND AWARDS
MSN Nursing

COURSE SUBJECT AREAS OFFERED OUTSIDE OF DEGREE PROGRAMS
Graduate—nursing.

SAN ANTONIO COLLEGE
San Antonio, Texas
SAC Online
http://www.accd.edu/sac/online/
San Antonio College was founded in 1925. It is accredited by Southern Association of Colleges and Schools. It first offered distance learning courses in 1996. Institutionally administered financial aid is available to distance learners.
Services Distance learners have accessibility to academic advising, bookstore, campus computer network, career placement assistance, e-mail services, library services, tutoring.
Contact Isabel Castaneda, Distance Education/SAC Online Secretary, San Antonio College, 1300 San Pedro Avenue, Fletcher Administration Center Building, Suite 221, San Antonio, TX 78212-4299. Telephone: 210-733-2045. Fax: 210-785-6494. E-mail: sac-online@mail.accd.edu.

DEGREES AND AWARDS
AA Criminal Justice

SAN DIEGO COMMUNITY COLLEGE DISTRICT
San Diego, California
http://www.sdccdonline.net
San Diego Community College District first offered distance learning courses in 2001. In fall 2007, there were 18,776 students enrolled in distance learning courses. Institutionally administered financial aid is available to distance learners.
Services Distance learners have accessibility to academic advising, bookstore, library services, tutoring.
Contact Dr. Andrea Henne, Dean, Online and Distributed Learning, San Diego Community College District, 3375 Camino del Rio South, Suite 125, San Diego, CA 92108. Telephone: 619-388-6750. E-mail: ahenne @sdccd.edu.

DEGREES AND AWARDS
AS Accounting; Business Administration

COURSE SUBJECT AREAS OFFERED OUTSIDE OF DEGREE PROGRAMS
Undergraduate—accounting and computer science; accounting and related services; air transportation; allied health and medical assisting services; American literature (United States and Canadian); American Sign Language (ASL); anthropology; apparel and textiles; applied mathematics; area, ethnic, cultural, and gender studies related; astronomy and astrophysics; audiovisual communications technologies; biological and physical sciences; biology; business administration, management and operations; business/commerce; business/corporate communications; business, management, and marketing related; business/managerial economics; business operations support and assistant services; chemistry; cognitive psychology and psycholinguistics; cognitive science; communication and journalism related; communication and media; communications technology; comparative literature; comparative psychology; computer and information sciences; computer and information sciences and support services related; computer/information technology administration and management; computer programming; computer science; computer software and media applications; computer systems networking and telecommunications; creative writing; criminal justice and corrections; data entry/microcomputer applications; economics; education; education related; engineering related; English; English as a second language; English composition; English language and literature related; fine and studio art; fire protection; genetics; health and physical education/fitness; health professions related; history; information science/studies; intercultural/multicultural and diversity studies; journalism; legal studies (non-professional general, undergraduate); liberal arts and sciences, general studies and humanities; library science; library science related; marketing; mathematics; mathematics and computer science; mathematics and statistics related; music; natural sciences; nutrition sciences; personality psychology; philosophy; physical sciences; political science and government; psychology; psychology related; real estate; social psychology; social sciences; social sciences related; sociology; speech and rhetoric; statistics; technical and business writing.

Non-credit—accounting and computer science; apparel and textiles; computer and information sciences; computer science; computer software and media applications.

SAN DIEGO STATE UNIVERSITY
San Diego, California
Academic Affairs
http://interwork.sdsu.edu/cdl

San Diego State University was founded in 1897. It is accredited by Western Association of Schools and Colleges. It first offered distance learning courses in 1984. In fall 2007, there were 971 students enrolled in distance learning courses. Institutionally administered financial aid is available to distance learners.

Services Distance learners have accessibility to academic advising, bookstore, e-mail services, library services, tutoring.

Contact Ms. Francesca Ringland, Director, Credit Community Education, College of Education, San Diego State University, 5500 Campanile Drive, San Diego, CA 92182. Telephone: 619-594-2193. E-mail: ringland@mail.sdsu.edu.

DEGREES AND AWARDS
Certificate Instructional Technology
MA Education Leadership–Pacific Cohorts
MAE Educational Technology
MS Biomedical Quality Systems; Regulatory Affairs; Rehabilitation Counseling

COURSE SUBJECT AREAS OFFERED OUTSIDE OF DEGREE PROGRAMS
Undergraduate—building/construction finishing, management, and inspection; business/commerce; business, management, and marketing related; educational/instructional media design; education related; education (specific levels and methods); education (specific subject areas); ethnic, cultural minority, and gender studies; geological and earth sciences/geosciences; gerontology; history; marketing; parks, recreation, and leisure related; physiology, pathology and related sciences; psychology.
Graduate—educational administration and supervision; educational/instructional media design; education (specific levels and methods).
Non-credit—business/commerce; computer programming; computer software and media applications; education; English as a second language; English composition; film/video and photographic arts; geological and earth sciences/geosciences; history.

SAN FRANCISCO STATE UNIVERSITY
San Francisco, California
Multimedia Studies Program
http://www.cel.sfsu.edu/msponline/

San Francisco State University was founded in 1899. It is accredited by Western Association of Schools and Colleges. It first offered distance learning courses in 1999. In fall 2007, there were 38 students enrolled in distance learning courses. Institutionally administered financial aid is available to distance learners.

Services Distance learners have accessibility to academic advising, bookstore.

Contact Richard Sinrich, Online Program Coordinator, MSP/CEL Online, San Francisco State University, MSP/CEL Online, 835 Market Street, Suite 600, San Francisco, CA 94103-1901. Telephone: 415-405-7700. Fax: 415-817-4299. E-mail: rsinrich@sfsu.edu.

DEGREES AND AWARDS
Programs offered do not lead to a degree or other formal award.

COURSE SUBJECT AREAS OFFERED OUTSIDE OF DEGREE PROGRAMS
Non-credit—computer software and media applications; design and applied arts; education (specific levels and methods); information science/studies.

SAN JOAQUIN DELTA COLLEGE
Stockton, California
Instructional Development
http://www.deltacollege.edu

San Joaquin Delta College was founded in 1935. It is accredited by Western Association of Schools and Colleges. It first offered distance learning courses in 1976. In fall 2007, there were 9,088 students enrolled in distance learning courses. Institutionally administered financial aid is available to distance learners.

Services Distance learners have accessibility to academic advising, bookstore, e-mail services, library services, tutoring.

Contact Dr. Matthew Wetstein, Interim Dean of Planning, Research, and Regional Education, San Joaquin Delta College, 5151 Pacific Avenue, Stockton, CA 95207. Telephone: 209-954-5039. Fax: 209-954-5600. E-mail: mwetstein@deltacollege.edu.

DEGREES AND AWARDS
Certificate Early Childhood Education Assistant; Merchandising; Supervision and Management
ATC Liberal Arts and Science

COURSE SUBJECT AREAS OFFERED OUTSIDE OF DEGREE PROGRAMS
Undergraduate—accounting and related services; American literature (United States and Canadian); anthropology; astronomy and astrophysics; biblical and other theological languages and literatures; business/commerce; business/corporate communications; chemistry; computer science; computer software and media applications; computer systems networking and telecommunications; creative writing; criminal justice and corrections; design and applied arts; education related; English composition; finance and financial management services; health and physical education/fitness; history; human development, family studies, and related services; legal studies (non-professional general, undergraduate); mathematics and statistics related; nursing; philosophy and religious studies related; political science and government; psychology; sales, merchandising, and related marketing operations (general); sociology; statistics.

SAN JOAQUIN VALLEY COLLEGE–ONLINE
Visalia, California
Contact SJVC Online, San Joaquin Valley College–Online, 3908 West Caldwell Avenue, Visalia, CA 93277. Telephone: 559-734-7582.

DEGREES AND AWARDS
AS Business Administration; Clinical Medical Assisting; Construction Management; Human Resource Administration; Medical Office Administration

SANTA MONICA COLLEGE
Santa Monica, California
SMC Online
http://smconline.org

Santa Monica College was founded in 1929. It is accredited by Western Association of Schools and Colleges. It first offered distance learning courses in 1999. Institutionally administered financial aid is available to distance learners.

Services Distance learners have accessibility to academic advising, bookstore, library services.

Contact Julie Yarrish, Associate Dean of Online Services and Support, Santa Monica College, 1900 Pico Boulevard, Santa Monica, CA 90405. Telephone: 310-434-3762. Fax: 310-434-3769. E-mail: yarrish_julie@smc.edu.

DEGREES AND AWARDS
Programs offered do not lead to a degree or other formal award.

COURSE SUBJECT AREAS OFFERED OUTSIDE OF DEGREE PROGRAMS
Undergraduate—accounting and computer science; accounting and related services; allied health diagnostic, intervention, and treatment

professions; architecture; behavioral sciences; biblical and other theological languages and literatures; biochemistry, biophysics and molecular biology; biological and physical sciences; biology; botany/plant biology; business administration, management and operations; business/commerce; cell biology and anatomical sciences; clinical child psychology; communication and journalism related; communication and media; computer programming; computer science; developmental and child psychology; ecology, evolution, and population biology; economics; education; English; English as a second language; English composition; entrepreneurial and small business operations; foods, nutrition, and related services; geological and earth sciences/geosciences; health services/allied health/health sciences; history; intercultural/multicultural and diversity studies; journalism; languages (foreign languages related); library science; marketing; music; nursing; nutrition sciences; pharmacology and toxicology; sociology; speech and rhetoric.

SANTA ROSA JUNIOR COLLEGE
Santa Rosa, California
http://online.santarosa.edu/
Santa Rosa Junior College was founded in 1918. It is accredited by Western Association of Schools and Colleges. It first offered distance learning courses in 1989. In fall 2007, there were 4,940 students enrolled in distance learning courses. Institutionally administered financial aid is available to distance learners.
Services Distance learners have accessibility to academic advising, bookstore, campus computer network, e-mail services, library services.
Contact Dr. Kris Abrahamson, Dean, Liberal Arts and Sciences, Santa Rosa Junior College, 1501 Mendocino Avenue, Santa Rosa, CA 95401. Telephone: 707-521-7950. Fax: 707-527-4794. E-mail: kabrahamson@santarosa.edu.

DEGREES AND AWARDS
AA Humanities; Social and Behavioral Sciences
AS Natural Sciences

COURSE SUBJECT AREAS OFFERED OUTSIDE OF DEGREE PROGRAMS
Undergraduate—accounting and related services; allied health and medical assisting services; anthropology; astronomy and astrophysics; atmospheric sciences and meteorology; behavioral sciences; business administration, management and operations; business/commerce; business/corporate communications; business operations support and assistant services; communication and journalism related; communication and media; communications technology; computer and information sciences; computer and information sciences and support services related; computer programming; computer science; computer software and media applications; computer systems networking and telecommunications; counseling psychology; creative writing; criminal justice and corrections; criminology; culinary arts and related services; economics; English; English composition; ethnic, cultural minority, and gender studies; family and consumer sciences/human sciences; fire protection; food science and technology; geological and earth sciences/geosciences; graphic communications; health professions related; human development, family studies, and related services; information science/studies; intercultural/multicultural and diversity studies; international/global studies; journalism; languages (foreign languages related); liberal arts and sciences, general studies and humanities; library science; library science related; marketing; mathematics; multi-/interdisciplinary studies related; philosophy; psychology; psychology related; real estate; sociology; visual and performing arts.

SARASOTA COUNTY TECHNICAL INSTITUTE
Sarasota, Florida
http://www.scti.edu
Sarasota County Technical Institute was founded in 1967. It first offered distance learning courses in 2000. In fall 2007, there were 500 students enrolled in distance learning courses. Institutionally administered financial aid is available to distance learners.
Services Distance learners have accessibility to academic advising, bookstore, career placement assistance, e-mail services.

Contact Scott Kennedy, Health Science Department Chair, Sarasota County Technical Institute, 4748 Beneva Road, Sarasota, FL 34233. Telephone: 941-924-1365 Ext. 62417. E-mail: scott_kennedy@sarasota.k12.fl.us.

DEGREES AND AWARDS
Programs offered do not lead to a degree or other formal award.

COURSE SUBJECT AREAS OFFERED OUTSIDE OF DEGREE PROGRAMS
Non-credit—education related; health professions related; medical basic sciences; technical and business writing.

SAVANNAH COLLEGE OF ART AND DESIGN
Savannah, Georgia
http://www.scad.edu
Savannah College of Art and Design was founded in 1978. It is accredited by Southern Association of Colleges and Schools. It first offered distance learning courses in 2003. In fall 2007, there were 500 students enrolled in distance learning courses. Institutionally administered financial aid is available to distance learners.
Services Distance learners have accessibility to academic advising, bookstore, campus computer network, career placement assistance, e-mail services, library services, tutoring.
Contact Ms. Ginger Hansen, Executive Director of Recruitment, Savannah College of Art and Design, PO Box 3146, Savannah, GA 31402-3146. Telephone: 912-525-5100. Fax: 912-525-5986. E-mail: ghunt@scad.edu.

DEGREES AND AWARDS
BA Digital Media; Visual Communication
Certificate Digital Publishing
Graduate Certificate Digital Publishing Management; Historic Preservation; Interactive Design; Typeface Design
MA Broadcast Design and Motion Graphics; Digital Photography; Graphic Design; Historic Preservation; Illustration Design; Interactive Design and Game Development; Interior Design; Painting

COURSE SUBJECT AREAS OFFERED OUTSIDE OF DEGREE PROGRAMS
Undergraduate—English composition; fine and studio art.
Graduate—fine and studio art.
See full description on page 442.

SAYBROOK GRADUATE SCHOOL AND RESEARCH CENTER
San Francisco, California
http://www.saybrook.edu/
Saybrook Graduate School and Research Center was founded in 1970. It is accredited by Western Association of Schools and Colleges. It first offered distance learning courses in 1971. In fall 2007, there were 479 students enrolled in distance learning courses. Institutionally administered financial aid is available to distance learners.
Services Distance learners have accessibility to academic advising, bookstore, campus computer network, library services.
Contact Ms. Rachel Napolin, Admissions Specialist, Saybrook Graduate School and Research Center, 747 Front Street, Third Floor, San Francisco, CA 94111. Telephone: 800-825-4480 Ext. 1206. Fax: 415-394-1206. E-mail: admissions@saybrook.edu.

DEGREES AND AWARDS
Graduate Certificate Building a Sustainable World; Community Health and Development; Creativity Studies; Dream Studies; Expressive Arts for Healing and Social Change; Leading Organizational Transformation; Organizational Consulting; Peace and Conflict Resolution (International focus); Socially Engaged Spirituality; Violence Prevention and Response
MA Human Science; Marriage and Family Therapy; Organizational Systems; Psychology in Creativity Studies specialization
PhD Human Science; Organizational Systems; Psychology

COURSE SUBJECT AREAS OFFERED OUTSIDE OF DEGREE PROGRAMS

Graduate—agriculture; allied health diagnostic, intervention, and treatment professions; alternative and complementary medical support services; alternative and complementary medicine and medical systems; business administration, management and operations; clinical child psychology; clinical psychology; cognitive science; community health services; community organization and advocacy; community psychology; counseling psychology; criminal justice and corrections; developmental and child psychology; educational administration and supervision; environmental psychology; ethnic, cultural minority, and gender studies; family and consumer sciences/human sciences; family psychology; gerontology; health psychology; housing and human environments; human development, family studies, and related services; industrial and organizational psychology; intercultural/multicultural and diversity studies; operations research; peace studies and conflict resolution; physiology, pathology and related sciences; psychology; psychology related; public administration and social service professions related; rehabilitation and therapeutic professions; social psychology; social sciences related; somatic bodywork and related therapeutic services; theological and ministerial studies; urban studies/affairs.

Non-credit—business administration, management and operations; educational administration and supervision; industrial and organizational psychology; psychology; psychology related; public administration and social service professions related; theology and religious vocations related.

See full description on page 444.

SCHENECTADY COUNTY COMMUNITY COLLEGE
Schenectady, New York
http://www.sunysccc.edu

Schenectady County Community College was founded in 1969. It is accredited by Middle States Association of Colleges and Schools. It first offered distance learning courses in 1998. In fall 2007, there were 775 students enrolled in distance learning courses. Institutionally administered financial aid is available to distance learners.
Services Distance learners have accessibility to academic advising, bookstore, campus computer network, e-mail services, library services, tutoring.
Contact Shirlee Dufort, Associate for Continuing Education, Schenectady County Community College, 78 Washington Avenue, Schenectady, NY 12305. Telephone: 518-381-1315. E-mail: dufortsa@gw.sunysccc.edu.

DEGREES AND AWARDS
Programs offered do not lead to a degree or other formal award.

COURSE SUBJECT AREAS OFFERED OUTSIDE OF DEGREE PROGRAMS

Undergraduate—accounting and related services; astronomy and astrophysics; biology; business administration, management and operations; computer software and media applications; criminal justice and corrections; culinary arts and related services; English composition; entrepreneurial and small business operations; fire protection; history; hospitality administration; human development, family studies, and related services; legal studies (non-professional general, undergraduate); mathematics; music; nutrition sciences; psychology; sociology; technical and business writing.

SCHILLER INTERNATIONAL UNIVERSITY
Largo, Florida
http://www.schiller.edu/

Schiller International University was founded in 1991. It is accredited by Accrediting Council for Independent Colleges and Schools. It first offered distance learning courses in 1999. In fall 2007, there were 197 students enrolled in distance learning courses. Institutionally administered financial aid is available to distance learners.
Services Distance learners have accessibility to academic advising, bookstore, career placement assistance, e-mail services, library services.

Contact Ms. Susan Russeff, Associate Director of Admissions, Schiller International University, 300 East Bay Drive, Largo, FL 33770. Telephone: 727-736-5082 Ext. 239. Fax: 727-734-0359. E-mail: admissions @schiller.edu.

DEGREES AND AWARDS
AS International Business
BA Interdepartmental Studies; International Relations and Diplomacy
BBA International Business; International Hotel and Tourism Management
MBA Business Administration; Financial Planning; International Hotel and Tourism Management; Management of Information Technology
MBAIB International Business
MIM Master of International Management in International Business

COURSE SUBJECT AREAS OFFERED OUTSIDE OF DEGREE PROGRAMS

Undergraduate—accounting and related services; business administration, management and operations; business/commerce; business/corporate communications; business/managerial economics; English composition; history; hospitality administration; human resources management; information science/studies; international business; international relations and affairs; management information systems; marketing; mathematics; physical sciences; political science and government; psychology; statistics.
Graduate—accounting and related services; business administration, management and operations; business/corporate communications; business/managerial economics; computer/information technology administration and management; finance and financial management services; hospitality administration; human resources management; industrial and organizational psychology; international business; legal research and advanced professional studies; marketing; sales, merchandising, and related marketing operations (specialized); statistics.

See full description on page 446.

SEATTLE CENTRAL COMMUNITY COLLEGE
Seattle, Washington
Distance Learning Program
http://www.seattlecentral.edu/distance

Seattle Central Community College was founded in 1966. It is accredited by Northwest Commission on Colleges and Universities. It first offered distance learning courses in 1990. In fall 2007, there were 1,200 students enrolled in distance learning courses. Institutionally administered financial aid is available to distance learners.
Services Distance learners have accessibility to academic advising, bookstore, campus computer network, e-mail services, library services.
Contact Ms. Queenie L. Baker, Director, Seattle Central Community College, 1701 Broadway, NP304, Seattle, WA 98122-2400. Telephone: 800-510-1724. Fax: 206-287-5562. E-mail: qbaker@sccd.ctc.edu.

DEGREES AND AWARDS
AA General Program; Liberal Arts

COURSE SUBJECT AREAS OFFERED OUTSIDE OF DEGREE PROGRAMS

Undergraduate—accounting and related services; anthropology; developmental and child psychology; English composition; film/video and photographic arts; geography and cartography; journalism; languages (foreign languages related); mathematics and statistics related; medieval and Renaissance studies; philosophy and religious studies related; sociology; statistics.

SEATTLE PACIFIC UNIVERSITY
Seattle, Washington
School of Education
http://www.spu.edu/spiral

Seattle Pacific University was founded in 1891. It is accredited by Northwest Commission on Colleges and Universities. It first offered distance learning courses in 1984. In fall 2007, there were 441 students enrolled in distance learning courses. Institutionally administered financial aid is available to distance learners.
Services Distance learners have accessibility to bookstore, campus computer network, e-mail services, library services.

Contact Kate Thrams, Distance Learning Program Coordinator, Seattle Pacific University, 3307 Third Avenue West, Seattle, WA 98119-1950. Telephone: 800-482-3848. Fax: 206-281-2271. E-mail: connect@spu.edu.

DEGREES AND AWARDS
Programs offered do not lead to a degree or other formal award.

COURSE SUBJECT AREAS OFFERED OUTSIDE OF DEGREE PROGRAMS
Undergraduate—linguistic, comparative, and related language studies. **Graduate**—astronomy and astrophysics; bilingual, multilingual, and multicultural education; computer software and media applications; curriculum and instruction; education; education (specific levels and methods); education (specific subject areas); English as a second/foreign language (teaching); geography and cartography; history; library science; mathematics; parks, recreation and leisure; special education.

SEMINOLE COMMUNITY COLLEGE
Sanford, Florida
Distance Learning Department
http://www.scc-fl.edu/dl
Seminole Community College was founded in 1966. It is accredited by Southern Association of Colleges and Schools. It first offered distance learning courses in 1970. In fall 2007, there were 3,100 students enrolled in distance learning courses. Institutionally administered financial aid is available to distance learners.
Services Distance learners have accessibility to academic advising, bookstore, campus computer network, career placement assistance, e-mail services, library services.
Contact Distance Learning Department, Seminole Community College, Distance Learning Department, 100 Weldon Boulevard, Sanford, FL 32773. Telephone: 407-708-2424. Fax: 407-708-2547. E-mail: sccdl@scc-fl.edu.

DEGREES AND AWARDS
AA Accounting; Advertising and Public Relations; Anthropology Pre-Major; Business, general; Economics (Business track); Economics (Liberal Arts track); General Studies; Interpersonal Communications; Journalism; Management Information Systems; Organizational Communication; Psychology; Public Relations and Organizational Communication; Social Work; Sociology
AS Computer Programming and Analysis (C++ Programming specialization); Computer Programming and Analysis Visual Basic Programming specialization; Computer Programming and Analysis; Programming and Analysis (WWW programming specialization); e-Business Technology (Security specialization); e-Business Technology (Software specialization); e-Business Technology (Technology specialization)
Certificate Computer Programming; Computer Science–Microsoft Certified Systems Administrator
Technical Certificate Accounting Applications; Computer Science–Microsoft Certified Systems Engineer; Office Software Applications; Office Support; e-Business Software (Database track); e-Business Software (Web Design track); e-Business Technology (Microsoft track)

COURSE SUBJECT AREAS OFFERED OUTSIDE OF DEGREE PROGRAMS
Undergraduate—accounting and computer science; accounting and related services; anthropology; applied mathematics; astronomy and astrophysics; atmospheric sciences and meteorology; behavioral sciences; biological and physical sciences; business administration, management and operations; business/commerce; business/corporate communications; business, management, and marketing related; business operations support and assistant services; communication and journalism related; communication and media; community health services; computer and information sciences; computer and information sciences and support services related; computer/information technology administration and management; computer programming; computer science; computer software and media applications; computer systems analysis; computer systems networking and telecommunications; construction engineering; criminal justice and corrections; criminology; data entry/microcomputer

applications; data processing; developmental and child psychology; economics; education; education related; education (specific subject areas); English; English composition; family psychology; fire protection; geography and cartography; geological and earth sciences/geosciences; health professions related; history; human development, family studies, and related services; legal research and advanced professional studies; legal support services; liberal arts and sciences, general studies and humanities; library science; library science related; management information systems; marketing; mathematics; mathematics and computer science; mathematics and statistics related; nutrition sciences; physical sciences; physical sciences related; political science and government; psychology; psychology related; public health; social sciences related; sociology; statistics; technical and business writing.
Non-credit—education (specific levels and methods); health and medical administrative services; security and protective services related.

SETON HALL UNIVERSITY
South Orange, New Jersey
MA in Counseling
http://www.setonworldwide.net
Seton Hall University was founded in 1856. It is accredited by Middle States Association of Colleges and Schools. It first offered distance learning courses in 1998. Institutionally administered financial aid is available to distance learners.
Services Distance learners have accessibility to academic advising, bookstore, campus computer network, career placement assistance, e-mail services, library services.
Contact Ms. Rosalie Maiorella, Program Administrator, Seton Hall University, 400 South Orange Avenue, South Orange, NJ 07079. Telephone: 973-313-6239. E-mail: setonworldwide@shu.edu.

DEGREES AND AWARDS
MA Counseling
See full description on page 448.

SETON HALL UNIVERSITY
South Orange, New Jersey
MA Education Leadership Management and Policy
http://www.shu.edu/academics/online_programs.cfm
Seton Hall University was founded in 1856. It is accredited by Middle States Association of Colleges and Schools. It first offered distance learning courses in 1998. Institutionally administered financial aid is available to distance learners.
Services Distance learners have accessibility to academic advising, bookstore, campus computer network, career placement assistance, e-mail services, library services.
Contact Ms. Cindy Jimenez, Program Coordinator, Seton Hall University, 400 South Orange Avenue, South Orange, NJ 07079. Telephone: 973-761-9087. Fax: 973-761-9325. E-mail: setonworldwide@shu.edu.

DEGREES AND AWARDS
MA Education Leadership, Management, and Policy (ELMP)
See full description on page 450.

SETON HALL UNIVERSITY
South Orange, New Jersey
MA in Strategic Communication and Leadership
http://www.shu.edu/academics/online_programs.cfm
Seton Hall University was founded in 1856. It is accredited by Middle States Association of Colleges and Schools. It first offered distance learning courses in 1998. Institutionally administered financial aid is available to distance learners.
Services Distance learners have accessibility to academic advising, bookstore, campus computer network, career placement assistance, e-mail services, library services.

Contact Ms. Cindy Jimenez, Program Coordinator, Seton Hall University, 400 South Orange Avenue, South Orange, NJ 07079. Telephone: 973-761-9087. Fax: 973-761-9325. E-mail: setonworldwide@shu.edu.

DEGREES AND AWARDS

MA Strategic Communication and Leadership

See full description on page 452.

SETON HALL UNIVERSITY
South Orange, New Jersey
Master of Healthcare Administration
http://www.shu.edu/academics/online_programs.cfm

Seton Hall University was founded in 1856. It is accredited by Middle States Association of Colleges and Schools. It first offered distance learning courses in 1998. Institutionally administered financial aid is available to distance learners.

Contact Ms. Cindy Jimenez, Program Coordinator, Seton Hall University, 400 South Orange Avenue, South Orange, NJ 07079. Telephone: 973-761-9087. Fax: 973-761-9325. E-mail: setonworldwide@shu.edu.

DEGREES AND AWARDS

MHA Healthcare Administration

See full description on page 454.

SETON HALL UNIVERSITY
South Orange, New Jersey
Programs in Nursing
http://www.shu.edu/academics/setonworldwide/about.cfm

Seton Hall University was founded in 1856. It is accredited by Middle States Association of Colleges and Schools. It first offered distance learning courses in 1998. Institutionally administered financial aid is available to distance learners.

Services Distance learners have accessibility to academic advising, bookstore, campus computer network, career placement assistance, e-mail services, library services.

Contact Ms. Cindy Jimenez, Program Coordinator, Seton Hall University, 400 South Orange Avenue, South Orange, NJ 07079. Telephone: 973-761-9087. Fax: 973-761-9325. E-mail: setonworldwide@shu.edu.

DEGREES AND AWARDS

BSN Nursing–RN to BSN
MSN Nursing

See full description on page 456.

SHASTA BIBLE COLLEGE
Redding, California
Individualized Distance Learning
http://www.shasta.edu

Shasta Bible College was founded in 1971. It is accredited by Transnational Association of Christian Colleges and Schools. It first offered distance learning courses in 1999. In fall 2007, there were 100 students enrolled in distance learning courses. Institutionally administered financial aid is available to distance learners.

Services Distance learners have accessibility to academic advising, bookstore, e-mail services, library services.

Contact Mr. Mark Mueller, Registrar and Enrollment Manager, Shasta Bible College, 2951 Goodwater Avenue, Redding, CA 96002. Telephone: 530-221-4275 Ext. 206. Fax: 530-221-6929. E-mail: admissions@shasta.edu.

DEGREES AND AWARDS

BA Christian Professional Studies
MA Christian Ministries; Christian Ministries
MS School and Church Administration

COURSE SUBJECT AREAS OFFERED OUTSIDE OF DEGREE PROGRAMS

Undergraduate—biblical studies; counseling psychology; education related; religious studies.
Graduate—counseling psychology; educational administration and supervision; education related.
Non-credit—biblical studies.

SHAWNEE STATE UNIVERSITY
Portsmouth, Ohio
Department of Nursing
http://www.shawnee.edu/acad/hs/bsn/index.html

Shawnee State University was founded in 1986. It is accredited by North Central Association of Colleges and Schools. It first offered distance learning courses in 1998. In fall 2007, there were 155 students enrolled in distance learning courses. Institutionally administered financial aid is available to distance learners.

Services Distance learners have accessibility to bookstore, e-mail services, library services.

Contact Dr. Mattie Burton, Chair, Nursing, Shawnee State University, 940 Second Street, Health Sciences Building, Room 121, Portsmouth, OH 45662. Telephone: 740-351-3378. E-mail: mburton@shawnee.edu.

DEGREES AND AWARDS

Programs offered do not lead to a degree or other formal award.

COURSE SUBJECT AREAS OFFERED OUTSIDE OF DEGREE PROGRAMS

Undergraduate—health professions related; health services/allied health/health sciences; nursing.
Non-credit—English; pharmacy, pharmaceutical sciences, and administration.

SHIPPENSBURG UNIVERSITY OF PENNSYLVANIA
Shippensburg, Pennsylvania
Extended Studies
http://www.ship.edu/extended/

Shippensburg University of Pennsylvania was founded in 1871. It is accredited by Middle States Association of Colleges and Schools. It first offered distance learning courses in 1998. In fall 2007, there were 182 students enrolled in distance learning courses. Institutionally administered financial aid is available to distance learners.

Services Distance learners have accessibility to academic advising, bookstore, campus computer network, career placement assistance, e-mail services, library services, tutoring.

Contact Dr. Christina M. Sax, Dean of Extended Studies, Shippensburg University of Pennsylvania, 1871 Old Main Drive, Shippensburg, PA 17257-2299. Telephone: 717-477-1348. Fax: 717-477-4050. E-mail: extended@ship.edu.

DEGREES AND AWARDS

MBA Business Administration
MSIS Information Systems

COURSE SUBJECT AREAS OFFERED OUTSIDE OF DEGREE PROGRAMS

Undergraduate—accounting and related services; biology; communication and media; computer science; criminal justice and corrections; economics; education; English; finance and financial management services; fine and studio art; geography and cartography; history; information science/studies; international business; management information systems; management sciences and quantitative methods; marketing; mathematics; mathematics and computer science; philosophy; physics; political science and government; psychology; social work; sociology; special education; speech and rhetoric.
Graduate—accounting and related services; biology; business administration, management and operations; communication and media; criminal justice and corrections; education; English; entrepreneurial and small business operations; geography and cartography; history; information

science/studies; international business; management information systems; political science and government; psychology; social work; sociology; special education.

SIENA HEIGHTS UNIVERSITY
Adrian, Michigan
http://www.sienaheights.edu

Siena Heights University was founded in 1919. It is accredited by North Central Association of Colleges and Schools. It first offered distance learning courses in 1995. In fall 2007, there were 450 students enrolled in distance learning courses. Institutionally administered financial aid is available to distance learners.

Services Distance learners have accessibility to academic advising, bookstore, e-mail services, library services.

Contact Lori Timmis, Director, Siena Heights University, 1247 East Siena Heights Drive, Adrian, MI 49221. Telephone: 517-264-7195. E-mail: ltimmis@sienaheights.edu.

DEGREES AND AWARDS

BA Multidisciplinary Studies
BAS Bachelor of Applied Science
BBA Business Administration

COURSE SUBJECT AREAS OFFERED OUTSIDE OF DEGREE PROGRAMS

Undergraduate—liberal arts and sciences, general studies and humanities.

SIERRA COLLEGE
Rocklin, California
Distance Learning Department
http://lrc.sierracollege.edu/dl

Sierra College was founded in 1936. It is accredited by Western Association of Schools and Colleges. It first offered distance learning courses in 1986. In fall 2007, there were 4,614 students enrolled in distance learning courses. Institutionally administered financial aid is available to distance learners.

Services Distance learners have accessibility to academic advising, bookstore, campus computer network, e-mail services, library services, tutoring.

Contact Suzanne Davenport, LRC Coordinator, Distance Learning, Sierra College, 5000 Rocklin Road, Rocklin, CA 95677. Telephone: 916-789-2638. Fax: 916-781-7193. E-mail: sdavenport@sierracollege.edu.

DEGREES AND AWARDS

Programs offered do not lead to a degree or other formal award.

COURSE SUBJECT AREAS OFFERED OUTSIDE OF DEGREE PROGRAMS

Undergraduate—agriculture; anthropology; applied mathematics; area, ethnic, cultural, and gender studies related; astronomy and astrophysics; biology; business/commerce; chemistry; communication and media; computer and information sciences; computer science; design and applied arts; developmental and child psychology; dramatic/theater arts and stagecraft; economics; English; English composition; fire protection; forestry; geography and cartography; health and physical education/fitness; history; library science; mathematics; mathematics and statistics related; music; philosophy; real estate; social psychology; sociology; statistics; technical and business writing.

SILVER LAKE COLLEGE
Manitowoc, Wisconsin
http://www.sl.edu

Silver Lake College was founded in 1869. It is accredited by North Central Association of Colleges and Schools. It first offered distance learning courses in 1986. In fall 2007, there were 220 students enrolled in distance learning courses. Institutionally administered financial aid is available to distance learners.

Services Distance learners have accessibility to academic advising, bookstore, campus computer network, career placement assistance, e-mail services, library services.

Contact Dr. George Grinde, Vice President of Academic Affairs, Silver Lake College, 2406 South Alverno Road, Manitowoc, WI 54220. Telephone: 920-686-6125. Fax: 920-684-7082. E-mail: ggrinde@silver.sl.edu.

DEGREES AND AWARDS

MS Management and Organizational Behavior

COURSE SUBJECT AREAS OFFERED OUTSIDE OF DEGREE PROGRAMS

Graduate—educational administration and supervision; educational assessment, evaluation, and research; education related.

SIMMONS COLLEGE
Boston, Massachusetts
http://www.simmons.edu/shs/academics/

Simmons College was founded in 1899. It is accredited by New England Association of Schools and Colleges. It first offered distance learning courses in 2001. In fall 2007, there were 141 students enrolled in distance learning courses. Institutionally administered financial aid is available to distance learners.

Services Distance learners have accessibility to academic advising, bookstore, campus computer network, e-mail services, library services, tutoring.

Contact Ms. Yolanda Mendez Rainey, Administrative Assistant, Simmons College, School for Health Studies, 300 The Fenway, Boston, MA 02115-5898. Telephone: 617-521-2518. Fax: 617-521-3032. E-mail: yolanda.rainey@simmons.edu.

DEGREES AND AWARDS

CAGS Clinical Genetics; Health Professions Education; Sports Nutrition
DPT Bridge Doctor of Physical Therapy

COURSE SUBJECT AREAS OFFERED OUTSIDE OF DEGREE PROGRAMS

Non-credit—developmental and child psychology; statistics.

SIMPSON COLLEGE
Indianola, Iowa
Division of Adult Learning
http://www.simpson.edu/dal

Simpson College was founded in 1860. It is accredited by North Central Association of Colleges and Schools. It first offered distance learning courses in 1996. In fall 2007, there were 250 students enrolled in distance learning courses. Institutionally administered financial aid is available to distance learners.

Services Distance learners have accessibility to academic advising, bookstore, campus computer network, career placement assistance, e-mail services, library services.

Contact Walter Pearson, Director, Simpson College, 701 North C Street, Indianola, IA 50125. Telephone: 515-961-1615. Fax: 515-961-1498. E-mail: walter.pearson@simpson.edu.

DEGREES AND AWARDS

Programs offered do not lead to a degree or other formal award.

COURSE SUBJECT AREAS OFFERED OUTSIDE OF DEGREE PROGRAMS

Undergraduate—accounting and related services; communication and media; computer science; criminal justice and corrections; English; finance and financial management services; human resources management; journalism; liberal arts and sciences, general studies and humanities; marketing.

Graduate—criminal justice and corrections; education (specific subject areas).

SINCLAIR COMMUNITY COLLEGE
Dayton, Ohio
Distance Learning Division
http://www.sinclair.edu/distance

Sinclair Community College was founded in 1887. It is accredited by North Central Association of Colleges and Schools. It first offered distance learning courses in 1979. In fall 2007, there were 5,000 students enrolled in distance learning courses. Institutionally administered financial aid is available to distance learners.

Services Distance learners have accessibility to academic advising, bookstore, e-mail services, library services.

Contact Ms. Linda M. Stowe, Coordinator of Distance Learning Services, Sinclair Community College, Distance Learning and Instructional Support Division, Room 14-223, 444 West Third Street, Dayton, OH 45402. Telephone: 937-512-2694. Fax: 937-512-2891. E-mail: linda.stowe@sinclair.edu.

DEGREES AND AWARDS

AA Liberal Arts and Sciences
AS Business Administration; Liberal Arts and Sciences
Certificate Programmer Analyst–Fast Track--Programmer Analyst Short-Term Certificate; Software Applications for the Professional; Web Programming–Visual Basic or Java Track Short-Term Certificate
Certification Human Services Short-Term Certificate; Medical Office Coding Specialist; Radiologic Technology Continuing Education Units (CEUs)

COURSE SUBJECT AREAS OFFERED OUTSIDE OF DEGREE PROGRAMS

Undergraduate—accounting and computer science; architectural engineering; behavioral sciences; business administration, management and operations; business, management, and marketing related; business operations support and assistant services; chemistry; civil engineering technology; communication and media; computer and information sciences; computer programming; computer software and media applications; computer systems networking and telecommunications; creative writing; developmental and child psychology; drafting/design engineering technologies; economics; English composition; entrepreneurial and small business operations; film/video and photographic arts; fine and studio art; history; human services; legal studies (non-professional general, undergraduate); liberal arts and sciences, general studies and humanities; marketing; mathematics; psychology; social psychology; sociology; speech and rhetoric; technical and business writing.
Non-credit—health professions related.

SIOUX FALLS SEMINARY
Sioux Falls, South Dakota
http://www.nabs.edu/learning/

Sioux Falls Seminary was founded in 1858. It is accredited by North Central Association of Colleges and Schools. It first offered distance learning courses in 2000. In fall 2007, there were 29 students enrolled in distance learning courses. Institutionally administered financial aid is available to distance learners.

Services Distance learners have accessibility to academic advising, bookstore, campus computer network, e-mail services, library services.

Contact Mr. Bryce H. Eben, Director of Enrollment Development, Sioux Falls Seminary, 1525 South Grange Avenue, Sioux Falls, SD 57105. Telephone: 605-336-6588 Ext. 706. Fax: 605-335-9090. E-mail: beben@sfseminary.edu.

DEGREES AND AWARDS
Programs offered do not lead to a degree or other formal award.

COURSE SUBJECT AREAS OFFERED OUTSIDE OF DEGREE PROGRAMS

Graduate—education (specific subject areas); religious/sacred music; theological and ministerial studies; theology and religious vocations related.

SKIDMORE COLLEGE
Saratoga Springs, New York
University Without Walls
http://www.skidmore.edu/uww

See full description on page 458.

SONOMA STATE UNIVERSITY
Rohnert Park, California
Liberal Studies Special Sessions Degree Programs
http://www.sonoma.edu/exed

Sonoma State University was founded in 1960. It is accredited by Western Association of Schools and Colleges. It first offered distance learning courses in 1996. In fall 2007, there were 120 students enrolled in distance learning courses. Institutionally administered financial aid is available to distance learners.

Services Distance learners have accessibility to academic advising, bookstore, campus computer network, career placement assistance, e-mail services, library services.

Contact Beth Warner, Administrative Coordinator, Sonoma State University, 1801 East Cotati Avenue, Rohnert Park, CA 94928-3609. Telephone: 707-664-3977. Fax: 707-664-2613. E-mail: beth.warner@sonoma.edu.

DEGREES AND AWARDS
BA Liberal Studies
MA Interdisciplinary Studies–Action for a Viable Future

COURSE SUBJECT AREAS OFFERED OUTSIDE OF DEGREE PROGRAMS

Undergraduate—educational/instructional media design; environmental design.
Non-credit—business administration, management and operations; business/corporate communications; business, management, and marketing related; computer/information technology administration and management; computer software and media applications; computer systems networking and telecommunications.

SOUTHEAST ARKANSAS COLLEGE
Pine Bluff, Arkansas
http://www.seark.edu/

Southeast Arkansas College was founded in 1991. It is accredited by North Central Association of Colleges and Schools. It first offered distance learning courses in 1995. In fall 2007, there were 719 students enrolled in distance learning courses. Institutionally administered financial aid is available to distance learners.

Services Distance learners have accessibility to e-mail services, library services.

Contact Daytra Demmings, Coordinator of Distance Learning, Southeast Arkansas College, 1900 Hazel Street, Pine Bluff, AR 71603. Telephone: 870-543-5992. Fax: 870-543-5937. E-mail: ddemmings@seark.edu.

DEGREES AND AWARDS
Programs offered do not lead to a degree or other formal award.

COURSE SUBJECT AREAS OFFERED OUTSIDE OF DEGREE PROGRAMS

Undergraduate—anthropology; applied mathematics; business administration, management and operations; business/commerce; business/corporate communications; business, management, and marketing related; business/managerial economics; computer/information technology administration and management; computer programming; computer science; computer software and media applications; computer systems analysis; computer systems networking and telecommunications; criminal justice and corrections; criminology; data entry/microcomputer applications; economics; English; English composition; entrepreneurial and small business operations; fire protection; foods, nutrition, and related services; geography and cartography; health and physical education/fitness; health professions related; history; insurance; international business; marketing; mathematics; mathematics and computer science; mathematics and statistics related; nursing; psychology; real estate; sociology; statistics.

SOUTHEAST COMMUNITY COLLEGE AREA
Lincoln, Nebraska
http://online.southeast.edu

Southeast Community College Area first offered distance learning courses in 1998. In fall 2007, there were 1,900 students enrolled in distance learning courses. Institutionally administered financial aid is available to distance learners.

Services Distance learners have accessibility to academic advising, bookstore, library services, tutoring.

Contact Robert Morgan, Director of Distance Learning, Southeast Community College Area, 4771 West Scott Road, Beatrice, NE 68310. Telephone: 402-228-8272. Fax: 402-228-2218. E-mail: bmorgan@southeast.edu.

DEGREES AND AWARDS

AA Early Childhood

AAS Business Administration; Radiologic Technology Program; Respiratory Care; Surgical Technology

Certification Food Service Training Program

License Nursing Home Administration

COURSE SUBJECT AREAS OFFERED OUTSIDE OF DEGREE PROGRAMS

Undergraduate—accounting and related services; biological and biomedical sciences related; business administration, management and operations; business/commerce; business/corporate communications; economics; English; English composition; foods, nutrition, and related services; health and medical administrative services; health professions related; history; human services; liberal arts and sciences, general studies and humanities; mathematics; philosophy; psychology; sales, merchandising, and related marketing operations (specialized); social psychology; speech and rhetoric; technical and business writing.

Non-credit—management sciences and quantitative methods; mathematics.

SOUTHEASTERN COMMUNITY COLLEGE
Whiteville, North Carolina
http://www.sccnc.info

Southeastern Community College was founded in 1964. It is accredited by Southern Association of Colleges and Schools. It first offered distance learning courses in 1980. In fall 2007, there were 5,000 students enrolled in distance learning courses. Institutionally administered financial aid is available to distance learners.

Services Distance learners have accessibility to academic advising, bookstore, career placement assistance, e-mail services, library services, tutoring.

Contact Ms. Angela Spears, Distance and e-Learning Technician, Southeastern Community College, PO Box 151, Whiteville, NC 28472. Telephone: 910-642-7141 Ext. 229. Fax: 910-642-5658. E-mail: aspears@sccnc.edu.

DEGREES AND AWARDS

AA Business Administration; College Transfer; Elementary, Middle Grades, and Special Education

AAB Business Administration

AAS Electronic Commerce

COURSE SUBJECT AREAS OFFERED OUTSIDE OF DEGREE PROGRAMS

Undergraduate—accounting and related services; biology; business administration, management and operations; chemistry; computer and information sciences; economics; English; English composition; history; mathematics; music; psychology; social sciences; sociology.

SOUTHEASTERN ILLINOIS COLLEGE
Harrisburg, Illinois
Distance Learning
http://sic.edu/virtual.htm

Southeastern Illinois College was founded in 1960. It is accredited by North Central Association of Colleges and Schools. It first offered distance learning courses in 1988. In fall 2007, there were 634 students enrolled in distance learning courses. Institutionally administered financial aid is available to distance learners.

Services Distance learners have accessibility to academic advising, bookstore, campus computer network, e-mail services, library services, tutoring.

Contact Mrs. Karla J. Lewis, Distance Learning Specialist, Southeastern Illinois College, 3575 College Road, Harrisburg, IL 62946. Telephone: 618-252-5400 Ext. 2265. Fax: 618-252-2713. E-mail: karla.lewis@sic.edu.

DEGREES AND AWARDS

Programs offered do not lead to a degree or other formal award.

COURSE SUBJECT AREAS OFFERED OUTSIDE OF DEGREE PROGRAMS

Undergraduate—business/commerce; communication and journalism related; computer software and media applications; education; English; family and consumer sciences/human sciences related; health professions related; history; mathematics; music; philosophy; political science and government; psychology; religious studies.

SOUTHEASTERN OKLAHOMA STATE UNIVERSITY
Durant, Oklahoma
http://www.se.edu/online-learning

Southeastern Oklahoma State University was founded in 1909. It is accredited by North Central Association of Colleges and Schools. It first offered distance learning courses in 2000. In fall 2007, there were 1,624 students enrolled in distance learning courses. Institutionally administered financial aid is available to distance learners.

Services Distance learners have accessibility to academic advising, bookstore, career placement assistance, library services.

Contact Dr. Linda Kallam, Director of Online Learning, Southeastern Oklahoma State University, 1405 North 4th, PMB 4178, Durant, OK 74701. Telephone: 580-745-2682. Fax: 580-745-7458. E-mail: lkallam@se.edu.

DEGREES AND AWARDS

Programs offered do not lead to a degree or other formal award.

COURSE SUBJECT AREAS OFFERED OUTSIDE OF DEGREE PROGRAMS

Undergraduate—accounting and related services; astronomy and astrophysics; biology; business administration, management and operations; business/commerce; business, management, and marketing related; communication and media; computer and information sciences; computer science; criminal justice and corrections; criminology; economics; education related; English composition; gerontology; health and physical education/fitness; history; languages (Romance languages); marketing; mathematics; music; nursing; physical sciences; political science and government; psychology; quality control and safety technologies; sociology; statistics.

Graduate—business administration, management and operations; counseling psychology; educational administration and supervision; educational assessment, evaluation, and research; education related; health and physical education/fitness.

Non-credit—accounting and related services; computer software and media applications; computer systems networking and telecommunications; creative writing; dramatic/theater arts and stagecraft; education related; family and consumer economics; health and physical education/fitness; languages (Romance languages); mathematics; nutrition sciences.

SOUTHEAST MISSOURI STATE UNIVERSITY
Cape Girardeau, Missouri
Southeast Online
http://online.semo.edu

Southeast Missouri State University was founded in 1873. It is accredited by North Central Association of Colleges and Schools. It first offered distance learning courses in 1999. In fall 2007, there were 2,076 students enrolled in distance learning courses. Institutionally administered financial aid is available to distance learners.

Services Distance learners have accessibility to academic advising, bookstore, campus computer network, career placement assistance, e-mail services, library services.

Contact Mrs. Robin Adkison Grebing, Director of Southeast Online, Southeast Missouri State University, Kent Library, Room 305, Mail Stop 4650, Cape Girardeau, MO 63701. Telephone: 573-986-7306. Fax: 573-986-6858. E-mail: radkison@semo.edu.

DEGREES AND AWARDS
BGS General Studies
BS Industrial Technology; Interdisciplinary Studies
BSBA Organizational Administration
BSN Nursing–RN to BSN completion
MBA General Management option

SOUTHEAST TECHNICAL INSTITUTE
Sioux Falls, South Dakota
http://www.southeasttech.edu

Southeast Technical Institute was founded in 1968. It is accredited by North Central Association of Colleges and Schools. It first offered distance learning courses in 2006. In fall 2007, there were 60 students enrolled in distance learning courses. Institutionally administered financial aid is available to distance learners.

Contact Jim Rokusek, Director of Students, Southeast Technical Institute, 2320 North Career Avenue, Sioux Falls, SD 57107. Telephone: 605-367-6109. Fax: 605-367-4372. E-mail: jim.rokusek@southeasttech.edu.

DEGREES AND AWARDS
Programs offered do not lead to a degree or other formal award.

SOUTHERN ARKANSAS UNIVERSITY TECH
Camden, Arkansas
http://www.sautech.edu

Southern Arkansas University Tech was founded in 1967. It is accredited by North Central Association of Colleges and Schools. It first offered distance learning courses in 1995. In fall 2007, there were 750 students enrolled in distance learning courses. Institutionally administered financial aid is available to distance learners.

Services Distance learners have accessibility to academic advising, bookstore, campus computer network, e-mail services, library services, tutoring.

Contact Robert D. Gunnels, Vice Chancellor for Instruction, Southern Arkansas University Tech, PO Box 3499, Camden, AR 71711. Telephone: 870-574-4521. Fax: 870-574-4477. E-mail: rgunnels@sautech.edu.

DEGREES AND AWARDS
AA General Studies
AS Business Administration

COURSE SUBJECT AREAS OFFERED OUTSIDE OF DEGREE PROGRAMS
Undergraduate—accounting and related services; biological and physical sciences; business administration, management and operations; computer science; computer systems networking and telecommunications; curriculum and instruction; education; English; geography and cartography; health and physical education/fitness; history; mathematics; philosophy; political science and government; psychology.

SOUTHERN CALIFORNIA SEMINARY
El Cajon, California
http://www.socalsem.edu

Southern California Seminary was founded in 1946. It is accredited by Transnational Association of Christian Colleges and Schools. It first offered distance learning courses in 2006. In fall 2007, there were 48 students enrolled in distance learning courses. Institutionally administered financial aid is available to distance learners.

Services Distance learners have accessibility to academic advising, bookstore, campus computer network, e-mail services, library services.

Contact Mr. Steve Perdue, Director of Admissions, Southern California Seminary, 2075 East Madison Avenue, El Cajon, CA 92019. Telephone: 888-389-7244. Fax: 619-442-4510. E-mail: sperdue@socalsem.edu.

DEGREES AND AWARDS
AA Biblical Studies
BA Biblical Studies
MABS Biblical Studies
MBS Master of Religious Studies (MRS)

SOUTHERN ILLINOIS UNIVERSITY EDWARDSVILLE
Edwardsville, Illinois
Office of Continuing Education
http://www.siue.edu/CE/

Southern Illinois University Edwardsville was founded in 1957. It is accredited by North Central Association of Colleges and Schools. It first offered distance learning courses in 1994. In fall 2007, there were 297 students enrolled in distance learning courses. Institutionally administered financial aid is available to distance learners.

Services Distance learners have accessibility to academic advising, bookstore, campus computer network, career placement assistance, e-mail services, library services, tutoring.

Contact Dr. Roger Maclean, Executive Director of Educational Outreach, Southern Illinois University Edwardsville, Campus Box 1084, Edwardsville, IL 62026. Telephone: 618-650-3210. Fax: 618-650-2629. E-mail: rmaclea@siue.edu.

DEGREES AND AWARDS
BS Nursing–RN to BS
BSN Nursing

COURSE SUBJECT AREAS OFFERED OUTSIDE OF DEGREE PROGRAMS
Undergraduate—nursing.
Graduate—business/commerce; education; engineering; nursing.

SOUTHERN MAINE COMMUNITY COLLEGE
South Portland, Maine
http://www.smccme.edu/ecampus/

Southern Maine Community College was founded in 1946. It is accredited by New England Association of Schools and Colleges. It first offered distance learning courses in 1999. In fall 2007, there were 1,000 students enrolled in distance learning courses. Institutionally administered financial aid is available to distance learners.

Services Distance learners have accessibility to academic advising, e-mail services, library services.

Contact Mr. Maurice Leavitt, Distance Learning Director, Southern Maine Community College, 2 Fort Road, South Portland, ME 04106. Telephone: 207-741-5789. E-mail: blackboard@smccme.edu.

DEGREES AND AWARDS
Programs offered do not lead to a degree or other formal award.

COURSE SUBJECT AREAS OFFERED OUTSIDE OF DEGREE PROGRAMS
Undergraduate—criminology; culinary arts and related services; dietetics and clinical nutrition services; English; mathematics; social sciences.

SOUTHERN METHODIST UNIVERSITY
Dallas, Texas
School of Engineering–Distance Learning
http://www.engr.smu.edu

Southern Methodist University was founded in 1911. It is accredited by Southern Association of Colleges and Schools. It first offered distance learning courses in 1968. In fall 2007, there were 500 students enrolled in distance learning courses. Institutionally administered financial aid is available to distance learners.

Services Distance learners have accessibility to academic advising, bookstore, campus computer network, career placement assistance, e-mail services, library services.

Contact Mr. Patrick Hicks, Director of Business Development, Southern Methodist University, PO Box 750335, Dallas, TX 75275-0335. Telephone: 214-768-1992. Fax: 214-768-8874. E-mail: phicks@engr.smu.edu.

DEGREES AND AWARDS

MS Computer Engineering; Computer Science; Environmental Engineering; Environmental Science (Environmental Systems Management major); Environmental Science (Hazardous and Waste Materials Management major); Environmental Science; Facilities Management; Information Engineering and Management; Manufacturing Systems Management; Operations Research; Packaging of Electronic and Optical Devices; Security Engineering; Software Engineering; Systems Engineering; Telecommunications
MSCE Civil Engineering
MSEE Electrical Engineering
MSEM Engineering Management
MSME Mechanical Engineering

COURSE SUBJECT AREAS OFFERED OUTSIDE OF DEGREE PROGRAMS

Graduate—civil engineering; civil engineering technology; computer and information sciences; computer and information sciences and support services related; computer engineering; computer engineering technologies; computer/information technology administration and management; computer science; computer software and media applications; computer systems networking and telecommunications; construction engineering; electrical and electronic engineering technologies; electrical, electronics and communications engineering; engineering design; engineering/industrial management; engineering mechanics; engineering related; engineering-related fields; engineering-related technologies; engineering science; engineering technologies related; engineering technology; environmental design; environmental/environmental health engineering; industrial engineering; information science/studies; mechanical engineering; mechanical engineering related technologies; systems engineering.

See full description on page 460.

SOUTHERN NEW HAMPSHIRE UNIVERSITY
Manchester, New Hampshire
SNHU Online
http://www.snhu.edu/online

Southern New Hampshire University was founded in 1932. It is accredited by New England Association of Schools and Colleges. It first offered distance learning courses in 1996. In fall 2007, there were 14,000 students enrolled in distance learning courses. Institutionally administered financial aid is available to distance learners.

Services Distance learners have accessibility to academic advising, bookstore, campus computer network, career placement assistance, e-mail services, library services, tutoring.

Contact Ms. Yvonne Simon, CEO, SNHU Online, Southern New Hampshire University, SNHU Online, 2500 North River Road, Manchester, NH 03106-1045. Telephone: 866-860-0449. Fax: 603-645-9706. E-mail: online@snhu.edu.

DEGREES AND AWARDS
AA Liberal Arts

AS Accounting; Business Administration; Information Technology; Marketing
BA Communications; English Language and Literature; Psychology (Child and Adolescent Development concentration); Psychology; Social Science
BS Accounting; Accounting/Finance; Accounting/Information Systems; Business Administration (Human Resource Management concentration); Business Administration (Organizational Leadership concentration); Business Administration (Small Business Management concentration); Business Administration; Business Studies (Accounting concentration); Business Studies (Business Administration concentration); Business Studies (Business Finance concentration); Business Studies (Human Resource Management concentration); Business Studies (Information Technology concentration); Business Studies (International Management concentration); Business Studies (Marketing concentration); Business Studies (Organizational Leadership concentration); Business Studies (Small Business Management concentration); Finance/Economics; Information Technology; International Business; Marketing; Technical Management
Certificate Accounting; Business Information Systems; Human Resource Management
Graduate Certificate Accounting; Human Resource Management; Integrated Marketing Communications; International Business; Marketing; Microfinance Management; Operations Management; Sport Management; Training and Development
MBA Global MBA
MS Accounting/Finance; Business Education; Justice Studies; Marketing; Organizational Leadership; Sport Management

COURSE SUBJECT AREAS OFFERED OUTSIDE OF DEGREE PROGRAMS

Undergraduate—accounting and computer science; accounting and related services; business administration, management and operations; business/commerce; business/corporate communications; business, management, and marketing related; communication and journalism related; communication and media; computer and information sciences; developmental and child psychology; economics; English language and literature related; entrepreneurial and small business operations; finance and financial management services; human resources management; information science/studies; international relations and affairs; liberal arts and sciences, general studies and humanities; marketing; psychology; social sciences.
Graduate—accounting and computer science; accounting and related services; business administration, management and operations; business/commerce; business/corporate communications; business, management, and marketing related; criminal justice and corrections; human resources management; international business; international/global studies; marketing; operations research.

SOUTHERN POLYTECHNIC STATE UNIVERSITY
Marietta, Georgia
http://dl.spsu.edu

Southern Polytechnic State University was founded in 1948. It is accredited by Southern Association of Colleges and Schools. It first offered distance learning courses in 1995. In fall 2007, there were 300 students enrolled in distance learning courses. Institutionally administered financial aid is available to distance learners.

Services Distance learners have accessibility to academic advising, bookstore, career placement assistance, e-mail services, library services.

Contact Dean Dawn Ramsey, Dean of Extended University, Southern Polytechnic State University, 1100 South Marietta Parkway, Atrium Building, Suite J-330, Marietta, GA 30060-2855. Telephone: 678-915-4287. Fax: 678-915-3576. E-mail: dramsey@spsu.edu.

DEGREES AND AWARDS
BS Information Technology
Certificate Specialty Construction
Graduate Certificate Communications Management; Content Development; Instructional Design; Technical Communication; Visual Communication and Graphics
MS Quality Assurance; Systems Engineering

COURSE SUBJECT AREAS OFFERED OUTSIDE OF DEGREE PROGRAMS

Undergraduate—building/construction finishing, management, and inspection; civil engineering technology; communication and journalism related; computer science; educational/instructional media design; electrical and electronic engineering technologies; engineering design; information science/studies; speech and rhetoric; statistics; textile sciences and engineering.

Graduate—communication and journalism related; computer and information sciences; computer engineering; computer programming; computer science; computer systems analysis; computer systems networking and telecommunications.

Non-credit—computer programming.

SOUTHERN UNION STATE COMMUNITY COLLEGE
Wadley, Alabama
http://www.suscc.edu
Southern Union State Community College was founded in 1922. It is accredited by Southern Association of Colleges and Schools. It first offered distance learning courses in 2001. In fall 2007, there were 1,000 students enrolled in distance learning courses. Institutionally administered financial aid is available to distance learners.
Services Distance learners have accessibility to academic advising, bookstore, career placement assistance, e-mail services, library services.
Contact Dean Tiffany Sanders, Dean of Student Services, Southern Union State Community College, 1701 Lafayette Parkway, Opelika, AL 36801. Telephone: 334-745-6437. E-mail: tsanders@suscc.edu.

DEGREES AND AWARDS
Programs offered do not lead to a degree or other formal award.

COURSE SUBJECT AREAS OFFERED OUTSIDE OF DEGREE PROGRAMS

Undergraduate—English composition; finance and financial management services; history; languages (classics and classical); legal professions and studies related; mathematics; sociology; speech and rhetoric.

SOUTH PIEDMONT COMMUNITY COLLEGE
Polkton, North Carolina
http://www.spcc.edu
South Piedmont Community College was founded in 1962. It is accredited by Southern Association of Colleges and Schools. It first offered distance learning courses in 1982. In fall 2007, there were 1,200 students enrolled in distance learning courses. Institutionally administered financial aid is available to distance learners.
Services Distance learners have accessibility to academic advising, bookstore, e-mail services, library services.
Contact Ms. Judith A. Smith, Associate Vice President, Distance Learning, South Piedmont Community College, PO Box 126, 680 Highway 74 West, Polkton, NC 28135. Telephone: 704-272-5397. E-mail: j-smith@spcc.edu.

DEGREES AND AWARDS
AAS Early Childhood Education

COURSE SUBJECT AREAS OFFERED OUTSIDE OF DEGREE PROGRAMS

Undergraduate—accounting and computer science; accounting and related services; allied health and medical assisting services; allied health diagnostic, intervention, and treatment professions; applied mathematics; behavioral sciences; biological and biomedical sciences related; biology; business administration, management and operations; business/commerce; business, management, and marketing related; business/managerial economics; carpentry; cell biology and anatomical sciences; chemistry; communication and media; communications technology; computer and information sciences; computer and information sciences and support services related; computer/information technology administration and management; computer programming; computer software and media applications; computer systems networking and telecommunications;

criminal justice and corrections; dietetics and clinical nutrition services; economics; education; educational administration and supervision; education related; education (specific levels and methods); education (specific subject areas); electrical/electronics maintenance and repair technology; English; English as a second language; English composition; English language and literature related; entrepreneurial and small business operations; finance and financial management services; foods, nutrition, and related services; geography and cartography; health professions related; health services/allied health/health sciences; heating, air conditioning, ventilation and refrigeration maintenance technology; history; human development, family studies, and related services; human services; intercultural/multicultural and diversity studies; legal professions and studies related; marketing; mathematics; nursing; psychology; psychology related; social sciences; sociology; special education; teaching assistants/aides.

Non-credit—health aides/attendants/orderlies.

SOUTHSIDE VIRGINIA COMMUNITY COLLEGE
Alberta, Virginia
http://www.southside.edu
Southside Virginia Community College was founded in 1970. It is accredited by Southern Association of Colleges and Schools.
Contact Ashley Leslie, Instructional Technologist, Southside Virginia Community College, 109 Campus Drive, Alberta, VA 23821. Telephone: 434-949-1097. E-mail: ashley.leslie@southside.edu.

DEGREES AND AWARDS
Programs offered do not lead to a degree or other formal award.

COURSE SUBJECT AREAS OFFERED OUTSIDE OF DEGREE PROGRAMS

Undergraduate—languages (East Asian).

SOUTHWESTERN ADVENTIST UNIVERSITY
Keene, Texas
Adult Degree Program
http://www.swau.edu/admissions/distancelearning/default.asp
Southwestern Adventist University was founded in 1894. It is accredited by Southern Association of Colleges and Schools. It first offered distance learning courses in 1978. In fall 2007, there were 108 students enrolled in distance learning courses. Institutionally administered financial aid is available to distance learners.
Services Distance learners have accessibility to academic advising, bookstore, e-mail services, library services.
Contact Dr. Robert Gardner, Director, Southwestern Adventist University, 100 West Hillcrest, Adult Degree Program, Keene, TX 76059. Telephone: 817-645-6204. Fax: 817-556-4742. E-mail: adp@swau.edu.

DEGREES AND AWARDS
AS Computer Information Systems; Office Technology
BA Business Administration; Computer Information Systems; English; History; International Affairs; Journalism; Mathematics; Religion; Social Sciences; Theology
BS Broadcasting; Business Management; Computer Information Systems; Computer Science; Corporate Communications; Criminal Justice; Elementary Education; History; Journalism; Mathematics; Nursing; Office Administration; Office Systems Administration; Psychology; Social Sciences

COURSE SUBJECT AREAS OFFERED OUTSIDE OF DEGREE PROGRAMS

Undergraduate—accounting and related services; biblical and other theological languages and literatures; business, management, and marketing related; education; English; history; psychology; theological and ministerial studies.
Graduate—business, management, and marketing related; education.

SOUTHWESTERN COLLEGE
Winfield, Kansas
Southwestern College Online
http://www.southwesterncollege.org

Southwestern College was founded in 1885. It is accredited by North Central Association of Colleges and Schools. It first offered distance learning courses in 2001. In fall 2007, there were 1,400 students enrolled in distance learning courses. Institutionally administered financial aid is available to distance learners.

Services Distance learners have accessibility to academic advising, bookstore, career placement assistance, library services, tutoring.

Contact Linda Bussman, Director of Enrollment Management, Southwestern College, 2040 South Rock Road, Wichita, KS 67207. Telephone: 888-684-5335 Ext. 214. Fax: 316-688-5218. E-mail: linda.bussman@sckans.edu.

DEGREES AND AWARDS

BA Pastoral Studies; Youth Ministry

BS Accounting; Business Administration; Business Quality Management; Computer Operations Technology; Computer Programming Technology; Criminal Justice; Human Resource Development; Nursing–RN to BSN; Operations Management; Security Management; Strategic Leadership

MA Specialized Ministries–Youth and Young Adult Ministry

MBA Business Administration

MS Leadership; Management; Security Administration

COURSE SUBJECT AREAS OFFERED OUTSIDE OF DEGREE PROGRAMS

Undergraduate—business/commerce; computer/information technology administration and management; economics; English; English composition; industrial production technologies; liberal arts and sciences, general studies and humanities; nursing; philosophy; social sciences.

Graduate—business administration, management and operations; education.

Non-credit—business, management, and marketing related.

SOUTHWESTERN COMMUNITY COLLEGE
Creston, Iowa
http://www.swcciowa.edu

Southwestern Community College was founded in 1966. It is accredited by North Central Association of Colleges and Schools. It first offered distance learning courses in 2000. In fall 2007, there were 135 students enrolled in distance learning courses. Institutionally administered financial aid is available to distance learners.

Services Distance learners have accessibility to academic advising, bookstore, campus computer network, e-mail services, library services, tutoring.

Contact Doug Greene, Director of Distance Learning, Southwestern Community College, 1501 West Townline Street, Creston, IA 50801. Telephone: 641-782-7081 Ext. 324. Fax: 641-782-3312. E-mail: greene@swcciowa.edu.

DEGREES AND AWARDS

AA Liberal Arts

COURSE SUBJECT AREAS OFFERED OUTSIDE OF DEGREE PROGRAMS

Undergraduate—accounting and related services; area studies; biology; cell biology and anatomical sciences; English composition; fine and studio art; geography and cartography; journalism; mathematics and statistics related; music; philosophy and religious studies related; sociology.

SOUTHWEST VIRGINIA COMMUNITY COLLEGE
Richlands, Virginia
Audiovisual and Distance Education Services
http://desweb.sw.edu/

Southwest Virginia Community College was founded in 1968. It is accredited by Southern Association of Colleges and Schools. It first offered distance learning courses in 1991. In fall 2007, there were 1,800 students enrolled in distance learning courses. Institutionally administered financial aid is available to distance learners.

Services Distance learners have accessibility to academic advising, bookstore, campus computer network, career placement assistance, e-mail services, library services, tutoring.

Contact Thomas A. Cash, Director of Distance and Distributed Learning, Southwest Virginia Community College, PO Box SVCC, Richlands, VA 24641. Telephone: 276-964-7280. Fax: 276-964-7686. E-mail: tom.cash@sw.edu.

DEGREES AND AWARDS

AAS Arts and Science degree program
AS General Studies
Certificate Network and Internet Administration

COURSE SUBJECT AREAS OFFERED OUTSIDE OF DEGREE PROGRAMS

Undergraduate—creative writing; developmental and child psychology; English composition; history; languages (Romance languages); mathematics and statistics related; sociology; statistics.

Non-credit—computer and information sciences and support services related.

SOUTHWEST WISCONSIN TECHNICAL COLLEGE
Fennimore, Wisconsin
http://www.swtc.edu/

Southwest Wisconsin Technical College was founded in 1967. It is accredited by North Central Association of Colleges and Schools. It first offered distance learning courses in 1989. In fall 2007, there were 800 students enrolled in distance learning courses. Institutionally administered financial aid is available to distance learners.

Services Distance learners have accessibility to academic advising, bookstore, career placement assistance, e-mail services, library services, tutoring.

Contact Kristal Davenport, Instructional Technology Support Specialist, Southwest Wisconsin Technical College, 1800 Bronson Boulevard, Fennimore, WI 53809. Telephone: 608-822-2426. Fax: 608-822-6019. E-mail: kdavenport@swtc.edu.

DEGREES AND AWARDS

Diploma Medical Transcription
Technical Certificate Medical Coding Specialist

COURSE SUBJECT AREAS OFFERED OUTSIDE OF DEGREE PROGRAMS

Undergraduate—accounting and related services; allied health and medical assisting services; applied mathematics; business/corporate communications; communication and journalism related; communication and media; computer and information sciences; computer programming; computer software and media applications; computer systems networking and telecommunications; cosmetology and related personal grooming services; culinary arts and related services; curriculum and instruction; economics; educational/instructional media design; foods, nutrition, and related services; health/medical preparatory programs; hospitality administration; human resources management; management information systems; mathematics; nursing; psychology; social sciences; sociology; statistics.

SPENCERIAN COLLEGE–LEXINGTON
Lexington, Kentucky

Spencerian College–Lexington was founded in 1997. It is accredited by Accrediting Council for Independent Colleges and Schools. It first offered distance learning courses in 2008. Institutionally administered financial aid is available to distance learners.

Services Distance learners have accessibility to campus computer network, e-mail services, library services.

Contact David Profita, Director of Admissions, Spencerian College–Lexington, 1575 Winchester Road, Lexington, KY 40505. Telephone: 859-977-5430. Fax: 859-224-7744. E-mail: dprofita@spencerian.edu.

DEGREES AND AWARDS
Programs offered do not lead to a degree or other formal award.

SPERTUS INSTITUTE OF JEWISH STUDIES
Chicago, Illinois
http://www.spertus.edu/
Spertus Institute of Jewish Studies was founded in 1924. It is accredited by North Central Association of Colleges and Schools. It first offered distance learning courses in 1994. In fall 2007, there were 250 students enrolled in distance learning courses. Institutionally administered financial aid is available to distance learners.
Services Distance learners have accessibility to academic advising, library services.
Contact Dr. Ellen LeVee, Assistant Dean for Jewish Studies, Spertus Institute of Jewish Studies, 610 South Michigan Avenue, Chicago, IL 60605. Telephone: 888-322-1794. Fax: 312-922-6406. E-mail: college@spertus.edu.

DEGREES AND AWARDS
MS Jewish Education–Master of Science in Jewish Education (MSJE)
MSJS Jewish Studies
DJS Jewish Studies

SPOON RIVER COLLEGE
Canton, Illinois
http://www.src.edu/
Spoon River College was founded in 1959. It is accredited by North Central Association of Colleges and Schools. It first offered distance learning courses in 1994. In fall 2007, there were 689 students enrolled in distance learning courses. Institutionally administered financial aid is available to distance learners.
Services Distance learners have accessibility to academic advising, bookstore, campus computer network, career placement assistance, e-mail services, library services, tutoring.
Contact Mr. Jim Genandt, Dean of Instruction, Spoon River College, 23235 North County 22, Canton, IL 61520. Telephone: 309-647-4645. Fax: 309-649-6215. E-mail: info@src.edu.

DEGREES AND AWARDS
Programs offered do not lead to a degree or other formal award.

COURSE SUBJECT AREAS OFFERED OUTSIDE OF DEGREE PROGRAMS
Undergraduate—American literature (United States and Canadian); biology; education; English; English composition; fine and studio art; graphic communications; health professions related; human development, family studies, and related services; philosophy and religious studies related; social sciences; statistics.

SPRING ARBOR UNIVERSITY
Spring Arbor, Michigan
http://www.arbor.edu/sauonline/home/index.aspx
Spring Arbor University was founded in 1873. It is accredited by North Central Association of Colleges and Schools. It first offered distance learning courses in 1998. In fall 2007, there were 290 students enrolled in distance learning courses. Institutionally administered financial aid is available to distance learners.
Services Distance learners have accessibility to academic advising, bookstore, campus computer network, e-mail services, library services.
Contact Mr. Jim Weidman, Director of SAUonline, Graduate Recruiter, Spring Arbor University, 106 East Main Street, ST22, Spring Arbor, MI 49283. Telephone: 517-750-6584. Fax: 517-750-2618. E-mail: james.weidman@arbor.edu.

DEGREES AND AWARDS
BA Management and Organizational Development
MA Spiritual Formation and Leadership
MAE Education
MBA Business
MCS Communication
MIM Organizational Management

COURSE SUBJECT AREAS OFFERED OUTSIDE OF DEGREE PROGRAMS
Undergraduate—business administration, management and operations; computer software and media applications; creative writing; criminal justice and corrections; English composition; finance and financial management services; history; hospitality administration; human resources management; marketing; music; philosophy; psychology; sociology.

STANFORD UNIVERSITY
Stanford, California
Stanford Center for Professional Development
http://scpd.stanford.edu
Stanford University was founded in 1891. It is accredited by Western Association of Schools and Colleges. It first offered distance learning courses in 1969. In fall 2007, there were 1,500 students enrolled in distance learning courses. Institutionally administered financial aid is available to distance learners.
Services Distance learners have accessibility to academic advising, bookstore, campus computer network, e-mail services, library services.
Contact Valeriana Allende, Customer Service Coordinator, Stanford University, 496 Lomita Mall, Durand Building, Room 300, Stanford, CA 94305-4036. Telephone: 650-725-3000. Fax: 650-725-2868. E-mail: vallende@stanford.edu.

DEGREES AND AWARDS
Graduate Certificate Artificial Intelligence; Biodesign; Bioinformatics; Cardiovascular Bioengineering; Clinical Informatics; Computer Architecture; Computer Hardware and VLSI Design; Computer Languages and Operating Systems; Computer Science–Foundations in Computer Science; Control and System Engineering; Data Mining and Applications (Statistics); Databases; Decision Analysis; Design for Customer Value and Market Success; Digital Communication; Electronic Circuits; Electronic Devices and Technology; Engineering Mechanics–Mathematical Foundations and Applications; Guidance and Control (Aeronautics and Astronautics); International Security; Management Science and Engineering; Nanoscale Materials Science; Networking (Electrical Engineering); Optics, Imaging, and Communications; Product Creation and Innovative Manufacturing; Quantitative Methods in Finance and Risk Management (Statistics); Risk Analysis (Management Science and Engineering); Signal Processing; Software Systems; Software Systems, advanced; Spacecraft Design and Operation proficiency; Telecommunications; Wireless Personal Communication
MS Aeronautics and Astronautics; Biomedical Informatics; Computer Science; Electrical Engineering; Engineering–Computational and Mathematical Engineering; Management Science and Engineering; Mechanical Engineering

COURSE SUBJECT AREAS OFFERED OUTSIDE OF DEGREE PROGRAMS
Graduate—aerospace, aeronautical and astronautical engineering; biomedical/medical engineering; biotechnology; chemical engineering; civil engineering; computer science; electrical, electronics and communications engineering; engineering; engineering design; engineering/industrial management; engineering mechanics; environmental/environmental health engineering; management sciences and quantitative methods; materials engineering; science, technology and society; statistics.
Non-credit—aerospace, aeronautical and astronautical engineering; civil engineering; computer science; electrical, electronics and communications engineering; engineering; materials engineering; mechanical engineering; statistics.

STATE UNIVERSITY OF NEW YORK AT BINGHAMTON
Binghamton, New York
EngiNet
http://www.binghamton.edu

State University of New York at Binghamton was founded in 1946. It is accredited by Middle States Association of Colleges and Schools. It first offered distance learning courses in 1989. In fall 2007, there were 181 students enrolled in distance learning courses. Institutionally administered financial aid is available to distance learners.

Services Distance learners have accessibility to academic advising, bookstore, campus computer network, career placement assistance, e-mail services, library services.

Contact Dr. Thomas F. Kowalik, Director, State University of New York at Binghamton, Continuing Education and Outreach, PO Box 6000, Binghamton, NY 13902-6000. Telephone: 607-777-2792. Fax: 607-777-6661. E-mail: kowalik@binghamton.edu.

DEGREES AND AWARDS

MEngr Computer Engineering; Electrical Engineering; Industrial Engineering; Materials Engineering; Mechanical Engineering

MS Computer Science; Electrical Engineering; Industrial Engineering; Mechanical Engineering

COURSE SUBJECT AREAS OFFERED OUTSIDE OF DEGREE PROGRAMS

Undergraduate—anthropology; area, ethnic, cultural, and gender studies related; comparative literature; computer and information sciences and support services related; creative writing; economics; English; health and physical education/fitness; health services/allied health/health sciences; international/global studies; languages (Romance languages); legal studies (non-professional general, undergraduate); linguistic, comparative, and related language studies; nursing; philosophy; political science and government; psychology; psychology related; social sciences; social sciences related; sociology.

Graduate—computer and information sciences; computer and information sciences and support services related; computer engineering; education; electrical, electronics and communications engineering; engineering; engineering science; health services/allied health/health sciences; industrial engineering; manufacturing engineering; mechanical engineering; mechanical engineering related technologies; nursing; public administration; social sciences; social sciences related; social work; systems science and theory.

Non-credit—accounting and computer science; accounting and related services; business administration, management and operations; business/commerce; business/corporate communications; business, management, and marketing related; business/managerial economics; business operations support and assistant services; communication and journalism related; communication and media; computer and information sciences; computer and information sciences and support services related; computer/information technology administration and management; computer programming; computer science; computer software and media applications; computer systems networking and telecommunications; construction management; creative writing; curriculum and instruction; entrepreneurial and small business operations; finance and financial management services; health and medical administrative services; health professions related; languages (Romance languages); legal professions and studies related; legal studies (non-professional general, undergraduate); liberal arts and sciences, general studies and humanities; management information systems; mathematics; technical and business writing.

STATE UNIVERSITY OF NEW YORK AT OSWEGO
Oswego, New York
Office of Distance Learning
http://www.oswego.edu/distance

State University of New York at Oswego was founded in 1861. It is accredited by Middle States Association of Colleges and Schools. It first offered distance learning courses in 1995. In fall 2007, there were 750 students enrolled in distance learning courses. Institutionally administered financial aid is available to distance learners.

Services Distance learners have accessibility to academic advising, bookstore, campus computer network, career placement assistance, e-mail services, library services, tutoring.

Contact Allison Lovallo, Associate Director, State University of New York at Oswego, Continuing Education, 166 Campus Center, Oswego, NY 13126. Telephone: 315-312-2270. Fax: 315-312-3078. E-mail: ced @oswego.edu.

DEGREES AND AWARDS

BA Communications; Public Justice

BS Vocational Teacher Preparation

MS Vocational Teacher Preparation

COURSE SUBJECT AREAS OFFERED OUTSIDE OF DEGREE PROGRAMS

Undergraduate—anthropology; archeology; biology; business administration, management and operations; business/managerial economics; chemistry; communication and journalism related; communication and media; computer and information sciences; computer science; computer systems networking and telecommunications; counseling psychology; criminal justice and corrections; developmental and child psychology; dramatic/theater arts and stagecraft; economics; educational psychology; education (specific subject areas); geological and earth sciences/geosciences; health services/allied health/health sciences; history; information science/studies; journalism; philosophy and religious studies related; psychology; public relations, advertising, and applied communication related; sociology.

Graduate—accounting and related services; anthropology; business administration, management and operations; counseling psychology; curriculum and instruction; economics; education; education (specific subject areas); gerontology; information science/studies; psychology.

See full description on page 462.

STATE UNIVERSITY OF NEW YORK AT PLATTSBURGH
Plattsburgh, New York
Distance Learning Office
http://www.plattsburgh.edu/academics/onlinelearning

State University of New York at Plattsburgh was founded in 1889. It is accredited by Middle States Association of Colleges and Schools. It first offered distance learning courses in 1990. In fall 2007, there were 905 students enrolled in distance learning courses. Institutionally administered financial aid is available to distance learners.

Services Distance learners have accessibility to academic advising, bookstore, campus computer network, e-mail services, library services, tutoring.

Contact Ms. Holly B. Heller-Ross, Interim Associate Dean, Library and Information Services, State University of New York at Plattsburgh, Feinberg Library, 2 Draper Avenue, Plattsburgh, NY 12901. Telephone: 564-5192. Fax: 564-4236. E-mail: hellerhb@plattsburgh.edu.

DEGREES AND AWARDS

BS Nursing

COURSE SUBJECT AREAS OFFERED OUTSIDE OF DEGREE PROGRAMS

Undergraduate—anthropology; area, ethnic, cultural, and gender studies related; biochemistry, biophysics and molecular biology; biology; biopsychology; business administration, management and operations; computer and information sciences; education; education related; English; entrepreneurial and small business operations; ethnic, cultural minority, and gender studies; geological and earth sciences/geosciences; health and physical education/fitness; health professions related; history; languages (Romance languages); library science related; marketing; mathematics; music; nursing; political science and government; psychology related; sales, merchandising, and related marketing operations (specialized); social sciences; sociology; statistics.

Graduate—business administration, management and operations; education; educational administration and supervision; educational/instructional media design; education related; entrepreneurial and small business operations; special education.

STATE UNIVERSITY OF NEW YORK COLLEGE AT CORTLAND
Cortland, New York
SUNY Cortland eLearning
http://www.cortland.edu/ir/index.asp
State University of New York College at Cortland was founded in 1868. It is accredited by Middle States Association of Colleges and Schools. It first offered distance learning courses in 1997. In fall 2007, there were 349 students enrolled in distance learning courses.
Services Distance learners have accessibility to academic advising, bookstore, campus computer network, career placement assistance, e-mail services, library services.
Contact Ms. Paula N. Warnken, Associate Provost for Information Resources, State University of New York College at Cortland, PO Box 2000, Cortland, NY 13045. Telephone: 607-753-5942. Fax: 607-753-5985. E-mail: warnken@cortland.edu.

DEGREES AND AWARDS
Programs offered do not lead to a degree or other formal award.

COURSE SUBJECT AREAS OFFERED OUTSIDE OF DEGREE PROGRAMS
Undergraduate—allied health diagnostic, intervention, and treatment professions; anthropology; business/managerial economics; communication and media; community health services; computer programming; computer software and media applications; creative writing; developmental and child psychology; economics; educational assessment, evaluation, and research; educational psychology; education (specific levels and methods); education (specific subject areas); English composition; ethnic, cultural minority, and gender studies; experimental psychology; film/video and photographic arts; finance and financial management services; fine and studio art; geography and cartography; health and physical education/fitness; health psychology; health services/allied health/health sciences; mathematics; mathematics and computer science; mental and social health services and allied professions; political science and government; psychology; public health; social psychology; special education; technical and business writing.
Graduate—allied health diagnostic, intervention, and treatment professions; community health services; developmental and child psychology; education; educational administration and supervision; educational psychology; education related; education (specific levels and methods); education (specific subject areas); geography and cartography; health and physical education/fitness; nutrition sciences; parks, recreation and leisure; public health.

STATE UNIVERSITY OF NEW YORK COLLEGE AT POTSDAM
Potsdam, New York
http://www.potsdam.edu/online
State University of New York College at Potsdam was founded in 1816. It is accredited by Middle States Association of Colleges and Schools. It first offered distance learning courses in 2002. In fall 2007, there were 202 students enrolled in distance learning courses. Institutionally administered financial aid is available to distance learners.
Services Distance learners have accessibility to academic advising, bookstore, campus computer network, e-mail services, library services.
Contact Ms. Lee Ghostlaw, Staff Assistant, Office of Extended Education, State University of New York College at Potsdam, 44 Pierrepont

Avenue, Potsdam, NY 13676. Telephone: 315-267-2166. Fax: 315-267-3088. E-mail: ghostllk@potsdam.edu.

DEGREES AND AWARDS
Programs offered do not lead to a degree or other formal award.

COURSE SUBJECT AREAS OFFERED OUTSIDE OF DEGREE PROGRAMS
Undergraduate—anthropology; behavioral sciences; biology; business administration, management and operations; business, management, and marketing related; business/managerial economics; communication and journalism related; community health services; data processing; economics; education (specific subject areas); entrepreneurial and small business operations; geography and cartography; geological and earth sciences/geosciences; languages (foreign languages related); management information systems; music; physical sciences; psychology; sociology.
Graduate—education (specific levels and methods).
Non-credit—accounting and related services; business administration, management and operations; business/commerce; communication and media; computer and information sciences; computer programming; computer software and media applications; creative writing; culinary arts and related services; data entry/microcomputer applications; entrepreneurial and small business operations; finance and financial management services; languages (Romance languages); linguistic, comparative, and related language studies; sales, merchandising, and related marketing operations (specialized).

STATE UNIVERSITY OF NEW YORK COLLEGE OF AGRICULTURE AND TECHNOLOGY AT MORRISVILLE
Morrisville, New York
http://www.morrisville.edu/
State University of New York College of Agriculture and Technology at Morrisville was founded in 1908. It is accredited by Middle States Association of Colleges and Schools. It first offered distance learning courses in 1997. In fall 2007, there were 193 students enrolled in distance learning courses. Institutionally administered financial aid is available to distance learners.
Services Distance learners have accessibility to academic advising, bookstore, campus computer network, e-mail services, library services.
Contact Office of Admission, State University of New York College of Agriculture and Technology at Morrisville, Morrisville, NY 13408. Telephone: 315-684-6046. Fax: 315-684-6427. E-mail: admissions@morrisville.edu.

DEGREES AND AWARDS
Certification Office Technology

COURSE SUBJECT AREAS OFFERED OUTSIDE OF DEGREE PROGRAMS
Undergraduate—accounting and related services; agricultural business and management; agriculture; business/commerce; computer/information technology administration and management; computer software and media applications; creative writing; English composition; hospitality administration; management sciences and quantitative methods; mathematics; technical and business writing.

STATE UNIVERSITY OF NEW YORK COLLEGE OF TECHNOLOGY AT CANTON
Canton, New York
SUNY Canton Online
http://www.canton.edu
State University of New York College of Technology at Canton was founded in 1906. It is accredited by Middle States Association of Colleges and Schools. It first offered distance learning courses in 1998. In fall 2007, there were 1,152 students enrolled in distance learning courses. Institutionally administered financial aid is available to distance learners.
Services Distance learners have accessibility to academic advising, bookstore, career placement assistance, e-mail services, library services.

Contact Barbara Porter, Registrar, State University of New York College of Technology at Canton, 34 Cornell Drive, Canton, NY 13617. Telephone: 315-386-7647. Fax: 315-379-3819. E-mail: porter@canton.edu.

DEGREES AND AWARDS
Programs offered do not lead to a degree or other formal award.

COURSE SUBJECT AREAS OFFERED OUTSIDE OF DEGREE PROGRAMS
Undergraduate—animal sciences; business administration, management and operations; computer and information sciences; criminal justice and corrections; physical sciences related; political science and government; sales, merchandising, and related marketing operations (specialized); social psychology.

STATE UNIVERSITY OF NEW YORK EMPIRE STATE COLLEGE
Saratoga Springs, New York
Center for Distance Learning
http://www.esc.edu/cdl

State University of New York Empire State College was founded in 1971. It is accredited by Middle States Association of Colleges and Schools. It first offered distance learning courses in 1979. In fall 2007, there were 7,272 students enrolled in distance learning courses. Institutionally administered financial aid is available to distance learners.
Services Distance learners have accessibility to academic advising, bookstore, campus computer network, career placement assistance, e-mail services, library services, tutoring.
Contact Ms. Shelly B. Dixon, Director of Outreach, State University of New York Empire State College, 111 West Avenue, Saratoga Springs, NY 12866. Telephone: 518-587-2100 Ext. 2300. Fax: 518-587-2660. E-mail: cdladvisor@esc.edu.

DEGREES AND AWARDS
AA Business, Management, and Economics; Community and Human Services; Cultural Studies; Educational Studies; Historical Studies; Human Development; Interdisciplinary Studies; Labor Studies; Science, Math, and Technology; Social Theory, Social Structure, and Change; the Arts
AS Business, Management, and Economics; Community and Human Services; Cultural Studies; Educational Studies; Historical Studies; Human Development; Interdisciplinary Studies; Labor Studies; Science, Math, and Technology; Social Theory, Social Structure, and Change; the Arts
BA Business, Management, and Economics; Community and Human Services; Cultural Studies; Educational Studies; Historical Studies; Human Development; Interdisciplinary Studies; Labor Studies; Science, Math, and Technology; Social Theory, Social Structure, and Change; the Arts
BPS Business, Management, and Economics
BS Business, Management, and Economics; Community and Human Services; Cultural Studies; Educational Studies; Historical Studies; Human Development; Interdisciplinary Studies; Labor Studies; Science, Math, and Technology; Social Theory, Social Structure, and Change; the Arts
MA Liberal Studies; Policy Studies
MAT Teaching
MBA Business Administration

COURSE SUBJECT AREAS OFFERED OUTSIDE OF DEGREE PROGRAMS
Undergraduate—accounting and related services; biology; communication and media; computer/information technology administration and management; criminal justice and corrections; education; English composition; finance and financial management services; fire protection; history; human development, family studies, and related services; international business; legal studies (non-professional general, undergraduate); management information systems; mathematics and statistics related; political science and government; social psychology; sociology; statistics.
Graduate—business/commerce; education; political science and government; social sciences.

See full description on page 464.

STATE UNIVERSITY OF NEW YORK INSTITUTE OF TECHNOLOGY
Utica, New York
Program in Accountancy
http://sln.suny.edu

State University of New York Institute of Technology was founded in 1966. It is accredited by Middle States Association of Colleges and Schools. It first offered distance learning courses in 1998. In fall 2007, there were 462 students enrolled in distance learning courses. Institutionally administered financial aid is available to distance learners.
Services Distance learners have accessibility to academic advising, bookstore, campus computer network, career placement assistance, e-mail services, library services.
Contact Ms. Marybeth Lyons, Assistant Vice President of Enrollment Management, State University of New York Institute of Technology, PO Box 3050, Utica, NY 13504-3050. Telephone: 315-792-7500. Fax: 315-792-7837. E-mail: smbl@sunyit.edu.

DEGREES AND AWARDS
MS Accountancy

COURSE SUBJECT AREAS OFFERED OUTSIDE OF DEGREE PROGRAMS
Undergraduate—accounting and related services; business administration, management and operations; business/commerce; communication and media; health and medical administrative services; health professions related; human resources management; nursing.
Graduate—accounting and related services; business administration, management and operations; business/commerce; communication and media; health and medical administrative services; health professions related; human resources management; nursing; taxation.

STATE UNIVERSITY OF NEW YORK INSTITUTE OF TECHNOLOGY
Utica, New York
Program in Health Services Administration
http://www.sln.suny.edu

State University of New York Institute of Technology was founded in 1966. It is accredited by Middle States Association of Colleges and Schools. It first offered distance learning courses in 1998. In fall 2007, there were 462 students enrolled in distance learning courses. Institutionally administered financial aid is available to distance learners.
Services Distance learners have accessibility to academic advising, bookstore, campus computer network, career placement assistance, e-mail services, library services.
Contact Ms. Marybeth Lyons, Assistant Vice President of Enrollment Management, State University of New York Institute of Technology, PO Box 3050, Utica, NY 13504-3050. Telephone: 315-792-7500. Fax: 315-792-7837. E-mail: smbl@sunyit.edu.

DEGREES AND AWARDS
MS Health Services Administration

COURSE SUBJECT AREAS OFFERED OUTSIDE OF DEGREE PROGRAMS
Undergraduate—accounting and related services; business administration, management and operations; business/commerce; communication and media; health and medical administrative services; health professions related; human resources management; nursing.
Graduate—accounting and related services; business administration, management and operations; business/commerce; communication and media; health and medical administrative services; health professions related; human resources management; nursing; taxation.

STATE UNIVERSITY OF NEW YORK INSTITUTE OF TECHNOLOGY
Utica, New York
SUNY Learning Network
http://sln.suny.edu

State University of New York Institute of Technology was founded in 1966. It is accredited by Middle States Association of Colleges and

Schools. It first offered distance learning courses in 1998. In fall 2007, there were 464 students enrolled in distance learning courses. Institutionally administered financial aid is available to distance learners.

Services Distance learners have accessibility to academic advising, bookstore, campus computer network, career placement assistance, e-mail services, library services.

Contact Ms. Marybeth Lyons, Assistant Vice President of Enrollment Management, State University of New York Institute of Technology, PO Box 3050, Utica, NY 13504-3050. Telephone: 315-792-7500. Fax: 315-792-7837. E-mail: smbl@sunyit.edu.

DEGREES AND AWARDS

BS Health Information Management (BS or BPS)
MBA Technology Management
MS Accountancy; Health Services Administration; Information Design and Technology

COURSE SUBJECT AREAS OFFERED OUTSIDE OF DEGREE PROGRAMS

Undergraduate—accounting and related services; business administration, management and operations; business/commerce; communication and media; health and medical administrative services; health professions related; human resources management; information science/studies; nursing.

Graduate—accounting and related services; business administration, management and operations; business/commerce; communication and media; health and medical administrative services; health professions related; human resources management; information science/studies; nursing; taxation; technical and business writing.

STEPHEN F. AUSTIN STATE UNIVERSITY
Nacogdoches, Texas
http://sfaonline.sfasu.edu/

Stephen F. Austin State University was founded in 1923. It is accredited by Southern Association of Colleges and Schools. It first offered distance learning courses in 1993. In fall 2007, there were 1,890 students enrolled in distance learning courses. Institutionally administered financial aid is available to distance learners.

Services Distance learners have accessibility to academic advising, bookstore, campus computer network, career placement assistance, e-mail services, library services, tutoring.

Contact Andra Floyd, Distance Education Support Specialist, Stephen F. Austin State University, SFA Box 13038, Nacogdoches, TX 75962. Telephone: 936-468-1919. Fax: 936-468-1308. E-mail: sfaonline@sfasu.edu.

DEGREES AND AWARDS

BS Interdisciplinary Studies EC-6, 4-8
BSN RN-BSN Transition Program
Certificate Elementary Education (post-Baccalaureate certification)
MA Music Education
MEd Educational Leadership with Principal Certification
MS Human Sciences; Resource Interpretation

COURSE SUBJECT AREAS OFFERED OUTSIDE OF DEGREE PROGRAMS

Undergraduate—accounting and related services; agriculture; astronomy and astrophysics; business administration, management and operations; business/corporate communications; curriculum and instruction; economics; educational psychology; family and consumer economics; finance and financial management services; foods, nutrition, and related services; hospitality administration; music; psychology; sales, merchandising, and related marketing operations (specialized); social work; special education; technical and business writing.

Graduate—educational administration and supervision; educational psychology; education related; education (specific levels and methods); forestry; music; psychology; public administration; special education.

STEVENS INSTITUTE OF TECHNOLOGY
Hoboken, New Jersey
Graduate School
http://stevens.edu/webcampus

Stevens Institute of Technology was founded in 1870. It is accredited by Middle States Association of Colleges and Schools. It first offered distance learning courses in 1999. In fall 2007, there were 1,200 students enrolled in distance learning courses. Institutionally administered financial aid is available to distance learners.

Services Distance learners have accessibility to academic advising, bookstore, campus computer network, career placement assistance, e-mail services, library services.

Contact Robert Zotti, Director, Online Learning, Stevens Institute of Technology, Castle Point on the Hudson, Howe Center, 12th Floor, Hoboken, NJ 07030. Telephone: 201-216-5231. Fax: 201-216-5090. E-mail: webcampus@stevens.edu.

DEGREES AND AWARDS

Graduate Certificate Atmospheric and Environmental Science and Engineering; Communications–Professional Communications; Computer Graphics; Computer Science–Elements of Computer Science; Cyber Security; Database Systems; Digital Signal Processing; Financial Engineering; Human Resources Management; Management Information Systems; Multimedia Technology; Networked Information Systems; Pharmaceutical Manufacturing Practices; Project Management for the Life Sciences Industries; Project Management; Quantitative Software Engineering; Secure Network Systems Design; Technology Management; Telecommunications Management; Wireless Communications
MBA Technology Management
ME Engineering Management; Networked Information Systems; Space Systems Engineering
MS Computer Science–CyberSecurity concentration; Computer Science; Financial Engineering; Information Systems; Management in Computer Science/Telecom with Security Management and Forensics; Management; Microelectronics and Photonics; Pharmaceutical Manufacturing; Project Management; Quantitative Software Engineering; Systems Engineering; Telecommunication Management

COURSE SUBJECT AREAS OFFERED OUTSIDE OF DEGREE PROGRAMS

Undergraduate—computer science; mathematics; physics.
Non-credit—engineering related.

See full description on page 466.

STRAYER UNIVERSITY
Washington, District of Columbia
http://www.strayer.edu

Strayer University was founded in 1892. It is accredited by Middle States Association of Colleges and Schools. It first offered distance learning courses in 1997. In fall 2007, there were 36,000 students enrolled in distance learning courses. Institutionally administered financial aid is available to distance learners.

Services Distance learners have accessibility to academic advising, bookstore, campus computer network, e-mail services, library services, tutoring.

Contact Chad Nyce, Vice President, Global Region, Strayer University, PO Box 487, Newington, VA 22122. Telephone: 703-339-1850. Fax: 703-339-4849. E-mail: info@strayer.edu.

DEGREES AND AWARDS

AA Accounting; Acquisition and Contract Management; Business Administration; Economics; General Studies; Information Systems; Marketing
BBA Acquisition and Contract Management; Banking; E-business; Finance; Hospitality and Tourism Management; Human Resource Management; Legal Studies; Management; Marketing; Retail Management
BS Accounting; Economics; Information Systems; International Business
Certificate Accounting; Business Administration; Information Systems
Diploma Accounting; Acquisition and Contract Management; Information Systems
MBA Business Administration

MEd Education
MHSA Health Services Administration
MPA Public Administration
MS Information Systems; Professional Accounting

COURSE SUBJECT AREAS OFFERED OUTSIDE OF DEGREE PROGRAMS

Undergraduate—accounting and related services; area, ethnic, cultural, and gender studies related; business/commerce; economics; English; English composition; finance and financial management services; history; information science/studies; international business; legal studies (non-professional general, undergraduate); linguistic, comparative, and related language studies; mathematics; political science and government; psychology; sales, merchandising, and related marketing operations (specialized); sociology.
Graduate—accounting and related services; business/commerce; economics; health services/allied health/health sciences; information science/studies; international business; legal research and advanced professional studies; mathematics.

See full description on page 468.

SULLIVAN COUNTY COMMUNITY COLLEGE
Loch Sheldrake, New York
http://www.sullivan.suny.edu/
Sullivan County Community College was founded in 1962. It is accredited by Middle States Association of Colleges and Schools.
Contact Office of Workforce Development, Continuing Education and Lifelong Learning, Sullivan County Community College, 112 College Road, Loch Sheldrake, NY 12759. Telephone: 845-434-5750 Ext. 4398. E-mail: workforce@sullivan.suny.edu.

DEGREES AND AWARDS
Programs offered do not lead to a degree or other formal award.

COURSE SUBJECT AREAS OFFERED OUTSIDE OF DEGREE PROGRAMS
Undergraduate—accounting and computer science; American literature (United States and Canadian); behavioral sciences; biological and physical sciences; business administration, management and operations; English; nursing.
Non-credit—accounting and computer science; business/commerce; communication and journalism related; construction trades related; dietetics and clinical nutrition services; education; engineering; English; entrepreneurial and small business operations; environmental control technologies; health professions related; insurance; legal professions and studies related; liberal arts and sciences, general studies and humanities; real estate.

SULLIVAN UNIVERSITY
Louisville, Kentucky
Global e-Learning
http://sullivanelearning.net
Sullivan University was founded in 1864. It is accredited by Southern Association of Colleges and Schools. It first offered distance learning courses in 1999. Institutionally administered financial aid is available to distance learners.
Services Distance learners have accessibility to academic advising, bookstore, campus computer network, career placement assistance, e-mail services, library services, tutoring.
Contact Global e-Learning, Sullivan University, Louisville, KY 40205. Telephone: 502-413-8830.

DEGREES AND AWARDS
AS Accounting; Business Management; Logistics and Distribution Management; Marketing and Sales Management
BS Human Resource Leadership
BSBA Accounting concentration; Finance concentration; Hospitality Management concentration; Logistics and Distribution Management concentration; Management concentration; Marketing concentration

Certificate Dispute Resolution Specialist; Employee Relations Specialist; Medical Coding; Organizational Diversity Specialist; Organizational Effectiveness Specialist
MSHRM Human Resource Leadership

SUMMIT PACIFIC COLLEGE
Abbotsford, British Columbia, Canada
http://www.summitpacific.ca
Summit Pacific College was founded in 1941. It is provincially chartered. It first offered distance learning courses in 1999. In fall 2007, there were 125 students enrolled in distance learning courses. Institutionally administered financial aid is available to distance learners.
Services Distance learners have accessibility to academic advising, bookstore, career placement assistance, tutoring.
Contact Rev. Robert McIntyre, Director, Distance Education, Summit Pacific College, 35235 Straiton Road, PO Box 1700, Abbotsford, BC V2S 7E7, Canada. Telephone: 604-851-7228. Fax: 604-853-8951. E-mail: distanceed@summitpacific.ca.

DEGREES AND AWARDS
Programs offered do not lead to a degree or other formal award.

COURSE SUBJECT AREAS OFFERED OUTSIDE OF DEGREE PROGRAMS
Undergraduate—biblical studies; pastoral counseling and specialized ministries; religious education; religious studies; theological and ministerial studies.
Non-credit—biblical studies; religious education; religious studies; theological and ministerial studies.

SYRACUSE UNIVERSITY
Syracuse, New York
Martin J. Whitman School of Management
http://whitman.syr.edu/mba/imba
Syracuse University was founded in 1870. It is accredited by Middle States Association of Colleges and Schools. It first offered distance learning courses in 1977. In fall 2007, there were 250 students enrolled in distance learning courses. Institutionally administered financial aid is available to distance learners.
Services Distance learners have accessibility to academic advising, bookstore, campus computer network, career placement assistance, e-mail services, library services.
Contact Pamela Suzadail, Assistant Director, External Programs, Syracuse University, 721 University Avenue, Syracuse, NY 13244-2450. Telephone: 315-443-8384. E-mail: pjsuzada@syr.edu.

DEGREES AND AWARDS
MBA iMBA
MS iMS Accounting

COURSE SUBJECT AREAS OFFERED OUTSIDE OF DEGREE PROGRAMS
Graduate—accounting and related services; business administration, management and operations; business/commerce; business/managerial economics; entrepreneurial and small business operations; finance and financial management services; management information systems; management sciences and quantitative methods; marketing; sales, merchandising, and related marketing operations (general).

SYRACUSE UNIVERSITY
Syracuse, New York
University College
http://www.suce.syr.edu/distance
Syracuse University was founded in 1870. It is accredited by Middle States Association of Colleges and Schools. It first offered distance learning courses in 1966. In fall 2007, there were 1,000 students enrolled in distance learning courses. Institutionally administered financial aid is available to distance learners.
Services Distance learners have accessibility to academic advising, bookstore, campus computer network, career placement assistance, e-mail services, library services.

Contact Dr. Geraldine de Berly, Associate Dean, University College, Syracuse University, 700 University Avenue, Suite 403, Syracuse, NY 13244-2530. Telephone: 315-443-5753. Fax: 315-443-4410. E-mail: gdeberly@uc.syr.edu.

DEGREES AND AWARDS
AA Liberal Arts
BA Liberal Studies
BPS Organizational Leadership
Certificate Organizational Leadership
CAGS Digital Libraries; Information Security Management; Information Security Management; Information Systems and Telecommunications Management; School Media
MA Advertising Design; Illustration
MBA iMBA
MS Communications Management; Information Management; Library and Information Science in School Media; Library and Information Science; Social Sciences; Telecommunications and Network Management

COURSE SUBJECT AREAS OFFERED OUTSIDE OF DEGREE PROGRAMS
Undergraduate—biological and physical sciences; business, management, and marketing related; computer and information sciences; English language and literature related; ethnic, cultural minority, and gender studies; liberal arts and sciences, general studies and humanities; science, technology and society; social sciences; speech and rhetoric; statistics; technical and business writing; visual and performing arts related.
Graduate—anthropology; business administration, management and operations; communication and media; computer and information sciences; computer/information technology administration and management; computer systems networking and telecommunications; ethnic, cultural minority, and gender studies; history; information science/studies; library science; library science related; management information systems; sociology; visual and performing arts related.
See full description on page 470.

TACOMA COMMUNITY COLLEGE
Tacoma, Washington
Distance Learning Program
http://www.tacomacc.edu/elearning/
Tacoma Community College was founded in 1965. It is accredited by Northwest Commission on Colleges and Universities. It first offered distance learning courses in 1975. In fall 2007, there were 3,500 students enrolled in distance learning courses. Institutionally administered financial aid is available to distance learners.
Services Distance learners have accessibility to academic advising, bookstore, e-mail services, library services, tutoring.
Contact Mr. Andy Duckworth, Coordinator, eLearning, Tacoma Community College, 6501 South 19th Street, Building 28, Room 126, Tacoma, WA 98466. Telephone: 253-460-3958. Fax: 253-460-4378. E-mail: aduckworth@tacomacc.edu.

DEGREES AND AWARDS
Programs offered do not lead to a degree or other formal award.

COURSE SUBJECT AREAS OFFERED OUTSIDE OF DEGREE PROGRAMS
Undergraduate—accounting and related services; allied health and medical assisting services; allied health diagnostic, intervention, and treatment professions; American literature (United States and Canadian); anthropology; applied mathematics; behavioral sciences; bilingual, multilingual, and multicultural education; biological and physical sciences; biology; botany/plant biology; business/commerce; chemistry; communication and journalism related; computer and information sciences; computer programming; computer science; creative writing; criminal justice and corrections; data entry/microcomputer applications; design and applied arts; developmental and child psychology; engineering;

engineering physics; engineering related; English as a second language; English composition; fine and studio art; geography and cartography; geological and earth sciences/geosciences; health and medical administrative services; health professions related; health services/allied health/health sciences; history; human development, family studies, and related services; human services; information science/studies; legal studies (nonprofessional general, undergraduate); library science; library science related; linguistic, comparative, and related language studies; mathematics; music; nursing; philosophy; physics; political science and government; psychology; social sciences; social work; sociology; speech and rhetoric.
Non-credit—business administration, management and operations; computer and information sciences; management information systems.

TAFT COLLEGE
Taft, California
http://www.taftcollege.edu
Taft College was founded in 1922. It is accredited by Western Association of Schools and Colleges. It first offered distance learning courses in 1997. In fall 2007, there were 1,250 students enrolled in distance learning courses. Institutionally administered financial aid is available to distance learners.
Services Distance learners have accessibility to academic advising, bookstore, campus computer network, e-mail services, library services, tutoring.
Contact Patti Bench, Distance Learning Coordinator, Taft College, 29 Emmons Park Drive, Taft, CA 93268. Telephone: 661-763-7757. Fax: 661-763-7816. E-mail: pbench@taft.org.

DEGREES AND AWARDS
AA Business Administration; Liberal Arts
AS Business, general; Criminal Justice Administration; Early Childhood Education

COURSE SUBJECT AREAS OFFERED OUTSIDE OF DEGREE PROGRAMS
Undergraduate—accounting and related services; applied mathematics; biological and physical sciences; business administration, management and operations; business/commerce; computer science; creative writing; criminal justice and corrections; economics; English; English composition; English language and literature related; geological and earth sciences/geosciences; history; human development, family studies, and related services; mathematics; mathematics and statistics related; psychology; psychology related; social sciences; social sciences related; sociology; statistics.

TAYLOR UNIVERSITY
Fort Wayne, Indiana
Center for Lifelong Learning
http://fw.taylor.edu/online
Taylor University was founded in 1938. It is accredited by North Central Association of Colleges and Schools. It first offered distance learning courses in 1941. In fall 2007, there were 1,300 students enrolled in distance learning courses. Institutionally administered financial aid is available to distance learners.
Services Distance learners have accessibility to academic advising, bookstore, e-mail services, library services.
Contact Carrie L. Meyer, Director of Online Learning and Instructional Technology, Taylor University, 1025 West Rudisill Boulevard, Fort Wayne, IN 46807-2197. Telephone: 260-744-8750. Fax: 260-744-8796. E-mail: tufwo.office@taylor.edu.

DEGREES AND AWARDS
AA Biblical Studies; Justice Administration–Ministry concentration; Justice Administration–Public Policy concentration; Liberal Arts–History concentration; Liberal Arts–Interdisciplinary concentration; Liberal Arts–Social Science concentration

BBA Business Administration
Certificate Biblical Studies; Biblical and Cultural Leadership; Christian Worker; Justice and Ministry; Leadership Development; Missions Studies; Professional Writing

COURSE SUBJECT AREAS OFFERED OUTSIDE OF DEGREE PROGRAMS

Undergraduate—American literature (United States and Canadian); area, ethnic, cultural, and gender studies related; area studies; behavioral sciences; biblical and other theological languages and literatures; biblical studies; biological and physical sciences; biology; business administration, management and operations; business/commerce; business, management, and marketing related; business/managerial economics; communication and journalism related; computer and information sciences; computer/information technology administration and management; computer science; counseling psychology; creative writing; criminal justice and corrections; developmental and child psychology; economics; education; educational/instructional media design; educational psychology; education related; English; English composition; English literature (British and Commonwealth); fine and studio art; geography and cartography; history; information science/studies; journalism; liberal arts and sciences, general studies and humanities; management information systems; marketing; mathematics; medieval and Renaissance studies; missionary studies and missiology; multi-/interdisciplinary studies related; music; pastoral counseling and specialized ministries; peace studies and conflict resolution; philosophy; philosophy and religious studies related; physical sciences; physical sciences related; political science and government; psychology; psychology related; religious education; religious/sacred music; religious studies; social psychology; social sciences; social sciences related; social work; sociology; speech and rhetoric; theological and ministerial studies; theology and religious vocations related.
Non-credit—accounting and related services; applied mathematics; biblical and other theological languages and literatures; biblical studies; business administration, management and operations; business/commerce; business/corporate communications; business, management, and marketing related; business operations support and assistant services; communication and journalism related; communication and media; computer and information sciences; computer and information sciences and support services related; computer/information technology administration and management; computer programming; computer software and media applications; computer systems networking and telecommunications; creative writing; data entry/microcomputer applications; data processing; English composition; entrepreneurial and small business operations; family and consumer economics; human development, family studies, and related services; human resources management; information science/studies; management information systems; marketing; mathematics; mathematics and computer science; public relations, advertising, and applied communication related; religious studies; sales, merchandising, and related marketing operations (general); sales, merchandising, and related marketing operations (specialized); technical and business writing; theological and ministerial studies.

TEMPLE UNIVERSITY
Philadelphia, Pennsylvania
Online Learning Program
http://www.temple.edu/distanceandsummer

Temple University was founded in 1884. It is accredited by Middle States Association of Colleges and Schools. It first offered distance learning courses in 1995. In fall 2007, there were 700 students enrolled in distance learning courses. Institutionally administered financial aid is available to distance learners.
Services Distance learners have accessibility to academic advising, bookstore, campus computer network, career placement assistance, e-mail services, library services, tutoring.
Contact Dr. Dominique Monolescu Kliger, Distance Learning Program Director, Temple University, 1301 Cecil B. Moore Avenue, 665 Ritter Annex Building, Philadelphia, PA 19122. Telephone: 215-204-2712. Fax: 215-204-2666. E-mail: online@temple.edu.

DEGREES AND AWARDS
MBA Business Administration–Online MBA

COURSE SUBJECT AREAS OFFERED OUTSIDE OF DEGREE PROGRAMS

Undergraduate—anthropology; architecture; area, ethnic, cultural, and gender studies related; communication and media; communications technology; crafts, folk art and artisanry; economics; education; educational/instructional media design; film/video and photographic arts; industrial and organizational psychology; journalism; mathematics; multi-/interdisciplinary studies related; music; nursing; physics; psychology; sales, merchandising, and related marketing operations (specialized).
Graduate—accounting and related services; business administration, management and operations; business/commerce; communication and media; communications technology; community health services; economics; educational administration and supervision; engineering; health professions related; journalism; music; physical sciences; social work.
Non-credit—botany/plant biology; business/corporate communications.

TEXAS A&M UNIVERSITY–COMMERCE
Commerce, Texas
Instructional Technology and Distance Learning
http://www.tamu-commerce.edu/itde/

Texas A&M University–Commerce was founded in 1889. It is accredited by Southern Association of Colleges and Schools. It first offered distance learning courses in 1993. In fall 2007, there were 2,560 students enrolled in distance learning courses. Institutionally administered financial aid is available to distance learners.
Services Distance learners have accessibility to academic advising, bookstore, campus computer network, career placement assistance, e-mail services, library services, tutoring.
Contact Dr. Charlotte A. Larkin, Director of Instructional Technology and Distance Education, Texas A&M University–Commerce, PO Box 3011, Commerce, TX 75429. Telephone: 903-886-5511. Fax: 903-886-5991. E-mail: charlotte_larkin@tamu-commerce.edu.

DEGREES AND AWARDS
BAA Applied Arts and Sciences degree
MBA Business Administration
MS Management; Technology Management (MS-TMGT)
PhD Educational Psychology

COURSE SUBJECT AREAS OFFERED OUTSIDE OF DEGREE PROGRAMS

Undergraduate—accounting and computer science; agricultural production; animal sciences; biology; botany/plant biology; business administration, management and operations; business/commerce; business, management, and marketing related; business/managerial economics; communication and media; computer and information sciences; computer science; creative writing; criminal justice and corrections; developmental and child psychology; economics; English; English composition; history; industrial engineering; journalism; management information systems; marketing; mathematics; psychology; social work; sociology.
Graduate—accounting and related services; agriculture; business, management, and marketing related; business/managerial economics; computer and information sciences; construction management; curriculum and instruction; economics; education; educational administration and supervision; educational/instructional media design; English composition; finance and financial management services; industrial engineering; library science related; marketing; psychology; radio, television, and digital communication; social work; special education.
Non-credit—economics; finance and financial management services.

TEXAS A&M UNIVERSITY–KINGSVILLE
Kingsville, Texas
Center for Distance Learning and Continuing Education
http://www.tamuk.edu/distancelearning

Texas A&M University–Kingsville was founded in 1925. It is accredited by Southern Association of Colleges and Schools. It first offered distance learning courses in 1992. In fall 2007, there were 2,150 students enrolled in distance learning courses. Institutionally administered financial aid is available to distance learners.
Services Distance learners have accessibility to academic advising, bookstore, campus computer network, career placement assistance, e-mail services, library services.

Contact Dr. Tadeo Reyna, Jr., Director, Texas A&M University–Kingsville, 700 University Boulevard, MSC 147, Kingsville, TX 78363-8202. Telephone: 361-593-2861 Ext. 2854. Fax: 361-593-2859. E-mail: t-reyna@tamuk.edu.

DEGREES AND AWARDS
Programs offered do not lead to a degree or other formal award.

COURSE SUBJECT AREAS OFFERED OUTSIDE OF DEGREE PROGRAMS
Undergraduate—accounting and computer science; agriculture; bilingual, multilingual, and multicultural education; business/corporate communications; communication disorders sciences and services; computer and information sciences; computer science; criminal justice and corrections; economics; education; English; family and consumer sciences/human sciences; finance and financial management services; geological and earth sciences/geosciences; history; management sciences and quantitative methods; marketing; physics; psychology; sociology.
Graduate—agriculture; bilingual, multilingual, and multicultural education; business administration, management and operations; communication disorders sciences and services; economics; education; educational administration and supervision; English; English as a second language; environmental/environmental health engineering; family and consumer sciences/human sciences; sociology.
Non-credit—computer programming; computer software and media applications.

TEXAS CHRISTIAN UNIVERSITY
Fort Worth, Texas
Cyberlearning
http://tcuglobal.edu

Texas Christian University was founded in 1873. It is accredited by Southern Association of Colleges and Schools. It first offered distance learning courses in 1999. In fall 2007, there were 172 students enrolled in distance learning courses. Institutionally administered financial aid is available to distance learners.
Services Distance learners have accessibility to academic advising, bookstore, campus computer network, career placement assistance, e-mail services, library services, tutoring.
Contact Mrs. Romana J. Hughes, Assistant Director of Learning Resources, Texas Christian University, Box 298970, Fort Worth, TX 76129. Telephone: 817-257-7434. Fax: 817-257-7393. E-mail: r.hughes @tcu.edu.

DEGREES AND AWARDS
Advanced Graduate Diploma Liberal Arts–Master of Liberal Arts
MSN Nursing

COURSE SUBJECT AREAS OFFERED OUTSIDE OF DEGREE PROGRAMS
Undergraduate—biology; dramatic/theater arts and stagecraft; fine and studio art; history.

TEXAS STATE TECHNICAL COLLEGE WACO
Waco, Texas
http://www.waco.tstc.edu/

Texas State Technical College Waco was founded in 1965. It is accredited by Southern Association of Colleges and Schools. It first offered distance learning courses in 1995. In fall 2007, there were 1,000 students enrolled in distance learning courses. Institutionally administered financial aid is available to distance learners.
Services Distance learners have accessibility to academic advising, bookstore, campus computer network, career placement assistance, e-mail services, library services, tutoring.
Contact Lance Zimmerman, Director, Distance Education, Texas State Technical College Waco, 3801 Campus Drive, Waco, TX 76705-1696. Telephone: 800-792-8784 Ext. 3257. Fax: 254-867-3470. E-mail: lance.zimmerman@tstc.edu.

DEGREES AND AWARDS
AAS Web Designer; Web Developer

COURSE SUBJECT AREAS OFFERED OUTSIDE OF DEGREE PROGRAMS
Undergraduate—computer programming; computer science; computer software and media applications; computer systems analysis; computer systems networking and telecommunications; data entry/microcomputer applications; English composition; mathematics.
Non-credit—business/commerce; computer programming; computer software and media applications; graphic communications.

TEXAS STATE UNIVERSITY–SAN MARCOS
San Marcos, Texas
Correspondence and Extension Studies
http://www.studyanywhere.txstate.edu

Texas State University–San Marcos was founded in 1899. It is accredited by Southern Association of Colleges and Schools. It first offered distance learning courses in 1953. In fall 2007, there were 2,000 students enrolled in distance learning courses. Institutionally administered financial aid is available to distance learners.
Services Distance learners have accessibility to bookstore, campus computer network, e-mail services, library services, tutoring.
Contact Carolyn Bettelheim, Administrative Assistant, Texas State University–San Marcos, Office of Correspondence Studies, 302 ASB North, 601 University Drive, San Marcos, TX 78666. Telephone: 512-245-2322. Fax: 512-245-8934. E-mail: corrstudy@txstate.edu.

DEGREES AND AWARDS
Programs offered do not lead to a degree or other formal award.

COURSE SUBJECT AREAS OFFERED OUTSIDE OF DEGREE PROGRAMS
Undergraduate—allied health and medical assisting services; American literature (United States and Canadian); behavioral sciences; biological and physical sciences; biology; business/commerce; cell biology and anatomical sciences; community psychology; comparative literature; creative writing; criminology; dance; developmental and child psychology; English; English composition; English language and literature related; English literature (British and Commonwealth); family psychology; fine and studio art; health and medical administrative services; health professions related; history; industrial and organizational psychology; journalism; languages (Romance languages); legal professions and studies related; liberal arts and sciences, general studies and humanities; mathematics; mathematics and computer science; music; philosophy; political science and government; psychology; psychology related; social psychology; social sciences; social sciences related; sociology.
Graduate—mathematics.

TEXAS TECH UNIVERSITY
Lubbock, Texas
Outreach and Distance Education
http://www.de.ttu.edu

Texas Tech University was founded in 1923. It is accredited by Southern Association of Colleges and Schools. It first offered distance learning courses in 1941. In fall 2007, there were 1,918 students enrolled in distance learning courses. Institutionally administered financial aid is available to distance learners.
Services Distance learners have accessibility to academic advising, bookstore, campus computer network, e-mail services, library services.
Contact Mrs. Michele L. Moskos, Marketing Director, Division of Outreach and Distance Education, Texas Tech University, Box 42191, Lubbock, TX 79409-2191. Telephone: 806-742-7200 Ext. 276. Fax: 806-742-7212. E-mail: distlearn@ttu.edu.

DEGREES AND AWARDS
BGS General Studies
BS Architecture; Horticultural and Turfgrass Sciences; Multidisciplinary Studies

Certificate Deaf and Hard of Hearing; Educational Diagnostician; Family and Consumer Sciences Education Teacher Education; Orientation and Mobility; Special Education, generic; Superintendent Professional; Visual Impairment

CAGS Autism; Crop Protection; Dual Impairments; Fibers and Textiles; Gerontology; Horticultural Landscape Management; Soil Management

MA Art Education; Technical Communication

MAg Agriculture

ME Engineering

MEd Educational Leadership and Principal Professional certification preparation; Instructional Technology (Distance Education emphasis); Special Education

MS Agricultural Education; Computer Science; Crop Science; Family Studies and Consumer Science Education; Horticultural and Turfgrass Sciences; Human Development and Family Studies (Gerontology emphasis); Multidisciplinary Science; Restaurant, Hotel, and Institutional Management; Software Engineering; Systems and Engineering Management

EdD Agricultural Education; Educational Leadership

PhD Computer Science; Systems and Engineering Management; Technical Communication and Rhetoric

COURSE SUBJECT AREAS OFFERED OUTSIDE OF DEGREE PROGRAMS

Undergraduate—accounting and related services; agricultural business and management; agriculture; American literature (United States and Canadian); anthropology; applied horticulture/horticultural business services; business administration, management and operations; developmental and child psychology; economics; educational psychology; English composition; English literature (British and Commonwealth); food science and technology; foods, nutrition, and related services; history; journalism; languages (Romance languages); legal studies (non-professional general, undergraduate); liberal arts and sciences, general studies and humanities; marketing; mathematics and statistics related; music; psychology; sales, merchandising, and related marketing operations (specialized); social psychology; sociology; technical and business writing.

Graduate—agriculture; animal sciences; architecture; chemical engineering; civil engineering; computer and information sciences and support services related; computer science; curriculum and instruction; education; educational administration and supervision; educational assessment, evaluation, and research; educational/instructional media design; education related; electrical and electronic engineering technologies; engineering; engineering related; English; English composition; environmental/environmental health engineering; family and consumer economics; gerontology; mathematics; mechanical engineering; music; petroleum engineering; plant sciences; special education; statistics; technical and business writing; textile sciences and engineering; visual and performing arts.

Non-credit—business administration, management and operations; languages (Romance languages).

TEXAS WOMAN'S UNIVERSITY
Denton, Texas
http://www.twuonline.com

Texas Woman's University was founded in 1901. It is accredited by Southern Association of Colleges and Schools. It first offered distance learning courses in 1994. In fall 2007, there were 4,700 students enrolled in distance learning courses. Institutionally administered financial aid is available to distance learners.

Services Distance learners have accessibility to academic advising, bookstore, campus computer network, career placement assistance, e-mail services, library services, tutoring.

Contact Ms. Julie Brown, DE Senior Administrative Assistant, Texas Woman's University, PO Box 425649, Denton, TX 76204. Telephone: 940-898-3409. Fax: 940-898-3416. E-mail: de@twu.edu.

DEGREES AND AWARDS
BGS General Studies
BS Health Studies
BSN Nursing–RN to BS
EMBA Business Administration

MAT Teaching
MLS Library Science
MOT COTA to MOT
MS Deaf Education; Family Studies; Food Systems Administration (Nutrition and Food Sciences); Health Studies; Kinesiology; Speech-Language Pathology
PhD Nursing

COURSE SUBJECT AREAS OFFERED OUTSIDE OF DEGREE PROGRAMS

Undergraduate—business administration, management and operations; computer and information sciences; English; family and consumer economics; health and physical education/fitness; health services/allied health/health sciences; history; nursing; sociology; visual and performing arts.

Graduate—bilingual, multilingual, and multicultural education; business administration, management and operations; business/commerce; communication disorders sciences and services; education; education related; family and consumer economics; health and physical education/fitness; health services/allied health/health sciences; library science; nursing; nutrition sciences; rehabilitation and therapeutic professions; school psychology; sociology; visual and performing arts.

Non-credit—computer software and media applications; English; English composition.

THOMAS COLLEGE
Waterville, Maine
Continuing Education Division
http://www.thomas.edu

Thomas College was founded in 1894. It is accredited by New England Association of Schools and Colleges. It first offered distance learning courses in 1995. In fall 2007, there were 100 students enrolled in distance learning courses. Institutionally administered financial aid is available to distance learners.

Services Distance learners have accessibility to academic advising, bookstore, campus computer network, e-mail services, library services.

Contact Libby LaRochelle, Administrative Assistant, Thomas College, 180 West River Road, Waterville, ME 04901. Telephone: 207-859-1102. Fax: 207-859-1114. E-mail: ced@thomas.edu.

DEGREES AND AWARDS
Programs offered do not lead to a degree or other formal award.

COURSE SUBJECT AREAS OFFERED OUTSIDE OF DEGREE PROGRAMS

Undergraduate—accounting and computer science; business administration, management and operations; business/commerce.

Graduate—business/commerce; business/managerial economics.

THOMAS EDISON STATE COLLEGE
Trenton, New Jersey
DIAL–Distance and Independent Adult Learning
http://www.tesc.edu

Thomas Edison State College was founded in 1972. It is accredited by Middle States Association of Colleges and Schools. It first offered distance learning courses in 1972. In fall 2007, there were 16,423 students enrolled in distance learning courses. Institutionally administered financial aid is available to distance learners.

Services Distance learners have accessibility to academic advising, library services.

Contact Mr. David Hoftiezer, Director of Admissions, Thomas Edison State College, 101 West State Street, Trenton, NJ 08608-1176. Telephone: 888-442-8372. Fax: 609-984-8447. E-mail: admissions@tesc.edu.

DEGREES AND AWARDS
AA Liberal Arts/General Studies
AAS Administrative Studies; Applied Computer Studies; Applied Electronic Studies; Applied Health Studies; Aviation Support; Construction and Facility Support; Dental Hygiene (through UMDNJ); Electrical/

Mechanical Systems and Maintenance; Environmental, Safety, and Security Technology; Mechanics and Maintenance; Occupational Studies

AS Business Administration (ASBA)

ASAST Air Traffic Control; Architectural Design; Aviation Flight Technology; Aviation Maintenance Technology; Biomedical Electronics; Civil and Construction Engineering Technology; Clinical Lab Science; Computer Science Technology; Electrical Technology; Electronic Engineering Technology; Engineering Graphics; Environmental Sciences; Fire Protection Science; Forestry; Horticulture; Laboratory Animal Science; Manufacturing Engineering Technology; Marine Engineering Technology; Mechanical Engineering Technology; Medical Imaging; Nondestructive Testing Technology; Nuclear Engineering Technology; Nuclear Medicine Technology; Radiation Protection; Radiation Therapy; Respiratory Care; Surveying

ASNSM Biology; Computer Science; Mathematics

ASPSS Administration of Justice; Child Development Services; Community Services; Emergency Disaster Services; Fitness and Wellness Services; Gerontology; Legal Services; Recreation Services; Social Services for Special Populations; Social Services

BA Anthropology; Art; Biology; Communications; Computer Science; Criminal Justice; Economics; English; Environmental Studies; Foreign Language; History; Humanities; Journalism; Labor Studies; Liberal Studies; Mathematics; Music; Natural Sciences/Mathematics; Philosophy; Photography; Political Science; Psychology; Religion; Social Sciences; Sociology; Theater

BS Administration of Justice; Advanced Imaging Sciences (with UMDNJ); Allied Dental Education (with UMDNJ); Child Development Services; Community Services; Dietetic Sciences (with UMDNJ); Emergency Disaster Services; Gerontology; Health Services Administration; Health Services Education and Management (with UMDNJ); Health Services; Health and Nutrition Counseling; Legal Services; Mental Health and Rehabilitation Services; Organizational Leadership (BSOL); Recreation Services; Social Services Administration; Social Services for Special Populations; Social Services

BSAST Air Traffic Control; Architectural Design; Aviation Flight Technology; Aviation Maintenance Technology; Biomedical Electronics; Civil Engineering Technology; Clinical Lab Science; Computer Science Technology; Construction; Cytotechnology; Dental Hygiene; Electrical Technology; Electronic Engineering Technology; Energy Utility Technology; Engineering Graphics; Environmental Sciences; Fire Protection Science; Forestry; Health Service Technology; Horticulture; Laboratory Animal Science; Manufacturing Engineering Technology; Marine Engineering Technology; Mechanical Engineering Technology; Medical Imaging; Nondestructive Testing Technology; Nuclear Engineering Technology; Nuclear Medicine Technology; Perfusion Technology; Radiation Protection; Radiation Therapy; Respiratory Care; Surveying

BSBA Accounting; Computer Information Systems; Entrepreneurship; Finance; Financial Institution Management; General Management; Hospital Health Care Administration; Hospitality Management; Human Resources Management/Organizational Management; International Business; Marketing; Operations Management; Public Administration; Real Estate

BSN Nursing

Certificate Post-baccalaureate Certificate in Clinical Trials Management; Post-baccalaureate Certificate in Homeland Security; Post-baccalaureate Certificate in Human Resource Management; Post-baccalaureate Certificate in Online Learning and Teaching; Post-baccalaureate Certificate in Organizational Management and Leadership; Post-baccalaureate Certificate in Public Service Leadership; Pre-associate Certificate in Accounting; Pre-associate Certificate in Computer Aided Design; Pre-associate Certificate in Computer Information Systems; Pre-associate Certificate in Computer Science; Pre-associate Certificate in Dental Assistant (jointly sponsored by UMDNJ and TESC); Pre-associate Certificate in Electronics; Pre-associate Certificate in Finance; Pre-associate Certificate in Fitness and Wellness Services; Pre-associate Certificate in Human Resource Management; Pre-associate Certificate in Labor Studies; Pre-associate Certificate in Marketing; Pre-associate Certificate in Operations Management; Pre-associate Certificate in Public Administration

Graduate Certificate Post-master's Certificate in Nurse Educator

MA Liberal Studies

MAEd Educational Leadership (MAEdL)

MSHRM Human Resources Management

MSM Management

MSN Nursing

See full description on page 472.

THREE RIVERS COMMUNITY COLLEGE
Norwich, Connecticut
http://www.trcc.commnet.edu/

Three Rivers Community College was founded in 1963. It is accredited by New England Association of Schools and Colleges. It first offered distance learning courses in 2000. In fall 2007, there were 352 students enrolled in distance learning courses. Institutionally administered financial aid is available to distance learners.

Services Distance learners have accessibility to academic advising, bookstore, career placement assistance, library services, tutoring.

Contact Mr. R. Kem Barfield, Director of Distance Learning and Educational Technology, Three Rivers Community College, 547 New London Turnpike, Norwich, CT 06360. Telephone: 860-383-5215. E-mail: kbarfield@trcc.commnet.edu.

DEGREES AND AWARDS

AS Computer Support Specialist; General Studies

COURSE SUBJECT AREAS OFFERED OUTSIDE OF DEGREE PROGRAMS

Undergraduate—accounting and related services; business administration, management and operations; computer and information sciences; education (specific subject areas); environmental/environmental health engineering; history; mathematics; nutrition sciences; psychology; sociology.

Non-credit—allied health and medical assisting services; computer software and media applications.

THREE RIVERS COMMUNITY COLLEGE
Poplar Bluff, Missouri
http://www.trcc.edu/

Three Rivers Community College was founded in 1966. It is accredited by North Central Association of Colleges and Schools. It first offered distance learning courses in 1996. In fall 2007, there were 1,000 students enrolled in distance learning courses. Institutionally administered financial aid is available to distance learners.

Services Distance learners have accessibility to academic advising, bookstore, e-mail services, library services.

Contact Cindy Clark, Registrar, Three Rivers Community College, 2080 Three Rivers Boulevard, Poplar Bluff, MO 63901. Telephone: 573-840-9665. Fax: 573-840-9666. E-mail: cclark@trcc.edu.

DEGREES AND AWARDS

Programs offered do not lead to a degree or other formal award.

COURSE SUBJECT AREAS OFFERED OUTSIDE OF DEGREE PROGRAMS

Undergraduate—accounting and computer science; agriculture; allied health and medical assisting services; American literature (United States and Canadian); biology; business administration, management and operations; computer and information sciences; computer science; creative writing; criminal justice and corrections; developmental and child psychology; English language and literature related; English literature (British and Commonwealth); health and medical administrative services; history; mathematics; nursing; psychology; social work; sociology; speech and rhetoric.

THUNDERBIRD SCHOOL OF GLOBAL MANAGEMENT
Glendale, Arizona
http://www.thunderbird.edu/prospective_students/ working_prof_degrees/gmbaod/index.htm

Thunderbird School of Global Management was founded in 1946. It is accredited by North Central Association of Colleges and Schools. It first offered distance learning courses in 2000. In fall 2007, there were 462 students enrolled in distance learning courses. Institutionally administered financial aid is available to distance learners.

Services Distance learners have accessibility to academic advising, bookstore, campus computer network, career placement assistance, e-mail services, library services, tutoring.

Contact Ms. Kimaya Girme, Assistant Director of Global Recruitment, Thunderbird School of Global Management, 1 Global Place, Glendale, AZ 85306-6000. Telephone: 800-457-6966. E-mail: admissions@thunderbird.edu.

DEGREES AND AWARDS

GMBA Global Master of Business Administration On-Demand; Global Master of Business Administration for Latin American Managers
MBA/MIM Kelley Direct MBA/M-GM Dual Degree–Thunderbird and Indiana University
MIM Post-MBA Master of Global Management

COURSE SUBJECT AREAS OFFERED OUTSIDE OF DEGREE PROGRAMS

Graduate—accounting and related services; business administration, management and operations; business/corporate communications; business, management, and marketing related; international business; management information systems; sales, merchandising, and related marketing operations (specialized).
Non-credit—business administration, management and operations; business/commerce; business/corporate communications; business, management, and marketing related; business/managerial economics; international business; international/global studies; marketing.

TIFFIN UNIVERSITY
Tiffin, Ohio
Tiffin Online
http://www.tiffin.edu/online

Tiffin University was founded in 1888. It is accredited by North Central Association of Colleges and Schools. It first offered distance learning courses in 2000. Institutionally administered financial aid is available to distance learners.

Services Distance learners have accessibility to academic advising, bookstore, career placement assistance, e-mail services, library services.
Contact Tiffin Online, Tiffin University, 155 Miami Street, Tiffin, OH 44883. Telephone: 800-968-6446.

DEGREES AND AWARDS

BBA Business Administration–Accelerated degree completion
BCJ Justice Administration
MBA General Management; Leadership concentration; Safety and Security Management concentration; Sports Management
MCJ Justice Administration
MH Humanities
MSCJ Crime Analysis; Criminal Behavior; Homeland Security Administration

TOMPKINS CORTLAND COMMUNITY COLLEGE
Dryden, New York
Instructional and Learning Resources
http://www.tc3.edu/e-tc3/

Tompkins Cortland Community College was founded in 1968. It is accredited by Middle States Association of Colleges and Schools. It first offered distance learning courses in 1997. In fall 2007, there were 1,800 students enrolled in distance learning courses. Institutionally administered financial aid is available to distance learners.

Services Distance learners have accessibility to bookstore, career placement assistance, e-mail services, library services, tutoring.

Contact Tony DeFranco, Coordinator of Learning Technology Services, Tompkins Cortland Community College, 170 North Street, PO Box 139, Dryden, NY 13053. Telephone: 607-844-8222 Ext. 4399. Fax: 607-844-6540. E-mail: defrant@tc3.edu.

DEGREES AND AWARDS

AAS Business Administration–Applied Management; Chemical Dependency Studies Counseling; Hotel and Restaurant Management; Paralegal Studies

COURSE SUBJECT AREAS OFFERED OUTSIDE OF DEGREE PROGRAMS

Undergraduate—accounting and related services; biotechnology; business/commerce; business/corporate communications; communication and media; computer and information sciences; computer programming; computer software and media applications; creative writing; criminal justice and corrections; developmental and child psychology; education (specific levels and methods); English; English as a second language; English composition; ethnic, cultural minority, and gender studies; fine and studio art; hospitality administration; human services; international business; legal studies (non-professional general, undergraduate); management sciences and quantitative methods; marketing; mathematics; mental and social health services and allied professions; nursing; psychology; psychology related; social psychology; sociology; visual and performing arts.
Non-credit—business, management, and marketing related; business operations support and assistant services; computer software and media applications; computer systems networking and telecommunications; data processing.

TREASURE VALLEY COMMUNITY COLLEGE
Ontario, Oregon
Division of Extended Learning
http://www.tvcc.cc

Treasure Valley Community College was founded in 1962. It is accredited by Northwest Commission on Colleges and Universities. It first offered distance learning courses in 1985. In fall 2007, there were 1,000 students enrolled in distance learning courses. Institutionally administered financial aid is available to distance learners.

Services Distance learners have accessibility to academic advising, bookstore, campus computer network, e-mail services, library services, tutoring.
Contact Robin Bagent, Distance Education, Treasure Valley Community College, 650 College Boulevard, Ontario, OR 97914. Telephone: 541-881-8822 Ext. 362. Fax: 541-881-2753. E-mail: rbagent@tvcc.cc.

DEGREES AND AWARDS

Programs offered do not lead to a degree or other formal award.

COURSE SUBJECT AREAS OFFERED OUTSIDE OF DEGREE PROGRAMS

Undergraduate—accounting and computer science; agricultural and domestic animal services; agricultural production; agriculture and agriculture operations related; alternative and complementary medical support services; biology; business administration, management and operations; business/commerce; chemistry; cognitive psychology and psycholinguistics; community psychology; computer and information sciences and support services related; computer programming; creative writing; education; ethnic, cultural minority, and gender studies; family and consumer sciences/human sciences; foods, nutrition, and related services; geological and earth sciences/geosciences; health and physical education/fitness; mathematics and statistics related; music; nutrition sciences; physical sciences; psychology; psychology related; real estate; social sciences; sociology.
Non-credit—real estate.

TRI-COUNTY COMMUNITY COLLEGE
Murphy, North Carolina
http://www.tricountycc.edu/

Tri-County Community College was founded in 1964. It is accredited by Southern Association of Colleges and Schools. It first offered distance learning courses in 1997. In fall 2007, there were 600 students enrolled in distance learning courses. Institutionally administered financial aid is available to distance learners.

Services Distance learners have accessibility to academic advising, bookstore, career placement assistance, e-mail services, library services.

Contact Mr. Wes Chastain, Distance Learning Coordinator/Technician, Tri-County Community College, 4600 East US 64, Murphy, NC 28906. Telephone: 828-837-6810. Fax: 828-837-3266. E-mail: wchastain@tricountycc.edu.

DEGREES AND AWARDS
Programs offered do not lead to a degree or other formal award.

COURSE SUBJECT AREAS OFFERED OUTSIDE OF DEGREE PROGRAMS
Undergraduate—accounting and computer science; accounting and related services; allied health and medical assisting services; anthropology; biology; business administration, management and operations; business, management, and marketing related; computer and information sciences; computer science; computer systems analysis; criminal justice and corrections; data entry/microcomputer applications; economics; education; English; history; marketing; social sciences; sociology.

Non-credit—accounting and computer science; accounting and related services; business administration, management and operations; computer and information sciences; computer and information sciences and support services related; computer programming; computer science.

TRINE UNIVERSITY
Angola, Indiana
http://www.tristate.edu/

Trine University was founded in 1884. It is accredited by North Central Association of Colleges and Schools. It first offered distance learning courses in 1995. In fall 2007, there were 312 students enrolled in distance learning courses. Institutionally administered financial aid is available to distance learners.

Services Distance learners have accessibility to bookstore, e-mail services, library services.

Contact Mr. Brad Grubb, Dean, School of Professional Studies, Trine University, 1 University Avenue, Angola, IN 46703. Telephone: 260-483-4949. Fax: 260-482-8553. E-mail: grubbb@tristate.edu.

DEGREES AND AWARDS
BBA Business

COURSE SUBJECT AREAS OFFERED OUTSIDE OF DEGREE PROGRAMS
Undergraduate—accounting and related services; business administration, management and operations; business/commerce; economics; fine and studio art; geological and earth sciences/geosciences; history; legal studies (non-professional general, undergraduate); liberal arts and sciences, general studies and humanities; marketing; social sciences.

TRINITY EPISCOPAL SCHOOL FOR MINISTRY
Ambridge, Pennsylvania
http://www.tesm.edu

Trinity Episcopal School for Ministry was founded in 1975. It is accredited by Association of Theological Schools in the United States and Canada. It first offered distance learning courses in 1997. In fall 2007, there were 45 students enrolled in distance learning courses. Institutionally administered financial aid is available to distance learners.

Services Distance learners have accessibility to academic advising, bookstore, campus computer network, career placement assistance, e-mail services, library services, tutoring.

Contact Rev. Deacon Travis S. Hines, Director, Center for Distance Learning, Trinity Episcopal School for Ministry, 311 11th Street, Ambridge, PA 15003. Telephone: 724-266-3838 Ext. 228. Fax: 724-266-4617. E-mail: thines@tesm.edu.

DEGREES AND AWARDS
Diploma Anglican Studies; Christian Ministry

COURSE SUBJECT AREAS OFFERED OUTSIDE OF DEGREE PROGRAMS
Graduate—biblical and other theological languages and literatures; biblical studies; missionary studies and missiology; religious studies; theological and ministerial studies; theology and religious vocations related.

Non-credit—biblical studies; missionary studies and missiology; religious studies; theological and ministerial studies; theology and religious vocations related.

TRITON COLLEGE
River Grove, Illinois
Alternative Learning at Triton
http://www.triton.edu

Triton College was founded in 1964. It is accredited by North Central Association of Colleges and Schools. It first offered distance learning courses in 1997. In fall 2007, there were 1,715 students enrolled in distance learning courses. Institutionally administered financial aid is available to distance learners.

Services Distance learners have accessibility to academic advising, bookstore, campus computer network, career placement assistance, e-mail services, library services, tutoring.

Contact Mr. Douglas Olson, Dean, Student Services, Triton College, 2000 Fifth Avenue, River Grove, IL 60171. Telephone: 708-456-0300 Ext. 3230. Fax: 708-582-3162. E-mail: wolson@triton.edu.

DEGREES AND AWARDS
AA the Arts
AS General Studies

COURSE SUBJECT AREAS OFFERED OUTSIDE OF DEGREE PROGRAMS
Undergraduate—accounting and related services; American literature (United States and Canadian); anthropology; architecture; area studies; astronomy and astrophysics; bilingual, multilingual, and multicultural education; bioethics/medical ethics; biology; business, management, and marketing related; chemistry; developmental and child psychology; dramatic/theater arts and stagecraft; economics; educational psychology; English composition; fine and studio art; health and physical education/fitness; history; languages (Romance languages); legal studies (non-professional general, undergraduate); liberal arts and sciences, general studies and humanities; linguistic, comparative, and related language studies; marketing; mathematics; medieval and Renaissance studies; music; nursing; philosophy; philosophy and religious studies related; psychology; real estate; religious studies; social psychology; social sciences; sociology; speech and rhetoric; statistics.

Non-credit—communication and journalism related; computer and information sciences; languages (foreign languages related); medical basic sciences; real estate.

TUFTS UNIVERSITY
Medford, Massachusetts
Fletcher School of Law and Diplomacy
http://www.fletcher.tufts.edu/gmap

Tufts University was founded in 1852. It is accredited by New England Association of Schools and Colleges. It first offered distance learning courses in 2000. In fall 2007, there were 42 students enrolled in distance learning courses. Institutionally administered financial aid is available to distance learners.

Services Distance learners have accessibility to academic advising, campus computer network, career placement assistance, e-mail services, library services.

Contact Nicole Sass, GMAP Program Coordinator, Tufts University, 160 Packard Avenue, Medford, MA 02155. Telephone: 617-627-2429. Fax: 617-627-3005. E-mail: nicole.sass@tufts.edu.

DEGREES AND AWARDS
MA International Affairs

COURSE SUBJECT AREAS OFFERED OUTSIDE OF DEGREE PROGRAMS
Graduate—international business; international relations and affairs.

TUI UNIVERSITY
Cypress, California
http://www.tuiu.edu

TUI University is accredited by Western Association of Schools and Colleges. It first offered distance learning courses in 1999. In fall 2007, there were 8,057 students enrolled in distance learning courses. Institutionally administered financial aid is available to distance learners.
Services Distance learners have accessibility to academic advising, bookstore, campus computer network, e-mail services, library services.
Contact Wei Ren, Registrar, TUI University, 5665 Plaza Drive, 3rd Floor, Cypress, CA 90630. Telephone: 800-375-9878. Fax: 714-827-7407. E-mail: registration@tuiu.edu.

DEGREES AND AWARDS
BS Business Administration; Computer Science; Health Sciences; Information Technology Management
MAE Education
MBA Business Administration
MHS Health Sciences
MS Information Technology Management
PhD Business Administration; Educational Leadership; Health Sciences
See full description on page 474.

TUNXIS COMMUNITY COLLEGE
Farmington, Connecticut
http://www.tunxis.commnet.edu/online

Tunxis Community College was founded in 1969. It is accredited by New England Association of Schools and Colleges. It first offered distance learning courses in 1996. In fall 2007, there were 1,800 students enrolled in distance learning courses. Institutionally administered financial aid is available to distance learners.
Services Distance learners have accessibility to academic advising, bookstore, library services, tutoring.
Contact Peter McCluskey, Director of Admissions, Tunxis Community College, 271 Scott Swamp Road, Farmington, CT 06032. Telephone: 860-255-3563. E-mail: tx-admissions@txcc.commnet.edu.

DEGREES AND AWARDS
AA Criminal Justice; General Studies/Liberal Arts
Certificate Corrections pre-Certification

COURSE SUBJECT AREAS OFFERED OUTSIDE OF DEGREE PROGRAMS
Undergraduate—anthropology; area, ethnic, cultural, and gender studies related; business administration, management and operations; communication and media; computer and information sciences; computer systems networking and telecommunications; criminal justice and corrections; criminology; dental support services and allied professions; developmental and child psychology; English; English composition; history; industrial and organizational psychology; linguistic, comparative, and related language studies; management information systems; music; philosophy; psychology; sociology.
Non-credit—business/commerce; computer and information sciences; criminal justice and corrections; education related; information science/ studies.

TYLER JUNIOR COLLEGE
Tyler, Texas
Learning Resources
http://www.tjc.edu/de

Tyler Junior College was founded in 1926. It is accredited by Southern Association of Colleges and Schools. It first offered distance learning courses in 1969. In fall 2007, there were 3,100 students enrolled in distance learning courses. Institutionally administered financial aid is available to distance learners.
Services Distance learners have accessibility to academic advising, bookstore, career placement assistance, e-mail services, library services, tutoring.
Contact Gay Howard, Secretary of Learning Resources, Tyler Junior College, PO Box 9020, Tyler, TX 75711. Telephone: 903-510-2529. Fax: 903-510-2643. E-mail: ghow@tjc.edu.

DEGREES AND AWARDS
AA General Studies
AAS Business Management; Computer Information Systems Network Administration; Emergency Medical Service Professions (Paramedic option); Health Information Technology

COURSE SUBJECT AREAS OFFERED OUTSIDE OF DEGREE PROGRAMS
Undergraduate—accounting and related services; American literature (United States and Canadian); astronomy and astrophysics; biology; business administration, management and operations; business/commerce; business/corporate communications; business operations support and assistant services; cell biology and anatomical sciences; computer and information sciences; computer and information sciences and support services related; computer/information technology administration and management; computer programming; computer science; computer software and media applications; computer systems analysis; computer systems networking and telecommunications; creative writing; criminal justice and corrections; economics; education; educational/instructional media design; English composition; fine and studio art; fire protection; health services/allied health/health sciences; history; languages (Romance languages); legal studies (non-professional general, undergraduate); legal support services; liberal arts and sciences, general studies and humanities; mathematics and statistics related; music; political science and government; psychology; sociology.
Non-credit—accounting and related services; business administration, management and operations; business/commerce; computer and information sciences; computer programming; computer software and media applications; educational/instructional media design; information science/ studies; management information systems.

UC SAN DIEGO EXTENSION
La Jolla, California
http://mediacenter.ucsd.edu/service_pages/
distance_learning.html

UC San Diego Extension first offered distance learning courses in 1995. In fall 2007, there were 500 students enrolled in distance learning courses. Institutionally administered financial aid is available to distance learners.
Services Distance learners have accessibility to academic advising, bookstore, campus computer network, career placement assistance, e-mail services, tutoring.
Contact Mr. Howard Laurence, Distance Learning Videoconferencing Facilities Manager, UC San Diego Extension, 9500 Gilman Drive, Mail Code 0504, La Jolla, CA 92093-0504. Telephone: 858-534-1174. E-mail: hlaurence@ucsd.edu.

DEGREES AND AWARDS
Programs offered do not lead to a degree or other formal award.

COURSE SUBJECT AREAS OFFERED OUTSIDE OF DEGREE PROGRAMS
Undergraduate—economics; engineering science.
Graduate—economics.
Non-credit—computer engineering technologies; engineering.

INSTITUTION PROFILES

UNIFICATION THEOLOGICAL SEMINARY
Barrytown, New York
http://www.uts.edu

Unification Theological Seminary was founded in 1975. It is accredited by Middle States Association of Colleges and Schools. It first offered distance learning courses in 1994. In fall 2007, there were 5 students enrolled in distance learning courses. Institutionally administered financial aid is available to distance learners.

Services Distance learners have accessibility to academic advising, bookstore, library services.

Contact Mr. Henry Christopher, Director of Admissions, Unification Theological Seminary, 30 Seminary Drive, Barrytown, NY 12507. Telephone: 845-752-3000 Ext. 200. Fax: 845-752-3016. E-mail: admissions @uts.edu.

DEGREES AND AWARDS
Programs offered do not lead to a degree or other formal award.

COURSE SUBJECT AREAS OFFERED OUTSIDE OF DEGREE PROGRAMS
Graduate—biblical studies; history; languages (East Asian); philosophy; philosophy and religious studies related; theological and ministerial studies.
Non-credit—biblical studies; history; languages (East Asian); philosophy; philosophy and religious studies related; theological and ministerial studies.

UNION COUNTY COLLEGE
Cranford, New Jersey
http://www.ucc.edu/DistanceEducation

Union County College was founded in 1933. It is accredited by Middle States Association of Colleges and Schools. It first offered distance learning courses in 1991. In fall 2007, there were 3,100 students enrolled in distance learning courses. Institutionally administered financial aid is available to distance learners.

Services Distance learners have accessibility to academic advising, bookstore, campus computer network, e-mail services, library services, tutoring.

Contact Dr. Barbara Gaba, Provost and Associate Vice President of Academic Affairs, Union County College, 12 West Jersey Street, Elizabeth, NJ 07201. Telephone: 908-965-6091.

DEGREES AND AWARDS
AA Business Administration
AAS Business Management; Computer Science
AS Information Systems Technology; Liberal Studies
Certificate Database Specialist; End-User Computing; Office Professional; Programming; Webmaster

COURSE SUBJECT AREAS OFFERED OUTSIDE OF DEGREE PROGRAMS
Undergraduate—accounting and related services; American Sign Language (ASL); astronomy and astrophysics; biological and physical sciences; chemistry; communication and media; criminal justice and corrections; economics; engineering; English; fine and studio art; history; mathematics; physics; political science and government; psychology; sociology.

UNION UNIVERSITY
Jackson, Tennessee
http://www.uu.edu

Union University was founded in 1823. It is accredited by Southern Association of Colleges and Schools. It first offered distance learning courses in 1999. In fall 2007, there were 2,000 students enrolled in distance learning courses. Institutionally administered financial aid is available to distance learners.

Services Distance learners have accessibility to academic advising, bookstore, campus computer network, career placement assistance, e-mail services, library services.

Contact Ms. Robin Navel, Director of Online Instruction and Training, Union University, 1050 Union University Drive, Jackson, TN 38305. Telephone: 731-661-5402. E-mail: rnavel@uu.edu.

DEGREES AND AWARDS
EdD Higher Education–School Administration

COURSE SUBJECT AREAS OFFERED OUTSIDE OF DEGREE PROGRAMS
Undergraduate—accounting and computer science; behavioral sciences; biological and physical sciences; business, management, and marketing related; computer science; education; library science; management information systems; marketing; mathematics and computer science; medical clinical sciences/graduate medical studies; nursing; physical science technologies; physics; psychology; religious studies; social psychology.
Graduate—education; educational administration and supervision; educational assessment, evaluation, and research; health professions related; religious studies.
Non-credit—religious studies.

UNITED STATES SPORTS ACADEMY
Daphne, Alabama
Continuing Education and Distance Learning
http://www.ussa.edu

United States Sports Academy was founded in 1972. It is accredited by Southern Association of Colleges and Schools. It first offered distance learning courses in 1995. In fall 2007, there were 900 students enrolled in distance learning courses. Institutionally administered financial aid is available to distance learners.

Services Distance learners have accessibility to academic advising, bookstore, campus computer network, e-mail services, library services.

Contact Mr. Craig Bogar, Assistant Dean of Student Services, United States Sports Academy, One Academy Drive, Daphne, AL 36526-7055. Telephone: 800-223-2668 Ext. 7147. Fax: 251-625-1035. E-mail: cbogar@ussa.edu.

DEGREES AND AWARDS
BS Sports Coaching; Sports Management; Sports Studies
Certification Coaching–National Coaching certification; International Sport Diploma; Sports Coaching (International certification); Sports Coaching; Sports Management (International certification); Sports Management; Sports Medicine
MSS Sports Coaching; Sports Fitness; Sports Management; Sports Medicine; Sports Studies
EdD Sports Management–Olympism emphasis; Sports Management

COURSE SUBJECT AREAS OFFERED OUTSIDE OF DEGREE PROGRAMS
Undergraduate—business, management, and marketing related; health and physical education/fitness.
Graduate—business administration, management and operations; entrepreneurial and small business operations; health and physical education/fitness; marketing.
Non-credit—business, management, and marketing related; health and physical education/fitness; parks, recreation and leisure; parks, recreation and leisure facilities management; parks, recreation, and leisure related.

THE UNIVERSITY OF AKRON
Akron, Ohio
Information Services
http://www.uakron.edu

The University of Akron was founded in 1870. It is accredited by North Central Association of Colleges and Schools. It first offered distance learning courses in 1994. In fall 2007, there were 18,939 students enrolled in distance learning courses. Institutionally administered financial aid is available to distance learners.

Services Distance learners have accessibility to academic advising, bookstore, campus computer network, career placement assistance, e-mail services, library services, tutoring.

The College Blue Book, 36th Edition

Contact Ms. Holly Harris Bane, Associate Vice President, Strategic Initiatives and Engagement, The University of Akron, Buchtel Hall 102, Akron, OH 44325-4703. Telephone: 330-972-7508. Fax: 330-972-8699. E-mail: harrisb@uakron.edu.

DEGREES AND AWARDS
Programs offered do not lead to a degree or other formal award.

COURSE SUBJECT AREAS OFFERED OUTSIDE OF DEGREE PROGRAMS

Undergraduate—accounting and related services; allied health and medical assisting services; allied health diagnostic, intervention, and treatment professions; anthropology; archeology; area, ethnic, cultural, and gender studies related; Army J.R.O.T.C/R.O.T.C; astronomy and astrophysics; audiovisual communications technologies; behavioral sciences; bilingual, multilingual, and multicultural education; biochemistry, biophysics and molecular biology; biological and physical sciences; biology; botany/plant biology; business administration, management and operations; business/commerce; business/corporate communications; business, management, and marketing related; business/managerial economics; business operations support and assistant services; cell biology and anatomical sciences; chemistry; communication and journalism related; communication and media; community health services; community organization and advocacy; computer and information sciences; computer science; computer software and media applications; computer systems networking and telecommunications; creative writing; criminal justice and corrections; criminology; curriculum and instruction; design and applied arts; dramatic/theater arts and stagecraft; economics; education; educational administration and supervision; educational assessment, evaluation, and research; educational/instructional media design; education related; education (specific levels and methods); education (specific subject areas); engineering related; engineering technology; English; English as a second/foreign language (teaching); English composition; English language and literature related; English literature (British and Commonwealth); ethnic, cultural minority, and gender studies; family and consumer sciences/human sciences; finance and financial management services; fire protection; foods, nutrition, and related services; geography and cartography; geological and earth sciences/geosciences; health and medical administrative services; health/medical preparatory programs; health professions related; health services/allied health/health sciences; history; hospitality administration; human resources management; journalism; languages (East Asian); languages (Germanic); languages (Romance languages); liberal arts and sciences, general studies and humanities; linguistic, comparative, and related language studies; mathematics; mathematics and computer science; mathematics and statistics related; medical basic sciences; microbiological sciences and immunology; music; nursing; peace studies and conflict resolution; pharmacy, pharmaceutical sciences, and administration; philosophy; philosophy and religious studies related; physical sciences; physical sciences related; political science and government; polymer/plastics engineering; psychology; public administration; public administration and social service professions related; real estate; sales, merchandising, and related marketing operations (general); sales, merchandising, and related marketing operations (specialized); security and protective services related; social and philosophical foundations of education; social sciences; social work; sociology; special education; speech and rhetoric; statistics; taxation; technical and business writing; technology education/industrial arts; urban studies/affairs; visual and performing arts; zoology/animal biology.
Graduate—accounting and related services; applied mathematics; bilingual, multilingual, and multicultural education; business administration, management and operations; communication disorders sciences and services; computer and information sciences; computer software and media applications; counseling psychology; curriculum and instruction; dramatic/theater arts and stagecraft; economics; education; educational administration and supervision; educational assessment, evaluation, and research; educational/instructional media design; educational psychology; education related; education (specific levels and methods); education (specific subject areas); engineering; English; English language and literature related; health professions related; history; human resources management; human services; information science/studies; legal research and advanced professional studies; mathematics; mathematics and computer science; mathematics and statistics related; nursing; political science

and government; psychology; psychology related; public administration; public health; school psychology; social and philosophical foundations of education; social psychology; social work; special education; speech and rhetoric; statistics; taxation; technology education/industrial arts; urban studies/affairs.
Non-credit—allied health and medical assisting services; area, ethnic, cultural, and gender studies related; communications technology; computer and information sciences; computer and information sciences and support services related; computer/information technology administration and management; computer programming; computer science; computer software and media applications; computer systems analysis; computer systems networking and telecommunications; curriculum and instruction; data entry/microcomputer applications; data processing; educational/instructional media design; education related; education (specific levels and methods); entrepreneurial and small business operations; human resources management; information science/studies; nursing.

THE UNIVERSITY OF ALABAMA
Tuscaloosa, Alabama
College of Continuing Studies
http://BamaByDistance.ua.edu
The University of Alabama was founded in 1831. It is accredited by Southern Association of Colleges and Schools. It first offered distance learning courses in 1991. In fall 2007, there were 5,000 students enrolled in distance learning courses. Institutionally administered financial aid is available to distance learners.
Services Distance learners have accessibility to academic advising, bookstore, campus computer network, e-mail services, library services.
Contact Ms. Nina Smith, Program Manager, Adult Student Services, The University of Alabama, Division of Academic Outreach, Box 870388, Tuscaloosa, AL 35487-0388. Telephone: 205-348-0089. Fax: 205-348-0249. E-mail: nsmith@ccs.ua.edu.

DEGREES AND AWARDS
BA Criminal Justice; Interdisciplinary Studies
BS Commerce and Business Administration (General Business); Commerce and Business Administration (Management); Consumer Sciences (Consumer Affairs); Consumer Sciences (Family Financial Planning and Counseling); Early Childhood Education; Human Development and Family Studies; Human Environmental Sciences–General Studies option; Human Environmental Sciences–Restaurant and Hospitality Management; Human Environmental Studies (General Studies); Interdisciplinary Studies; Mechanical Engineering; Mechanical Engineering; Nursing; Restaurant and Hospitality Management (Executive Restaurant and Hospitality Management); Restaurant and Hospitality Management (Restaurant, Hotel, and Meetings Management)
BSN Nursing
MA Counselor Education (Rehabilitation); Educational Leadership; Elementary Education; Health Studies (Health Promotion); Higher Education Administration; Management (Global Business Management); Management; Secondary Education (Curriculum, Teaching, and Learning); Secondary Education (Second Language Acquisition and Teaching); Special Education (Gifted and Talented)
MLIS Library and Information Science; Library and Information Studies–Master of Library and Information Studies
MS Aerospace Engineering; Human Environmental Sciences (Consumer Quality Management); Human Environmental Sciences (Family Financial Planning and Counseling); Human Environmental Sciences (General Studies); Human Environmental Sciences (Human Nutrition); Human Environmental Sciences (Interactive Technology); Human Environmental Sciences (Restaurant and Hospitality Management); Human Environmental Sciences–Food and Nutrition; Nursing; Operations Management
MSAE Aerospace Engineering
MSN Instructional Leadership for Nurse Educators; Nursing–Case Management for Rural Populations/Clinical Nurse Leader; Nursing–RN to BSN/MSN
MSW Social Work
EdD Educational Administration; Higher Education Administration (Executive Cohort); Higher Education Administration; Instructional Leadership for Nurse Educators; Instructional Leadership
PhD Instructional Leadership

COURSE SUBJECT AREAS OFFERED OUTSIDE OF DEGREE PROGRAMS

Undergraduate—accounting and related services; American literature (United States and Canadian); astronomy and astrophysics; biological and physical sciences; biology; business/commerce; business, management, and marketing related; communication and media; computer and information sciences; computer science; computer systems networking and telecommunications; creative writing; criminal justice and corrections; economics; education (specific levels and methods); engineering; English; English composition; English language and literature related; English literature (British and Commonwealth); family and consumer economics; family and consumer sciences/human sciences; family and consumer sciences/human sciences business services; family and consumer sciences/human sciences related; finance and financial management services; foods, nutrition, and related services; geography and cartography; health professions related; history; hospitality administration; human development, family studies, and related services; journalism; languages (Romance languages); liberal arts and sciences, general studies and humanities; linguistic, comparative, and related language studies; mathematics; philosophy; philosophy and religious studies related; political science and government; psychology; public relations, advertising, and applied communication related; religious studies; sales, merchandising, and related marketing operations (specialized); social sciences; social sciences related.

Graduate—aerospace, aeronautical and astronautical engineering; computer and information sciences and support services related; engineering mechanics; family and consumer economics; finance and financial management services; health professions related; library science; nursing.

See full description on page 476.

THE UNIVERSITY OF ALABAMA IN HUNTSVILLE
Huntsville, Alabama
Engineering Management Distance Learning Programs
http://www.engdl.uah.edu/

The University of Alabama in Huntsville was founded in 1950. It is accredited by Southern Association of Colleges and Schools. It first offered distance learning courses in 1992. In fall 2007, there were 150 students enrolled in distance learning courses. Institutionally administered financial aid is available to distance learners.

Services Distance learners have accessibility to academic advising, bookstore, e-mail services, library services.

Contact Dr. Dawn R. Utley, Associate Director of Distance Learning, The University of Alabama in Huntsville, N136 Technology Hall, ISEEM Department, Huntsville, AL 35899. Telephone: 256-824-6075. Fax: 256-824-6608. E-mail: utley@ise.uah.edu.

DEGREES AND AWARDS

MSE Engineering Management; Industrial Engineering; Missile Systems Engineering; Rotorcraft Systems Engineering; Systems Engineering
PhD Industrial and Systems Engineering

COURSE SUBJECT AREAS OFFERED OUTSIDE OF DEGREE PROGRAMS

Graduate—engineering/industrial management; industrial engineering; mechanical engineering; operations research; quality control and safety technologies; statistics; systems engineering.

UNIVERSITY OF ALASKA ANCHORAGE, KODIAK COLLEGE
Kodiak, Alaska
http://www.koc.alaska.edu

University of Alaska Anchorage, Kodiak College was founded in 1968. It is accredited by Northwest Commission on Colleges and Universities. In fall 2007, there were 700 students enrolled in distance learning courses. Institutionally administered financial aid is available to distance learners.

Services Distance learners have accessibility to academic advising, bookstore, e-mail services, library services, tutoring.

Contact Jennifer Myrick, Registrar, University of Alaska Anchorage, Kodiak College, 117 Benny Benson Drive, Kodiak, AK 99615. Telephone: 907-486-1235. Fax: 907-486-1264. E-mail: jmyrick@kodiak.alaska.edu.

DEGREES AND AWARDS

Programs offered do not lead to a degree or other formal award.

COURSE SUBJECT AREAS OFFERED OUTSIDE OF DEGREE PROGRAMS

Undergraduate—accounting and computer science; biological and physical sciences; education.

UNIVERSITY OF ALASKA FAIRBANKS
Fairbanks, Alaska
Center for Distance Education and Independent Learning
http://distance.uaf.edu

University of Alaska Fairbanks was founded in 1917. It is accredited by Northwest Commission on Colleges and Universities. It first offered distance learning courses in 1964. In fall 2007, there were 2,000 students enrolled in distance learning courses. Institutionally administered financial aid is available to distance learners.

Services Distance learners have accessibility to bookstore, campus computer network, e-mail services, library services, tutoring.

Contact Tina Johnson, Communications Coordinator, University of Alaska Fairbanks, PO Box 756700, Fairbanks, AK 99775. Telephone: 800-277-8060. Fax: 907-479-3443. E-mail: distance@uaf.edu.

DEGREES AND AWARDS

Programs offered do not lead to a degree or other formal award.

COURSE SUBJECT AREAS OFFERED OUTSIDE OF DEGREE PROGRAMS

Undergraduate—accounting and related services; American literature (United States and Canadian); anthropology; applied mathematics; bilingual, multilingual, and multicultural education; biological and physical sciences; biology; business administration, management and operations; business/commerce; business, management, and marketing related; communication and journalism related; computer and information sciences; computer science; computer software and media applications; criminal justice and corrections; design and applied arts; drafting/design engineering technologies; dramatic/theater arts and stagecraft; economics; education; educational administration and supervision; English; English composition; English language and literature related; ethnic, cultural minority, and gender studies; film/video and photographic arts; fine and studio art; geography and cartography; gerontology; health professions related; health psychology; history; human development, family studies, and related services; human resources management; journalism; languages (classics and classical); languages (Romance languages); legal studies (non-professional general, undergraduate); liberal arts and sciences, general studies and humanities; library science; linguistic, comparative, and related language studies; marketing; mathematics; mathematics and computer science; mathematics and statistics related; music; nutrition sciences; personality psychology; political science and government; psychology; psychometrics and quantitative psychology; public relations, advertising, and applied communication related; radio, television, and digital communication; real estate; social psychology; social sciences; social sciences related; social work; sociology; statistics; technical and business writing; technology education/industrial arts.

Graduate—computer and information sciences; counseling psychology; curriculum and instruction; educational administration and supervision; education related; education (specific levels and methods); family psychology; health psychology; human development, family studies, and related services; intercultural/multicultural and diversity studies; legal professions and studies related; psychology; psychology related.

See full description on page 478.

UNIVERSITY OF ALASKA, PRINCE WILLIAM SOUND COMMUNITY COLLEGE
Valdez, Alaska
http://www.pwscc.edu
University of Alaska, Prince William Sound Community College was founded in 1978. It is accredited by Northwest Commission on Colleges and Universities. Institutionally administered financial aid is available to distance learners.
Services Distance learners have accessibility to academic advising, bookstore.
Contact Ms. Shannon Foster, Registrar, University of Alaska, Prince William Sound Community College, PO Box 97, Valdez, AK 99686. Telephone: 907-834-1632. Fax: 907-834-1635. E-mail: sfoster@pwscc.edu.

DEGREES AND AWARDS
Programs offered do not lead to a degree or other formal award.

COURSE SUBJECT AREAS OFFERED OUTSIDE OF DEGREE PROGRAMS
Undergraduate—behavioral sciences; English composition; environmental control technologies; speech and rhetoric.

THE UNIVERSITY OF ARIZONA
Tucson, Arizona
Extended University, Distance Learning Program
http://www.ceao.arizona.edu/dist/
The University of Arizona was founded in 1885. It is accredited by North Central Association of Colleges and Schools. It first offered distance learning courses in 1972. In fall 2007, there were 900 students enrolled in distance learning courses. Institutionally administered financial aid is available to distance learners.
Services Distance learners have accessibility to bookstore, campus computer network, e-mail services, library services.
Contact Colleen Reed, Program Coordinator, The University of Arizona, PO Box 210158, University Services Building, Room 301, Tucson, AZ 85721-0158. Telephone: 520-626-2079. Fax: 520-626-1102. E-mail: distance@email.arizona.edu.

DEGREES AND AWARDS
Graduate Certificate Digital Information Management; Gerontology; Optical Sciences
MEngr Engineering
MS Optical Sciences

COURSE SUBJECT AREAS OFFERED OUTSIDE OF DEGREE PROGRAMS
Undergraduate—agriculture; agriculture and agriculture operations related; psychology; psychology related.
Graduate—educational psychology; education (specific levels and methods); engineering; engineering mechanics; gerontology; industrial engineering; library science; mechanical engineering; special education.

THE UNIVERSITY OF ARIZONA
Tucson, Arizona
Independent Study through Correspondence
http://www.outreachcollege.arizona.edu
The University of Arizona was founded in 1885. It is accredited by North Central Association of Colleges and Schools. It first offered distance learning courses in 1941. In fall 2007, there were 1,600 students enrolled in distance learning courses. Institutionally administered financial aid is available to distance learners.
Services Distance learners have accessibility to bookstore, e-mail services, library services.
Contact Mrs. Yvette M. Wingfield, Program Coordinator Senior, The University of Arizona, University Services Building, 888 North Euclid, #323, Tucson, AZ 85721. Telephone: 800-772-7480. Fax: 520-626-5667. E-mail: wingy@u.arizona.edu.

DEGREES AND AWARDS
Programs offered do not lead to a degree or other formal award.

COURSE SUBJECT AREAS OFFERED OUTSIDE OF DEGREE PROGRAMS
Undergraduate—accounting and computer science; animal sciences; anthropology; atmospheric sciences and meteorology; cell biology and anatomical sciences; civil engineering technology; family and consumer sciences/human sciences business services; geography and cartography; geological and earth sciences/geosciences; history; mathematics; physics; political science and government; psychology; sociology.
Graduate—family and consumer economics; geological and earth sciences/geosciences.

UNIVERSITY OF ARKANSAS
Fayetteville, Arkansas
Division for Continuing Education
http://globalcampus.uark.edu
University of Arkansas was founded in 1871. It is accredited by North Central Association of Colleges and Schools. It first offered distance learning courses in 1998. In fall 2007, there were 1,000 students enrolled in distance learning courses. Institutionally administered financial aid is available to distance learners.
Services Distance learners have accessibility to bookstore, e-mail services, library services.
Contact Gary McHenry, Director, University of Arkansas, Office of Credit Studies, 2 East Center Street, Fayetteville, AR 72701. Telephone: 479-575-3648. Fax: 479-575-7232. E-mail: gmchenry@uark.edu.

DEGREES AND AWARDS
BS Human Resource Development
MBA/M Ed Elementary Education/Reading; Physical Education; Special Education; Workforce Development Education
MBA/MS Agricultural, Food, and Life Sciences non-thesis (Food Safety emphasis)
MSN Nursing

COURSE SUBJECT AREAS OFFERED OUTSIDE OF DEGREE PROGRAMS
Undergraduate—curriculum and instruction; developmental and child psychology; dramatic/theater arts and stagecraft; English composition; geography and cartography; history; industrial and organizational psychology; journalism; languages (Germanic); languages (Romance languages); legal studies (non-professional general, undergraduate); mathematics and statistics related; microbiological sciences and immunology; philosophy and religious studies related; social work; sociology.
Graduate—agricultural and food products processing; education (specific subject areas).

UNIVERSITY OF ARKANSAS AT LITTLE ROCK
Little Rock, Arkansas
Extended Programs
http://ualr.edu/extendedprograms
University of Arkansas at Little Rock was founded in 1927. It is accredited by North Central Association of Colleges and Schools. It first offered distance learning courses in 1975. In fall 2007, there were 3,810 students enrolled in distance learning courses. Institutionally administered financial aid is available to distance learners.
Services Distance learners have accessibility to academic advising, bookstore, e-mail services, library services.
Contact Donna Rae Eldridge, Director of Online and Off-Campus Programs, University of Arkansas at Little Rock, UALR Extended Programs, 2801 South University Avenue, Little Rock, AR 72204. Telephone: 501-569-3003. Fax: 501-569-8560. E-mail: dreldridge@ualr.edu.

DEGREES AND AWARDS
BA Criminal Justice; Liberal Arts; Mathematics
BBA Management

BS Community Health Promotion; Mathematics
MA Orientation and Mobility; Rehabilitation Counseling; Rehabilitation Teaching
MEd Learning Systems Technology
MS Criminal Justice

COURSE SUBJECT AREAS OFFERED OUTSIDE OF DEGREE PROGRAMS

Undergraduate—accounting and related services; American Sign Language (ASL); anthropology; archeology; area, ethnic, cultural, and gender studies related; astronomy and astrophysics; atmospheric sciences and meteorology; biology; botany/plant biology; building/construction finishing, management, and inspection; business administration, management and operations; business, management, and marketing related; communication and journalism related; communication and media; community health services; construction management; construction trades related; creative writing; criminal justice and corrections; criminology; data entry/microcomputer applications; developmental and child psychology; economics; education; education related; education (specific levels and methods); English; English composition; English language and literature related; ethnic, cultural minority, and gender studies; finance and financial management services; foods, nutrition, and related services; genetics; geography and cartography; geological and earth sciences/geosciences; gerontology; health and physical education/fitness; health professions related; health psychology; health services/allied health/health sciences; history; human resources management; journalism; languages (foreign languages related); liberal arts and sciences, general studies and humanities; management information systems; marketing; mathematics; mathematics and statistics related; multi-/interdisciplinary studies related; music; nursing; philosophy; philosophy and religious studies related; physical sciences; physical sciences related; political science and government; psychology; psychology related; real estate; religious studies; social work; sociology; speech and rhetoric; statistics; technical and business writing.

Graduate—biology; business administration, management and operations; business, management, and marketing related; criminal justice and corrections; economics; education; educational administration and supervision; educational assessment, evaluation, and research; educational/instructional media design; educational psychology; education related; education (specific levels and methods); English; finance and financial management services; gerontology; history; human resources management; languages (foreign languages related); marketing; mathematics; political science and government; psychopharmacology; real estate; rehabilitation and therapeutic professions; social and philosophical foundations of education; social work; special education; technical and business writing.

UNIVERSITY OF ARKANSAS AT PINE BLUFF
Pine Bluff, Arkansas
http://www.uaex.edu/AQFI
University of Arkansas at Pine Bluff was founded in 1873. It is accredited by North Central Association of Colleges and Schools. It first offered distance learning courses in 1997. Institutionally administered financial aid is available to distance learners.
Services Distance learners have accessibility to academic advising, campus computer network, e-mail services.
Contact Dr. Carole Engle, Director and Chair, University of Arkansas at Pine Bluff, 1200 North University Drive, Mail Slot 4912, Pine Bluff, AR 71601. Telephone: 870-575-8523. Fax: 870-575-4637. E-mail: cengle@uaex.edu.

DEGREES AND AWARDS
Programs offered do not lead to a degree or other formal award.

COURSE SUBJECT AREAS OFFERED OUTSIDE OF DEGREE PROGRAMS

Undergraduate—accounting and related services; agricultural business and management; agriculture; American literature (United States and Canadian); animal sciences; apparel and textiles; architectural engineering; bilingual, multilingual, and multicultural education; biological and physical sciences; biology; business administration, management and

operations; business/corporate communications; chemistry; communication and media; computer and information sciences; computer science; economics; education; English; fishing and fisheries sciences and management.

Graduate—education; fishing and fisheries sciences and management.

Non-credit—Air Force J.R.O.T.C/R.O.T.C; bilingual, multilingual, and multicultural education; business operations support and assistant services; carpentry; computer/information technology administration and management.

UNIVERSITY OF BRIDGEPORT
Bridgeport, Connecticut
Office of Distance Learning
http://www.bridgeport.edu/online
University of Bridgeport was founded in 1927. It is accredited by New England Association of Schools and Colleges. It first offered distance learning courses in 1997. In fall 2007, there were 300 students enrolled in distance learning courses. Institutionally administered financial aid is available to distance learners.
Services Distance learners have accessibility to academic advising, bookstore, campus computer network, e-mail services, library services, tutoring.
Contact Claude A. Perrottet, Coordinator, Distance Learning Programs, University of Bridgeport, 126 Park Avenue, Bridgeport, CT 06604. Telephone: 203-576-4853. Fax: 203-576-4537. E-mail: ubonline@bridgeport.edu.

DEGREES AND AWARDS
BS Dental Hygiene Online (degree completion program); General Studies
Certification Marriage Education (for credit); Marriage Education (non-credit)
MS Computer Science; Human Nutrition; Technology Management

COURSE SUBJECT AREAS OFFERED OUTSIDE OF DEGREE PROGRAMS

Undergraduate—area, ethnic, cultural, and gender studies related; business/commerce; business, management, and marketing related; counseling psychology; dental support services and allied professions; developmental and child psychology; economics; entrepreneurial and small business operations; foods, nutrition, and related services; history; human development, family studies, and related services; human services; liberal arts and sciences, general studies and humanities; mathematics and statistics related; music; philosophy; philosophy and religious studies related; political science and government; psychology; religious studies; sales, merchandising, and related marketing operations (general); social psychology; social sciences; sociology.

Graduate—foods, nutrition, and related services.

Non-credit—human development, family studies, and related services.

THE UNIVERSITY OF BRITISH COLUMBIA
Vancouver, British Columbia, Canada
Distance Education and Technology
http://olt.ubc.ca
The University of British Columbia was founded in 1915. It is provincially chartered. It first offered distance learning courses in 1949. In fall 2007, there were 4,172 students enrolled in distance learning courses. Institutionally administered financial aid is available to distance learners.
Services Distance learners have accessibility to academic advising, bookstore, campus computer network, career placement assistance, e-mail services, library services, tutoring.
Contact Linda Haftner, Student Advisor, The University of British Columbia, Enrolment Services, 1874 East Mall, Room 2016, Brock Hall, Vancouver, BC V6T 1Z1, Canada. Telephone: 604-822-3768. Fax: 604-822-5945. E-mail: linda.haftner@ubc.ca.

DEGREES AND AWARDS
Graduate Certificate Rehabilitation Sciences; Technology-Based Distributed Learning; Technology-Based Learning for Schools
MET Educational Technology–Master of Educational Technology

COURSE SUBJECT AREAS OFFERED OUTSIDE OF DEGREE PROGRAMS

Undergraduate—agricultural business and management; agriculture; animal sciences; area studies; civil engineering; computer and information sciences; dental support services and allied professions; education; educational/instructional media design; English; environmental control technologies; ethnic, cultural minority, and gender studies; film/video and photographic arts; foods, nutrition, and related services; forestry; geography and cartography; history; landscape architecture; languages (Romance languages); library science related; medieval and Renaissance studies; metallurgical engineering; music; nursing; philosophy; political science and government; psychology; rehabilitation and therapeutic professions; social work; soil sciences.
Graduate—education; educational/instructional media design; rehabilitation and therapeutic professions.
Non-credit—English composition.

UNIVERSITY OF CALGARY
Calgary, Alberta, Canada
Teaching and Learning Centre at University of Calgary
http://tlc.ucalgary.ca

University of Calgary was founded in 1945. It is provincially chartered. It first offered distance learning courses in 1977.
Services Distance learners have accessibility to academic advising, bookstore, campus computer network, career placement assistance, e-mail services, library services.
Contact Joanne Carruthers, E-Learning Coordinator, University of Calgary, Teaching and Learning Centre, 540 Bio Science Building, 2500 University Drive NW, Calgary, AB T2N 1N4, Canada. Telephone: 403-220-7364. Fax: 403-282-0730. E-mail: carruthe@ucalgary.ca.

DEGREES AND AWARDS

BCR Community Rehabilitation
BN Nursing
Certificate Adult Learning; E-Learning; Environmental Management; Human Resource Management; Management, general; Teacher Assistant
MEd Education–Master of Education

COURSE SUBJECT AREAS OFFERED OUTSIDE OF DEGREE PROGRAMS

Undergraduate—nursing; social work.
Graduate—education; educational administration and supervision; educational assessment, evaluation, and research; educational/instructional media design; educational psychology; social work.
Non-credit—education (specific levels and methods).

UNIVERSITY OF CALIFORNIA, DAVIS
Davis, California
UC Davis Extension
http://extension.ucdavis.edu/unit/online_learning/

University of California, Davis was founded in 1905. It is accredited by Western Association of Schools and Colleges. It first offered distance learning courses in 1987. In fall 2007, there were 600 students enrolled in distance learning courses. Institutionally administered financial aid is available to distance learners.
Services Distance learners have accessibility to academic advising, bookstore, library services.
Contact Bill Heekin, Director of Student Services, University of California, Davis, 1333 Research Park Drive, Davis, CA 95616. Telephone: 530-757-8777. Fax: 530-757-8696. E-mail: bheekin@unexmail.ucdavis.edu.

DEGREES AND AWARDS

Programs offered do not lead to a degree or other formal award.

COURSE SUBJECT AREAS OFFERED OUTSIDE OF DEGREE PROGRAMS

Undergraduate—allied health and medical assisting services; computer and information sciences; computer programming; computer systems analysis; education; food science and technology; health professions related; languages (Romance languages); natural resources and conservation related; public health.
Non-credit—allied health and medical assisting services; computer engineering technologies; computer/information technology administration and management; computer programming; computer science.

UNIVERSITY OF CALIFORNIA, LOS ANGELES
Los Angeles, California
University Extension
http://www.uclaextension.edu

University of California, Los Angeles was founded in 1919. It is accredited by Western Association of Schools and Colleges. It first offered distance learning courses in 1996. In fall 2007, there were 4,000 students enrolled in distance learning courses. Institutionally administered financial aid is available to distance learners.
Services Distance learners have accessibility to academic advising, bookstore, campus computer network, e-mail services, library services, tutoring.
Contact Program Representative, University of California, Los Angeles, 10995 LeConte, Los Angeles, CA 90024. Telephone: 310-825-2648. Fax: 310-267-4793. E-mail: dstlrng@unex.ucla.edu.

DEGREES AND AWARDS

Programs offered do not lead to a degree or other formal award.

COURSE SUBJECT AREAS OFFERED OUTSIDE OF DEGREE PROGRAMS

Graduate—archeology; business administration, management and operations; business/commerce; design and applied arts; economics; film/video and photographic arts; health and physical education/fitness; languages (foreign languages related); liberal arts and sciences, general studies and humanities; mathematics; philosophy and religious studies related; psychology; social sciences; technical and business writing; visual and performing arts.

UNIVERSITY OF CALIFORNIA, RIVERSIDE
Riverside, California
University Extension
http://www.extension.ucr.edu

University of California, Riverside was founded in 1954. It is accredited by Western Association of Schools and Colleges. It first offered distance learning courses in 1994. In fall 2007, there were 200 students enrolled in distance learning courses. Institutionally administered financial aid is available to distance learners.
Services Distance learners have accessibility to academic advising, bookstore, library services.
Contact Jon Kindschy, Director of Sciences, University of California, Riverside, Riverside, CA 92507. Telephone: 951-827-5804 Ext. 1622. E-mail: sciences@ucx.ucr.edu.

DEGREES AND AWARDS

Programs offered do not lead to a degree or other formal award.

COURSE SUBJECT AREAS OFFERED OUTSIDE OF DEGREE PROGRAMS

Non-credit—agriculture and agriculture operations related; applied horticulture/horticultural business services; atmospheric sciences and meteorology; computer software and media applications; education related; geography and cartography; nursing; plant sciences.

UNIVERSITY OF CENTRAL FLORIDA
Orlando, Florida
Center for Distributed Learning
http://online.ucf.edu

University of Central Florida was founded in 1963. It is accredited by Southern Association of Colleges and Schools. It first offered distance learning courses in 1996. In fall 2007, there were 9,431 students enrolled in distance learning courses. Institutionally administered financial aid is available to distance learners.
Services Distance learners have accessibility to academic advising, bookstore, campus computer network, e-mail services, library services.

Contact Ms. Lori Allison, Coordinator, University of Central Florida, 3100 Technology Parkway, Suite 234, Orlando, FL 32826-3271. Telephone: 407-823-4910. Fax: 407-207-4911. E-mail: lallison@mail.ucf.edu.

DEGREES AND AWARDS

BA Interdisciplinary Studies
BS Health Services Administration; Information Systems Technology; Interdisciplinary Studies; Radiologic Sciences; Technical Education and Industry Training
BSET Engineering Technology
BSN Nursing
Graduate Certificate Community College Education; Educational Media; Gifted Education; Initial Teacher Professional Preparation; Instructional Design for Simulations; Instructional/Educational Technology; Nonprofit Management; Nursing Education; Pre-Kindergarten Handicapped Endorsement; Professional Writing; Special Education; e-Learning Professional Development
MA Career and Technical Education; English, Technical Communication track; Exceptional Education; Instructional Technology/Media E-Learning or Instructional Systems; Instructional Technology/Media-Educational Technology track
MEd Exceptional Education; Instructional Technology/Media-Educational Media track
MM Nonprofit Management
MS Criminal Justice; Forensic Science–Forensic Analysis track; Forensic Science–Forensic Biochemistry track
MSN Nursing–Leadership and Management track; Nursing–Nurse Educator track

COURSE SUBJECT AREAS OFFERED OUTSIDE OF DEGREE PROGRAMS

Undergraduate—computer and information sciences and support services related; education related; health and medical administrative services; legal professions and studies related; nursing; philosophy and religious studies related; sociology; statistics.
Graduate—chemistry; educational/instructional media design; education related; health and medical administrative services; nursing; public administration; public administration and social service professions related; technical and business writing.

UNIVERSITY OF CENTRAL MISSOURI
Warrensburg, Missouri
Department of Nursing
http://www.ucmo.edu/ucmonline
University of Central Missouri was founded in 1871. It is accredited by North Central Association of Colleges and Schools. It first offered distance learning courses in 1993. In fall 2007, there were 2,500 students enrolled in distance learning courses. Institutionally administered financial aid is available to distance learners.
Services Distance learners have accessibility to academic advising, bookstore, campus computer network, career placement assistance, e-mail services, library services, tutoring.
Contact Dr. Linda Mulligan, Graduate Nursing Program Coordinator, University of Central Missouri, Nursing, UHC 106, Warrensburg, MO 64093. Telephone: 660-543-4775. Fax: 660-543-8304. E-mail: mulligan@ucmo.edu.

DEGREES AND AWARDS
BS Nursing
MS Nursing and Rural Family Nursing

COURSE SUBJECT AREAS OFFERED OUTSIDE OF DEGREE PROGRAMS

Undergraduate—computer science; criminal justice and corrections; curriculum and instruction; educational assessment, evaluation, and research; educational psychology; education (specific subject areas); foods, nutrition, and related services; health and physical education/fitness; library science; religious studies; technology education/industrial arts.

Graduate—criminal justice and corrections; curriculum and instruction; educational assessment, evaluation, and research; educational psychology; geography and cartography; library science; nursing; special education; technology education/industrial arts.
Non-credit—accounting and related services; computer programming; computer software and media applications; computer systems networking and telecommunications; entrepreneurial and small business operations.

See full description on page 480.

UNIVERSITY OF CENTRAL MISSOURI
Warrensburg, Missouri
Department of Criminal Justice
http://www.ucmo.edu/ucmonline
University of Central Missouri was founded in 1871. It is accredited by North Central Association of Colleges and Schools. It first offered distance learning courses in 1993. In fall 2007, there were 2,500 students enrolled in distance learning courses. Institutionally administered financial aid is available to distance learners.
Services Distance learners have accessibility to academic advising, bookstore, campus computer network, career placement assistance, e-mail services, library services, tutoring.
Contact Dr. Gene Bonham, Graduate Program Coordinator, University of Central Missouri, Department of Criminal Justice, Humphreys 300, Warrensburg, MO 64093. Telephone: 660-543-8836. Fax: 660-543-8306. E-mail: lbonham@ucmo.edu.

DEGREES AND AWARDS
MS Criminal Justice

COURSE SUBJECT AREAS OFFERED OUTSIDE OF DEGREE PROGRAMS

Undergraduate—computer science; criminal justice and corrections; curriculum and instruction; educational assessment, evaluation, and research; educational psychology; education (specific subject areas); foods, nutrition, and related services; health and physical education/fitness; library science; religious studies; technology education/industrial arts.
Graduate—criminal justice and corrections; curriculum and instruction; educational assessment, evaluation, and research; educational psychology; geography and cartography; library science; nursing; special education; technology education/industrial arts.
Non-credit—accounting and related services; computer programming; computer software and media applications; computer systems networking and telecommunications; entrepreneurial and small business operations.

See full description on page 482.

UNIVERSITY OF CENTRAL MISSOURI
Warrensburg, Missouri
School of Technology
http://www.ucmo.edu/ucmonline
University of Central Missouri was founded in 1871. It is accredited by North Central Association of Colleges and Schools. It first offered distance learning courses in 1993. In fall 2007, there were 2,500 students enrolled in distance learning courses. Institutionally administered financial aid is available to distance learners.
Services Distance learners have accessibility to academic advising, bookstore, campus computer network, career placement assistance, e-mail services, library services, tutoring.
Contact Dr. Ronald C. Woolsey, Graduate Program Coordinator, University of Central Missouri, School of Technology, G 009 F, Warrensburg, MO 64093. Telephone: 660-543-4340. E-mail: woolsey@ucmo.edu.

DEGREES AND AWARDS
MS Industrial Management

COURSE SUBJECT AREAS OFFERED OUTSIDE OF DEGREE PROGRAMS

Undergraduate—computer science; criminal justice and corrections; curriculum and instruction; educational assessment, evaluation, and research; educational psychology; education (specific subject areas); foods, nutrition, and related services; health and physical education/fitness; library science; religious studies; technology education/industrial arts.

Graduate—criminal justice and corrections; curriculum and instruction; educational assessment, evaluation, and research; educational psychology; geography and cartography; library science; nursing; special education; technology education/industrial arts.

Non-credit—accounting and related services; computer programming; computer software and media applications; computer systems networking and telecommunications; entrepreneurial and small business operations.

See full description on page 484.

UNIVERSITY OF CENTRAL MISSOURI
Warrensburg, Missouri
Master of Science Physical Education/Exercise and Sport Science
http://www.ucmo.edu/ucmonline

University of Central Missouri was founded in 1871. It is accredited by North Central Association of Colleges and Schools. It first offered distance learning courses in 1993. In fall 2007, there were 2,500 students enrolled in distance learning courses. Institutionally administered financial aid is available to distance learners.

Services Distance learners have accessibility to academic advising, bookstore, campus computer network, career placement assistance, e-mail services, library services, tutoring.

Contact Dr. H. Scott Strohmeyer, Graduate Program Coordinator, University of Central Missouri, Department of Health and Human Performance, Humphreys 216, Warrensburg, MO 64093. Telephone: 660-543-8191. Fax: 660-543-8847. E-mail: strohmeyer@ucmo.edu.

DEGREES AND AWARDS
MS Physical Education Exercise and Sport Science

COURSE SUBJECT AREAS OFFERED OUTSIDE OF DEGREE PROGRAMS

Undergraduate—computer science; criminal justice and corrections; curriculum and instruction; educational assessment, evaluation, and research; educational psychology; education (specific subject areas); health and physical education/fitness; library science; nursing; psychology; religious studies; technology education/industrial arts.

Graduate—criminal justice and corrections; curriculum and instruction; educational assessment, evaluation, and research; educational psychology; geography and cartography; library science; nursing; technology education/industrial arts.

Non-credit—accounting and related services; computer programming; computer software and media applications; entrepreneurial and small business operations; legal support services.

See full description on page 486.

UNIVERSITY OF CINCINNATI
Cincinnati, Ohio
Distance Learning Programs
http://www.uc.edu/distance

University of Cincinnati was founded in 1819. It is accredited by North Central Association of Colleges and Schools. It first offered distance learning courses in 1984. In fall 2007, there were 4,349 students enrolled in distance learning courses. Institutionally administered financial aid is available to distance learners.

Services Distance learners have accessibility to academic advising, bookstore, campus computer network, e-mail services, library services, tutoring.

Contact Dr. Melody Clark, University of Cincinnati.

DEGREES AND AWARDS

AAS Early Childhood Education; Fire Science Technology

BEd Early Childhood Education

BS Addiction Studies; Clinical Laboratory Science; Fire Science Technology; Health Information Management; Special Education–Sign Language Interpreting track (Bachelor Completion program)

Certificate Curriculum and Instruction in Medical Education for Healthcare Professionals; Medical Biller/Coder; Postsecondary Literacy Instruction; Software Productivity

MEd Curriculum and Instruction (for Health Care Professionals); Educational Leadership

MS Criminal Justice; Pharmaceutical Sciences, Cosmetic Science emphasis

MSN Nurse Midwifery; Nursing–Women's Health Nurse Practitioner

PharmD Pharmacy

COURSE SUBJECT AREAS OFFERED OUTSIDE OF DEGREE PROGRAMS

Undergraduate—accounting and related services; anthropology; business/commerce; communication disorders sciences and services; computer and information sciences; computer software and media applications; criminal justice and corrections; economics; education; engineering related; English; geography and cartography; geological and earth sciences/geosciences; history; liberal arts and sciences, general studies and humanities; mathematics; philosophy; philosophy and religious studies related; psychology.

Graduate—communication disorders sciences and services; education related; engineering related.

Non-credit—accounting and computer science; accounting and related services; business/commerce; business operations support and assistant services; computer and information sciences; computer programming; publishing; technical and business writing.

UNIVERSITY OF CINCINNATI RAYMOND WALTERS COLLEGE
Cincinnati, Ohio
Outreach and Continuing Education
http://www.rwc.uc.edu

University of Cincinnati Raymond Walters College was founded in 1967. It is accredited by North Central Association of Colleges and Schools. It first offered distance learning courses in 1995. In fall 2007, there were 465 students enrolled in distance learning courses. Institutionally administered financial aid is available to distance learners.

Services Distance learners have accessibility to academic advising, bookstore, campus computer network, career placement assistance, e-mail services, library services, tutoring.

Contact Janice Ooten, Program Manager, University of Cincinnati Raymond Walters College, 9555 Plainfield Road, Cincinnati, OH 45236-1096. Telephone: 513-936-1533. Fax: 513-745-8315. E-mail: janice.ooten@uc.edu.

DEGREES AND AWARDS

Programs offered do not lead to a degree or other formal award.

COURSE SUBJECT AREAS OFFERED OUTSIDE OF DEGREE PROGRAMS

Undergraduate—biology; business administration, management and operations; computer/information technology administration and management; computer software and media applications; English composition; film/video and photographic arts; foods, nutrition, and related services; health professions related; library science; psychology; sociology.

UNIVERSITY OF COLORADO AT BOULDER
Boulder, Colorado
Center for Advanced Engineering and Technology Education (CAETE)
http://caete.colorado.edu

University of Colorado at Boulder was founded in 1876. It is accredited by North Central Association of Colleges and Schools. It first offered distance learning courses in 1983. In fall 2007, there were 400 students enrolled in distance learning courses. Institutionally administered financial aid is available to distance learners.

Services Distance learners have accessibility to academic advising, bookstore, campus computer network, career placement assistance, e-mail services, library services.

Contact Robin M.W. McClanahan, Marketing Manager, University of Colorado at Boulder, CAETE, 435 UCB, Boulder, CO 80309. Telephone: 303-492-0212. Fax: 303-492-5987. E-mail: caete@colorado.edu.

DEGREES AND AWARDS

Graduate Certificate Computer and Network Security; Engineering Management; Leadership and Ethical Decision Making; Managing Applied Research in Technology; Managing Innovation; Performance Excellence in Technology Management; Power Electronics; Project Management; Quality Systems for Product and Process Engineering; Research and Development; Software Engineering; Wireless Network and Technologies

ME Aerospace Engineering; Computer Science; Electrical and Computer Engineering; Engineering Management; Telecommunications

MS Aerospace Engineering; Electrical and Computer Engineering; Telecommunications

COURSE SUBJECT AREAS OFFERED OUTSIDE OF DEGREE PROGRAMS

Graduate—aerospace, aeronautical and astronautical engineering; biomedical/medical engineering; civil engineering; computer engineering; computer science; computer systems networking and telecommunications; electrical and electronic engineering technologies; engineering/industrial management; environmental/environmental health engineering; mechanical engineering.

Non-credit—aerospace, aeronautical and astronautical engineering; biomedical/medical engineering; civil engineering; computer engineering; computer science; computer systems networking and telecommunications; electrical and electronic engineering technologies; engineering/industrial management; environmental/environmental health engineering; mechanical engineering.

UNIVERSITY OF COLORADO AT COLORADO SPRINGS
Colorado Springs, Colorado
http://www.uccs.edu/~online/

University of Colorado at Colorado Springs was founded in 1965. It is accredited by North Central Association of Colleges and Schools. It first offered distance learning courses in 1996. In fall 2007, there were 610 students enrolled in distance learning courses. Institutionally administered financial aid is available to distance learners.

Services Distance learners have accessibility to academic advising, campus computer network, e-mail services, library services.

Contact Dana Rocha, Director, Campus Wide Extended Studies, University of Colorado at Colorado Springs, 1420 Austin Bluffs Parkway, MH 308, ADM 10, Colorado Springs, CO 80933-7150. Telephone: 719-262-4662. E-mail: drocha@uccs.edu.

DEGREES AND AWARDS

MA Curriculum and Instruction–Educational Leadership; English as a Second Language Education program; Online Principal Licensure program and Masters Degree in Curriculum and Instruction

MBA Business Administration

ME Engineering Management; Space Studies; Systems Engineering

MSN Nurse Practitioner and Clinical Specialist

COURSE SUBJECT AREAS OFFERED OUTSIDE OF DEGREE PROGRAMS

Undergraduate—American literature (United States and Canadian); area, ethnic, cultural, and gender studies related; biological and biomedical sciences related; chemistry; communication and media; economics; English composition; geography and cartography; gerontology; health professions related; history; languages (Middle/Near Eastern and Semitic); mathematics; mechanical engineering; military studies; nursing; psychology; sociology.

Graduate—aerospace, aeronautical and astronautical engineering; business/commerce; criminal justice and corrections; educational administration and supervision; health professions related; mechanical engineering; nursing; public administration.

UNIVERSITY OF COLORADO DENVER
Denver, Colorado
CU Online
http://cuonline.edu/petersons

University of Colorado Denver was founded in 1912. It is accredited by North Central Association of Colleges and Schools. It first offered distance learning courses in 1996. In fall 2007, there were 4,612 students enrolled in distance learning courses. Institutionally administered financial aid is available to distance learners.

Services Distance learners have accessibility to academic advising, bookstore, career placement assistance, e-mail services, library services, tutoring.

Contact Naomi Wahls, Learning Management Resource Support Coordinator, University of Colorado Denver, Campus Box 198, PO Box 173364, Denver, CO 80217-3364. Telephone: 303-315-3700. Fax: 303-315-3711. E-mail: help@cuonline.edu.

DEGREES AND AWARDS

BA English–Writing; Sociology

Certificate Designing and Implementing Web-based Learning Environments; Early Literacy; Professional Writing

License Early Childhood Special Education, Specialist; Special Education Generalist

MA Early Childhood Education; Information and Learning Technologies, School Library; eLearning Design and Implementation

MBA Business Administration

MEngr Geographic Information Systems (GIS)

MPA Public Administration

MS Information Systems; Management and Organization

COURSE SUBJECT AREAS OFFERED OUTSIDE OF DEGREE PROGRAMS

Undergraduate—accounting and related services; American literature (United States and Canadian); anthropology; biochemistry, biophysics and molecular biology; biology; cell biology and anatomical sciences; civil engineering; communication and media; computer programming; creative writing; dramatic/theater arts and stagecraft; economics; electrical, electronics and communications engineering; engineering; engineering science; English; English composition; ethnic, cultural minority, and gender studies; fine and studio art; geography and cartography; geological and earth sciences/geosciences; history; industrial and organizational psychology; languages (classics and classical); liberal arts and sciences, general studies and humanities; linguistic, comparative, and related language studies; mathematics and statistics related; mechanical engineering; music; philosophy and religious studies related; physics; political science and government; psychology; social psychology; sociology; statistics; technical and business writing.

Graduate—accounting and related services; architecture; business administration, management and operations; business/commerce; business/corporate communications; business, management, and marketing related; business/managerial economics; education; education related; electrical, electronics and communications engineering; engineering; engineering design; engineering/industrial management; engineering related; engineering technologies related; history; management information systems; management sciences and quantitative methods; marketing; political science and government; public administration; public administration and social service professions related; public policy analysis; sales, merchandising, and related marketing operations (general); sales, merchandising, and related marketing operations (specialized).

See full description on page 488.

UNIVERSITY OF CONNECTICUT
Storrs, Connecticut
Center for Continuing Studies
http://continuingstudies.uconn.edu/onlinecourses
University of Connecticut was founded in 1881. It is accredited by New England Association of Schools and Colleges. It first offered distance learning courses in 2001. In fall 2007, there were 500 students enrolled in distance learning courses. Institutionally administered financial aid is available to distance learners.
Services Distance learners have accessibility to academic advising, bookstore, campus computer network, career placement assistance, e-mail services, library services, tutoring.
Contact Dr. Judy Buffolino, Director of Distance Education, University of Connecticut, Center for Continuing Studies, Distance Education Office, One Bishop Circle, Unit 4056, Storrs, CT 06269-4056. Telephone: 860-486-1080. Fax: 860-486-0756. E-mail: judy.buffolino@uconn.edu.

DEGREES AND AWARDS
BGS Law and Society; Occupational Safety and Health focus; Web Technology focus
MPS Homeland Security Leadership; Human Resource Management; Humanitarian Services Administration

COURSE SUBJECT AREAS OFFERED OUTSIDE OF DEGREE PROGRAMS
Undergraduate—area, ethnic, cultural, and gender studies related; behavioral sciences; computer and information sciences and support services related; computer/information technology administration and management; computer programming; computer software and media applications; criminal justice and corrections; ethnic, cultural minority, and gender studies; health professions related; health services/allied health/health sciences; liberal arts and sciences, general studies and humanities; multi-/interdisciplinary studies related; sociology.
Graduate—criminology; health professions related; human resources management; human services; security and protective services related.
Non-credit—health professions related.

See full description on page 490.

UNIVERSITY OF DALLAS
Irving, Texas
Center for Distance Education
http://www.thedallasmba.com
University of Dallas was founded in 1955. It is accredited by American Academy for Liberal Education. It first offered distance learning courses in 1970. In fall 2007, there were 800 students enrolled in distance learning courses. Institutionally administered financial aid is available to distance learners.
Services Distance learners have accessibility to academic advising, bookstore, career placement assistance, library services, tutoring.
Contact Ms. Alounda Joseph, Director of Enrollment Processes, University of Dallas, 1845 East Northgate Drive, Irving, TX 75062-4736. Telephone: 800-832-5622. Fax: 972-721-5356. E-mail: ajoseph@gsm.udallas.edu.

DEGREES AND AWARDS
Graduate Certificate Health Services Management; Information Assurance; Information Technology; Marketing Management; Project Management; Sports and Entertainment Management; Supply Chain Management/Market Logistics
MBA Accounting; Corporate Finance; Global Business; Health Services Management; Information Assurance; Information Technology; Interdisciplinary (custom curriculum); Marketing Management; Not-for-Profit; Project Management; Sports and Entertainment Management; Supply Chain Management/Market Logistics
MM Information Assurance; Information Technology; Marketing Management; Project Management

COURSE SUBJECT AREAS OFFERED OUTSIDE OF DEGREE PROGRAMS
Graduate—accounting and related services; business administration, management and operations; computer and information sciences; computer and information sciences and support services related; computer systems analysis; computer systems networking and telecommunications; finance and financial management services; health and medical administrative services; international business; management information systems; marketing; sales, merchandising, and related marketing operations (general); sales, merchandising, and related marketing operations (specialized).

See full description on page 492.

UNIVERSITY OF DENVER
Denver, Colorado
University College
http://www.universitycollege.du.edu
University of Denver was founded in 1864. It is accredited by North Central Association of Colleges and Schools. It first offered distance learning courses in 1996. In fall 2007, there were 400 students enrolled in distance learning courses. Institutionally administered financial aid is available to distance learners.
Services Distance learners have accessibility to academic advising, bookstore, campus computer network, career placement assistance, e-mail services, library services.
Contact Mr. Mark Guthrie, Director of Enrollment and Advising, University of Denver, 2211 South Josephine, Denver, CO 80208. Telephone: 303-871-7582. Fax: 303-871-3070. E-mail: maguthri@du.edu.

DEGREES AND AWARDS
BA Bachelor of Arts completion program
Certificate Alternative Dispute Resolution–Certificate of Advanced Study; Arts and Literature–Certificate of Advanced Study; Broadband–Certificate of Advanced Study; Computer Information Systems–Certificate of Advanced Study; Database Administration–Certificate of Advanced Study; Distributed Object-Oriented Analysis and Design–Certificate of Advanced Study; Environmental Information Management–Certificate of Advanced Study; Environmental Management–Certificate of Advanced Study; Environmental Policy–Certificate of Advanced Study; Environmental Project Management–Certificate of Advanced Study; Environmental, Health, and Safety Management–Certificate of Advanced Study; Geographic Information Systems–Certificate of Advanced Study; Human Resource Administration–Certificate of Advanced Study; Information Security–Certificate of Advanced Study; Information Systems Security–Certificate of Advanced Study; Leadership–Certificate of Advanced Study; Modern Languages–Certificate of Advanced Study; Natural Resource Management–Certificate of Advanced Study; Organizational Security–Certificate of Advanced Study; Project Management–Certificate of Advanced Study; Public Relations and Marketing Communications–Certificate of Advanced Study; Technology Management–Certificate of Advanced Study; Telecommunications Management and Policy–Certificate of Advanced Study; Telecommunications Networks–Certificate of Advanced Study; Telecommunications Technology–Certificate of Advanced Study; Training and Development–Certificate of Advanced Study; Web Design and Development Technologies–Certificate of Advanced Study
MLS Liberal Studies–Master of Liberal Studies
MPS Applied Communication–Master of Professional Studies in Applied Communication; Human Resource Administration–Master of Professional Studies in Human Resource Administration; Organizational Leadership–Master of Professional Studies in Organizational Leadership
MS Computer Information Systems–Master of Applied Science in Computer Information Systems; Environmental Policy and Management–Master of Applied Science in Environmental Policy and Management; Knowledge and Information Technologies–Master of Applied Science in Knowledge and Information Technologies; Security Management–

Master of Applied Science in Security Management; Technology Management–Master of Applied Science in Technology Management; Telecommunications–Master of Applied Science in Telecommunications

COURSE SUBJECT AREAS OFFERED OUTSIDE OF DEGREE PROGRAMS

Undergraduate—business/corporate communications; public policy analysis; science, technology and society; social sciences related.
Graduate—business administration, management and operations; communication and media; computer and information sciences; computer and information sciences and support services related; computer/information technology administration and management; computer systems networking and telecommunications; creative writing; liberal arts and sciences, general studies and humanities; linguistic, comparative, and related language studies; natural resources management and policy.

See full description on page 494.

UNIVERSITY OF DUBUQUE
Dubuque, Iowa
Theological Seminary
http://udts.dbq.edu/distance/index.htm
University of Dubuque was founded in 1852. It is accredited by North Central Association of Colleges and Schools. It first offered distance learning courses in 2000. In fall 2007, there were 150 students enrolled in distance learning courses. Institutionally administered financial aid is available to distance learners.
Services Distance learners have accessibility to academic advising, bookstore, campus computer network, career placement assistance, e-mail services, library services.
Contact Ms. Margaret (Peggy) Sell, Director of Seminary Admissions, University of Dubuque, 2000 University Avenue, Dubuque, IA 52001. Telephone: 800-369-8987. Fax: 563-589-3110. E-mail: psell@dbq.edu.

DEGREES AND AWARDS
Certificate Commissioned Lay Pastor
MDiv Distance M.Div.; Unclassified Student Status

COURSE SUBJECT AREAS OFFERED OUTSIDE OF DEGREE PROGRAMS
Graduate—theological and ministerial studies.

UNIVERSITY OF DUBUQUE
Dubuque, Iowa
http://www.dbq.edu/
University of Dubuque was founded in 1852. It is accredited by North Central Association of Colleges and Schools. It first offered distance learning courses in 2007. In fall 2007, there were 43 students enrolled in distance learning courses. Institutionally administered financial aid is available to distance learners.
Services Distance learners have accessibility to academic advising, bookstore, campus computer network, career placement assistance, e-mail services, library services, tutoring.
Contact Dean Gail Hodge, Associate Dean for Professional Programs, University of Dubuque, 2000 University Avenue, Dubuque, IA 52001. Telephone: 563-589-3349. Fax: 563-589-3416. E-mail: ghodge@dbq.edu.

DEGREES AND AWARDS
Programs offered do not lead to a degree or other formal award.

COURSE SUBJECT AREAS OFFERED OUTSIDE OF DEGREE PROGRAMS
Undergraduate—biology; business, management, and marketing related; communication and media; computer and information sciences; education; English language and literature related; environmental psychology; nutrition sciences; religious studies; sociology.

THE UNIVERSITY OF FINDLAY
Findlay, Ohio
Global Campus
http://www.findlay.edu
The University of Findlay was founded in 1882. It is accredited by North Central Association of Colleges and Schools. It first offered distance learning courses in 1998. In fall 2007, there were 661 students enrolled in distance learning courses. Institutionally administered financial aid is available to distance learners.
Services Distance learners have accessibility to academic advising, bookstore, campus computer network, career placement assistance, e-mail services, library services, tutoring.
Contact Mrs. Heather L. Riffle, Assistant to the Dean, Graduate and Professional Studies, The University of Findlay, 1000 North Main Street, Findlay, OH 45840. Telephone: 419-434-4600. Fax: 419-434-5517. E-mail: riffle@findlay.edu.

DEGREES AND AWARDS
BS Business Management; Criminal Justice Administration; Environmental, Safety, and Health Management
MAE Education–Human Resource Development Strand
MBA Business Administration
MS Environmental, Safety, and Health Management

COURSE SUBJECT AREAS OFFERED OUTSIDE OF DEGREE PROGRAMS
Undergraduate—accounting and related services; biblical studies; business administration, management and operations; business/commerce; business/managerial economics; chemistry; communication and journalism related; computer science; criminal justice and corrections; criminology; economics; ethnic, cultural minority, and gender studies; fine and studio art; history; human resources management; international business; marketing; mathematics; philosophy and religious studies related; religious studies; social sciences; sociology; statistics; visual and performing arts.
Graduate—accounting and related services; business administration, management and operations; business/corporate communications; business/managerial economics; educational assessment, evaluation, and research; educational/instructional media design; environmental control technologies; human resources management; marketing; public administration; sales, merchandising, and related marketing operations (general).
Non-credit—business, management, and marketing related; business/managerial economics; management information systems; management sciences and quantitative methods.

UNIVERSITY OF FLORIDA
Gainesville, Florida
UF EDGE
http://ufedge.eng.ufl.edu
University of Florida was founded in 1853. It is accredited by Southern Association of Colleges and Schools. It first offered distance learning courses in 1964. In fall 2007, there were 300 students enrolled in distance learning courses. Institutionally administered financial aid is available to distance learners.
Services Distance learners have accessibility to academic advising, bookstore, campus computer network, career placement assistance, e-mail services, library services, tutoring.
Contact Ruth Bryant, Program Assistant, University of Florida, College of Engineering, E-117 CSE, PO Box 116100, Gainesville, FL 32611-6100. Telephone: 352-392-9670. Fax: 352-846-2255. E-mail: rbrya@eng.ufl.edu.

DEGREES AND AWARDS
MS Civil Engineering; Computer Engineering (Bioinformatics track); Computer Engineering (General track); Electrical and Computer Engineering; Environmental Engineering (Systems Ecology and Ecological Engineering track); Environmental Engineering (Water Resources Planning and Management track); Environmental Engineering (Water, Wastewater, and Stormwater Engineering track); Materials Science and Engineering; Mechanical and Aerospace Engineering (Dynamics and Control track);

Mechanical and Aerospace Engineering (Fundamentals of Thermal Fluids Transport track); Mechanical and Aerospace Engineering (Solid Mechanics and Design track); Systems Engineering

COURSE SUBJECT AREAS OFFERED OUTSIDE OF DEGREE PROGRAMS

Graduate—civil engineering; computer engineering; engineering; environmental/ environmental health engineering; industrial engineering; materials science; mechanical engineering; systems engineering.

Non-credit—aerospace, aeronautical and astronautical engineering; civil engineering; computer engineering; engineering; environmental/ environmental health engineering; industrial engineering; materials engineering; materials science; mechanical engineering; systems engineering.

See full description on page 496.

UNIVERSITY OF HAWAII–WEST OAHU
Pearl City, Hawaii
http://www.uhwo.hawaii.edu/dl

University of Hawaii–West Oahu was founded in 1976. It is accredited by Western Association of Schools and Colleges. It first offered distance learning courses in 1981. In fall 2007, there were 200 students enrolled in distance learning courses. Institutionally administered financial aid is available to distance learners.

Services Distance learners have accessibility to academic advising, bookstore, campus computer network, career placement assistance, e-mail services, library services, tutoring.

Contact LeeAnne Santos, Academic Advisor, Distance Learning, University of Hawaii–West Oahu, Student Services Office, 96-129 Ala Ike, Pearl City, HI 96782. Telephone: 808-454-4700. Fax: 808-453-6075. E-mail: leeanne@hawaii.edu.

DEGREES AND AWARDS

BA Business Administration–General Business Administration and Accounting; Public Administration: Health Care Administration; Social Sciences: Applied Track; Social Sciences: Early Childhood Edu, Political Sci

Certificate Disaster Preparedness and Emergency Management; Health Care Administration; Substance Abuse and Addictions Studies

COURSE SUBJECT AREAS OFFERED OUTSIDE OF DEGREE PROGRAMS

Undergraduate—accounting and related services; anthropology; business administration, management and operations; business, management, and marketing related; clinical psychology; counseling psychology; criminal justice and corrections; criminology; developmental and child psychology; economics; history; human resources management; philosophy; political science and government; psychology; psychology related; public administration; public administration and social service professions related; social sciences; social sciences related; sociology; statistics.

UNIVERSITY OF HOUSTON–DOWNTOWN
Houston, Texas
http://www.uhd.edu/academic/distance.htm

University of Houston–Downtown was founded in 1974. It is accredited by Southern Association of Colleges and Schools. It first offered distance learning courses in 1994. In fall 2007, there were 1,756 students enrolled in distance learning courses. Institutionally administered financial aid is available to distance learners.

Services Distance learners have accessibility to academic advising, bookstore, campus computer network, career placement assistance, e-mail services, library services.

Contact Dr. Gail S.M. Evans, Assistant Vice President, Academic Affairs–Distance Education, University of Houston–Downtown, One Main Street, 950S, Houston, TX 77002. Telephone: 713-221-8003. Fax: 713-221-8922. E-mail: evansg@uhd.edu.

DEGREES AND AWARDS
Programs offered do not lead to a degree or other formal award.

COURSE SUBJECT AREAS OFFERED OUTSIDE OF DEGREE PROGRAMS

Undergraduate—accounting and related services; business administration, management and operations; business, management, and marketing related; communication and media; computer/information technology administration and management; criminal justice and corrections; education; English; finance and financial management services; marketing; philosophy; political science and government; psychology; social sciences; statistics.

UNIVERSITY OF HOUSTON–VICTORIA
Victoria, Texas
School of Business Administration
http://www.uhv.edu/

University of Houston–Victoria was founded in 1973. It is accredited by Southern Association of Colleges and Schools. It first offered distance learning courses in 1996. In fall 2007, there were 2,000 students enrolled in distance learning courses. Institutionally administered financial aid is available to distance learners.

Services Distance learners have accessibility to academic advising, bookstore, campus computer network, career placement assistance, e-mail services, library services, tutoring.

Contact Ms. Chari Norgard, Senior Director, Student and Academic Services, University of Houston–Victoria, 3007 North Ben Wilson, Victoria, TX 77901-4450. Telephone: 361-570-4290. Fax: 361-570-4314. E-mail: norgardc@uhv.edu.

DEGREES AND AWARDS
BA History
BBA Business, general; Management; Marketing
BS Criminal Justice; Psychology
MBA Business Administration; Global MBA
MEd Special Education
MS Computer Information System; Economic Development and Entrepreneurship

COURSE SUBJECT AREAS OFFERED OUTSIDE OF DEGREE PROGRAMS

Undergraduate—accounting and related services; biology; communication and journalism related; computer and information sciences; education; English composition; history; nursing; psychology.

Graduate—accounting and related services; computer and information sciences; education; entrepreneurial and small business operations; psychology.

See full description on page 498.

UNIVERSITY OF IDAHO
Moscow, Idaho
Engineering Outreach
http://www.outreach.uidaho.edu/eo/

University of Idaho was founded in 1889. It is accredited by Northwest Commission on Colleges and Universities. It first offered distance learning courses in 1976. In fall 2007, there were 391 students enrolled in distance learning courses. Institutionally administered financial aid is available to distance learners.

Services Distance learners have accessibility to academic advising, bookstore, campus computer network, e-mail services, library services.

Contact Ms. Diane Bancke, Administrative Manager, University of Idaho, Engineering Outreach, PO Box 441014, Moscow, ID 83844-1014. Telephone: 800-824-2889. Fax: 208-885-9249. E-mail: outreach@uidaho.edu.

DEGREES AND AWARDS

Certificate Applied Geotechnics; Communication Systems; Electric Machines and Drives; Heating, Ventilation, and Air Conditioning (HVAC) Systems; Material Design, advanced; Power System Protection and Relaying; Secure and Dependable Computing Systems; Structural Engineering; Water Resources Engineering
MAT Teaching Mathematics

MEngr Biological and Agricultural Engineering (Water Management emphasis); Civil Engineering; Computer Engineering; Electrical Engineering; Mechanical Engineering
MS Biological and Agricultural Engineering (Water Management emphasis); Computer Engineering; Computer Science; Electrical Engineering; Geological Engineering

COURSE SUBJECT AREAS OFFERED OUTSIDE OF DEGREE PROGRAMS

Undergraduate—agricultural/biological engineering and bioengineering; biology; chemical engineering; civil engineering; computer engineering; computer programming; computer science; geography and cartography; mathematics and statistics related; mechanical engineering; psychology; statistics.
Graduate—accounting and computer science; agricultural/biological engineering and bioengineering; applied mathematics; business administration, management and operations; business, management, and marketing related; chemical engineering; civil engineering; computer engineering; computer science; electrical and electronic engineering technologies; engineering; engineering technology; environmental/environmental health engineering; geological/geophysical engineering; materials engineering; mathematics; mathematics and computer science; mathematics and statistics related; mechanical engineering; mechanical engineering related technologies; psychology; psychology related; statistics.

UNIVERSITY OF IDAHO
Moscow, Idaho
Independent Study in Idaho
http://www.uidaho.edu/isi

University of Idaho was founded in 1889. It is accredited by Northwest Commission on Colleges and Universities. It first offered distance learning courses in 1973. In fall 2007, there were 538 students enrolled in distance learning courses. Institutionally administered financial aid is available to distance learners.
Services Distance learners have accessibility to bookstore, library services.
Contact Jeanne Workman, Registration Coordinator, University of Idaho, Independent Study in Idaho, PO Box 443225, Moscow, ID 83844-3225. Telephone: 877-464-3246. Fax: 208-885-5738. E-mail: indepst@uidaho.edu.

DEGREES AND AWARDS
Programs offered do not lead to a degree or other formal award.

COURSE SUBJECT AREAS OFFERED OUTSIDE OF DEGREE PROGRAMS

Undergraduate—accounting and related services; agricultural business and management; anthropology; biology; business/commerce; criminal justice and corrections; dental support services and allied professions; economics; education related; English; English composition; environmental/environmental health engineering; family and consumer economics; finance and financial management services; health and medical administrative services; health and physical education/fitness; history; human development, family studies, and related services; journalism; library science; library science related; linguistic, comparative, and related language studies; mathematics; microbiological sciences and immunology; museum studies; music; philosophy; physics; political science and government; psychology; real estate; social sciences; social sciences related; sociology; special education.
Graduate—library science; library science related.

UNIVERSITY OF ILLINOIS AT CHICAGO
Chicago, Illinois
Office of External Education
http://www.uic.edu/depts/uionline/

University of Illinois at Chicago was founded in 1946. It is accredited by North Central Association of Colleges and Schools. It first offered distance learning courses in 1998. In fall 2007, there were 5,518 students enrolled in distance learning courses. Institutionally administered financial aid is available to distance learners.
Services Distance learners have accessibility to academic advising, bookstore, campus computer network, e-mail services, library services.

Contact UIC Online Programs, University of Illinois at Chicago, External Education, MC 140, 1333 South Halsted Street, Suite 205, Chicago, IL 60607. Telephone: 312-355-0423. Fax: 312-413-9730. E-mail: online@uic.edu.

DEGREES AND AWARDS
BSN Nursing–BSN Completion Program for RNs
Certificate Advanced Community Public Health Practice; Advanced Nursing Leadership; Advanced Practice Forensic Nurse; Advanced Practice Palliative Care; Basic Community Public Health Practice; Bioinformatics; Electromagnetics Technology Campus Certificate; Emergency Preparedness and Continuity Planning; Engineering Law and Management Campus Certificate; Environmental Health Informatics Campus Certificate; Health Informatics; Nursing–School Nurse; Public Health Informatics; Teaching/Learning in Nursing and Health Sciences; Wireless Communication Technology Campus Certificate
MEngr Engineering
MHPE Health Professions Education
MPH Public Health Informatics
MS Health Informatics

COURSE SUBJECT AREAS OFFERED OUTSIDE OF DEGREE PROGRAMS

Graduate—accounting and related services; business administration, management and operations; business/commerce; business, management, and marketing related; business/managerial economics; chemical engineering; economics; education (specific subject areas); electrical and electronic engineering technologies; electrical, electronics and communications engineering; engineering; engineering related; engineering technology; finance and financial management services; health professions related; health services/allied health/health sciences; information science/studies; marketing; medical illustration and informatics; nursing; pharmacy, pharmaceutical sciences, and administration; public health; social work; statistics.
Non-credit—allied health and medical assisting services; business administration, management and operations; business/commerce; business/corporate communications; business, management, and marketing related; English as a second language; health professions related; marketing; medical clinical sciences/graduate medical studies; nursing; pharmacy, pharmaceutical sciences, and administration; public administration and social service professions related; public health; social work; technical and business writing.

UNIVERSITY OF ILLINOIS AT SPRINGFIELD
Springfield, Illinois
Office of Technology-Enhanced Learning
http://online.uis.edu

University of Illinois at Springfield was founded in 1969. It is accredited by North Central Association of Colleges and Schools. It first offered distance learning courses in 1984. In fall 2007, there were 2,353 students enrolled in distance learning courses. Institutionally administered financial aid is available to distance learners.
Services Distance learners have accessibility to academic advising, bookstore, campus computer network, career placement assistance, e-mail services, library services, tutoring.
Contact Dr. Ray Schroeder, Director of Office of Technology and Enhanced Learning, University of Illinois at Springfield, OTEL, Brookens, Room 426, One University Plaza, MS BRK 425, Springfield, IL 62703-5407. Telephone: 217-206-7531. Fax: 217-206-7539. E-mail: schroeder.ray@uis.edu.

DEGREES AND AWARDS
BA Economics; English; History; Liberal Studies; Mathematical Sciences; Philosophy
BBA Business Administration
BS Computer Science
MA Environmental Studies–Natural Resources and Sustainable Development concentration; Legal Studies; Teacher Leadership
MPA Public Administration
MPH Public Health

MS Computer Science; Human Services–Social Services Administration concentration; Management Information Systems

COURSE SUBJECT AREAS OFFERED OUTSIDE OF DEGREE PROGRAMS

Undergraduate—accounting and related services; business administration, management and operations; business, management, and marketing related; chemistry; communication and journalism related; communication and media; computer science; criminal justice and corrections; economics; education related; English; fine and studio art; history; languages (foreign languages related); liberal arts and sciences, general studies and humanities; mathematics; multi-/interdisciplinary studies related; philosophy; political science and government; psychology; social work; sociology; visual and performing arts.

Graduate—business administration, management and operations; communication and media; computer science; education related; environmental/ environmental health engineering; human services; legal professions and studies related; management information systems; political science and government; public administration; public health.

UNIVERSITY OF ILLINOIS AT URBANA–CHAMPAIGN
Champaign, Illinois
Academic Outreach
http://www.outreach.uiuc.edu

University of Illinois at Urbana–Champaign was founded in 1867. It is accredited by North Central Association of Colleges and Schools. It first offered distance learning courses in 1995. In fall 2007, there were 5,324 students enrolled in distance learning courses. Institutionally administered financial aid is available to distance learners.

Services Distance learners have accessibility to academic advising, bookstore, campus computer network, career placement assistance, e-mail services, library services, tutoring.

Contact Arathi Kylasam, Marketing Coordinator, University of Illinois at Urbana–Champaign, 302 East John Street, Suite 1702, MC 433, Champaign, IL 61820. Telephone: 217-244-7882. Fax: 217-265-8226. E-mail: outreachinfo@uiuc.edu.

DEGREES AND AWARDS

Certificate Crop Sciences; Dairy Science; Horticulture
Certification Library and Information Science K-12
Endorsement Middle Grades
CAGS Library and Information Science
Graduate Certificate Business Management for Engineers; Community College Teaching and Learning; Computer Science/Computer Security; Computer Science/Information Systems; Computer Science/Networks and Distributed Systems; Computer Science/Software Engineering; Computer Science/System Software; Environmental and Water Resources Engineering; French Translation; Mechanical Engineering/Materials Failure Analysis; Mechanical Engineering/Materials; Strategic Technology Management; Systems Engineering
MCS Computer Science
MEd Community College Teaching and Learning (Ed.M); Curriculum, Technology, and Education Reform; Diversity and Equity Issues in Education emphasis; Educational Leadership and Policy emphasis; Global Human Resource Development; Global Studies in Education; Health Profession Education emphasis; New Learning and New Literacies emphasis
MLIS LEEP–Library and Information Science
MS Agricultural Education; Crop Sciences; Natural Resources and Environmental Sciences
MSME Mechanical Engineering

COURSE SUBJECT AREAS OFFERED OUTSIDE OF DEGREE PROGRAMS

Undergraduate—anthropology; area, ethnic, cultural, and gender studies related; business administration, management and operations; classical and ancient studies; computer and information sciences; design and applied arts; educational psychology; English; English composition; ethnic, cultural minority, and gender studies; fine and studio art; history;

human development, family studies, and related services; languages (foreign languages related); languages (Germanic); languages (Romance languages); liberal arts and sciences, general studies and humanities; mathematics; mathematics and statistics related; philosophy; philosophy and religious studies related; political science and government; psychology; sociology.

Graduate—agriculture; business administration, management and operations; clinical/medical laboratory science and allied professions; computer and information sciences; computer/information technology administration and management; computer science; computer systems networking and telecommunications; curriculum and instruction; education; education (specific subject areas); engineering; health professions related; human resources management; international business; library science; materials engineering; mathematics; mechanical engineering; nursing; pharmacy, pharmaceutical sciences, and administration; public administration.

Non-credit—architecture; architecture related; business/commerce; computer and information sciences; computer engineering technologies; computer programming; computer software and media applications; construction trades related; creative writing; English; English composition; environmental design; fine and studio art; fire protection; information science/studies; landscape architecture; marketing; public administration; public health; technical and business writing.

UNIVERSITY OF ILLINOIS AT URBANA–CHAMPAIGN
Champaign, Illinois
College of Engineering
http://online.engr.uiuc.edu

University of Illinois at Urbana–Champaign was founded in 1867. It is accredited by North Central Association of Colleges and Schools. It first offered distance learning courses in 1998. In fall 2007, there were 240 students enrolled in distance learning courses. Institutionally administered financial aid is available to distance learners.

Services Distance learners have accessibility to academic advising, bookstore, campus computer network, career placement assistance, e-mail services, library services.

Contact Mrs. Laura A. Miller, Director of Engineering Online Programs, University of Illinois at Urbana–Champaign, Office of Continuing Engineering Education, 400 Engineering Hall, MC-268, 1308 West Green Street, Urbana, IL 61801. Telephone: 217-333-6634. Fax: 217-333-0015. E-mail: ocee@uiuc.edu.

DEGREES AND AWARDS

CAGS Business Management for Engineers

Graduate Certificate Computer Security; Environmental and Water Resources Engineering; Information Systems; Materials Engineering; Materials Failure Analysis; Networks and Distributed Systems; Software Engineering; Strategic Technology Management; System Software; Systems Engineering

MCS Computer Science–Master of Computer Science

MSME Mechanical Engineering

COURSE SUBJECT AREAS OFFERED OUTSIDE OF DEGREE PROGRAMS

Undergraduate—management sciences and quantitative methods.

Graduate—civil engineering; computer science; computer systems analysis; computer systems networking and telecommunications; data processing; engineering; entrepreneurial and small business operations; genetics; management sciences and quantitative methods; materials engineering; materials science; mathematics; mechanical engineering; systems engineering.

Non-credit—computer science; engineering; genetics; management sciences and quantitative methods; mechanical engineering.

UNIVERSITY OF ILLINOIS AT URBANA–CHAMPAIGN
Champaign, Illinois
Curriculum, Technology, and Education Reform Program
http://www.cter.ed.uiuc.edu/

University of Illinois at Urbana–Champaign was founded in 1867. It is accredited by North Central Association of Colleges and Schools. It first offered distance learning courses in 1999. In fall 2007, there were 34 students enrolled in distance learning courses. Institutionally administered financial aid is available to distance learners.

Services Distance learners have accessibility to academic advising, campus computer network, e-mail services, tutoring.

Contact Ms. Helen Katz, Office Support Specialist, University of Illinois at Urbana–Champaign, Educational Psychology, 225 Education Building, 1310 South 6th Street, Champaign, IL 61820. Telephone: 217-333-5242. Fax: 217-244-7620. E-mail: hnkatz@uiuc.edu.

DEGREES AND AWARDS

MEd Curriculum, Technology, and Education Reform (CTER)

UNIVERSITY OF ILLINOIS AT URBANA–CHAMPAIGN
Champaign, Illinois
Graduate School of Library and Information Science
http://www.lis.uiuc.edu/

University of Illinois at Urbana–Champaign was founded in 1867. It is accredited by North Central Association of Colleges and Schools. It first offered distance learning courses in 1996. In fall 2007, there were 350 students enrolled in distance learning courses. Institutionally administered financial aid is available to distance learners.

Services Distance learners have accessibility to academic advising, bookstore, campus computer network, career placement assistance, e-mail services, library services, tutoring.

Contact Penny Ames, GSLIS Admissions, University of Illinois at Urbana–Champaign, 501 East Daniel Street, Champaign, IL 61820. Telephone: 800-982-0914. Fax: 217-244-3302. E-mail: lis-apply@uiuc.edu.

DEGREES AND AWARDS

CAGS Library and Information Science
MS Library and Information Science

COURSE SUBJECT AREAS OFFERED OUTSIDE OF DEGREE PROGRAMS

Graduate—communications technology; computer and information sciences; computer/information technology administration and management; computer software and media applications; educational/instructional media design; library science; science, technology and society.

Non-credit—computer and information sciences; library science; science, technology and society.

THE UNIVERSITY OF KANSAS
Lawrence, Kansas
http://www.ContinuingEd.ku.edu/is

The University of Kansas was founded in 1866. It is accredited by North Central Association of Colleges and Schools. In fall 2007, there were 2,000 students enrolled in distance learning courses. Institutionally administered financial aid is available to distance learners.

Services Distance learners have accessibility to bookstore.

Contact Enrollment Coordinator, The University of Kansas, KUCE Independent Study, 1515 St. Andrews Drive, Lawrence, KS 66047. Telephone: 785-864-7886. Fax: 785-864-7895. E-mail: enroll@ku.edu.

DEGREES AND AWARDS

Programs offered do not lead to a degree or other formal award.

COURSE SUBJECT AREAS OFFERED OUTSIDE OF DEGREE PROGRAMS

Undergraduate—anthropology; area, ethnic, cultural, and gender studies related; atmospheric sciences and meteorology; biology; classical and ancient studies; cognitive psychology and psycholinguistics; creative writing; curriculum and instruction; developmental and child psychology; economics; English; English composition; English literature (British and Commonwealth); ethnic, cultural minority, and gender studies; geography and cartography; geological and earth sciences/geosciences; history; human development, family studies, and related services; liberal arts and sciences, general studies and humanities; mathematics; philosophy; political science and government; psychology; public administration and social service professions related; religious studies; social psychology; sociology; statistics.

Graduate—behavioral sciences; curriculum and instruction; educational administration and supervision; English literature (British and Commonwealth); history; psychology; special education.

UNIVERSITY OF LA VERNE
La Verne, California
Distance Learning Center
http://www.ulv.edu/ulvonline/

University of La Verne was founded in 1891. It is accredited by Western Association of Schools and Colleges. It first offered distance learning courses in 1996. In fall 2007, there were 2,400 students enrolled in distance learning courses. Institutionally administered financial aid is available to distance learners.

Services Distance learners have accessibility to academic advising, bookstore, campus computer network, career placement assistance, e-mail services, library services, tutoring.

Contact Melissa Duran, Academic Advisor, University of La Verne, 1950 Third Street, La Verne, CA 91750. Telephone: 800-468-4858. Fax: 909-971-2294. E-mail: degreeinfo@ulv.edu.

DEGREES AND AWARDS

BS Organizational Management; Public Administration
MBA Business Administration

COURSE SUBJECT AREAS OFFERED OUTSIDE OF DEGREE PROGRAMS

Non-credit—astronomy and astrophysics; education; educational psychology; education related; English; English as a second language; English composition; English language and literature related; English literature (British and Commonwealth); ethnic, cultural minority, and gender studies; geological and earth sciences/geosciences; history; special education.

UNIVERSITY OF LETHBRIDGE
Lethbridge, Alberta, Canada
http://www.uleth.ca/

University of Lethbridge was founded in 1967. It is provincially chartered. It first offered distance learning courses in 2001. In fall 2007, there were 134 students enrolled in distance learning courses. Institutionally administered financial aid is available to distance learners.

Services Distance learners have accessibility to academic advising, bookstore, campus computer network, career placement assistance, e-mail services, library services, tutoring.

Contact Inquiries, University of Lethbridge, 4401 University Drive, Lethbridge, AB T1K 3M4, Canada. Telephone: 403-329-2233. E-mail: inquiries@uleth.ca.

DEGREES AND AWARDS

Programs offered do not lead to a degree or other formal award.

COURSE SUBJECT AREAS OFFERED OUTSIDE OF DEGREE PROGRAMS

Undergraduate—computer software and media applications; education related.
Graduate—education; educational assessment, evaluation, and research; education related.

UNIVERSITY OF LOUISVILLE
Louisville, Kentucky
Division of Distance and Continuing Education
http://www.delphi.louisville.edu
University of Louisville was founded in 1798. It is accredited by Southern Association of Colleges and Schools. It first offered distance learning courses in 1992. In fall 2007, there were 1,600 students enrolled in distance learning courses. Institutionally administered financial aid is available to distance learners.
Services Distance learners have accessibility to academic advising, bookstore, campus computer network, career placement assistance, e-mail services, library services, tutoring.
Contact Shelly Reid, Program Coordinator, University of Louisville, Delphi Center for Teaching and Learning, Burhans Hall, Shelby Campus, Louisville, KY 40292. Telephone: 502-852-6456. Fax: 502-852-8573. E-mail: online@louisville.edu.

DEGREES AND AWARDS
BA Communication
BS Administration of Justice; Communication; Nursing–Accelerated RN to BSN; Workforce Leadership (formerly Occupational Training and Development)
Graduate Certificate Data Mining
MA Higher Education
MS Administration of Justice; Civil Engineering–Transportation Engineering specialization; Computer Science; Human Resource Education

COURSE SUBJECT AREAS OFFERED OUTSIDE OF DEGREE PROGRAMS
Undergraduate—anthropology; archeology; behavioral sciences; dramatic/theater arts and stagecraft; English; ethnic, cultural minority, and gender studies; geography and cartography; health and physical education/fitness; languages (classics and classical); philosophy; political science and government; psychology; sociology; statistics.
Graduate—bioethics/medical ethics; communication and media; education; educational psychology; nursing; social work; special education.
Non-credit—business, management, and marketing related; human resources management.

THE UNIVERSITY OF MAINE AT AUGUSTA
Augusta, Maine
University of Maine System Network for Education and Technology (UNET)
http://www.uma.maine.edu
The University of Maine at Augusta was founded in 1965. It is accredited by New England Association of Schools and Colleges. It first offered distance learning courses in 1986. In fall 2007, there were 3,000 students enrolled in distance learning courses. Institutionally administered financial aid is available to distance learners.
Services Distance learners have accessibility to academic advising, bookstore, campus computer network, e-mail services, library services, tutoring.
Contact Sheri Fraser, Director of Academic and Career Advising, The University of Maine at Augusta, 46 University Drive, Augusta, ME 04330. Telephone: 207-621-3390. Fax: 207-621-3171. E-mail: fraser@maine.edu.

DEGREES AND AWARDS
AA Liberal Studies; Social Services
AS Business Administration; Library and Information Services
BA Liberal Studies
BS Accounting; Applied Science–Bachelor of Applied Science; Library and Information Services; Management; Mental Health and Human Services

COURSE SUBJECT AREAS OFFERED OUTSIDE OF DEGREE PROGRAMS
Undergraduate—accounting and related services; American Sign Language (ASL); anthropology; applied mathematics; behavioral sciences; business administration, management and operations; business/commerce; business/corporate communications; business, management, and marketing related; business/managerial economics; business operations support and assistant services; communication and media; community health services; comparative literature; computer and information sciences; computer and information sciences and support services related; computer software and media applications; counseling psychology; creative writing; criminal justice and corrections; criminology; developmental and child psychology; economics; English; English composition; family and consumer sciences/human sciences; finance and financial management services; health professions related; history; human development, family studies, and related services; human resources management; human services; information science/studies; languages (Romance languages); liberal arts and sciences, general studies and humanities; library science; library science related; management sciences and quantitative methods; marketing; mathematics; mathematics and statistics related; mental and social health services and allied professions; music; nursing; nutrition sciences; philosophy; physical sciences; political science and government; psychology; social psychology; social sciences; social sciences related; sociology; statistics; taxation; technical and business writing.

UNIVERSITY OF MAINE AT FORT KENT
Fort Kent, Maine
http://www.umfk.maine.edu/distance/
University of Maine at Fort Kent was founded in 1878. It is accredited by New England Association of Schools and Colleges. It first offered distance learning courses in 1989. In fall 2007, there were 400 students enrolled in distance learning courses. Institutionally administered financial aid is available to distance learners.
Services Distance learners have accessibility to academic advising, bookstore, campus computer network, career placement assistance, e-mail services, library services, tutoring.
Contact Donald K. Eno, Academic Outreach Coordinator, University of Maine at Fort Kent, 23 University Drive, Fort Kent, ME 04743. Telephone: 207-834-7835. Fax: 207-834-8604. E-mail: deno@maine.edu.

DEGREES AND AWARDS
AA General Studies, Criminal Justice Sequence
BS Rural Public Safety Administration
BSN Nursing–RN to BSN
BUS University Studies

COURSE SUBJECT AREAS OFFERED OUTSIDE OF DEGREE PROGRAMS
Undergraduate—anthropology; astronomy and astrophysics; behavioral sciences; business/commerce; business, management, and marketing related; communication and media; creative writing; criminal justice and corrections; developmental and child psychology; economics; education related; education (specific levels and methods); English; geography and cartography; geological and earth sciences/geosciences; health professions related; history; liberal arts and sciences, general studies and humanities; music; nursing; philosophy; political science and government; psychology; public administration; public policy analysis; real estate; sociology; special education.
Non-credit—criminal justice and corrections.

UNIVERSITY OF MAINE AT MACHIAS
Machias, Maine
Distance Learning
http://www.umm.maine.edu/content/page.
php?cat=6&content_id=9
University of Maine at Machias was founded in 1909. It is accredited by New England Association of Schools and Colleges. It first offered distance learning courses in 1990. In fall 2007, there were 1,652 students enrolled in distance learning courses. Institutionally administered financial aid is available to distance learners.
Services Distance learners have accessibility to academic advising, bookstore, campus computer network, e-mail services, library services, tutoring.

Contact Linda Schofield, Instructional Technologist, University of Maine at Machias, Distance Education, Torrey Hall, 9 O'Brien Avenue, Machias, ME 04654. Telephone: 207-255-1241. Fax: 207-255-4864. E-mail: lschof@maine.edu.

DEGREES AND AWARDS
Programs offered do not lead to a degree or other formal award.

COURSE SUBJECT AREAS OFFERED OUTSIDE OF DEGREE PROGRAMS
Undergraduate—accounting and computer science; American literature (United States and Canadian); American Sign Language (ASL); business/commerce; business, management, and marketing related; community psychology; creative writing; economics; education; education (specific levels and methods); English; English composition; English language and literature related; entrepreneurial and small business operations; foods, nutrition, and related services; health psychology; natural resources and conservation related; philosophy; political science and government; psychology; psychology related; social sciences; sociology; statistics.

UNIVERSITY OF MANAGEMENT AND TECHNOLOGY
Arlington, Virginia
http://www.umtweb.edu
University of Management and Technology was founded in 1998. It is accredited by Distance Education and Training Council. It first offered distance learning courses in 1998. In fall 2007, there were 5,000 students enrolled in distance learning courses. Institutionally administered financial aid is available to distance learners.
Services Distance learners have accessibility to academic advising, bookstore, library services, tutoring.
Contact Dr. J. Davidson Frame, Academic Dean, University of Management and Technology, 1901 North Fort Myer Drive, Suite 700, Arlington, VA 22209. Telephone: 703-516-0035. Fax: 703-516-0985. E-mail: davidson.frame@umtweb.edu.

DEGREES AND AWARDS
ABA Business Administration
AS Computer Science; Criminal Justice; General Studies; Information Technology
BBA Criminal Justice Administration; Human Resources Management; Information Technology Management; International Management; Management; Marketing Management
BS Computer Science–Information Systems; Computer Science–Information Technology; Computer Science–Software Engineering; Computer Science; Criminal Justice; General Studies; Information Technology
Certificate Acquisition Management; Information Technology; Project Management; Public Administration
Graduate Certificate Project Management
MBA Management; Project Management
MS Criminal Justice; Information Technology–IT Management; Information Technology–IT Project Management; Information Technology–Management Information Systems
MSCS Computer Science; Software Engineering
MSM Acquisition Management; Management; Project Management

COURSE SUBJECT AREAS OFFERED OUTSIDE OF DEGREE PROGRAMS
Undergraduate—accounting and computer science; applied mathematics; behavioral sciences; business administration, management and operations; business, management, and marketing related; computer and information sciences; computer/information technology administration and management; computer programming; computer science; computer software and media applications; computer systems analysis; computer systems networking and telecommunications; criminal justice and corrections; criminology; economics; English; finance and financial management services; history; human resources management; international business; international/global studies; management information systems; management sciences and quantitative methods; mathematics; psychology; public administration; science technologies related; science, technology and society; statistics; technical and business writing.

Graduate—accounting and computer science; business administration, management and operations; business/commerce; criminal justice and corrections; criminology; economics; linguistic, comparative, and related language studies; management information systems; psychology.

UNIVERSITY OF MANITOBA
Winnipeg, Manitoba, Canada
Distance and Online Education
http://www.umanitoba.ca/distance
University of Manitoba was founded in 1877. It is provincially chartered. It first offered distance learning courses in 1950. In fall 2007, there were 3,500 students enrolled in distance learning courses. Institutionally administered financial aid is available to distance learners.
Services Distance learners have accessibility to academic advising, bookstore, campus computer network, e-mail services, library services.
Contact Student Support, University of Manitoba, Distance and Online Education, 188D Extended Education Complex, Winnipeg, MB R3T 2N2, Canada. Telephone: 204-474-8012. Fax: 204-474-7660. E-mail: de_info@umanitoba.ca.

DEGREES AND AWARDS
BA General degree studies–3-year general degree; Geography
BN Nursing–Baccalaureate program for Registered Nurses
BSW Social Work
Graduate Certificate Education–Post-Baccalaureate Diploma in Education program

UNIVERSITY OF MARYLAND, COLLEGE PARK
College Park, Maryland
E-Learning
http://www.onlinestudies.umd.edu
University of Maryland, College Park was founded in 1856. It is accredited by Middle States Association of Colleges and Schools. It first offered distance learning courses in 2000. In fall 2007, there were 250 students enrolled in distance learning courses. Institutionally administered financial aid is available to distance learners.
Services Distance learners have accessibility to academic advising, bookstore, library services.
Contact Paul E. Roche, EdD, Senior Project Manager, University of Maryland, College Park, 2103 Reckord Armory, Office of Professional Studies, College Park, MD 20742. Telephone: 301-405-8989. Fax: 301-314-9572. E-mail: proche@umd.edu.

DEGREES AND AWARDS
Graduate Certificate Graduate Certificate in Public Health Informatics
MEngr Professional Master of Engineering in Fire Protection
MLS Life Sciences
See full description on page 500.

UNIVERSITY OF MARYLAND UNIVERSITY COLLEGE
Adelphi, Maryland
http://www.umuc.edu
University of Maryland University College was founded in 1947. It is accredited by Middle States Association of Colleges and Schools. It first offered distance learning courses in 1972. In fall 2007, there were 33,000 students enrolled in distance learning courses. Institutionally administered financial aid is available to distance learners.
Services Distance learners have accessibility to academic advising, bookstore, campus computer network, career placement assistance, e-mail services, library services, tutoring.
Contact Advisor, University of Maryland University College, 3501 University Boulevard East, Adelphi, MD 20783. Telephone: 800-888-UMUC. E-mail: emteam@umuc.edu.

DEGREES AND AWARDS
BA Asian Studies; Communication Studies; English; History; Humanities

BS Accounting; Business Administration; Computer Information Technology; Computer Science; Computer Studies; Computer and Information Science; Criminal Justice; Emergency Management; Environmental Management; Finance; Fire Science; General Studies; Gerontology; Global Business and Public Policy; Homeland Security; Human Resource Management; Information Assurance; Information Systems Management; Investigative Forensics; Legal Studies; Management Studies; Marketing; Political Science; Psychology; Social Science

EMBA Business Administration

Graduate Certificate Accounting and Information Technology; Accounting; Bioinformatics; Biotechnology Management; Chief Information Officer (CIO); Database Systems Technologies; Distance Education Leadership; Distance Education, Globalization, and Development; E-Business; Environmental Management; Financial Management in Organizations; Foundations of Distance Education; Foundations of Human Resource Management; Foundations of Information Technology; Health Care Administration; Homeland Security Management; Informatics; Information Assurance; Integrated Direct Marketing; Integrative Supply Chain Management; International Marketing; International Trade; Nonprofit and Association Financial Management; Policy and Management in Distance Education; Procurement and Contract Management; Project Management; Public Relations; Software Engineering; Systems Analysis; Teaching and Training at a Distance; Technology in Distance Education; Telecommunications Management

MBA Business Administration

MDE Distance Education

MEd Instructional Technology

MIM International Management

MS Accounting and Financial Management; Accounting and Information Technology; Biotechnology; Computer Systems Management; E-Commerce; Environmental Management; Financial Management and Information Systems; Health Administration Informatics; Health Care Administration; Information Technology; Management; Technology Management; Telecommunications Management

DM Management

COURSE SUBJECT AREAS OFFERED OUTSIDE OF DEGREE PROGRAMS

Undergraduate—accounting and related services; anthropology; area studies; biology; business administration, management and operations; chemistry; communication and media; computer and information sciences; criminal justice and corrections; economics; fire protection; gerontology; human resources management; information science/studies; international business; journalism; mathematics; psychology; sales, merchandising, and related marketing operations (general); social sciences; sociology.

Graduate—accounting and related services; business administration, management and operations; business, management, and marketing related; computer/information technology administration and management; computer systems networking and telecommunications; educational/instructional media design; education (specific levels and methods); education (specific subject areas); entrepreneurial and small business operations; health and medical administrative services; human resources management; international business; marketing; public administration; sales, merchandising, and related marketing operations (general).

UNIVERSITY OF MARY WASHINGTON
Fredericksburg, Virginia

University of Mary Washington was founded in 1908. It is accredited by Southern Association of Colleges and Schools.

Contact Mrs. Sue Lafayette, Testing/Proctor Administrator, University of Mary Washington, 121 University Boulevard, Fredericksburg, VA 22406. Telephone: 540-286-8012. Fax: 540-286-8005. E-mail: sclarkla @umw.edu.

DEGREES AND AWARDS
Programs offered do not lead to a degree or other formal award.

COURSE SUBJECT AREAS OFFERED OUTSIDE OF DEGREE PROGRAMS

Graduate—engineering.

UNIVERSITY OF MASSACHUSETTS BOSTON
Boston, Massachusetts
Corporate, Continuing and Distance Education
http://ccde.umb.edu/dl

University of Massachusetts Boston was founded in 1964. It is accredited by New England Association of Schools and Colleges. It first offered distance learning courses in 2001. In fall 2007, there were 1,500 students enrolled in distance learning courses. Institutionally administered financial aid is available to distance learners.

Services Distance learners have accessibility to academic advising, bookstore, campus computer network, career placement assistance, e-mail services, library services, tutoring.

Contact Ms. Katharine Grant Galaitsis, Director of Online Education, University of Massachusetts Boston, Corporate, Continuing, and Distance Education, 100 Morrissey Boulevard, Boston, MA 02125-3393. Telephone: 617-287-7918. Fax: 617-287-7297. E-mail: kitty.galaitsis@ umb.edu.

DEGREES AND AWARDS

BA Community Studies completer program

BS Nursing–RN to BS

Certificate Community, Media, and Technology; Frank J. Manning Certificate in Gerontology; Fundamentals of Information Technology

Graduate Certificate Critical and Creative Thinking (Focus on Creativity at Work); Education–Adapting Curriculum Frameworks for All Learners; Gerontology–Management of Aging Services track; Instructional Technology Design; Instructional Technology for Educators; Special Education–Orientation and Mobility

MA Linguistics–Applied Linguistics, ESL concentration

MEd Counseling–Family Therapy track; Counseling–Mental Health Counseling track; Counseling–Rehabilitation Counseling track; Counseling–School Guidance track; Instructional Design; Special Education–Orientation and Mobility; Special Education–Teaching of Students with Visual Impairments

MS Gerontology–Management of Aging Services track

PMC Nursing–Gerontological/Adult and Family Nurse Practitioner

COURSE SUBJECT AREAS OFFERED OUTSIDE OF DEGREE PROGRAMS

Undergraduate—anthropology; archeology; biology; business administration, management and operations; classical and ancient studies; communication and media; community organization and advocacy; community psychology; computer and information sciences; computer/information technology administration and management; computer science; criminal justice and corrections; economics; English; English composition; environmental/environmental health engineering; geography and cartography; history; international relations and affairs; languages (classics and classical); languages (Romance languages); liberal arts and sciences, general studies and humanities; linguistic, comparative, and related language studies; management information systems; marketing; mathematics; music; natural resources and conservation related; nursing; nutrition sciences; physics; political science and government; psychology; social sciences; sociology; statistics; technology education/industrial arts.

Graduate—biological and physical sciences; counseling psychology; criminal justice and corrections; education; educational/instructional media design; educational psychology; education (specific subject areas); English; English as a second/foreign language (teaching); gerontology; history; international relations and affairs; linguistic, comparative, and related language studies; nursing; peace studies and conflict resolution; school psychology; sociology; special education; statistics; student counseling and personnel services; technology education/industrial arts.

Non-credit—business, management, and marketing related; counseling psychology; human services.

UNIVERSITY OF MASSACHUSETTS LOWELL
Lowell, Massachusetts
Continuing Studies and Corporate Education
http://continuinged.uml.edu/online

University of Massachusetts Lowell was founded in 1894. It is accredited by New England Association of Schools and Colleges. It first offered distance learning courses in 1995. In fall 2007, there were 3,100 students enrolled in distance learning courses. Institutionally administered financial aid is available to distance learners.

Services Distance learners have accessibility to academic advising, bookstore, campus computer network, e-mail services, library services.
Contact Amy Yacus, Assistant Director of Marketing and Outreach, University of Massachusetts Lowell, One University Avenue, Lowell, MA 01854-2881. Telephone: 800-480-3190. Fax: 978-934-4064. E-mail: amy_yacus@uml.edu.

DEGREES AND AWARDS

AS Information Technology

BA Liberal Arts (BLA); Psychology

BS Information Technology; Information Technology, Business minor

Certificate Contemporary Communications; Data/Telecommunications; Information Technology; Multimedia Applications; Paralegal Studies; Security Management and Homeland Security; UNIX; Website Design and Development

Graduate Certificate Behavioral Intervention in Autism; Clinical Pathology; Domestic Violence Prevention; Forensic Criminology; Foundations of Business; Plastics Engineering Fundamentals; Security Studies

MA Criminal Justice

MBA Business Administration

MEd Curriculum and Instruction; Educational Administration; Reading and Language

COURSE SUBJECT AREAS OFFERED OUTSIDE OF DEGREE PROGRAMS

Non-credit—educational/instructional media design; education related.

UNIVERSITY OF MEDICINE AND DENTISTRY OF NEW JERSEY
Newark, New Jersey
http://shrp.umdnj.edu/

University of Medicine and Dentistry of New Jersey was founded in 1970. It is accredited by Middle States Association of Colleges and Schools. It first offered distance learning courses in 1998. In fall 2007, there were 350 students enrolled in distance learning courses. Institutionally administered financial aid is available to distance learners.

Services Distance learners have accessibility to academic advising, bookstore, campus computer network, e-mail services, library services.
Contact Ms. Diane Hanrahan, Manager of Admission, University of Medicine and Dentistry of New Jersey, 65 Bergen Street, Room 149, Newark, NJ 07107. Telephone: 973-972-8515. Fax: 973-972-7463. E-mail: hanrahdi@umdnj.edu.

DEGREES AND AWARDS

BS Health Sciences

MS Clinical Nutrition; Health Sciences; Health Systems; Psychiatric Rehabilitation

DH Sc Clinical Nutrition (DCN)

PhD Health Sciences

COURSE SUBJECT AREAS OFFERED OUTSIDE OF DEGREE PROGRAMS

Undergraduate—health professions related; nutrition sciences.
Graduate—health professions related; nutrition sciences.

UNIVERSITY OF MICHIGAN
Ann Arbor, Michigan
College of Engineering
http://interpro.engin.umich.edu

University of Michigan was founded in 1817. It is accredited by North Central Association of Colleges and Schools. It first offered distance learning courses in 1996. In fall 2007, there were 750 students enrolled in distance learning courses. Institutionally administered financial aid is available to distance learners.

Services Distance learners have accessibility to academic advising, bookstore, campus computer network, career placement assistance, e-mail services, library services, tutoring.
Contact Sandra Hines, Manager, University of Michigan, CoE, 2401 Plymouth Road, Suite A/B, Ann Arbor, MI 48105-1093. Telephone: 734-647-7176. E-mail: hinesone@umich.edu.

DEGREES AND AWARDS

ME Automotive Engineering; Energy Systems; Global Automotive and Manufacturing Engineering; Manufacturing Engineering; Pharmaceutical Engineering
MEngr Automotive Engineering

UNIVERSITY OF MICHIGAN–DEARBORN
Dearborn, Michigan
http://dln.engin.umd.umich.edu

University of Michigan–Dearborn was founded in 1959. It is accredited by North Central Association of Colleges and Schools. It first offered distance learning courses in 2003. In fall 2007, there were 250 students enrolled in distance learning courses. Institutionally administered financial aid is available to distance learners.

Services Distance learners have accessibility to academic advising, bookstore, campus computer network, e-mail services, library services.
Contact Susan Guinn, Distance Learning Program Manager, University of Michigan–Dearborn, College of Engineering and Computer Science, 4901 Evergreen Road, 2040 PEC, Dearborn, MI 48128-1491. Telephone: 313-593-4000. Fax: 313-593-4070. E-mail: sguinn@umich.edu.

DEGREES AND AWARDS

MS Engineering Management; Software Engineering
MSE Automotive Systems Engineering; Computer Engineering; Industrial and Systems Engineering

COURSE SUBJECT AREAS OFFERED OUTSIDE OF DEGREE PROGRAMS

Undergraduate—computer and information sciences; computer science.
Graduate—computer and information sciences; computer engineering; computer science; engineering; engineering/industrial management; engineering science; mechanical engineering.
Non-credit—engineering science.

UNIVERSITY OF MICHIGAN–FLINT
Flint, Michigan
Distance Learning Program
http://online.umflint.edu/

University of Michigan–Flint was founded in 1956. It is accredited by North Central Association of Colleges and Schools. It first offered distance learning courses in 2000. In fall 2007, there were 2,796 students enrolled in distance learning courses. Institutionally administered financial aid is available to distance learners.

Services Distance learners have accessibility to academic advising, bookstore, campus computer network, career placement assistance, e-mail services, library services.
Contact Ms. Kimberly Buster-Williams, Director of Admissions, University of Michigan–Flint, 245 University Pavilion, Flint, MI 48502-1950. Telephone: 810-762-3300. Fax: 810-762-3272. E-mail: kbwill@umflint.edu.

DEGREES AND AWARDS
BBA Business Administration
BSN Nursing
Certificate Africana Studies
MA Technology in Education (Global)
MBA Business Administration
MPA Educational Administration–WebPlus! MPA Program
MS Computer and Information Systems

COURSE SUBJECT AREAS OFFERED OUTSIDE OF DEGREE PROGRAMS
Undergraduate—accounting and related services; allied health diagnostic, intervention, and treatment professions; business/commerce; computer science; management sciences and quantitative methods; marketing; mathematics; nursing; social work.
Graduate—accounting and related services; business administration, management and operations; human resources management; management sciences and quantitative methods; marketing.
Non-credit—accounting and related services; business administration, management and operations; business/commerce; business/corporate communications; business, management, and marketing related; computer software and media applications; educational administration and supervision; educational assessment, evaluation, and research; educational/instructional media design; education (specific subject areas); management information systems; sales, merchandising, and related marketing operations (specialized); teaching assistants/aides.

UNIVERSITY OF MINNESOTA, CROOKSTON
Crookston, Minnesota
Office of Continuing Education
http://www.umcrookston.edu/online
University of Minnesota, Crookston was founded in 1966. It is accredited by North Central Association of Colleges and Schools. It first offered distance learning courses in 1990. In fall 2007, there were 680 students enrolled in distance learning courses. Institutionally administered financial aid is available to distance learners.
Services Distance learners have accessibility to academic advising, bookstore, campus computer network, career placement assistance, e-mail services, library services, tutoring.
Contact Michelle A. Christopherson, Director, Center for Adult Learning, University of Minnesota, Crookston, 208 Selvig Hall, 2900 University Avenue, Crookston, MN 56716-5001. Telephone: 218-281-8679. Fax: 218-281-8676. E-mail: mchristo@umn.edu.

DEGREES AND AWARDS
BS Bachelor of Applied Health; Bachelor of Manufacturing Management Online; Business Online
Certificate Hotel, Restaurant, and Institutional Management

COURSE SUBJECT AREAS OFFERED OUTSIDE OF DEGREE PROGRAMS
Undergraduate—accounting and related services; agricultural and food products processing; biology; business administration, management and operations; data entry/microcomputer applications; data processing; economics; English composition; English language and literature related; entrepreneurial and small business operations; foods, nutrition, and related services; health and medical administrative services; industrial production technologies; information science/studies; management information systems; manufacturing engineering; marketing; mathematics; microbiological sciences and immunology; philosophy; physics; psychology; sociology; speech and rhetoric; statistics.

UNIVERSITY OF MINNESOTA, DULUTH
Duluth, Minnesota
http://www.d.umn.edu/goto/ini
University of Minnesota, Duluth was founded in 1947. It is accredited by North Central Association of Colleges and Schools. It first offered distance learning courses in 1980. In fall 2007, there were 600 students enrolled in distance learning courses. Institutionally administered financial aid is available to distance learners.
Services Distance learners have accessibility to academic advising, bookstore, campus computer network, e-mail services, library services.

Contact Torina Stark, Program Coordinator, University of Minnesota, Duluth, 251 Darland Administration, 1049 University Drive, Duluth, MN 55812. Telephone: 218-726-8146. E-mail: tstark@d.umn.edu.

DEGREES AND AWARDS
Programs offered do not lead to a degree or other formal award.

COURSE SUBJECT AREAS OFFERED OUTSIDE OF DEGREE PROGRAMS
Undergraduate—area, ethnic, cultural, and gender studies related; astronomy and astrophysics; education (specific subject areas); English composition; health and physical education/fitness; history; psychology; sociology; special education.
Graduate—education (specific subject areas); special education.

UNIVERSITY OF MINNESOTA, MORRIS
Morris, Minnesota
College of Continuing Education-GenEdWeb Program
http://genedweb.morris.umn.edu
University of Minnesota, Morris was founded in 1959. It is accredited by North Central Association of Colleges and Schools. It first offered distance learning courses in 1997. In fall 2007, there were 100 students enrolled in distance learning courses. Institutionally administered financial aid is available to distance learners.
Services Distance learners have accessibility to academic advising, bookstore, campus computer network, e-mail services, library services, tutoring.
Contact Ms. Karen M. Cusey, Program Associate/GenEdWeb Program Coordinator, University of Minnesota, Morris, 225 Community Services Building, 600 East 4th Street, Morris, MN 56267. Telephone: 800-842-0030. Fax: 320-589-1661. E-mail: genedweb@morris.umn.edu.

DEGREES AND AWARDS
Programs offered do not lead to a degree or other formal award.

COURSE SUBJECT AREAS OFFERED OUTSIDE OF DEGREE PROGRAMS
Undergraduate—creative writing; education; education (specific subject areas); English composition; geography and cartography; history; international and comparative education; legal studies (non-professional general, undergraduate); multi-/interdisciplinary studies related; political science and government; psychology; sociology; statistics.

UNIVERSITY OF MINNESOTA, TWIN CITIES CAMPUS
Minneapolis, Minnesota
Independent and Distance Learning
http://www.cce.umn.edu/petersons
University of Minnesota, Twin Cities Campus was founded in 1851. It is accredited by North Central Association of Colleges and Schools. It first offered distance learning courses in 1941. In fall 2007, there were 4,000 students enrolled in distance learning courses. Institutionally administered financial aid is available to distance learners.
Services Distance learners have accessibility to academic advising, bookstore, campus computer network, career placement assistance, e-mail services, library services, tutoring.
Contact Information Center Receptionist, University of Minnesota, Twin Cities Campus, College of Continuing Education, 20 Classroom Office Building, 1994 Buford Avenue, Saint Paul, MN 55108. Telephone: 800-234-6564. Fax: 612-625-1511. E-mail: info@cce.umn.edu.

DEGREES AND AWARDS
Programs offered do not lead to a degree or other formal award.

COURSE SUBJECT AREAS OFFERED OUTSIDE OF DEGREE PROGRAMS
Undergraduate—accounting and related services; agriculture; allied health diagnostic, intervention, and treatment professions; applied horticulture/horticultural business services; biochemistry, biophysics and

molecular biology; biology; biology/biotechnology laboratory technician; biopsychology; business administration, management and operations; business/corporate communications; business, management, and marketing related; business/managerial economics; business operations support and assistant services; cell biology and anatomical sciences; communication and journalism related; communication and media; comparative literature; computer software and media applications; computer systems networking and telecommunications; developmental and child psychology; ecology, evolution, and population biology; economics; English; English language and literature related; English literature (British and Commonwealth); entrepreneurial and small business operations; ethnic, cultural minority, and gender studies; family and consumer economics; family and consumer sciences/human sciences; finance and financial management services; fine and studio art; food science and technology; foods, nutrition, and related services; genetics; geological and earth sciences/geosciences; health and medical administrative services; health/medical preparatory programs; health professions related; health services/allied health/health sciences; human resources management; journalism; languages (classics and classical); languages (Germanic); languages (Romance languages); languages (Slavic, Baltic and Albanian); liberal arts and sciences, general studies and humanities; linguistic, comparative, and related language studies; marketing; materials science; mathematics; music; nursing; operations research; personality psychology; philosophy; physics; physiology, pathology and related sciences; psychology; public health; public relations, advertising, and applied communication related; publishing; rehabilitation and therapeutic professions; social work; speech and rhetoric; technical and business writing; work and family studies.

Graduate—biochemistry, biophysics and molecular biology; communication and media; liberal arts and sciences, general studies and humanities; public health; social work; speech and rhetoric.

See full description on page 502.

UNIVERSITY OF MISSOURI–COLUMBIA
Columbia, Missouri
Center for Distance and Independent Study
http://online.missouri.edu/mu/pgd.html

University of Missouri–Columbia was founded in 1839. It is accredited by North Central Association of Colleges and Schools. It first offered distance learning courses in 1941. In fall 2007, there were 6,042 students enrolled in distance learning courses. Institutionally administered financial aid is available to distance learners.

Services Distance learners have accessibility to academic advising, bookstore, e-mail services, library services.

Contact Mr. Ehren Oncken, Academic Advisor, University of Missouri–Columbia, 136 Clark Hall, Columbia, MO 65211-4200. Telephone: 800-609-3727 Ext. 4. Fax: 573-882-6808. E-mail: onckene@missouri.edu.

DEGREES AND AWARDS
BGS Online Bachelor of General Studies (degree completion program)

COURSE SUBJECT AREAS OFFERED OUTSIDE OF DEGREE PROGRAMS
Undergraduate—accounting and related services; American literature (United States and Canadian); anthropology; area, ethnic, cultural, and gender studies related; area studies; astronomy and astrophysics; atmospheric sciences and meteorology; behavioral sciences; biblical and other theological languages and literatures; biology; business administration, management and operations; business/commerce; business, management, and marketing related; business/managerial economics; business operations support and assistant services; classical and ancient studies; computer and information sciences; creative writing; curriculum and instruction; developmental and child psychology; economics; education; educational psychology; education related; English; English composition; English language and literature related; English literature (British and Commonwealth); environmental psychology; ethnic, cultural minority, and gender studies; film/video and photographic arts; finance and financial management services; geography and cartography; geological and earth sciences/geosciences; gerontology; health and physical education/fitness;

health professions related; history; human development, family studies, and related services; human resources management; intercultural/multicultural and diversity studies; international relations and affairs; languages (classics and classical); languages (foreign languages related); languages (Germanic); languages (Romance languages); liberal arts and sciences, general studies and humanities; linguistic, comparative, and related language studies; marketing; mathematics; mathematics and statistics related; mental and social health services and allied professions; parks, recreation and leisure; philosophy; philosophy and religious studies related; physics; political science and government; psychology; psychology related; religious studies; social psychology; social work; sociology; statistics; technical and business writing.

Graduate—business operations support and assistant services; counseling psychology; curriculum and instruction; education; educational administration and supervision; educational assessment, evaluation, and research; educational psychology; education related; gerontology; mental and social health services and allied professions; sociology; urban studies/affairs.

Non-credit—city/urban, community and regional planning; fire protection; forestry; human resources management; journalism; languages (Romance languages); work and family studies.

UNIVERSITY OF MISSOURI–COLUMBIA
Columbia, Missouri
MU Direct: Continuing and Distance Education
http://online.missouri.edu/mu/pgd.html

University of Missouri–Columbia was founded in 1839. It is accredited by North Central Association of Colleges and Schools. It first offered distance learning courses in 1990. In fall 2007, there were 1,420 students enrolled in distance learning courses. Institutionally administered financial aid is available to distance learners.

Services Distance learners have accessibility to academic advising, bookstore, campus computer network, e-mail services, library services, tutoring.

Contact Emily Marschall, Assistant, MU Direct Student Inquiries, University of Missouri–Columbia, 103 Whitten Hall, Columbia, MO 65211-6300. Telephone: 800-545-2604. Fax: 573-882-5071. E-mail: mudirect@missouri.edu.

DEGREES AND AWARDS
BHS Radiologic Sciences (Bachelor's completion program–Radiography); Respiratory Therapy (Bachelor's completion program)
BSN Nursing–RN to BSN online option (Bachelor's completion program)
Graduate Certificate Food Safety and Defense; Personal Financial Planning
MA Architectural Studies; Gerontology (Human Development and Family Studies); Journalism (Media Management); Journalism (Strategic Communications); Library Science; Youth Development (Human Development and Family Studies)
MEd Business and Marketing Education; Early Childhood Education; Early Childhood Special Education; Educational Leadership; Gifted Education; Journalism Education; Learning Systems Design and Development; Literacy; Mental Health Practices in Schools; Social Studies Education; Teaching English to Speakers of Other Languages (TESOL); Technology in Schools
MHA Health Services Management (Executive Program)
MS Architectural Studies; Family Nurse Practitioner; Gerontological Nurse Practitioner; Health Informatics (Executive Program); Leadership in Nursing and Healthcare Systems; Mental Health Nurse Practitioner; Nursing Education; Nursing–Clinical Nurse Specialist; Pediatric Nurse Practitioner; Personal Financial Planning; Public Health or School Health Nursing
PhD Architectural Studies

COURSE SUBJECT AREAS OFFERED OUTSIDE OF DEGREE PROGRAMS
Undergraduate—agricultural and food products processing; agricultural business and management; food science and technology; foods, nutrition, and related services; health professions related; nuclear engineering; nursing; plant sciences.

Graduate—agricultural and food products processing; agricultural business and management; economics; education; educational administration and supervision; educational/instructional media design; educational psychology; education related; education (specific subject areas); food science and technology; foods, nutrition, and related services; health and medical administrative services; information science/studies; journalism; library science; library science related; mental and social health services and allied professions; nuclear engineering; nursing; public relations, advertising, and applied communication related; radio, television, and digital communication; school psychology; technology education/industrial arts.

Non-credit—agricultural business and management; business, management, and marketing related; city/urban, community and regional planning; criminal justice and corrections; criminology; education; educational assessment, evaluation, and research; education related; education (specific levels and methods); fire protection; forestry; health/medical preparatory programs; health professions related; health services/allied health/health sciences; human resources management; languages (foreign languages related); medical illustration and informatics; personal and culinary services related; soil sciences; wildlife and wildlands science and management.

THE UNIVERSITY OF MONTANA–WESTERN
Dillon, Montana
Division of Outreach
http://outreach.umwestern.edu
The University of Montana–Western was founded in 1893. It is accredited by Northwest Commission on Colleges and Universities. It first offered distance learning courses in 1989. In fall 2007, there were 300 students enrolled in distance learning courses. Institutionally administered financial aid is available to distance learners.
Services Distance learners have accessibility to academic advising, bookstore, career placement assistance, e-mail services, library services.
Contact Vickie Lansing, Director of Continuing Education and Extension Programs, The University of Montana–Western, 710 South Atlantic Street, Dillon, MT 59725. Telephone: 406-683-7537. Fax: 406-683-7809. E-mail: v_lansing@umwestern.edu.

DEGREES AND AWARDS
Programs offered do not lead to a degree or other formal award.

COURSE SUBJECT AREAS OFFERED OUTSIDE OF DEGREE PROGRAMS
Undergraduate—business, management, and marketing related; computer software and media applications; education; education (specific levels and methods); English composition; geological and earth sciences/geosciences; history; liberal arts and sciences, general studies and humanities; library science related; mathematics; philosophy; psychology.
Non-credit—computer software and media applications; legal professions and studies related; medical basic sciences.

UNIVERSITY OF NEBRASKA AT KEARNEY
Kearney, Nebraska
Division of Continuing Education
http://ecampus.unk.edu
University of Nebraska at Kearney was founded in 1903. It is accredited by North Central Association of Colleges and Schools. It first offered distance learning courses in 1986. In fall 2007, there were 900 students enrolled in distance learning courses. Institutionally administered financial aid is available to distance learners.
Services Distance learners have accessibility to academic advising, bookstore, campus computer network, career placement assistance, e-mail services, library services, tutoring.
Contact Gloria Vavricka, Director of eCampus, University of Nebraska at Kearney, Communications Center, Kearney, NE 68849-4220. Telephone: 308-865-8390. Fax: 308-865-8090. E-mail: vavrickag@unk.edu.

DEGREES AND AWARDS
Endorsement English as a Second Language–ESL; Gifted Graduate Endorsement; Library Media Graduate Endorsement; Vocational Diversified Occupations endorsement
MAE Curriculum and Instruction K-12; Curriculum and Instruction–Special Education and Reading; Reading K-12; School Principalship, K-6 or 7-12; Special Education–Gifted Education
MS Biology
MSE Instructional Technology

UNIVERSITY OF NEVADA, RENO
Reno, Nevada
Independent Study and Division of Continuing Education
http://istudy.unr.edu
University of Nevada, Reno was founded in 1874. It is accredited by Northwest Commission on Colleges and Universities. It first offered distance learning courses in 1944. In fall 2007, there were 3,500 students enrolled in distance learning courses. Institutionally administered financial aid is available to distance learners.
Services Distance learners have accessibility to bookstore, campus computer network, e-mail services, library services.
Contact Carley Ries, Associate Director, University of Nevada, Reno, Independent Learning, Mail Stop 050, Reno, NV 89557. Telephone: 775-784-4652. Fax: 775-784-1280. E-mail: istudy@unr.edu.

DEGREES AND AWARDS
Programs offered do not lead to a degree or other formal award.

COURSE SUBJECT AREAS OFFERED OUTSIDE OF DEGREE PROGRAMS
Undergraduate—accounting and related services; American literature (United States and Canadian); anthropology; area, ethnic, cultural, and gender studies related; area studies; business/commerce; business/managerial economics; communication and media; computer and information sciences; counseling psychology; creative writing; criminal justice and corrections; curriculum and instruction; developmental and child psychology; economics; educational psychology; education related; English; English as a second/foreign language (teaching); English composition; fine and studio art; foods, nutrition, and related services; geography and cartography; history; hospitality administration; languages (Germanic); languages (Romance languages); library science; linguistic, comparative, and related language studies; marketing; mathematics; music; psychology; social work; sociology; statistics.
Graduate—counseling psychology; curriculum and instruction; education; education related; library science; psychology related.

UNIVERSITY OF NEW HAVEN
West Haven, Connecticut
http://www.newhaven.edu/
University of New Haven was founded in 1920. It is accredited by New England Association of Schools and Colleges.
Contact Ms. Nancy Baker, Registrar, University of New Haven, 300 Boston Post Road, West Haven, CT 06516. Telephone: 203-932-7307. E-mail: ncarroll@newhaven.edu.

DEGREES AND AWARDS
Programs offered do not lead to a degree or other formal award.

COURSE SUBJECT AREAS OFFERED OUTSIDE OF DEGREE PROGRAMS
Undergraduate—communication and journalism related; computer engineering.
Graduate—communications technology; education; education (specific subject areas).

UNIVERSITY OF NEW ORLEANS
New Orleans, Louisiana
UNO Metropolitan College
http://alt.uno.edu

University of New Orleans was founded in 1958. It is accredited by Southern Association of Colleges and Schools. It first offered distance learning courses in 1980. In fall 2007, there were 7,000 students enrolled in distance learning courses. Institutionally administered financial aid is available to distance learners.

Services Distance learners have accessibility to academic advising, bookstore, campus computer network, e-mail services, library services, tutoring.

Contact Dr. Carl E. Drichta, Associate Vice Chancellor and Dean, University of New Orleans, Lakefront Campus, Education 122, New Orleans, LA 70148. Telephone: 504-280-7100. Fax: 504-280-7317. E-mail: cdrichta@uno.edu.

DEGREES AND AWARDS
Programs offered do not lead to a degree or other formal award.

COURSE SUBJECT AREAS OFFERED OUTSIDE OF DEGREE PROGRAMS

Undergraduate—accounting and computer science; American literature (United States and Canadian); American Sign Language (ASL); anthropology; applied mathematics; architectural engineering; architectural engineering technology; area, ethnic, cultural, and gender studies related; behavioral sciences; bioethics/medical ethics; biological and biomedical sciences related; biological and physical sciences; biology; business administration, management and operations; business/corporate communications; business, management, and marketing related; business/managerial economics; chemistry; city/urban, community and regional planning; civil engineering; classical and ancient studies; community organization and advocacy; comparative literature; computer and information sciences; computer programming; computer science; computer systems analysis; creative writing; curriculum and instruction; developmental and child psychology; economics; education; educational administration and supervision; educational assessment, evaluation, and research; education (specific levels and methods); education (specific subject areas); electrical and electronic engineering technologies; engineering; engineering-related fields; English; English as a second language; English composition; English language and literature related; English literature (British and Commonwealth); entrepreneurial and small business operations; finance and financial management services; geography and cartography; geological and earth sciences/geosciences; geological/geophysical engineering; gerontology; health professions related; history; hospitality administration; human resources management; journalism; languages (foreign languages related); languages (Germanic); languages (Romance languages); liberal arts and sciences, general studies and humanities; linguistic, comparative, and related language studies; management information systems; management sciences and quantitative methods; marketing; mathematics; mathematics and computer science; mathematics and statistics related; mechanical engineering; medieval and Renaissance studies; music; natural resources and conservation related; naval architecture and marine engineering; personality psychology; philosophy; philosophy and religious studies related; physical sciences; physics; political science and government; psychology; psychometrics and quantitative psychology; public administration; public administration and social service professions related; real estate; social sciences; sociology; special education; speech and rhetoric; statistics; systems engineering; technical and business writing; urban studies/affairs.

Graduate—accounting and computer science; American literature (United States and Canadian); American Sign Language (ASL); anthropology; applied mathematics; architectural engineering; architectural engineering technology; area, ethnic, cultural, and gender studies related; behavioral sciences; biological and biomedical sciences related; biological and physical sciences; biology; business administration, management and operations; business/corporate communications; business, management, and marketing related; business/managerial economics; chemistry; city/urban, community and regional planning; civil engineering; classical and ancient studies; comparative literature; computer and information sciences; computer programming; computer science; computer systems

analysis; creative writing; curriculum and instruction; developmental and child psychology; dramatic/theater arts and stagecraft; economics; education; educational administration and supervision; educational assessment, evaluation, and research; educational/instructional media design; education (specific levels and methods); education (specific subject areas); electrical and electronic engineering technologies; engineering; engineering-related fields; English; English as a second language; English composition; English language and literature related; English literature (British and Commonwealth); entrepreneurial and small business operations; finance and financial management services; geography and cartography; geological and earth sciences/geosciences; geological/geophysical engineering; gerontology; health professions related; history; hospitality administration; human resources management; journalism; languages (foreign languages related); languages (Germanic); languages (Romance languages); liberal arts and sciences, general studies and humanities; linguistic, comparative, and related language studies; management information systems; management sciences and quantitative methods; marketing; mathematics; mathematics and computer science; mathematics and statistics related; mechanical engineering; medieval and Renaissance studies; music; natural resources and conservation related; naval architecture and marine engineering; personality psychology; philosophy; philosophy and religious studies related; physical sciences; physics; political science and government; psychology; psychometrics and quantitative psychology; public administration; public administration and social service professions related; real estate; social sciences; sociology; special education; speech and rhetoric; statistics; systems engineering; technical and business writing; urban studies/affairs.

Non-credit—business, management, and marketing related; communication and journalism related; creative writing; English composition; finance and financial management services; liberal arts and sciences, general studies and humanities; mathematics.

UNIVERSITY OF NORTH ALABAMA
Florence, Alabama
Educational Technology Services/Distance Learning
http://distance.una.edu

University of North Alabama was founded in 1830. It is accredited by Southern Association of Colleges and Schools. It first offered distance learning courses in 1997. In fall 2007, there were 1,000 students enrolled in distance learning courses. Institutionally administered financial aid is available to distance learners.

Services Distance learners have accessibility to academic advising, bookstore, campus computer network, career placement assistance, e-mail services, library services, tutoring.

Contact Ms. B.J. Wilson, Coordinator of Distance Learning, University of North Alabama, UNA Box 5005, Florence, AL 35632-0001. Telephone: 877-765-6110. Fax: 256-718-3923. E-mail: bhwilson@una.edu.

DEGREES AND AWARDS

BS Sociology

BSN Nursing–RN to BSN

MBA Business Administration–Online MBA program

COURSE SUBJECT AREAS OFFERED OUTSIDE OF DEGREE PROGRAMS

Undergraduate—accounting and related services; area studies; business, management, and marketing related; communication and media; computer and information sciences; criminal justice and corrections; economics; education; English; English composition; finance and financial management services; foods, nutrition, and related services; geography and cartography; gerontology; history; marketing; nursing; philosophy; political science and government; psychology; social work; sociology.

Graduate—accounting and related services; area studies; business administration, management and operations; business/commerce; education; English; geography and cartography.

THE UNIVERSITY OF NORTH CAROLINA AT CHAPEL HILL
Chapel Hill, North Carolina
School of Journalism and Mass Communication
http://jomc.unc.edu/de

The University of North Carolina at Chapel Hill was founded in 1789. It is accredited by Southern Association of Colleges and Schools. It first offered distance learning courses in 2003. In fall 2007, there were 40 students enrolled in distance learning courses. Institutionally administered financial aid is available to distance learners.

Services Distance learners have accessibility to campus computer network, e-mail services, library services.

Contact Ms. Louise Spieler, Assistant Dean for Distance Education and Executive Education, The University of North Carolina at Chapel Hill, School of Journalism and Mass Communication, Campus Box 3365, Chapel Hill, NC 27599. Telephone: 919-843-8137. Fax: 919-843-8138. E-mail: lspieler@unc.edu.

DEGREES AND AWARDS
Programs offered do not lead to a degree or other formal award.

COURSE SUBJECT AREAS OFFERED OUTSIDE OF DEGREE PROGRAMS
Graduate—communication and journalism related; communication and media; journalism; radio, television, and digital communication.

THE UNIVERSITY OF NORTH CAROLINA AT CHAPEL HILL
Chapel Hill, North Carolina
The William and Ida Friday Center for Continuing Education
http://fridaycenter.unc.edu

The University of North Carolina at Chapel Hill was founded in 1789. It is accredited by Southern Association of Colleges and Schools. It first offered distance learning courses in 1941. In fall 2007, there were 3,800 students enrolled in distance learning courses. Institutionally administered financial aid is available to distance learners.

Services Distance learners have accessibility to academic advising, bookstore, career placement assistance, library services.

Contact Carol McDonnell, Student Services Manager, The University of North Carolina at Chapel Hill, CB #1020, Chapel Hill, NC 27599-1020. Telephone: 800-862-5669. Fax: 919-962-5549. E-mail: carol_mcdonnell@unc.edu.

DEGREES AND AWARDS
Programs offered do not lead to a degree or other formal award.

COURSE SUBJECT AREAS OFFERED OUTSIDE OF DEGREE PROGRAMS
Undergraduate—accounting and related services; anthropology; area studies; astronomy and astrophysics; biology; business administration, management and operations; business/corporate communications; chemistry; communication and media; computer and information sciences; creative writing; criminal justice and corrections; dramatic/theater arts and stagecraft; economics; English as a second language; English composition; ethnic, cultural minority, and gender studies; fine and studio art; foods, nutrition, and related services; geography and cartography; geological and earth sciences/geosciences; history; hospitality administration; journalism; languages (classics and classical); languages (foreign languages related); languages (Romance languages); languages (Slavic, Baltic and Albanian); mathematics and statistics related; music; parks, recreation and leisure; philosophy; physics; political science and government; psychology; religious studies; sociology; statistics.
Non-credit—area, ethnic, cultural, and gender studies related; business/corporate communications; business, management, and marketing related; creative writing; ethnic, cultural minority, and gender studies; fine and studio art; history; music; nursing; philosophy; political science and government.

See full description on page 504.

THE UNIVERSITY OF NORTH CAROLINA AT CHARLOTTE
Charlotte, North Carolina
Continuing Education, Extension and Summer Programs
http://www.DistanceEd.uncc.edu

The University of North Carolina at Charlotte was founded in 1946. It is accredited by Southern Association of Colleges and Schools. It first offered distance learning courses in 1985. In fall 2007, there were 604 students enrolled in distance learning courses. Institutionally administered financial aid is available to distance learners.

Services Distance learners have accessibility to academic advising, bookstore, campus computer network, career placement assistance, e-mail services, library services, tutoring.

Contact Mary Faye Englebert, Associate Director, The University of North Carolina at Charlotte, 9201 University City Boulevard, Charlotte, NC 28223. Telephone: 704-687-4594. Fax: 704-687-4305. E-mail: mfengleb@uncc.edu.

DEGREES AND AWARDS
BA Elementary Education
BSET Electrical Engineering Technology; Fire Science
BSN Nursing–RN to BSN completion
Graduate Certificate Education, Academically or Intellectually Gifted Add-On Teacher Licensure; Education, Middle and Secondary Education Teacher Licensure; Information Security and Privacy; Special Education, Adapted Curriculum; Special Education, General Curriculum Teacher licensure
MEd Education, Middle Grades; Elementary Education; Reading, Language, and Literacy
MSA Education and School Administration
MSN Community and Public Health, School Nurse option; Nurse Educator

COURSE SUBJECT AREAS OFFERED OUTSIDE OF DEGREE PROGRAMS
Undergraduate—business, management, and marketing related; classical and ancient studies; computer and information sciences; education; engineering; English as a second language; history; mathematics; nursing; political science and government; psychology related; sociology.
Graduate—biology; education; information science/studies; nursing; statistics.
Non-credit—accounting and computer science; accounting and related services; architecture; building/construction finishing, management, and inspection; business administration, management and operations; business/commerce; business/corporate communications; business, management, and marketing related; business operations support and assistant services; civil engineering; computer software and media applications; counseling psychology; electrical and electronic engineering technologies; engineering; film/video and photographic arts; finance and financial management services; fire protection; geography and cartography; health and medical administrative services; hospitality administration; human resources management; legal support services; marketing; mechanical engineering; nursing; public administration and social service professions related; sales, merchandising, and related marketing operations (specialized); taxation.

THE UNIVERSITY OF NORTH CAROLINA AT GREENSBORO
Greensboro, North Carolina
Division of Continual Learning and Summer Session
http://www.uncg.edu/dcl

The University of North Carolina at Greensboro was founded in 1891. It is accredited by Southern Association of Colleges and Schools. It first offered distance learning courses in 1972. In fall 2007, there were 1,426 students enrolled in distance learning courses. Institutionally administered financial aid is available to distance learners.

Services Distance learners have accessibility to academic advising, bookstore, campus computer network, career placement assistance, e-mail services, library services.

Contact William H. Taylor, Director of Distance Learning and Summer Session, The University of North Carolina at Greensboro, Division of Continual Learning, 915 Northridge Street, PO Box 26170, Greensboro, NC 27402-6170. Telephone: 336-315-7044. Fax: 336-315-7737. E-mail: whtaylor@uncg.edu.

DEGREES AND AWARDS

BA Liberal Studies (Humanities concentration)

BS Education–Birth-Kindergarten Teacher Licensure

BSN Nursing

Certificate Conflict Resolution; Nonprofit Management (post-Baccalaureate)

MA Conflict Resolution; Dance Education; Liberal Studies

MEd Curriculum and Instruction; Educational Administration–School Administration; Special Education (cross-categorical emphasis)

MLIS Library and Information Studies

MSN Nursing

PMC Counseling–School Counseling, advanced

COURSE SUBJECT AREAS OFFERED OUTSIDE OF DEGREE PROGRAMS

Undergraduate—anthropology; classical and ancient studies; communication disorders sciences and services; dance; geological and earth sciences/geosciences; health professions related; history; human development, family studies, and related services; languages (Germanic); liberal arts and sciences, general studies and humanities; mathematics; mathematics and statistics related; multi-/interdisciplinary studies related; philosophy; psychology; social sciences; sociology; statistics.

Graduate—classical and ancient studies; curriculum and instruction; dance; educational assessment, evaluation, and research; education related; liberal arts and sciences, general studies and humanities; library science; library science related; nursing; peace studies and conflict resolution; special education; student counseling and personnel services.

Non-credit—business administration, management and operations; health and medical administrative services; pharmacy, pharmaceutical sciences, and administration; veterinary biomedical and clinical sciences.

THE UNIVERSITY OF NORTH CAROLINA WILMINGTON
Wilmington, North Carolina
Division of Academic Affairs
http://www.uncw.edu/extension

The University of North Carolina Wilmington was founded in 1947. It is accredited by Southern Association of Colleges and Schools. It first offered distance learning courses in 1992. In fall 2007, there were 467 students enrolled in distance learning courses. Institutionally administered financial aid is available to distance learners.

Services Distance learners have accessibility to academic advising, bookstore, campus computer network, career placement assistance, e-mail services, library services, tutoring.

Contact Dr. Beth A. Barton, Director, The University of North Carolina Wilmington, Administration Building, Room 23, 444 Western Boulevard, Jacksonville, NC 28546. Telephone: 910-455-2310. Fax: 910-451-5266. E-mail: bartonb@uncw.edu.

DEGREES AND AWARDS

Programs offered do not lead to a degree or other formal award.

COURSE SUBJECT AREAS OFFERED OUTSIDE OF DEGREE PROGRAMS

Undergraduate—business administration, management and operations; criminal justice and corrections; education (specific subject areas); English; history; nursing; psychology; social work.

Graduate—chemistry; education (specific subject areas); liberal arts and sciences, general studies and humanities.

UNIVERSITY OF NORTH DAKOTA
Grand Forks, North Dakota
Division of Continuing Education
http://www.conted.und.edu

University of North Dakota was founded in 1883. It is accredited by North Central Association of Colleges and Schools. It first offered distance learning courses in 1970. In fall 2007, there were 709 students enrolled in distance learning courses. Institutionally administered financial aid is available to distance learners.

Services Distance learners have accessibility to academic advising, bookstore, campus computer network, career placement assistance, e-mail services, library services, tutoring.

Contact Ms. Heidi Flaten, Coordinator, University of North Dakota, Gustafson Hall, Room 205, 3264 Campus Road, Stop 9021, Grand Forks, ND 58202-9021. Telephone: 877-450-1842. Fax: 701-777-6401. E-mail: distancedegreeprograms@mail.und.edu.

DEGREES AND AWARDS

BA Social Science

BGS General Studies

BS Chemical Engineering; Civil Engineering; Electrical Engineering; Mechanical Engineering; Nursing

Endorsement English Language Learner/English as a Second Language

Graduate Certificate Autistic Spectrum Disorders; Geographic Information Sciences; Health Administration; Instructional Design & Technology

MA Counseling; Forensic Psychology

MBA Business Administration

MEd Education Leadership; Special Education

MPA Public Administration

MS Early Childhood Education; Elementary Education; General Studies (Secondary Education); Instructional Design and Technology; Space Studies

MSN Nursing–Education specialization

MSW Social Work

EdD Educational Leadership

PhD Higher Education

COURSE SUBJECT AREAS OFFERED OUTSIDE OF DEGREE PROGRAMS

Undergraduate—accounting and related services; anthropology; behavioral sciences; bilingual, multilingual, and multicultural education; business administration, management and operations; business/managerial economics; chemical engineering; chemistry; civil engineering; communication and journalism related; communication and media; criminal justice and corrections; dietetics and clinical nutrition services; economics; education; education (specific levels and methods); education (specific subject areas); English composition; geography and cartography; history; industrial and organizational psychology; linguistic, comparative, and related language studies; mathematics; mechanical engineering; nursing; personality psychology; physical sciences; physics; psychology; religious studies; social psychology; social sciences; social sciences related; social work; sociology; statistics.

Graduate—business administration, management and operations; education (specific subject areas); English as a second/foreign language (teaching); public administration; social work.

Non-credit—computer programming; computer software and media applications; graphic communications; health and medical administrative services; health professions related; heating, air conditioning, ventilation and refrigeration maintenance technology; human resources management; legal support services; mathematics; real estate.

UNIVERSITY OF NORTHERN IOWA
Cedar Falls, Iowa
Division of Continuing Education
http://www.uni.edu/contined/cp/distance.shtml

University of Northern Iowa was founded in 1876. It is accredited by North Central Association of Colleges and Schools. It first offered distance learning courses in 1941. In fall 2007, there were 1,200 students enrolled in distance learning courses. Institutionally administered financial aid is available to distance learners.

Services Distance learners have accessibility to academic advising, bookstore, campus computer network, career placement assistance, e-mail services, library services.

Contact Dr. Kent Johnson, Associate Director of Continuing Education Credit Programs, University of Northern Iowa, Cedar Falls, IA 50614-0223. Telephone: 319-273-5970. Fax: 319-273-2872. E-mail: kent.johnson@uni.edu.

DEGREES AND AWARDS
BLS Liberal Studies

COURSE SUBJECT AREAS OFFERED OUTSIDE OF DEGREE PROGRAMS

Undergraduate—accounting and related services; area studies; communication and media; criminology; education; English; family and consumer economics; geography and cartography; health and physical education/fitness; marketing; mathematics; music; psychology; religious studies; social work; sociology.

Graduate—criminology; education; geography and cartography; religious studies; social work; sociology.

UNIVERSITY OF NORTH FLORIDA
Jacksonville, Florida
http://www.unf.edu/

University of North Florida was founded in 1965. It is accredited by Southern Association of Colleges and Schools. It first offered distance learning courses in 1997. In fall 2007, there were 1,480 students enrolled in distance learning courses. Institutionally administered financial aid is available to distance learners.

Services Distance learners have accessibility to academic advising, bookstore, campus computer network, career placement assistance, e-mail services, library services, tutoring.

Contact Dr. Julia A. Watkins, Assistant Professor, University of North Florida, 1 UNF Drive, Jacksonville, FL 32224-7699. Telephone: 904-620-1468. E-mail: jwatkins@unf.edu.

DEGREES AND AWARDS
Programs offered do not lead to a degree or other formal award.

COURSE SUBJECT AREAS OFFERED OUTSIDE OF DEGREE PROGRAMS

Undergraduate—building/construction finishing, management, and inspection; computer and information sciences; computer programming; creative writing; curriculum and instruction; dietetics and clinical nutrition services; education; English composition; health and medical administrative services; health services/allied health/health sciences; music; nursing; nutrition sciences; philosophy; public health; special education.

Graduate—building/construction finishing, management, and inspection; dietetics and clinical nutrition services; education; educational administration and supervision; health services/allied health/health sciences; public health.

UNIVERSITY OF NORTH TEXAS
Denton, Texas
Center for Distributed Learning
http://www.untecampus.com

University of North Texas was founded in 1890. It is accredited by Southern Association of Colleges and Schools. It first offered distance learning courses in 1995. In fall 2007, there were 9,458 students enrolled in distance learning courses. Institutionally administered financial aid is available to distance learners.

Services Distance learners have accessibility to academic advising, bookstore, campus computer network, career placement assistance, e-mail services, library services, tutoring.

Contact Amber Bryant, Senior Marketing Specialist, University of North Texas, PO Box 310889, Denton, TX 76203-0889. Telephone: 940-369-8096. Fax: 940-369-7619. E-mail: amberb@unt.edu.

DEGREES AND AWARDS
BA General Studies
BAA Applied Technology and Performance Improvement; Organizational Development
Certificate E-Commerce; Retailing–Five Course Sequence in Retailing; TESOL
Certification Texas Teacher Certification–Secondary Education
Endorsement Gifted and Talented Education
Graduate Certificate Behavior Analysis; Gifted Education; Hospitality Management; Library and Information Sciences; Merchandising; Specialist Certificate in Aging; Volunteer and Community Resource Management
MA Anthropology; Applied Gerontology
MBA Management; Marketing
MEd Education–Secondary Education; Educational Administration
MLS Library Science
MS Applied Gerontology; Computer Education and Cognitive Systems; Educational Administration and Supervision; Educational Psychology; Hospitality Management; Information Sciences; Merchandising; Teaching and Learning with Technology
MSE Applied Technology, Training, and Development

COURSE SUBJECT AREAS OFFERED OUTSIDE OF DEGREE PROGRAMS

Undergraduate—anthropology; apparel and textiles; behavioral sciences; biology; business administration, management and operations; business/commerce; business, management, and marketing related; chemistry; computer and information sciences; computer/information technology administration and management; computer software and media applications; curriculum and instruction; data entry/microcomputer applications; developmental and child psychology; economics; education; educational administration and supervision; educational assessment, evaluation, and research; educational/instructional media design; educational psychology; electrical and electronic engineering technologies; engineering-related technologies; engineering technologies related; English composition; family and consumer economics; fine and studio art; food science and technology; geological and earth sciences/geosciences; health and physical education/fitness; history; hospitality administration; human development, family studies, and related services; journalism; library science; library science related; linguistic, comparative, and related language studies; marketing; mathematics; music; nutrition sciences; psychology related; public administration; rehabilitation and therapeutic professions; sales, merchandising, and related marketing operations (specialized); social sciences; social work; sociology; special education; technical and business writing.

Graduate—anthropology; apparel and textiles; behavioral sciences; business administration, management and operations; business, management, and marketing related; chemistry; communications technology; community organization and advocacy; computer and information sciences; computer software and media applications; curriculum and instruction; developmental and child psychology; education; educational administration and supervision; educational assessment, evaluation, and research; educational/instructional media design; educational psychology; education related; electrical and electronic engineering technologies; family and consumer economics; food science and technology; gerontology; health and medical administrative services; hospitality administration; human development, family studies, and related services; human resources management; industrial and organizational psychology; information science/studies; library science; library science related; linguistic, comparative, and related language studies; marketing; rehabilitation and therapeutic professions; sales, merchandising, and related marketing operations (specialized); social and philosophical foundations of education; social sciences; special education.

Non-credit—behavioral sciences; business administration, management and operations; education; educational administration and supervision; educational psychology; gerontology; library science; library science related; marketing; rehabilitation and therapeutic professions; school psychology; special education.

UNIVERSITY OF NORTHWESTERN OHIO
Lima, Ohio
Division of Distance Learning
http://www.unoh.edu

University of Northwestern Ohio was founded in 1920. It is accredited by North Central Association of Colleges and Schools. It first offered distance learning courses in 1993. In fall 2007, there were 800 students enrolled in distance learning courses. Institutionally administered financial aid is available to distance learners.

Services Distance learners have accessibility to academic advising, bookstore, campus computer network, career placement assistance, e-mail services, library services, tutoring.

Contact Mr. Rick Morrison, Director of Admissions, University of Northwestern Ohio, 1441 North Cable Road, Lima, OH 45805. Telephone: 419-998-3120. Fax: 419-229-6926. E-mail: rmorris@unoh.edu.

DEGREES AND AWARDS

AAS Agribusiness; Automotive Management; Information Systems Technology; Legal Assisting; Marketing; Marketing, Management, and Technology; Medical Assistant Technology; Secretarial (Administrative, Legal, Medical); Travel Management; Word Processing–Administrative Support

BS Accounting; Business Administration; Health Care Administration

COURSE SUBJECT AREAS OFFERED OUTSIDE OF DEGREE PROGRAMS

Undergraduate—accounting and related services; agricultural business and management; allied health and medical assisting services; business administration, management and operations; business operations support and assistant services; computer and information sciences; electrical and power transmission installation.

UNIVERSITY OF OKLAHOMA
Norman, Oklahoma
College of Continuing Education
http://www.outreach.ou.edu

University of Oklahoma was founded in 1890. It is accredited by North Central Association of Colleges and Schools. It first offered distance learning courses in 1941. In fall 2007, there were 50,000 students enrolled in distance learning courses. Institutionally administered financial aid is available to distance learners.

Services Distance learners have accessibility to academic advising, bookstore, campus computer network, career placement assistance, e-mail services, library services.

Contact Larry D. Hayes, Information Assistant, Office of the Vice President for University Outreach, University of Oklahoma, University OUTREACH, 1700 Asp Avenue, Norman, OK 73072. Telephone: 800-522-0772 Ext. 4414. Fax: 405-325-7196. E-mail: lhayes@ou.edu.

DEGREES AND AWARDS

BA Liberal Studies

MA Advanced Programs; Liberal Studies

PhD Advanced Programs

COURSE SUBJECT AREAS OFFERED OUTSIDE OF DEGREE PROGRAMS

Undergraduate—anthropology; astronomy and astrophysics; business administration, management and operations; business/corporate communications; chemistry; communication and media; dramatic/theater arts and stagecraft; economics; education; engineering; English composition; finance and financial management services; geography and cartography; geological and earth sciences/geosciences; health and physical education/fitness; history; journalism; library science related; marketing; mathematics; philosophy; political science and government; sociology.

See full description on page 506.

UNIVERSITY OF OREGON
Eugene, Oregon
Distance Education
http://de.uoregon.edu

University of Oregon was founded in 1872. It is accredited by Northwest Commission on Colleges and Universities. It first offered distance learning courses in 1996. In fall 2007, there were 850 students enrolled in distance learning courses. Institutionally administered financial aid is available to distance learners.

Services Distance learners have accessibility to academic advising, bookstore, campus computer network, e-mail services, library services.

Contact Sonya Faust, Program Coordinator, University of Oregon, 1277 University of Oregon, Eugene, OR 97403-1277. Telephone: 541-346-4231. Fax: 541-346-3545. E-mail: disted@uoregon.edu.

DEGREES AND AWARDS

MS Applied Information Management

COURSE SUBJECT AREAS OFFERED OUTSIDE OF DEGREE PROGRAMS

Undergraduate—astronomy and astrophysics; economics; geography and cartography; geological and earth sciences/geosciences; linguistic, comparative, and related language studies; multi-/interdisciplinary studies related; physics; political science and government; science, technology and society; visual and performing arts related.

Graduate—history; information science/studies; management information systems.

UNIVERSITY OF PENNSYLVANIA
Philadelphia, Pennsylvania
Distance Education
http://www.upenn.edu/programs/distance.php

University of Pennsylvania was founded in 1740. It is accredited by Middle States Association of Colleges and Schools. It first offered distance learning courses in 1995. In fall 2007, there were 300 students enrolled in distance learning courses. Institutionally administered financial aid is available to distance learners.

Services Distance learners have accessibility to academic advising, bookstore, campus computer network, career placement assistance, e-mail services, library services.

Contact Ms. Miriam Wright, Manager, Recruitment and Admissions, University of Pennsylvania, College of General Studies, 3440 Market Street, Suite 100, Philadelphia, PA 19104-3335. Telephone: 215-898-7326. Fax: 215-573-2053. E-mail: cgs@sas.upenn.edu.

DEGREES AND AWARDS
Programs offered do not lead to a degree or other formal award.

COURSE SUBJECT AREAS OFFERED OUTSIDE OF DEGREE PROGRAMS

Undergraduate—anthropology; biological and physical sciences; cell biology and anatomical sciences; English composition; geological and earth sciences/geosciences; liberal arts and sciences, general studies and humanities; mathematics; psychology; social sciences.

Graduate—anthropology; English composition; psychology.

Non-credit—English as a second language.

UNIVERSITY OF PENNSYLVANIA
Philadelphia, Pennsylvania
School of Arts and Sciences
http://www.sas.upenn.edu/elp/online/index.php

University of Pennsylvania was founded in 1740. It is accredited by Middle States Association of Colleges and Schools. It first offered distance learning courses in 2004. In fall 2007, there were 42 students enrolled in distance learning courses. Institutionally administered financial aid is available to distance learners.

Services Distance learners have accessibility to academic advising, e-mail services.

Contact Ms. Karen Asenavage, Distributed Learning Coordinator, University of Pennsylvania, 110 Fisher-Bennett Hall, 3340 Walnut Street, Philadelphia, PA 19104-6274. Telephone: 215-898-8084. Fax: 215-898-2684. E-mail: elponline@sas.upenn.edu.

DEGREES AND AWARDS
Programs offered do not lead to a degree or other formal award.

COURSE SUBJECT AREAS OFFERED OUTSIDE OF DEGREE PROGRAMS
Non-credit—biological and biomedical sciences related; business/corporate communications; English as a second language; English composition.

UNIVERSITY OF PHOENIX
Phoenix, Arizona
http://www.uoponline.com
University of Phoenix was founded in 1989. It is accredited by North Central Association of Colleges and Schools. It first offered distance learning courses in 1989. In fall 2007, there were 224,880 students enrolled in distance learning courses. Institutionally administered financial aid is available to distance learners.
Services Distance learners have accessibility to academic advising, bookstore, campus computer network, library services, tutoring.
Contact Mr. Owen Murray, Vice President, Marketing, University of Phoenix, Mail Stop CF-K903, 4615 East Elwood Street, Phoenix, AZ 85040-1958. Telephone: 602-557-1662. Fax: 602-557-1898. E-mail: owen.murray@phoenix.edu.

DEGREES AND AWARDS
AA Accounting; Business; Communications; Criminal Justice; Elementary Education; Financial Services; General Studies; Health Administration; Health Care Administration–Medical Records; Health Care Administration–Pharmacy Practice; Hospitality, Travel, and Tourism; Human Services Management; Information Technology; Information Technology/Networking; Information Technology/Visual Communications; Paraprofessional Education; Psychology; Sports Management
BEd Education
BS Business Hospitality Management; Business/Accounting; Business/Business Administration; Business/Communication; Business/E-Business; Business/Finance; Business/Global Business Management; Business/Information Systems; Business/Integrated Supply Chain and Operations Management; Business/Management; Business/Marketing; Business/Organizational Innovation; Business/Public Administration; Business/Retail Management; Criminal Justice Administration; Health Administration; Health Administration/Health Information Systems; Health Administration/Long-Term Care; Health Care Services; Human Services; Human Services/Management; Information Technology; Information Technology/Business Systems Analysis; Information Technology/Information Systems Security; Information Technology/Multimedia and Visual Communication; Information Technology/Networking and Telecommunications; Information Technology/Software Engineering; Information Technology/Visual Communication; Management; Organizational Security and Management; Psychology
BSN Licensed Practical Nurse to Bachelor of Science in Nursing; Licensed Vocational Nurse to Bachelor of Science in Nursing; Nursing–RN to BSN
MA Curriculum and Instruction–Adult Education; Education–Administration and Supervision specialization; Education–Computer Education; Education–Curriculum and Instruction; Education–Early Childhood Education specialization; Education/Adult Education and Training; Education/Cross-Categorical Special Education; Education/Curriculum and Instruction–English and Language Education; Education/Curriculum and Instruction–Mathematics Education; Education/ESL; Education/Elementary Teacher Education; Education/Secondary Teacher Education
MBA Accounting; Business Administration; Business Administration/Marketing; Global Management; Human Resource Management; Public Administration; Spanish; Technology Management
MBA/MHMS Business Administration/Health Care Management
MHA Education; Gerontology; Health Administration–Master of Health Administration; Informatics

MISM Information Systems
MM Human Resource Management; International; Management; Public Administration
MS Accountancy; Administration of Justice and Security; Administration of Justice and Security; Counseling/Community Counseling; Counseling/Marriage and Family Counseling; Counseling/Marriage, Family, and Child Therapy; Counseling/Mental Health Counseling; Counseling/School Counseling; Psychology
MSN Family Nurse Practitioner; Informatics; Nursing for Nurse Practitioners; Nursing–Master of Business Administration, Health Care Management; Nursing–Nursing/Health Care Education; Nursing; Nursing/Health Care Education
DBA Business Administration
DH Sc Health Administration–Doctor of Health Administration (DHA)
DM Organizational Leadership, Information Systems and Technology specialization; Organizational Leadership/Information Systems and Technology; Organizational Management
EdD Educational Leadership; Educational Leadership, Curriculum and Instruction specialization; Educational Leadership/Education Technology
PhD Higher Education Administration

COURSE SUBJECT AREAS OFFERED OUTSIDE OF DEGREE PROGRAMS
Undergraduate—business operations support and assistant services; computer science; human resources management; nursing.
Graduate—accounting and related services; education; gerontology; human resources management; marketing; nursing.

UNIVERSITY OF PITTSBURGH
Pittsburgh, Pennsylvania
School of Nursing
http://www.nursing.pitt.edu
University of Pittsburgh was founded in 1787. It is accredited by Middle States Association of Colleges and Schools. In fall 2007, there were 300 students enrolled in distance learning courses. Institutionally administered financial aid is available to distance learners.
Services Distance learners have accessibility to campus computer network, e-mail services, library services.
Contact Mr. Scott Coulson, Associate Director, University of Pittsburgh, 219 Victoria Building, Pittsburgh, PA 15261. Telephone: 412-624-2419. E-mail: slc28@pitt.edu.

DEGREES AND AWARDS
Programs offered do not lead to a degree or other formal award.

COURSE SUBJECT AREAS OFFERED OUTSIDE OF DEGREE PROGRAMS
Undergraduate—nursing.
Graduate—nursing.
Non-credit—nursing.

UNIVERSITY OF PITTSBURGH AT BRADFORD
Bradford, Pennsylvania
http://www.upb.pitt.edu/
University of Pittsburgh at Bradford was founded in 1963. It is accredited by Middle States Association of Colleges and Schools. It first offered distance learning courses in 1995. In fall 2007, there were 67 students enrolled in distance learning courses. Institutionally administered financial aid is available to distance learners.
Services Distance learners have accessibility to academic advising, bookstore, campus computer network, career placement assistance, e-mail services, library services.
Contact Mr. Bernie Picklo, Academic Technology Integrator, University of Pittsburgh at Bradford, 300 Campus Drive, Bradford, PA 16701-2898. Telephone: 814-362-7644. Fax: 814-362-5279. E-mail: bjp47@pitt.edu.

DEGREES AND AWARDS
AA Liberal Studies

COURSE SUBJECT AREAS OFFERED OUTSIDE OF DEGREE PROGRAMS

Undergraduate—biology; business, management, and marketing related; chemistry; computer and information sciences; computer science; criminal justice and corrections; economics; management information systems; marketing; nursing.

UNIVERSITY OF PITTSBURGH AT JOHNSTOWN
Johnstown, Pennsylvania
http://www.upj.pitt.edu

University of Pittsburgh at Johnstown was founded in 1927. It is accredited by Middle States Association of Colleges and Schools. It first offered distance learning courses in 1994. In fall 2007, there were 45 students enrolled in distance learning courses. Institutionally administered financial aid is available to distance learners.

Services Distance learners have accessibility to career placement assistance, e-mail services, library services.

Contact Dr. Janet L. Grady, Director, Nursing Program, University of Pittsburgh at Johnstown, 141 Biddle Hall, Johnstown, PA 15904. Telephone: 814-269-2995. Fax: 814-269-2957. E-mail: jgrady@pitt.edu.

DEGREES AND AWARDS
Programs offered do not lead to a degree or other formal award.

COURSE SUBJECT AREAS OFFERED OUTSIDE OF DEGREE PROGRAMS

Graduate—nursing.

UNIVERSITY OF ST. AUGUSTINE FOR HEALTH SCIENCES
St. Augustine, Florida
Division of Distance Education
http://www.usa.edu

University of St. Augustine for Health Sciences was founded in 1978. It is accredited by Distance Education and Training Council. It first offered distance learning courses in 1979. In fall 2007, there were 557 students enrolled in distance learning courses. Institutionally administered financial aid is available to distance learners.

Services Distance learners have accessibility to academic advising, bookstore, e-mail services, library services, tutoring.

Contact Dr. Debra Gray, Transitional DPT Program Director, University of St. Augustine for Health Sciences, 1 University Boulevard, St. Augustine, FL 32086. Telephone: 904-826-0084 Ext. 262. Fax: 904-826-0085. E-mail: info@usa.edu.

DEGREES AND AWARDS
DPT Transitional Doctor of Physical Therapy
OTD Transitional Doctor of Occupational Therapy

COURSE SUBJECT AREAS OFFERED OUTSIDE OF DEGREE PROGRAMS

Graduate—rehabilitation and therapeutic professions.
Non-credit—health professions related.

UNIVERSITY OF ST. FRANCIS
Joliet, Illinois
http://www.stfrancis.edu/

University of St. Francis was founded in 1920. It is accredited by North Central Association of Colleges and Schools. It first offered distance learning courses in 1997. In fall 2007, there were 1,536 students enrolled in distance learning courses. Institutionally administered financial aid is available to distance learners.

Services Distance learners have accessibility to academic advising, bookstore, campus computer network, career placement assistance, e-mail services, library services, tutoring.

Contact Ms. Sandra Sloka, Director, Graduate and Degree Completion Admissions, University of St. Francis, 500 Wilcox Street, Joliet, IL 60435. Telephone: 800-735-7500. Fax: 815-740-5032. E-mail: ssloka@stfrancis.edu.

DEGREES AND AWARDS
BS Applied Organizational Management; Health Care Leadership; Organizational Leadership
BSN Nursing Fast Track
MBA Business Administration
MS Health Services Administration; Training and Development
MSM Management
MSN Clinical Specialist; Nurse Practitioner

COURSE SUBJECT AREAS OFFERED OUTSIDE OF DEGREE PROGRAMS

Undergraduate—business administration, management and operations; communication and media; computer and information sciences; English; fine and studio art; health professions related; history; nursing; philosophy and religious studies related; social sciences.
Graduate—business administration, management and operations; educational assessment, evaluation, and research; health and medical administrative services; nursing.

UNIVERSITY OF ST. MICHAEL'S COLLEGE
Toronto, Ontario, Canada

University of St. Michael's College was founded in 1852. It is provincially chartered. It first offered distance learning courses in 2005. In fall 2007, there were 20 students enrolled in distance learning courses. Institutionally administered financial aid is available to distance learners.

Services Distance learners have accessibility to academic advising, campus computer network, e-mail services, library services.

Contact Dr. Anne Anderson, CSJ, Dean, Faculty of Theology, University of St. Michael's College, 81 St. Mary Street, Toronto, ON M5S 1J4, Canada. Telephone: 416-926-7265. Fax: 416-926-7294. E-mail: anne.anderson@utoronto.ca.

DEGREES AND AWARDS
Programs offered do not lead to a degree or other formal award.

COURSE SUBJECT AREAS OFFERED OUTSIDE OF DEGREE PROGRAMS

Undergraduate—theology and religious vocations related.
Graduate—theology and religious vocations related.
Non-credit—theology and religious vocations related.

UNIVERSITY OF ST. THOMAS
St. Paul, Minnesota
http://www.stthomas.edu/

University of St. Thomas was founded in 1885. It is accredited by North Central Association of Colleges and Schools. It first offered distance learning courses in 1994. In fall 2007, there were 95 students enrolled in distance learning courses. Institutionally administered financial aid is available to distance learners.

Services Distance learners have accessibility to bookstore, campus computer network, e-mail services, library services.

Contact Dr. Rosann Cahill, Associate Director, Web and Media Services, University of St. Thomas, Mail #5048, 2115 Summit Avenue, St. Paul, MN 55105. Telephone: 651-962-6272. E-mail: rfcahill@stthomas.edu.

DEGREES AND AWARDS
MBA Health Service

COURSE SUBJECT AREAS OFFERED OUTSIDE OF DEGREE PROGRAMS

Undergraduate—education (specific levels and methods); languages (Germanic); music; philosophy.

Graduate—educational administration and supervision; educational assessment, evaluation, and research; educational/instructional media design; health professions related.
Non-credit—education.

UNIVERSITY OF SASKATCHEWAN
Saskatoon, Saskatchewan, Canada
Extension Credit Studies
http://www.ccde.usask.ca
University of Saskatchewan was founded in 1907. It is provincially chartered. It first offered distance learning courses in 1941. In fall 2007, there were 1,500 students enrolled in distance learning courses. Institutionally administered financial aid is available to distance learners.
Services Distance learners have accessibility to academic advising, bookstore, campus computer network, e-mail services, library services, tutoring.
Contact Ms. Grace Milashenko, Independent Studies Coordinator, University of Saskatchewan, Centre for Continuing and Distance Education, 427 Williams Building, 221 Cumberland Avenue North, Saskatoon, SK S7N 1M3, Canada. Telephone: 306-966-5562. Fax: 306-966-5590. E-mail: grace.milashenko@usask.ca.

DEGREES AND AWARDS
Programs offered do not lead to a degree or other formal award.

COURSE SUBJECT AREAS OFFERED OUTSIDE OF DEGREE PROGRAMS
Undergraduate—agricultural business and management; agriculture; anthropology; archeology; computer science; curriculum and instruction; economics; education (specific levels and methods); education (specific subject areas); English; English as a second/foreign language (teaching); English as a second language; English literature (British and Commonwealth); geography and cartography; geological and earth sciences/geosciences; history; mathematics; music; nursing; philosophy; political science and government; psychology; religious studies; sociology.
Graduate—educational psychology; education related.
Non-credit—agricultural business and management; agriculture and agriculture operations related; applied horticulture/horticultural business services; botany/plant biology; educational/instructional media design; education related; education (specific subject areas); English as a second/foreign language (teaching); English as a second language; landscape architecture; soil sciences.

THE UNIVERSITY OF SCRANTON
Scranton, Pennsylvania
http://scrantonuniversityonline.com
The University of Scranton was founded in 1888. It is accredited by Middle States Association of Colleges and Schools.
Contact The University of Scranton Online, The University of Scranton, Scranton, PA 18510. Telephone: 866-373-9547.

DEGREES AND AWARDS
MBA Online MBA in Health Care Management; Online MBA

UNIVERSITY OF SIOUX FALLS
Sioux Falls, South Dakota
http://www.usiouxfalls.edu/
University of Sioux Falls was founded in 1883. It is accredited by North Central Association of Colleges and Schools. It first offered distance learning courses in 2000. In fall 2007, there were 160 students enrolled in distance learning courses. Institutionally administered financial aid is available to distance learners.
Services Distance learners have accessibility to academic advising, bookstore, campus computer network, career placement assistance, e-mail services, library services.
Contact Phyllis Thompson, Associate Dean of Academic Affairs and Registrar, University of Sioux Falls, 1101 West 22nd Street, Jorden Hall,

Sioux Falls, SD 57105. Telephone: 605-331-6651. Fax: 605-331-6615. E-mail: phyllis.thompson@usiouxfalls.edu.

DEGREES AND AWARDS
Programs offered do not lead to a degree or other formal award.

COURSE SUBJECT AREAS OFFERED OUTSIDE OF DEGREE PROGRAMS
Undergraduate—education (specific subject areas); English; fine and studio art; geography and cartography; health and physical education/fitness; health professions related; history; religious education; sociology.
Graduate—education; educational administration and supervision; educational assessment, evaluation, and research.

UNIVERSITY OF SOUTH ALABAMA
Mobile, Alabama
USA Online
http://usaonline.southalabama.edu
University of South Alabama was founded in 1963. It is accredited by Southern Association of Colleges and Schools. It first offered distance learning courses in 1999. In fall 2007, there were 1,886 students enrolled in distance learning courses. Institutionally administered financial aid is available to distance learners.
Services Distance learners have accessibility to academic advising, bookstore, e-mail services, library services.
Contact Norma Jean Tanner, Director of Admissions, University of South Alabama, MH 2500, Mobile, AL 36688-0002. Telephone: 251-460-6141. Fax: 251-460-7876. E-mail: admiss@usouthal.edu.

DEGREES AND AWARDS
BSN Nursing
Certification Educational Administration; Educational Media (Library Media)
MEd Educational Leadership; Educational Media (Library Media); Special Education (Gifted)
MS Instructional Design and Development
MSN Nursing

COURSE SUBJECT AREAS OFFERED OUTSIDE OF DEGREE PROGRAMS
Undergraduate—biological and biomedical sciences related; communication and journalism related; computer and information sciences; education; educational psychology; engineering; gerontology; nursing; psychology; sociology.
Graduate—biology; educational administration and supervision; educational/instructional media design; education (specific levels and methods); gerontology; nursing; sociology; special education.

THE UNIVERSITY OF SOUTH DAKOTA
Vermillion, South Dakota
Division of Continuing and Distance Education
http://www.usd.edu/ce
The University of South Dakota was founded in 1862. It is accredited by North Central Association of Colleges and Schools. It first offered distance learning courses in 1957. In fall 2007, there were 1,259 students enrolled in distance learning courses. Institutionally administered financial aid is available to distance learners.
Services Distance learners have accessibility to academic advising, bookstore, campus computer network, career placement assistance, e-mail services, library services, tutoring.
Contact Secretary, The University of South Dakota, Division of Continuing and Distance Education, 414 East Clark Street, Vermillion, SD 57069. Telephone: 800-233-7937. Fax: 605-677-6118. E-mail: ceinfo@usd.edu.

DEGREES AND AWARDS
AA General Studies
Certificate Alcohol and Drug Abuse Studies
Graduate Certificate Alcohol and Drug Abuse Studies; Long-Term Care Management
MA Educational Administration/Adult and Higher Education; Educational Administration/Elementary School Principal; Educational Administration/

Pre-K-12 Principal; Educational Administration/School District Superintendent; Educational Administration/Secondary School Principal
MBA Business Administration; Health Services Administration specialization
MS Administrative Studies/Health Services Administration; Administrative Studies/Interdisciplinary Studies; Administrative Studies/Long-Term Care Administration; Administrative Studies/Organizational Leadership; Technology for Education and Training

COURSE SUBJECT AREAS OFFERED OUTSIDE OF DEGREE PROGRAMS

Undergraduate—behavioral sciences; biology; chemistry; creative writing; criminal justice and corrections; criminology; dramatic/theater arts and stagecraft; education; English; English composition; history; liberal arts and sciences, general studies and humanities; mathematics; microbiological sciences and immunology; music; nursing; physical sciences; physiology, pathology and related sciences; psychology; public relations, advertising, and applied communication related; social sciences related; sociology; speech and rhetoric; statistics.

Graduate—counseling psychology; criminal justice and corrections; education; speech and rhetoric.

UNIVERSITY OF SOUTHERN CALIFORNIA
Los Angeles, California
Technology Enhanced Learning and Distance Learning Initiative
http://tel.usc.edu
University of Southern California was founded in 1880. It is accredited by Western Association of Schools and Colleges. It first offered distance learning courses in 1972. In fall 2007, there were 1,585 students enrolled in distance learning courses. Institutionally administered financial aid is available to distance learners.
Services Distance learners have accessibility to academic advising, bookstore, campus computer network, career placement assistance, e-mail services, library services, tutoring.
Contact Dr. Suh-Pyng Ku, Vice Provost and Executive Director for Continuing Education and Summer Programs, University of Southern California, Los Angeles, CA 90089-0874. Telephone: 213-740-9767. E-mail: suhpyng.ku@marshall.usc.edu.

DEGREES AND AWARDS
Certificate of Completion Differentiated Curriculum for Gifted Students; Education of Twice-Exceptional Students; Program of Professional Preparation Reading Certificate; School Business Management
Graduate Certificate Astronautical Engineering; Clinical Research Design and Management; Engineering Technology Commercialization; Food Safety; Geographic Information Science and Technology; Gerontology; Network Centric Systems; Patient and Product Safety; Petroleum Engineering (Smart Oilfield Technologies); Preclinical Drug Development; System Safety and Security; Systems Architecture Engineering
MA Gerontology; Long-Term Care Administration; Master of Academic Medicine
MCM Construction Management
MS Aerospace Engineering; Aerospace and Mechanical Engineering (Computational Fluid and Solid Mechanics); Aerospace and Mechanical Engineering (Dynamics and Control); Astronautical Engineering; Biomedical Engineering (Medical Imaging and Imaging Informatics); Biomedical Engineering; Chemical Engineering; Civil Engineering (Construction Engineering); Civil Engineering (Structural Engineering); Computer Engineering; Computer Science (Computer Networking); Computer Science (Computer Security); Computer Science (Multimedia and Creative Technologies); Computer Science (Software Engineering); Computer Science; Engineering Management; Geographic Information Science and Technology; Industrial and Systems Engineering; Materials Engineering; Mechanical Engineering; Medical Device and Diagnostic Engineering; Petroleum Engineering (Smart Oilfield Technologies); Petroleum Engineering; Product Development Engineering; Regulatory Science; System Safety and Security; Systems Architecture Engineering

MSEE Electrical Engineering (Computer Networks); Electrical Engineering (Multimedia and Creative Technologies); Electrical Engineering (VLSI Design); Electrical Engineering

COURSE SUBJECT AREAS OFFERED OUTSIDE OF DEGREE PROGRAMS
Non-credit—aerospace, aeronautical and astronautical engineering; engineering related.

UNIVERSITY OF SOUTHERN INDIANA
Evansville, Indiana
Distance Education Programming
http://www.usi.edu/distance
University of Southern Indiana was founded in 1965. It is accredited by North Central Association of Colleges and Schools. It first offered distance learning courses in 1994. In fall 2007, there were 1,853 students enrolled in distance learning courses. Institutionally administered financial aid is available to distance learners.
Services Distance learners have accessibility to academic advising, bookstore, campus computer network, e-mail services, library services.
Contact Mr. Dana R. Willett, Director, Instructional Technology Services, University of Southern Indiana, 8600 University Boulevard, Room FA41, Evansville, IN 47712. Telephone: 800-813-4238. Fax: 812-465-7131. E-mail: dwillett@usi.edu.

DEGREES AND AWARDS
BS Health Professions and Related Sciences; Radiologic and Imaging Sciences
BSN Nursing
MHA Health Administration
MSN Nursing
MSOT Occupational Therapy

COURSE SUBJECT AREAS OFFERED OUTSIDE OF DEGREE PROGRAMS
Undergraduate—biology; communication and media; computer/information technology administration and management; dental support services and allied professions; economics; education; educational psychology; education (specific levels and methods); English; English composition; English literature (British and Commonwealth); fine and studio art; gerontology; health and medical administrative services; history; journalism; languages (foreign languages related); linguistic, comparative, and related language studies; nursing; political science and government; psychology; public relations, advertising, and applied communication related; radio, television, and digital communication; speech and rhetoric; visual and performing arts.
Graduate—economics; education; education (specific subject areas); health professions related; marketing; nursing; social work.
Non-credit—accounting and computer science; audiovisual communications technologies; communication and journalism related; computer and information sciences; computer software and media applications; film/video and photographic arts; health professions related; human resources management; legal professions and studies related; nursing; sales, merchandising, and related marketing operations (general).

UNIVERSITY OF SOUTHERN MAINE
Portland, Maine
USU Distance Learning Program
http://www.usm.maine.edu/eap/distanceeducation
University of Southern Maine was founded in 1878. It is accredited by New England Association of Schools and Colleges. It first offered distance learning courses in 1983. In fall 2007, there were 800 students enrolled in distance learning courses. Institutionally administered financial aid is available to distance learners.
Services Distance learners have accessibility to academic advising, bookstore, campus computer network, e-mail services, library services.

Contact Ms. Ann E. Clarey, Director of Center for Technology-Enhanced Learning, University of Southern Maine, PO Box 9300, Portland, ME 04104-9300. Telephone: 207-780-4540. Fax: 207-228-8094. E-mail: clarey@usm.maine.edu.

DEGREES AND AWARDS
BSN Nursing–RN to BSN
Certificate Applied Research and Evaluation Methods; Foundations of Holistic Health; Health Policy and Management; Mental Health Rehabilitation Technician–Community; Nonprofit Management
Certification Unified K-8 General and Special Education
MS Ed Adult Education

COURSE SUBJECT AREAS OFFERED OUTSIDE OF DEGREE PROGRAMS
Undergraduate—anthropology; communication and media; community health services; English composition; health professions related; liberal arts and sciences, general studies and humanities; mathematics and statistics related; music; nursing; psychology; sociology.
Graduate—education; educational assessment, evaluation, and research; public policy analysis; social work.
Non-credit—information science/studies.

UNIVERSITY OF SOUTHERN MISSISSIPPI
Hattiesburg, Mississippi
Department of Continuing Education
http://www.usm.edu/lec/des
University of Southern Mississippi was founded in 1910. It is accredited by Southern Association of Colleges and Schools. It first offered distance learning courses in 1941. In fall 2007, there were 2,970 students enrolled in distance learning courses. Institutionally administered financial aid is available to distance learners.
Services Distance learners have accessibility to academic advising, bookstore, campus computer network, e-mail services, library services.
Contact Ms. Sheri L. Rawls, Director, Learning Enhancement Center, University of Southern Mississippi, Learning Enhancement Center, 118 College Drive, #9649, Hattiesburg, MS 39406-0001. Telephone: 601-266-5518. Fax: 601-266-4560. E-mail: sheri.rawls@usm.edu.

DEGREES AND AWARDS
BS Construction Technology
BSN Nursing–RN to BSN
MAT Teaching of Languages (MATL)
MEd Music Education–Master of Music Education
MLIS Library Information Science
MS Child and Family Studies; Economic Development; Sport Coaching Education; Sport Management; Workforce Training and Development
PhD Human Capital Development

COURSE SUBJECT AREAS OFFERED OUTSIDE OF DEGREE PROGRAMS
Undergraduate—accounting and related services; anthropology; biblical studies; biology; chemistry; community health services; community organization and advocacy; comparative literature; creative writing; criminal justice and corrections; criminology; educational administration and supervision; educational assessment, evaluation, and research; education related; engineering technologies related; English; English composition; English literature (British and Commonwealth); foods, nutrition, and related services; geography and cartography; health and physical education/fitness; health professions related; human development, family studies, and related services; liberal arts and sciences, general studies and humanities; library science related; linguistic, comparative, and related language studies; management information systems; marketing; mathematics and statistics related; microbiological sciences and immunology; music; nursing; philosophy and religious studies related; social work; sociology; special education; technical and business writing.
Graduate—biochemistry, biophysics and molecular biology; biology; city/urban, community and regional planning; cognitive psychology and psycholinguistics; communication and media; community health services; construction engineering technology; criminal justice and corrections; curriculum and instruction; demography and population; economics;

education; educational administration and supervision; educational assessment, evaluation, and research; geography and cartography; health and physical education/fitness; human development, family studies, and related services; linguistic, comparative, and related language studies; marketing; music; nursing; parks, recreation, and leisure related; public health; social and philosophical foundations of education; social work; special education; statistics.

UNIVERSITY OF SOUTH FLORIDA
Tampa, Florida
Educational Outreach
http://www.outreach.usf.edu/
University of South Florida was founded in 1956. It is accredited by Southern Association of Colleges and Schools. It first offered distance learning courses in 1983. In fall 2007, there were 16,932 students enrolled in distance learning courses. Institutionally administered financial aid is available to distance learners.
Services Distance learners have accessibility to academic advising, bookstore, campus computer network, career placement assistance, e-mail services, library services.
Contact Office of the Registrar, University of South Florida, 4202 East Fowler Avenue, SVC 1034, Tampa, FL 33620. Telephone: 813-974-2000. Fax: 813-974-5271. E-mail: asktheregistrar@admin.usf.edu.

DEGREES AND AWARDS
BS AS to BS Applied Sciences
BSN Nursing–RN completion program for Associate degree-holding nurses
Graduate Certificate Children's Mental Health; Clinical Investigation; Digital Music Education; Disaster Management; ESOL; Engineering Technology Management; Entrepreneurship; Gerontology; Gifted Education; Health Sciences; Hearing Specialist–Early Intervention; Homeland Security; Humanitarian Assistance; Infection Control; Instructional Technology–Distance Education; Instructional Technology–Web Design; Occupational Health Nursing; Process Engineering; Public Health Generalist; Public Health Policy and Programs; Regulatory Affairs–Medical Devices; Total Quality Management Engineering; Transportation Systems Analysis; Wireless Engineering
MA Career and Technical Education; Gifted Education; Library and Information Science; Music Education; Physical Education
ME Chemical Engineering
MEd Curriculum and Instruction–Secondary Education, TESOL specialization
MEngr Civil and Environmental Engineering
MPH Public Health Administration; Public Health Practice
MSE Industrial Engineering
MSEE Electrical Engineering
MSEM Engineering Management

COURSE SUBJECT AREAS OFFERED OUTSIDE OF DEGREE PROGRAMS
Undergraduate—anthropology; archeology; area, ethnic, cultural, and gender studies related; area studies; biology; chemistry; criminal justice and corrections; curriculum and instruction; education; engineering; English; English composition; ethnic, cultural minority, and gender studies; fine and studio art; geography and cartography; geological and earth sciences/geosciences; history; languages (Romance languages); liberal arts and sciences, general studies and humanities; library science; mathematics; mathematics and computer science; music; natural sciences; nursing; nutrition sciences; philosophy; philosophy and religious studies related; social sciences; sociology; visual and performing arts.
Graduate—accounting and computer science; biomedical/medical engineering; business administration, management and operations; business, management, and marketing related; business/managerial economics; chemical engineering; chemistry; civil engineering technology; computer and information sciences; computer engineering; computer programming; computer software and media applications; construction engineering; criminal justice and corrections; criminology; curriculum and instruction; education; educational administration and supervision; educational assessment, evaluation, and research; educational/instructional media design; educational psychology; education (specific levels and methods);

education (specific subject areas); electrical and electronic engineering technologies; electrical, electronics and communications engineering; engineering; engineering design; engineering/industrial management; English; English as a second/foreign language (teaching); environmental/ environmental health engineering; health services/allied health/health sciences; industrial engineering; information science/studies; languages (Germanic); library science; marketing; materials engineering; mechanical engineering; music; nursing; psychology; public administration; public health; public policy analysis; quality control and safety technologies; social and philosophical foundations of education; special education; systems engineering; visual and performing arts.

Non-credit—business administration, management and operations; communication and journalism related; computer programming; computer software and media applications; creative writing; English as a second language; entrepreneurial and small business operations; finance and financial management services; journalism; publishing.

THE UNIVERSITY OF TENNESSEE
Knoxville, Tennessee
Department of Distance Education and Independent Study
http://www.anywhere.tennessee.edu
The University of Tennessee was founded in 1794. It is accredited by Southern Association of Colleges and Schools. It first offered distance learning courses in 1941. In fall 2007, there were 2,356 students enrolled in distance learning courses. Institutionally administered financial aid is available to distance learners.
Services Distance learners have accessibility to academic advising, bookstore, campus computer network, e-mail services, library services.
Contact Ms. Caroline C. Bowers, Assistant Director, Distance Education, The University of Tennessee, 208 Conference Center Building, 600 Henley Street, Knoxville, TN 37996-4126. Telephone: 800-670-8657. Fax: 865-974-4684. E-mail: cbowers1@utk.edu.

DEGREES AND AWARDS
Graduate Certificate Applied Statistical Strategies; Computational Fluid Dynamics; Engineering Management; Nuclear Criticality Safety; Reliability and Maintainability Engineering
MBA Aerospace; Executive; Physician Executive; Professional (weekend) program
MCE Public Works option
MS Agricultural and Extension Education; Engineering Management; Environmental Engineering; Information Sciences; Instructional Technology (WebIT); Nuclear Engineering; Rehabilitation Counseling; Reliability and Maintainability Engineering; Social Work, Advanced Standing Program; Social Work, Extended Study Program

COURSE SUBJECT AREAS OFFERED OUTSIDE OF DEGREE PROGRAMS
Undergraduate—agricultural business and management; American literature (United States and Canadian); anthropology; applied mathematics; astronomy and astrophysics; business administration, management and operations; chemistry; creative writing; curriculum and instruction; economics; education; English; English composition; English language and literature related; English literature (British and Commonwealth); geography and cartography; history; languages (Germanic); languages (Romance languages); liberal arts and sciences, general studies and humanities; mathematics; physics; political science and government; psychology; religious studies; sociology; technical and business writing.
Non-credit—computer/information technology administration and management; creative writing; English composition; languages (foreign languages related); languages (Romance languages); mathematics; technology education/industrial arts.

THE UNIVERSITY OF TENNESSEE AT MARTIN
Martin, Tennessee
Office of Extended Campus and Continuing Education
http://www.utm.edu
The University of Tennessee at Martin was founded in 1900. It is accredited by Southern Association of Colleges and Schools. It first offered distance learning courses in 1992. In fall 2007, there were 939 students enrolled in distance learning courses. Institutionally administered financial aid is available to distance learners.
Services Distance learners have accessibility to academic advising, bookstore, campus computer network, career placement assistance, e-mail services, library services.
Contact Dr. Tommy Cates, Director, The University of Tennessee at Martin, Office of Online and University Studies, 227 Administration Building, Martin, TN 38238-5050. Telephone: 731-881-7589. E-mail: tcates@utm.edu.

DEGREES AND AWARDS
BUS University Studies
MBA Business Administration
MS Ed Counseling; Education Administration and Supervision
MS Agriculture and Natural Resources Systems Management
MSE Education

COURSE SUBJECT AREAS OFFERED OUTSIDE OF DEGREE PROGRAMS
Non-credit—accounting and related services; business administration, management and operations; computer and information sciences; crafts, folk art and artisanry; criminal justice and corrections; education; education (specific levels and methods); human development, family studies, and related services.

THE UNIVERSITY OF TEXAS AT BROWNSVILLE
Brownsville, Texas
Academic Computing
http://www.utb.edu
The University of Texas at Brownsville was founded in 1973. It is accredited by Southern Association of Colleges and Schools. It first offered distance learning courses in 2003. In fall 2007, there were 3,332 students enrolled in distance learning courses. Institutionally administered financial aid is available to distance learners.
Services Distance learners have accessibility to academic advising, bookstore, campus computer network, career placement assistance, e-mail services, library services, tutoring.
Contact Rene Sainz, Assistant Director of Distance Education Office, The University of Texas at Brownsville, 80 Fort Brown, Brownsville, TX 78520. Telephone: 956-574-6695 Ext. 6695. Fax: 956-574-6751. E-mail: deonline@utb.edu.

DEGREES AND AWARDS
BA Criminal Justice
BN Nursing; Nursing
BSAST Bachelor of Applied Technology
Advanced Graduate Diploma Master in Mathematics
MBA Business Administration
MEd Educational Technology; Masters Teacher Certification

COURSE SUBJECT AREAS OFFERED OUTSIDE OF DEGREE PROGRAMS
Undergraduate—behavioral sciences; bilingual, multilingual, and multicultural education; computer science; curriculum and instruction; English composition; mathematics; mathematics and statistics related; social sciences related.
Graduate—developmental and child psychology; education related.
Non-credit—accounting and related services; business administration, management and operations; computer software and media applications; computer systems networking and telecommunications; criminal justice and corrections; culinary arts and related services; dance; English as a second language; foods, nutrition, and related services; ground transportation; medical basic sciences; real estate.

THE UNIVERSITY OF TEXAS AT DALLAS
Richardson, Texas
Global On-Line MBA
http://som.utdallas.edu/globalmba/

The University of Texas at Dallas was founded in 1969. It is accredited by Southern Association of Colleges and Schools. It first offered distance learning courses in 1999. In fall 2007, there were 250 students enrolled in distance learning courses. Institutionally administered financial aid is available to distance learners.

Services Distance learners have accessibility to academic advising, campus computer network, e-mail services, library services.

Contact George Barnes, Director, The University of Texas at Dallas, 800 West Campbell Road, Mail Station 27, Richardson, TX 75080-3021. Telephone: 972-883-2783. Fax: 972-883-6598. E-mail: gbarnes@utdallas.edu.

DEGREES AND AWARDS
MBA Global MBA On-line

THE UNIVERSITY OF TEXAS AT EL PASO
El Paso, Texas
http://academics.utep.edu/online

The University of Texas at El Paso was founded in 1913. It is accredited by Southern Association of Colleges and Schools. It first offered distance learning courses in 1997. In fall 2007, there were 634 students enrolled in distance learning courses. Institutionally administered financial aid is available to distance learners.

Services Distance learners have accessibility to campus computer network, e-mail services, library services.

Contact Instructional Support Services, The University of Texas at El Paso. Telephone: 915-747-5059. E-mail: iss@utep.edu.

DEGREES AND AWARDS
BSN Nursing–RN to BSN
Certificate Nurse Clinician Educator
MFA Creative Writing

COURSE SUBJECT AREAS OFFERED OUTSIDE OF DEGREE PROGRAMS
Undergraduate—accounting and related services; anthropology; criminal justice and corrections; developmental and child psychology; education; educational administration and supervision; educational assessment, evaluation, and research; educational psychology; education related; English; liberal arts and sciences, general studies and humanities; linguistic, comparative, and related language studies; nursing; political science and government.

Graduate—creative writing; education; nursing.

THE UNIVERSITY OF TEXAS AT SAN ANTONIO
San Antonio, Texas
Distance Learning Center
http://dlat.utsa.edu

The University of Texas at San Antonio was founded in 1969. It is accredited by Southern Association of Colleges and Schools. It first offered distance learning courses in 1993. In fall 2007, there were 4,081 students enrolled in distance learning courses. Institutionally administered financial aid is available to distance learners.

Services Distance learners have accessibility to academic advising, bookstore, campus computer network, career placement assistance, e-mail services, library services, tutoring.

Contact Mr. Bill Angrove, Director of the Distance Learning Center, The University of Texas at San Antonio, 6900 North Loop 1604 West, San Antonio, TX 78249-0617. Telephone: 210-458-5855. Fax: 210-458-7378. E-mail: bill.angrove@utsa.edu.

DEGREES AND AWARDS
Certificate Paralegal Online Certificate program
MS Management of Technology

COURSE SUBJECT AREAS OFFERED OUTSIDE OF DEGREE PROGRAMS
Undergraduate—accounting and related services; anthropology; biological and physical sciences; biology; business administration, management and operations; business/commerce; business, management, and marketing related; cell biology and anatomical sciences; civil engineering; civil engineering technology; communication and media; computer programming; computer science; economics; education related; engineering; English composition; geography and cartography; geological and earth sciences/geosciences; health and physical education/fitness; health services/allied health/health sciences; information science/studies; languages (Romance languages); linguistic, comparative, and related language studies; marketing; mathematics; mechanical engineering; physical sciences; political science and government; psychology; sales, merchandising, and related marketing operations (specialized); technical and business writing.

Graduate—biology; business administration, management and operations; business, management, and marketing related; computer science; curriculum and instruction; economics; engineering; engineering/industrial management; engineering technologies related; languages (Romance languages); management information systems; management sciences and quantitative methods; mathematics; neuroscience; political science and government; psychology; technology education/industrial arts.

Non-credit—legal professions and studies related.

THE UNIVERSITY OF TEXAS AT TYLER
Tyler, Texas
Interactive Television
http://www.uttyler.edu

The University of Texas at Tyler was founded in 1971. It is accredited by Southern Association of Colleges and Schools. It first offered distance learning courses in 1991. Institutionally administered financial aid is available to distance learners.

Services Distance learners have accessibility to academic advising, bookstore, career placement assistance, e-mail services, library services.

Contact Bonnie Purser, Admissions Assistant, The University of Texas at Tyler, Enrollment Management, 3900 University Boulevard, Tyler, TX 75799. Telephone: 903-566-7202. Fax: 903-566-7068. E-mail: bpurser@uttyler.edu.

DEGREES AND AWARDS
BBA Business Administration
BEd BSIS-EC4
BN Nursing
BS Health Professions; Interdisciplinary Studies–Early Childhood through Grade Four (Education); Technology–Human Resource Development
BSN LVN to Bachelor of Science in Nursing; Nursing–RN Option; Nursing
MBA Business Administration
MEd Educational Leadership
MS Kinesiology; Technology–Human Resource Development
MSN Nursing–Administration and Education options; Nursing–RN to MSN; Nursing

COURSE SUBJECT AREAS OFFERED OUTSIDE OF DEGREE PROGRAMS
Undergraduate—accounting and related services; anthropology; archeology; biology; business/commerce; business/corporate communications; community health services; computer science; criminal justice and corrections; criminology; curriculum and instruction; education (specific levels and methods); finance and financial management services; fire protection; geography and cartography; health and physical education/fitness; health professions related; history; human resources management; industrial production technologies; marketing; mathematics; nursing; political science and government; psychology; sales, merchandising, and related marketing operations (specialized); sociology; special education; statistics; technology education/industrial arts.

Graduate—business administration, management and operations; computer science; health professions related; human resources management;

management sciences and quantitative methods; nursing; public administration; quality control and safety technologies; special education.

THE UNIVERSITY OF TEXAS OF THE PERMIAN BASIN
Odessa, Texas
REACH Program Center
http://www.utpb.edu/reach/
The University of Texas of the Permian Basin was founded in 1969. It is accredited by Southern Association of Colleges and Schools. It first offered distance learning courses in 1996. In fall 2007, there were 1,663 students enrolled in distance learning courses. Institutionally administered financial aid is available to distance learners.
Services Distance learners have accessibility to academic advising, bookstore, e-mail services, library services, tutoring.
Contact Lynn Rogers, Administrative Secretary, The University of Texas of the Permian Basin, 4901 East University Drive, Odessa, TX 79762-0001. Telephone: 432-552-2870. Fax: 432-522-2871. E-mail: rogers_l@utpb.edu.

DEGREES AND AWARDS
BA Criminal Justice
MBA Business Administration
MS Kinesiology

COURSE SUBJECT AREAS OFFERED OUTSIDE OF DEGREE PROGRAMS
Undergraduate—American literature (United States and Canadian); behavioral sciences; cognitive psychology and psycholinguistics; communication and media; computer and information sciences; computer science; criminology; curriculum and instruction; education; educational psychology; education related; education (specific levels and methods); education (specific subject areas); English as a second language; English composition; English language and literature related; English literature (British and Commonwealth); fine and studio art; health and physical education/fitness; history; human development, family studies, and related services; liberal arts and sciences, general studies and humanities; mathematics; music; philosophy and religious studies related; psychology; sociology; special education; visual and performing arts; visual and performing arts related.
Graduate—criminal justice and corrections; criminology; curriculum and instruction; educational administration and supervision; educational psychology; education (specific levels and methods); education (specific subject areas); English language and literature related; finance and financial management services; health and physical education/fitness; psychology; special education; statistics.

THE UNIVERSITY OF TEXAS SYSTEM
Austin, Texas
UT TeleCampus
http://www.telecampus.utsystem.edu
The University of Texas System is accredited by Southern Association of Colleges and Schools. It first offered distance learning courses in 1999. In fall 2007, there were 5,005 students enrolled in distance learning courses. Institutionally administered financial aid is available to distance learners.
Services Distance learners have accessibility to academic advising, bookstore, campus computer network, library services, tutoring.
Contact Dr. Darcy Hardy, Director, The University of Texas System, 702 Colorado, Suite 4.100, Austin, TX 78701. Telephone: 888-TEXAS-16. Fax: 512-499-4715. E-mail: telecampus@utsystem.edu.

DEGREES AND AWARDS
BS Criminal Justice (completion degree)
BSAST Health Services Technology (BAT)
BSN Nursing–RN to BSN
Certificate Blood Bank Technology; Border Administration; Border Studies; Chess in Education Online; Evidence-based Practice; Master Technology Teacher; Paralegal; Physical Therapy (IMPRINTS); Reading Specialist

Certification Alternative Teacher; Health Science Technology Teacher; Master Reading Teacher; Trade & Industrial (T&I) Education
Endorsement English as a Second Language (ESL)
Graduate Certificate Nursing Education
MAT Science Education
MBA Business Administration and Management
MEd Curriculum and Instruction; Educational Technology; Instructional Specialist (Bilingual Education or Early Childhood Education); Kinesiology
MPA Public Administration
MS Human Resource Development; Kinesiology
PhD Nursing

COURSE SUBJECT AREAS OFFERED OUTSIDE OF DEGREE PROGRAMS
Undergraduate—accounting and related services; biology; clinical/medical laboratory science and allied professions; computer and information sciences; computer and information sciences and support services related; computer systems networking and telecommunications; creative writing; curriculum and instruction; developmental and child psychology; economics; education; educational/instructional media design; education related; education (specific subject areas); English; English as a second language; English composition; English language and literature related; fine and studio art; geological and earth sciences/geosciences; health professions related; history; information science/studies; liberal arts and sciences, general studies and humanities; linguistic, comparative, and related language studies; mathematics; mathematics and statistics related; music; physical sciences; physical sciences related; political science and government; psychology; social and philosophical foundations of education; social sciences; social sciences related; sociology; statistics.
Graduate—allied health and medical assisting services; computer and information sciences; curriculum and instruction; education; educational/instructional media design; educational psychology; education related; education (specific subject areas); English as a second/foreign language (teaching); health professions related; nursing; political science and government; social and philosophical foundations of education; teaching assistants/aides.
Non-credit—allied health and medical assisting services; clinical/medical laboratory science and allied professions; legal support services; political science and government.
See full description on page 508.

UNIVERSITY OF THE INCARNATE WORD
San Antonio, Texas
Universe Online
http://www.uiw.edu/online
University of the Incarnate Word was founded in 1881. It is accredited by Southern Association of Colleges and Schools. It first offered distance learning courses in 2000. In fall 2007, there were 1,250 students enrolled in distance learning courses. Institutionally administered financial aid is available to distance learners.
Services Distance learners have accessibility to academic advising, bookstore, career placement assistance, library services, tutoring.
Contact Dr. Cyndi Wilson Porter, Dean, Virtual University/Director, Universe Online, University of the Incarnate Word, CPO #324, 4301 Broadway, San Antonio, TX 78209. Telephone: 877-827-2709. Fax: 210-829-2756. E-mail: virtual@uiwtx.edu.

DEGREES AND AWARDS
AA Business; Information Systems; Liberal Studies
BA Administration; Human Resources; Organizational Development
BAA Applied Arts and Sciences (BAAS)
BBA Business Administration
MA Administration–Communication Arts; Instructional Technology; Organizational Development
MBA General Program; International
See full description on page 510.

UNIVERSITY OF THE PACIFIC
Stockton, California
Center for Professional and Continuing Education
http://www.pacific.edu/cpce
University of the Pacific was founded in 1851. It is accredited by Western Association of Schools and Colleges. It first offered distance learning courses in 1995. In fall 2007, there were 2,750 students enrolled in distance learning courses. Institutionally administered financial aid is available to distance learners.
Contact Valerie Seimas, Interim Program Coordinator, University of the Pacific, 3601 Pacific Avenue, Stockton, CA 95211. Telephone: 209-946-2424 Ext. 65005. Fax: 209-946-3916. E-mail: cpce@pacific.edu.

DEGREES AND AWARDS
Programs offered do not lead to a degree or other formal award.

COURSE SUBJECT AREAS OFFERED OUTSIDE OF DEGREE PROGRAMS
Undergraduate—behavioral sciences; communication and media; counseling psychology; creative writing; dance; English; movement and mind-body therapies.
Graduate—curriculum and instruction; education related; education (specific subject areas).
Non-credit—behavioral sciences; counseling psychology.

UNIVERSITY OF THE SCIENCES IN PHILADELPHIA
Philadelphia, Pennsylvania
http://www.usp.edu
University of the Sciences in Philadelphia was founded in 1821. It is accredited by Middle States Association of Colleges and Schools. It first offered distance learning courses in 2000. In fall 2007, there were 123 students enrolled in distance learning courses. Institutionally administered financial aid is available to distance learners.
Services Distance learners have accessibility to academic advising, bookstore, campus computer network, e-mail services, library services.
Contact Ms. Joyce D'Angelo, Admission Counselor, College of Graduate Studies, University of the Sciences in Philadelphia, 600 South 43rd Street, Philadelphia, PA 19104-4418. Telephone: 215-596-8937. Fax: 215-895-1185. E-mail: j.dangel@usp.edu.

DEGREES AND AWARDS
MBA Pharmaceutical Business
MS Biomedical Writing

COURSE SUBJECT AREAS OFFERED OUTSIDE OF DEGREE PROGRAMS
Undergraduate—information science/studies.
Graduate—allied health diagnostic, intervention, and treatment professions; health professions related; health services/allied health/health sciences.

UNIVERSITY OF THE SOUTHWEST
Hobbs, New Mexico
http://www.usw.edu/
University of the Southwest was founded in 1962. It is accredited by North Central Association of Colleges and Schools. It first offered distance learning courses in 1994. In fall 2007, there were 300 students enrolled in distance learning courses. Institutionally administered financial aid is available to distance learners.
Services Distance learners have accessibility to academic advising, bookstore, campus computer network, e-mail services, library services, tutoring.
Contact Evelyn Rising, Acting Registrar, University of the Southwest, 6610 North Lovington Highway, Hobbs, NM 88240. Telephone: 575-392-6561 Ext. 1031. Fax: 575-392-6006. E-mail: erising@usw.edu.

DEGREES AND AWARDS
BS Criminal Justice

MSE Counseling (Mental Health); Curriculum and Instruction–Bilingual; Curriculum and Instruction–Reading; Curriculum and Instruction–TESOL; Curriculum and Instruction; Early Childhood Education; Educational Administration; Educational Diagnostician; School Business Administration; School Counseling; Special Education

COURSE SUBJECT AREAS OFFERED OUTSIDE OF DEGREE PROGRAMS
Undergraduate—accounting and related services; biblical studies; bilingual, multilingual, and multicultural education; biology; business administration, management and operations; business, management, and marketing related; computer and information sciences; computer science; creative writing; criminal justice and corrections; developmental and child psychology; economics; education; English as a second language; English composition; history; industrial and organizational psychology; marketing; psychology; religious studies; social psychology; sociology.

UNIVERSITY OF THE VIRGIN ISLANDS
Saint Thomas, Virgin Islands
http://www.uvi.edu
University of the Virgin Islands was founded in 1962. It is accredited by Middle States Association of Colleges and Schools. It first offered distance learning courses in 2003. Institutionally administered financial aid is available to distance learners.
Services Distance learners have accessibility to campus computer network, career placement assistance, e-mail services, library services.
Contact Monifa Potter, Registrar's Office, University of the Virgin Islands, Registrar's Office, #2 John Brewer's Bay, St. Thomas, VI 00802. Telephone: 340-693-1160. Fax: 340-693-1167. E-mail: registrar@uvi.edu.

DEGREES AND AWARDS
Programs offered do not lead to a degree or other formal award.

COURSE SUBJECT AREAS OFFERED OUTSIDE OF DEGREE PROGRAMS
Undergraduate—accounting and computer science; accounting and related services; astronomy and astrophysics; atmospheric sciences and meteorology; audiovisual communications technologies; communication and journalism related; communication and media; computer and information sciences; computer programming; computer science; English; English composition; English language and literature related; geography and cartography; journalism; social sciences related.
Graduate—business administration, management and operations; public administration and social service professions related.

THE UNIVERSITY OF TOLEDO
Toledo, Ohio
Division of Distance and eLearning
http://www.utoledo.edu/dl
The University of Toledo was founded in 1872. It is accredited by North Central Association of Colleges and Schools. It first offered distance learning courses in 1995. In fall 2007, there were 5,000 students enrolled in distance learning courses. Institutionally administered financial aid is available to distance learners.
Services Distance learners have accessibility to academic advising, bookstore, campus computer network, career placement assistance, e-mail services, library services, tutoring.
Contact James Ham, Coordinator, eLearning Student Services Management, The University of Toledo, eLearning and Academic Support, MS 516, Toledo, OH 43606-3390. Telephone: 419-530-8835. Fax: 419-530-8836. E-mail: utdl@utoledo.edu.

DEGREES AND AWARDS
AAB Accounting Technology; Business Management Technology–FastTrack option; Business Management Technology; Computer Software Specialist; Information Services and Support; Marketing and Sales Technology; Programming and Software Development
AIS Interdisciplinary program in Technical Studies

BA Adult Liberal Studies; Interdisciplinary Studies (BA or BS)
BS Computer Science and Engineering Technology; Criminal Justice; Health Care Administration; Health Information Management; Information Technology
Certificate Accounting Software Applications; Accounting Technology; Accounting for Health Care and Non-Profit; Applied Organizational Technology; Business Management Technology; Computer Software Specialist; Diversity Management; Information Services and Support; Legal Secretarial Certificate; Management Accounting; Marketing and Sales Technology; Nursing Education; Post-Baccalaureate Certificate in Health Information Administration; Preparation for Certified Bookkeeper exam; Preparation for Certified Bookkeeper exam; Programming and Software Development; Web Design
MEd Early Childhood Education Pre-K-3 (Non-licensure); Special Education–Early Childhood Intervention Specialist
MLS Liberal Studies
MSE Engineering
MSN Nurse Educator; Nurse Educator

COURSE SUBJECT AREAS OFFERED OUTSIDE OF DEGREE PROGRAMS

Undergraduate—allied health and medical assisting services; area, ethnic, cultural, and gender studies related; communication and media; computer and information sciences; computer/information technology administration and management; criminology; curriculum and instruction; developmental and child psychology; economics; education; education related; engineering technologies related; English; English composition; ethnic, cultural minority, and gender studies; film/video and photographic arts; geography and cartography; health professions related; history; human resources management; journalism; legal studies (non-professional general, undergraduate); liberal arts and sciences, general studies and humanities; mathematics; music; nutrition sciences; philosophy; philosophy and religious studies related; political science and government; psychology; public administration and social service professions related; religious studies; social sciences; social work; sociology; statistics; technical and business writing; visual and performing arts related.
Graduate—counseling psychology; curriculum and instruction; education; educational assessment, evaluation, and research; education related; engineering; engineering related; liberal arts and sciences, general studies and humanities; philosophy; political science and government; special education.

See full description on page 512.

UNIVERSITY OF TORONTO
Toronto, Ontario, Canada
School of Continuing Studies
http://learn.utoronto.ca
University of Toronto was founded in 1827. It is provincially chartered. It first offered distance learning courses in 1944. In fall 2007, there were 5,000 students enrolled in distance learning courses. Institutionally administered financial aid is available to distance learners.
Services Distance learners have accessibility to academic advising, bookstore, e-mail services.
Contact Margaret White, Program Assistant, University of Toronto, School of Continuing Studies, 158 St. George Street, Toronto, ON M5S 2V8, Canada. Telephone: 416-978-7697. Fax: 416-978-5673. E-mail: margaret.white@utoronto.ca.

DEGREES AND AWARDS
Programs offered do not lead to a degree or other formal award.

COURSE SUBJECT AREAS OFFERED OUTSIDE OF DEGREE PROGRAMS

Non-credit—accounting and related services; business administration, management and operations; business/corporate communications; business/managerial economics; communication and media; computer/information technology administration and management; economics; finance and financial management services; human resources management; insurance; languages (East Asian); languages (foreign languages related); languages

(Germanic); languages (Romance languages); languages (South Asian); management information systems; management sciences and quantitative methods; marketing; taxation.

UNIVERSITY OF UTAH
Salt Lake City, Utah
Distance Education
http://continue.utah.edu/distance
University of Utah was founded in 1850. It is accredited by Northwest Commission on Colleges and Universities. It first offered distance learning courses in 1941. In fall 2007, there were 1,000 students enrolled in distance learning courses. Institutionally administered financial aid is available to distance learners.
Services Distance learners have accessibility to bookstore.
Contact Michelle Lynch, Program Coordinator, University of Utah, 1901 East South Campus Drive, Room 1215, Salt Lake City, UT 84112-9359. Telephone: 800-467-8839. Fax: 801-581-6267. E-mail: distance@aoce. utah.edu.

DEGREES AND AWARDS
Programs offered do not lead to a degree or other formal award.

COURSE SUBJECT AREAS OFFERED OUTSIDE OF DEGREE PROGRAMS

Undergraduate—anthropology; area, ethnic, cultural, and gender studies related; biology; chemistry; creative writing; developmental and child psychology; economics; education (specific subject areas); English literature (British and Commonwealth); finance and financial management services; fine and studio art; foods, nutrition, and related services; history; mathematics; mathematics and statistics related; music; political science and government; psychology; social psychology; social sciences; special education; statistics.
Non-credit—real estate.

UNIVERSITY OF VERMONT
Burlington, Vermont
Distance Learning Network
http://learn.uvm.edu
University of Vermont was founded in 1791. It is accredited by New England Association of Schools and Colleges. It first offered distance learning courses in 2000. In fall 2007, there were 275 students enrolled in distance learning courses. Institutionally administered financial aid is available to distance learners.
Services Distance learners have accessibility to academic advising, bookstore, campus computer network, career placement assistance, e-mail services, library services, tutoring.
Contact Carol Vallett, Dean, Continuing Education, University of Vermont, Continuing Education, 322 South Prospect Street, Burlington, VT 05401. Telephone: 800-639-3210. Fax: 802-656-0266. E-mail: carol.vallett@ uvm.edu.

DEGREES AND AWARDS
Programs offered do not lead to a degree or other formal award.

COURSE SUBJECT AREAS OFFERED OUTSIDE OF DEGREE PROGRAMS

Undergraduate—accounting and computer science; agriculture; allied health diagnostic, intervention, and treatment professions; American literature (United States and Canadian); anthropology; business/managerial economics; community organization and advocacy; computer science; education; English; gerontology; international relations and affairs; languages (Romance languages); library science; nursing; nutrition sciences; psychology; psychology related; public administration; religious studies; social work; sociology; speech and rhetoric; statistics; teaching assistants/ aides.
Graduate—communication disorders sciences and services; education (specific levels and methods); electrical and electronic engineering technologies; library science; nursing; public administration; religious studies; social work; speech and rhetoric.

Non-credit—accounting and related services; business administration, management and operations; business/managerial economics; communication disorders sciences and services; computer/information technology administration and management; computer programming; computer science; computer software and media applications; engineering; English; food science and technology; languages (Romance languages); mathematics; mathematics and statistics related; music; nursing; nutrition sciences; psychology; social work; statistics.

UNIVERSITY OF VIRGINIA
Charlottesville, Virginia
Educational Technologies
http://www.scps.virginia.edu/
University of Virginia was founded in 1819. It is accredited by Southern Association of Colleges and Schools. It first offered distance learning courses in 1983. In fall 2007, there were 830 students enrolled in distance learning courses. Institutionally administered financial aid is available to distance learners.
Services Distance learners have accessibility to academic advising, bookstore, e-mail services, library services.
Contact Office of Admissions, University of Virginia, PO Box 400160, Charlottesville, VA 22904. Telephone: 434-982-3200. Fax: 434-924-3587. E-mail: undergrad-admission@virginia.edu.

DEGREES AND AWARDS
ME Engineering

COURSE SUBJECT AREAS OFFERED OUTSIDE OF DEGREE PROGRAMS
Undergraduate—accounting and related services; computer/information technology administration and management.
Graduate—education.
Non-credit—business administration, management and operations; computer/information technology administration and management; human resources management.

THE UNIVERSITY OF VIRGINIA'S COLLEGE AT WISE
Wise, Virginia
http://www.uvawise.edu
The University of Virginia's College at Wise was founded in 1954. It is accredited by Southern Association of Colleges and Schools. It first offered distance learning courses in 1995. In fall 2007, there were 100 students enrolled in distance learning courses. Institutionally administered financial aid is available to distance learners.
Services Distance learners have accessibility to academic advising, bookstore, campus computer network, career placement assistance, e-mail services, library services, tutoring.
Contact Mr. P. Scott Bevins, Director of Institutional Research, The University of Virginia's College at Wise, One College Avenue, Wise, VA 24219. Telephone: 276-376-1066. Fax: 276-376-4669. E-mail: pb8q@uvawise.edu.

DEGREES AND AWARDS
Programs offered do not lead to a degree or other formal award.

COURSE SUBJECT AREAS OFFERED OUTSIDE OF DEGREE PROGRAMS
Undergraduate—business administration, management and operations; computer science; economics; library science.

UNIVERSITY OF WASHINGTON
Seattle, Washington
Online Learning
http://onlinelearning.washington.edu/ol/
University of Washington was founded in 1861. It is accredited by Northwest Commission on Colleges and Universities. In fall 2007, there were 9,700 students enrolled in distance learning courses. Institutionally administered financial aid is available to distance learners.
Services Distance learners have accessibility to academic advising, bookstore, campus computer network, e-mail services, library services.

Contact General Information, University of Washington, 4311 11th Avenue, NE, Seattle, WA 98105-4608. Telephone: 800-543-2320. Fax: 206-685-9359. E-mail: onlinelearning@extn.washington.edu.

DEGREES AND AWARDS
Certificate Brain Research in Education; Business Foundations; Computer Programming–C Programming; Computer Programming–C++ Programming; Computer Programming–Java 2 Programming; Construction Management; Curriculum Integration in Action; Data Resource Management; Database Management; Distance Learning Design and Development; Embedded and Real-Time Systems Programming; Facility Management; Fiction Writing; Gerontology; Heavy Construction Project Management; Infrastructure Construction; Internet Programming; Object-Oriented Analysis and Design Using UML; Project Management; Quantitative Construction Management; School Library Media Specialist; Site Planning; Web Administration; Web Consultant for Small Business; Web Technology Essentials

CCCPE Paralegal

MAE Aerospace Engineering

MEE Electrical Engineering

MLIS Library and Information Science

MS Aeronautics and Astronautics; Construction Engineering; Strategic Planning for Critical Infrastructure

MSE Manufacturing Engineering; Materials Science and Engineering

MSME Mechanical Engineering

COURSE SUBJECT AREAS OFFERED OUTSIDE OF DEGREE PROGRAMS
Undergraduate—accounting and related services; American literature (United States and Canadian); anthropology; applied mathematics; archeology; astronomy and astrophysics; atmospheric sciences and meteorology; building/construction finishing, management, and inspection; business/corporate communications; chemistry; cognitive psychology and psycholinguistics; communication and media; computer engineering; computer programming; computer science; construction engineering technology; creative writing; criminology; curriculum and instruction; developmental and child psychology; economics; education; educational psychology; English; English as a second language; English composition; ethnic, cultural minority, and gender studies; geography and cartography; geological and earth sciences/geosciences; gerontology; history; international business; journalism; languages (Modern Greek); languages (Slavic, Baltic and Albanian); library science; marketing; materials engineering; mathematics; mathematics and statistics related; mechanical engineering; pharmacy, pharmaceutical sciences, and administration; philosophy; political science and government; psychology; religious studies; social psychology; sociology; speech and rhetoric; statistics; technical and business writing; urban studies/affairs.

Graduate—building/construction finishing, management, and inspection; city/urban, community and regional planning; civil engineering; computer science; construction engineering technology; electrical and electronic engineering technologies; engineering/industrial management; engineering related; gerontology; library science; library science related; materials engineering; mechanical engineering; political science and government.

Non-credit—business administration, management and operations; city/urban, community and regional planning; computer and information sciences; computer and information sciences and support services related; computer/information technology administration and management; computer programming; computer software and media applications; computer systems analysis; creative writing; English; English as a second language; information science/studies.

See full description on page 514.

UNIVERSITY OF WATERLOO
Waterloo, Ontario, Canada
Distance and Continuing Education
http://de.uwaterloo.ca

University of Waterloo was founded in 1957. It is provincially chartered. It first offered distance learning courses in 1968. In fall 2007, there were 4,500 students enrolled in distance learning courses. Institutionally administered financial aid is available to distance learners.

Services Distance learners have accessibility to academic advising, bookstore, campus computer network, e-mail services, library services, tutoring.

Contact Information and Student Services, Distance and Continuing Education Office, University of Waterloo, Waterloo, ON N2L 3G1, Canada. Telephone: 519-888-4050. Fax: 519-746-4607. E-mail: distance@uwaterloo.ca.

DEGREES AND AWARDS

BA English; Humanities; Liberal Studies; Philosophy; Religious Studies; Social Development Studies; Social Sciences
BS Science, general non-major
MM Management Sciences–Master of Management Sciences Online (MMSC)

COURSE SUBJECT AREAS OFFERED OUTSIDE OF DEGREE PROGRAMS

Undergraduate—accounting and related services; American literature (United States and Canadian); anthropology; area, ethnic, cultural, and gender studies related; area studies; astronomy and astrophysics; biblical and other theological languages and literatures; biblical studies; biochemistry, biophysics and molecular biology; biological and biomedical sciences related; biological and physical sciences; biology; business/managerial economics; cell biology and anatomical sciences; chemistry; community organization and advocacy; computer and information sciences; computer science; criminology; developmental and child psychology; ecology, evolution, and population biology; economics; educational psychology; English composition; English literature (British and Commonwealth); ethnic, cultural minority, and gender studies; finance and financial management services; geological and earth sciences/geosciences; gerontology; history; human development, family studies, and related services; insurance; international relations and affairs; languages (classics and classical); languages (foreign languages related); languages (Germanic); languages (Modern Greek); languages (Romance languages); languages (Slavic, Baltic and Albanian); legal studies (non-professional general, undergraduate); liberal arts and sciences, general studies and humanities; linguistic, comparative, and related language studies; mathematics; mathematics and statistics related; medieval and Renaissance studies; microbiological sciences and immunology; multi-/interdisciplinary studies related; peace studies and conflict resolution; philosophy; philosophy and religious studies related; physical sciences; physics; physiology, pathology and related sciences; psychology; psychology related; religious studies; social psychology; social sciences; social sciences related; social work; sociology; statistics.
Graduate—management information systems.
Non-credit—chemistry; mathematics and statistics related; physics.

UNIVERSITY OF WEST FLORIDA
Pensacola, Florida
Online Campus/Academic Technology Center
http://onlinecampus.uwf.edu

University of West Florida was founded in 1963. It is accredited by Southern Association of Colleges and Schools. It first offered distance learning courses in 1995. In fall 2007, there were 4,800 students enrolled in distance learning courses. Institutionally administered financial aid is available to distance learners.

Services Distance learners have accessibility to academic advising, bookstore, campus computer network, e-mail services, library services, tutoring.

Contact Mrs. Sharon Cobb, Program Coordinator, Academic Technology Center, University of West Florida, 11000 University Parkway, Building 77, Room 138A, Pensacola, FL 32514. Telephone: 850-473-7468. Fax: 850-474-2807. E-mail: scobb@uwf.edu.

DEGREES AND AWARDS

BA Exceptional Student Education
BS Career and Technical Studies Education–Vocational Program Development; Career and Technical Studies Education–Vocational Teacher Education; Health Sciences, Allied Health; Health Sciences, Health Care Professional; Health Sciences, Medical Information Technology; IIT Networking and Telecommunications with e-Learning Systems; Information Engineering Technology; Maritime Studies; Oceanography
MA Special Education
MEd Career and Technical Education (CTE); Education and Training Management Subspecialty/Human Performance Technology; Education and Training Management Subspecialty/Instructional Technology; Education–Comprehensive Masters in Education; Instructional Technology
MS Acquisition and Contract Administration (MSA); Biomedical/Pharmaceutical (MSA); Criminal Justice Administration (MSA); Database Administration (MSA); Education Leadership (MSA); Health Care Administration (MSA); Human Performance Technology (MSA); Leadership (MSA); Nursing Administration; Public Administration (MSA); Public Health; Software Engineering Administration

COURSE SUBJECT AREAS OFFERED OUTSIDE OF DEGREE PROGRAMS

Undergraduate—anthropology; archeology; biological and biomedical sciences related; biology; business/corporate communications; communication and media; communications technology; computer programming; computer science; computer software and media applications; computer systems networking and telecommunications; data entry/microcomputer applications; economics; engineering technologies related; English; English composition; fine and studio art; history; liberal arts and sciences, general studies and humanities; mathematics; mathematics and statistics related; philosophy; physical sciences; physical sciences related; political science and government; religious studies; statistics; technical and business writing.
Graduate—accounting and computer science; allied health diagnostic, intervention, and treatment professions; behavioral sciences; business administration, management and operations; computer science; educational/instructional media design; education related; health services/allied health/health sciences; information science/studies; political science and government; public administration and social service professions related; special education.
Non-credit—business, management, and marketing related; communications technology; computer engineering; education related; education (specific subject areas); human resources management; technology education/industrial arts.

UNIVERSITY OF WINDSOR
Windsor, Ontario, Canada
Continuing Education
http://www.uwindsor.ca/flexible

University of Windsor was founded in 1857. It is provincially chartered. It first offered distance learning courses in 1985. In fall 2007, there were 1,100 students enrolled in distance learning courses. Institutionally administered financial aid is available to distance learners.

Services Distance learners have accessibility to academic advising, bookstore, campus computer network, career placement assistance, e-mail services, library services, tutoring.

Contact Mr. Marty Lowman, Supervisor, Student Information Resource Centre (SIRC), University of Windsor, Windsor, ON N9B 3P4, Canada. Telephone: 519-253-3000 Ext. 1414. Fax: 519-971-3623. E-mail: askme@uwindsor.ca.

DEGREES AND AWARDS

BA Liberal and Professional Studies; Political Science
BBA Accounting–General Accounting Track (BBS)
BComm Business Administration–Honours Business Administration; Commerce–Bachelor of Commerce Program for University Graduates
BS General Science
Certificate Arts Management; Business Administration; Labour Studies

COURSE SUBJECT AREAS OFFERED OUTSIDE OF DEGREE PROGRAMS
Undergraduate—nursing.

UNIVERSITY OF WISCONSIN COLLEGES
Madison, Wisconsin
UWC On-line
http://www.online.uwc.edu
University of Wisconsin Colleges is accredited by North Central Association of Colleges and Schools. It first offered distance learning courses in 1998. In fall 2007, there were 1,400 students enrolled in distance learning courses. Institutionally administered financial aid is available to distance learners.
Services Distance learners have accessibility to academic advising, bookstore, campus computer network, e-mail services, library services, tutoring.
Contact Ms. Leanne Johnson, DE Coordinator, University of Wisconsin Colleges, 644 West Washington Avenue, Madison, WI 53703-2638. Telephone: 608-263-9553. Fax: 608-262-7872. E-mail: decoordinator@uwc.edu.

DEGREES AND AWARDS
AAS Liberal Arts

COURSE SUBJECT AREAS OFFERED OUTSIDE OF DEGREE PROGRAMS
Undergraduate—anthropology; biology; business/commerce; chemistry; communication and journalism related; creative writing; economics; English; English composition; ethnic, cultural minority, and gender studies; geography and cartography; geological and earth sciences/geosciences; history; journalism; mathematics; mathematics and computer science; mathematics and statistics related; music; natural sciences; philosophy; political science and government; psychology; social sciences; sociology; statistics; visual and performing arts related.
Non-credit—English; mathematics.

UNIVERSITY OF WISCONSIN–GREEN BAY
Green Bay, Wisconsin
BSN–LINC Online RN–BSN Program
http://www.bsnlinc.wisconsin.edu/
University of Wisconsin–Green Bay was founded in 1968. It is accredited by North Central Association of Colleges and Schools. It first offered distance learning courses in 2000. In fall 2007, there were 137 students enrolled in distance learning courses. Institutionally administered financial aid is available to distance learners.
Services Distance learners have accessibility to academic advising, bookstore, campus computer network, e-mail services, library services.
Contact Jennifer Schwahn, Advisor, University of Wisconsin–Green Bay, 2420 Nicolet Drive, MAC Hall, A-309, Green Bay, WI 54311-7001. Telephone: 920-465-2826. Fax: 920-465-2854. E-mail: schwahnj@uwgb.edu.

DEGREES AND AWARDS
BSN Professional Program in Nursing

UNIVERSITY OF WISCONSIN–LA CROSSE
La Crosse, Wisconsin
http://www.uwlax.edu/
University of Wisconsin–La Crosse was founded in 1909. It is accredited by North Central Association of Colleges and Schools. It first offered distance learning courses in 1995. In fall 2007, there were 200 students enrolled in distance learning courses. Institutionally administered financial aid is available to distance learners.
Services Distance learners have accessibility to academic advising, bookstore, campus computer network, career placement assistance, e-mail services, library services, tutoring.

Contact Terry Wirkus, DE Site Support Coordinator, University of Wisconsin–La Crosse, 1725 State Street, La Crosse, WI 54601. Telephone: 608-785-8049. Fax: 608-785-8825. E-mail: wirkus.terr@uwlax.edu.

DEGREES AND AWARDS
Programs offered do not lead to a degree or other formal award.

COURSE SUBJECT AREAS OFFERED OUTSIDE OF DEGREE PROGRAMS
Undergraduate—health professions related; linguistic, comparative, and related language studies; nursing; ophthalmic and optometric support services and allied professions.
Graduate—accounting and related services; business administration, management and operations; economics; educational psychology; finance and financial management services; microbiological sciences and immunology; parks, recreation and leisure facilities management; sales, merchandising, and related marketing operations (general).

UNIVERSITY OF WISCONSIN–PARKSIDE
Kenosha, Wisconsin
http://www.uwp.edu/
University of Wisconsin–Parkside was founded in 1968. It is accredited by North Central Association of Colleges and Schools. It first offered distance learning courses in 1996. In fall 2007, there were 28 students enrolled in distance learning courses. Institutionally administered financial aid is available to distance learners.
Services Distance learners have accessibility to academic advising, bookstore, campus computer network, career placement assistance, e-mail services, library services, tutoring.
Contact Bradley R. Piazza, Assistant Dean of the School of Business, University of Wisconsin–Parkside, 900 Wood Road, PO Box 2000, Kenosha, WI 53141-2000. Telephone: 262-595-2046. Fax: 262-595-2680. E-mail: bradley.piazza@uwp.edu.

DEGREES AND AWARDS
Programs offered do not lead to a degree or other formal award.

COURSE SUBJECT AREAS OFFERED OUTSIDE OF DEGREE PROGRAMS
Graduate—accounting and computer science; accounting and related services; business administration, management and operations; business, management, and marketing related; business/managerial economics; economics; finance and financial management services; management information systems; management sciences and quantitative methods; sales, merchandising, and related marketing operations (general); statistics.

UNIVERSITY OF WISCONSIN–PLATTEVILLE
Platteville, Wisconsin
Bachelor of Science in Business Administration at a Distance
http://www.uwplatt.edu/disted/degrees/bsad/index.html
University of Wisconsin–Platteville was founded in 1866. It is accredited by North Central Association of Colleges and Schools. It first offered distance learning courses in 1978. In fall 2007, there were 375 students enrolled in distance learning courses. Institutionally administered financial aid is available to distance learners.
Services Distance learners have accessibility to academic advising, bookstore, campus computer network, career placement assistance, e-mail services, library services.
Contact Kim Maier, Admission Specialist, BS in Business Administration at a Distance, University of Wisconsin–Platteville, 2100 Ullsvik Hall, 1 University Plaza, Platteville, WI 53818-3099. Telephone: 800-362-5460. Fax: 608-342-1071. E-mail: maierk@uwplatt.edu.

DEGREES AND AWARDS
BSBA Business Administration

Certificate Human Resource Management; International Business; Leadership and Human Performance; Marketing

UNIVERSITY OF WISCONSIN–PLATTEVILLE
Platteville, Wisconsin
Distance Learning Center
http://www.uwplatt.edu/disted

University of Wisconsin–Platteville was founded in 1866. It is accredited by North Central Association of Colleges and Schools. It first offered distance learning courses in 1978. In fall 2007, there were 1,100 students enrolled in distance learning courses. Institutionally administered financial aid is available to distance learners.

Services Distance learners have accessibility to academic advising, bookstore, campus computer network, career placement assistance, e-mail services, library services.

Contact Admission Specialist, University of Wisconsin–Platteville, 2100 Ullsvik Hall, 1 University Plaza, Platteville, WI 53818-3099. Telephone: 800-362-5460. Fax: 608-342-1071. E-mail: disted@uwplatt.edu.

DEGREES AND AWARDS
BS Business Administration; Criminal Justice
Certificate Human Resource Management; International Business; Leadership and Human Performance; Marketing
Advanced Graduate Diploma Criminal Justice
Graduate Certificate Advanced Project Management; Engineering Management; Geotechnical Engineering; Project Management; Structural Engineering; Structural/Geotechnical Engineering
MS Criminal Justice; Engineering; Project Management

COURSE SUBJECT AREAS OFFERED OUTSIDE OF DEGREE PROGRAMS
Non-credit—business administration, management and operations; criminology.

UNIVERSITY OF WISCONSIN–PLATTEVILLE
Platteville, Wisconsin
Master of Science in Education, Adult Education at a Distance
http://www.uwplatt.edu/mse/AdultEd.htm

University of Wisconsin–Platteville was founded in 1866. It is accredited by North Central Association of Colleges and Schools. It first offered distance learning courses in 1978. In fall 2007, there were 33 students enrolled in distance learning courses. Institutionally administered financial aid is available to distance learners.

Services Distance learners have accessibility to academic advising, bookstore, campus computer network, career placement assistance, e-mail services, library services.

Contact Master of Science in Education–Adult Education at a Distance, University of Wisconsin–Platteville, 2100 Ullsvik Hall, 1 University Plaza, Platteville, WI 53818-3099. Telephone: 800-362-5460. Fax: 608-342-1071. E-mail: disted@uwplatt.edu.

DEGREES AND AWARDS
MSE Adult Education

UNIVERSITY OF WISCONSIN–PLATTEVILLE
Platteville, Wisconsin
Online Bachelor of Science in Criminal Justice
http://www.uwplatt.edu/disted/degrees/bscj/index.html

University of Wisconsin–Platteville was founded in 1866. It is accredited by North Central Association of Colleges and Schools. It first offered distance learning courses in 1978. In fall 2007, there were 35 students enrolled in distance learning courses. Institutionally administered financial aid is available to distance learners.

Services Distance learners have accessibility to academic advising, bookstore, campus computer network, career placement assistance, e-mail services, library services.

Contact Kim Maier, Admission Specialist, Bachelor of Science in Criminal Justice, University of Wisconsin–Platteville, 2100 Ullsvik Hall, 1 University Plaza, Platteville, WI 53818-3099. Telephone: 800-362-5460. Fax: 608-342-1071. E-mail: maierk@uwplatt.edu.

DEGREES AND AWARDS
BS Criminal Justice

UNIVERSITY OF WISCONSIN–PLATTEVILLE
Platteville, Wisconsin
Online Master of Science in Criminal Justice
http://www.uwplatt.edu/disted/degrees/cj/index.html

University of Wisconsin–Platteville was founded in 1866. It is accredited by North Central Association of Colleges and Schools. It first offered distance learning courses in 1978. In fall 2007, there were 100 students enrolled in distance learning courses. Institutionally administered financial aid is available to distance learners.

Services Distance learners have accessibility to academic advising, bookstore, campus computer network, career placement assistance, e-mail services, library services.

Contact Clint Nemitz, Admission Specialist, Online Master of Science in Criminal Justice, University of Wisconsin–Platteville, 2100 Ullsvik Hall, 1 University Plaza, Platteville, WI 53818-3099. Telephone: 800-362-5460. Fax: 608-342-1071. E-mail: nemitzc@uwplatt.edu.

DEGREES AND AWARDS
Advanced Graduate Diploma Criminal Justice
MSCJ Criminal Justice

COURSE SUBJECT AREAS OFFERED OUTSIDE OF DEGREE PROGRAMS
Non-credit—criminal justice and corrections; criminology.

UNIVERSITY OF WISCONSIN–PLATTEVILLE
Platteville, Wisconsin
Online Master of Science in Engineering
http://www.uwplatt.edu/disted/degrees/eng/index.html

University of Wisconsin–Platteville was founded in 1866. It is accredited by North Central Association of Colleges and Schools. It first offered distance learning courses in 1978. In fall 2007, there were 110 students enrolled in distance learning courses. Institutionally administered financial aid is available to distance learners.

Services Distance learners have accessibility to academic advising, bookstore, campus computer network, career placement assistance, e-mail services, library services.

Contact Clint Nemitz, Admission Specialist, Online Master of Science in Engineering, University of Wisconsin–Platteville, 2100 Ullsvik Hall, 1 University Plaza, Platteville, WI 53818-3099. Telephone: 800-362-5460. Fax: 608-342-1071. E-mail: nemitzc@uwplatt.edu.

DEGREES AND AWARDS
Graduate Certificate Engineering Management; Geotechnical Engineering; Structural Engineering; Structural/Geotechnical Engineering
MSE Engineering

UNIVERSITY OF WISCONSIN–PLATTEVILLE
Platteville, Wisconsin
Online Master of Science in Project Management
http://www.uwplatt.edu/disted/degrees/pm/index.html

University of Wisconsin–Platteville was founded in 1866. It is accredited by North Central Association of Colleges and Schools. It first offered distance learning courses in 1978. In fall 2007, there were 250 students enrolled in distance learning courses. Institutionally administered financial aid is available to distance learners.

Services Distance learners have accessibility to academic advising, bookstore, campus computer network, career placement assistance, e-mail services, library services.

Contact Clint Nemitz, Admission Specialist, Online Master of Science in Project Management, University of Wisconsin–Platteville, 2100 Ullsvik Hall, 1 University Plaza, Platteville, WI 53818-3099. Telephone: 800-362-5460. Fax: 608-342-1071. E-mail: nemitzc@uwplatt.edu.

DEGREES AND AWARDS

CAGS Project Management
Graduate Certificate Project Management
MS Project Management

COURSE SUBJECT AREAS OFFERED OUTSIDE OF DEGREE PROGRAMS

Non-credit—quality control and safety technologies.

UNIVERSITY OF WISCONSIN–STOUT
Menomonie, Wisconsin
Office of Continuing Education
http://www.uwstout.edu/outreach/ces

University of Wisconsin–Stout was founded in 1891. It is accredited by North Central Association of Colleges and Schools. It first offered distance learning courses in 1980. In fall 2007, there were 3,500 students enrolled in distance learning courses. Institutionally administered financial aid is available to distance learners.
Services Distance learners have accessibility to academic advising, bookstore, campus computer network, career placement assistance, e-mail services, library services, tutoring.
Contact Sandra White, Credit Outreach Program Manager III, University of Wisconsin–Stout, Outreach Services, 140 Vocational Rehabilitation Building, Menomonie, WI 54751-0790. Telephone: 715-232-1610. Fax: 715-232-3385. E-mail: whites@uwstout.edu.

DEGREES AND AWARDS

BS Career and Technical Education; Golf Enterprise Management; Information and Communication Technologies; Management
Certificate Gaming Management; Human Resource Management; Quality Management Certificate
Certification Early Childhood/Middle Childhood; Health Science Occupations; Reading Teacher Certification; Traffic Safety Education
Graduate Certificate E-Learning and Online Teaching Graduate Certificate
MS Career and Technical Education; Education; Information Communication Technologies; Manufacturing Engineering; Technology Management; Training and Development; Vocational Rehabilitation Counseling

COURSE SUBJECT AREAS OFFERED OUTSIDE OF DEGREE PROGRAMS

Undergraduate—business, management, and marketing related; chemistry; developmental and child psychology; economics; education; human resources management.
Graduate—business administration, management and operations; developmental and child psychology; education; human resources management; library science; management sciences and quantitative methods; science technologies related; social sciences; technology education/industrial arts.
Non-credit—computer systems networking and telecommunications; education (specific levels and methods); gerontology; human development, family studies, and related services; human resources management.

UNIVERSITY OF WISCONSIN–STOUT
Menomonie, Wisconsin
Program in Vocational Rehabilitation
http://www.uwstout.edu/programs/msvr/

University of Wisconsin–Stout was founded in 1891. It is accredited by North Central Association of Colleges and Schools. It first offered distance learning courses in 2002. In fall 2007, there were 55 students enrolled in distance learning courses. Institutionally administered financial aid is available to distance learners.
Services Distance learners have accessibility to academic advising, bookstore, campus computer network, career placement assistance, e-mail services, library services.
Contact Debra Homa, PhD, Vocational Rehabilitation Program Director, University of Wisconsin–Stout, 250F Vocational Rehabilitation Building,

Department of Rehabilitation and Counseling, Menomonie, WI 54751. Telephone: 715-232-1113. Fax: 715-232-2356. E-mail: homad@uwstout.edu.

DEGREES AND AWARDS

MS Vocational Rehabilitation–Rehabilitation Counseling

COURSE SUBJECT AREAS OFFERED OUTSIDE OF DEGREE PROGRAMS

Graduate—counseling psychology; health professions related; rehabilitation and therapeutic professions.

UNIVERSITY OF WISCONSIN–SUPERIOR
Superior, Wisconsin
http://www2.uwsuper.edu/cee/dlc/direct/

University of Wisconsin–Superior was founded in 1893. It is accredited by North Central Association of Colleges and Schools. It first offered distance learning courses in 1978. In fall 2007, there were 272 students enrolled in distance learning courses. Institutionally administered financial aid is available to distance learners.
Services Distance learners have accessibility to academic advising, bookstore, campus computer network, career placement assistance, e-mail services, library services, tutoring.
Contact Peter Nordgren, Director, University of Wisconsin–Superior, Distance Learning Center, PO Box 2000, Belknap and Catlin, Superior, WI 54880. Telephone: 715-394-8487. Fax: 715-394-8139. E-mail: pnordgre@uwsuper.edu.

DEGREES AND AWARDS

BS Communicating Arts, Speech Communication concentration; Elementary Education; Individualized major

COURSE SUBJECT AREAS OFFERED OUTSIDE OF DEGREE PROGRAMS

Undergraduate—accounting and computer science; American literature (United States and Canadian); astronomy and astrophysics; biology; business administration, management and operations; communication and journalism related; communication and media; counseling psychology; curriculum and instruction; education; English; fine and studio art; history; human services; mathematics and computer science; physical sciences; social sciences.
Graduate—education; educational administration and supervision; health psychology.
Non-credit—gerontology.

See full description on page 516.

UNIVERSITY OF WISCONSIN–WHITEWATER
Whitewater, Wisconsin
http://www.uww.edu/conteduc/distance/index.htm

University of Wisconsin–Whitewater was founded in 1868. It is accredited by North Central Association of Colleges and Schools. It first offered distance learning courses in 1980. In fall 2007, there were 1,636 students enrolled in distance learning courses. Institutionally administered financial aid is available to distance learners.
Services Distance learners have accessibility to bookstore, campus computer network, e-mail services, library services.
Contact Lorna Y. Wong, Director, Instructional Technology Services, University of Wisconsin–Whitewater, 800 West Main Street, Whitewater, WI 53190. Telephone: 262-472-7795. Fax: 262-472-1285. E-mail: disted@uww.edu.

DEGREES AND AWARDS

BA Liberal Studies
BBA Business Administration (General Business)
BS Political Science
MBA Business Administration and Online Masters of Business Administration
MSE School Business Management; School Business Management

COURSE SUBJECT AREAS OFFERED OUTSIDE OF DEGREE PROGRAMS

Undergraduate—accounting and computer science; anthropology; area, ethnic, cultural, and gender studies related; business administration, management and operations; business, management, and marketing related; communication and journalism related; communication and media; creative writing; curriculum and instruction; economics; education; education related; English; English as a second language; ethnic, cultural minority, and gender studies; history; journalism; languages (foreign languages related); library science; management information systems; marketing; political science and government.

Graduate—accounting and related services; area, ethnic, cultural, and gender studies related; business administration, management and operations; business, management, and marketing related; communication and journalism related; creative writing; economics; English; English as a second language; finance and financial management services; history; journalism; management information systems; marketing; political science and government; psychology related.

UNIVERSITY OF WYOMING
Laramie, Wyoming
Outreach School
http://outreach.uwyo.edu/ocp
University of Wyoming was founded in 1886. It is accredited by North Central Association of Colleges and Schools. In fall 2007, there were 3,930 students enrolled in distance learning courses. Institutionally administered financial aid is available to distance learners.

Services Distance learners have accessibility to academic advising, bookstore, campus computer network, career placement assistance, e-mail services, library services, tutoring.

Contact Ms. Judith E. Atencio, Program Manager, Outreach Credit Programs, University of Wyoming, Department 3274, 1000 East University Avenue, Laramie, WY 82071. Telephone: 800-448-7801. Fax: 307-766-4048. E-mail: occ@uwyo.edu.

DEGREES AND AWARDS

BA Criminal Justice; Social Sciences

BGS Bachelor of Applied Science, Organizational Leadership concentration

BS Business Administration; Family and Consumer Sciences (Family and Community Services option); Family and Consumer Sciences (Professional Child Development option); Psychology; Social Sciences

BSN Nursing–RN to BSN

Certificate Family and Consumer Sciences (Early Childhood Program Director's certificate); Land Surveying; Real Estate

Endorsement Early Childhood Birth to Five Endorsement; Early Childhood Special Education; Literacy Program (Wyoming Reading Endorsement); Principal Endorsement Program

MA Education–Adult and Post-Secondary Education; Education–Educational Leadership; Education–Special Education; Education–Teaching and Learning

MBA Executive Master of Business Administration

MPA Public Administration

MS Education–Instructional Technology; Kinesiology and Health; Nursing–Nurse Educator option; Speech-Language Pathology

MSW Social Work

COURSE SUBJECT AREAS OFFERED OUTSIDE OF DEGREE PROGRAMS

Undergraduate—agriculture; American literature (United States and Canadian); astronomy and astrophysics; biological and biomedical sciences related; botany/plant biology; business/commerce; chemistry; communication and media; criminal justice and corrections; education; English composition; English literature (British and Commonwealth); ethnic, cultural minority, and gender studies; family and consumer economics; foods, nutrition, and related services; geography and cartography; history; liberal arts and sciences, general studies and humanities; mathematics; music; nursing; physics; real estate; social psychology; statistics.

Graduate—business administration, management and operations; education; educational/instructional media design; health professions related; nursing; public administration; social work.

See full description on page 518.

UPPER IOWA UNIVERSITY
Fayette, Iowa
External Degree
http://www.uiu.edu
Upper Iowa University was founded in 1857. It is accredited by North Central Association of Colleges and Schools. It first offered distance learning courses in 1973. In fall 2007, there were 1,900 students enrolled in distance learning courses. Institutionally administered financial aid is available to distance learners.

Services Distance learners have accessibility to academic advising, bookstore, campus computer network, career placement assistance, e-mail services, library services.

Contact Carol J. Katsumes, Assistant Director, External Degree Program, Upper Iowa University, PO Box 1861, Fayette, IA 52142. Telephone: 888-877-3742. Fax: 563-425-5353. E-mail: moreinfo@uiu.edu.

DEGREES AND AWARDS

AA Business, general; Liberal Arts

BS Accounting; Business Administration; Criminal Justice; Emergency and Disaster Management; Finance; Health Services Administration; Human Resources Management; Human Services; Interdisciplinary Studies; Management; Marketing; Psychology; Public Administration; Public Administration–Fire Science emphasis; Public Administration–Law Enforcement emphasis; Social Sciences; Technology and Information Management

Certificate Emergency and Disaster Management; Human Resources Management; Marketing; Organizational Communications; Organizational Leadership

COURSE SUBJECT AREAS OFFERED OUTSIDE OF DEGREE PROGRAMS

Undergraduate—accounting and related services; astronomy and astrophysics; biology; business administration, management and operations; business/corporate communications; business, management, and marketing related; communication and media; counseling psychology; criminal justice and corrections; criminology; English; English composition; entrepreneurial and small business operations; finance and financial management services; health professions related; health services/allied health/health sciences; history; human resources management; human services; industrial and organizational psychology; international business; legal studies (non-professional general, undergraduate); liberal arts and sciences, general studies and humanities; management information systems; management sciences and quantitative methods; marketing; mathematics; mathematics and statistics related; natural sciences; philosophy and religious studies related; physical sciences; political science and government; psychology; psychology related; public administration; public administration and social service professions related; public relations, advertising, and applied communication related; social psychology; social sciences; social sciences related; sociology; statistics.

Non-credit—accounting and computer science; accounting and related services; biological and physical sciences; biology; communication and media; English composition; history; industrial and organizational psychology; international business; management information systems; marketing; political science and government; psychology; public administration; sociology; statistics.

See full description on page 520.

UTAH STATE UNIVERSITY
Logan, Utah
Independent and Distance Education
http://distance.usu.edu
Utah State University was founded in 1888. It is accredited by Northwest Commission on Colleges and Universities. It first offered distance learning courses in 1983. In fall 2007, there were 6,700 students enrolled in distance learning courses. Institutionally administered financial aid is available to distance learners.

Services Distance learners have accessibility to academic advising, bookstore, campus computer network, e-mail services, library services.

Contact Staff Assistant, Independent and Distance Education, Utah State University, 5055 Old Main Hill, Logan, UT 84322-5055. Telephone: 800-233-2137. Fax: 435-797-9700. E-mail: distance.info@usu.edu.

DEGREES AND AWARDS

AAS Office Support Systems; Ornamental Horticulture
AS General Studies
BS Accounting; Business; Communicative Disorders and Deaf Education (post-Bachelors); Computer Science; Entrepreneurship; Psychology; Special Education
Endorsement Distance Learning; Reading, Elementary Education; Reading, Secondary Education; School Library Media; Utah Mathematics Endorsement Project
ME Electrical/Computer Engineering
MEd Elementary Education; Health, Physical Education, and Recreation; Instructional Technology–Educational Technology emphasis; Secondary Education; Special Education
MFHD Family and Human Development
MS Agricultural Systems Technology, Family and Consumer Sciences Education and Extension emphasis; Agricultural Systems Technology, Secondary/Post-Secondary Agricultural Education emphasis; Business Information Systems; Computer Science; English/Technical Writing Specialization Online; Psychology–School Counseling specialization; Special Education
MSW Social Work
EdD Distance Doctorate

COURSE SUBJECT AREAS OFFERED OUTSIDE OF DEGREE PROGRAMS

Undergraduate—accounting and related services; anthropology; applied mathematics; biology; business administration, management and operations; business operations support and assistant services; chemistry; communication disorders sciences and services; data entry/microcomputer applications; data processing; economics; English; English literature (British and Commonwealth); family and consumer economics; family and consumer sciences/human sciences; history; human resources management; liberal arts and sciences, general studies and humanities; mathematics; mathematics and statistics related; philosophy; physical sciences; physics; psychology; social psychology; social sciences; social work; sociology; special education; statistics.
Graduate—agriculture and agriculture operations related; business administration, management and operations; computer programming; computer science; computer software and media applications; computer systems analysis; computer systems networking and telecommunications; curriculum and instruction; education; educational administration and supervision; educational assessment, evaluation, and research; educational/instructional media design; educational psychology; education (specific levels and methods); education (specific subject areas); English; family and consumer sciences/human sciences; human development, family studies, and related services; human resources management; library science related; psychology; school psychology; social sciences related; special education.

See full description on page 522.

UTAH VALLEY STATE COLLEGE
Orem, Utah
Department of Distance Education
http://www.uvu.edu/disted

Utah Valley State College was founded in 1941. It is accredited by Northwest Commission on Colleges and Universities. It first offered distance learning courses in 1988. In fall 2007, there were 12,000 students enrolled in distance learning courses. Institutionally administered financial aid is available to distance learners.
Services Distance learners have accessibility to academic advising, bookstore, campus computer network, career placement assistance, e-mail services, library services, tutoring.
Contact Karen Merrick, Assistant Director of Support Services, Utah Valley State College, 800 West University Parkway, MS 149, Orem, UT 84058. Telephone: 888-425-4412. Fax: 801-863-7298. E-mail: dehelp@uvu.edu.

DEGREES AND AWARDS

AS Communication; Criminal Justice; General Studies
ASM Business Management Associate of Science
BS Aviation Science

COURSE SUBJECT AREAS OFFERED OUTSIDE OF DEGREE PROGRAMS

Undergraduate—accounting and related services; air transportation; American literature (United States and Canadian); anthropology; astronomy and astrophysics; atmospheric sciences and meteorology; behavioral sciences; biological and physical sciences; biology; business administration, management and operations; business/corporate communications; business, management, and marketing related; communication and journalism related; communication and media; computer and information sciences; creative writing; dramatic/theater arts and stagecraft; electrical/electronics maintenance and repair technology; English; English composition; fire protection; history; hospitality administration; languages (foreign languages related); legal studies (non-professional general, undergraduate); management information systems; ocean engineering; philosophy; political science and government; psychology; public relations, advertising, and applied communication related; social sciences; sociology; zoology/animal biology.

UTAH VALLEY STATE COLLEGE
Orem, Utah
Global Aviation Degree Center
http://www.aviationuniversity.com

Utah Valley State College was founded in 1941. It is accredited by Northwest Commission on Colleges and Universities. It first offered distance learning courses in 1997. In fall 2007, there were 1,500 students enrolled in distance learning courses. Institutionally administered financial aid is available to distance learners.
Services Distance learners have accessibility to academic advising, bookstore, campus computer network, career placement assistance, e-mail services, library services, tutoring.
Contact Theo Okawa, Aviation Advisor, Utah Valley State College, 800 West University Parkway, MS 114, Orem, UT 84058-5999. Telephone: 888-901-7192 Ext. 7837. Fax: 801-764-7815. E-mail: okawath@uvsc.edu.

DEGREES AND AWARDS

AAS Aviation Job Ready degree
AS Aviation (baccalaureate degree transfer)
BS Aviation Administration/Management; Aviation Professional Pilot

COURSE SUBJECT AREAS OFFERED OUTSIDE OF DEGREE PROGRAMS

Undergraduate—aerospace, aeronautical and astronautical engineering; biology; English composition; English language and literature related; fine and studio art; health and physical education/fitness; history; mathematics; philosophy; physical sciences; social sciences; social sciences related.
Graduate—aerospace, aeronautical and astronautical engineering.

UTICA COLLEGE
Utica, New York
http://www.uticaonline.edu

Utica College was founded in 1946. It is accredited by Middle States Association of Colleges and Schools. It first offered distance learning courses in 2000. In fall 2007, there were 1,003 students enrolled in distance learning courses. Institutionally administered financial aid is available to distance learners.
Services Distance learners have accessibility to academic advising, bookstore, campus computer network, e-mail services, library services, tutoring.
Contact Dr. Stephen P. Neun, Assistant Vice President for Academic Affairs, Utica College, 1600 Burrstone Road, Office of Graduate and Extended Studies, Utica, NY 13502. Telephone: 315-792-3002. E-mail: sneun@utica.edu.

DEGREES AND AWARDS

BS Criminal Justice, Economic Crime Investigation; Cybersecurity and Information Assurance

Certificate Financial Crime Investigation

MBA Business Administration–Economic Crime and Fraud Management; Business Administration–Professional Accountancy

MS Economic Crime Management

DPT Physical Therapy–Transitional Doctorate of Physical Therapy

COURSE SUBJECT AREAS OFFERED OUTSIDE OF DEGREE PROGRAMS

Undergraduate—biology; economics; English; gerontology; liberal arts and sciences, general studies and humanities; mathematics; psychology.

VALLEY CITY STATE UNIVERSITY
Valley City, North Dakota
North Dakota Interactive Video Network
http://distancelearning.vcsu.edu
Valley City State University was founded in 1890. It is accredited by North Central Association of Colleges and Schools. It first offered distance learning courses in 2000. In fall 2007, there were 80 students enrolled in distance learning courses. Institutionally administered financial aid is available to distance learners.
Services Distance learners have accessibility to academic advising, bookstore, campus computer network, career placement assistance, e-mail services.
Contact Jody Klier, Registrar, Valley City State University, 101 College Street SW, Valley City, ND 58072. Telephone: 701-845-7295 Ext. 7297. Fax: 701-845-7299. E-mail: jody.klier@vcsu.edu.

DEGREES AND AWARDS
Programs offered do not lead to a degree or other formal award.

COURSE SUBJECT AREAS OFFERED OUTSIDE OF DEGREE PROGRAMS

Undergraduate—communication and journalism related; English as a second language; English composition; health and physical education/fitness; library science; psychology; speech and rhetoric; technology education/industrial arts.

Graduate—education; technology education/industrial arts.

VANDERBILT UNIVERSITY
Nashville, Tennessee
MS in Nursing
http://www.nursing.vanderbilt.edu
Vanderbilt University was founded in 1873. It is accredited by Southern Association of Colleges and Schools. It first offered distance learning courses in 1996. In fall 2007, there were 203 students enrolled in distance learning courses. Institutionally administered financial aid is available to distance learners.
Services Distance learners have accessibility to academic advising, bookstore, campus computer network, career placement assistance, e-mail services, library services.
Contact Admissions Counselor, Vanderbilt University, Godchaux Hall 207, 461 21st Av S, Nashville, TN 37240. Telephone: 888-333-9192. Fax: 615-343-0333. E-mail: vusn-admissions@vanderbilt.edu.

DEGREES AND AWARDS

MSN Acute Care Nurse Practitioner; Adult Nurse Practitioner; Clinical Management; Clinical Research Management; Health System Management; Neonatal Nurse Practitioner; Nursing Informatics; Pediatric Nurse Practitioner; Psychiatric Mental Health Nurse Practitioner

DNP Nursing Practice

PhD Nursing Science

VANGUARD UNIVERSITY OF SOUTHERN CALIFORNIA
Costa Mesa, California
http://www.vanguard.edu/eec
Vanguard University of Southern California was founded in 1920. It is accredited by Western Association of Schools and Colleges. It first offered distance learning courses in 2002. In fall 2007, there were 250 students enrolled in distance learning courses. Institutionally administered financial aid is available to distance learners.
Services Distance learners have accessibility to academic advising, bookstore, career placement assistance, e-mail services, library services, tutoring.
Contact Adm. Bren Martin, Technology and Learning, Vanguard University of Southern California, 55 Fair Drive, Costa Mesa, CA 92626. Telephone: 714-668-6196 Ext. 3441. Fax: 714-966-5460. E-mail: bmartin@vanguard.edu.

DEGREES AND AWARDS
Programs offered do not lead to a degree or other formal award.

COURSE SUBJECT AREAS OFFERED OUTSIDE OF DEGREE PROGRAMS

Undergraduate—curriculum and instruction; education; educational administration and supervision; education related; human development, family studies, and related services.

VERMONT TECHNICAL COLLEGE
Randolph Center, Vermont
http://www.vtc.edu
Vermont Technical College was founded in 1866. It is accredited by New England Association of Schools and Colleges. It first offered distance learning courses in 1996. In fall 2007, there were 140 students enrolled in distance learning courses. Institutionally administered financial aid is available to distance learners.
Services Distance learners have accessibility to academic advising, bookstore, campus computer network, e-mail services, library services.
Contact Michael Dempsey, Registrar, Vermont Technical College, PO Box 500, Randolph Center, VT 05061. Telephone: 802-728-1302. Fax: 802-728-1597. E-mail: mdempsey@vtc.vsc.edu.

DEGREES AND AWARDS
Programs offered do not lead to a degree or other formal award.

COURSE SUBJECT AREAS OFFERED OUTSIDE OF DEGREE PROGRAMS

Undergraduate—architectural history and criticism; computer and information sciences; dental support services and allied professions; history; social sciences related.

VINCENNES UNIVERSITY
Vincennes, Indiana
Distance Education/Degree Completion
http://www.vinu.edu/distance
Vincennes University was founded in 1801. It is accredited by North Central Association of Colleges and Schools. It first offered distance learning courses in 1989. In fall 2007, there were 1,705 students enrolled in distance learning courses. Institutionally administered financial aid is available to distance learners.
Services Distance learners have accessibility to academic advising, bookstore, campus computer network, career placement assistance, e-mail services, library services, tutoring.
Contact Mr. Donald E. Kaufman, Dean of Continuing Studies, Vincennes University, 1002 North First Street, Classroom Building A, Vincennes, IN 47591. Telephone: 812-888-5343. Fax: 812-888-2054. E-mail: dkaufman@vinu.edu.

DEGREES AND AWARDS

AAS Accounting; Business Management; Funeral Service Education; General Studies–Business Studies; General Studies; Law Enforcement Studies; Pharmacy Technician; Technology Apprenticeship–General Studies option

AS Behavioral Sciences; Business Administration; Funeral Service Education; General Studies–Surgical Technology Degree completion; General Studies; Health Information Management; Information Technology; Law Enforcement Studies; Liberal Arts/ Social Science Concentration; Social Work; Technology Apprenticeship
Certificate of Completion Behavioral Science–Substance Abuse Certificate; Community Rehabilitation; Surgical Technology–First Assist
Certificate General Studies–Customized Certificate
Graduate Certificate Surgical Technology accelerated option, Certificate of Graduation

COURSE SUBJECT AREAS OFFERED OUTSIDE OF DEGREE PROGRAMS

Undergraduate—accounting and related services; allied health and medical assisting services; applied mathematics; behavioral sciences; business administration, management and operations; business/commerce; business, management, and marketing related; business operations support and assistant services; chemistry; community health services; computer and information sciences; computer/information technology administration and management; creative writing; criminal justice and corrections; developmental and child psychology; economics; education; English composition; entrepreneurial and small business operations; fire protection; funeral service and mortuary science; history; information science/studies; liberal arts and sciences, general studies and humanities; mathematics; pharmacy, pharmaceutical sciences, and administration; psychology; rehabilitation and therapeutic professions; sales, merchandising, and related marketing operations (specialized); social sciences; social work; sociology; speech and rhetoric.

VIRGINIA POLYTECHNIC INSTITUTE AND STATE UNIVERSITY
Blacksburg, Virginia
Institute for Distance and Distributed Learning
http://vto.vt.edu

Virginia Polytechnic Institute and State University was founded in 1872. It is accredited by Southern Association of Colleges and Schools. It first offered distance learning courses in 1983. In fall 2007, there were 5,853 students enrolled in distance learning courses. Institutionally administered financial aid is available to distance learners.
Services Distance learners have accessibility to academic advising, bookstore, campus computer network, career placement assistance, e-mail services, library services, tutoring.
Contact Mrs. Angie A. Starr, Enrollment Services Coordinator, Virginia Polytechnic Institute and State University, Office of Distance Learning and Summer Sessions, 902 Prices Fork Road (0392), Blacksburg, VA 24061. Telephone: 540-231-1264. Fax: 540-231-2079. E-mail: vto@vt.edu.

DEGREES AND AWARDS

Certificate Undergraduate Humanistic Traditions
License Career and Technical Education; Professional Studies
Graduate Certificate Computer Engineering; Information Technology–Business Information Systems Module; Information Technology–Communications Module; Information Technology–Decision Support Systems; Information Technology–Networking; Liberal Arts; Natural Resources; Political Science–Environmental Politics and Policy; Political Science–Foundations of Political Analysis; Political Science–Information Policy and Society; Software Development
MA Instructional Technology; Political Science
MS Agricultural and Life Sciences; Career and Technical Education; Civil Infrastructure Engineering; Civil and Environmental Engineering; Computer Engineering; Electrical and Computer Engineering; Engineering Administration; Health Promotions; Information Technology; Natural Resources; Ocean Engineering; Systems Engineering

COURSE SUBJECT AREAS OFFERED OUTSIDE OF DEGREE PROGRAMS

Undergraduate—agriculture; agriculture and agriculture operations related; apparel and textiles; applied horticulture/horticultural business services; civil engineering; communication and media; computer engineering; computer science; education (specific levels and methods); education (specific subject areas); electrical and electronic engineering technologies; engineering; English composition; ethnic, cultural minority, and gender studies; fishing and fisheries sciences and management; geography and cartography; history; hospitality administration; human resources management; languages (Romance languages); linguistic, comparative, and related language studies; marketing; mathematics; music; philosophy; physics; political science and government; religious studies; science technologies related; sociology.
Graduate—accounting and related services; aerospace, aeronautical and astronautical engineering; agriculture and agriculture operations related; applied horticulture/horticultural business services; computer engineering; computer science; curriculum and instruction; educational administration and supervision; education related; education (specific subject areas); English; ethnic, cultural minority, and gender studies; forestry; geography and cartography; liberal arts and sciences, general studies and humanities; management information systems; marketing; mathematics; mechanical engineering; natural resources management and policy; political science and government; public administration; science technologies related; urban studies/affairs; veterinary biomedical and clinical sciences.
Non-credit—animal sciences; applied horticulture/horticultural business services; architecture; business administration, management and operations; business/commerce; computer and information sciences; computer software and media applications; education; engineering; engineering technologies related; forestry; history; marketing; music; natural resources conservation and research; plant sciences; public health; real estate; work and family studies.

See full description on page 524.

WAKE TECHNICAL COMMUNITY COLLEGE
Raleigh, North Carolina
http://www.waketech.edu

Wake Technical Community College was founded in 1958. It is accredited by Southern Association of Colleges and Schools. It first offered distance learning courses in 1986. In fall 2007, there were 3,512 students enrolled in distance learning courses. Institutionally administered financial aid is available to distance learners.
Services Distance learners have accessibility to academic advising, bookstore, career placement assistance, e-mail services, library services, tutoring.
Contact Diana Osborne, Head, Distance Education Support Department, Wake Technical Community College, 9101 Fayetteville Road, Raleigh, NC 27603-5696. Telephone: 919-866-5616. Fax: 919-773-6190. E-mail: dgosborne@waketech.edu.

DEGREES AND AWARDS

AA General degree
AAS Web Technologies
AGS General Education

COURSE SUBJECT AREAS OFFERED OUTSIDE OF DEGREE PROGRAMS

Undergraduate—accounting and related services; allied health and medical assisting services; American literature (United States and Canadian); anthropology; architectural technology; astronomy and astrophysics; biology; biomathematics and bioinformatics; business/commerce; business operations support and assistant services; chemistry; civil engineering technology; computer and information sciences and support services related; computer software and media applications; computer systems networking and telecommunications; construction management; cosmetology and related personal grooming services; criminal justice and corrections; culinary arts and related services; dental support services and allied professions; drafting/design engineering technologies; economics; electrical and electronic engineering technologies; engineering technology; English composition; English literature (British and Commonwealth); geological and earth sciences/geosciences; heating, air conditioning, ventilation and refrigeration maintenance technology; heavy/industrial equipment maintenance technologies; history; human services; landscape architecture; marketing; mathematics; pharmacy, pharmaceutical sciences, and administration; philosophy; physics; plumbing and related water supply services; political science and government; polymer/plastics engineering; psychology; real estate; religious studies; social work; sociology.

Non-credit—accounting and related services; business administration, management and operations; computer and information sciences and support services related; computer programming; computer software and media applications; data entry/microcomputer applications; data processing; English as a second language; entrepreneurial and small business operations; family and consumer economics; film/video and photographic arts; languages (foreign languages related); legal support services; sales, merchandising, and related marketing operations (general); technical and business writing.

WALDEN UNIVERSITY
Minneapolis, Minnesota
http://www.WaldenU.edu/

Walden University was founded in 1970. It is accredited by North Central Association of Colleges and Schools. It first offered distance learning courses in 1970. In fall 2007, there were 29,456 students enrolled in distance learning courses. Institutionally administered financial aid is available to distance learners.

Services Distance learners have accessibility to academic advising, bookstore, campus computer network, career placement assistance, e-mail services, library services, tutoring.

Contact Enrollment Advisor, Walden University, 1001 Fleet Street, Baltimore, MD 21202. Telephone: 866-492-5336. E-mail: info@waldenu.edu.

DEGREES AND AWARDS

BS Business Administration; Child Development; Computer Information Systems; Psychology
Certificate Engineering/Engineering Management Certificates; Post-Baccalaureate Teacher Preparation programs (with MAT option); Post-Doctoral Psychology Certificates
Endorsement Special Education Endorsement programs (with MS Education option)
Graduate Certificate Government Management; Nonprofit Management
MBA Business Administration
MHA Healthcare Administration
MISM Master of Information Systems Management
MPA Public Administration
MPH Public Health
MS Education; Mental Health Counseling; Nonprofit Management and Leadership; Nursing–BSN track; Nursing–RN track; Psychology; Software Engineering; Systems Engineering
EdD Education
PhD Applied Management and Decision Sciences; Education; Health Services; Human Services; Psychology; Public Health; Public Policy and Administration

See full description on page 526.

WASHBURN UNIVERSITY
Topeka, Kansas
Division of Continuing Education
http://www.washburn.edu/ce

Washburn University was founded in 1865. It is accredited by North Central Association of Colleges and Schools. It first offered distance learning courses in 1999. In fall 2007, there were 2,900 students enrolled in distance learning courses. Institutionally administered financial aid is available to distance learners.

Services Distance learners have accessibility to academic advising, bookstore, campus computer network, career placement assistance, e-mail services, library services.

Contact Dr. Timothy W. Peterson, Dean of Continuing Education, Washburn University, 1700 SW College Avenue, Topeka, KS 66621. Telephone: 785-670-1399. Fax: 785-670-1028. E-mail: tim.peterson@washburn.edu.

DEGREES AND AWARDS

BAA Human Services; Technology Administration
BHS Health Services Administration/Health Services Administration and Medical Imaging
BLS Administrative Communications–Liberal Studies
BS Criminal Justice

COURSE SUBJECT AREAS OFFERED OUTSIDE OF DEGREE PROGRAMS

Undergraduate—allied health diagnostic, intervention, and treatment professions; American literature (United States and Canadian); biology; business, management, and marketing related; chemistry; education; English composition; health and physical education/fitness; history; human services; military studies; music; nursing; political science and government; psychology; public administration; social work; sociology; technology education/industrial arts.
Graduate—criminal justice and corrections; education; liberal arts and sciences, general studies and humanities.
Non-credit—computer software and media applications; education; human resources management; social sciences related.

WASHINGTON STATE UNIVERSITY
Pullman, Washington
Distance Degree Programs
http://www.online.wsu.edu

Washington State University was founded in 1890. It is accredited by Northwest Commission on Colleges and Universities. It first offered distance learning courses in 1991. In fall 2007, there were 2,700 students enrolled in distance learning courses. Institutionally administered financial aid is available to distance learners.

Services Distance learners have accessibility to academic advising, bookstore, campus computer network, career placement assistance, e-mail services, library services, tutoring.

Contact Student Services, Washington State University, 104 Van Doren Hall, PO Box 645220, Pullman, WA 99164-5220. Telephone: 800-222-4978. Fax: 509-335-4850. E-mail: distance@wsu.edu.

DEGREES AND AWARDS

BA Business Administration; Criminal Justice; Human Development; Humanities; Social Sciences; Women's Studies
BSN Nursing–RN to BSN
Certificate Early Childhhood Development and Care; Organic Agriculture; Professional Writing
MS Agriculture

COURSE SUBJECT AREAS OFFERED OUTSIDE OF DEGREE PROGRAMS

Undergraduate—anthropology; economics; English; history; international business; marketing; mathematics; political science and government; psychology; sociology.

See full description on page 528.

WAYLAND BAPTIST UNIVERSITY
Plainview, Texas
http://www.wbu.edu/

Wayland Baptist University was founded in 1908. It is accredited by Southern Association of Colleges and Schools. It first offered distance learning courses in 1998. In fall 2007, there were 1,655 students enrolled in distance learning courses. Institutionally administered financial aid is available to distance learners.

Services Distance learners have accessibility to academic advising, e-mail services, library services.

Contact Mr. Jay Sample, Virtual Campus Director, Wayland Baptist University, 1900 West 7th Street, CMB 420, Plainview, TX 79072. Telephone: 806-291-1725. Fax: 806-291-1957. E-mail: samplej@wbu.edu.

DEGREES AND AWARDS

MA Management
MCM Christian Ministry
MEd Education
MPA Public Administration

COURSE SUBJECT AREAS OFFERED OUTSIDE OF DEGREE PROGRAMS

Undergraduate—accounting and related services; business administration, management and operations; criminal justice and corrections; economics; education related; finance and financial management services; health and medical administrative services; history; management information systems; marketing; music; physical sciences; political science and government; psychology; religious education; religious studies; sociology.

Graduate—accounting and related services; business administration, management and operations; counseling psychology; economics; education related; health and medical administrative services; human resources management; management information systems; public administration; religious education; religious studies.

WAYNE STATE COLLEGE
Wayne, Nebraska
Regional Education and Distance Learning
http://www.wsc.edu

Wayne State College was founded in 1910. It is accredited by North Central Association of Colleges and Schools. It first offered distance learning courses in 1997. In fall 2007, there were 1,130 students enrolled in distance learning courses. Institutionally administered financial aid is available to distance learners.

Services Distance learners have accessibility to academic advising, bookstore, campus computer network, career placement assistance, e-mail services, library services.

Contact Dr. Craig Kinsella, Director of Continuing Education, Wayne State College, 1111 Main Street, Wayne, NE 68787. Telephone: 402-375-7217. Fax: 402-375-7204. E-mail: crkinse1@wsc.edu.

DEGREES AND AWARDS

MBA Business Administration

COURSE SUBJECT AREAS OFFERED OUTSIDE OF DEGREE PROGRAMS

Undergraduate—business administration, management and operations; counseling psychology; criminal justice and corrections; economics; education; education (specific subject areas); English; industrial production technologies; multi-/interdisciplinary studies related; natural sciences; physical sciences; physics; special education; speech and rhetoric.

Graduate—business administration, management and operations; communications technologies and support services related; counseling psychology; criminal justice and corrections; economics; education; educational administration and supervision; education (specific subject areas); industrial production technologies; mathematics; parks, recreation and leisure facilities management; psychology; special education.

WEBER STATE UNIVERSITY
Ogden, Utah
Distance Learning and Independent Study
http://departments.weber.edu/ce/dl

Weber State University was founded in 1889. It is accredited by Northwest Commission on Colleges and Universities. It first offered distance learning courses in 1990. In fall 2007, there were 8,000 students enrolled in distance learning courses. Institutionally administered financial aid is available to distance learners.

Services Distance learners have accessibility to academic advising, bookstore, campus computer network, career placement assistance, e-mail services, library services, tutoring.

Contact Susan Smith, Office of Distance Learning, Weber State University, 4005 University Circle, Ogden, UT 84408-4005. Telephone: 801-626-6600. Fax: 801-626-8035. E-mail: dist-learn@weber.edu.

DEGREES AND AWARDS

AAS Clinical Laboratory Technician; Health Information Technology
AS Criminal Justice; General Studies
BS Clinical Laboratory Sciences; Health Administrative Services; Health Information Management; Health Promotion; Radiological Sciences
Certificate Health Care Coding and Classification; Radiological Sciences

COURSE SUBJECT AREAS OFFERED OUTSIDE OF DEGREE PROGRAMS

Undergraduate—accounting and related services; anthropology; building/construction finishing, management, and inspection; business administration, management and operations; chemistry; communication and media; computer and information sciences; computer and information sciences and support services related; computer science; English; English composition; geography and cartography; geological and earth sciences/geosciences; gerontology; health and medical administrative services; history; human development, family studies, and related services; linguistic, comparative, and related language studies; mathematics; microbiological sciences and immunology; music; philosophy; physics; political science and government; psychology; technical and business writing; zoology/animal biology.

Graduate—clinical/medical laboratory science and allied professions; health and medical administrative services.

See full description on page 530.

WEBSTER UNIVERSITY
St. Louis, Missouri
Online Learning Center
http://www.webster.edu/online

Webster University was founded in 1915. It is accredited by North Central Association of Colleges and Schools. It first offered distance learning courses in 1998. In fall 2007, there were 2,125 students enrolled in distance learning courses. Institutionally administered financial aid is available to distance learners.

Services Distance learners have accessibility to academic advising, bookstore, career placement assistance, e-mail services, library services, tutoring.

Contact Matt Nolan, Director, Graduate and Evening Student Admissions, Webster University, 470 East Lockwood Avenue, St. Louis, MO 63119. Telephone: 314-968-7089. Fax: 314-968-7462. E-mail: nolan@webster.edu.

DEGREES AND AWARDS

Certificate Web Site Design; Web Site Development
Graduate Certificate Decision Support Systems; Government Contracting; MBA Certificate in Global Commerce; Web Services
MA Business and Organizational Security Management; Communications Management; Human Resources Development; Human Resources Management; Information Technology Management; International Relations; Management and Leadership; Procurement and Acquisitions Management; Public Relations
MAT Educational Technology; Multidisciplinary Studies
MBA Business Administration
MS Environmental Management; Finance

COURSE SUBJECT AREAS OFFERED OUTSIDE OF DEGREE PROGRAMS

Undergraduate—computer and information sciences; languages (foreign languages related); mathematics; philosophy; public relations, advertising, and applied communication related; religious education.

Graduate—business, management, and marketing related; communication and journalism related; computer and information sciences and support services related; education; educational administration and supervision; finance and financial management services; management information systems; marketing; security and protective services related.

WESTCHESTER COMMUNITY COLLEGE
Valhalla, New York
http://www.sunywcc.edu/

Westchester Community College was founded in 1946. It is accredited by Middle States Association of Colleges and Schools. It first offered distance learning courses in 1997. In fall 2007, there were 1,100 students enrolled in distance learning courses. Institutionally administered financial aid is available to distance learners.

Services Distance learners have accessibility to academic advising, bookstore, library services, tutoring.

Contact Margi Winters, PhD, Assistant Dean for Distance Learning, Westchester Community College, 75 Grasslands Road, Valhalla, NY 10595. Telephone: 914-606-8677. Fax: 914-606-8550. E-mail: margi.winters@sunywcc.edu.

DEGREES AND AWARDS

AA Liberal Arts/Humanities; Liberal Arts/Social Science; Liberal Arts/Social Science

COURSE SUBJECT AREAS OFFERED OUTSIDE OF DEGREE PROGRAMS

Undergraduate—accounting and related services; American literature (United States and Canadian); anthropology; area, ethnic, cultural, and gender studies related; behavioral sciences; biological and physical sciences; biology; business/commerce; chemistry; communication and media; computer and information sciences; computer and information sciences and support services related; computer programming; computer science; computer systems analysis; computer systems networking and telecommunications; criminal justice and corrections; data processing; dietetics and clinical nutrition services; economics; English; English as a second language; English composition; English language and literature related; geography and cartography; health and physical education/fitness; history; human development, family studies, and related services; languages (Romance languages); management information systems; mathematics; mathematics and computer science; natural sciences; nursing; nutrition sciences; philosophy; philosophy and religious studies related; political science and government; psychology; religious studies; sales, merchandising, and related marketing operations (specialized); social psychology; social sciences; sociology; technical and business writing.

WESTERN KENTUCKY UNIVERSITY
Bowling Green, Kentucky
Distance Learning
http://www.wku.edu/reachu

Western Kentucky University was founded in 1906. It is accredited by Southern Association of Colleges and Schools. It first offered distance learning courses in 1999. In fall 2007, there were 4,175 students enrolled in distance learning courses. Institutionally administered financial aid is available to distance learners.

Services Distance learners have accessibility to academic advising, bookstore, career placement assistance, e-mail services, library services, tutoring.

Contact Ms. Cindy Troutman, Distance Learning Program Specialist, Western Kentucky University, Distance Learning, 1906 College Heights Boulevard, 61084, Bowling Green, KY 42101-1084. Telephone: 270-745-5173. Fax: 270-745-2107. E-mail: cindy.troutman@wku.edu.

DEGREES AND AWARDS

AAS Paramedicine completion
AS Interdisciplinary Early Childhood Education
BS Computer Information Technology; Consumer and Family Sciences, Child Studies emphasis; Technology Management
Certificate Canadian Studies; International Student Services
Endorsement Gifted and Talented Graduate Teaching Endorsement
Graduate Certificate Women's Studies
MA Exceptional Education; Mathematics Education
MBA eMBA
MS Biology Education; Communication Disorders; Library Media Education; Physical Education Pedagogy; Technology Management

WESTERN MICHIGAN UNIVERSITY
Kalamazoo, Michigan
Department of Distance Education
http://atis.wmich.edu/

Western Michigan University was founded in 1903. It is accredited by North Central Association of Colleges and Schools. It first offered distance learning courses in 1996. In fall 2007, there were 1,766 students enrolled in distance learning courses. Institutionally administered financial aid is available to distance learners.

Services Distance learners have accessibility to academic advising, bookstore, campus computer network, career placement assistance, e-mail services, library services.

Contact Teri Cleveland, Office Assistant, Western Michigan University, Academic Technology and Instructional Services, 1343 Ellsworth Hall, Kalamazoo, MI 49008-5232. Telephone: 269-387-4199. Fax: 269-387-4226. E-mail: teresa.cleveland@wmich.edu.

DEGREES AND AWARDS

MAE Educational Technology

COURSE SUBJECT AREAS OFFERED OUTSIDE OF DEGREE PROGRAMS

Undergraduate—air transportation; anthropology; apparel and textiles; area studies; biological and biomedical sciences related; biological and physical sciences; computer software and media applications; counseling psychology; economics; education; educational administration and supervision; educational assessment, evaluation, and research; educational/instructional media design; education related; engineering; English; English composition; ethnic, cultural minority, and gender studies; family and consumer economics; family and consumer sciences/human sciences; family and consumer sciences/human sciences related; film/video and photographic arts; geography and cartography; history; industrial engineering; languages (Romance languages); medieval and Renaissance studies; music; natural sciences; public administration and social service professions related; rehabilitation and therapeutic professions; religious studies; sales, merchandising, and related marketing operations (specialized); science, technology and society; social work; sociology.

Graduate—computer engineering; computer science; counseling psychology; developmental and child psychology; economics; educational/instructional media design; engineering/industrial management; family and consumer economics; film/video and photographic arts; history; human resources management.

WESTERN NEBRASKA COMMUNITY COLLEGE
Sidney, Nebraska
Information Technology
http://www.wncc.net

Western Nebraska Community College was founded in 1926. It is accredited by North Central Association of Colleges and Schools. It first offered distance learning courses in 1994. In fall 2007, there were 175 students enrolled in distance learning courses. Institutionally administered financial aid is available to distance learners.

Services Distance learners have accessibility to academic advising, bookstore, campus computer network, career placement assistance, e-mail services, library services, tutoring.

Contact Mr. Mark A. Sinner, Interactive Television Technical Coordinator, Western Nebraska Community College, 1601 East 27th Street, Scottsbluff, NE 69361. Telephone: 308-635-6142. Fax: 308-635-6100. E-mail: sinnerm@wncc.net.

DEGREES AND AWARDS

Programs offered do not lead to a degree or other formal award.

COURSE SUBJECT AREAS OFFERED OUTSIDE OF DEGREE PROGRAMS

Undergraduate—criminal justice and corrections; developmental and child psychology; education related; English composition; foods, nutrition, and related services; nursing; psychology related; sociology.

WESTERN SEMINARY
Portland, Oregon
Center for Lifelong Learning
http://www.westernseminary.edu

Western Seminary was founded in 1927. It is accredited by Northwest Commission on Colleges and Universities. It first offered distance learning courses in 1981. In fall 2007, there were 141 students enrolled in distance learning courses. Institutionally administered financial aid is available to distance learners.

Services Distance learners have accessibility to academic advising, bookstore, career placement assistance, e-mail services, library services.
Contact James Stewart, Director of Distance Education, Western Seminary, 5511 SE Hawthorne Boulevard, Portland, OR 97215. Telephone: 877-517-1800. Fax: 503-517-1801. E-mail: jstewart@westernseminary.edu.

DEGREES AND AWARDS

Programs offered do not lead to a degree or other formal award.

COURSE SUBJECT AREAS OFFERED OUTSIDE OF DEGREE PROGRAMS

Graduate—biblical and other theological languages and literatures; biblical studies; religious education; religious studies; theological and ministerial studies; theology and religious vocations related.

Non-credit—biblical and other theological languages and literatures; biblical studies; religious education; religious studies; theological and ministerial studies; theology and religious vocations related.

WESTERN WASHINGTON UNIVERSITY
Bellingham, Washington
Extended Education and Summer Programs
http://www.ExtendedEd.wwu.edu

Western Washington University was founded in 1893. It is accredited by Northwest Commission on Colleges and Universities. It first offered distance learning courses in 1941. In fall 2007, there were 304 students enrolled in distance learning courses. Institutionally administered financial aid is available to distance learners.

Services Distance learners have accessibility to academic advising, bookstore, campus computer network, career placement assistance, e-mail services, library services, tutoring.
Contact Barbara (Bunny) Starbuck, Distance Learning Assistant, Western Washington University, MS 5293, 516 High Street, Bellingham, WA 98225-5996. Telephone: 360-650-3650. Fax: 360-650-6858. E-mail: eesp.distedpeters@wwu.edu.

DEGREES AND AWARDS

Programs offered do not lead to a degree or other formal award.

COURSE SUBJECT AREAS OFFERED OUTSIDE OF DEGREE PROGRAMS

Undergraduate—American literature (United States and Canadian); anthropology; area studies; biblical and other theological languages and literatures; communication and journalism related; community health services; creative writing; curriculum and instruction; developmental and child psychology; economics; educational administration and supervision; education (specific levels and methods); education (specific subject areas); engineering technologies related; English; English as a second/foreign language (teaching); English as a second language; ethnic, cultural minority, and gender studies; history; human development, family studies, and related services; human services; languages (East Asian); languages (Modern Greek); languages (Romance languages); library science related; management sciences and quantitative methods; mathematics; medieval and Renaissance studies; music; parks, recreation, and leisure related; psychology; social work; sociology; special education.

WESTERN WYOMING COMMUNITY COLLEGE
Rock Springs, Wyoming
Extended Education
http://www.wwcc.wy.edu/dist_ed/

Western Wyoming Community College was founded in 1959. It is accredited by North Central Association of Colleges and Schools. It first offered distance learning courses in 1988. In fall 2007, there were 1,400 students enrolled in distance learning courses. Institutionally administered financial aid is available to distance learners.

Services Distance learners have accessibility to academic advising, bookstore, campus computer network, career placement assistance, e-mail services, library services, tutoring.
Contact Ms. Christine Lustik, Director of Distance Education, Western Wyoming Community College, 2500 College Drive, C-571, PO Box 428, Rock Springs, WY 82902. Telephone: 307-382-1757. Fax: 307-382-1812. E-mail: clustik@wwcc.wy.edu.

DEGREES AND AWARDS

AA General Studies

AAS Office Information Systems

AS Accounting; Business Administration; Computer Information Systems; Economics; General Studies; Marketing

Certificate Accounting; Western American Studies

Certification Web Site Development Certificate

COURSE SUBJECT AREAS OFFERED OUTSIDE OF DEGREE PROGRAMS

Undergraduate—accounting and related services; anthropology; applied mathematics; biological and physical sciences; business administration, management and operations; business/commerce; business operations support and assistant services; communication and journalism related; computer science; computer software and media applications; economics; education (specific levels and methods); English composition; ethnic, cultural minority, and gender studies; history; philosophy; psychology; social work; sociology.

WESTFIELD STATE COLLEGE
Westfield, Massachusetts
http://wsc.ma.edu/Academics/
Division_of_Graduate_and_Continuing_Education/

Westfield State College was founded in 1838. It is accredited by New England Association of Schools and Colleges. It first offered distance learning courses in 2003. In fall 2007, there were 150 students enrolled in distance learning courses. Institutionally administered financial aid is available to distance learners.

Services Distance learners have accessibility to bookstore, campus computer network, career placement assistance, e-mail services, library services.
Contact Mr. Cornel Hurston, IT Coordinator, Continuing Education/Graduate Studies, Westfield State College, Division of Graduate and Continuing Studies, 333 Western Avenue, Westfield, MA 01086. Telephone: 413-572-8028. Fax: 413-572-5227. E-mail: churston@wsc.ma.edu.

DEGREES AND AWARDS

BS Business Management Online

COURSE SUBJECT AREAS OFFERED OUTSIDE OF DEGREE PROGRAMS

Undergraduate—biology; computer and information sciences; computer science; criminal justice and corrections; education; history; liberal arts and sciences, general studies and humanities; music; philosophy; psychology; public administration; social sciences.

Graduate—education; history; public administration.

WEST HILLS COMMUNITY COLLEGE
Coalinga, California
Learning Resources Division
http://www.westhillscollege.com/

West Hills Community College was founded in 1932. It is accredited by Western Association of Schools and Colleges. It first offered distance learning courses in 1989. In fall 2007, there were 3,000 students enrolled in distance learning courses. Institutionally administered financial aid is available to distance learners.

Services Distance learners have accessibility to academic advising, bookstore, campus computer network, career placement assistance, e-mail services, library services, tutoring.

Contact M. Susan Whitener, Dean of Learning Resources and Web Services, West Hills Community College, 9900 Cody Avenue, Coalinga, CA 93210. Telephone: 559-925-3404. Fax: 559-925-3830. E-mail: susanwhitener@westhillscollege.com.

DEGREES AND AWARDS
AA Administration of Justice–Law Enforcement; Liberal Arts; Psychology; Social Science
AS Administration of Justice–Law Enforcement

COURSE SUBJECT AREAS OFFERED OUTSIDE OF DEGREE PROGRAMS
Non-credit—accounting and computer science; accounting and related services; alternative and complementary medical support services; alternative and complementary medicine and medical systems; animal sciences; applied horticulture/horticultural business services; business/corporate communications; computer and information sciences; computer software and media applications; creative writing; developmental and child psychology; English as a second language; gerontology; health and medical administrative services; health professions related; health services/allied health/health sciences; languages (Romance languages); mathematics and computer science; real estate; technical and business writing; veterinary biomedical and clinical sciences.

WEST LOS ANGELES COLLEGE
Culver City, California
Distance Learning Center
http://www.wlac.edu/online

West Los Angeles College was founded in 1969. It is accredited by Western Association of Schools and Colleges. It first offered distance learning courses in 1999. In fall 2007, there were 4,700 students enrolled in distance learning courses. Institutionally administered financial aid is available to distance learners.

Services Distance learners have accessibility to academic advising, bookstore, campus computer network, library services, tutoring.

Contact Mr. Eric Jean Ichon, Distance Learning Coordinator, West Los Angeles College, 9000 Overland Avenue, HLRC 4A, Culver City, CA 90230. Telephone: 310-287-4305. Fax: 310-287-4418. E-mail: ichone@wlac.edu.

DEGREES AND AWARDS
Programs offered do not lead to a degree or other formal award.

COURSE SUBJECT AREAS OFFERED OUTSIDE OF DEGREE PROGRAMS
Undergraduate—accounting and computer science; air transportation; allied health and medical assisting services; American literature (United States and Canadian); anthropology; applied mathematics; area, ethnic, cultural, and gender studies related; behavioral sciences; business administration, management and operations; business/commerce; business, management, and marketing related; business/managerial economics; business operations support and assistant services; computer and information sciences; computer/information technology administration and management; computer science; creative writing; criminal justice and corrections; data entry/microcomputer applications; dental support services and allied professions; dentistry and oral sciences (advanced/graduate); design and applied arts; dramatic/theater arts and stagecraft; economics; education; English; English as a second language; English

composition; English language and literature related; fire protection; foods, nutrition, and related services; health and physical education/fitness; health/medical preparatory programs; health services/allied health/health sciences; history; information science/studies; international relations and affairs; languages (foreign languages related); languages (South Asian); legal professions and studies related; legal studies (non-professional general, undergraduate); legal support services; liberal arts and sciences, general studies and humanities; library science; marketing; mathematics; music; philosophy; political science and government; psychology; real estate; sales, merchandising, and related marketing operations (specialized); social sciences; social sciences related; speech and rhetoric; technical and business writing; visual and performing arts; work and family studies.

WEST SHORE COMMUNITY COLLEGE
Scottville, Michigan
http://www.westshore.edu

West Shore Community College was founded in 1967. It is accredited by North Central Association of Colleges and Schools. It first offered distance learning courses in 1998. In fall 2007, there were 350 students enrolled in distance learning courses. Institutionally administered financial aid is available to distance learners.

Services Distance learners have accessibility to academic advising, bookstore, career placement assistance, e-mail services, library services, tutoring.

Contact Patti Davidson, Director of Distance Learning and Information Technology, West Shore Community College, 3000 North Stiles Road, Scottville, MI 49454-0277. Telephone: 231-843-5830. Fax: 231-845-0207. E-mail: pldavidson@westshore.edu.

DEGREES AND AWARDS
AGS General Studies

COURSE SUBJECT AREAS OFFERED OUTSIDE OF DEGREE PROGRAMS
Undergraduate—American literature (United States and Canadian); biology; botany/plant biology; business administration, management and operations; business, management, and marketing related; computer and information sciences; criminal justice and corrections; English composition; geological and earth sciences/geosciences; history; liberal arts and sciences, general studies and humanities; marketing; mathematics; mathematics and statistics related; music; public relations, advertising, and applied communication related; sociology.

WEST TEXAS A&M UNIVERSITY
Canyon, Texas
http://www.wtonline.wtamu.edu

West Texas A&M University was founded in 1909. It is accredited by Southern Association of Colleges and Schools. It first offered distance learning courses in 1997. In fall 2007, there were 3,055 students enrolled in distance learning courses. Institutionally administered financial aid is available to distance learners.

Services Distance learners have accessibility to academic advising, bookstore, career placement assistance, e-mail services, library services.

Contact Mr. Shawn Thomas, Director, Admissions, West Texas A&M University, Office of Admissions, WTAMU Box 60907, Canyon, TX 79016-0001. Telephone: 806-651-2020. Fax: 806-651-5285. E-mail: admissions@mail.wtamu.edu.

DEGREES AND AWARDS
BGS General Studies
BSN Nursing–RN to BSN completion
MBA Business Administration
MEd Instructional Technology
MS Agricultural Business Economics

COURSE SUBJECT AREAS OFFERED OUTSIDE OF DEGREE PROGRAMS
Undergraduate—education.

Graduate—accounting and computer science; educational assessment, evaluation, and research; education (specific subject areas).

WEST VIRGINIA STATE UNIVERSITY
Institute, West Virginia
http://www.wvstateu.edu/
West Virginia State University was founded in 1891. It is accredited by North Central Association of Colleges and Schools. It first offered distance learning courses in 1998. In fall 2007, there were 240 students enrolled in distance learning courses. Institutionally administered financial aid is available to distance learners.
Services Distance learners have accessibility to bookstore, campus computer network, e-mail services, library services, tutoring.
Contact Dr. John Teeuwissen, Assistant Vice President for Academic Affairs, West Virginia State University, 131 Ferrell Hall, PO Box 1000, Institute, WV 25112. Telephone: 304-766-3147. Fax: 304-766-4251. E-mail: johntee@wvstateu.edu.

DEGREES AND AWARDS
Programs offered do not lead to a degree or other formal award.

COURSE SUBJECT AREAS OFFERED OUTSIDE OF DEGREE PROGRAMS
Undergraduate—business administration, management and operations; communication and journalism related; communication and media; computer and information sciences; computer science; education; English; English composition; film/video and photographic arts; health professions related; social work; technical and business writing.
Graduate—communication and media; film/video and photographic arts.

WEST VIRGINIA UNIVERSITY
Morgantown, West Virginia
Extended Learning
http://elearn.wvu.edu/
West Virginia University was founded in 1867. It is accredited by North Central Association of Colleges and Schools. It first offered distance learning courses in 1987. In fall 2007, there were 4,461 students enrolled in distance learning courses. Institutionally administered financial aid is available to distance learners.
Services Distance learners have accessibility to academic advising, bookstore, campus computer network, career placement assistance, e-mail services, library services, tutoring.
Contact Ms. Cindy K. Hart, Coordinator of Distance Learning, West Virginia University, 707 Allen Hall, PO Box 6808, Morgantown, WV 26506-6808. Telephone: 304-293-3852. Fax: 304-293-3853. E-mail: lkhart@mail.wvu.edu.

DEGREES AND AWARDS
BA Multidisciplinary Studies; Regents Bachelor of Arts
BSN Nursing–RN to BSN
Certificate Integrated Marketing Communications
EMBA Business Administration
MA Elementary Education; Secondary Education–Science emphasis; Secondary Education–Social Studies emphasis; Special Education
MLS Legal Studies
MPH Public Health
MS Athletic Coaching; Integrated Marketing Communications; Rehabilitation Counseling; Software Engineering; Sports Management
MSE Physical Education Teacher Education
MSN Nursing
MSOT Occupational Therapy

COURSE SUBJECT AREAS OFFERED OUTSIDE OF DEGREE PROGRAMS
Graduate—engineering technologies related; marketing.
Non-credit—computer software and media applications; education; engineering related; finance and financial management services; forensic psychology; health professions related; health services/allied health/health sciences; legal support services; management information systems;

nursing; pharmacy, pharmaceutical sciences, and administration; technology education/industrial arts; veterinary biomedical and clinical sciences.

WEST VIRGINIA UNIVERSITY AT PARKERSBURG
Parkersburg, West Virginia
http://www.wvup.edu/dl/OnlineEd/index.htm
West Virginia University at Parkersburg was founded in 1961. It is accredited by North Central Association of Colleges and Schools. It first offered distance learning courses in 1999. In fall 2007, there were 1,331 students enrolled in distance learning courses. Institutionally administered financial aid is available to distance learners.
Services Distance learners have accessibility to academic advising, bookstore, campus computer network, e-mail services, library services, tutoring.
Contact Violet Mosser, Admissions Counselor, West Virginia University at Parkersburg, 300 Campus Drive, Parkersburg, WV 26104. Telephone: 304-424-8213. Fax: 304-424-8354. E-mail: violet.mossor@mail.wvu.edu.

DEGREES AND AWARDS
AA General degree
AAS Business Technology; Multi-Craft Technology
AS Business Administration

COURSE SUBJECT AREAS OFFERED OUTSIDE OF DEGREE PROGRAMS
Undergraduate—accounting and related services; biological and physical sciences; biology; business administration, management and operations; business/commerce; business/corporate communications; business, management, and marketing related; business/managerial economics; business operations support and assistant services; communication and journalism related; community health services; computer and information sciences; computer/information technology administration and management; criminal justice and corrections; dramatic/theater arts and stagecraft; English composition; English language and literature related; health and physical education/fitness; health professions related; history; human resources management; intercultural/multicultural and diversity studies; management information systems; marketing; mathematics; nursing; philosophy; psychology; social sciences; sociology; technology education/industrial arts.
Non-credit—accounting and computer science; business/corporate communications; business operations support and assistant services; communication and media; communications technologies and support services related; computer and information sciences; computer/information technology administration and management; construction trades related; crafts, folk art and artisanry; dance; fishing and fisheries sciences and management; foods, nutrition, and related services; quality control and safety technologies; technical and business writing.

WESTWOOD ONLINE
Denver, Colorado
http://www.westwood.edu
Westwood Online is accredited by Accrediting Commission of Career Schools and Colleges of Technology. It first offered distance learning courses in 2002. In fall 2007, there were 350 students enrolled in distance learning courses. Institutionally administered financial aid is available to distance learners.
Services Distance learners have accessibility to academic advising, bookstore, campus computer network, career placement assistance, e-mail services, library services, tutoring.
Contact Kim Beckman, Area Vice President, Westwood Online, Denver, CO 80221. Telephone: 303-635-7750 Ext. 11510. E-mail: kbeckman@westwood.edu.

DEGREES AND AWARDS
AAS Computer Network Engineering; Graphic Design and Multimedia; Software Engineering
BS Animation; Business Administration–Accounting concentration; Business Administration–Marketing and Sales concentration; Business–

Fashion Merchandising; Computer Network Management; Criminal Justice; E-Business Management; Game Art and Design; Game Software Development; Information Systems Security; Visual Communications; Web Design and Multimedia
MBA Business Administration

COURSE SUBJECT AREAS OFFERED OUTSIDE OF DEGREE PROGRAMS

Undergraduate—accounting and related services; business administration, management and operations; computer programming; computer software and media applications; computer systems networking and telecommunications; criminal justice and corrections; design and applied arts.

See full description on page 532.

WHARTON COUNTY JUNIOR COLLEGE
Wharton, Texas
http://www.wcjc.edu/
Wharton County Junior College was founded in 1946. It is accredited by Southern Association of Colleges and Schools. It first offered distance learning courses in 1993. In fall 2007, there were 930 students enrolled in distance learning courses. Institutionally administered financial aid is available to distance learners.
Services Distance learners have accessibility to bookstore, e-mail services, library services, tutoring.
Contact Ms. Lisa Shoppa, Distance Learning Program Assistant, Wharton County Junior College, 911 Boling Highway, Wharton, TX 77488. Telephone: 979-532-6336. Fax: 979-532-6567. E-mail: lisas@wcjc.edu.

DEGREES AND AWARDS
Programs offered do not lead to a degree or other formal award.

COURSE SUBJECT AREAS OFFERED OUTSIDE OF DEGREE PROGRAMS

Undergraduate—accounting and computer science; allied health and medical assisting services; American literature (United States and Canadian); behavioral sciences; biology; business administration, management and operations; business/commerce; business, management, and marketing related; computer and information sciences; computer science; computer software and media applications; computer systems networking and telecommunications; creative writing; criminal justice and corrections; English; English composition; English language and literature related; English literature (British and Commonwealth); geological and earth sciences/geosciences; history; liberal arts and sciences, general studies and humanities; marketing; psychology; sociology; speech and rhetoric.
Non-credit—English as a second language; fire protection.

WHEELING JESUIT UNIVERSITY
Wheeling, West Virginia
http://www.wju.edu/adulted/
Wheeling Jesuit University was founded in 1954. It is accredited by North Central Association of Colleges and Schools. It first offered distance learning courses in 2000. In fall 2007, there were 188 students enrolled in distance learning courses. Institutionally administered financial aid is available to distance learners.
Services Distance learners have accessibility to academic advising, bookstore, campus computer network, career placement assistance, e-mail services, library services, tutoring.
Contact Rebecca Forney, Associate Dean, Wheeling Jesuit University, 316 Washington Avenue, Wheeling, WV 26003. Telephone: 304-243-2250. Fax: 304-243-4441. E-mail: bforney@wju.edu.

DEGREES AND AWARDS
BS Healthcare Leadership
BSN Nursing–RN to MSN
CCCPE Accelerated Certification for Teaching
MSN Nursing

COURSE SUBJECT AREAS OFFERED OUTSIDE OF DEGREE PROGRAMS
Undergraduate—education; health professions related; nursing.
Graduate—nursing.

WICHITA STATE UNIVERSITY
Wichita, Kansas
Media Resources Center
http://www.mrc.twsu.edu/mrc/telecourse
Wichita State University was founded in 1895. It is accredited by North Central Association of Colleges and Schools. It first offered distance learning courses in 1982. In fall 2007, there were 619 students enrolled in distance learning courses. Institutionally administered financial aid is available to distance learners.
Services Distance learners have accessibility to bookstore, library services.
Contact Mary Morriss, Telecourse Coordinator, Wichita State University, 1845 Fairmount, Wichita, KS 67260-0057. Telephone: 316-978-7766. Fax: 316-978-3560. E-mail: morriss@mrc.twsu.edu.

DEGREES AND AWARDS
Programs offered do not lead to a degree or other formal award.

COURSE SUBJECT AREAS OFFERED OUTSIDE OF DEGREE PROGRAMS
Undergraduate—accounting and related services; anthropology; astronomy and astrophysics; communication and media; family and consumer economics; geography and cartography; gerontology; history; music; psychology; sociology; speech and rhetoric.

WIDENER UNIVERSITY
Chester, Pennsylvania
http://www.widener.edu/uc
Widener University was founded in 1821. It is accredited by Middle States Association of Colleges and Schools. It first offered distance learning courses in 1996. In fall 2007, there were 310 students enrolled in distance learning courses. Institutionally administered financial aid is available to distance learners.
Services Distance learners have accessibility to academic advising, bookstore, campus computer network, career placement assistance, e-mail services, library services.
Contact Dr. Emily C. Richardson, Dean, University College, Widener University, One University Place, Chester, PA 19013. Telephone: 610-499-4282. E-mail: ecrichardson@widener.edu.

DEGREES AND AWARDS
AA Liberal Arts
AS General Studies
BA Liberal Studies; Organizational Development and Leadership
BS Allied Health; Professional Studies

WILFRID LAURIER UNIVERSITY
Waterloo, Ontario, Canada
Office of Teaching Support Services
http://www.wlu.ca/disted
Wilfrid Laurier University was founded in 1911. It is provincially chartered. It first offered distance learning courses in 1978. In fall 2007, there were 3,000 students enrolled in distance learning courses. Institutionally administered financial aid is available to distance learners.
Services Distance learners have accessibility to academic advising, bookstore, campus computer network, career placement assistance, e-mail services, library services.
Contact Lisa Fanjoy, Manager, Distance and Continuing Education, Wilfrid Laurier University, Office of Teaching Support Services, 75 University Avenue West, Waterloo, ON N2L 3C5, Canada. Telephone: 519-884-0710 Ext. 4106. Fax: 519-884-6063. E-mail: lfanjoy@wlu.ca.

DEGREES AND AWARDS
BA General Studies

COURSE SUBJECT AREAS OFFERED OUTSIDE OF DEGREE PROGRAMS
Undergraduate—accounting and related services; American literature (United States and Canadian); anthropology; astronomy and astrophysics; biology; biopsychology; botany/plant biology; business/commerce; cognitive psychology and psycholinguistics; communication and media; developmental and child psychology; economics; English; English literature (British and Commonwealth); finance and financial management services; fine and studio art; geography and cartography; geological and earth sciences/geosciences; history; languages (Germanic); languages (Romance languages); philosophy; psychology; psychology related; religious studies; social work; sociology; visual and performing arts.
Non-credit—English composition.

WILLIAMSON CHRISTIAN COLLEGE
Franklin, Tennessee
http://www.williamsoncc.edu
Williamson Christian College was founded in 1997. It is accredited by Association for Biblical Higher Education. It first offered distance learning courses in 2000. In fall 2007, there were 20 students enrolled in distance learning courses. Institutionally administered financial aid is available to distance learners.
Services Distance learners have accessibility to academic advising, bookstore, career placement assistance, e-mail services, library services.
Contact Mr. Steve Smith, Registrar, Williamson Christian College, 200 Seaboard Lane, Franklin, TN 37067. Telephone: 615-771-7821. Fax: 615-771-7810. E-mail: ssmith@williamsoncc.edu.

DEGREES AND AWARDS
BS Leadership and Ministry; Management and Ethics

COURSE SUBJECT AREAS OFFERED OUTSIDE OF DEGREE PROGRAMS
Undergraduate—biblical studies; religious studies; theological and ministerial studies.

WILLISTON STATE COLLEGE
Williston, North Dakota
http://www.wsc.nodak.edu/distance/
Williston State College was founded in 1957. It is accredited by North Central Association of Colleges and Schools. It first offered distance learning courses in 2000. In fall 2007, there were 409 students enrolled in distance learning courses. Institutionally administered financial aid is available to distance learners.
Services Distance learners have accessibility to academic advising, bookstore, campus computer network, e-mail services, library services, tutoring.
Contact Mrs. Wanda Mae Meyer, Director for Distance Learning, Williston State College, 1410 University Avenue, Williston, ND 58801. Telephone: 701-774-4231. Fax: 701-772-4211. E-mail: wanda.meyer@wsc.nodak.edu.

DEGREES AND AWARDS
AAS Administrative Assistant–Accounting option; Administrative Assistant–Health Information Management option; Administrative Assistant–Information Processing option; Entrepreneurship; Marketing/Management; Medical Transcription; Paraeducator; Speech Language Pathology Assistant
Certificate of Completion Entrepreneurship
Certificate Administrative Assistant–Front Office option; Administrative Assistant–Information Processing option; Administrative Assistant–Medical Billing and Coding option; Entrepreneurship; Marketing/Management; Medical Transcription

COURSE SUBJECT AREAS OFFERED OUTSIDE OF DEGREE PROGRAMS
Undergraduate—accounting and computer science; biology; business, management, and marketing related; business/managerial economics; chemistry; computer science; English composition; history; mathematics; music; psychology; sociology.

WILMINGTON UNIVERSITY
New Castle, Delaware
http://www.wilmu.edu/distancelearning
Wilmington University was founded in 1967. It is accredited by Middle States Association of Colleges and Schools. It first offered distance learning courses in 2007. In fall 2007, there were 800 students enrolled in distance learning courses. Institutionally administered financial aid is available to distance learners.
Services Distance learners have accessibility to academic advising, bookstore, campus computer network, career placement assistance, e-mail services, library services, tutoring.
Contact Laura Leipold, e-Recruiter, Wilmington University, 47 Reads Way, New Castle, DE 19720. Telephone: 302-295-1179. E-mail: laura.m.leipold@wilmu.edu.

DEGREES AND AWARDS
Programs offered do not lead to a degree or other formal award.

COURSE SUBJECT AREAS OFFERED OUTSIDE OF DEGREE PROGRAMS
Undergraduate—allied health and medical assisting services; business administration, management and operations; criminal justice and corrections; human resources management; marketing.
Graduate—business administration, management and operations; computer and information sciences; criminal justice and corrections.

WISCONSIN INDIANHEAD TECHNICAL COLLEGE
Shell Lake, Wisconsin
http://www.witc.edu
Wisconsin Indianhead Technical College was founded in 1912. It is accredited by North Central Association of Colleges and Schools. It first offered distance learning courses in 1991. In fall 2007, there were 1,793 students enrolled in distance learning courses. Institutionally administered financial aid is available to distance learners.
Services Distance learners have accessibility to academic advising, bookstore, career placement assistance, e-mail services, library services, tutoring.
Contact Dr. Diane Vertin, Vice President, Academic Affairs, Wisconsin Indianhead Technical College, 505 Pine Ridge Drive, Shell Lake, WI 54871. Telephone: 715-468-2815 Ext. 2331. Fax: 715-468-2819. E-mail: diane.vertin@witc.edu.

DEGREES AND AWARDS
AD Information Technology–Web Analyst/Programmer

COURSE SUBJECT AREAS OFFERED OUTSIDE OF DEGREE PROGRAMS
Undergraduate—accounting and related services; agricultural and food products processing; agricultural business and management; agriculture; applied mathematics; business administration, management and operations; business/commerce; business operations support and assistant services; communication and media; computer and information sciences; computer programming; foods, nutrition, and related services; human development, family studies, and related services; nursing; psychology; public relations, advertising, and applied communication related; sales, merchandising, and related marketing operations (specialized); sociology; statistics.
Non-credit—accounting and related services; agricultural and food products processing; agricultural business and management; agriculture; applied mathematics; business administration, management and operations; business/commerce; business operations support and assistant services; communication and media; computer and information sciences;

computer programming; foods, nutrition, and related services; human development, family studies, and related services; nursing; psychology; public relations, advertising, and applied communication related; sales, merchandising, and related marketing operations (specialized); sociology; statistics.

WORCESTER POLYTECHNIC INSTITUTE
Worcester, Massachusetts
Advanced Distance Learning Network
http://www.online.wpi.edu
Worcester Polytechnic Institute was founded in 1865. It is accredited by New England Association of Schools and Colleges. It first offered distance learning courses in 1979. In fall 2007, there were 400 students enrolled in distance learning courses. Institutionally administered financial aid is available to distance learners.
Services Distance learners have accessibility to academic advising, bookstore, campus computer network, career placement assistance, e-mail services, library services.
Contact Pamela S. Shelley, Assistant Director, Distance Learning, Worcester Polytechnic Institute, 100 Institute Road, Worcester, MA 01609-2280. Telephone: 508-831-6789. Fax: 508-831-5694. E-mail: online@wpi.edu.

DEGREES AND AWARDS
CGMS Management
Graduate Certificate Environmental Engineering; Fire Protection Engineering
MBA Management
MS Environmental Engineering; Fire Protection Engineering

COURSE SUBJECT AREAS OFFERED OUTSIDE OF DEGREE PROGRAMS
Graduate—business administration, management and operations; environmental/environmental health engineering; fire protection; marketing.

WORCESTER STATE COLLEGE
Worcester, Massachusetts
http://www.worcester.edu/
Worcester State College was founded in 1874. It is accredited by New England Association of Schools and Colleges. It first offered distance learning courses in 2000. In fall 2007, there were 405 students enrolled in distance learning courses. Institutionally administered financial aid is available to distance learners.
Services Distance learners have accessibility to bookstore, campus computer network, e-mail services, library services.
Contact Dr. William White, Dean of Graduate and Continuing Education, Worcester State College, Office of Graduate and Continuing Education, 486 Chandler Street, Worcester, MA 01602-2597. Telephone: 508-929-8811. Fax: 508-929-8100. E-mail: wwhite@worcester.edu.

DEGREES AND AWARDS
Programs offered do not lead to a degree or other formal award.

COURSE SUBJECT AREAS OFFERED OUTSIDE OF DEGREE PROGRAMS
Undergraduate—biology; business administration, management and operations; communication and media; computer and information sciences; economics; English; health professions related; history; mathematics; philosophy; psychology; statistics.
Graduate—English; health professions related; history.
Non-credit—business administration, management and operations; communication and media; computer and information sciences; computer science; entrepreneurial and small business operations; film/video and photographic arts; human resources management; human services; public relations, advertising, and applied communication related.

WYTHEVILLE COMMUNITY COLLEGE
Wytheville, Virginia
http://www.wcc.vccs.edu/
Wytheville Community College was founded in 1967. It is accredited by Southern Association of Colleges and Schools. It first offered distance learning courses in 1981. In fall 2007, there were 800 students enrolled in distance learning courses. Institutionally administered financial aid is available to distance learners.
Services Distance learners have accessibility to academic advising, bookstore, campus computer network, career placement assistance, e-mail services, library services, tutoring.
Contact Dean Kathy Havens, Dean of Student Services, Wytheville Community College, 1000 East Main Street, Wytheville, VA 24382. Telephone: 276-223-4751. E-mail: havek@wcc.vccs.edu.

DEGREES AND AWARDS
Programs offered do not lead to a degree or other formal award.

COURSE SUBJECT AREAS OFFERED OUTSIDE OF DEGREE PROGRAMS
Undergraduate—accounting and related services; biology; business operations support and assistant services; computer and information sciences; computer programming; computer software and media applications; computer systems analysis; computer systems networking and telecommunications; cosmetology and related personal grooming services; developmental and child psychology; drafting/design engineering technologies; economics; English composition; health and physical education/fitness; health professions related; history; marketing; ophthalmic and optometric support services and allied professions; physics; psychology; religious studies.

YORK COUNTY COMMUNITY COLLEGE
Wells, Maine
http://www.yccc.edu
York County Community College was founded in 1994. It is accredited by New England Association of Schools and Colleges. It first offered distance learning courses in 1999. In fall 2007, there were 300 students enrolled in distance learning courses. Institutionally administered financial aid is available to distance learners.
Services Distance learners have accessibility to academic advising, bookstore, campus computer network, career placement assistance, e-mail services, library services, tutoring.
Contact Fred Quistgard, Director of Admissions, York County Community College, 112 College Drive, Wells, ME 04090. Telephone: 207-646-9282 Ext. 311. Fax: 207-641-0837. E-mail: fquistgard@yccc.edu.

DEGREES AND AWARDS
Programs offered do not lead to a degree or other formal award.

COURSE SUBJECT AREAS OFFERED OUTSIDE OF DEGREE PROGRAMS
Undergraduate—accounting and related services; American literature (United States and Canadian); applied mathematics; business administration, management and operations; business/commerce; business/corporate communications; business, management, and marketing related; business operations support and assistant services; computer and information sciences; computer/information technology administration and management; computer programming; computer software and media applications; culinary arts and related services; English composition; English language and literature related; hospitality administration; human development, family studies, and related services; management information systems; psychology; religious studies; sociology; technical and business writing.

YORK TECHNICAL COLLEGE
Rock Hill, South Carolina
Distance Learning Department
http://www.yorktech.com

York Technical College was founded in 1961. It is accredited by Southern Association of Colleges and Schools. It first offered distance learning courses in 1995. In fall 2007, there were 3,400 students enrolled in distance learning courses. Institutionally administered financial aid is available to distance learners.

Services Distance learners have accessibility to academic advising, bookstore, campus computer network, career placement assistance, e-mail services, library services, tutoring.

Contact Anita McBride, Department Manager, York Technical College, 452 South Anderson Road, Rock Hill, SC 29730. Telephone: 803-981-7044. Fax: 803-981-7193. E-mail: mcbride@yorktech.com.

DEGREES AND AWARDS

AA General degree
AAB Accounting–Associate of Business

COURSE SUBJECT AREAS OFFERED OUTSIDE OF DEGREE PROGRAMS

Undergraduate—accounting and related services; biological and physical sciences; business administration, management and operations; business/commerce; computer science; developmental and child psychology; economics; English; English composition; environmental/environmental health engineering; history; mathematics; nursing; philosophy; psychology; sociology.

Non-credit—computer and information sciences and support services related.

YORK UNIVERSITY
Toronto, Ontario, Canada
http://www.yorku.ca/

York University was founded in 1959. It is provincially chartered. It first offered distance learning courses in 1994. In fall 2007, there were 8,000 students enrolled in distance learning courses. Institutionally administered financial aid is available to distance learners.

Services Distance learners have accessibility to academic advising, bookstore, campus computer network, e-mail services, library services, tutoring.

Contact Ms. Amalia Syligardakis, Manager, e-Learning Services, York University, Office of Computing Technology and e-Learning Services, 4700 Keele Street, Room 2120, TEL Building, Toronto, ON M3J 1P3, Canada. Telephone: 416-736-2100 Ext. 30705. Fax: 416-736-5637. E-mail: amalias@yorku.ca.

DEGREES AND AWARDS

BA Business Economics
BBA Administrative Studies

COURSE SUBJECT AREAS OFFERED OUTSIDE OF DEGREE PROGRAMS

Undergraduate—accounting and related services; business administration, management and operations; business/corporate communications; business/managerial economics; communication and media; economics; English language and literature related; film/video and photographic arts; geography and cartography; health professions related; history; human development, family studies, and related services; human resources management; liberal arts and sciences, general studies and humanities; management sciences and quantitative methods; marketing; mathematics; nursing; philosophy; political science and government; psychology related; public administration; public administration and social service professions related; religious studies; social sciences; social work; sociology; statistics; visual and performing arts related.

YOUNGSTOWN STATE UNIVERSITY
Youngstown, Ohio
http://www.ysu.edu/distancelearning/

Youngstown State University was founded in 1908. It is accredited by North Central Association of Colleges and Schools. It first offered distance learning courses in 1999. In fall 2007, there were 1,000 students enrolled in distance learning courses. Institutionally administered financial aid is available to distance learners.

Services Distance learners have accessibility to academic advising, bookstore, campus computer network, career placement assistance, e-mail services, library services, tutoring.

Contact Dr. Annette M. Burden, Associate Professor and Interim Director of Distance Learning, Youngstown State University, Department of Mathematics and Statistics, One University Plaza, Youngstown, OH 44555-0001. Telephone: 330-941-1814. Fax: 330-941-3270. E-mail: amburden@ysu.edu.

DEGREES AND AWARDS

BS BSAS in Allied Health; BSAS in Criminal Justice; BSAS in Public Health
MHSA Master of Health and Human Services
MPH Public Health

COURSE SUBJECT AREAS OFFERED OUTSIDE OF DEGREE PROGRAMS

Undergraduate—criminal justice and corrections; economics; foods, nutrition, and related services; geological and earth sciences/geosciences; health and physical education/fitness; health professions related; history; mathematics; nursing; philosophy.

Graduate—educational administration and supervision; educational/instructional media design; health professions related; public administration; public health.

Non-credit—accounting and related services; allied health and medical assisting services; American literature (United States and Canadian); business administration, management and operations; business, management, and marketing related; business/managerial economics; business operations support and assistant services; computer and information sciences; computer software and media applications; computer systems networking and telecommunications; creative writing; English language and literature related; entrepreneurial and small business operations; health and medical administrative services; public relations, advertising, and applied communication related; sales, merchandising, and related marketing operations (specialized); technical and business writing.

YUBA COLLEGE
Marysville, California
Learning Resource Center
http://www.yubaonline.edu

Yuba College was founded in 1927. It is accredited by Western Association of Schools and Colleges. It first offered distance learning courses in 1975. In fall 2007, there were 2,729 students enrolled in distance learning courses. Institutionally administered financial aid is available to distance learners.

Services Distance learners have accessibility to academic advising, bookstore, campus computer network, career placement assistance, e-mail services, library services, tutoring.

Contact Ms. Jeanette O'Bryan, Distributive Education Support Specialist, Yuba College, 2088 North Beale Road, Marysville, CA 95901. Telephone: 530-741-6754. Fax: 530-741-6824. E-mail: jobryan@yccd.edu.

DEGREES AND AWARDS

AAS General Studies

COURSE SUBJECT AREAS OFFERED OUTSIDE OF DEGREE PROGRAMS

Undergraduate—accounting and computer science; agricultural business and management; agriculture and agriculture operations related; animal sciences; anthropology; applied mathematics; astronomy and astrophysics; behavioral sciences; biology; chemistry; communication and media; computer and information sciences and support services related; computer programming; computer systems networking and telecommunications; ecology, evolution, and population biology; economics; education related; education (specific subject areas); English composition;

foods, nutrition, and related services; liberal arts and sciences, general studies and humanities; mathematics and computer science; music; personality psychology; plant sciences; psychology; psychology related; sociology; veterinary biomedical and clinical sciences.

In-Depth Descriptions

The following two-page descriptions were prepared for this book by the institutions. An institution's absence from this section does not constitute an editorial decision. Rather, in-depth descriptions were offered as an open forum for institutions to expand upon the information provided in the previous section of this book. The descriptions are arranged alphabetically by institution name.

ADAMS STATE COLLEGE

Extended Studies
Alamosa, Colorado

Adams State College (ASC), which was founded in 1921, is located in the San Luis Valley in south-central Colorado in the city of Alamosa. Alamosa, at an elevation of 7,500 feet above sea level, is surrounded by mountain ranges with peaks rising up to 14,000 feet above sea level. The student body is composed of approximately 2,500 individuals from various ethnic and racial backgrounds. Adams State College is accredited by the Higher Learning Commission of the North Central Association of Colleges and Schools. The School of Education is currently accepted as a candidate in the Teacher Education Accreditation Council (TEAC).

Distance Learning Program

Adams State College has been providing education to off-campus students for more than twenty-five years. In the past year, more than 18,000 students took advantage of one of the options offered through Extended Studies.

The Distance Degree Program offers a Bachelor of Arts (B.A.) degree in business administration, interdisciplinary studies, and sociology; a Bachelor of Science (B.S.) degree in business administration; and the Associate of Arts (A.A.) and Associate of Science (A.S.) degrees.

Certificate programs are available in alternative dispute resolution (mediation), legal investigation, legal nurse consultant training, legal secretary studies, management information systems, paralegal studies, and victim advocacy. Students who are not interested in degree programs can enroll in a choice of more than 200 independent-study/correspondence courses in accounting, business, business finance, business management, business strategy, criminology, economics, education, English, geology, history, management, marketing, math, psychology, social theory, social welfare, and sociology.

Delivery Media

A variety of course delivery options are available to students, including online delivery, print materials, and face-to-face instruction at various sites. Students enrolling in an online or correspondence course are provided with a printed study guide outlining course requirements. Students send completed course work directly to the instructor. Some courses require proctored examinations, while others have online examinations. All ASC instructors are available by telephone, fax, e-mail, and surface mail.

Programs of Study

The B.A. and B.S. degrees in business administration require 120 semester credits for graduation; 45 must be junior- or senior-level credits, and a minimum of 30 credits must be completed with ASC. B.A./B.S. degree requirements include 40 semester credits in general education and approximately 40 in electives and 40 in the major field (specific requirements subject to the academic major). A maximum of 90 semester credits can be transferred to ASC, of which a maximum of 60 may be from junior/community colleges. Admitted students must maintain active status by enrolling in at least one ASC course per semester.

A.A. and A.S. degree program requirements include 43 semester credits in general education and 17 in electives. Students must complete general education course work to satisfy requirements from the following eight areas: oral and written communication, human behavior and institutions, history and culture, and arts and literature (6 credits each); quantitative thinking (3 credits) and speech fundamentals (3 credits; speech is required for A.A. and A.S. degrees only); science foundations and issues (8 credits); and health and fitness (2 credits). For specific course titles that meet these require-

ments, students should visit the ASC Web site at http://exstudies.adams.edu/degree.html.

Transfer credit is accepted from accredited institutions recommended by the American Association of Collegiate Registrars and Admissions Officers. Credits from a nonaccredited institution may be petitioned for transfer after the student has completed at least 24 semester credits at ASC with a C (2.0 GPA) average or better. Students may petition the appropriate academic chair for approval of courses that are not accepted during the normal admission and transfer process.

Special Programs

Courses that have attracted the interest of many students include the popular certificate programs in paralegal studies, alternative dispute resolution (mediation), legal investigation, legal nurse consultant training, legal secretary studies, and victim advocacy.

More than 200 six-week, noncredit, online interactive courses are available to students who are not interested in a standard academic program but are seeking a short-term solution to a current need. These courses are designed to provide the student with new skills and knowledge or to improve current skills. The categories of courses include business management, computer and software applications, entrepreneur studies, health, Internet, personal enrichment, small business, and Web page design. For a complete listing, students should visit http://www.ed2go.com/adams/.

ASC offers a wide range of online and independent-study graduate courses that have been developed for teachers. Many schools and school districts allow these courses to be used for in-service training or recertification purposes. Customized graduate certificate programs are designed to meet the professional development needs of educators.

Student Services

Free unofficial transfer evaluations are offered to students who are interested in a degree program. The ASC adviser provides students with a free, preliminary, unofficial credit evaluation upon request. Students must provide copies of transcripts or grade reports showing previous college work. Students have the opportunity to see how their previous college work might meet ASC's requirements. The unofficial evaluation is subject to change based on the outcome of the official admission evaluation and acceptance of transfer credits by the Admissions Office.

Credit Options

For the bachelor's degrees, students may transfer in a maximum of 90 semester credits to ASC. The remaining 30 semester credits must be completed with ASC. Only 60 credits from community colleges may be applied to the degree. For the associate degree, students may transfer in a maximum of 45 semester credits, with the remaining 15 credits completed at ASC.

ASC participates in the College-Level Examination Program (CLEP) (general or subject exams). Students who have performed satisfactorily in college-level courses before college entrance and have demonstrated a requisite achievement (minimum scores of 50th percentile) on tests of the College Board College-Level Examination Program may submit the results to ASC for consideration for college credit. The Records Office records the college credit based on determinations made by the appropriate school's department chair. The maximum credit on the general exams is 18 semester hours (in the areas of humanities, natural science, and social science). The semester hours of credit for each subject exam, as well as credit by examination in total, are determined by the appropriate school's dean.

Military and civilian training is also considered for credit. The chair of the academic department in which the degree is earned evaluates any military and civilian training and makes the decision as to how credit will be awarded. ASC uses the American Council on Education Guides for credit recommendations. Military service credit is processed when official documents or transcripts are received at ASC. Courses found in the American Council on Education Guide or on transcripts (CCAF, AARTS, SMART) can be evaluated. Locally conducted (base- or post-level) courses are generally not acceptable due to their unstructured and changing content.

Faculty

Approximately 65 percent of the faculty members in the Distance Degree Program have a Ph.D. and are full-time professors on campus at ASC. All professors have experience working with distance learners.

Admission

Transfer students with at least 12 transferable college credits are not required to submit ACT or SAT scores or their high school transcript but must submit the admission application, application fee, and official transcripts from all colleges previously attended. First-time freshman students must submit the program application fee, the application for admission, and high school transcripts with ACT or SAT scores. The Distance Degree Program application fee is $25. For admission and application information and details, students should visit http://exstudies.adams.edu/degree.html.

Tuition and Fees

Course tuition for undergraduate credit is $130 per semester hour; for graduate credit, it is $140 per semester hour. Tuition must be submitted with the registration for the course. Some courses may have additional fees for materials. For course details, applicants should see the specific course description at http://extudies.adams.edu/ind_study/independ.html.

Financial Aid

Students admitted to the Distance Degree Program are eligible to apply for financial aid. Also, company-sponsored tuition and military tuition assistance programs may be used for ASC courses. Eligible military personnel should process DANTES applications through their education office.

Applying

Students can find course and degree application information, application and registration forms, and more answers to their questions by visiting the Extended Studies Web site.

CONTACT

Distance Degree Programs
Extended Studies
Adams State College
208 Edgemont Boulevard
Alamosa, Colorado 81102

Phone: 800-548-6679 (toll-free)
Fax: 719-587-7974
E-mail: ascadvisor@adams.edu
Web site: http://exstudies.adams.edu

AIU ONLINE–AMERICAN INTERCONTINENTAL UNIVERSITY
Accelerated Degrees
Hoffman Estates, Illinois

American InterContinental University (AIU) Online is one of the premier online universities in the United States. With a tradition of educating students for more than thirty-five years, AIU has created an online education environment that combines the most sophisticated in Internet technology with the tradition of excellent higher education. American InterContinental University is accredited by the Commission on Colleges of the Southern Association of Colleges and Schools (1866 Southern Lane, Decatur, Georgia 30033-4097; telephone: 404-679-4500) to award associate, bachelor's, and master's degrees. This umbrella accreditation includes the following branch campuses of the University: AIU Buckhead, AIU Dunwoody, AIU South Florida, AIU London, AIU Houston, AIU Los Angeles, and AIU Online (originating in Illinois).

Distance Learning Program

AIU Online's Virtual Campus provides a rich, interactive education. AIU Online offers degree programs with classrooms as close as any Internet-connected computer, so students have access to a complete campus experience 24 hours a day, seven days a week. An education through AIU Online provides students with an opportunity to continue their education and advance their career opportunities without disrupting their current lifestyles and schedules.

Delivery Media

The Web-based degree programs delivered through AIU Online are specifically designed for the student who accesses the course from a home or work personal computer. Recommended PC specifications are provided to students at the time of enrollment.

Programs of Study

All AIU Online degree programs can be taken at an accelerated pace, so students finish their degree sooner; e.g., an M.B.A. can be completed in as little as ten months.

Business: Today's increasingly complicated business environments demand that existing and future business professionals have a comprehensive knowledge of the economic climate in the modern workforce. The business administration program includes many sought-after concentrations that students can choose from to tailor their business degree to a specific field of interest. Business concentrations include accounting and finance, health-care management, human resource management, international business, manage-ment, marketing, operations management, organizational psychology and development, and project management.

The B.B.A. degree programs provide an in-depth study of business, management, and marketing and give students a strong foundation for continued studies should they wish to advance their business education in the future.

The accelerated M.B.A. degree program helps ensure that a student is professionally up-to-date and prepared to meet the challenges of today's increasingly complicated business environments. An online education earned through AIU Online gives students the knowledge and understanding of the economic climate in the modern workplace.

Information Technology (IT): As the modern business world becomes increasingly dependent on computers, the demand for IT professionals may continue to grow. AIU Online's degree programs in information technology offer a real-world education and can help qualify a student to meet the demands.

The Bachelor of Information Technology (B.I.T.) provides students with the relevant, up-to-date knowledge to pursue exciting, in-demand IT careers. This curriculum focuses on the development of appropriate business and programming skills, the use of networks, education in data administration, and the completion of IT projects. Concentrations in computer forensics, computer systems, Internet security, network administration, and program-ming empower students to direct their degree program in a specific area of interest

The Master of Information Technology (M.I.T.), with concentrations in Internet security and IT project management, combines the technology and Internet security portions of the course work with key information management courses to help ensure success in the job market.

Visual Communications: AIU Online also offers a Bachelor of Fine Arts in visual communication, with available concentrations in digital design and Web design, completely online. These programs are designed to educate and develop artistic and imaginative students who are interested in such career opportunities as flash animator, Web designer, and computer illustrator. All required graphics software is included in the cost of course materials.

Criminal Justice: The growing emphasis on homeland security has created an unprecedented demand for criminal justice and security professionals. This accelerated degree program helps students prepare for such vital, in-demand career opportunities as FBI officers, correction officers, security analysts, U.S. customs agents, and directors of security.

The B.S. in criminal justice, with available concentrations in forensic science, law enforcement, and special populations provides students with a foundation in some of the most interesting aspects of the industry, including criminology, the causes of crime, and typologies and victims.

Education: For students who have a passion for learning and inspiring others, AIU Online offers a Master of Education degree program. This program can provide the spark for an individual to advance their career as a teacher, corporate instructor, or military trainer. Available concentrations include curriculum and instruction, educational assessment and evaluation, instructional technology, and leadership of educational organizations.

Health-Care Management: Health care is one of the fastest-growing fields. Whether a student is looking to pursue a new career opportunity in health-care management or upgrade an existing one, AIU Online's accelerated health-care management degree programs can help ensure he or she is prepared to meet the challenge in less time.

The B.B.A. with a concentration. in health-care management helps provide a solid foundation for those interested in a management position in health care, whether in a hospital, long-term-care facility, insurance company, managed-care organization, pharmaceutical company, or one of the many other health-care-related industries.

The M.B.A. with a concentration in health-care management is designed to provide a unique, market-relevant combination of a comprehensive business education with real-world, health-care-focused deliverables. This degree helps turn managers into executives and arms them with the knowledge, skills, and experience necessary to succeed.

Marketing: Today's complicated business models demand qualified marketing professionals in the management, planning, implementation, and evaluation of marketing and advertising functions. AIU Online offers accelerated, career-focused B.B.A. and M.B.A. degree programs for students interested in pursuing rewarding career opportunities in the ever-changing, fast-paced marketing industry.

The B.B.A. with a concentration in marketing is designed to deliver a solid foundation for business marketing professionals by combining a core education in business with a focus on topics relevant to various marketing careers. This degree provides the experience-based education that helps students qualify for a wide variety of challenging, interesting career opportunities.

The M.B.A. with a concentration in marketing can be completed in as little as ten months and combines the specialized curriculum of an executive M.B.A. with a focused training in marketing management disciplines. The result is a program that provides the advanced knowledge, skills, and practical experience-based education necessary to qualify for top marketing positions.

Organizational Psychology and Development: As the career-focused society spends more and more time at the office, there is a growing need for knowledgeable professionals with a modern, up-to-date understanding of the principles of psychology as they apply to the workplace. AIU Online's accelerated degree program with a concentration in organizational psychology and development prepares graduates for career opportunities in business or management, with specific emphasis on rel-

evant knowledge of such issues as group dynamics, performance appraisal, training and development, and conflict management.

The B.B.A. with a concentration in organizational psychology and development is designed to help prepare business and management professionals to drive their careers forward with up-to-date knowledge and applicable, real-world experience-based learning.

The M.B.A. with a concentration in organizational psychology and development can be completed in as little as ten months. This real-world degree program is designed to be immediately applicable to issues facing today's modern workplaces. The experience-based curriculum focuses on preparing business and management professionals to pursue leadership roles within their organizations.

Student Services

To help ensure an overall high-quality educational experience and academic success, AIU Online provides a range of student support services, including admissions, academics, financial aid, career services, and technical support. All services are accessible through the University's Virtual Campus. Students also have access to their account information, degree plan, and personal information 24 hours a day through this secure Web site.

Credit Options

In addition to college credit earned at accredited postsecondary institutions, the following can also be evaluated for lower-level academic credit equivalency at AIU: military credit/MOS, experiential learning, professional training and certification, standardized assessments/examinations, CLEP or DSST examination, course-challenge examinations, and Advanced Placement (AP) examination.

Through AIU's Prior Learning Assessment program, the University may award proficiency credit for learning that has taken place outside the traditional academic setting. This experience includes employment, noncollegiate or school-based education, or other appropriate life experiences. The outcomes of the noncollegiate learning experience must be documented, applicable to the program of study, and assessed as being similar to or meeting the requirements of learning gained through college-level learning experiences.

Faculty

AIU Online provides experienced faculty members with advanced degrees, who bring their real-world experience and ex-

pertise to their students. All faculty members teaching online receive training and guidance in online delivery methods and pedagogy.

Admission

To be considered for admission to AIU Online, applicants must submit a complete application for admission and a $50 application fee and fulfill all admission requirements for the program. Selection of students for admission into degree programs of study is based on an individual assessment of each applicant. Each applicant must submit proof of high school graduation or the equivalent and participate in an admissions interview arranged by a University admissions adviser. If the applicant's first language is not English or if the applicant graduated from a non-English-speaking university, a minimum TOEFL score of 500 (undergraduate) or 550 (graduate) or other acceptable proof of English proficiency must be submitted

Tuition and Fees

Tuition and fee schedules for programs of study are reviewed with students at the time of acceptance.

Financial Aid

The AIU Online Financial Aid Department is committed to providing financial aid available to those who qualify. AIU Online participates in various federal, state, and private student financial assistance programs. These financial aid programs are designed to provide assistance to students who are currently enrolled or accepted for enrollment but whose financial resources are unable to meet the full cost of their education. In addition, alternative financing options are available to those who qualify.

Applying

To apply for admission, a prospective student should submit an online application at http://www.aiuonline.edu along with a $50 application fee and complete a personal telephone interview.

CONTACT

Robyn Palmersheim
Vice President of Admissions
American InterContinental University
  Online
5550 Prairie Stone Parkway, Suite 400
Hoffman Estates, Illinois 60192

Phone: 877-701-3800 (toll-free)
E-mail: info@aiuonline.edu
Web site: http://www.aiuonline.edu

AMERICAN MILITARY UNIVERSITY
Distance Learning Programs
Charles Town, West Virginia

American Military University (AMU) is part of the American Public University System and is an institution of higher learning licensed by the West Virginia Higher Education Policy Commission. AMU is accredited by the Distance Education and Training Council (DETC) and the Higher Learning Commission of the North Central Association of Colleges and Schools (NCA). In addition, AMU is a member of the Servicemembers Opportunity Colleges (SOC). The University focuses on the educational needs of working adults, with special emphasis on the military, national security, and public safety communities. Founded in 1991, the University System offers distance learning degree programs to 30,000 students, who study from more than 100 countries around the world. The University has continuously broadened its curricula, expanding to include homeland security, national security, criminal justice, intelligence, management, business administration, information technology, education, security management, psychology, sports management, and many others. The University System is headquartered in Charles Town, West Virginia, with administrative offices in Manassas, Virginia.

Distance Learning Program

AMU's courses are offered online and are accessible around the clock through the Electronic Campus from wherever students have Internet access. Classes start monthly, and students are led through the eight-week or sixteen-week courses via an online classroom with a qualified instructor.

Delivery Media

AMU delivers and supports its courses through its Electronic Campus, with classrooms served by Educator® courseware by Ucompass. Through these electronic classrooms, students communicate with professors and each other using LISTSERV, discussion boards, streaming video, student lounge chat rooms, and e-mail. Through this system, students are able to interact with each other and with professors, submit assignments, receive feedback, and take examinations. Electronic communications are supplemented by phone consultations during professors' office hours, with classes restricted to 25 students to ensure adequate student-professor interaction.

Programs of Study

AMU offers more than 100 associate, bachelor's, and master's degree programs and certificates. Academic programs of study include business administration, criminal justice, education, emergency and disaster management, fire science management, history, homeland security, information technology, intelligence studies, international relations, military history, national security, political science, psychology, public administration, public health, security management, space studies, sports management, and transportation and logistics. To view a complete list of degrees offered by AMU, students may visit http://www.amu.apus.edu/Academics/Degree-Programs/index.htm.

Graduate programs are twelve-course programs with a comprehensive final examination, thesis option, or applied research project at the end of all course work. Core courses are required, and major courses allow students to make choices depending on their professional goals. Within the major courses, students may have an opportunity to specify a concentration that offers a choice of classes within the academic discipline, allowing students to focus on specific areas of interest. Finally, each student rounds out the program with electives, which vary according to the degree program.

Graduate certificate programs are for students who prefer a certificate instead of a full graduate degree. They focus on a particular topical area or set of issues. A certificate is more focused and concentrated than a master's degree. Typically, graduate certificates require a minimum of 15 semester hours.

Undergraduate programs include associate degrees and bachelor's degrees, undergraduate certificates, and minors. All degree programs include a general education component. Associate degree programs require a minimum of 60 semester hours, and bachelor's degree programs require a minimum of 120 semester hours. In most cases, bachelor's degree programs are made up of general education, core, major, and elective requirements. In many programs, students have the opportunity to select specific concentrations within the degree program or opt for a general program. Students seeking a bachelor's degree may also elect to minor in a second academic discipline.

Undergraduate certificate programs are available to students who seek a shorter program focused on career development or knowledge of a specific discipline. Students are required to take a minimum of 15 semester hours, although some certificates may require up to 27 semester hours. In some cases, credits from a certificate program can be applied to an associate or bachelor's degree.

Students should consult the Undergraduate Catalog (http://www.amu.apus.edu/Catalog/08/undergraduate/index.htm) or Graduate Catalog (http://

www.amu.apus.edu/Catalog/08/ graduate/index.htm) for the most updated information on AMU's degree programs.

Student Services
The Student Services department is staffed to assist students as needed via e-mail, phone, and even online chat rooms. All students experience AMU's online orientation program that prepares them for distance learning, including navigating the electronic campus, using the classroom functions, and understanding transfer credit and tuition and financial aid options. Many Student Services functions are available online, and it is easy for students to submit changes and check their status.

Credit Options
Credits may be earned through AMU via traditional courses, challenge examinations, and independent study. Courses may be audited without credit. AMU accepts transfer credit from accredited institutions; training and experience credit recommended by the American Council on Education; CCAF, AARTS, and SMARTS military transcripts; credit by examination (CLEP, DANTES, etc.); and PONSI programs.

Credit acceptance by program is as follows: associate degree, up to 45 semester hours; bachelor's degree, up to 90 semester hours; and graduate degree, up to 15 semester hours.

Faculty
AMU's faculty brings real-world experience and world-class credentials to the online learning experience. More than 500 adjunct faculty members, along with more than 100 full-time faculty members, work together to ensure AMU students achieve appropriate learning outcomes. All faculty members meet traditional accreditation standards with regard to degrees and professional preparedness.

Admission
Graduate students must possess an accredited baccalaureate degree. Undergraduate students must have a high school diploma or GED certificate. No examinations are required for admission.

Tuition and Fees
Tuition is $250 per semester hour for undergraduate programs. Graduate program tuition is $275 per semester hour. There is no admission fee. All undergraduate students earning academic credit receive AMU's book grant, covering 100 percent of the costs of all textbooks. Transfer credit evaluations are subject to a one-time fee of $100, and all students who have attended other institutions of higher learning are required to submit a transfer evaluation by the end of their first semester at AMU. There is a graduation fee of $100.

Financial Aid
AMU accepts military tuition assistance, GI Bill and VA educational benefits, and corporate tuition assistance. Students may be eligible for federal student aid loans and grants, and AMU has an installment payment plan as well. AMU is committed to providing the military and public safety communities with a high-quality, low-cost education, assisting in achieving their educational goals.

Applying
The application process is easy and is completed online. There is no cost to apply for admission, and applicants are conditionally admitted upon submission of the online application form. A student ID is issued, and applicants receive a password via e-mail, allowing them to log in to the electronic campus, complete their online orientation, and register for courses.

CONTACT

Admissions
American Military University
American Public University System
111 West Congress Street
Charles Town, West Virginia 25414

Phone: 877-777-9081, menu option 2 (toll-free)
E-mail: info@apus.edu
Web site: http://www.amuonline.com/

AMRIDGE UNIVERSITY
Distance Learning Programs
Montgomery, Alabama

Founded in 1967, Amridge University is an independent, coeducational institution dedicated to the spirit of its ideals and Christian heritage. All of Amridge University's programs are taught from a Christian perspective. Amridge University is the home of one of the nation's leading universities offering distance learning programs and services to adults nationally. In 1999, Amridge University was selected by the U.S. Department of Education as a Distance Education Demonstration Program Institution. One of fifteen initial participants in the nation, Amridge University partnered with the U.S. Department of Education, serving as a national model for distance education. As a result, the U.S. Congress recently changed the law regarding distance education, making it more accessible to more students. Accredited by the Southern Association of Colleges and Schools, Amridge University grants bachelor's, master's, and doctoral degrees—all available via a distance learning format.

Distance Learning Program
Amridge University programs are designed with the adult learner in mind. Eighty percent of Amridge's students are employed while they are attending. Courses can be taken anywhere there is Internet access and at any time. Amridge University has enrolled thousands of students in distance learning courses throughout the United States and internationally.

Delivery Media
Utilizing state-of-the-art technologies, Amridge University's distance learning programs are delivered to students over the Internet. Students participate via online discussion groups, testing, e-mail, and telephone. Some courses are streamed live over the Internet and can be viewed as the class is being taught or at the student's convenience. The flexibility of the programs ensures continuity for students in transit, such as military personnel, clergy, or salespeople who must move while still in school.

Programs of Study
Amridge University programs are structured with the traditional program in mind. Distance education is approved by the Southern Association of Colleges

and Schools and the U.S. Department of Education, ensuring that distance education students receive the same high-quality education as on-campus students. Faculty and student services for online students are available to distance learning students. Amridge University ensures that students have regular contact with faculty and staff members via e-mail and telephone. Residency is only required in certain programs. No residency is required for undergraduates.

Undergraduate degrees are awarded in biblical studies, business administration, homeland security, human development, human resource management, liberal studies, management communication, and public safety and criminal justice. These degrees promote biblical and Christian ministry skills, human development skills, knowledge in the arts, and management communication skills.

Graduate degrees are awarded in counseling/family therapy, organizational leadership, and religious studies. These degrees prepare students for careers and professions that provide support and services for the well-being of individuals, families, or society; foster leadership, counseling, and family therapy skills; and develop knowl-

edge and biblical and Christian ministry skills. Some of the counseling degrees are designed to help prepare students for licensure.

Doctoral degrees include family therapy and ministry. These degrees are advanced professional degrees for community organizations and church-related vocations, with a concentration designed to prepare participants to counsel families and individuals.

Amridge University students are fully matriculated students of Amridge University with full student privileges, rights, and responsibilities.

Special Programs
Amridge University has developed fully accredited programs of study to help working adults obtain their bachelor's degree in a timely manner through its programs. All undergraduate courses are 4 semester hours, rather than 3. A student only has to take three courses (12 semester hours) to be a full-time student and eligible for maximum financial aid benefits. Also, fewer courses are required for degree completion.

Amridge University is one of only a few institutions participating in the expansion of eArmyU colleges and universities. eArmyU is the Army's popular e-learning virtual university, offering thousands of soldiers the opportunity to earn a college degree during their enlistment. With the flexibility of eArmyU, soldier-students are able to continue their education uninterrupted and complete their degrees in a timely manner while they serve.

Student Services
Amridge University provides support for all aspects of the distance learning experience. ProQuest Religion Database and First Search library programs give students access to 65 online

databases, including the Library of Congress. Students have access to the collections of 150 theological schools online. Personal academic advising is performed via phone or e-mail. Students also receive personal evaluations of their degree program.

Credit Options

Fulfillment of some degree requirements is possible by passing the CLEP/DANTES tests or Excelsior examinations and through credit for lifetime learning and credit for military experience.

Faculty

The instructional faculty members total 85. Seventy-six percent of the full-time faculty members hold doctoral degrees, 100 percent hold master's degrees, and 100 percent hold terminal degrees.

Faculty members are specialized in their areas and have training in distance learning delivery.

Admission

There is a rolling admission plan. Admission requirements are verification of high school graduation or passage of the GED test for undergraduates and demonstrated proficiency in computer literacy. Ninety percent of applicants are accepted.

Tuition and Fees

The graduate tuition cost per semester hour is $510. Undergraduate tuition per semester hour is $260. A comprehensive fee of $400 per semester is required of all graduate students.

Financial Aid

Aid from institutionally generated funds is provided on the basis of academic

merit, financial need, or other criteria. A limited number of scholarships is available. Priority is given to early applicants. Federal funding available includes Pell and FSEOG grants, Academic Competitiveness Grants, and National SMART grants for undergraduates, the Federal Work-Study Program, and FFEL subsidized and unsubsidized loans for undergraduates and graduates. Eighty percent of students receive financial aid.

Applying

Prospective students must submit a $50 nonrefundable fee along with the completed application for admission. During the first semester, graduate students must submit letters of recommendation, transcripts, and test scores.

CONTACT

Rick Johnson
Amridge University
1200 Taylor Road
Montgomery, Alabama 36117

Phone: 800-351-4040 Ext. 7513 (toll-free)
E-mail: admissions@amridgeuniversity.edu
Web site: http://www.amridgeuniversity.edu

ATHABASCA UNIVERSITY

Quality Learning. Anywhere. Anytime.

Athabasca, Alberta, Canada

Athabasca University (AU), Canada's Open University, is a publicly funded university in the province of Alberta, Canada. AU is one of the world's foremost and fastest growing online and distance education specialists, serving 34,000 students worldwide.

As an open university, AU strives to eliminate barriers that prevent people from pursuing university studies. By providing access to flexible online and distance learning, AU helps people continue their studies regardless of where they live, their educational backgrounds, and their career or family obligations. AU is committed to innovation, flexibility in learning, and excellence in teaching, research, and scholarship.

AU is a full member of the Association of Universities and Colleges of Canada, the Association of Commonwealth Universities, the International Council for Open and Distance Education, the Canadian Association for Distance Education, the Canadian Association for Graduate Studies, the Canadian Virtual University, the Circumpolar Universities Association, the Global University Alliance, and the Inter-American Distance Education Consortium.

Distance Learning Program

AU, Canada's largest online and distance education university, offers more than 700 courses in over sixty undergraduate and graduate degree, diploma, and certificate programs. The flexibility of online and distance learning allows students to complete courses or programs on a full-time or part-time basis and to study when and where it is convenient for them. Many students also complete selected AU courses to satisfy specific program requirements at other universities and colleges.

Enrollment in AU courses has increased by 41 percent in the last five years, totaling 34,000 students in the 2005–06 academic year. Ninety-eight percent of AU graduates say they would recommend AU to others.

Delivery Media

AU uses a variety of distance learning methods, including multimedia online activities, print materials, Web, e-mail, the Internet, CD-ROMs, CDs, DVDs, computer software, audio/videoconferencing, TV, and radio. A particular course might use any combination of these methods. Students have support from professors, tutors, advisers, and a variety of specialized student services support staff members by e-mail and phone (toll-free in Canada and the United States).

Programs of Study

Graduate degree programs offered are Doctor of Education, Master of Arts–Integrated Studies, Executive Master of Business Administration, Executive Master of Business Administration in Project Management, Master of Counselling, Master of Distance Education, Master of Health Studies, Master of Nursing, and Master of Science–Information Systems.

Graduate diplomas offered are Advanced Graduate Diploma in Advanced Nursing Practice, Advanced Graduate Diploma in Distance Education (Technology), Graduate Diploma in Heritage Resource Management, Advanced Graduate Diploma in Management, and Advanced Graduate Diploma in Project Management.

Undergraduate degrees offered are Bachelor of Arts (three- or four-year) in anthropology, English, French, history, humanities, information systems, labour studies, political economy, political science, psychology, sociology, and women's studies; Bachelor of Arts (four-year) in Canadian studies; Bachelor of Commerce in accounting or e-commerce; Bachelor of General Studies (three-year) in applied studies or arts and science; Bachelor of Health Administration; Bachelor of Human Resources and Labour Relations; Bachelor of Management (three- or four-year) with majors in human resources management or marketing; Bachelor of Nursing (four-year; post-RN or post-LPN); Bachelor of Professional Arts (four-year) in communication studies, criminal justice, human services, or governance, law, and management; Bachelor of Science (four-year) in human science or computing and information systems.

Undergraduate University certificates are offered in accounting, advanced accounting, administration, career development, computers and management information systems, computing and information systems, counseling women, English language studies, French language proficiency, health development administration, heritage resource management, human resources and labour relations, labour studies, and public administration.

Undergraduate University diplomas are offered in arts and inclusive education.

Special Programs

AU is a founding partner in Canadian Virtual University (CVU), an innovative partnership of Canada's leading universities in online and distance learning. Students can select from among 2,000 courses in the CVU catalogue and apply them to programs at any partner university. Students who take courses from more than one partner university can save money on fees. Some courses are available in both French and English. Students should visit CVU's Web site at http://www.cvu-uvc.ca for course and program information.

AU's many partnerships with other postsecondary institutions and organizations provide a variety of learning options for students. For more information, students should visit http://www.athabascau.ca/collab/collab.php.

Student Services
AU takes pride in providing exceptional service to students. Services such as advising, counselling, registration support, help for students with disabilities, a long-distance library, and more are available. The first point of contact is the Information Centre at 800-788-9041 (toll-free in Canada and the U.S.) or 780-675-6100 (international). Students can also visit http://www.askau.ca for a quick answer to most general questions.

Credit Options
AU grants academic credit for courses completed at other recognized postsecondary institutions. AU course credits are also eligible for transfer to programs at other higher education institutions worldwide.

Some of AU's undergraduate degree programs include a post-diploma option, which allows a student who has previously completed an appropriate two-year diploma from an accredited college to receive advanced standing (typically receiving credit for the first two years of university study).

Students can also apply for a prior learning assessment, a process through which relevant, informal university-level learning, such as learning derived from work or life experience, is evaluated for credit toward an AU credential.

Faculty
As of March 31, 2006, AU's faculty comprised 152 full-time professors, 168 part-time professors, and 322 part-time tutors.

Admission
Undergraduate students may apply for admission to programs or register in courses year-round. Anyone 16 years or older is eligible for admission. (Some programs and courses may have academic or geographic restrictions).

Graduate programs typically require students to have a bachelor's degree from a recognized postsecondary institution. Additional admission requirements vary from program to program. Students should consult AU's academic calendar or Web site for more information.

Tuition and Fees
Course fees include the cost of textbooks, course materials, and tuition. As of September 1, 2007, the cost for an undergraduate 3-credit course was Can$591 (Alberta), Can$689 (rest of Canada), and Can$884 (international). Graduate program fees vary by program. Students should consult the academic calendar or the program office of a particular graduation program for precise fee information.

Financial Aid
Financial assistance is available to full- and part-time students from Alberta Students Finance or the financial aid agency where a student resides. The amount of assistance available varies according to need and provincial regulations in force. Alberta students can obtain a financial aid package from Athabasca University. Out-of-province students should contact their local financial aid agency.

AU offers nearly 200 scholarships, leadership awards, and bursaries to graduate and undergraduate students on the basis of academic achievement or financial need. All students are automatically considered for many of the academic scholarships; several others are available by application or nomination. Students should visit http://www.athabascau.ca/registrar/studawrds.php for more information on student awards.

Applying
Students may apply for admission to undergraduate programs year-round and start most courses on the first day of any month. To apply, students must complete a General Application Form and submit it along with the application fee. Students may apply online at the AU Web site or by fax or mail. Application forms are available in the academic calendar and on the Web site.

Application deadlines for graduate programs can be found in the academic calendar or on the AU Web site.

CONTACT
Athabasca University Information Centre
1 University Drive
Athabasca, Alberta
  Canada T9S 3A3
Phone: 780-675-6100 (international)
       800-788-9041 (toll-free in Canada and the U.S.)
Fax: 780-675-6437
E-mail: inquire@athabascau.ca
Web site: http://www.athabascau.ca

AUBURN UNIVERSITY
Graduate Outreach Program
Auburn, Alabama

Auburn University was chartered in 1856 as the East Alabama Male College. In 1872, Auburn became a state institution—the first land-grant university in the South to be separate from a state university. Auburn University is Alabama's premier engineering and business institution. U.S. News & World Report's "America's Best Colleges" ranks both Auburn's College of Business and its College of Engineering among the nation's top fifty programs at public institutions. Auburn's Graduate Outreach Program has been ranked by GetEducated.com's "Top 25 Best Buys" for Web-based distance learning graduate-degree programs. Auburn is dedicated to serving the state and the nation through instruction, research, and extension. Auburn University is accredited by the Commission on Colleges of the Southern Association of Colleges and Schools.

The campus consists of more than 1,800 acres, with a student body of approximately 24,000. Auburn University, the largest school in the state of Alabama, is located in east-central Alabama. The city of Auburn has a population of about 40,000. Auburn is known for its small-town, friendly atmosphere and is often referred to as "the loveliest village on the Plain."

Distance Learning Program

In response to industry's request, Auburn's College of Engineering began offering courses to off-campus students through the Graduate Outreach Program in 1984. The Graduate Outreach Program allows professionals the opportunity to continue their education while maintaining full-time employment. The program serves more than 400 students in forty-eight states. The M.B.A. program is accredited by AACSB International–The Association to Advance Collegiate Schools of Business. The programs in the College of Engineering are accredited by the Accreditation Board of Engineering and Technology (ABET).

Note for international inquirers: Due to material distribution methods, the current distance learning program service area is limited to the U.S. and Canada and to U.S. military personnel with APO or FPO mailing addresses.

Delivery Media

The Graduate Outreach Program makes every effort to ensure that the off-campus students receive the same high-quality education as on-campus students. Live classes are recorded daily and distributed by streaming video and in DVD format. Professors establish telephone office hours and/or e-mail communication so that off-campus students may receive answers to any questions they may have. E-mail accounts are established for the Graduate Outreach Program students. Most faculty members also utilize the Internet to post handouts and class materials.

Programs of Study

The Graduate Outreach Program offers master's degrees in seven disciplines in engineering—aerospace engineering, chemical engineering, civil engineering, computer science and software engineering, industrial and systems engineering, materials engineering, and mechanical engineering—as well as the Master of Management Information Systems, Master of Accounting, and Master of Business Administration. These programs are all nonthesis and without residency requirements. Each candidate must pass an on-campus, comprehensive, final oral examination covering the program of study to graduate. The examination covers the major and minor subjects, including any research or special projects involved.

In the Master of Business Administration program, students may earn a concentration in finance, health-care administration, human resource management, management information systems, management of technology, marketing, or operations management. The program consists of 36 to 42 semester hours of course work, including eight core courses and four electives. Applicants are required to complete a course in calculus and statistics prior to entering the program. Students with nonbusiness undergraduate degrees may be required to pass foundations exams in economics, finance, marketing, management, and accounting. Incoming students are also advised to have a working knowledge of word processing and spreadsheet software and an elementary understanding of database applications. M.B.A. students must visit the campus for five days during their final semester prior to graduating for on-campus presentations.

Nondegree professional development courses are available for those who need to meet job requirements or professional certification.

Special Programs

Career and job placement assistance is available through Auburn University's Career and Student Development Services. Accessibility to the R. B. Draughon Library is also available. A valid Auburn University student identification card is required to check out resources. The Division of University Computing provides University-wide computing and networking services to students. Computer accounts are free of charge to currently enrolled students.

Credit Options

Graduate credit taken in residence at another approved graduate school may be transferred to Auburn University but is not accepted until the student has completed at least 9 hours of work in the Graduate School at Auburn University. No prior commitment is made concerning whether transfer credit can be accepted. A student must earn at least 21 semester hours or half of the total hours required for a master's degree (whichever is greater) at Auburn University. No transfer credit is approved without two official transcripts. No course in which a grade lower than B was earned may be transferred.

Faculty

The Auburn University faculty consists of more than 1,200 members. Eighty percent of the faculty members hold a doctoral degree, and 88 percent hold a terminal degree in their field.

Admission

An applicant to the Graduate School must hold a bachelor's degree or its equivalent from an accredited college or university. The Graduate Record Examinations (GRE) is required for admission to the College of Engineering, and the Graduate Management Admission Test (GMAT) is required for admission to the M.B.A. program. Students whose native language is not English must submit scores of the Test of English as a Foreign Language (TOEFL) for admission to the M.B.A. program. Admission is based on the grade point average of university-level courses, GRE or GMAT scores, and recommendation letters from instructors and supervisors. Students can be informed by the Graduate Outreach Program on how they can enroll as off-campus students once they are accepted by the Graduate School.

Tuition and Fees

The Graduate Outreach Program fees are $546 per credit hour for engineering and $568 for business. Registration schedules and fee bills are mailed to the student prior to the beginning of each quarter.

Financial Aid

Military personnel who have been accepted into the Graduate School may apply for tuition aid through DANTES at their local education office. Many of the Graduate Outreach Program students receive tuition assistance through their employer's tuition reimbursement plan. The Auburn University Office of Student Financial Aid assists in the awarding of grants, loans, and scholarships for qualified full-time students.

Applying

To apply for admission, a prospective student must return a Graduate School application, an M.B.A. application (if applicable), a nonrefundable application fee of $25 for U.S. citizens or $50 for non-U.S. citizens, three letters of recommendation, GRE or GMAT scores, and two official transcripts of all undergraduate and subsequent course work from the respective institutions. Graduate School applicants may apply online at http://www.grad.auburn.edu. This ensures a quicker response in most cases.

CONTACT

Wanda Lambert
Graduate Outreach Program
202 Ramsay Hall
Auburn University
Auburn, Alabama 36849-5331
Phone: 888-844-5300 (toll-free)
Fax: 334-844-2502
E-mail: lambewf@eng.auburn.edu
Web site: http://www.gop.auburn.edu

BAKER COLLEGE

Baker Online
Flint, Michigan

Baker College, which was founded in the true American tradition as a small business college in 1911, is a private, nonprofit, accredited, coeducational institution. The College has more than a dozen campuses and branch locations in the Midwest and has a total enrollment of more than 31,500 students. The College is uniquely designed for one purpose: to provide high-quality higher education that enables graduates to be successful throughout their challenging and rewarding careers. The College offers diploma, certificate, and associate, bachelor's, and master's degree programs in business, technical, and health service fields. Total commitment to students' employment success is uniquely evident in all aspects of the College's operations.

Baker College is accredited by the Higher Learning Commission of the North Central Association of Colleges and Schools. Baker College is an equal opportunity/affirmative action institution.

Distance Learning Program

Baker Online offers the convenience of classroom accessibility 24 hours a day, seven days a week, from virtually anywhere in the world. It is not a self-paced program. Courses begin and end on specific dates and classwork is assigned deadlines, but as long as students have Internet access, they have access to their courses.

Delivery Media

Students are required to have a computer with the following minimum requirements: a Pentium III or higher system, Windows XP Professional or higher, a 56K (minimum) modem, Internet Explorer 5.5 or Netscape 4.7 or higher (AOL is not compatible), and Microsoft Office XP Professional. A CD-ROM drive and an Internet service provider are required. The virtual classroom is the common meeting area for all students taking classes online. Communication is accomplished by sending messages back and forth from the student's computer to the classroom computer. Each classroom has a unique name, and only students taking that class have access to the virtual classroom. This ensures privacy for all students.

Programs of Study

Baker Online offers the delivery of high-quality, respected courses and programs that enable a student to earn an associate, bachelor's, or master's degree at home, on the road, or anywhere in the world.

The Associate of Business Administration degree has been designed specifically for the online college environment, where students have a variety of choices in filling out the degree plan. The curriculum gives students a good background of business facts and knowledge upon which to build or enhance a career in business.

The Bachelor of Business Administration degree is a program designed for the working professional that combines core course work with independent research and experiential credit to provide a contemporary business degree for today's business environment. Each core course contains focused study in the content area, accompanied by independent research.

The Master of Business Administration degree program seeks to combine the best of conventional academic training with the best of field-based learning. Most typical business disciplines are represented in the curriculum because the College believes that a successful manager must be conversant with different aspects of running any of today's organizations or companies. Students may also elect to focus their studies in one of the following areas: computer information systems, healthcare management, human resource management, industrial management, integrated health care, international business, leadership studies, or marketing.

The Master of Science in Information Systems degree is designed for information systems professionals who are responsible for managing the development, acquisition, implementation, and operation of information systems in a variety of organizational settings. The program emphasizes information systems theory and its application to business opportunities and challenges. In addition, the program addresses mission-critical issues such as strategic planning, risk management, financial considerations, project management, and quality assurance.

Special Programs

Baker Online offers undergraduate courses at all levels to support all of the campuses and their program offerings as a convenience for students who may have trouble commuting to a campus. Baker Online publishes a listing each quarter showing which classes will be offered.

Student Services

Every Baker College student is assigned an e-mail account on the BakerNet system. Through this system, students can communicate with each other and their instructors and with members of the graduate school staff. Students may also use their accounts to access the World Wide Web. They also have access to the Baker College Library System and FALCON, a consortium of libraries that supports an online catalog database of more than 500,000 holdings. Students also have access to InfoTrac periodical indexing databases, the UMI/ProQuest General Periodicals On-Disc full-article imaging station, Books-in-Print with Reviews, and all available Internet and World Wide Web resources.

Baker College offers a renowned Lifetime Employment Service, with access to thousands of career opportunities and employment databases, to all students. This service can be used for the rest of one's life.

Credit Options
Baker College recognizes the expediency of understandable and universally accepted standards related to transfer of academic credit. The College follows the Michigan Association of Collegiate Registrars and Admissions Officers Official Policies and recognizes the College-Level Examination Program (CLEP) or other standardized tests.

Faculty
The focus of Baker's faculty is somewhat different from that of traditional universities. Instead of placing an emphasis on empirical research, Baker values practitioner-oriented education. Faculty members remain continually active in their professions by consulting, conducting seminars, running their own businesses, writing, volunteering in their communities, and working with other organizations. The faculty-student ratio in distance education is 1:12.

Admission
Graduate program candidates must have a bachelor's degree from an accredited institution and a 2.5 or better GPA in their undergraduate work, be able to display appropriate communication skills, submit three letters of reference, submit a current resume, and have completed no less than three years of full-time work. Undergraduates must have graduated from high school, completed a GED program, or passed an Ability to Benefit assessment before entering.

Tuition and Fees
Undergraduate tuition for the 2007–08 school year was $185 per credit hour. Graduate tuition was $315 per credit hour. The cost of books ranges from $200 to $250 per quarter.

Financial Aid
Students who are accepted into Baker College may be considered for several forms of state, federal, and institutional financial aid. Students are requested to complete the Free Application for Federal Student Aid (FAFSA) and return it directly to the College.

Applying
Baker College uses a rolling admission process, so there are no deadlines for applications. Students are allowed to begin in any quarter. Once the Admissions Committee receives an application, applicants usually receive a decision in approximately four weeks. Once accepted, students participate in a three-week online orientation. They are not required to visit a campus at any time.

CONTACT

Chuck J. Gurden
Vice President for Admissions
Center for Graduate Studies
Baker Online
1116 West Bristol Road
Flint, Michigan 48507-9843

Phone: 810-766-4390
          800-469-3165 (toll-free)
Fax: 810-766-4399
E-mail: adm-ol@baker.edu
Web site: http://www.bakercollegeonline.com

BELLEVUE UNIVERSITY
Online Programs
Bellevue, Nebraska

Bellevue University is one of Nebraska's largest fully accredited independent colleges. It is accredited by the Higher Learning Commission of the North Central Association of Colleges and Schools (30 North LaSalle Street, Suite 2400, Chicago, Illinois 60602-2504; telephone: 800-621-7440). Programs serve the needs of nearly 7,000 students annually and cater to working adult students as well as traditional undergraduate students. Benefits include accelerated degree completion programs, online programs, an online library, and cooperative credit transfer agreements. Associate degrees are accepted in full, and credit is given for corporate and military training as well as life experience.

Distance Learning Program

Bellevue University is an information-age institution of higher learning with progressive options for online graduate and undergraduate degrees. Graduate and undergraduate programs, online, on campus, and in centers throughout the region, prepare students for an ever-changing environment.

Delivery Media

With Web access, students earn degrees online, where they take classes, participate in discussions with professors and fellow students, conduct research at the online library, and interact with their online adviser. Online classes are small to give the Cyber-Active® Learning advantage that characterizes Bellevue University.

Programs of Study

Undergraduate programs are offered in an accelerated, cohort-based format. The adult education program prepares students for instructional responsibilities in professional education settings, such as vocational education, adult education, and training. The program in advertising management provides students the skills and knowledge necessary to understand advertising campaigns. The program in business emphasizes techniques, procedures, and methods for managing the technical functions of business. The business information systems program prepares students who do not have computer technology degrees or course work for management within information technol-

ogy (IT) and positions with technical applications. The program in corporate communication emphasizes the development of a broad range of communication skills and the application of those skills to communicating with internal and external stakeholders. The corrections administration and management program provides students the skills and knowledge necessary for the professional oversight of modern correctional programs. The program in criminal justice administration focuses on management and opportunities in the criminal justice system and is designed for individuals working in, or closely associated with, the criminal justice system. The health-care management program provides a systems perspective for those interested in pursuing management opportunities in health care. The human and social services administration program focuses on essential managerial knowledge and covers issues involved in administering agencies, such as board governance, voluntarism, and public policy issues. The degree program in investigations gives students an advanced knowledge of investigations, both in the private and public sectors. The leadership program provides students the theoretical and practical preparation they need to assume positions of leadership in the professional ranks of organizations. The legal studies program teaches about the American legal system and how to advance within a legal environment or framework. The logistics management program is designed for individuals interested in or already working in logistics management and sup-

ply chain management. The degree program in long-term-care administration prepares students as leaders and culture change advocates throughout the long-term-care continuum. The management program gives students a comprehensive background in the skills, methods, and theories that undergird all effective management. The management information systems program emphasizes business knowledge and management skills for individuals working in the management information systems field. The program in management of health-care informatics is designed for students interested in the management of electronic records and information in the health-care arena. The management of human resources program covers methods and practices of the human resource management professional. The marketing management program emphasizes the techniques and methods of managing and planning in marketing. The interdisciplinary program in organizational systems management provides the knowledge and skills necessary for a broad range of organizational supervisory positions rather than a single particular career. The security management program provides students with the theoretical and practical knowledge necessary for a career in the security field. The software development program cross-trains mainframe and other specialties to competency in Web-based technologies. The program in technical sales emphasizes communication, critical thinking, and problem-solving skills essential to the effective application of basic business and technical sales skills. The program in Web technologies provides a comprehensive study of the information technology industry, presented in an integrated format built around a common project management theme.

The Master of Arts in human services is a nonlicensure degree that enhances personal communication and leadership skills and provides an introduction to the variety of functions that are required of leaders in the human services arena. The Master of Arts in leadership combines leadership philosophy, derived from great leaders and their writings, with concepts and theoretical models of organizational leadership. Students in the Master of Arts in management program develop a working knowledge of the application of quantitative techniques, marketing analysis, human resource management, financial analysis, influencing behavior in organizations, and sensitivity to the legal environment in which operations occur. The Master of Business Administration (M.B.A.) program covers the tools and methods required to run a business. The program permits an individual working full-time to complete all the requirements for the M.B.A. degree in eighteen months (two classes per term). M.B.A. concentrations are offered in accounting, executive coaching, finance, health care, human resource management, international management, management information systems, marketing, and supply chain management. The Executive Master of Business Administration (eMBA) brings together mid- to senior-level managers with direct profit and loss responsibility to share real-world management concepts and gain valuable networking experiences. The Master in Healthcare Administration (M.H.A.) program provides clinical healthcare providers with an opportunity to pursue planning, organizing, leading, and controlling. The Master of Public Administration prepares students to become outstanding managers and leaders prepared to handle the complexities and challenges present in the public sector. The Master of Public Health (M.P.H.) program develops students into contributors to the viability and success of the many organizations in the field of public health. Skills mastered are reflective of knowledge identified by the curricula of the Graduate Schools of Public Health, and the course curriculum is designed to comply with the accrediting body of public health education programs. The Master of Science in computer information systems program has strong elements of both business and computer/telecommunication subjects. Students with business or computer undergraduate preparation typically finish the program with 36 credits of graduate work. For students without a computer background, there are 9 additional prerequisite credits. The Master of Science in human capital management is designed to equip graduates to be more effective in designing human capital development programs and measuring the effectiveness of investment in human capital resources within the corporate setting. The Master of Science in instructional design prepares students to be master educators in the application of instructional technology for both online and traditional classrooms, emphasizing the integration of theory and practice. The Master of Science in management of information systems was created for mid-level IT managers and future chief information officers who need to keep pace with the rapidly changing world of enterprise technology. The Master of Science in organizational performance prepares students to become effective managers, leaders, and facilitators of individual performance improvements, organizational development, and change. The Master of Science in security management prepares students to function effectively at the director level in a broad spectrum of homeland security and related occupations.

Credit Options

Bellevue University grants credit for college-level learning that a student has obtained outside of regionally accredited college settings. Procedures are in place to assess student learning from non–regionally accredited institutions, American Council on Education recommendations, corporate training or programs, CLEP/DSST tests (formerly known as DANTES), and the Experiential Learning Assessment.

Faculty

The Bellevue University full-time and adjunct faculty consists of 388 full- and part-time members who teach students from freshman to graduate level. The student-faculty ratio is 22:1. For most classes and programs, Bellevue University employs adjunct faculty members who are professionals in their respective fields. Faculty members are screened to ensure each is current on issues and technology.

Admission

Online degree completion programs are offered in an accelerated format. To qualify for undergraduate programs, students must have at least 60 credit hours from an accredited institution or an associate degree. To qualify for graduate programs, students must have a baccalaureate degree from an accredited institution and a minimum 2.5 GPA over the course of the last two years of undergraduate work. For some programs, two letters of recommendation and a completed essay are required.

Tuition and Fees

Online undergraduate tuition for a 36-hour major program is $11,880; for the 9-hour Signature Series, it is $2970. Undergraduate fees include the nonrefundable application/assessment fee ($50) and student fees ($150). The estimated total cost for an online undergraduate program is $15,050. This figure excludes the cost of books.

Tuition for the graduate online programs is as follows: the Master of Business Administration, Master of Science in security management, and the Master of Science in computer information systems, $405 per credit hour; or $14,580 for cohort programs (excluding books). The application fee is $75 for all online graduate programs. The general college fee is $45 per semester, or $150 for cohort programs.

Financial Aid

Financial aid assists students with the costs of attending college. This assistance comes from the federal and state government, the institution, and private sources. Financial aid includes grants, scholarships, work-study programs, and student loans. Grants and scholarships do not have to be repaid.

Applying

Individuals interested in applying should transmit the application online or by mail, pay fees, and submit transcripts for evaluation. Admissions counselors work with students to complete the official admissions process. An educational degree plan is completed for each student, defining the requirements needed to achieve each student's degree goal.

CONTACT

Bellevue University
1000 Galvin Road South
Bellevue, Nebraska 68005
Phone: 402-293-2000
            800-756-7920 (toll-free)
E-mail: info@bellevue.edu
Web site: http://www.bellevue.edu

BRENAU UNIVERSITY

Online Studies

Gainesville, Georgia

Brenau University, founded in 1878, is a historic, private, comprehensive university in Gainesville, Georgia, with the bold mission of preparing students to live extraordinary lives.

The University serves two populations: a coeducational population of nontraditional students and a single-gender population of women. Brenau students are able to take classes in an array of formats: day, evening, weekend, and online.

Brenau's Online Studies division offers degree and certificate programs entirely online, with a focus on collaborative learning. Campus-based classes serve a growing population of working adult men and women in four locations across the state (Atlanta, Augusta, Gainesville, and Kings Bay). Brenau has provided a single-gender liberal arts education to residential and nonresidential Women's College students since the University's founding.

Brenau University is regionally accredited by the Southern Association of Colleges and Schools.

Distance Learning Program

Brenau University provides high-quality educational experiences through the delivery of graduate and undergraduate programs utilizing the latest distance learning technology. Programs delivered in the online format are designed to provide maximum flexibility without compromising learning outcomes or academic rigor.

Delivery Media

Online classes are delivered via the Internet. Common software programs are used to enhance the delivery of course materials. Dialogue among students, using an asynchronous discussion board system, is central to the collaborative learning goal. Online students, like their professors, bring with them varied life and work experiences that, when shared with classmates, provide relevant and enlightening applications of theory to real-world situations.

Programs of Study

Brenau University currently offers undergraduate degree programs entirely online in the areas of business administration, human resources management, liberal studies, and nursing. Graduate degree programs are offered in business and education.

The Associate of Arts (A.A.) in liberal studies degree program is designed for the nontraditional, first-time college student or the student with very little college experience. This 60-hour degree program allows for flexibility in scheduling and course selection and can be completed in as little as five semesters.

Brenau's RN-to-B.S.N. bridge program provides registered nurses the opportunity for career advancement by earning a bachelor's degree. An experienced and academically qualified faculty of registered nurses offers this 31-hour program. The clinical portion of this program may be completed in the student's local community, supervised by a Brenau nursing faculty member.

The Bachelor of Business Administration (B.B.A.) in accounting or business administration is a 120-credit degree program. These undergraduate business degree programs, which include courses in organizational behavior, ethics, and international business, can be completed in approximately four years.

The Bachelor of Science (B.S.) in human resources management is a 120-hour degree program. This undergraduate degree program features courses in recruiting/selection, management, benefits, and compensation and can be completed in four years, entirely online.

M.B.A. degrees in accounting, business administration, health-care management, and project management are available from the Department of Business Administration, which has a long history of offering high-quality M.B.A. programs. Students can reach their professional goals easily with Brenau's accelerated ten-course, 30-hour general M.B.A.; the twelve-course, 36-hour M.B.A. in project management; the eleven-course, 33-hour M.B.A. in health-care management; or the twelve-course, 36-hour M.B.A. in accounting. Many states have adopted the 150-hour educational requirement to sit for the CPA exam; Brenau students meet this requirement by earning their M.B.A. degrees, earning a postgraduate certificate in accounting, or enrolling as special status students to acquire the required number of credits.

The M.Ed. degree in early childhood or middle grades education is available from the School of Education. The early childhood M.Ed., a long-standing degree offering at Brenau, is a twelve-course, 34- or 36-hour program, depending on the student's choice of a capstone activity (comprehensive exam or research project). The M.Ed. in middle grades education prepares professionals to teach children in grades four through eight. Students develop a variety of appropriate teaching methods and strategies that are specifically geared to the middle-grade learner. This program is an twelve-course, 34- or

36-hour degree program, depending on the student's choice of a capstone activity (comprehensive exam or research project).

Special Programs

Brenau University's accelerated M.B.A. program in business administration is designed so that students may complete it in five semesters. Classes are small and offer students asynchronous discussion and work-related collaborative projects. These activities are designed to guarantee participation in online classes.

Student Services

In addition to online application, advising, registration, and tuition payment, other student services include writing and math tutors, career services (job search and career selection), mental health counseling, and disability support services through the campus Learning Center. The Brenau Trustee Library catalog is available online using the popular Voyager software, and supplemental materials are offered via the GALILEO database, document delivery, and interlibrary loan.

Credit Options

For undergraduate programs, 45 credit hours must be completed at Brenau University. The residency requirement (Brenau credit hours) for the nursing degree is 31 hours. Alternative credit options toward a Brenau University undergraduate degree (credit earned from advanced-placement exams, international baccalaureate programs, CLEP, military credit, experiential credit, or challenge exams) are limited to a total of 27 hours.

Brenau University may accept up to 6 hours of transfer credit from other regionally accredited institutions as part of a planned graduate program of study upon approval of the respective department chair.

Faculty

Classes are taught by professors who are trained and certified in online course facilitation. Professors teaching in graduate programs have doctorates in their fields and corporate and/or practical experience.

Admission

Prospective students should submit a completed application, a $35 application fee, and transcripts from all institutions previously attended. Standardized test scores (GMAT, GRE, MAT, TOEFL) must be sent from testing services for graduate program admission.

Tuition and Fees

Online tuition is $462 per semester credit hour ($125 technology fee per semester). Tuition rates are addressed prior to each academic year. Tuition is payable by check, money order, or credit card (Visa, MasterCard, and Discover). Brenau offers a military tuition discount for online classes.

Financial Aid

Online students who qualify are eligible for all need-based financial aid programs, including Pell Grants, other federal grants and loan programs, state-direct loans for students in nursing, and institutional grants. Program-specific funds are also available. The FAFSA financial aid application is available online.

A total of 2,293 (73 percent) Brenau University students received some type of financial aid this past academic year. The Office of Financial Aid receives student loan applications (phone: 800-252-5119 Ext. 6152, toll-free).

Applying

The completed application, a $35 application fee, and official transcripts and test scores should be sent directly to the Office of Admissions, 500 Washington Street, SE, Gainesville, Georgia 30501. Military applicants should include a copy of a valid military I.D. or DD214. Online College representatives are available by phone at 800-252-5119 (toll-free) and e-mail.

CONTACT

Heather S. Gibbons, Ph.D.
Associate Vice President for IT and Online Studies
Brenau University
500 Washington Street, SE
Gainesville, Georgia 30501

Phone: 770-718-5327
Fax: 770-718-5329
E-mail: online@brenau.edu
Web site: http://online.brenau.edu

CALIFORNIA INSTITUTE OF INTEGRAL STUDIES
Online Degree Programs
San Francisco, California

California Institute of Integral Studies (CIIS) in San Francisco is an accredited university offering an online M.A. in transformative leadership and an online Ph.D. in transformative studies in a unique learning community. Residential Ph.D., Psy.D., M.A., and B.A. completion degrees in psychology and other disciplines are also offered. The Institute's commitment to the study and practice of multiple cultural and spiritual traditions and to their expression throughout the activities of the community promotes a stimulating learning environment with rigorous scholarship and a supportive community.

Distance Learning Program

The master's degree program in transformative leadership has been created for individuals who want to take the initiative and find ways to express their passion for making a contribution to the world. The program provides a context where students can prepare themselves in a community of like-minded individuals, explore their own mission in life, and develop the skills needed to make it a reality. The culminating capstone action project grounds students' work in the real world.

The primary focus of the doctoral program in transformative studies is to develop thought-leaders who are committed to exploring leading-edge issues in innovative ways, combining scholarship, creativity, and self-inquiry. The program places great value in developing the ability to participate in scholarly discourse through publication and on the importance of viewing academic inquiry as an opportunity for personal and social transformation, while grounding transformative processes in academic depth, rigor, and imagination.

Current information about the programs and courses is available on the CIIS Web site (http://www.ciis.edu/online/), by telephone, or in person at CIIS in San Francisco.

Delivery Media

The M.A. and Ph.D. are offered as 36-semester-unit programs. The doctoral program also requires a dissertation. Both programs are offered in online format using community-based learning through CIIS's Web-based virtual campus, in which students, faculty members, and staff members interact.

Students from both online programs participate in mandatory weeklong intensives in a San Francisco Bay Area retreat setting. Intensives are held at the beginning of each semester. Distance students generally take all their courses on the virtual campus.

Student Services

The CIIS Library, Registrar's, Business Office, and Financial Aid Department are well prepared to support online students with their specific needs.

Faculty

CIIS online programs attract a faculty of distinguished scholars from all over the world. The online-degree faculty members bring practical experience and intellectual expertise relevant to transformation and change and the pedagogies appropriate for an online learning environment.

Admission

CIIS online programs attract self-motivated individuals who are passionate about the relationship between personal and social transformation, and want to combine rigorous scholarship with creativity and commitment. Typically, candidates have professional experience and are seeking to enhance their abilities through study, action, reflection, and scholarship.

Both master's and doctoral programs are also attractive to those wishing to make a career transition, those looking to approach change differently in their current site of practice, and those who require a program that caters to working professionals and find the virtual campus a convenient venue.

Tuition and Fees

For 2007–08, full-time tuition for the M.A. program, at 9 units per semester, was $7020 ($14,040 per year). For the Ph.D. program, at 9 units per semester, tuition was $8325 ($16,650 per year).

Financial Aid

Financial assistance through scholarships, loans, and grants is awarded on the basis of merit and/or need. A serious attempt is made to extend a personalized, concerned approach to student financial needs while complying with governmental and donor regulations. General financial aid programs include Federal Pell Grants, Federal Supplemental Educational Opportunity Grants (FSEOG), Institute scholarships, diversity scholarships, international scholarships, Veterans Administration Educational Benefits, Federal Family Education Loan Programs (FFELP), Federal Stafford Student Loans, and other loan and scholarship opportunities based on merit or need.

Applying

Applicants must meet the general admissions requirements of the Institute. In addition to official transcripts and an autobiographical statement, applicants must submit the following: two letters of recommendation, a critical writing essay, a resume, and a goal statement. Ph.D. applicants should include a statement telling how they will use the resources of the curriculum to advance a chosen inquiry.

Complete admission information and applications are available through the CIIS Web site or through the Admissions Office.

CONTACT

Admissions Counselor
California Institute of Integral Studies
1453 Mission Street
San Francisco, California 94103

Phone: 415-575-6154
Fax: 415-575-1268
E-mail: admissions@ciis.edu
Web site: http://www.ciis.edu

CALIFORNIA STATE UNIVERSITY, DOMINGUEZ HILLS

College of Extended and International Education

Carson, California

California State University, Dominguez Hills (CSUDH), is a national leader in distance learning, named by Forbes *magazine as one of the top cyber universities. Founded in 1960, the University is one of twenty-three California State University (CSU) campuses and has the largest distance learning program in the CSU system. The University offered its first distance learning degree in 1974, and in 1995 offered one of the first online master's degree programs ever approved by the Western Association of Schools and Colleges.*

CSU Dominguez Hills continues to be in the forefront of distance learning technology and academic excellence, garnering numerous awards, including the Best Distance Learning Teacher from the U.S. Distance Learning Association, an Omni Intermedia Award, an Aegis Award, two Telly Awards, and a Top 100 Video Producer Award.

The CSU Dominguez Hills campus is located in the South Bay area of Los Angeles and is accredited by the Western Association of Schools and Colleges.

Distance Learning Program

The distance learning unit is part of the College of Extended and International Education, whose mission is to extend the resources of the University to better serve the educational needs of its communities. The University has more than 4,000 students enrolled in distance learning programs in all fifty states and more than sixty countries.

Delivery Media

All distance learning courses have a Web site, and participants can interact with faculty and staff members via e-mail, telephone, and correspondence. Courses are conducted via live Webcast, where students participate in a live, interactive educational environment, including video transmission of the lecture; via asynchronous Internet, where participants log in at their convenience to complete class assignments and engage in discussion groups with their peers; via television, where CSUDH broadcasts 24 hours a day on cable systems throughout southern California; and via correspondence.

Programs of Study

CSU Dominguez Hills currently offers ten degree and ten certificate programs via distance learning. There are no on-campus requirements for any CSUDH distance learning program. Programs include the following:

Master of Arts in Behavioral Science: Negotiation, Conflict Resolution, and Peacebuilding. Taught via asynchronous Internet, the program teaches participants valuable skills and knowledge that may be applied directly to police work, counseling, human resources management, labor relations, supervision, administration, alternative dispute resolution, arbitration, public policy, social work, teaching, intercultural and community conflicts, corporate contracts, and purchasing (telephone: 310-243-2162; e-mail: negotiation@csudh.edu; Web site: http://www.csudh.edu/negcon).

Master of Arts in the Humanities. Taught via correspondence, the degree offers an interdisciplinary approach to the disciplines of the humanities—history, literature, philosophy, music, and art—with emphasis on their interrelating effects and influences (telephone: 310-243-3190; e-mail: huxonline@csudh.edu; Web site: http://www.csudh.edu/hux).

Master of Business Administration. Taught via asynchronous Internet, the M.B.A. at CSUDH provides a solid qualification in business management with courses that are wide-ranging in content, covering the essential areas of knowledge and skills required in today's competitive business environment (telephone: 310-243-2714; e-mail: cryan@csudh.edu; Web site: http://mbaonline.csudh.edu).

Master of Public Administration. Taught via asynchronous Internet, the program is designed to provide a high-quality graduate professional education for individuals entering or currently employed in public service and nonprofit professions (telephone: 310-243-2395; e-mail: mpaonline@csudh.edu; Web site: http://mpaonline.csudh.edu).

Master of Science in Nursing and Bachelor of Science in Nursing. Taught via asynchronous Internet, the bachelor's completion program prepares graduates to function as leaders, managers, and resource people in a variety of health-care settings. The graduate program prepares professional nurses for advanced and specialized practice. Role emphasis options include clinical nurse specialist in gerontological nursing and nursing education (telephone: 310-243-3741; e-mail: eeinfo@csudh.edu; Web site: http://www.csudh.edu/msn or http://www.csudh.edu/bsn).

Master of Science in Quality Assurance and Bachelor of Science in Quality Assurance. Taught via asynchronous Internet, the bachelor's program provides the academic environment and the requisite course of study to blend the basic sciences, technologies, management principles, quality concepts, and statistical tools needed to prepare professionals for careers in quality assurance and to serve working professionals seeking career enhancement. Master's degree students receive education in both the technical and administrative foundations of quality assurance, an interdisciplinary profession used in management in manufacturing, service, government, and health-care organizations (telephone: 310-243-3880; e-mail: msqa@csudh.edu; Web site: http://www.csudh.edu/msqa or http://www.csudh.edu/bsqa).

Bachelor of Science in Applied Studies. Taught via live broadcasts on the Web and cable television, as well as archived broadcasts and Web sites, the program enables students with associate degrees to complete their bachelor's degree entirely via distance learning. Eighteen courses representing a wide spectrum of management and liberal arts courses help students to become leaders in their profession and advance in their careers. (telephone: 866-278-6789; e-mail: appliedstudiestv@csudh.edu; Web site: http://www.appliedstudies.tv).

Quality Management, Quality Engineering, Quality Auditing, Reliability Engineering, and Software Quality Engineering Certificates of Completion. Taught via asynchronous Internet, the certificate completion programs in quality assurance allow professionals to gain certification in specialized areas of quality and prepare for American Society for Quality exams. Students who successfully complete three master's degree–level courses and the associated capstone course can earn a certificate of completion (telephone: 310-243-3880; e-mail: msqa@csudh.edu; Web site: http://www.csudh.edu/msqa).

Assistive Technology Certificate. Taught via asynchronous Internet, the program prepares individuals to comply with state and federal laws that require that school personnel be prepared to offer a full range of assistive technology services to disabled people. The program is useful to educational administrators, teachers, special education teachers, occupational and physical therapists, speech and language specialists, rehabilitation specialists, program specialists, resource specialists, and psychologists (telephone: 310-243-3741; e-mail: paul_richard@ocde.k12.ca.us; Web site: http://www.csudh.edu/at).

Community College Teaching Certificate. Taught via asynchronous Internet, the program is designed to enhance the skills and the employability of potential community college instructors (telephone: 310-243-2781; e-mail: dulloa@csudh.edu; Web site: http://www.csudh.edu/ccteaching).

Production and Inventory Control Certificate. Taught via asynchronous In-

ternet, the program provides a broad education in the principles of production and inventory control. The program is taught by professionals currently employed in the field who are certified in production and inventory management (telephone: 310-243-3741; e-mail: smackay@csudh.edu; Web site: http://www.csudh.edu/lapicsonline).

Purchasing Certificate. Taught via asynchronous Internet, the program provides a broad education in the principles of procurement management and also helps students prepare for the Certified Purchasing Manager exam (telephone: 310-243-3741; e-mail: smackay@csudh.edu; Web site: http://www.csudh.edu/purchasingonline).

Technical Writing Certificate of Completion. The Technical Writing Certificate of Completion introduces students to the many aspects of contemporary technical writing practices and helps them develop the skills and confidence to communicate complex technical concepts simply and effectively (telephone: 310-243-3730; e-mail: bwald@lists.csudh.edu; Web site: http://www.csudh.edu/extension/technicalwriting.htm).

Special Programs

The Center for Training and Development at CSUDH works closely with the business community to develop custom-designed training programs to help meet the demands of the fast-paced workplace of the new millennium. Programs are delivered via distance learning, on-site, and on the CSUDH campus.

Student Services

Faculty members are available to students via e-mail, telephone, and mail. Student services available at a distance include academic advising, technical support, online tutoring, and access to the library and bookstore.

Credit Options

Depending on the specific program, students may transfer credit earned at other accredited colleges and universities. For more information, students should visit the CSUDH distance learning Web site.

Faculty

CSU Dominguez Hills has more than 100 faculty members teaching distance learning courses. Most of these faculty members have doctoral degrees in their chosen fields.

Admission

Admission requirements vary for each program. Students should consult the CSUDH distance learning Web site for specific program requirements.

Tuition and Fees

Tuition and fees vary for each program. For specific cost information, students should consult the CSUDH distance learning Web site.

Financial Aid

More than $30 million in financial aid is disbursed to CSUDH students each year. Approximately 68 percent of CSUDH students receive some form of financial assistance, and most financial aid programs are available to qualified distance learning students. For further information, students should visit the financial aid Web site (http://www.csudh.edu/fin_aid/default.htm).

Applying

Application processes vary for each program, and campus visits are not required for any program. Students should consult the CSUDH distance learning Web site for specific application information.

CONTACT

Registration Office
College of Extended and International Education
California State University, Dominguez Hills
1000 East Victoria Street
Carson, California 90747
Phone: 310-243-3741
       877-GO-HILLS (toll-free)
Fax: 310-516-3971
E-mail: eeinfo@csudh.edu
Web site: http://dominguezonline.csudh.edu

CANISIUS COLLEGE
On-Line Master of Science in Physical Education Program
Buffalo, New York

Founded by members of the Society of Jesus (Jesuits) in 1870, Canisius College consists of the College of Arts and Sciences, the Wehle School of Business, and the School of Education and Human Services. The Graduate Division at Canisius College was formally established in the 1930s and has grown to become one of the most respected schools in Western New York. Its graduates have become leaders in business, education, sciences, human resources, communication, and other fields, due largely in part to their Canisius master's degree. Time and again, the high quality of a Canisius College education is recognized by respected publications and college ranking lists. The College also meets the rigorous standards needed to receive the endorsement of several key, national higher education accrediting agencies. Canisius' School of Education and Human Services, through which the On-Line Master of Science in Physical Education Program is offered, is accredited by the National Council for Accreditation of Teacher Education (NCATE).

Distance Learning Program
This program is designed for physical education professionals who already possess initial or provisional teaching certification in physical education. It is ideal for coaches and others with demanding schedules who need to balance work, family, and continuing education.

Delivery Media
Unlike other programs that require some on-campus attendance, 100 percent of the On-Line Master of Science in Physical Education Program can be completed on the Web. Participants take their classes using a computer that is linked to the Web. As with most online experiences, a faster connection enhances this interactive experience.

Canisius College uses an instructional program called ANGEL for its online courses. ANGEL is a Web-based course management and collaboration portal that helps educators manage course material and communicate quickly, easily, and effectively. With ANGEL, students can take surveys, quizzes, and tests; send and receive course mail; post to threaded discussions and chat rooms; upload assignments using drop-boxes; and more. Students can check their progress and grades at any time

during the course and can create groups and teams for project or committee work.

Programs of Study
The Physical Education Department offers graduate study leading to the Master of the Science degree. The program is designed to develop job-related competencies with a goal of producing physical education professionals, sports scientists, and health educators who are knowledgeable and skilled in the administration of physical activity programs. The program is focused on K–12 physical education teaching.

The On-Line Master of Science in Physical Education Program requires the completion of 33 credits (11 courses). The program can be completed in as little as four semesters or about 15 months. By taking two courses each semester, the program can be completed in two years. However, a candidate must complete all master's degree requirements within five years. Exceptions to this policy must be approved by the director and program chair as well as the associate dean.

Student Services
Information Technology Services (ITS), the information systems service organization at Canisius, provides information technology resources for instruction, research, and college administration. The ITS Help Desk has experienced, qualified staff members and extensive facilities with which to diagnose and correct many computer problems. Call-in and e-mail service are available for Canisius College students and faculty and staff members.

Credit Options
No more than 6 credits of graduate course work is accepted in transfer from other institutions. The grades must have been at least B and must have been earned within the five-year time limit for completion of degree requirements. All transfer credits must coordinate with the candidate's program of study at Canisius College, as approved by the program director or the associate dean. Any exceptions may only be made with the approval of the program director or the associate dean.

Faculty
Faculty and staff in the School of Education and Human Services are dedicated educators; 75 percent hold a doctoral degree in their field.

Admission
Although the program is designed for certified physical education teachers, candidates without certification are occasionally accepted into the program if it serves their purposes. The program is focused on K–12 physical education teaching.

To be considered for admission to Canisius College's online master's degree program in physical education, candidates are required to submit a completed graduate application (available online), two official transcripts from the degree-granting institution, and two letters of recommendation. In terms of the undergraduate record, candidates with less than a 2.7 cumulative GPA in their undergraduate course work are reviewed by the program director for an admissions decision and may establish additional requirements (e.g., Graduate Record Exam (GRE) scores, etc.).

Tuition and Fees

Tuition for the program during the 2008–09 school year is $667 per credit hour.

Financial Aid

Students may apply for federal student aid as well as private scholarships.

Applying

New graduate students are admitted three times a year: spring (mid-January), summer (May–June), and fall (late August). There are no deadlines for applying; Canisius operates on a rolling admissions basis. The Graduate Application for the School of Education and Human Services can be completed online for free. Students should complete their applications at least one month prior to the term they wish to begin.

CONTACT

School of Education and Human Services
Horan-O'Donnell 014
Canisius College
2001 Main Street
Buffalo, New York 14208-1098
Phone: 716-888-2545
　　　800-950-2505 (toll-free)
E-mail: graded@canisius.edu
Web site: http://www.canisius.edu/
　GradEd

CAPELLA UNIVERSITY
Online Learning
Minneapolis, Minnesota

Capella University is an accredited university that offers online graduate and undergraduate programs for professionals pursuing advancement in the fields of business management, health care administration, higher education, information technology, K–12 education, mental health, and public safety. Capella was founded in 1993 and today is a national leader in online education, with more than 23,000 students from all fifty states and fifty-six other countries. For more information, students should visit http://www.capella.edu or call 888-CAPELLA (227-3552).

Capella University is accredited by the The Higher Learning Commission and is a member of the North Central Association of Colleges and Schools (NCA), http://www.ncahlc.org.

Distance Learning Program

The mission of Capella University is to extend access to high-quality doctoral, master's, bachelor's, and certificate programs for adults seeking to maximize their personal and professional potential. This mission is fulfilled through innovative programs that are responsive to the needs of adult learners. Faculty members are selected for a strong combination of academic and professional experience. A key part of their instructional method is to encourage students to share current workplace challenges as problem-solving opportunities for the entire class.

Capella offers seventeen degree programs, eighty-nine graduate and undergraduate specializations, and sixteen certificate programs. The online university currently serves more than 23,000 adults from all fifty states and fifty-six other countries.

Delivery Media

The Capella online courseroom places the student at the center of the learning experience. The content of each course is developed to align with industry and professional standards, so students learn what is relevant in the field. Many course assignments may be tailored to apply to the student's work situation.

The instructor serves as an expert guide and discussion leader. Active online discussions involve the instructor and other students each week in sharing diverse perspectives and feedback on course assign-

ments. Many Capella courses incorporate interactive media that bring the topic to life and graphically illustrate key concepts.

Programs of Study

Capella University's programs are offered through five schools.

The School of Education offers the Ph.D. in education (nine specializations), the M.S. in education (ten specializations), and three graduate certificates. More than 2,500 educators have chosen Capella University to advance their education and achieve personal and professional goals. Capella's online education degree and certificate programs in K–12, higher education, and continuing and adult education are designed to improve teaching and leadership effectiveness in diverse educational settings. Capella graduates are found throughout the U.S. in leadership roles such as superintendent, principal, and dean.

The School of Human Services offers the Ph.D. in human services (five specializations), the Ph.D. in public safety (three specializations), the M.S. in human services (seven specializations, including two counseling specializations accredited by the American Counseling Association's Council for Accreditation of Counseling and Related Educational Programs [CACREP]), the M.S. in public safety (three specializations), and eight graduate certificates. These programs prepare students to pursue their passion for social change

in a variety of institutional, agency, community, and educational settings. Capella University is one of few online universities to offer M.S. and Ph.D. programs with a specialization in criminal justice. In addition, CACREP has accredited two of Capella's clinical counseling specializations: marital, couple, and family counseling/therapy and mental health counseling.

The Harold Abel School of Psychology offers the clinically oriented Psy.D. program (two specializations), the Ph.D. in psychology (three specializations), the M.S. in psychology (ten specializations), and one specialist certificate. The school offers a range of academic and professionally oriented online psychology degree specializations. Students develop critical thinking skills to understand and apply key psychological principles in diverse work settings.

The School of Business and Technology offers the Ph.D. in organization and management (five specializations), the Ph.D. in information technology (two specializations), the M.B.A. (seven specializations), the M.S. in organization and management (three specializations), the M.S. in information technology (five specializations), and four graduate certificates. In these programs, faculty members combine professional business and technology experience with a solid academic foundation in fundamental principles that drive business success. The programs are competency-based so that students can take practical solutions from the courseroom into the workplace. The information technology curriculum reflects the skills associated with leading IT certifications, such as CCNA®, CCNP®, MCSE, CISSP®, and PMP.

The School of Undergraduate Studies offers the B.S. in business (seven specializations), the B.S. in information technology (seven specializations), and the B.S. in public safety. Through relevant and practical course work, students gain knowledge and skills that can make an immediate impact in their career—even before they graduate. Students in the information technology bachelor's program benefit from a relevant curriculum that addresses essential IT competencies in project management, information security, enterprise systems integration, application development, network architecture and design, systems design and programming, and graphics multimedia. The B.S. in business program develops foundational knowledge and scholarship related to current issues in the areas of accounting, business administration, finance, human resource management, management and leadership, and marketing.

Special Programs

Capella's enrollment counselors take a respectful, consultative approach in helping prospective students investigate their educational options. They offer details on Capella programs and specializations, provide a customized estimate of the time and cost to complete a Capella program, and supply other information that prospective students seek in order to make a well-informed decision.

Academic advisers work with each Capella University student to guide them in planning and completing their educational program. Academic advisers help students plan course sequences, develop a long-term educational plan, and understand the requirements for degree completion.

The Capella University Library offers a team of librarians dedicated exclusively to working with Capella students and faculty and staff members. The library provides the full range of academic resources and services, including databases and online services, reference services, interlibrary loans, and training in research methodology.

Capella University's Writing Program fosters the connection between clear thinking and clear writing. Program faculty members have extensive writing and teaching experience and are eager to help students achieve a level of writing excellence that will advance their academic pursuits and life goals.

Effective, skilled career counselors can be essential allies during educational pursuits. Capella's career services staff members help students recognize their strengths and focus energy in the right direction. Although job placement is not

provided, career services professionals provide award-winning online resources, assist with career planning and development, and deliver one-to-one career guidance and job search assistance. Capella graduates have lifetime access to Capella Career Center services.

The Capella Alumni Association creates lifelong opportunities for continued professional and academic networking and growth. Capella University graduates become part of a nationwide and international network of educated practitioners.

All doctoral programs and some master's and certificate programs involve academic residencies, on-site learning experiences that vary in length and number. A residency advances academic learning, research or clinical skills, and community building—all integral to the Capella model of the personal, professional, and intellectual transformation into a "scholar-practitioner." For example, Ph.D. students participate in three 1-week residential colloquia at specific points in their program. Each one is timed to support success in the next stage of the doctoral program.

Credit Options

Adults typically bring a wealth of experience and knowledge to their education. Not only is this prior learning welcomed and valued in the Capella educational environment, but it may also apply toward a Capella degree program. Course work from regionally accredited or internationally recognized institutions may transfer directly into a Capella program. In some business and IT programs, Capella students may also earn credit by demonstrating relevant, college-level knowledge gained outside the classroom, such as through professional certifications. At the bachelor's degree level, students may be able to gain credit for military training and national testing exams such as ACE, DSST, and CLEP. In these ways, prior learning may shorten the time and reduce the cost of earning a Capella degree.

Faculty

Capella has 942 faculty members—132 core, full-time faculty members and faculty administrators as well as 810 adjunct faculty members. Capella faculty members live in all fifty U.S. states and seven other countries. Eighty percent of the faculty hold doctoral degrees.

Admission

Capella University was founded with a commitment to extend access to high-quality higher education. To achieve this goal, Capella admits applicants who have received the appropriate qualifying degree or course work from accredited institutions or programs and who have a qualifying grade point average. Some programs or specializations have additional requirements; an enrollment counselor can provide details.

Tuition and Fees

The application fee is $75 ($175 for international applicants). Tuition costs vary for each school within the University. Current tuition rates are found at http://www.capella.edu/inc/pdf/tuition_chart.pdf.

Financial Aid

More than three quarters (78 percent) of Capella University students receive some form of financial aid to support their education investment. Sources include federal loans and grants, employer tuition reimbursement, military education benefits, scholarships, and grants. Capella offers an online financial aid application and assistance to those who would like to secure educational funding to help finance their academic program. Enrollment counselors can provide more information about financial aid and other ways to reduce tuition costs.

Applying

Capella's eAdmissions tool makes it easy to apply online at http://www.capella.edu. Admission requirements vary depending on the program and the school. The details of admission can be found in the catalog, available on request. For more information, prospective students should contact the University.

CONTACT

Capella University
225 South 6th Street, 9th Floor
Minneapolis, Minnesota 55402
Phone: 888-227-2736 (toll-free)
          612-339-8650 (international)
Fax: 612-977-5060
E-mail: info@capella.edu
Web site: http://www.capella.edu

CMU CENTRAL MICHIGAN UNIVERSITY

CENTRAL MICHIGAN UNIVERSITY

CMU Off-Campus Programs

Mount Pleasant, Michigan

Since its founding in 1892, Central Michigan University (CMU) has grown from a small teachers' college into a world-class Midwestern university offering more than 150 programs at the bachelor's level and nearly sixty programs at the master's, specialist, and doctoral levels. CMU is accredited by the Higher Learning Commission of the North Central Association of Colleges and Schools. This accreditation includes all on- and off-campus programs. Central Michigan University is an institutional member of the Council for Adult and Experiential Learning, the Adult Education Association, the Alliance: An Association of Alternative Degree Programs for Adults, and the National Association of Institutions in Military Education.

Distance Learning Program

Programs are offered in a compressed format to help balance the demands of work, school, family, and other obligations. The compressed format does not mean easier courses. CMU's Off-Campus Programs are held to the same academic standards that on-campus courses must meet. To help ensure success in the compressed format, procedures and support services are fast and accessible.

Delivery Media

Students have a choice of delivery formats: online, print-based learning packages, or classroom-based courses at more than sixty locations in North America.

Online courses use Web technology to involve the student in interactive learning. Students can interact with instructors and others through e-mail, chat sessions, and message forums. Student lecture materials and assignments are all online. Textbooks are required.

Learning packages are print-based courses that use textbooks and study guides but may also include audio and videocassettes as well as the use of e-mail and Internet chat rooms to enrich the content.

Classes are also available in evening or weekend formats at locations throughout the United States, Canada, and Mexico. An up-to-date listing of locations is available at http://www.cel.cmich.edu/locations.

Programs of Study

CMU Off-Campus Programs offers undergraduate, graduate, and doctoral degree programs.

Undergraduate program offerings are available at centers in Michigan and online through CMU Online. The Bachelor of Science (B.S.) degree with a major in administration is for students wishing to pursue an administrative career. The core courses provide a foundation in the concepts and applications critical to becoming a successful, effective administrator. Graduates of this program are prepared for careers as production supervisors, human resource administrators, and small business administrators. General education and elective courses allow students to acquire basic skills and learn to communicate with people in other disciplines and jobs and provide an emphasis in liberal arts and natural or social sciences.

The B.S. degree with an option in community development prepares students for work in the public sector or human services area. Courses focus on the general theory and practice of community along with interaction of community institutions in a community setting. Graduates go on to careers in political office, the public health professions, directing community education, and more. The community services concentration prepares students for employment at community agencies, for providing community services, and for work in nonprofit organizations; many of the courses are focused in sociology. The public administration concentration is for those wishing to work in local, state, or federal government positions; many of the courses are centered on political science.

The Master of Science in Administration (M.S.A.) degree is a 36-semester-hour program that approaches administration and management from a broader perspective than other graduate degrees. This interdisciplinary program was developed to meet the needs of administrators in both the public and nonprofit sectors. Concentrations are available at locations throughout North America, with two concentrations (general administration and information resource management) available completely online. Core courses provide students with quantitative analysis, and concentration courses allow them to tailor the program to their individual areas of interest.

Among the other M.S.A. concentrations offered, the acquisition administration concentration deals with purchasing inventory, and the general administration concentration gives an excellent foundation in management principals and is applicable to a wide variety of administrative settings. The health services administration concentration equips students to proactively meet the challenges faced in a health-care facility or in hospital administration. The concentration in human resource administration helps students develop their human resource management skills, focusing on the areas of labor relations, staffing, training, and organizational development. An information resource management concentration enables students to develop a comprehensive approach to the management of information systems in an organization to ensure that the chosen technology solution is the most appropriate one. The leadership concentration enhances abilities to think creatively, manage knowledge effectively, develop a vision, establish direction, and motivate staff. The public administration concentration prepares students for careers in public administration. Students get in-depth information on public policy making and regulatory, budgetary, and personnel issues.

CMU offers an online M.B.A. program in a cohort format (a group of students admitted to the program with a specific start date who follow a planned sequence of courses). The program, which is suited for working professionals seeking a program in advanced managerial study, has a concentration in management information systems (MIS) and an emphasis in enterprise software (SAP). This eighteen-month, 31-credit program includes the two-week face-to-face SAP Academy. To participate in this program, students must show evidence of computer literacy with a working knowledge of advanced business computer applications in spreadsheet, database, and presentation graphics. Applicants must also submit a GMAT score. An SAP Graduate Certificate is available for those not looking to pursue a full M.B.A. program. This is a 16-credit-hour program designed to be completed in nine months. The courses are offered online, with the exception of the SAP Academy. The program is also offered in a cohort format.

An M.B.A. program with a concentration in value-driven organization (VDO) is offered online in the cohort format. This is a 31-credit hour program that is completed in eighteen months. The program is designed to meet the needs of experienced business people seeking a career-enhancing M.B.A. degree from an AACSB-accredited business school. The focus of this M.B.A. program is on the voice of the customer (marketing research methodologies), corporate governance and social responsibility, and process improvement (Six Sigma methods used to enhance processes and increase efficiencies). The GMAT is required for admission to the M.B.A./VDO program.

The Master of Science (M.S.) degree in nutrition and dietetics is designed to provide advanced training in human nutritional sciences for new and experienced professionals. The program is designed to provide graduates with the quantitative and methodological knowledge necessary to better interpret the scientific literature to conduct their own nutritional research. It is available completely online.

The M.A. in education is a continuing education program for teachers; it presumes the individual is already trained and qualified in the technical aspects of the field. Concentrations available within the program are adult education (teaching in an adult education environment), community college (currently only available in Canada, this concentration is for effective teaching in a community college environment), and instructional (for K-12 curriculum and instruction). The M.A. in education degree is offered at select locations throughout the United States and Canada.

The M.A. in educational leadership with an emphasis in charter school administration leadership is offered in a cohort format. The program is geared toward the growing needs of charter school administration. Course topics include leadership in a charter school, administration within diverse populations, school and community relations, and principles of educational administration. This is a 33-credit-hour program.

Special Programs
The Doctor of Health Administration (D.H.A.) is a 63-credit program that is cutting-edge, academically sound, practice-based, and flexible. Designed for leaders in the health-care field, the online format, combined with six weekend seminars, provides the ultimate combination of academic rigor and practical convenience.

Student Services
All services are available online and/or by a toll-free phone call. The service ranked highest by CMU's current students and graduates is the nationally recognized Off-Campus Library Services. Document delivery provides students with books, copies of journal articles, and other materials free of charge.

Credit Options
Credits earned through distance learning Off-Campus Programs are recorded on Central Michigan University's transcripts in the same manner as credits earned in on-campus courses. These courses are part of the regular offerings of Central Michigan University. Relevant transfer credit and prior learning credits are also options.

Faculty
Faculty members are selected from the main campus in Mount Pleasant, Michigan; from other universities; and from the executive ranks of government, business, and industry. Approval of all faculty members is done by department chairpersons on the basis of their academic and professional qualifications.

Admission
Students must be admitted to CMU in order to take distance learning Off-Campus Programs courses. The minimum requirement for admission to CMU undergraduate programs is a high school diploma or GED certificate. Undergraduate applicants must posses a GPA of 2.0 or higher. For those with GPAs lower than the required 2.0, conditional admission may be granted. One official transcript from all previously attended institutions should be provided to CMU.

Graduate applicants must have a baccalaureate or equivalent degree from an institution that has received regional accreditation or recognized standing at the time the student attended. Graduate applicants must have an overall grade point average of at least 2.7 in their bachelor's studies. Applicants whose GPA is between 2.3 and 2.7 may be considered for conditional admission. GMAT or GRE scores are not required (except for the online M.B.A. program).

D.H.A. applicants must have a master's degree of at least 27 semester hours or have earned a professional doctorate (such as M.D., D.O., J.D., or Pharm.D.) from a U.S. regionally accredited university.

Tuition and Fees
Tuition for the 2008–09 academic year is as follows: undergraduate, $325 per credit hour; master's-level degrees, $425 per credit hour (except M.S. in nutrition and dietetics, $485 per credit hour; M.B.A. core courses and VDO concentration, $655 per credit hour; and M.B.A. SAP concentration courses, $1000 per credit hour); and D.H.A., $850 per credit hour. Military personnel (active duty and retired) and their dependents are eligible for a discounted tuition rate of $250 per credit hour at both the undergraduate and graduate levels of select programs. This rate does not apply at the doctoral level or to the M.B.A. program offerings. Additional fees include a $50 admission fee and a $50 graduation fee.

Financial Aid
Financial aid is available to those students who qualify. Students interested in financial aid are encouraged to contact CMU for more information.

Applying
Students interested in taking classes through CMU Off-Campus Programs are encouraged to apply for admission to Central Michigan University. Admission applications can be downloaded from the Web site.

CONTACT
CMU Off-Campus Programs
Central Michigan University
Mount Pleasant, Michigan 48859
Phone: 877-268-4636 (toll-free)
Fax: 989-774-1822
E-mail: cmuoffcampus@cmich.edu
Web site: http://www.cmuoffcampus.
com

CHARTER OAK STATE COLLEGE
New Britain, Connecticut

Charter Oak State College, one of America's leading distance learning colleges for adults, was established in 1973 by the Connecticut Legislature to provide an alternate way for adults to earn a college degree. Recognized as the College that offers "degrees without boundaries," Charter Oak responds to the degree-completion needs of adult learners. The College, which is regionally accredited by the New England Association of Schools and Colleges and is a Servicemembers Opportunity College, awards bachelor's and associate degrees.

Charter Oak's flexible degree-completion programs are designed to assist adult learners in achieving their educational objectives as they continue to meet career, family, and financial obligations.

Students can complete their degree credit requirements by combining credits earned by taking Charter Oak online courses with credits earned—no matter how long ago—from regionally accredited colleges and universities, noncollegiate-sponsored instruction, standardized testing such as CLEP and Dantes, work or military experience, contract learning, and portfolio assessment.

Individualized professional advisement is a hallmark of Charter Oak State College. Each student benefits from one-on-one support from an academic counselor who specializes in the student's chosen field of study. Counselors, who are accessible via telephone, e-mail, fax, and U.S. mail, work closely with students to customize a degree-completion program geared to personal goals.

Distance Learning Program
Charter Oak State College provides all of its services using distance technology. The College offers an expansive selection of five-, eight-, and fifteen-week quality online courses. Textbooks may be purchased electronically from an authorized bookstore.

Programs of Study
Charter Oak State College offers four degrees in general studies: Associate in Arts, Associate in Science, Bachelor of Arts, and Bachelor of Science. To earn an associate degree, a student must complete at least 60 credits; a bachelor's degree requires at least 120 credits. The College accepts up to 90 community college credits toward a bachelor's degree.

A Charter Oak degree is more than an accumulation of the required number of credits. At least one half of the credits toward a degree must be earned in subjects traditionally included in the liberal arts and sciences—humanities, mathematics, natural sciences, and social sciences. Achievement in these areas demonstrates breadth of learning. To demonstrate depth of learning, students who pursue a baccalaureate degree must complete a concentration consisting of at least 36 credits.

A concentration plan, accompanied by an essay, must be submitted to the faculty for approval. Concentrations may be constructed in many areas, including applied arts, art history, the behavioral sciences, business, child study, communication, computer science, engineering studies, fire service administration, health-care administration, human services, individualized studies, languages, liberal studies, literature, music history, the natural sciences, organizational management and leadership, paralegal studies, public safety administration, religious studies, the social sciences, and technology studies. As a graduation requirement, students must also submit an academic autobiography that provides them the opportunity to reflect on their educational experiences and demonstrate their writing ability and understanding of their degree program.

Special Programs
The College has evaluated a number of noncollegiate courses and programs for which it awards credit toward Charter Oak degree programs. Many health-care specialties from hospital-based programs are included, such as medical laboratory technician, nurse practitioner, physician assistant, radiologic technologist, registered nurse, and respiratory therapist or technician. The College also evaluates state and municipal police officer training. Other evaluations include the Child Development Associate (CDA) credential; the FAA Airman Certificate; Famous Artists School in Westport, Connecticut; Institute of Children's Literature in West Redding, Connecticut; the National Opticianry Competency Examination; the Contact Lens Registry Examination; and several fire certifications, including Fire Marshal, Deputy Fire Marshal, Fire Inspector, Fire Fighter III, Fire Officer I or II, and Fire Service Instructor I or II.

Credit Options
Students can transfer credits from other regionally accredited colleges and universities. Age of credits is not a factor in most concentrations. There is no limit to the number of credits that can be earned using standardized examinations, prior learning—including ACE-evaluated military credits and ACE- and PONSI-evaluated noncollegiate learning—and portfolio assessment

Faculty

Full-time faculty members, from public and independent institutions of higher education in Connecticut, serve as consulting examiners at Charter Oak. Distance learning faculty members come from all over the United States and possess appropriate degrees and/or experience.

Admission

Admission is open to any person 16 years or older, regardless of level of formal education, who is able to demonstrate college-level achievement. To be admitted, a student must have earned 9 college-level credits from acceptable sources of credit.

Tuition and Fees

All students pay a $75 application fee. Connecticut residents pay a first-year matriculation fee of $685 for an associate degree or $995 for a bachelor's degree. Nonresidents pay a first-year matriculation fee of $965 for an associate degree or $1310 for a bachelor's degree. Active-duty service members and their spouses pay in-state resident's rates for all Charter Oak fees and services. All students pay a graduation fee of $195. Tuition for online and video-based courses is $177 per credit for Connecticut residents and $247 per credit for nonresidents. There is a $40 registration fee for all students. A Comprehensive Enrollment Fee, combining matriculation and 12 credits per year is available at a rate reflecting a 10 percent discount.

Financial Aid

Financial aid is available to eligible Charter Oak students from federal, state, and institutional sources. All students who wish to apply for aid must complete the Free Application for Federal Student Aid (FAFSA). The FAFSA may be completed online and can be accessed at http://www.fafsa.ed.gov. Charter Oak's forms can be accessed online at http://www.charteroak.edu/sfa. The Charter Oak State College school code is 032343.

Applying

Charter Oak reviews applications on a rolling basis; students may matriculate at anytime during the year.

CONTACT

Admissions Office
Charter Oak State College
55 Paul J. Manafort Drive
New Britain, Connecticut 06053-2150
Phone: 860-832-3855
Fax: 860-832-3999
Web site:
http://www.charteroak.edu

CITY UNIVERSITY OF SEATTLE
Distance Learning Option
Bellevue, Washington

> *City University of Seattle is a private not-for-profit institution of higher education. Its mission is to change lives for good by offering high quality and relevant lifelong education to anyone with the desire to learn.*
>
> *City University of Seattle's programs cover a variety of academic fields, ranging from business management and technology to psychology and communications. The majority of faculty members actively work in the fields they teach. The combination of innovative program design and outstanding instruction makes City University of Seattle an exceptional institution of higher learning.*

Distance Learning Program

In keeping with its mission of providing convenient, accessible education, City University of Seattle offers most of its degree programs through distance learning (DL), utilizing the World Wide Web. City University of Seattle serves approximately 5,000 students annually through DL.

Delivery Media

City University of Seattle delivers distance learning course work utilizing the Blackboard Course Management System. Delivered through asynchronous interaction on the World Wide Web, City University of Seattle distance learning courses are designed for optimum learning anywhere, anytime. Highly qualified faculty members, who are working in the fields they teach, provide distance learning students with real-world application of course material. In addition, structured discussions provide students the opportunity to exchange in dialogue with peers without the need of traveling to a classroom.

Programs of Study

City University of Seattle's undergraduate programs prepare students to compete in today's marketplace. Students may complete a Bachelor of Science (B.S.) or a Bachelor of Arts (B.A.) degree. Within these degrees, students may pursue one of several areas of study, including accounting, business administration, communications, computer systems, and psychology. Undergraduate courses are 5 credits each; 180 credits are required for completion of a B.S. degree, and students typically transfer the first two years of study.

City University of Seattle's graduate business program prepares management professionals for leadership roles at local, national, and international levels. Students may pursue a Master of Business Administration (M.B.A.) or a Master of Science in either project management or computer systems. Most graduate courses are worth 3 credits; total required credits range from 45 to 60. Students may also pursue a Master of Education (M.Ed.) in literacy. Total required credits for this program is 48.

Special Programs

City University of Seattle has an "open-door" admissions policy for most programs. Students may begin course work at the start of any quarter once accepted to their program of study.

All of City University of Seattle's programs are geared for adult students. From its student body to its faculty and staff, City University of Seattle is a community of professionals. All who are associated with the University understand the needs of adult learners who are seeking high-quality education that applies to their individual lifestyle.

Student Services

Students may register online or by phone. Academic advising and assistance is available from a distance learning adviser by phone, fax, or e-mail. Students have full access to the library via the Internet and a toll-free phone number, and a mailing service for circulation of books and articles is available as well.

Credit Options

Students may transfer up to 90 approved lower-division and 45 approved upper-division credits from approved institutions for baccalaureate programs. The Prior Learning Experience Program lets students earn credits through documented experimental learning. Students may receive credit for the CLEP or other standardized tests. Graduate students may transfer up to 12 credits from approved programs.

Faculty

There are more than 350 faculty members included in the distance learning program. Faculty members have, at minimum, a master's degree and professional experience in the fields they teach.

Admission

Undergraduate programs are generally open to applicants over 18 years of age who hold a high school diploma or GED. Admission to graduate programs requires that students hold a baccalaureate degree from an accredited or otherwise recognized institution. Additional requirements apply to education programs. International students whose first language is not English are required to submit a TOEFL score of at least 540 for admission to undergraduate programs and 550 for graduate programs.

Tuition and Fees

For 2007–08, tuition was $295 per undergraduate credit hour and $500 per graduate credit hour. The tuition rate is the same for both in-class and distance learning study. Other fees may apply, depending on the specific course

of study. Additional fees apply for certificate completion, graduation application, course registration, and various tests or examinations that the student may request. All initial applicants for certificate or degree programs pay a nonrefundable application fee of $50. Tuition and fees are subject to annual review on July 1.

Textbooks and other instructional materials are additional. While the number of required texts and other course materials vary with each course, textbooks typically cost between $100 and $150 each.

Financial Aid

For information, students should contact the Financial Aid Office at 800-426-5596 (toll-free).

Applying

DL students may enroll on a rolling admissions basis. Students must speak with an academic adviser to complete the initial enrollment. Students should then submit the application form, nonrefundable application fee, transcripts, and admission documents to the Office of Admissions.

CONTACT

Office of Admissions
City University of Seattle
11900 NE First Street
Bellevue, Washington 98005

Phone: 425-737-1010
          800-422-4898 (toll-free)
Fax: 425-709-5361
E-mail: info@cityu.edu
Web site: http://www.cityu.edu

CLARION UNIVERSITY OF PENNSYLVANIA

Office of Extended Studies and Distance Education
Clarion, Pennsylvania

Clarion University of Pennsylvania seeks to excel in all that it does and challenges students to develop their talents, extend their intellectual capacities and interests, expand their creative abilities, and develop a respect and enthusiasm for learning that will continue throughout their lives. Clarion University is primarily an undergraduate institution with selected graduate programs. Instructional programs—delivered on campus, throughout the state, and beyond via distance-learning technologies—range from associate degree and certificate programs to baccalaureate degree programs in the arts and sciences and professional fields, graduate programs in selected fields, and continuing education.

Distance Learning Program

Clarion University has offered distance education credit courses since fall 1996. Since that time, Clarion has offered hundreds of interactive television (ITV) and online classes around the state and over the Internet. In the past five years, Clarion has expanded its online programming significantly. The University now offers four undergraduate and five graduate degree programs fully online, and more will soon be added.

The courses required to support these degrees meet the same curricular and instructional standards as classes delivered on campus, and they are taught by the same faculty members currently teaching in the traditional classrooms. As a result, the degree a student earns online offers the same quality and accreditation as a degree earned through the University's traditional on-campus program.

Delivery Media

To take advantage of the latest technology in Blackboard and to minimize additional plug-in downloads, students should have, at minimum, Microsoft Windows 2000 or XP or Macintosh OS 10.2 or 10.3.

Web pages are best viewed in Microsoft Internet Explorer 5.2 (for Macintosh OS 10.2 or 10.3), Microsoft Internet Explorer 5.5 or 6.0 (for Windows), Netscape Navigator 7.1 or higher (for Windows or Macintosh OS 10.2 or 10.3), Firefox 1.0 (for Windows or Macintosh OS 10.2 or 10.3), Safari 1.0 (for Macintosh 10.2), and Safari 1.1 or 1.2 (for Macintosh OS 10.3). Macintosh users in accounting, chemistry, and math courses must use OS 10.3.9 with Safari 1.3 in order to view all homework content. Though Blackboard is not compatible with the America Online (AOL) browser, students can connect using AOL and then use Internet Explorer or Netscape.

Students should also have Adobe Acrobat 5.0 higher, a display/monitor with 256 colors and 800x600 resolution or higher (1024x768 recommended), a minimum of a 56K modem connection, an e-mail account, and McAfee antivirus software (available without charge through a license agreement).

Microsoft Office has a number of viewer programs that enable students who do not have the software installed on their home computers to view the documents that have been posted. Plug-ins are available for Adobe Acrobat, QuickTime, Shockwave, RealPlayer, Windows Media Player, and Microsoft Office Viewers at http://www.clarion.edu/academic/adeptt/blackboard/plugins.htm.

Programs of Study

Nondegree programs include the Instructional Technology Specialist Certificate (ITSC) Program; the graduate-level Secondary Teacher Certification Program, with certification in biology, chemistry, earth and space science, English, general science, modern languages, physics, and social studies; and the Radiologic Sciences Prerequisite Program, which is designed to meet the general education credit requirements set for radiography students by the American Society of Radiologic Technologists (ASRT).

Undergraduate programs offered are the Associate of Arts (A.A.) in arts and sciences; the Associate of Science (A.S.) in early childhood education; the Bachelor of Science (B.S.) in liberal studies, with a concentration in library science; and a degree-completion program leading to the Bachelor of Science in Nursing (B.S.N.).

Graduate programs include the Master of Business Administration (M.B.A.), the Master of Science (M.S.) in rehabilitative sciences, the Master of Science (M.S.) in mass media arts and journalism, the Master of Science of Library Science (M.S.L.S.), and the Master of Science in Nursing (M.S.N.) with family nurse practitioner concentration.

Special Programs

Internships and study-abroad opportunities are available.

Student Services

Clarion University libraries offer services designed to support research and information needs of off-campus students and faculty members. Distance education support includes reference and information assistance, access to online resources, online tutorials, and interlibrary loan. Technical help is available through Blackboard Help at 866-434-8882.

Credit Options

Clarion University affirms its commitment to maximize access to higher education for all Pennsylvanians through the Academic Passport to the Pennsylvania State System of Higher Education, applying credit toward graduation for all equivalent college course work completed for the associate degree. High school students who earn a 3 or higher on an AP exam may be granted at least 3 credits. A maximum of 60 credits may be earned through the College-Level Examination Program (CLEP). Some graduate programs allow students to transfer credit for graduate courses taken at other regionally accredited institutions for course work of higher academic caliber in accepted fields of study. No more than 30 percent of the total credits for any degree may be transfer credits.

Faculty

Clarion faculty members draw upon a broad mix of academic expertise and field experience in their teaching and research. Most faculty members hold doctorates and have worked extensively in their fields. All professors are selected by the academic departments. In most cases, departments employ only full-time tenured or tenure-track faculty members to teach online classes. At Clarion, faculty members are committed to helping each individual learn

and grow and will go to significant lengths to help students succeed. The University's student-faculty ratio is 19:1.

Admission

Undergraduate applicants must be graduates of an approved secondary school or hold a General Educational Development (GED) high school equivalency diploma issued by the Pennsylvania (or associated state) Department of Education. Home schooled applicants must be graduates of a Department of Education–approved home school association program.

Most applicants should have completed 4 units of mathematics (typically algebra 1, algebra 2, and geometry), 3 units of science (typically biology and chemistry), 4 units of English, and 4 units in the social sciences (typically world cultures, history, social studies, psychology, and sociology). There are no foreign language requirements for applicants, but two or more years of a foreign language are strongly encouraged.

Applicants for graduate programs should have a bachelor's degree in a related field from a regionally accredited institution.

Tuition and Fees

Full-time undergraduate tuition and fees are $2935 and $3031 per semester for Pennsylvania residents and nonresidents, respectively. Graduate residents pay $3598 per semester for full-time study, while nonresidents pay $3705.

Financial Aid

Online students are eligible to use federal financial aid (Pell and SEOG grants, Stafford Loans) for which they qualify per the FAFSA. Since their educational costs are lower, they may not receive the maximum grant or loan amounts. Associate and baccalaureate degree students who enroll in more than 50 percent of their courses online are not eligible to use a PHEAA state grant for which they might otherwise qualify. Master's-degree students are eligible only for Stafford Loans as their source of federal financial aid. They are not eligible for PELL, SEOG, or PHEAA grants. Distance education students are subject to the same financial aid regulations and conditions as any student taking courses on campus.

Applying

Undergraduate applicants must submit the completed application, the nonrefundable $30 application, official high school transcripts, SAT or ACT scores, and letters of recommendation. Graduate applicants must send in the completed application, the nonrefundable $30 application fee, official transcripts, three sealed recommendation forms, and a resume; students should check online for other requirements. Applicants should write "online" on the application form beside the name of the program. Undergraduate applications are accepted on a rolling basis. The graduate deadlines for the fall and the spring semesters are August 1 and December 1, respectively.

CONTACT

Lynne M. Lander Fleisher, Associate Director
Office of Extended Programs
131 Harvey Hall
Clarion University of Pennsylvania
840 Wood Street
Clarion, Pennsylvania 16214-1232

Phone: 814-393-2778
E-mail: lfleisher@clarion.edu
Web site: http://www.clarion.edu/academic/distance/index.
    shtml

COLORADO STATE UNIVERSITY
College of Business, Distance M.B.A. Program
Fort Collins, Colorado

Colorado State University's College of Business offers a comprehensive M.B.A. program to professionals around the world who desire not only to learn the concepts and theories behind sound business practices but also to understand how to apply these ideas to their day-to-day operations. The Distance M.B.A. Program is offered through mixed-media DVD technology and video streaming called BizCast; students gain the benefit of the full lectures, student discussions, questions, and special topics presented by the guest speakers. Students are at a distance—not in isolation.

CSU strives to make all of its students feel part of the activities experienced on the main campus. The degree earned is not a diluted form of the on-campus degree but rather encompasses the same academic content and rigor as the on-campus M.B.A. program. Our distance M.B.A. students earn an M.B.A. from Colorado State University, not an online or distance degree.

Accredited by AACSB International–The Association of Advance Collegiate Schools of Business more than thirty years ago, the Distance M.B.A. Program at Colorado State University was the first to earn this coveted accreditation and remains one of the only distance M.B.A. programs to be so accredited. The program strives to provide students with the knowledge, skills, and functional competencies they need to become effective decision makers and leaders in a business environment that is becoming more global, more competitive, and increasingly dynamic.

Distance Learning Program

Founded more than forty years ago and one of the nation's oldest distance degree programs, the Distance M.B.A. Program delivers a high-quality education while providing students with the flexibility needed to earn their degrees. This program was the first distance M.B.A. program to earn the coveted AACSB International accreditation nearly forty years ago and remains one of the only distance/online M.B.A. programs with the prestigious accreditation. Program content is cross-functional and has a strong emphasis on leadership, entrepreneurship, and global issues. Nearly 2,000 professionals have earned their M.B.A. degrees through the CSU Distance M.B.A. Program.

Most individuals in the CSU Distance M.B.A. Program are working professionals, with an average of thirteen years of work experience. They are drawn from all fifty states, many provinces in Canada, and, increasingly, from around the world. Over the years, U.S. military personnel have been frequent participants in the program and continue to be heavy sup-

porters of this flexible and convenient M.B.A. program. The average age of the distance students is 33; their average GMAT score is 580.

The Distance M.B.A. Program at CSU offers active duty military personnel, National Guard personnel, reservists, and veterans a Military Tuition Reduction Program to help bridge the funding gap found in graduate education. Likewise, a Federal and State Employee Tuition Reduction Program is available.

Delivery Media

Distance M.B.A. students are linked to each other and to the epicenter of the M.B.A. programs at CSU through a technologically advanced classroom and an online communications network. By virtue of the unique connectedness, all students come together as one class, even though they may be located across the country or in another part of the world.

The classroom lectures and discussions are recorded using a mixed-media DVD format for the distance M.B.A. stu-

dents and are shipped the following day. The DVD format gives CSU's distance M.B.A. students a direct link to the classroom, the on-campus students, and the professors. In addition to lectures and discussions being delivered using the DVD technology, students also are part of the unique M.B.A. intranet for communication with professors, other students in the sections, and team members. The chat rooms and threaded discussions keep students engaged with others in the program, assignments, and group collaboration.

As a complement to delivery of the full classroom dynamic to distance students through the mixed-media DVD, the College of Business also provides lecture content via video streaming called Biz-Cast. Students around the world have access to BizCast within 48 hours of each class with the added feature of download capabilities to overcome the issue of firewalls.

Program of Study

The Distance M.B.A. Program is designed to serve the needs of working professionals who need flexibility in schedule and location. There is no requirement to come to the campus during the course of the program; however, over 50 percent of the Distance M.B.A. Program graduates come to take part in commencement each year. The 36-credit program may be completed in as little as twenty-one months, or a student may take up to five years to complete the program; summer classes are required regardless of the time sequence selected. The College's M.B.A. adviser works with students throughout the program to match course offerings with professional and personal schedules. There is no thesis required in this program.

In this comprehensive and progressive M.B.A. degree program, students study the five major functional areas of a business and the interrelationship among those areas. Students are not only exposed to the concepts and theories of modern business practices but they also have the opportunity to apply those concepts and theories to their own companies/businesses or to others around them. This application-based course of study is lauded by CSU's students as immediately valuable in their day-to-day professional lives.

Student Services
A student in the Colorado State University Distance M.B.A. Program is afforded all the student–support services offered to those on campus. Each student is assigned to an M.B.A. adviser to help with course sequencing or special situations impacting program participation. In addition, each student has electronic access to the main CSU library's business databases and the library's reference materials, journals, and periodicals. Students can even sign up to receive books and articles directly from the library. In addition, each student has access to technical support and an operations assistant for the M.B.A. intranet.

Credit Options
The Distance M.B.A. Program offers courses in a lock-step sequencing mode, so each class builds on the previous classes. Because of the lock-step sequencing of the program and because of the group collaboration, CSU does not accept transfer credits; however, there are no prerequisites for the program. For students who feel they could benefit from a refresher with accounting, finance, and statistics, an MBA Survival Kit is available through the bookstore. These self-paced CDs take students through the basics of each of these subject areas providing foundation knowledge and confidence.

Faculty
What differentiates CSU's Distance M.B.A. Program from other programs is the high quality of its faculty members, who not only teach the material but also demonstrate how to apply it to the business world. With the exception of a few extraordinary individuals with private-industry experience, the professors who teach in the M.B.A. program are full-time faculty members with Ph.D.'s in their disciplines. Their research efforts and work in their respective industries keep the faculty members in the forefront of what is happening in business today.

Admission
Admission to the Distance M.B.A. Program is predicated on an individual's performance at the undergraduate level; their professional experience, including management of projects or people; GMAT scores; and their application materials. A balance of these four criteria is sought in the determination for admission. In special cases, petitions for GMAT waivers are considered.

Colorado State University seeks to balance each class with a representation of industries, years of experience, and a mix of undergraduate degree concentrations. In addition, attention is paid to provide a balance along gender lines and a rich mix of backgrounds. Applicants with all types of undergraduate backgrounds are encouraged to apply. The program does not have prerequisites.

Tuition and Fees
For the 2007–08 academic year, tuition for the distance M.B.A. courses was $620 per credit hour. The $620-per-credit-hour cost includes the production of the course-delivery DVDs, shipping, access

to BizCast, receipt of Microsoft 2007 Operating System and Office Suite 2007, the M.B.A. intranet, technical support, production assistance, and all other student services. Students are responsible for their own textbooks and course materials.

Financial Aid
Federal financial aid is available to qualified students admitted to the Distance M.B.A. Program who take at least 5 credits per semester. More information can be obtained from the Financial Aid Office (http://sfs.colostate.edu/B2000.cfm; 800-491-4622 Ext. 7). Students may also complete the Free Application for Federal Student Aid on the Web at http://www.fafsa.ed.gov. The Montgomery GI Bill, Tuition Assistance, and third-party billing are also available. Students interested in using their veterans benefits may call 800-491-4622, Ext. 8.

Applying
The application deadlines for the Distance M.B.A. Program are July 15 for the fall semester and December 8 for the spring semester. Applicants must submit a resume, a cover letter that reflects carefully considered reasons for pursuing a business degree at the master's level, GMAT scores (unless a petition for a waiver to the GMAT is submitted and approved), TOEFL scores (for international students), a completed data sheet for the College of Business, three references from individuals who know the applicant's work, two copies of official transcripts in sealed envelopes, a completed Graduate School Web Application, and a $50 application fee. To request an admissions packet, students should contact the College.

CONTACT
Matt Leland
M.B.A. Program Assistant
Colorado State University College of Business
1270 Campus Delivery
Fort Collins, Colorado 80523-1270
Phone: 800-491-4622 Ext. 1 (toll-free)
Fax: 970-491-3481
E-mail: matt.leland@colostate.edu
Web site: http://www.CSUdistanceMBA.com

COLORADO STATE UNIVERSITY
Continuing Education
Fort Collins, Colorado

Colorado State University has served the people of Colorado as the state's land-grant university since 1870. Today, the campus in Fort Collins is home to 25,000 students pursuing degrees at all levels in a wide range of subjects in liberal arts, engineering, business, natural resources, agriculture, and the sciences. The University's instructional outreach activities go far beyond the campus and the state of Colorado.

Distance Learning Program

Colorado State University's online and distance learning courses are designed to begin or to finish a degree, to explore new topics, to enrich life, and to give students an opportunity to develop a level of proficiency in professional development. Approximately 12,000 students from all over the country and overseas are enrolled in distance education courses from Colorado State University.

Delivery Media

Colorado State offers courses in online, print, and mixed-media formats. All courses are supported by Colorado State University faculty members. Students may contact course faculty members via telephone, fax, e-mail, or regular mail. Students should call Continuing Education or visit the Web site for contact information for an instructor.

Programs of Study

As an institution, Colorado State has been involved in online and distance learning since 1967 and was one of the first schools to utilize technology in distance education.

Independent Study: Correspondence Study and Online Courses remove the traditional boundaries of time and location for the distance learner. Through the use of a study guide, textbooks, the Internet, and applicable reference materials, students have the opportunity to participate in an indi-

vidualized mode of instruction offering a high degree of flexibility. Students interested in correspondence courses may enroll at any time, set their own pace, and choose the most convenient time and place to study. Online courses are taught according to the regular University semester schedule.

Distance Degrees offer working professionals the opportunity to earn credit from Colorado State without coming to campus. These are semester-based courses that use DVD/VCD, online, and mixed-media formats. Whether students are working on their degree or taking courses to stay current in their field, distance degrees offer the flexibility to pursue educational objectives as work schedules permit.

Courses are available in several disciplines, including agriculture, business, communication/public affairs, computer science, engineering, fire and emergency services administration, human resource development, merchandising, and statistics.. Distance Degree students are located throughout the United States and Canada and at U.S. military APO and FPO addresses. At this time, only correspondence courses and online courses and degrees are available to overseas students. Thousands of motivated people have earned their degrees, and countless others have taken individual courses to enhance their skill base or keep current with the latest technology.

Special Programs

Colorado State also provides other distance education opportunities. These courses are open-entry/open-exit, meaning students may register at any time and take six months to complete the course. Many of the courses can be used for specific programs, such as Child Care Administration Certification or Seed Analyst Training.

The state of Colorado requires certification of all child-care center directors and substitute directors by the State Department of Human Services. Certification requires both experience working with young children and specific education. Colorado State University is proud to offer courses through distance education that may satisfy some of the educational requirements. Other states may have individual specific educational requirements. Students should contact the appropriate agency in their area for further information.

For instructors wanting to enhance their teaching, Colorado State offers a Postsecondary Teaching Certificate Program, consisting of three 3-credit courses: Models of Teaching, Communication and Classrooms, and Educators, Systems, and Change. In this program, new instructors acquire a practical overview of a range of effective teaching models, ideas for engaging students while addressing measurable learning objectives, and approaches to promote critical and creative thinking. Experienced instructors update and energize their teaching repertoires, connecting personal knowledge with established research on effective classroom practices. Students in the program can earn graduate credit for advanced course work in postsecondary education and apply the 9 credits toward a master's or doctoral degree.

An innovative Seed Analyst Training Program consisting of four distance learning (correspondence) courses has been developed by the National Seed Storage Laboratory and Colorado State University. The courses were prepared over a two-year period by University professors and other experts with the support of the Colorado seed industry. The four courses cover the basics of seed analyst training: Seed Anatomy and Identification, Seed Development and Metabolism, Seed Purity Analysis, and Seed Germination and Viability.

Counseling through the University Center for Advising and Student Achievement is offered to all those interested in continuing their education. There is no fee for academic advising services. Students may schedule an appointment with an academic adviser by calling 970-491-7095. The Extended University Programs librarian is available to assist students with identifying and accessing library materials. Students should call 970-491-6952 to speak with the librarian.

Credit Options

All credits earned through distance education are recorded on a Colorado State University transcript. Distance education courses are the same as on-campus courses and are accredited by the same organizations as the University. A student currently enrolled in a degree program elsewhere is responsible for checking with the appropriate official at the degree-granting institution to make certain the course applies.

Faculty

Distance education faculty members must meet the same high standards any Colorado State University faculty member must meet. Most of the distance faculty members are faculty members within the department granting the course credit. Faculty members are available to answer questions and give feedback via telephone, fax, e-mail, or regular mail.

Admission

Anyone who has the interest, desire, background, and ability may register for distance learning courses. However, if prerequisites are listed for a course, they must be met. Registration in distance learning courses does not constitute admission to Colorado State University.

Tuition and Fees

Tuition for distance degrees for the 2007–08 academic year was $584 per credit (business courses), $520 per credit (weekly videotaped courses), or $419 per credit (online courses). Tuition for other distance education courses for the 2007–08 academic year was $223 per credit for undergraduate courses and $280 per credit for graduate courses. For current tuition information, students should visit the Web site.

Financial Aid

Colorado State University courses are approved for the DANTES program. Eligible military personnel should process DANTES applications through their education office. For information regarding veterans' benefits, students should contact the VA office at Colorado State University. With the exception of distance degrees, distance learning is not a degree-granting program and is therefore not eligible for federal grants. Students are encouraged to seek scholarship aid from organizations and local civic groups that may sponsor such study.

Applying

To complete a distance degree, admittance to the University is required. There is no application for distance education. Students should simply register for the course(s) of interest by mail or fax or online and pay the tuition. For more information about these and other distance courses from Colorado State University, or for registration information, students should contact the University.

CONTACT

Phone: 970-491-5288
          877-491-4336 (toll-free)
Fax: 970-491-7885
E-mail: info@learn.colostate.edu
Web site: http://www.learn.colostate.edu

COLORADO TECHNICAL UNIVERSITY

Colorado Technical University Online
Accelerated Degrees

Colorado Springs, Colorado

Since 1965, Colorado Technical University has helped thousands of students achieve success in business, management, and technology careers. Academic programs are continually evaluated and updated for relevance and currency. Colorado Technical University is accredited by the Higher Learning Commission of the North Central Association of Colleges and Schools. For more information, students should visit the NCA Higher Learning Commission Web site at http://www.ncahigherlearningcommission.org.

Distance Learning Program

Colorado Technical University Online provides students with a high-quality education relevant to the needs and demands of the ever-evolving business and technical job markets. Colorado Tech Online offers innovative, career-relevant degree programs completely online, so students can learn anywhere, anytime, on any PC with Internet access. Each program's content is continually updated and instantly applicable.

Delivery Media

Colorado Tech Online offers one of the best online platforms available. All courses are taught in a multimedia format that provides a rich, dynamic, interactive classroom experience. The programs offer many opportunities for students to adapt their learning experiences to their own personal styles. Students who prefer to have a hard copy of notes can print the presentations. Students also control the pace of an instructor's presentation. Students participate in discussions with the instructors and other students. Since the participants are employed in a variety of interesting professions, students gain insightful knowledge and learn from each other's experiences.

Programs of Study

Colorado Tech Online offers associate, bachelor's, and master's degrees in a variety of career-relevant fields, including business, criminal justice, health-care management, information technology, and marketing. The bachelor's degrees and master's degrees can be completed in as little as fifteen months. (The fifteen-month bachelor's degree is a 2+2 program and assumes that all associate-level requirements have been met through an associate degree or the equivalent. Colorado Tech Online students with no previous college experience can complete this degree in about 2½ years.) All of Colorado Tech Online's degree programs incorporate Colorado Technical University (CTU) Academic Certificates that students earn as they progress through the programs, without additional courses or added costs.

Colorado Tech Online is a Registered Educational Provider (REP) of the Project Management Institute™ (PMI), the world's leading not-for-profit project management professional association. CTU has been reviewed and approved by PMI and has agreed to abide by PMI-established quality assurance criteria.

Business: Colorado Tech Online's School of Business can help prepare versatile managers with the business and management skills they need to provide creative leadership vision, while solving modern business problems effectively and efficiently.

The Associate of Science in Business Administration (A.A.B.A.) degree programs emphasize a strong base of business fundamentals, including critical thinking and decision-making skills.

The Bachelor of Science in Business Administration (B.S.B.A.) degree programs emphasize practical competencies, creative leadership approaches, and the development of critical-thinking skills. Students can select from several career-relevant concentrations, including finance, health-care management, human resource management, international business, management, marketing, and project management.

The Master of Science in Management (M.S.M.) degree programs are designed to help provide immediate management applications, along with the knowledge and understanding of the critical skills necessary to analyze and solve various business problems. Available concentrations include business management and project management.

The Master of Business Administration (M.B.A.) degree program features an array of career-relevant concentrations, including accounting, finance, health-care management, human resource management, insurance risk management, logistics/supply chain management, mediation and dispute resolution, operations management, and technology management.

Students can also select the Executive M.B.A. degree program, which delivers immediate management applications, along with the knowledge and understanding of the critical skills necessary to analyze and solve various business problems. The emphasis is on real-world skills and knowledge that managers need to succeed in today's business world. This Executive M.B.A. program also incorporates information technology management and project management competencies.

Criminal Justice: The Colorado Tech Online School of Criminal Justice helps prepare students for a wide variety of careers in law enforcement, corrections, the court systems, and security by providing in-depth criminal justice knowledge in addition to strong business and management skills appropriate to the industry.

The Associate of Science in Criminal Justice (A.S.C.J.) is designed to help prepare students to enter the criminal justice field in a variety of first-tier positions. Students are exposed to the foundational areas of the discipline: investigation and law enforcement, law and courts, and corrections and parole. The program also addresses juvenile delinquency and the juvenile justice system.

The Bachelor of Science in Criminal Justice (B.S.C.J.) offers students a component of forensic study not usually available at the undergraduate level. This degree program can help prepare students for positions such as police officer, deputy sheriff, fraud investigator, highway patrol officer, and more. Additional training and/or education may be required for certain positions.

The Master of Science in Management (M.S.M.) with a concentration in criminal justice is designed to help prepare students to pursue positions of leadership in the criminal justice systems. The degree program addresses such topics as homeland security, law enforcement management, and public administration.

Information Technology: Colorado Tech Online develops curricula to reflect current market conditions by incorporating relevant, industry-current material into course content.

The Associate of Science in Information Technology (A.S.I.T.) can help students develop the capabilities needed to assume in-demand positions throughout the growing IT industry.

The Bachelor of Science in Business Administration (B.S.B.A.), with a concentration in information technology, gives students the technical skills and strong management skills they need to help position themselves for career advancement in this growing industry.

With the Bachelor of Science in Information Technology (B.S.I.T.), students acquire a practical, real-world education from instructors who are also IT professionals. In addition to important undergraduate foundation studies, students learn computer programming languages, computer network systems operations, and software engineering skills. Available concentrations include network management, security, and software systems engineering.

The Master of Science in Management (M.S.M.) degree program includes two technology-related concentrations: information systems security and IT management. The M.S.M. in information systems security provides a strong foundation for students to help advance their technical skills to plan, manage, certify, and accredit an organization's security plan. The M.S.M. in IT management is designed as a broad-based IT management curriculum that provides an understanding of computer architecture, networking and telecommunication, database management, and business and financial management strategies.

Student Services

Colorado Tech Online provides technical support 24/7 via an online help desk as well as a toll-free telephone number.

For research and curriculum support, Colorado Tech Online students have access to a full academic library completely online. The texts, journals, articles, and thousands of other resources are accessible whenever a student needs them.

The Career Services Department is staffed by skilled professionals who assist students with their career planning process. The department's full range of services includes career development strategies, job search strategies, interviewing tips, and resume and cover letter assistance.

Credit Options

Students with college credit or military experience may be eligible for the Colorado Tech Online Baccalaureate Degree Completion Program. If eligible, this program may reduce the time required to complete a degree program.

Faculty

Colorado Tech Online's faculty members have advanced degrees and are established professionals in their fields, giving students valuable opportunities to derive insights and real-world perspectives from their experiences. They bring situation-specific relevance to every course, so students receive an education they can apply in the real world. Colorado Tech Online also limits the number of students enrolled in each class to encourage interaction with, and personal attention from, instructors.

Admission

To be considered for admission to Colorado Tech Online, applicants must submit an application and $50 application fee and fulfill all admission requirements for the program. Applicants are contacted to arrange for a personal telephone interview and for the necessary school transcripts to be submitted. TOEFL scores are required from nonnative speakers of English.

Tuition and Fees

Tuition amounts vary depending on the program. Students should call an Admissions Advisor for more information.

Financial Aid

Financial aid is available for those who qualify.

CONTACT

Colorado Technical University Online
4435 North Chestnut Street, Suite E
Colorado Springs, Colorado 80907
Phone: 800-416-8904 (toll-free)
Web site: http://www.ctuonline.edu

CORBAN COLLEGE
Adult Studies Online Programs
Salem, Oregon

Corban College is an independent, Christian liberal arts college and is accredited by the Northwest Commission on Colleges and Universities. Its core purpose is to educate Christians who will make a difference in the world for Jesus Christ.

The College offered its first distance learning program in 1994, which developed into a uniquely online format in 1997. It now offers two online degree-completion programs for Christian students in the areas of business and organizational leadership and family studies.

Distance Learning Program

Corban's online degree-completion programs are specifically and conveniently formatted for the Christian student who has two years of college credit and desires a Christian college education but is unable to attend on-campus classes. With only a three-day residency orientation, the entirety of the sixteen-month programs is completed from home via computer.

Delivery Media

Online course work requires an IBM-compatible computer system, Internet access, and completion of an initial orientation, which is held on campus. Complete precourse training is provided for all students via self-paced tutorials, hands-on workshops, and follow-up technical support.

Course instruction is accomplished by utilizing facilitated discussion forums, live chat conferences, and collaborative project reports, which are supported by Internet course-management software, audio-video and keyboard conferencing programs, e-mail, and telephone.

Programs of Study

Corban offers two degree-completion programs entirely online. Individual online courses are also offered to assist students in completing general education requirements.

The online degree-completion programs lead to a B.S. or B.A. degree.

Students enrolling in the degree-completion program must have completed 60 semester hours of transferable credit. A total of 128 semester hours is required for the bachelor's degree. The online degree-completion programs in both business and organizational leadership and family studies are excellent preparation for graduate study.

The business and organizational leadership online degree-completion program is 41 semester hours in length. The program develops leadership, analytical, and problem-solving skills with a Christian perspective. Course work provides expertise in values-driven decision making, organizational systems management, and strategic planning—three of the most important aspects of business and public administration.

The family studies online degree-completion program is 44 semester hours in length. It uses an applied interdisciplinary approach, focusing on the study of family dynamics and the relationships between families and the society at large. The curriculum is integrated with biblical principles and is taught by Christian professionals. Optional tracks for these programs include mental health and strategic management.

Special Programs

Students are given the opportunity to earn college credit for prior learning through the Prior Learning Assessment program. Students learn how to identify, document, and describe appropriate prior learning experiences. Weekend classes are offered both online and on campus and are designed to meet general education requirements. The course offerings vary in length. Internships and research projects are required in the online degree-completion programs. They are generally completed within the workplace or in a related local business or agency.

Student Services

Online students enjoy complete access to the same College services as campus students via Web-based communication, fax, or telephone. In addition to academic advising and project mentoring, financial aid, the registrar's office, technical support, the campus bookstore, and library services are available. Online library resources include EBSCOhost, ERIC, Academic Universe, ProQuest Direct, OPALL, OCLC, and other comprehensive databases.

Credit Options

Qualifying college credit may be transferred, subject to the approval of the College registrar. Students may earn a maximum of 32 semester hours of credit through college-level exams (CLEP, DANTES) and 30 semester hours of credit through the Prior Learning Assessment program.

Admission

Enrollment in the online degree-completion programs requires applicants to have a minimum of 60 semester hours of transferable college credit as well as profession of a personal faith in Jesus Christ.

Tuition and Fees

The 2008 tuition for the online degree-completion programs is $16,158. Tuition includes all textbooks and graduation fees.

Financial Aid

Financial aid is available through federal and state financial aid programs. For further information, students should contact the financial aid office at 800-845-3005 (toll-free) or via e-mail at aid@corban.edu.

Applying

Applicants for online degree-completion programs must complete an application and submit transcripts, two references, an acceptable writing sample, and a profession of faith in Jesus Christ.

CONTACT

Adult Degree Programs Online
Corban College
5000 Deer Park Drive, SE
Salem, Oregon 97301

Phone: 800-764-1383 (toll-free)
Fax: 503-375-7583
E-mail: adp@corban.edu
Web site: http://www.corban.edu

DARTON COLLEGE
Online Division
Albany, Georgia

> *Darton College, a two-year unit of the University System of Georgia, is located in Albany (population 100,000), the hub of southwest Georgia, surrounded by rural cotton, pecan, and peanut farms. Darton prides itself on student success, as measured by its two-year graduates' high pass rates on state licensing tests and their success after transferring to four-year institutions. Students can pursue more than seventy 2-year transfer and career associate degrees.*
>
> *As an accredited institution, Darton College takes online education to a higher level. The College believes that real life-changing learning happens in an environment of academic excellence, challenge, and personal connection. Darton College is a recognized leader in state distance learning initiatives.*

Distance Learning Program

Darton offers numerous online courses that are conveniently available through the Internet. Credit courses are offered through a course management system, GeorgiaVIEW (formerly WebCT), where students attend classes in an online environment. Students can access their Darton online course using any Internet connection—anytime, anywhere. Each week, students participate in class discussion, post their assignments, and review faculty and peer feedback. Much of the course work can be done offline.

Delivery Media

Distance learning courses are supported through Channel 19 telecasts, Web-based instruction, GSAMS videoconferencing, the Darton College Library, the Georgia Library Catalogs, the Darton College Bookstore, the Division of Online Learning, and the Instructional Technology and Distance Learning Department. Students choose a convenient time and place to access their courses through the Internet. Online courses use a broad spectrum of technology-based instructional methods, including online multimedia presentations, e-mail, discussion forums, chat rooms, faculty Web pages, and online assessment. All students enrolled at Darton College automatically receive a campus e-mail account to facilitate access to instructional technology.

Course schedules and requirements for online classes are determined by individual course instructors. Off-campus computer hardware and Internet access are the responsibility of the student.

Programs of Study

Several associate degrees and certificates are available.

The Associate of Arts (A.A.) is offered in English, history, Spanish, or speech communication.

The Associate of Applied Science (A.A.S.) is offered in management or office administration (administrative support).

The Associate of Science (A.S.) is offered completely online in allied health (health information technology, histologic technology, medical laboratory technology, or respiratory care), business administration, business education, computer information systems, criminal justice, economics, general studies, office administration (secretarial science), political science, prelaw, psychology, social work, sociology, and teacher education (early childhood, middle grade, secondary education, or special education).

The Associate of Science is offered partially online in biology, environmental science, forensic science, forestry, nuclear medicine technology, nursing, predentistry, premedicine, preoptometry, or pre–veterinary medicine. Students in these programs must come to the campus to complete their laboratory requirements.

Fully online certificates are available in accounting, addiction counseling, cancer registry management, criminal justice management, general management, homeland security, logistics and supply chain management, management and marketing, marketing, medical coding, teacher communications and crisis skills, or technology.

Student Services

Many services are available to both on-campus and distance learners through the Darton Library, via distance learning modules, and through cooperation between the library, the University System of Georgia, and regional and national InterLibrary Loan systems. Georgia Library Learning Online (GALILEO) is available without restriction at https://gil.darton.edu/. GALILEO provides access to multiple information resources, including secured access to licensed products. More than 100 research databases that index thousands of periodicals and scholarly journals are also available through GALILEO, with more than 2,000 journal titles provided in full text. Other resources include encyclopedias, business directories, and government publications. Streaming media are available through cooperation with the Offices of Instructional Technology and Distance Learning. The instructional technology help desk is open during regular campus hours and can troubleshoot student computer connections to the network during normal business hours.

Credit Options
Students can get credit for courses taken online from other institutions and sources of instruction. The maximum number of transfer hours is 42. The Cooperative Education Program provides academic credit for a student's work experience if the work is related to the student's major field of study.

Faculty
Darton College has 217 faculty members, 41 percent of whom are full-time. The student-faculty ratio is 20:1.

Admission
To apply to Darton College's online programs, students must have a high school diploma or the equivalent. In addition, applicants must be highly motivated and able to complete course work on time. Georgia colleges require a placement test to determine whether an applicant must take learning support classes. All applicants must take the placement test unless exempted by the admissions office.

Tuition and Fees
In 2007–08, tuition per credit was $99. With courses of 3 credits or more, a technology fee of $48 is charged in addition to the tuition of $99 per credit. A full-time student taking 12 credits paid a reduced rate of $1236.

Financial Aid
The Darton College Foundation, Inc., and other sources provide scholarship opportunities for students. Darton College Foundation scholarships can be used in addition to other state and federal financial aid. All students applying for scholarships must also complete the Free Application for Federal Student Aid, available online at http://www.fafsa.ed.gov. Scholarship applications are available from the Darton College Office of Financial Aid, and applicants are considered for all scholarships for which they are qualified. The priority deadline for scholarship applications is April 1.

Applying
Distance learning applicants follow the same procedures as those for traditional enrollment at Darton College. Students must complete an easy, step-by-step online application and pay the $20 admission fee. Applicants must also submit an official copy of their high school transcript and SAT or ACT scores; nontraditional students are not required to send in test scores. Transfer students must also submit official transcripts from all colleges and universities previously attended. To guarantee admission, all application materials should be sent to Darton College at least two weeks before the beginning of the semester.

CONTACT
Dr. Janice Hilyard, Dean
Division of Online Learning
Darton College
2400 Gillionville Road
Albany, Georgia 31707
Phone: 229-317-6732
Fax: 229-317-6682
E-mail: Janice.hilyard@darton.edu
Web site: http://online.darton.edu/degrees/

DEPAUL UNIVERSITY

School for New Learning
Center for Online Education
Chicago, Illinois

DePaul University is nationally recognized for its innovative academic programs that combine hands-on learning and personal attention to help students achieve their personal and career goals. With more than 23,000 students hailing from all fifty states in the U.S. and over 100 other countries, DePaul combines multiple perspectives, experience-based learning, and small class sizes to give them a practical education for a global marketplace.

Nowhere is the value of life experience more respected than in the School for New Learning (SNL), one of DePaul's nine colleges and schools. Established thirty-five years ago, SNL is a national leader in the design and delivery of competence-based learning for adults. At SNL, students are able to earn college credit for their past life and work experiences, reap the value of prior college courses, and tailor a personalized course of study to achieve their own goals. The program is designed for adults age 24 and older, to accommodate the complexities of their lives.

Because DePaul and SNL are fully accredited and nationally known for their high academic standards, the Bachelor of Arts degree students earn will be honored by employers and other universities worldwide. SNL's unique program is recognized as an NGO (Non-Governmental Organization) by the United Nations.

Distance Learning Program

SNL's online education program allows students to earn a Bachelor of Arts degree entirely online. Students work intensively with their faculty mentors and professional advisers, experts in their chosen focus area, to plan their degree programs. They can complete their courses fully online or, if they live in the Chicago area, they can choose to take a combination of on-campus and online courses to fulfill their degree requirements. SNL's online courses are interdisciplinary and aimed at developing competence that can be applied immediately in their lives. Students also may register for online courses through other DePaul colleges and schools, such as the School of Computer Science, Telecommunications, and Information Systems.

Flexible and rigorous, the School for New Learning provides students with excellent learning opportunities and individualized attention. Networking and real-world relevance are also built into the program through the professional adviser.

Delivery Media

Students complete the online education program using a range of electronic media, including course management systems such as Blackboard, e-mail, podcasts, Webconferencing, VoIP, WIKIs, and blogs. SNL's delivery media change with the development of new technology. The highly interactive system keeps students well-connected with faculty members, advisers, professional experts, and classmates.

Programs of Study

Graduates receive a Bachelor of Arts degree from DePaul University. The degree is competence-based, consisting of fifty requirements allocated across three areas: lifelong learning, liberal arts, and focus area. Students determine their focus areas based on their personal and career goals; about 60 percent of current SNL students graduate with a focus related to business.

There are various ways to earn credit toward a degree, including interdisciplinary, competence-based DePaul courses, transfer courses, proficiency examinations, demonstration of prior learning, and independent study. Students generally master two competencies per course; most part-time students complete the degree in just over three years.

In order to ensure both academic quality and focus-area expertise, students work with a personal academic committee consisting of a faculty mentor and a professional adviser throughout their time at SNL. As an adult learner, they chair their own committee, decide on their own externship and major project, and identify the skills they need to develop in order to further their personal goals through their focus area. Their faculty mentor helps them plan their degree programs. Their professional advisers are experts in the students' focus-area fields who help them determine the competencies needed to meet their career goals.

Student Services

Online learning students are able to access admission, registration, identification cards, extensive online and campus-based library resources, career counseling, writing and math assistance, financial aid, academic advising, the bookstore, and more—entirely online. Unlike many online programs, the admissions staff members at SNL are skilled and experienced student advisers. Advisers have no quotas to meet; their only goal is to help students achieve theirs. The DePaul Writing

Center provides writing support via e-mail and Web cams; services include tutoring and editing of papers.

Credit Options

Any course from an accredited institution, with a grade of C- or better, is eligible for transfer credit, regardless of how long ago the course was completed.

Faculty

SNL faculty members are dedicated to teaching adults in a student-centered, individualized, and collaborative environment. All are experienced in the fields in which they teach, and nearly all have terminal or graduate degrees.

Admission

To be considered for admission, applicants must be 24 years old or older, proficient in the use of the English language, and have completed a high school diploma or equivalent.

Students must have access to a computer with an Internet connection and an e-mail account. Hardware and software requirements are a Pentium 4 or newer computer with Windows 2000 Professional, XP Home, or Professional edition; at least 512 MB of RAM; a 40 gigabyte or larger hard drive; a 56K baud dial-up modem or high-speed connection (DSL or cable); a sound card; speakers; a CD-ROM drive; a monitor with 1024 x 728 pixel resolution or better; and a printer. Macintosh users must have OS 9.2.2 (or higher) with comparable features.

Tuition and Fees

Tuition and fees for the 2007–08 academic year were $422 per credit hour. Most SNL courses were four credit hours, or $1,688. The cost of textbooks varies from class to class.

Financial Aid

Students are eligible to apply for financial aid and scholarships. For more information, students should visit DePaul's financial aid Web site at http://www.depaul.edu/financial_aid.

Applying

Applications are accepted year-round. Interested students should visit SNL's Web site at http://www.snlonline.edpaul.edu to request additional information about the program as well as an application for admission.

CONTACT

Center for Distance Education
School for New Learning
DePaul University
25 East Jackson Boulevard
Chicago, Illinois 60604
Phone: 312-362-8001
        866-SNL-FORU (toll-free)
Fax: 312-362-8809
E-mail: snlonline@depaul.edu
Web site: http://www.snlonline.depaul.edu

DEVRY UNIVERSITY

Online Center

Oakbrook Terrace, Illinois

DeVry University provides high-quality, career-oriented associate, bachelor's, and master's degree programs in technology, health-care technology, business, and management. More than 48,000 students are enrolled across eighty-five locations in twenty-four states and Canada. DeVry University is accredited by the Higher Learning Commission and is a member of the North Central Association of Colleges and Schools (NCA). DeVry University, a division of DeVry Inc. (NYSE: DV), is based in Oakbrook Terrace, Illinois. For more information about DeVry University, students should visit http://www.devry.edu.

Distance Learning Program

Distance learning, delivered through DeVry University's Online Center, integrates today's high-tech, Internet-based capabilities with DeVry's proven educational methodologies. The innovative "anytime, anywhere" educational delivery system extends the offering of DeVry programs to students who reside beyond the geographic reach of DeVry locations or whose schedules preclude their attending on-site. The result is solid education enhanced by the latest in interactive information technology, which enables students to send messages and receive feedback from instructors as well as participate in various group and team activities with fellow online students. DeVry University Online has more than 8,800 enrolled undergraduate and graduate students.

Delivery Media

Typical distance learning technologies include the undergraduate site (http://www.devry.edu/online) and graduate site (http://online.keller.edu), which are accessible 24 hours a day, seven days a week. DeVry Online offers course syllabi and assignments; a virtual library and other Web-based resources; e-mail, threaded conversations, and chat rooms; text and course materials available through an online bookstore;

CD-ROM companion disks; and study notes or instructor lectures for student review.

Programs of Study

DeVry University Online currently offers associate degree programs in accounting technology, health-information technology, and network systems administration. Bachelor's degrees are available in business administration, computer information systems, game and simulation programming, information technology, network and communications management, and technical management. DeVry University's graduate-level programs include master's degrees in accounting and financial management, business administration, human resource management, information systems management, network and communications management, project management, and public administration. Graduate certificates are also available for students who wish to develop their expertise in these graduate-level programs without completing a degree or who wish to specialize in one of these areas within their degree program.

Undergraduate students must achieve a cumulative grade point average of at least 2.0 (on a 4.0 scale) and satisfactorily complete all curriculum require-

ments to graduate. Graduate students must achieve a cumulative grade point average of at least 3.0 as well as fulfill the graduation requirements for their specific programs.

Student Services

In addition to offering high-quality education online, DeVry is committed to providing online students with access to a full range of support services, including admission and registration information, academic advising, and financial aid information. DeVry University maintains an online library with full-text periodical databases and online short courses for self-instruction. DeVry Online staff members are available to assist students with administrative matters as well as with education-related issues. Students can complete all administrative details online, including purchasing books.

Faculty

Instructors for online courses are drawn from DeVry's faculty throughout North America as well as from leading organizations in business and technology, creating a systemwide student-faculty community. To ensure their effective delivery of course material as well as their ability to facilitate relevant and meaningful participation from all class members, faculty members teaching online courses complete specialized instruction to prepare them to teach via this medium. As a result, online students are provided with a comprehensive learning experience that enables them to master course content.

Admission

DeVry University's admission process is streamlined, so students learn quickly whether they have been accepted. Applicants must complete a personal interview with an admissions representative and complete a written application. Applicants should visit DeVry University's Web site for further details (http://www.devry.edu).

For admission to undergraduate programs, specific requirements must be met regarding age, prior education, demonstrated proficiency in the basic and prerequisite skills needed for college-level work in the chosen field of study, and computer literacy. Each undergraduate applicant pays a $50 application fee.

For regular graduate admission, applicants must hold a baccalaureate degree from a regionally accredited U.S. institution (international applicants must hold a degree equivalent to a U.S.

baccalaureate degree). Applicants who meet baccalaureate degree requirements and whose undergraduate cumulative grade point average is 2.7 or higher are eligible for admission. Applicants with a cumulative GPA below 2.7 must demonstrate quantitative and verbal skills proficiency in one of several possible standardized tests.

Tuition and Fees

Tuition charges are calculated each semester per credit hour enrolled. Within each semester, hours 1–11 are charged at one credit-hour rate; hours 12 and above are charged at a lower rate. Hourly rates are available at the University's Web site and vary by program and location. Online students attending more than 19 credit hours are charged the standard tuition rate plus

the per-credit-hour rate for each additional credit hour. All new students pay a $50 deposit, which is credited toward the first semester's tuition.

For graduate online students, tuition is $2050 per course. After acceptance into the graduate school, new students pay a $100 deposit, which is credited toward the first term's tuition.

Financial Aid

Federal Stafford Student Loan money is available to graduate students through the Federal Family Education Loan Program (FFELP). Undergraduate students who qualify can take advantage of the five major federal financial aid programs in which DeVry is eligible to participate. Undergraduate students may also qualify for state-funded programs and DeVry scholarships.

CONTACT

DeVry University
One Tower Lane
Oakbrook Terrace, Illinois 60181
Phone: 800-839-9009 (toll-free)
Web site: http://www.devry.edu/online
       http://online.keller.edu

DREXEL UNIVERSITY
Drexel University Online
Philadelphia, Pennsylvania

Founded in 1891, Drexel University is a leader in the integration of technology into academics. Drexel University is committed to providing high-quality education online by offering a convenient way to earn a reputable, accredited degree with no career interruption, commuting, or fixed class hours. Drexel University has more than 90,000 alumni and 1,000 full-time faculty members. Known as Philadelphia's technological university, Drexel is among the top 50 private, nonprofit, national doctoral/research universities in the United States and is ranked by U.S. News & World Report *as one of "America's Best Colleges for 2008."*

Distance Learning Program

Drexel University Online specializes in innovative, Internet-based distance education programs for working professionals in the United States and abroad. A pioneer in online education, Drexel has offered programs online since 1996. Using the same rigorous academic standards (admission criteria, curricula, accreditation, and exams), Drexel's online programs are taught by the same distinguished faculty members and lead to the same high-quality degree as those received on the campus.

Delivery Media

Drexel University's online courses require a student to have a personal computer with an Internet connection and use a Web browser to access the e-learning environment. Course instruction is delivered primarily asynchronously (i.e., where the teacher and learner are not physically at the same place at the same time). Instructional materials come in text, graphics, audio, and video formats and are available online 24/7. Students interact directly with each other and faculty members through e-mail, threaded discussions (online discussion boards), chat, and Web-based whiteboard facilities. All readings, assignments, quizzes, and exams are prespecified, monitored on a continuous basis, and submitted online.

Programs of Study

Drexel has more than sixty bachelor's, master's, and certificate programs online. Drexel's online Bachelor of Science degree programs offered through the College of Nursing include RN-B.S.N. and RN-B.S.N.-M.S.N. programs, which focus on industry-current issues in nursing. In these programs, which are accredited by the National League for Nursing Accrediting Commission (NLNAC) and Commission on Collegiate Nursing Education (CCNE), students arrange to complete clinicals in their area. An RN license is required for admission to the programs. A B.S. in health services administration program is also available.

Bachelor of Science programs are also offered in communication, communications and applied technology, computing technology and security, education, general studies–individualized studies, general studies with a minor in business, professional studies, and psychology. The programs are designed for adult learners, who can transfer up to 135 out of 180 quarter credits.

Drexel's master's degree online programs offered through the College of Nursing include M.S.N. in nursing education and faculty role, nursing leadership in health systems management, clinical trials research, acute-care nurse practitioner (NP)*, adult psychi-

atric–mental health (NP)*, completion program for NPs, and innovation and intra/entrepreneurship in advanced nursing practice. Programs are accredited by the National League for Nursing Accrediting Commission (NLNAC) and the CCNE and prepare nurses to move into managerial or leadership roles in their desired fields. Post-master's certificates are also available.

MBA Anywhere™ program provides a broadly based management curriculum with available concentrations in marketing, finance, information systems strategy, engineering management, and entrepreneurship. This program optimizes the students' leadership potential in a twenty-four-month, part-time cohort format and is accredited by AACSB International, the highest accreditation for U.S. business schools.

Online master's degrees through Drexel's College of Engineering are available in engineering management, electrical engineering, software engineering, and computer science. Drexel University's College of Engineering is the third-largest private engineering college in the United States, with numerous faculty recognitions, highly ranked programs, and research accomplishments. Its curricula are accredited by the Accreditation Board for Engineering and Technology, Inc. (ABET), the leading authority on educational standards for the engineering and science professions.

Drexel, an internationally recognized center for education and research in all facets of information science and systems, also offers online M.S. degree programs in library and information science and in information systems. The M.S. program in library and information science is a top-ranked, ALA-accredited program that allows students to specialize in management of digital information or information/

library services. The M.S. program in information systems features a wide range of courses that cover all stages of systems engineering as a life-cycle process.

Ranked as one of America's Best Graduate Schools for 2008 by *U.S. News & World Report,* Drexel's College of Education offers M.S. degrees in educational administration: collaborative leadership, global and international education, higher education, the science of instruction, learning technologies, math learning and teaching, and teaching, learning, and curriculum.

The teacher certification program certifies students in elementary education or secondary education in the areas of biology, chemistry, physics, earth and space science, general science, environmental education, and/or mathematics. The certification program can be incorporated into the master's program or can be completed as a stand-alone program.

Add-on certificates available include instructional technology specialist, principal's certification, and teaching English as a second language. These programs incorporate current research on teaching and expose teachers to the latest developments in instructional technology.

Drexel's online M.S. in clinical research organization and management program allows students to earn the experience and knowledge necessary to conduct investigations in the increasingly complex and highly regulated clinical field. A five-course certificate of study is also available.

Programs accompanied by an * require on-campus attendance.

Special Programs

Drexel offers an undergraduate certificate program in retail leadership and medical billing and coding. Graduate nursing certificates are available in clinical trials research, complementary and integrative therapies, innovation and intra/entrepreneurship in advanced nursing practice, nursing education and faculty role, and nursing leadership in health systems management. Additional graduate certificates are available in education, engineering management, epidemiology and biostatistics, health-care informatics, and toxicology and industrial hygiene.

Student Services

Online students have access to library facilities, career services, individual tutoring, learning resources, the writing center, and 24/7 technical support.

Credit Options

Students pursuing bachelor's degree programs may receive transfer credit for previous studies at an accredited college, CLEP exams, military training, Skillsoft, and more. The maximum number of transfer credits varies according to the student's program.

Faculty

Drexel has more than 1,000 full-time faculty members, 90 percent of whom hold Ph.D.'s. Many of them are distinguished authorities in their fields, including several members of the National Academies of Science and Engineering. Drexel's online programs are taught by the same distinguished faculty members who teach on campus.

Admission

All Drexel online programs run on ten-week quarters beginning in January, March, June, and September, with the exception of the M.S. and certificate in clinical research, which begin three times a year, in January, May, and August. Admissions requirements vary across programs. Students should visit the Web site for specific program information.

Tuition and Fees

Tuition rates vary across programs. Interested students should visit the Web site listed in the Contact section (http://www.drexel.com/petersons) for specific program rates. Students are required to purchase textbooks. There are no application fees when applying online.

Financial Aid

Students may apply for scholarships, loans, grants, federal and state aid, and more. Drexel is part of the Servicemembers Opportunity Colleges (SOC) Consortium, welcoming adult students from the military who are using military aid or the Montgomery G.I. Bill benefits to cover their education costs. Deferred tuition payment plans are also available for students receiving reimbursement.

Applying

Application deadlines are typically six weeks before the start of classes. There is not an application fee, and applications are accepted on a rolling basis. Students should visit the Web site for more information.

CONTACT

Drexel University Online
Drexel University
3001 Market Street
One Drexel Plaza, Suite 300
Philadelphia, Pennsylvania 19104

Phone: 866-440-1949 (toll-free)
Fax: 215-895-0525
E-mail: info@drexel.com
Web site: http://www.drexel.com/petersons

DUKE UNIVERSITY

Nicholas School of the Environment and Earth Sciences
Duke Environmental Leadership Program

Durham, North Carolina

Located in Durham, North Carolina, Duke University is at the heart of a world-renowned center of excellence in medicine, research, high technology, and education, incorporating a sophisticated and unique blend of history, culture, and ethnic diversity. Noted for its magnificent Gothic architecture and its academic excellence, Duke is among the smallest of the nation's leading universities, having a total enrollment of about 12,000. Its spacious campus is bounded on the east by residential sections of Durham and on the west by the Duke Forest.

The Nicholas School of the Environment and Earth Sciences is one of the world's premier graduate and professional schools for the interdisciplinary study of the environment, combining resources from the biological, physical, and social sciences. Located in the heart of the Duke campus, the School functions as an environmental forum, an intellectual hub drawing input from all disciplines at Duke—law, business, medicine, science, and engineering. The goal is to develop critical and creative leaders who will shape tomorrow's Earth. No other university—and no other environmental school—takes such a broad approach to environmental science and policy.

Distance Learning Program

Through the Duke Environmental Leadership (DEL) Program, the Nicholas School of the Environment and Earth Sciences offers a rigorous online and on-campus Master of Environmental Management (M.E.M.) degree program designed specifically for midcareer environmental professionals and business executives. The DEL M.E.M. is an innovative, two-year program composed of courses taught through a combination of written and electronic formats, case studies, and weeklong, intensive on-campus sessions. Driven by a broad perspective of interdisciplinary and global themes, strategic approaches to environmental management, communication, and effective leadership, the DEL M.E.M. offers an alternative to traditional full-semester courses, allowing students to update their education while maintaining a commitment to their jobs and families.

Delivery Media

The DEL M.E.M. uses advanced interactive technologies to complement the face-to-face sessions on campus. Students use the Blackboard platform as their learning portal to complete individual and group course work and to participate in chat sessions and online meetings. In addition, DEL-sponsored bulletin boards, videoconferences, and conference calls reinforce the curriculum, and Duke e-mail accounts are available through Duke's Office of Information Technology.

Students must arrange network access with a local Internet service provider (ISP) and are strongly encouraged to have broadband access to the Internet via a cable modem, DSL, or satellite connection.

Program of Study

The DEL M.E.M. is a two-year, 30-credit program. Requirements include the orientation course at the Duke campus (1 credit); core modules, including ecosystems science and management, economics of environmental management, environmental law and policy, and program management for environmental professionals (12 credits); focused modules developed around more specialized themes (12 credits); an environmental leadership module, which involves prominent leaders from the private, public, and not-for-profit sectors in Washington, D.C. (1 credit); and a master's project directly related to the student's current employment (4 credits).

Through the DEL Program, students can also enroll in 1-credit intensive short courses and independent studies. More information on the short-course program and a list of upcoming courses can be found online.

Student Services

DEL M.E.M. students receive complete student services, including registration, academic advising, library resources, and access to the bookstore, at a distance and during on-campus sessions. Technical support is available online or, for personal support, via e-mail and telephone during business hours, with limited hours during weekends and evenings. The IT orientation during the first on-campus session introduces students to the programs and packages preinstalled on the DEL laptop computers. Matriculating students each receive a laptop computer that remains the property of Duke until graduation, at which time ownership is transferred to the student. Much of the curriculum during the first session aims to help students gain familiarity with online education and master new learning techniques.

Credit Options

Credit from other institutions may be considered on a case-by-case basis; however, due to the nature of the DEL M.E.M. program, acceptance of transfer credits is unlikely.

Faculty

The Nicholas School is known for the strength of its faculty members, as measured by their scholarly achievement, commitment to high-quality education, and impact on the most important environmental and natural resource challenges. More than 50 faculty members hold primary or joint appointments in the School, and a large number have secondary or adjunct status with other units or institutions.

Admission

The admissions committee seeks the following in the selection process: five years of relevant work experience (required to apply), evidence of leadership potential and an established background in fields directly related to the environment, self-motivation and commitment to learn at a distance, a working knowledge of personal computers for word processing and data analysis, an undergraduate degree from an accredited four-year college or university, written sponsorship from the applicant's employer, and proficiency in English.

Tuition and Fees

In summer 2007, tuition was $53,200 for four semesters. Students are billed on a semester basis in four equal payments. Tuition includes books, other class materials, and various Duke student fees, including a required technology fee that provides a laptop computer and technology support. Tuition does not cover travel to and from the campus, lodging, or meals during the on-campus sessions.

Financial Aid

At this time, the DEL Program does not award scholarships or grants to students. However, financial aid is available to U.S. citizens and permanent residents through various student loan programs.

Applying

Candidates are requested to apply online by March 1, but applications may be accepted after the final deadline on a space-available basis and with prior approval. A complete application includes an application form; three letters of recommendation; a sponsor letter written on company letterhead stating that the employer endorses the applicant's participation in the program and grants the necessary time off to attend classes; resume; completed essay questions; and official, confidential transcripts from all colleges and universities previously attended, including official English translations if the original is not in English.

A 90-minute online diagnostic test is also part of the application process. The test includes one timed essay question and two multipart data interpretation questions. Information about the test is forwarded to applicants upon submission of a complete application.

Official TOEFL scores are required for applicants whose first language is not English.

There is a nonrefundable application fee of $65 if the application is submitted prior to March 1 or $75 after March 1.

CONTACT

Duke Environmental Leadership Program Office
Nicholas School of the Environment and Earth Sciences
Levine Science Research Center, Room A106
Box 90328
Duke University
Durham, North Carolina 27708-0328

Phone: 919-613-8082
Fax: 919-613-9002
E-mail: del@nicholas.duke.edu
Web site: http://www.nicholas.duke.edu/del

EAST CAROLINA UNIVERSITY
Division of Continuing Studies
Greenville, North Carolina

Founded in 1907, East Carolina University (ECU) is the third-largest of the sixteen institutions in the University of North Carolina system and offers baccalaureate, master's, specialist, and doctoral degrees in the liberal arts and sciences and professional fields, including medicine. Fully accredited by the Southern Association of Colleges and Schools, the University's goal is to provide students with a rich and distinctive educational experience. ECU's commitment to providing outstanding off-campus educational opportunities is long-standing; the University offered its first distance education course in 1947. The Division of Continuing Studies provides a portal at http://www.options.ecu.edu to the resources of the University as well as assistance that allows adult learners to choose programs that fit their schedules and academic goals. East Carolina University is constantly evaluating and updating its distance learning programs to take advantage of the latest technology and is committed to meeting the evolving needs of the lifelong learner.

Distance Learning Program

East Carolina University's academic community has developed a diverse offering of distance learning programs in direct response to the needs of students. A number of fully online programs are currently available, with additional programs under development. ECU is committed to providing programs designed to meet the professional needs and demanding schedules of busy, working adults. For more information on the latest offerings, students should visit the Web site for the Division of Continuing Studies, which is listed in the Contact section of this description.

Delivery Media

East Carolina University's Web-based courses are faculty-member created Web sites that contain course materials and interactive tools. Most utilize the Blackboard Course Management System. Faculty members may employ a variety of communication tools within their courses, including threaded discussion groups, small-group work, asynchronous Web-based chats, and instant messaging. In addition, faculty members may elect to deliver essential components of their courses via audio and video streaming, by distribution of CDs, or by using desktop videoconferencing technologies.

Programs of Study

Graduate programs are offered in art education (M.A.Ed.); business administration/finance (M.B.A.); business administration/health-care management (M.B.A.); business administration/hospitality management (M.B.A.); business administration/management information systems (M.B.A.); business administration/security studies (M.B.A.); business education (M.A.Ed.); construction management (M.C.M.); criminal justice (M.S.); educational specialist/administration and supervision (Ed.S.); English/technical and professional communications (M.A.); health education (M.A. or M.A.Ed.); instructional technology (M.A.Ed. or M.S.); library science (M.L.S.); music education* (M.M.); nursing/adult nurse practitioner studies (M.S.N.); nursing/clinical nurse specialist studies (M.S.N.); nursing/family nurse practitioner studies* (M.S.N.); nursing/nursing leadership* (M.S.N.); nursing/neonatal nurse practitioner studies* (M.S.N.); nursing/nurse midwifery* (M.S.N.); nursing/nursing education (M.S.N.); nutrition (M.S.); occupational

safety (M.S.); psychology* (M.A.); science education (M.A.Ed.); software engineering (M.S.); special education (M.A.Ed.); speech, language, and auditory pathology* (M.S.); technology systems/computer networking management (M.S.); technology systems/digital communications (M.S.); technology systems/industrial distribution and logistics (M.S.); technology systems/information security (M.S.); technology systems/manufacturing systems (M.S.); technology systems/performance improvement (M.S.); and vocational education/information technologies (M.S.).

Undergraduate degree completion programs are available in birth–kindergarten education (B.S.), business administration (B.S.B.A.), communication/media studies (B.S.), health information management (B.S.), health services management (B.S.), hospitality management (B.S.), industrial technology/bioprocess manufacturing (B.S.), industrial technology/industrial distribution and logistics (B.S.), industrial technology/industrial supervision (B.S.), industrial technology/information and computer technology (B.S.), industrial technology/manufacturing systems (B.S.), information technologies (B.S.B.E.), and registered nurse/Bachelor of Science in Nursing (RN to B.S.N.).

Graduate certificates are offered in assistive technology, community college instruction, computer network professional studies, distance instruction, health-care management, information assurance, multicultural literature, performance improvement, professional communication, security studies, virtual reality in education and training, and Web site developer studies.

Post-master's nursing certificates can be earned in clinical nurse specialist studies, family nurse practitioner studies*, neonatal nurse practitioner studies*, nurse midwifery*, and nursing education.

Add-on teacher licensure programs are offered in driver's education and instructional technology specialist studies.

For the programs listed above, the * denotes programs for which some on-campus attendance is required.

Student Services

Distance learners at East Carolina University have access to library services, the campus network, e-mail accounts, the bookstore, registration, and academic advising at a distance. Academic advisers are available by phone, e-mail, fax, and in person to assist students with course selection.

Credit Options

Transfer credit is granted on academic course work within degree-specific limits, and no credit is granted on the basis of professional experience. CLEP course credit may also be available.

Faculty

ECU's approximately 1,300 full-time faculty members, the majority of whom hold terminal degrees, teach both the on-campus and distance-learning courses.

Admission

Before registering for a course, students must first apply and be admitted to ECU. Students may be admitted as degree-seeking or as nondegree/visiting students. Admission for students seeking a degree is based on their previous academic record and standardized test scores. In addition, graduate students are required to submit letters of recommendation.

Tuition and Fees

Undergraduate tuition and technology fees are $98 per semester hour for in-state residents and $453 per semester hour for out-of-state students. Graduate tuition and technology fees are $158 per semester hour for in-state residents and $664 per semester hour for out-of-state students. Graduate busi-

ness-student tuition and technology fees are $218 per semester hour for in-state residents and $724 per semester hour for out-of-state students. Graduate students taking undergraduate courses are charged graduate tuition. Rates are projected and subject to change without prior written notice.

Financial Aid

Distance learning students are eligible to apply for financial aid and are encouraged to contact the Office of Financial Aid at 252-328-6610, faques@ecu.edu, or via the Web at http://www.ecu.edu/financial/ for more information.

Applying

Prospective students must submit an application, accompanied by a fee of $60, for admission. Applications can also be obtained online from the Division of Continuing Studies at the Web site listed in the Contact section. While most programs accept students year-round, students are urged to apply early.

CONTACT

Carolyn Dunn
Division of Continuing Studies
404-E Self-Help Center
East Carolina University
Greenville, North Carolina 27858-4353
Phone: 252-328-9218
          800-398-9275 (toll-free)
E-mail: options@ecu.edu
Web site: http://www.options.ecu.edu

EASTERN MICHIGAN UNIVERSITY

EMU-Online and Independent Learning

Ypsilanti, Michigan

Eastern Michigan University (EMU) is a public, comprehensive, metropolitan university that offers programs in the arts, sciences, and professions. Founded in 1849, the University comprises more than 22,000 students, who are served by 660 full-time faculty members as well as more than 1,500 staff members—on campus, off campus, and online. EMU offers undergraduate, graduate, specialist, doctoral, and certificate programs in its Colleges of Arts and Sciences, Business, Education, Health and Human Services, and Technology.

EMU continues to be the largest producer of educational personnel in the United States, including the largest producer of special education personnel and mathematics and science teachers, and is among the top ten producers of educational administrators. The University is fully accredited by the North Central Association of Colleges and Schools.

EMU's Continuing Education Office offers programs and courses online, at off-campus locations throughout the state, on weekends, in the evening, and in accelerated formats.

Distance Learning Program

EMU's Distance Education program offers students two options. EMU-Online courses allow students to attend classes when it's convenient—early in the morning, during the weekend, or even at 2 a.m. Whether students live 5 or 500 miles from EMU's campus, they can learn conveniently, using a computer from their home, office, hotel room, military base, or "virtually" any other location in the world. Independent learning courses have flexible enrollment periods that allow students to learn at their own pace. They can avoid commuting and parking while satisfying general education requirements. Course work can be submitted via Internet, fax, or U.S. mail.

Delivery Media

EMU-Online courses are delivered online. Some Independent learning courses are delivered online and may be accompanied by DVDs and printed course materials. Students

may interact online and via e-mail, mail, telephone, or fax.

Programs of Study

EMU-Online offers the Master of Arts in educational media and technology; Master of Science in earth science education; Master of Science in engineering management; Master of Science in human nutrition; Master of Science in human nutrition through the Coordinated Program in Dietetics (CPD); Master of Science in integrated marketing communications; Master of Science in quality management; Bachelor of Science in applied technology (degree-completion program); Bachelor of Science in dietetics (CPD); Bachelor of Science in technology management (degree-completion program); graduate certificate in educational media and technology; graduate certificate in geographic information systems (GIS) for educators; and graduate certificate in human resource management.

Special Programs

Prior learning assessment is offered if students are seeking credit for prior learning through portfolio assessment. A free workshop helps students identify competencies and document experience to create a portfolio to present for assessment by faculty members in appropriate departments.

Student Services

Distance learners can complete their education entirely online. Registration, book purchases, discussions, homework assignments, library services, and exams are all available at the click of a mouse.

Credit Options

Students may transfer credits from another institution or earn credits through examinations, portfolio assessment, military training, or business training.

Faculty

More than 200 faculty members from EMU's academic departments currently teach online and independent learning courses at EMU.

Admission

Students may register for courses via the Internet, mail, fax and in person.

Tuition and Fees

Out-of-state students can take EMU-Online courses at in-state tuition rates. In 2007–08, per-credit-hour rates for Michigan and Ohio residents were $213.50 for all levels (100–400) of undergraduate courses, $373.50 for lower-level (500–600) graduate courses, and $429.75 for upper-level (700–999) graduate courses.

Fees include $40 per semester for registration, the $21 per credit hour general fee, $110 for late registration, $10 per credit hour for technology, $27 for payment plan (for fall/winter only), $33 per month for late payments, and $20 for returned checks and declined charge cards. Program support fees also apply and vary by program. In addition to tuition and other applicable fees,

online students are assessed an additional $40-per-credit-hour program fee. For specific continuing education program fees, candidates should visit http://www.emich.edu/controller/sbs/tuitionfeesoutline.html.

All tuition and fees are subject to change by action of the EMU Board of Regents without prior notice and at any time.

Financial Aid

For financial aid information, students should visit http://www.emich.edu/finaid/ or call 734-487-0455.

Applying

For information on undergraduate admissions, prospective students should visit http://www.emich.edu/admissions or call 800-GO-TO-EMU (toll-free).

Each graduate program has its own requirements for admissions. Students should contact the graduate coordinator in their department of interest to determine which of these are required. For more information, students should call 800-GO-TO-EMU (toll-free).

CONTACT

EMU-Online and Independent Learning
Continuing Education
Eastern Michigan University
101 Boone Hall
Ypsilanti, Michigan 48197

Phone: 800-777-3521 (toll-free)
E-mail: distance.education@emich.edu
Web site: http://www.emuonline.edu
http://www.ce.emich.edu

EXCELSIOR COLLEGE

Learning Services

Albany, New York

As a private institution with no residency requirement, Excelsior College—an accredited leader in distance education—has devoted itself to making college degrees more accessible to busy, working adults. Ranked number one by U.S. News & World Report for transfer students, the College accepts credits from a broad array of sources, including Excelsior College® Examinations and courses. As a result, many students find that most or all of their prior college-level credits transfer into their Excelsior College degree program.

Excelsior College offers associate, bachelor's, master's, and certificate programs in liberal arts (including criminal justice), business, health science and technology, and nursing. The College's self-paced degree programs are accessible worldwide, allowing students to complete their degrees from any location.

Excelsior College is accredited by the Commission on Higher Education of the Middle States Association of Colleges and Schools, 3624 Market Street, Philadelphia, Pennsylvania 19104; telephone: 215-662-5606. All of the College's academic programs are registered (i.e., approved) by the New York State Education Department, and its examinations are recognized by the American Council on Education, Center for Adult Learning and Educational Credentials, for the award of college-level credit.

The associate, baccalaureate, and master's degree programs in nursing are accredited by the National League for Nursing Accrediting Commission (NLNAC), 61 Broadway, New York, New York 10006; telephone 800-669-1656 (toll-free). The NLNAC is a specialized accrediting agency recognized by the U.S. Secretary of Education. The baccalaureate degree programs in electronics engineering technology and nuclear engineering technology are accredited by the Technology Accreditation Commission (TAC) of the Accreditation Board for Engineering and Technology (ABET) 111 Market Place, Baltimore, Maryland 21202; telephone: 410-347-7700. The TAC of ABET is a specialized accrediting agency recognized by the U.S. Secretary of Education.

Distance Learning Program

Excelsior College programs are designed to help busy adults pursue their degree at a distance through whatever combination of courses, exams, and training that fits their situation. The College accepts credits from Excelsior College courses and exams; classroom and online courses from other accredited colleges and universities; other college-level proficiency examinations, such as CLEP and DANTES; and military, academy, and corporate training recognized for college credit by the American Council on Education (ACE), Center for Adult Learning and Educational Credentials, National Program on Noncollegiate Sponsored Instruction (PONSI), or training evaluated for college credit by Excelsior College.

Currently, the College has more than 30,000 students enrolled in its associate, baccalaureate, and master's degree programs and has more than 120,000 graduates worldwide.

Programs of Study

Excelsior College offers over forty degree and certificate programs through distinct schools in four major areas.

In the School of Business and Technology, thirteen undergraduate business programs lead to degrees in such fields as accounting, finance, global business, management information systems, management of human resources, marketing, operations management, and risk management and insurance. The College

also offers both a Master of Business Administration (M.B.A.) program and a certificate in entrepreneurship that can be completed entirely at a distance. The GMAT is not required for the M.B.A., and students may transfer up to 24 previously earned graduate credits into the program. A dozen undergraduate technology degree programs educate students in fields such as computer technology, electronics engineering technology, electronics technology, information technology, and nuclear technology. The College awards college credit for approved industry training in several fields, including fossil fuel plant technology, information technology, and nuclear utility power plant training.

Students in the School of Liberal Arts can earn associate or baccalaureate degrees in majors that include biology, chemistry, communication, criminal justice, economics, geography, geology, history, literature, mathematics, music, philosophy, physics, political science, psychology, sociology, or world language and literature. In addition, a liberal studies option provides flexibility for students to pursue a range of interests while focusing on a particular discipline. The School offers two associate and two baccalaureate degrees, a certificate in homeland security, and a Master of Arts in liberal studies that can be earned entirely online. Master's students can now focus studies to match their interests and career goals by choosing one of five tracks: Issues in Today's Society, Global Strategies, Educational Leadership, Natural Science and Society, and Self-Design. The Graduate Record Examinations (GRE) are not required.

The Excelsior College School of Nursing is an NLN Center of Excellence and one of the largest distance education nursing programs in the world. All programs are NLNAC accredited. The school has been selected to receive the Best School Award from the American Assembly for Men in Nursing for two years in a row. The nursing components of the associate degree programs are made up of guided independent study and nationally recognized Excelsior College Examinations. The nursing components of the bachelor's degree comprise 30 transfer credits (validated by successful completion of the NCLEX-RN), Excelsior College Examinations, and courses. Students can earn credit for General Education requirements through of wide variety of sources.

Excelsior College offers an online Master of Science degree in nursing, with specializations in clinical systems management and nursing education, plus an RN-M.S. in nursing program.

The School of Health Sciences expands the College's offerings in health care with online certificate programs in end-of-life care, health-care informatics, and health-care management. The Bachelor of Science in health sciences, available to students with at least 20 undergraduate credits in the health sciences, offers concentrations in end-of-life care, gerontology, health education, and management.

Special Programs

Through its Office of Military Education, Excelsior College has addressed educational needs of the members of the U.S. armed forces. The College awards credit for military training recognized for college credit by the American Council on Education. Ten programs, including associate degrees in aviation, technical studies, and administrative/management studies, and bachelor's degrees in liberal arts and health sciences, are specially designed to meet the needs of military personnel. DANTES-funded Excelsior College Examinations are free to all active duty military, National Guard, and Reserve Component personnel. Special discounted fees and tuition are available to military personnel, military family members, veterans, and DoD civilians. Special partnerships allow active duty personnel to take Excelsior College distance courses that may be 100 percent covered by military tuition assistance. A college military deployment policy holds the status of deployed students without extension or penalty fees until their return.

Student Services

Excelsior College students draw on a team of experienced academic advisers who assist in the development of individualized degree completion plans.

Enrolled students can use Excelsior College Course Search, a searchable database of courses (in online, CD-ROM, or MP3 format) and examinations, to find credit sources to meet their degree requirements. It is the most comprehensive database of such offerings available today.

Students take advantage of a variety of online services through a customized Web user account, including paying bills online and viewing billing transactions, viewing transcript and graduation status, viewing course and exam registration status, and utilizing resources for career development, job hunting, resume writing, and other opportunities.

The Excelsior College Virtual Library gives students online access to millions of the world's most current and authoritative resources. The Electronic Peer Network (EPN) provides a Web-based community where students can join online study groups and buy and sell textbooks, among other things. For those who seek help as they study for Excelsior College Exams, the Online Writing and Online Tutoring Services connect students to experienced tutors and to select online practice exams.

Tuition and Fees

Undergraduate tuition for Excelsior College distance courses is $290 per credit hour. There is a $75 application fee. Excelsior College charges an $895 undergraduate fee at enrollment, which covers a student's initial evaluation, academic advisement, and program planning services for one year; a $440 undergraduate annual fee for each year after, which covers the ongoing evaluation of academic records submitted by a student; and a $245 (AAS/AOS) or $495 (associate and baccalaureate) fee for a final evaluation and verification of all academic records prior to program completion and graduation. A $15 discount is applied to the graduation fee for every credit earned through Excelsior College courses up to the full amount of the graduation fee. Different fees and fee structures apply to

military students and graduate programs. Students can choose to pay their Excelsior College enrollment and annual service expenses, tuition, and exams fees through special payment plans. Complete details can be found on the Excelsior College Web site.

Graduate tuition is $390 per credit hour. There is a $100 application fee. Excelsior College changes an annual $215 graduate student fee and $130 for a final evaluation and verification of all academic records prior to completion and graduation.

Financial Aid

Excelsior College offers more than fifteen options for financing a degree, including scholarships and private loan programs. Veterans Affairs educational benefits and New York State financial aid programs are also available. Excelsior College offers several flexible payment plan options that allow students to spread the cost of fees and tuition over several installments. Excelsior College is a Title IV-eligible educational institution offering federal financial assistance (Pell Grants, Stafford Loans, and PLUS Loans) to students who qualify. As a Title IV-eligible educational institution, students attending Excelsior College may qualify for the Hope Scholarship or Lifetime Learning Credit on their taxes.

Applying

Students apply to the degree program of their choice and receive an unofficial evaluation of how prior credit may apply to their degree program. They then enroll as a matriculated student. Application and enrollment are available online, by mail, or by fax.

CONTACT

Admissions Office
Excelsior College
7 Columbia Circle
Albany, New York 12203
Phone: 518-464-8500 Ext. 27
        888-647-2388 Ext. 27
        (toll-free)
E-mail: admissions@excelsior.edu
Web site: http://www.excelsior.edu

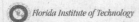
Florida Institute of Technology

FLORIDA INSTITUTE OF TECHNOLOGY
University College–Distance Learning–Virtual Campus
Melbourne, Florida

Florida Institute of Technology is an accredited, coeducational, independently controlled and supported university. It is committed to the pursuit of excellence in teaching and research in the sciences, engineering, technology, management, and related disciplines as well as to providing the challenges that motivate students to reach their full academic and professional potential. Today, over 4,700 students are enrolled, with more than 3,300 students on the Melbourne campus and the others at Florida Tech's off-campus sites. All of the off-campus students and more than 1,000 on-campus students are enrolled in graduate programs. Florida Tech offers 140 degree programs in science and engineering, aviation, business, education, humanities, psychology, and communication. Doctoral degrees are offered in twenty-two disciplines, while more than seventy master's degrees are offered. The university is organized into six academic units: the College of Aeronautics, College of Business, College of Engineering, College of Psychology and Liberal Arts, College of Science, and University College, which encompasses the Distance Learning and Extended Studies Divisions.

Distance Learning Program

University College is a multi-faceted hub of higher education, research initiatives, consulting, and professional development centers, and it consists of four divisions: Distance Learning, Extended Studies, Professional Development, and Applied Research.

Academic offerings include over thirty-five graduate degree and certificate programs offered at ten U.S. sites in five East Coast states, including a well-established distance learning program with online classes taught through the Virtual Campus. These off-campus sites are located in: Redstone Arsenal, Alabama; Orlando, Melbourne, Rockledge/Kennedy Space Center, Florida; Aberdeen Proving Ground and Patuxent River, Maryland; Picatinny/Lakehurst, New Jersey; and Fort Lee, Alexandria/Quantico, and Hampton Roads, Virginia. Distance learning courses are taught through the Virtual Campus.

Mission critical to University College is its dedication to encouraging diversity and inclusion while serving the needs of a global workforce of adult learners.

Graduate degree programs are taught in business and management, logistics and contract management, engineering, project management, operations research and computer science-related disciplines.

Extended Studies began in August 1972 as "Off-Campus Programs," when 42 students enrolled in a master's degree program in electrical engineering at the Naval Air Test Center, Patuxent River, Maryland. Graduate programs in University College have grown to more than 1,400 students per year enrolled in thirty-five degree programs. Since the 1972 beginning, over 16,000 Florida Tech master's degrees have been conferred on off-campus candidates representing the military services, federal and local government, and a wide variety of business and industry sectors.

Florida Tech's extended studies and distance learning programs are conducted in a very traditional manner, with admission and graduation standards the same as those required on campus. Curricula and course content are tailored to meet the needs of the students and their employers, while maintaining the highest possible academic quality and integrity.

Florida Institute of Technology is accredited by the Commission on Colleges of the Southern Association of Colleges and Schools to award associate, baccalaureate, master's, education specialist, and doctoral degrees.

Delivery Media

With Blackboard as the learning management system, courses are offered via the Internet. Text information is supported by audio and video clips. Interaction between instructors and students is provided through e-mail, synchronous chats, and asynchronous threaded discussions.

Programs of Study

Degrees offered through distance learning include the Professional Master of Business Administration (PMBA), with concentrations in acquisition and contract management, e-business, human resource management, and information systems; the Master of Public Administration (M.P.A.); and the Master of Science (M.S.) in acquisition and contract management, computer information systems, human resources management, logistics management, management (with concentrations in acquisition and contract management, e-business, human resources management, information systems, logistics management, and transportation management), materiel acquisition management, systems management (with a concentration in operations research), project management (with concentrations in information systems and operations research), and operations research.

These graduate programs require a set of core requirements and a set of electives, with some programs and courses requiring the completion of specific prerequisites prior to enrollment. All courses are 3 semester hours.

Additional information about Florida Tech's academic and admission policies may be found at http://uc.fit.edu/dl/academics/ and http://uc.fit.edu/dl/admissions/. Course prerequisites are available in the University College catalog at http://uc.fit.edu/es/catalog/ or by contacting the Virtual Campus directly http://uc/fit.edu/dl.

For those seeking an alternative to a master's degree program, graduate certificate programs are offered through distance learning in the following areas of study: business management, contract management, e-business, human resources management, information systems management, logistics, materiel acquisition management, program management, quality management, systems management and transportation management. Each certificate program requires the completion of five 3-hour courses.

Student Services
Florida Tech's Library Information Network (LINK) and its many valuable resources and features are provided via remote access through http://www.lib.fit.edu/pubs/distancelearning/. Access is granted to registered students via a personal identification number and password for certain restricted databases.

Academic advising for distance learning students is provided through e-mail, fax, or telephone contact on a request basis.

All students are eligible to use the university's career placement services.

Credit Options
If the courses constitute a logical part of the student's program, up to a maximum of 12 semester hours of transfer credit from regionally accredited institutions may be transferred to Florida Tech (for one master's degree only), under certain conditions. For details, students should see http://uc.fit.edu/dl/academics/. Transfer credit from foreign universities is considered on a case-by-case basis, subject to certain limitations. The same rules apply as given above.

Some courses presented by certain military schools, plus the resident courses of the U.S. Army Command and General Staff College, Fort Leavenworth, Kansas, have been evaluated by Florida Tech, and specific courses have been found acceptable for transfer to designated degree programs without charge to the student. Information about the specific courses found acceptable and the Florida Tech equivalents is available from University College in Melbourne.

Faculty
The faculty members of University College have a passion for educating. Each day, they make an impact. Their choice for a career in higher education is one of dedication and determination, allowing them to share their passion and excitement for teaching. Faculty members are aware that adult learners, no matter where they are employed, come to Florida Tech expecting a cutting-edge education because they must have up-to-date information in order to compete in a knowledge-based environment. Teaching at Florida Tech is an exciting adventure because they are working with willing minds in a quest to do more and to be better than ever before. The synergistic partnership between students and teachers leaves both parties with a well-deserved sense of achievement.

Adjunct faculty member Jim Bryant, Ph. D., shares his level of enthusiasm and motivation for teaching: "I get excited about teaching because it gives me the opportunity to tell students about actual events that take place using the knowledge they are learning in the classroom...helping people reach for their next goal and the happiness they receive in that accomplishment."

Admission
Admission to graduate study is granted to qualified applicants. Successful applicants for the master's degree will have received a bachelor's degree from a regionally accredited institution or its equivalent internationally. As a general rule, an undergraduate cumulative grade point average (GPA) of at least 3.0 is required for regular admission. Individual academic units may have higher minimum standards. For further details, students should visit http://uc.fit.edu/dl/admissions.

Tuition and Fees
For the latest information about tuition and fees policies, students should refer to the university's Web site at http://uc.fit.edu/dl/academics/tuition.

Financial Aid
As a general rule, a graduate student must be enrolled half-time (at least 5 credit hours per term) as a regular student in a degree program and must be a U.S. citizen or an eligible noncitizen to qualify for federal and/or state financial aid. Financial aid forms are available through the University's Office of Financial Aid.

Applying
Application information is available online at http://uc.fit.edu/dl/admissions/. Applicants must sign and mail an affidavit attesting to the accuracy of the application to the university's Graduate Admission Office. Official transcripts are required from all colleges and universities attended. Students may begin the online application process anytime at http://www.fit.edu/paws/.

CONTACT
University College
Attention: Virtual Campus Administration
Florida Institute of Technology
150 West University Boulevard
Melbourne, Florida 32901
Phone: 864-226-2257
           888-225-2239 (toll-free in the U.S.)
Fax: 864-226-2258
E-mail: pvassar@fit.edu
           uc@fit.edu
Web site: http://uc.fit.edu/dl

FRANKLIN UNIVERSITY
The Virtual Campus
Columbus, Ohio

Franklin University's primary objective is to provide services and programs for students who work full- or part-time. Franklin is focused on providing students with a supportive environment that allows achievement of goals and provides a practical education with immediate application in the workplace. Students learn from professionals who practice what they teach, are accessible, have a wealth of experience, and exhibit a true commitment to teaching and learning. Franklin University is an independent, nonprofit institution that celebrated its 100th anniversary in 2002. It has offered online courses since 1996 and currently offers sixteen undergraduate majors as well as an online Vantage M.B.A.® Program through its Virtual Campus. In 1998, the University unveiled the Community College Alliance (CCA) Program, which encourages community college graduates to obtain a bachelor's degree by combining on-campus classes at their community colleges with online classes through Franklin. In addition, Franklin was chosen as one of the initial institutions partnering with the U.S. Army to offer online learning opportunities for soldiers through the eArmyU Program and has served more than 1,500 students to date through the Virtual Campus.

Distance Learning Program
Franklin University has a total distance education enrollment of over 4,000 students, an online Vantage M.B.A.® Program enrollment of over 200 students, and an eArmyU enrollment of nearly 600.

Delivery Media
Students in Franklin's Virtual Campus access courses, programs, and student services via the Internet. All of Franklin's Virtual Campus classes are designed to incorporate electronic communication tools that include chat rooms, bulletin boards, whiteboards, e-mail, and a grade book that can be accessed by students and faculty members online.

The Balanced Learning Format (BLF) course design and delivery format provides students with a wide range of offerings to meet their learning needs and busy schedules. With three-, six-, twelve-, and fifteen-week course lengths, new classes start every few weeks. The BLF allows students to anticipate consistent time commitments from week to week and from class to class. Franklin University uses a team of instructional designers, faculty members, and developers to create courses. This guarantees students consistent course outcomes, experiential learning, and consistent grading criteria.

Programs of Study
Franklin serves degree-seeking candidates, students who want to continue their education, and those who are interested in experiencing online learning. Franklin's Virtual Campus offers sixteen undergraduate programs and one graduate degree program, the Vantage Master of Business Administration® (M.B.A.). The online Vantage M.B.A.® Program is a seventeen-month program consisting of six-week courses and two 3-day, high-intensity learning residencies. Admitted students can enter the M.B.A. program at multiple points along the academic calendar. The online graduate program enables students to continue their careers, balance family and social commitments, and still reach their educational goals.

Sixteen bachelor's degree completion majors are offered online: accounting, applied management, business administration, business forensics, computer science, eMarketing, financial management, forensic accounting, health-care management, human resources management, information technology, management, management information sciences (MIS), marketing, public safety management, and Web development.

Franklin University continually updates its programs and schedules to stay current with industry trends and the ever-changing job market.

Student Services
Through Franklin University's student-centered approach, each student is matched with a Student Services Associate (SSA) who, along with the course faculty members, becomes an important contact at the University. SSAs serve as both an initial and long-term resource, working from initial application through graduation.

The Community College Alliance (CCA) program is an educational alliance with more than 245 two-year colleges in thirty-two states. The CCA enables community college graduates, or those with equivalent credit, to earn a bachelor's degree from Franklin without leaving their community. Students complete their degrees through a combination of on-site courses at the community college and online courses through Franklin. For more information, students may visit the program's Web site at http://alliance.franklin.edu.

Credit Options
Franklin University has a credit transfer policy that is more student-friendly than those at most other institutions. More than 75 percent of Franklin students have transferred credit from other colleges and universities. Students also can earn credit outside the classroom through the College-Level

Examination Program (CLEP), Franklin University Proficiency Exams (FUPE), and Prior Learning Portfolios.

Faculty

Franklin faculty members enrich the virtual classroom with special talents and abilities drawn from successful careers in business, industry, government, and social service. Franklin University faculty members are working professionals who provide both excellence in teaching and real-world experience.

Admission

Admission to the Franklin M.B.A. program is based on the following selection criteria: a baccalaureate degree from a regionally accredited college or university, a minimum of three years of full-time work experience, a minimum cumulative undergraduate GPA of 2.75

on a 4.0 scale (GMAT scores are considered if the GPA is below 2.75), and a score of 550 (paper-based) or 213 (computer-based) or better on the Test of English as a Foreign Language (TOEFL).

To apply transfer credits from another institution, all official transcripts should be directly forwarded to Franklin University from the previous institution(s); however, a student can begin a distance learning course before the transcripts have been received.

Tuition and Fees

For the 2007–08 academic year, tuition for undergraduate online courses from Franklin University is $266 per credit hour for standard courses and $318 per credit hour for computer science, MIS, and information technology courses. For online Vantage M.B.A.® Program courses, tuition is $413 per credit hour.

Financial Aid

Franklin offers a variety of financial aid options, including a deferred-payment plan for students whose employers offer a tuition reimbursement program. More than 75 percent of Franklin students receive some type of financial assistance through grants, scholarships, loans, employer tuition reimbursement, and student employment. Franklin University awards approximately 250 scholarships every year to new and current students.

Applying

Anyone who is a graduate of an accredited high school or has passed the GED test is eligible for admission as a degree-seeking undergraduate student. Those seeking a bachelor's degree must complete an admission application and forward an official high school transcript or an official GED test score report to Franklin.

CONTACT

Franklin University Virtual Campus
201 South Grant Avenue
Columbus, Ohio 43215

Phone: 877-341-6300 (toll-free)
E-mail: info@franklin.edu
Web site: http://www.franklin.edu

GENESEE COMMUNITY COLLEGE

Distance Learning

Batavia, New York

Genesee Community College (GCC) is located outside Batavia, New York, between Buffalo and Rochester, nestled amid the scenic villages and farmland of the Genesee region. Since its founding in 1966 as part of the State University of New York (SUNY), Genesee has become one of the most respected community colleges in the United States. With about 7,000 full-time and part-time students, Genesee is the college of choice for students across New York State and the country and also from many different nations around the globe. In a 2006 survey, Genesee Community College ranked among the highest in student satisfaction. The College has earned acclaim for its innovative academic programs, powerful technological tools available to students, and growing distance learning programs. Genesee graduates consistently find good jobs or successfully transfer to baccalaureate colleges and universities.

Distance Learning Program

Genesee Community College distance learning courses are convenient, flexible, and high quality. Instead of conventional class attendance, distance learning courses use communication media that free the student from specific time and location restraints.

Each distance learning course is different, but all involve regular communications and written work: short papers, field research, term papers, or semester projects. Online discussions, Web links, individual and group assignments, and student assessments are conducted in Blackboard, Genesee's course-management software. A few courses require proctored exams, on-campus science labs, or presentations. All requirements are detailed in each course syllabus and described on http://www.genesee.edu/DL.

Delivery Media

Courses use a combination of textbooks, study guides, e-mail, online course management software, video and audio programs, online discussions, remote library services, and other media. Online courses require a high-speed Internet connection and an intermediate or higher level of familiarity with e-mail, accessing Web materials, word processing, file transfer, and other computer-related skills.

Genesee distance learning courses use Blackboard course-management software and are accessed from the College's main Web page. Online tutorials familiarize students with the system. Optional technical orientations take place at the start of each semester, when students may choose to come to the Batavia campus to learn how Blackboard and Genesee e-mail work.

Programs of Study

Nearly half of Genesee Community College's fifty-nine degree programs are designed to allow 50 percent or more of the course work to be completed online through the distance learning format. Associate in Science (A.S.) and Associate in Arts (A.A.) degrees are for students who intend to pursue bachelor's degrees after graduation. These degrees provide a broad liberal arts background paralleling the first two years of most bachelor's degree programs. The Associate in Applied Science (A.A.S.) degree provides more career-specific courses to enable graduates to enter their chosen careers after graduation. Many A.A.S. students also transfer to bachelor's programs. Certificate programs are for students who

wish to upgrade job skills or for those who already have a degree and wish to be retrained. Interested students should always talk with an academic adviser to determine which program best meets their needs.

The A.A. is offered in liberal arts (humanities and social science). The A.S. is available in accounting, alcohol and substance abuse, business administration, computer information systems, criminal justice, economic crime investigation, general studies, human services, sports management, and teacher education transfer. The A.A.S. is offered in accounting, criminal justice, human services, and fitness, recreation, and sports management. Certificate programs include accounting, criminal justice, early childhood education, entrepreneurship, general education, gerontology, and teaching assistant certification.

Student Services

During technical orientation, the bookstore and records and business offices are open, and picture ID/library cards may be obtained. Computer Services staff members help students log into online courses using Blackboard. Other services available to Genesee distance learners include academic and career advising, financial aid assistance, counseling, and tutoring.

Credit Options

Distance learning courses are equivalent to campus-based courses in meeting requirements or elective-credit needs for Genesee Community College and other colleges' degree programs and majors.

Faculty

Unlike some baccalaureate institutions and universities, community colleges

---

specialize in teaching. Genesee faculty members are experts in providing useful content and career skills. Online courses are taught by top Genesee faculty members, who use technology to teach concepts, supplement textbook information, and enable content-specific communication. Instructors quickly fill in where technology cannot by directing students' study, answering questions, and helping apply learned information.

Admission

High school graduates and GED certificate recipients are invited to apply to Genesee for certificate and degree programs. The application is free at http://www.genesee.edu/admissions. Some students are advised or required to take a placement test to ascertain best course selection.

Tuition and Fees

Genesee's out-of-state tuition is among the lowest in New York State. Information is available at http://www.genesee.edu/depts/admissions/financial/costs.cfm. Fees total about $300 per academic year.

Financial Aid

Genesee Community College awards nearly $15 million in aid in each year. Online students are eligible for grants, scholarships, or loans, depending on need and completion of the financial aid application. Interested students should visit http://www.genesee.edu/depts/admissions/financial/.

Applying

In addition to completing the free application form (http://www.genesee.edu/admissions), applicants for certificate and degree programs must submit official high school transcripts or GED scores. Students who wish to take courses but not enroll in a degree or certificate program can apply simply by completing the application.

CONTACT

Robert G. Knipe, Dean
Distance Learning
Genesee Community College
One College Road
Batavia, New York 14020-9704
Phone: 585-345-6969
Fax: 585-343-0433
E-mail: rgknipe@genesee.edu
Web site: http://www.genesee.edu/DL

GEORGIA INSTITUTE OF TECHNOLOGY
Center for Distance Learning
Atlanta, Georgia

Founded in 1885, the Georgia Institute of Technology is the Southeast's largest technological institution. Georgia Tech is located on a 330-acre campus near downtown Atlanta—the financial, communications, and cultural hub of the Southeast. The Institute's mission is to be a leader among those few technological universities whose alumni, faculty, students, and staff define, expand, and communicate the frontiers of knowledge and innovation.

Georgia Tech ranks seventh among the nation's public universities for undergraduates, according to the 2007 rankings by U.S. News & World Report. *They consistently rank Georgia Tech's College of Engineering in the nation's top five. Georgia Tech also makes their list of the top graduate engineering programs in the country; eight of the engineering options were ranked in the top ten, with four in the top five. In terms of producing African American engineering graduates,* Diverse: Issues in Higher Education *ranks Tech first at the bachelor's level, second at the master's level, and first at the doctoral level.*

In addition to its high-quality undergraduate and graduate instructional programs, Tech has a world-class research program, with $480 million in new grants and contracts awarded during the 2007 fiscal year. This ranks Tech as the South's number one public institution in engineering research.

Distance Learning Program
Georgia Tech's Center for Distance Learning serves more than 600 distance learning students and is housed within a unit that reports directly to the provost. Georgia Tech is accredited by the Southern Association of Colleges and Schools. Engineering disciplines are accredited by the Accrediting Board for Engineering and Technology, Inc.

Delivery Media
Video cameras record instructor presentations and student-instructor interaction during regular Georgia Tech graduate classes. The captured lectures are encoded and placed on a video-on-demand server and made available to off-campus students, who take courses without having to come to the campus. Selected courses are available at some locations via videoconferencing, Web-casting, and the Internet. Students enrolled in the program communicate with their Georgia Tech professor by telephone, fax, and/or e-mail. Students have access to the Georgia Tech Electronic Library and the computer system via a business or home computer and an Internet connection. Access is also provided over the Internet. Every student is expected to have access to a high-quality computer with a printer and

Internet access. (High-speed connection is highly recommended.)

Programs of Study
The Georgia Tech video-based distance delivery program provides high-quality graduate-level courses that can be applied to several master's degree programs. The School of Aerospace Engineering offers two master's degrees, the Master of Science in Aerospace Engineering (M.S.A.E.) and the Master of Science (M.S.). The M.S.A.E is generally referred to as a designated degree, while the M.S. is referred to as an undesignated degree. The difference between the two degree programs is that the designated degree program includes the completion of all academic course work required for a Bachelor of Science in Aerospace Engineering degree. The Master of Science in Electrical and Computer Engineering is offered with options in computer engineering, digital signal processing, power, and telecommunications; all options require 30 hours of course work. The M.S. and the Master of Science in Environmental Engineering (M.S.Env.E.) degrees are offered with concentrations in water quality, surface and subsurface systems, hazardous and solid waste, and air quality; all programs require 30 hours of

course work or the equivalent. The Master of Science in Industrial Engineering is offered with specializations in automation, production and logistics systems, and statistical process control and quality assurance; it requires 30 hours of course work and students must hold an undergraduate degree from an ABET-accredited engineering curriculum. The Master of Science in Operations Research (M.S.O.R.) is a program for students who likely have a background in engineering, mathematics, the physical sciences, or computer science. The Master of Science in Mechanical Engineering is offered with specializations in thermal science and mechanical systems; it requires 30 hours of course work. The Master of Science in Medical Physics (M.S.M.P.) degree program is intended to prepare students with a bachelor's degree in science or engineering for productive careers as medical physicists. Students have the choice of a thesis or a nonthesis option in the medical physics curriculum. Both options include seven required courses (21 credit hours) and a clinical rotation (3 credit hours). The thesis option includes an additional 6 credit hours for the preparation of a thesis and the elective for a total of 33 credit hours.

New for the 2009 academic year, Georgia Tech announces the availability of a Master of Science degree in computational science and engineering (CSE). This interdisciplinary degree is offered by the Colleges of Computing, Engineering, and Sciences. Participating units from these colleges include the Computational Science and Engineering Division, Department of Biomedical Engineering, and Schools of Aerospace Engineering, Civil and Environmental Engineering, Industrial and Systems Engineering, Biology, Chemistry and Biochemistry, and Mathematics.

The curriculum has been structured to impart students with solid CSE foundational knowledge and skills and includes technical specialization courses that enhance a student's domain expertise. Advanced elective courses will enable students to specialize in a domain and technical expertise focusing on their particular interests. The optional thesis portion of the program requires completion of an interdisciplinary research project. CSE master's students will be well prepared for work in software systems engineering, Web technologies, software for consumer product and drug design, financial engineering, and many more industries. In government, graduates may pursue work in software and systems, modeling and simulation, systems integration, data mining and visualization, high-performance computing, and computational modeling. Academic career possibilities include research and education in departments concerned with the development and application of computational models in engineering, the sciences, and computing.

The master's in CSE requires a minimum of 30 semester hours. This includes a set of required courses defining a core body of knowledge in CSE (12 hours). A set of technical elective courses focusing on developing a more in-depth knowledge of computational techniques as well as the application of computational methods in an application domain (12 hours) is also required. This set of courses will typically form a body of material in close alignment with the student's selected home unit and form a minor course of study aligned with the home unit. Finally, either a thesis or additional technical electives (6 hours) are required.

Specific information on admission and degree requirements for any program can be obtained by calling the academic coordinators for each area. Students should call the contact name for additional information.

Special Programs

Georgia Tech offers every graduate-level credit course in all of the above listed disciplines via video-on-demand download via the Internet. This new system enables qualified students around the world to earn a Georgia Tech master's degree completely online.

All Georgia Tech online graduate courses use state-of-the-art streaming audio and video technologies synchronized with slides, simulations, and other multimedia and make maximum use of the pedagogical advantages offered by Web-based courseware and instruction. Further information about these new online degree programs is available at the Georgia Tech Center for Distance Learning Web site at the address listed in the Contact section.

A Certificate in Manufacturing provides students with the fundamentals in support of education and research in manufacturing. Each student pursuing the certificate develops knowledge and skills in a particular discipline coupled with a general knowledge of the entire manufacturing enterprise and an ability to work well as a member of a team. The certificate emphasizes the philosophy that it is not possible to educate engineers, managers, or scientists in all aspects of manufacturing. Accordingly, the program is structured to broaden and enhance the education of students who are enrolled in traditional academic disciplines. The program encourages students to develop knowledge in multiple disciplines from class work and experiences in multidisciplinary team activities. Thus, the program balances technical depth with a broad exposure and comprehension of the realistic problems and solution methodologies that are faced by manufacturing industries every day. The Certificate in Manufacturing is obtained as part of a graduate degree program (M.S. or Ph.D.) from the Georgia Institute of Technology. Students must complete a graduate degree to obtain the certificate. The certificate program consists of a set of key courses that are fundamental to manufacturing, from which the students select 12 semester hours. Students are also required to attend seminars.

Credit Options

Students earn credit toward their degree by registering for and completing courses online. Requirements for each course are the same as for on-campus students enrolled in the course. A student may receive transfer credit of up to 6 hours for graduate-level courses (approved by the academic adviser) taken at an accredited institution in the United States or Canada and not used for credit toward another degree.

Faculty

There are 961 full-time faculty members at Georgia Tech. Of these, 96 percent hold doctoral degrees. Sixteen percent, or 150 faculty members, teach in the Distance Learning Program.

Admission

Admission requirements vary among the academic disciplines. To apply, individuals should contact the academic adviser or admissions office in the School to which he or she is applying.

Tuition and Fees

Tuition for in-state and out-of-state students for the 2007–08 academic year was $875 per credit hour. Fees are subject to change each year. Students were assessed a technology fee of $103 per semester; students must also purchase their own textbooks and software.

Financial Aid

There are financial aid programs available through Georgia Tech for distance learning students. Most employers have programs that will help students pay the course fees. The Department of Veterans Affairs has approved the Georgia Tech Video Program as independent study. Georgia Tech has a memorandum of understanding with DANTES and with the Air Force.

Applying

Application materials can be obtained from the School to which the student is applying. Applicants must submit an Application for Admission, three letters of recommendation, a biographical sketch, two official transcripts of all previous college work, and scores from the Graduate Record Examinations (GRE). Decisions are made by the individual Schools.

CONTACT

Student Support Services Manager
Center for Distance Learning
Georgia Institute of Technology
Atlanta, Georgia 30308-1031

Phone: 404-894-3378
Fax: 404-894-8924
E-mail: cdlops@dlpe.gatech.edu
Web site: http://www.cdl.gatech.edu/

GRANTHAM UNIVERSITY

The College of Computer Science and Engineering Technology
The Mark Skousen School of Business
The College of Arts and Sciences

Kansas City, Missouri

Established in 1951, Grantham University is a private institution that specializes in educating the working adult student. Grantham's mission is to level the playing field by making a high-quality college education available to adult learners, based on the combined academic and economic principles of accessibility, affordability, and academic accountability. Since 1951, Grantham has contributed to the formal education of thousands of working adults. Students from each of the fifty states and many countries around the world have discovered the benefits and convenience of the Grantham distance education model.

Grantham University has designed its degree programs to meet the needs of busy working adults. Students can complete their course work at the times and places that fit their busy schedules.

Grantham University is accredited by the Accrediting Commission of the Distance Education and Training Council, 1601 18th Street NW, Washington, D.C. 20009 (http://www.detc.org).

Distance Learning Program

Grantham University's degree programs are offered through distance education, or e-learning, formats. Its programs are 100 percent online and do not require on-campus or in-classroom attendance. Students enjoy self-paced, self-directed methods of study and course completion. This unique method of learning is advantageous for those students with full-time jobs or who have family or other commitments that do not allow them to participate in a regular classroom environment.

Other students who are attracted to Grantham University are those who travel extensively or find that the nearest college or university may be hundreds of miles away. Grantham University also attracts thousands of military students who appreciate the benefit of being able to complete classes from almost anywhere in the world. Grantham's military students never have to worry about frequent deployments or transfers, because they can take their course work with them and complete it when and where it is convenient.

Grantham offers both undergraduate and graduate degree programs. All of Grantham University's degree programs include an emphasis on both theory and applications, and each program also incorporates general studies courses designed to help students learn to communicate clearly, formulate and analyze problems, and develop well-thought-out solutions.

Delivery Media

Grantham utilizes the latest technologies to deliver courses electronically to students worldwide. Students have access to course materials, announcements, e-mails, and grades through Grantham's online student portal. On-line testing and grading provides students with immediate results to ensure that they can work at their own pace. New students are required to take an orientation course that is designed to help them understand Grantham's distance learning model and to inform them of the wide array of services offered by Grantham.

Programs of Study

Associate and bachelor's degree programs are offered in business administration, business management, computer engineering technology, computer science, criminal justice, electronics engineering technology, general studies and interdisciplinary studies.

A Master of Business Administration degree if offered with specialties in project management or information management, and a Master of Science in Information Technology degree is offered with specialties in information management-project management and information management technology.

A student is given eight weeks to complete each course, but can accelerate course completion based on study habits and time devoted to the material.

Students must complete 61–65 credit hours (depending on program) for an associate degree, of which 25 percent of those credit hours must be completed with Grantham. The bachelor's programs require 121–126 credit hours, of which 25 percent of the credit hours must be completed with Grantham. The master's degree programs require 36 credit hours, of which 75 percent of the credit hours must be completed with Grantham.

Credit Options

Grantham University makes every effort to apply college credit for military training and previous course work whenever possible. CLEP testing and DSST exams along with military and work-related training courses may be eligible for transfer credit. More information about transfer of credit is available on Grantham's Web site.

Faculty

Grantham's faculty, administration, and advisers comprise educators, business executives, industry professionals, and entrepreneurs. Among the advisers are Dr. Herbert I. London, founder, endowed chair, and former Dean of

Students at New York University's Gallatin School of Individualized Study; John Ashford, an adviser to Fortune 100 companies as chairman and CEO of the Hawthorne Group; David E. Baker, Brig. Gen. (USAF, Ret.), a decorated fighter pilot and senior vice president for the Stanford Washington Research Group; and Rear Admiral Karen Harmeyer, former Chief Staff Officer, Navy Surgeon General, OPNAV 093R.

Admission

Students wishing to apply to Grantham must have earned a high school diploma or GED equivalent. Applicants with high school or previous education in another country and who do not reside in the United States, the United Kingdom, or Canada must demonstrate English-language proficiency. Students should visit the University's Web site to read more about the English-language proficiency tests accepted by Grantham.

Tuition and Fees

Grantham University's standard tuition rate is $265 per credit hour, which includes a technology and textbook grant that covers the cost of required textbooks and software. Grantham's tuition rate for service members, veterans, and military family members is $250 per credit hour, which includes a technology and textbook grant.

Financial Aid

Grantham University offers its students financing options through SLM Financial Corporation, a Sallie Mae company, and Education One, a Chase company. Prospective students who require financing for tuition and fees may contact Grantham's Admissions Department for more information about applying for these student loans.

Grantham University provides scholarships for active duty military service members, National Guard members, Reservists, veterans, military family members, and law enforcement professionals.

Applying

Students may apply to Grantham at any time. Grantham University offers continuous enrollment. Students may apply 24 hours a day, 365 days a year using the school's online enrollment services.

CONTACT

Admissions Department
Grantham University
7200 Northwest 86th Street
Kansas City, Missouri 64153

Phone: 800-955-2527 (toll-free)
Fax: 816-595-5757
E-mail: admissions@grantham.edu
Web site: http://www.grantham.edu

INDIANA STATE UNIVERSITY

Distance Learning Program

Terre Haute, Indiana

> *Indiana State University is a medium-sized, comprehensive university accredited by the North Central Association of Colleges and Schools. Founded in 1865, the University has grown to serve a student population of approximately 10,000, including students from throughout the United States and sixty-one other countries.*
>
> *Attention to and concern for the individual is reflected in the institution's offerings. Flexible and responsive programs are designed to facilitate student attainment of academic, vocational, and personal goals. Classes are designed to meet the needs of full-time and part-time students.*
>
> *In addition to offering distance programs and courses, the University offers undergraduate and graduate programs in more than 100 areas of study on the Indiana State University campus in Terre Haute, Indiana.*

Distance Learning Program

Indiana State University (ISU) has offered distance learning since 1969. Many courses and programs can be completed entirely via distance learning; others require minimal campus visits. All distance programs are available in Indiana. Numerous programs and courses can be completed by out-of-state and international students. More than 1,000 students enroll in ISU distance learning courses each semester.

Delivery Media

Courses are offered primarily via the Internet. Selected courses are offered via desktop videoconferencing and live I-TV (accessible at selected receive sites). Equipment requirements vary, depending on course format.

Programs of Study

Students may complete individual undergraduate or graduate courses. Each semester, approximately 200 courses are offered via distance learning, including professional development courses for teachers, principals, administrators, counselors, and other educational specialists.

In addition, eligible students may complete numerous undergraduate and graduate degrees and professional development programs.

Undergraduate degree programs include an Associate of Science in general aviation flight technology and bachelor's degree completion programs in business administration, career and technical education, community health promotion, criminology and criminal justice, electronics technology, industrial technology management, human resource development, insurance and risk management, mechanical engineering technology, and nursing.

Undergraduate certificate programs are offered in corrections, law enforcement, and private security and loss prevention. Also offered is a driver education instructor license program.

Graduate degree programs include a doctoral program in technology management and master's programs in criminology, electronics and computer technology, health and safety, human resource development, nurs-

ing, and student affairs and higher education. The University also offers a Master of Public Administration (M.P.A.) via distance learning.

Graduate certificate/licensure programs are offered in the following areas: driver education instructor license, family nurse practitioner studies, middle/secondary teaching, nursing education, public administration, public personnel administration, school administration, school library media services, special education (mild interventions), teaching English as a second or foreign language, visual impairment, and vocational business education.

Special Programs

DegreeLink is a bachelor's degree completion program that enables individuals to transfer previously earned credit to Indiana State University, and complete selected bachelor degrees via distance learning. Students may transfer credit earned from Ivy Tech Community College, Vincennes University, and other accredited institutions.

The Master of Public Administration (M.P.A.) is a 36-hour program designed for working professionals who have experience in public or nonprofit organizations, and now seek a graduate-level degree for career advancement.

The Library Media Services Certification Program consists of 27 hours of library and media courses leading to graduate licensure/certification in school library media services.

The Master of Science in nursing includes specializations in family nurse practitioner studies, nursing administration, and nursing education.

The Master of Science in electronics and computer technology program is a 32-semester-hour (minimum) program that includes a focus, or concentration, in instrumentation, systems, and automation.

The Ph.D. in technology management is offered through the College of Technology in cooperation with a consortium of four other universities. Course work includes a general technology core, a technical specialization, cognate studies, an internship, and a research core and dissertation.

Student Services

Indiana State University offers distance learners a comprehensive package of services, including online registration, credit transfer assistance, academic advisement, a virtual bookstore, library services, technical support, and career counseling. Financial assistance programs include financial aid, scholarships, student loans, and veterans benefits programs. The Office of Distance Support Services offers one-stop assistance to individuals interested in pursuing undergraduate and graduate courses and programs via distance learning.

Credit Options

Students earn credit by registering for and completing semester-based courses offered on campus or via distance learning. In addition, undergraduate students may opt to earn credit via year-based study. Selected programs enable undergraduates to earn credit for prior work experience, by examination, and through portfolios. Graduate students are eligible to transfer selected credit; each department determines the number of hours transferable.

Faculty

Distance courses are developed and taught by Indiana State University faculty members. Working with instructional designers and media specialists, faculty members transform on-campus courses to distance formats.

Admission

Admission requirements vary by program of study. For information, prospective students should visit http://www.indstate.edu/distance.

Tuition and Fees

Distance learners are eligible for fee waivers that equate to in-state fees. For details, students should visit http://www.indstate.edu/distance.

Applying

Individuals may obtain undergraduate and graduate applications, information, and assistance by contacting the Office of Distance Support Services or visiting http://www.indstate.edu/distance.

CONTACT

Office of Distance Support Services
Erickson Hall, Room 122
Indiana State University
Terre Haute, Indiana 47809
Phone: 812-237-8080
       888-237-8080 (toll-free)
Fax: 812-237-8540
E-mail: studentservices@indstate.edu
Web site: http://www.indstate.edu/distance

INDIANA UNIVERSITY

INDIANA UNIVERSITY

INDIANA UNIVERSITY
School of Continuing Studies
Bloomington, Indiana

Indiana University (IU) was established in 1820 in Bloomington, Indiana. There are now eight IU campuses located throughout the state of Indiana. Indiana University has more than 1,048 authorized degree programs. For fall semester 2007, the all-campus enrollment was 99,122 students (graduate and undergraduate).

Indiana University has offered undergraduate distance education courses since 1912 and high school distance education courses since 1925. It is accredited by the Higher Learning Commission and is a member of the North Central Association of Colleges and Schools.

Distance Learning Program

The IU School of Continuing Studies (SCS) offers a wide range of self-paced undergraduate and high school courses through online and correspondence study as well as semester-based online courses. In 2007, the School broadened its curriculum by adding online upper-division courses taught by the IU campus in Richmond; further such collaborations with other IU campuses will make an even greater diversity of high-quality courses available to students in the near future. Each year, registrations in the program top 14,000. The School of Continuing Studies has won fifty-four course awards from the University Continuing Education Association.

Delivery Media

SCS courses use the Web, e-mail, CD-ROMs, and audio cassettes and videotapes. Students may interact with their instructors by toll-free phone, e-mail, and the Web.

Programs of Study

SCS students can take individual courses, earn an Indiana University high school diploma, or complete all degree requirements leading to an IU Associate of Arts in General Studies (60 semester credit hours) or an IU Bachelor of General Studies (120 semester credit hours). Students may earn both degrees online.

SCS courses are open to all students. In fact, many students at other educational institutions use SCS courses to fulfill degree or diploma requirements at their home institution.

Student Services

Students should visit the IU School of Continuing Studies Web site to find course information and registration forms. Students can contact the School 24 hours a day, seven days a week. They enjoy a one-on-one relationship with their instructors either by phone or e-mail. Students enrolling in SCS courses receive a free IU e-mail account. Through the IU Bloomington Libraries Distance Education Services, students can obtain a library code for borrowing books; order books, articles, and other library materials to be delivered free of charge; get reference help; and learn how to search the library's catalog and databases.

Credit Options

Students can use a variety of options for earning credit toward their Associate of Arts in General Studies and their Bachelor of General Studies. Students who started their college education at another accredited college or university should be able to transfer a considerable number of credits to Indiana University. Other options include credit by examination, credit for self-acquired competency, and military service credit.

Students pursuing the Associate of Arts in General Studies must successfully complete at least 15 of the 60 required credit hours at Indiana University or through SCS distance education courses. Students pursuing the Bachelor of General Studies degree must successfully complete at least 30 of the 120 required credit hours at Indiana University or through SCS distance education courses.

Faculty

The 2007–08 SCS teaching faculty included 40 high school instructors and 120 university instructors.

Admission

Admission to Indiana University is not required for taking SCS courses. Students need only fill out a registration form for the desired courses.

Students wanting to earn an Associate of Arts in General Studies or a Bachelor of General Studies must submit an admission application to the General Studies Degree Program office. For more information, students should contact the General Studies Degree Program as listed below.

Tuition and Fees

The 2007–08 fee for undergraduate SCS courses was $145.06 per credit hour for Indiana residents and $164.22 per credit hour for nonresidents. The 2007–08 fee for high school SCS courses was $132.50 per 1-credit course and $66.25 per half-credit course. Students seeking admission to the General Studies Degree Program pay a $50 application fee ($65 for international students). Fees are subject to change.

Financial Aid

At this time, Indiana University is unable to administer federal or state financial aid for students enrolled in SCS courses.

Applying

There are no residency requirements for registering for SCS courses or applying to the General Studies Degree Program, and no on-campus meetings are required; these programs are open to students worldwide.

CONTACT

School of Continuing Studies
Owen Hall
Indiana University
790 East Kirkwood Avenue
Bloomington, Indiana 47405-7101

Phone: 812-855-2292
        800-334-1011 (toll-free)
E-mail: scs@indiana.edu
Web site: http://scs.indiana.edu

KANSAS STATE UNIVERSITY

Division of Continuing Education Distance Education

Manhattan, Kansas

Kansas State University (K-State) was founded on February 16, 1863, as a land-grant institution under the Morrill Act. Originally located on the grounds of the old Bluemont Central College, which was chartered in 1858, the University was moved to its present site in 1875.

The 664-acre campus is in Manhattan, 125 miles west of Kansas City via Interstate 70, in the rolling Flint Hills of northeast Kansas. The Salina campus, 70 miles west of Manhattan, was established through a merger of the former Kansas College of Technology with the University. This was made possible by an enactment of the 1991 Kansas Legislature.

K-State is accredited by the North Central Association of Colleges and Schools (NCA). One of the six universities governed by the Kansas Board of Regents, Kansas State University continues to fulfill its historic educational mission in teaching, research, and public service.

Distance Learning Program

Kansas State University innovatively offers high-quality courses and degree programs to students who are not geographically located near the Manhattan campus. K-State utilizes cutting-edge technologies that enhance the learning environment and extend it far beyond the University's physical boundaries.

Adults across the country want to complete their education, advance their careers, or change their professions. Success requires dedication, self-direction, and perseverance on the part of the student. Distance education offered by K-State provides people with an opportunity to pursue these goals without leaving a current job or family. K-State offers bachelor's degrees, master's degrees, and certificate programs at a distance.

Delivery Media

K-State offers more than 450 courses per semester through a variety of delivery methods. Most courses follow regular K-State semester dates. Some courses require minimum computer system requirements. Courses are offered in a variety of subject areas, and

students can take many of these without enrolling in a degree program.

Delivery methods include use of videotapes and audiotapes, the Web, listservs, e-mail, discussion rooms, guided study, desktop video, community-based outreach courses, independent study, and correspondence course work.

Programs of Study

K-State has been offering degree completion programs through distance education for more than thirty years. The goal of the Distance Education Degree Completion Programs is to help students complete the last two years of a Bachelor of Science degree. K-State staff is available to help students get started, stay directed, and earn a Bachelor of Science degree.

A student's requirements include a minimum of 30 K-State hours, with 20 of the last 30 hours earned from K-State. Students may transfer a maximum of 60 credit hours to K-State from other institutions. The average student completes a bachelor's degree in two to six years; the pace is up to the student.

Bachelor's degree completion programs are offered in animal sciences

and industry, early childhood education, elementary education (southwest Kansas only), dietetics, food science and industry, general business, interdisciplinary social science, and technology management.

Master's degree programs offered include academic advising; agribusiness; chemical engineering; civil engineering; educational computing, design, and online learning/classroom technology; educational leadership; electrical engineering; engineering management; food science and industry; gerontology; industrial/organizational psychology; mechanical engineering; merchandising; personal financial planning; software engineering; and youth development.

Special Programs

Certificate/endorsement programs are also offered. These programs include an academic advising graduate certificate; applied statistics graduate certificate; business administration graduate certificate; conflict resolution graduate and undergraduate certificates; early childhood administration credential and endorsement; educational computing, design, and online learning/classroom technology graduate certificate; food safety and defense graduate certificate; engineering professional-development hours; ESL endorsement in elementary and secondary education (limited to Kansas teachers); food science graduate and nondegree undergraduate certificates; gerontology graduate certificate; occupational health psychology graduate certificate; organizational leadership graduate certificate; personal financial planning graduate certificate; public administration graduate certificate; and youth development graduate certificate.

K-State is a member of Service Members Opportunity College for the

SOCAD-2 flexible-degree network. This network guarantees worldwide transfer of credit for military personnel who take courses from participating colleges and universities.

Student Services

Students in degree programs receive advising from the college offering the degree. The Division of Continuing Education also has Program Coordinators for each college who can provide assistance.

Library services are available to students enrolled in degree completion programs.

The technical support help desk can provide a variety of technical support services once a student is enrolled in a distance education course.

For information about all the student services, students should visit the Student Services Web site at http://www.dce.k-state.edu/studentservices.

Faculty

Kansas State University is an accredited institution offering credit courses through distance education. Distance education courses are taught by faculty members who teach K-State on-campus courses.

Admission

Each distance education degree program has specific admission requirements and procedures. Admission information is available for each program at the Web address listed in the Contact section.

Tuition and Fees

Distance education tuition at K-State is the same for both in-state and out-of-state students. Tuition is the cost for an academic course and includes a per-credit-hour charge. It also includes additional tuition components such as student services, TELENET 2 media fee, engineering equipment and mainte-

nance, licensing, tape/Web media, and distance education support.

Financial Aid

Students may be eligible for financial aid for distance education courses if federal requirements are met, if they are admitted and enrolled in a degree program in Kansas State University, and if they are enrolled in a minimum of 6 credit hours of Kansas State University course work.

Scholarships are also available to students enrolled in degree programs.

Applying

The application process for each program varies. For complete information on a specific program, students can access the Web site listed below or contact the Division of Continuing Education at 785-532-5575 or at the toll-free number listed in the Contact section, or by e-mail at the address listed in the Contact section.

CONTACT

Division of Continuing Education
Kansas State University
13 College Court Building
Manhattan, Kansas 66506-6002

Phone: 785-532-5575
        800-622-2KSU (toll-free)
Fax: 785-532-5637
E-mail: informationdce@k-state.edu
Web site: http://www.dce.k-state.edu/distance

KEISER UNIVERSITY

Keiser University eCampus

Fort Lauderdale, Florida

For over thirty years, Keiser University has provided high-quality career education and now offers degree programs online to prepare students for high-demand professions. Associate, bachelor's, and master's degrees are offered with a student-centered approach and curriculum that is in pace with technology and workforce demand trends.

Keiser University is accredited by the Commission on Colleges of the Southern Association of Colleges and Schools (1866 Southern Lane, Decatur, Georgia 30033-4097; 404-679-4501) to award associate, bachelor's, and master's degrees.

Keiser University eCampus offers degrees in fields that are in high demand and provides job placement assistance to all its students and alumni. The University researches trends for growing fields and tailors its curriculum to prepare students for entry into rewarding careers.

Distance Learning Program

Online learning is not impersonal at Keiser University Online. From admissions to faculty, Keiser University Online staff members are dedicated to superior student care accomplished through accessible staff and faculty members who foster a student-centered learning community, state-of-the-practice online classroom technology and user-friendly format to enhance learning, a one-class-at-a-time approach that allows busy students to focus on their education and develop the skills to excel, and extensive online resources that include information and access to all student services.

Delivery Media

Students should contact eCampus for technical requirements at admissions@ keiseruniversity.edu.

Programs of Study

Keiser University eCampus offers fully online programs and is a division of the Fort Lauderdale campus. Students interact with their instructors and each other using advanced technology, from anywhere at anytime.

The Master's in Business Administration (M.B.A.) is offered online.

Bachelor's degrees are offered online in accounting, business administration, criminal justice, health science, health services administration, homeland security, information technology management, legal studies, management information systems (MIS), and nursing (RN to B.S.N.).

Associate degrees are offered online in accounting, criminal justice, health services administration, information technology, medical assisting, and paralegal studies.

All online students must log in at least three times a week and actively participate in class. Each student must maintain satisfactory progress. Students must maintain a C average or better during each grading period.

Student Services

Keiser University Online programs are Web-based courses, designed by qualified faculty and staff members to create an interesting and interactive learning environment. Keiser's virtual classroom is comfortable, and courses can be taken easily by anyone with access to the World Wide Web. Lesson plans, assignments, and class schedules are posted online, while student-teacher interaction and student-student interac-

tion also occur over the Internet. Scheduled discussions, e-mail messages, live chats, and real-time group discussions are a few of the opportunities for interacting during an online course.

Online students have access to all Keiser University resources, from the bookstore to on-campus libraries. In addition, online access to information and services includes application, enrollment and registration procedures, financial aid information, tuition and fee information, course schedules and outlines, course demonstrations, faculty information, and an e-mail directory. Online students also have access to online academic advising and technical support through e-mail or telephone.

Credit Options

Credit for courses or degrees completed at another institution by students enrolling at Keiser University are subject to approval by the Dean of Academic Affairs. These courses or degrees must be similar in content and duration to those offered in the program for which the student has applied. The Dean of Academic Affairs considers only official transcripts mailed directly to Keiser University. Students are responsible for having official transcripts sent to Keiser University from their transfer institutions. Keiser University requires that, as a minimum, the student must complete the last 25 percent of credits in a program of study at the University. All transfer students are informed in writing of any credits accepted as transferable. Preliminary notification is presented, in most cases, prior to enrollment, but in no case, later than the end of the transfer student's first semester.

Admission

In order to be considered for enrollment at Keiser University, all applicants must supply verification of high school graduation (such as a transcript or diploma), verification of GED completion (GED scores or GED diploma), or proof of graduation from an international institution comparable to a U.S. secondary school.

Home schooled applicants who have a high school diploma are also considered for admission. Home schooled applicants should present their SAT or ACT scores with their application.

Students should make arrangements to take Keiser University's entrance examination (administered at the University) or provide results of their SAT or ACT exam. The University requirements for admission are a combined score of 800 on the SAT and a composite score of 17 on the ACT. In addition, students in Keiser University's medical programs must sign a Statement of Good Health prior to entrance into the program.

Keiser University is proud of the international character of its student body and welcomes students from other nations. All international students must be fluent in English before they enroll. Applicants must furnish proof that they can read, write, and speak English fluently. Keiser University has been approved by the United States Department of Immigration for students to pursue their studies at any of the University's campuses. The University can accept only F-1 visas based upon the student's program of study. International student applicants must meet the following requirements for admission to Keiser University: successful completion of a secondary school program that is equivalent to high school in the U.S., certification of financial ability to meet tuition and other necessary expenses or ability to qualify for financial aid as an eligible noncitizen, and the required minimum TOEFL score of 500 on the paper-based test or 225 on the computer-based test if the primary language is not English.

Applications for international students can be obtained through the Admissions Office. Students should apply at least two months prior to the start of the program.

Tuition and Fees

Students should contact the Admissions Department for current information on tuition and fees.

Financial Aid

Keiser University offers a number of financial aid programs to its students, including Federal Pell Grants, Federal Supplemental Educational Opportunity Grants (FSEOG), Keiser University Academic Scholarships, Federal Stafford Student Loans, Federal PLUS Loans, and Federal Perkins Loans.

Applying

Applications are accepted on an ongoing basis and can be accessed online at the University Web site at http://online.keiseruniversity.edu.

CONTACT

Admissions Director
Keiser University eCampus
1900 West Commercial Boulevard
Fort Lauderdale, Florida 33309

Phone: 954-351-4040
      866-KEISER-1 (866-534-7371, toll-free)
E-mail: admissions@keiseruniversity.edu
Web site: http://online.keiseruniversity.edu

KETTERING UNIVERSITY

Graduate Studies Department

Flint, Michigan

Kettering University, formerly known as GMI Engineering & Management Institute, is a highly respected private college located in Flint, Michigan. For nearly ninety years, Kettering University has proudly been recognized for providing students worldwide with specialized, practical, high-quality, and real-world education in engineering, automotive systems, manufacturing, business, management, and the sciences.

Kettering University is accredited by the North Central Association of Colleges and Schools of North America (NCA), the Accreditation Board for Engineering and Technology (ABET), and the Association of Collegiate Business Schools and Programs (ACBSP).

As featured in the 2008 edition of "America's Best Colleges Guide," published by U.S. News & World Report, Kettering University maintains its top Number One ranking for its Industrial and Manufacturing Engineering program—marking its eighth consecutive year at first place. In addition, two other Kettering undergraduate programs rank tops in the country for undergraduate engineering schools at which the highest degree awarded is a bachelor's or master's degree. These rankings include third for the Mechanical Engineering program and seventh for the Electrical and Computer Engineering program.

Known in the industry as "America's Co-Op College," Kettering University works with more than 700 undergraduate co-op employers—including various manufacturing and automotive companies, banks, hospitals, government agencies, and corporations.

Kettering University also offers first-class graduate and continuing education programs that develop leaders for the real world. Designed for the working professional, Kettering's master's degree programs are offered on campus as well as off campus through distance learning methods. The convenience, flexibility, and portability of distance learning makes Kettering's graduate programs available virtually anywhere in the world through CD-ROM, DVD, or online video-streaming. Participating employers make Kettering's graduate programs available to their employees at more than 130 off-site learning centers around the world.

Distance Learning Program

Kettering University's convenient and flexible graduate programs are available virtually anywhere through distance learning methods that include DVD, online video-streaming, Internet/Web, and CD-ROM (students must have access to RealPlayer for viewing class lectures on CD and online video-streaming formats). Kettering's distance learning is also supported by Blackboard.

Delivery Media

On-campus graduate courses are presented to students in a high-tech classroom/television studio on the Kettering campus to digitally capture the entire class presentation, lecture materials, case studies, question-answer sessions, and other contents presented. These class sessions are recorded onto CD-ROMs, DVDs, and Internet video-streaming formats.

Distance learning students get the same class experience and materials that on-campus students receive, without ever setting foot on campus. Since courses are recorded, distance learning students receive the course content/materials one week after on-campus students.

Students can select the delivery format that best suits their needs. Kettering ships course materials (such as CDs and DVDs) to the student on a weekly basis, or students can simply view their courses online through video-streaming on Blackboard. Exams are sent to and proctored by a site coordinator/proctor assigned to a specific learning center or by a designated proctor for independent students.

Programs of Study

Most of Kettering University's graduate degrees are Master of Science degree programs that consist of ten core classes, totaling 40 credit hours. (This does not include any prerequisite courses that may apply for some programs.) Kettering also offers an M.B.A. program with several concentrations, totaling 48 credit hours. Kettering designed the master's programs to be terminal professional degrees for engineers, managers, and business professionals. The programs are particularly attractive to working professionals who want to extend and broaden their related skills. Although designed as terminal degrees, they also provide preparation for study at the doctoral level.

Graduate students have up to six years to complete the degree requirements. The textbooks are free, and the GMAT or GRE is not required for admission.

Kettering University's master's degree programs include an M.B.A. (with leadership, general, or technical concentrations), engineering (with concentrations available in automotive systems (on campus only)), electrical and computer engineering, industrial engineering (on campus only), manufacturing engineering, manufacturing engineering–lean manufacturing (on campus only), mechanical cognate, and mechanical design; engineering management, with a concentration available in lean manufacturing (on campus only); information technology; manufacturing management; manufacturing operations; and operations management.

To learn more about Kettering University's graduate programs, including courses, prerequisites, and admission requirements, prospective students should visit the University's Web site.

Credit Options

Credits are earned by completing courses; however, students may transfer up to 8 credit hours. Credit may be transferred for grades of B or better and is granted only for completed graduate study. Credit is not given for experi-ence. Anyone interested in transfer credit should obtain an application for transfer credit from the Graduate Office.

Faculty

Kettering University's excellent faculty and staff members are truly committed to educating and preparing future leaders for a global workplace. The majority of the University's graduate programs are taught by nationally ranked faculty members who hold doctorate degrees in addition to having practical experience in their respective fields of study.

Professors announce office hours for students to clarify materials, ask questions, or obtain assistance. Students may contact professors during office hours via e-mail, phone or voice-mail, fax, or online bulletin boards.

Admission

Only students with at least a bachelor's degree are accepted into Kettering's graduate programs. A bachelor's degree in engineering from an ABET-accredited institution is required for admission to any of the Master of Science in engineering degree programs. Two letters of recommendation are also required for engineering students as well as for the manufacturing operations program. Other requirements include a minimum 3.0 grade point average in undergraduate work and two supervisor recommendations. Certain other requirements must be met for some programs. The same requirements apply to on-campus and distance learning students.

Tuition and Fees

Tuition for graduate studies during the 2008–09 academic year is $674 per credit hour. There are no application or registration fees for U.S. applicants. There is a $50 application fee for international applicants.

Applying

Application deadlines are as follows: for the summer 2008 term, the deadline was June 16; for fall 2008, the deadline is September 15; for the winter 2009 term, the deadline is December 15; and for spring 2009, the deadline is March 23.

CONTACT

Kettering University
1700 West Third Avenue
Flint, Michigan 48504-4898

Phone: 866-584-7237 Ext. 4 (toll-free)
Fax: 810-762-9935
E-mail: gradoff@kettering.edu
Web site: http://www.kettering.edu

LOCK HAVEN UNIVERSITY OF PENNSYLVANIA

eCampus Programs

Lock Haven, Pennsylvania

Lock Haven University of Pennsylvania (LHUP) encourages academic excellence. The University's educational programs are designed to develop the intellectual skills and talents of all students. Through formal and informal instruction, students are guided to achieve their full potential. Students gain a better self-understanding, a sense of individual and community responsibility, and knowledge of cultural diversity and the global community. The institution is accredited by the Middle States Association of Colleges and Schools, and distance education is included in the scope of the accreditation.

"This educational experience at LHUP has helped me to focus my goals and redefine them more clearly and has also given me the opportunity to achieve greater insight into this world. This has been the best experience of my life."
Carolyne M. Timko, M.L.A.; Blossburg, Pennsylvania.

Distance Learning Program

Lock Haven University (LHUP) provides students with the opportunity to complete a full degree program or to complete individual courses either at a local education center or in the convenience of their homes.

Delivery Media

Lock Haven University offers distance learning programs via videoconferencing-based technologies or Web-based technologies to create a fully online experience. The videoconferencing sites are limited to sites contracting with the University. Web-based technologies include a full-featured course-management system, Web-casting of lectures, resource materials, threaded discussions, journaling, real-time chat discussions, document sharing, and other instructional methods that create active and engaged learning communities.

Programs of Study

Students can complete some of their LHUP General Education requirements through the distance learning program as a nonmatriculating student. Four master's degree programs are also available. These include the Master of Education in Alternative Education program (online), Master of Education in

Teaching and Learning program (online), Master of Liberal Arts (online), and Master of Health Science in Physician Assistant Studies program (distributed learning).

Noncredit certificates are available in business, construction, health care, Internet design and technical programs, networking and CompTIA certification prep, Microsoft certification prep, paralegal studies and legal secretary studies, and video game design and development. K-12 teachers can also take continuing education classes and receive Act 48 credit.

Special Programs

Lock Haven University encourages students to consider studying abroad. LHUP has a large and diverse international program, providing many opportunities for its students to study abroad for periods ranging from several weeks in a semester to a year or more. The University has direct exchange programs with institutions in Australia, China, Costa Rica, Croatia, England, Finland, France, Germany, Italy, Japan, Mexico, Poland, Russia, Scotland, Spain, and Ukraine. The University offers interested and qualified students an opportunity to participate in various

internship programs that provide field experiences to supplement classroom learning.

Student Services

The course management system organizes information, services, and resources relevant to distance learners. Forms are available online to apply for admissions and/or register for courses. The Stevenson Library caters to online students, providing a catalog of resources and access to databases and full-text journals online.

Credit Options

The various subject examinations offered through the College Board's Advanced Placement (AP) program are approved and credit is awarded based on a test score of 3 or higher. With the exception of only one General Examination (English Composition) and four subject tests (Business Law, Educational Psychology, College Composition, and Freshman English) offered through the College Board's College-Level Examination Program (CLEP), degree credit may be earned by candidates who achieve a scaled score equivalent to the 50th percentile or higher using current national norms for each test. There is no limit to the number of courses for which CLEP or AP may award credit. A maximum of 6 graduate semester hours may be transferred and applied toward most graduate degrees.

Faculty

Of the 259 faculty members, 91 percent are full-time. Faculty members are noted for their diverse expertise, their interest in interdisciplinary study and their dedication to working with adult students. In addition to teaching, faculty members advise students, formulate program policy, and supervise independent study and capstone projects.

Admission

Admission requirements vary by program. Generally, undergraduates should have completed college-preparatory course work in high school, have a satisfactory command of the English language, and should have taken either the SAT or the ACT. In general, graduate students must have a baccalaureate degree from an accredited institution and a minimum GPA of 3.0.

Tuition and Fees

Tuition and fees are set by the Board of Governors of the Pennsylvania State System of Higher Education once a year.

For the 2007–08 academic year, undergraduate tuition was $216 per credit for Pennsylvania residents and $456 per credit for nonresidents; the distance education fee was 10 percent of the tuition. Graduate in-state tuition was $345 per credit, and out-of-state students paid $552 per credit. For graduate and undergraduate students, the tuition technology fee was $43 for residents and $65 for nonresidents.

For current information, students should check the Web site at http://www.lhup.edu/financial-services/bursar/. The cost of noncredit courses and certificate programs may vary.

Financial Aid

Financial aid to meet the costs of attending LHUP is available from a variety of programs, including grants, loans, and scholarships. The majority of these programs provide funds based on computed financial need, but some non-need-based programs are also available. To apply for financial aid, students must complete the Free Application for Federal Student Aid (FAFSA). Pennsylvania residents should complete this form as provided by the Pennsylvania Higher Education Assistance Agency and any supplemental forms required for the Pennsylvania State Grant. Of all full-time matriculated undergraduates who enrolled in 2003, 77 percent of undergraduates had their financial need fully met.

Applying

Application procedures vary by program, and students should contact the distance education office for specific information. Applicants are required to submit the completed application, a $25 application fee, all high school transcripts, and official SAT or ACT scores. In addition, graduate programs require official transcripts of all undergraduate and graduate work; students applying to the Master of Education programs must also submit three letters of recommendation and a writing sample. International students must also submit TOEFL scores. All applications are processed on a rolling basis.

CONTACT

Dr. Carlos Morales, Executive Director
eCampus
Lock Haven University of Pennsylvania
Lock Haven, Pennsylvania 17745
Phone: 570-484-2404
       877-268-4688 (toll-free)
Fax: 570-484-2638
E-mail: cmorales@lhup.edu
Web site: http://www.ecampus.lhup.edu/

LYNN UNIVERSITY
Institute for Distance Learning
Boca Raton, Florida

Founded in 1962 and located in Boca Raton, Florida, Lynn University is a private coeducational institution whose primary purposes are education; the preservation, discovery, dissemination, and creative application of knowledge; and the preparation of its graduates with the academic foundation for lifelong learning. Service, scholarly activity that includes research, and ongoing professional development allow the faculty, in conjunction with the entire University community, to fulfill its purposes: facilitating student-centered learning and fostering the intellectual life of the University.

Distance Learning Program

The Institute for Distance Learning provides students with easy access to online courses from anywhere in the world where Internet access is available. Most online courses follow a term calendar of six 8-week terms per year. Start dates for graduate courses and adult undergraduate courses are in August, October, January, March, May, and July. Online courses associated with the Day Division follow the Day Division schedule.

Online courses reside on the online course management system and can only be accessed by students and faculty members engaged in online course work.

The online degree programs facilitated by Lynn University's Institute for Distance Learning offer undergraduate and graduate degrees that combine a comprehensive general education with a study in a major and validation of prior learning experience.

A student's credit hours are earned through instruction (distance learning or traditional classroom), transfer credits from an accredited college or university, military service course credits (DANTES), Florida Department of Law Enforcement (FDLE) or a similar state training facility, professional training or certification as recognized by the American Council on Education (ACE) or the College Level Examination Pro-gram (CLEP), and/or a student's professional experience or experiential learning.

Lynn University is approved by the Commission on Colleges of the Southern Association of Colleges and Schools (SACS) (1866 Southern Lane, Decatur, Georgia 30033-4097; telephone: 404-679-4501) to offer complete distance learning degree programs via the Web.

Delivery Media

Internet technology encourages interactions between faculty members and students, students and other students, and students and resources (books, journals, electronic library services, and the Internet). Courses are delivered using Blackboard, a student-friendly platform that affords learners the opportunity to complete assignments and engage in learning activities at convenient times. Distance learning courses are delivered in an accelerated format, with six 8-week class terms per academic year. Students may begin their studies during any of the terms.

Programs of Study

Lynn University offers online courses leading to seven graduate and undergraduate degrees. Students can find the course schedule at http://www.lynn.edu/pm.

Master's-level online graduate degree programs are offered in administration, with a specialization in criminal justice or in emergency planning and administration; business administration, with a specialization in aviation management, financial valuation and investment management, hospitality management, international business, marketing, mass communication and media management, or sports and athletics administration; and in educational leadership, with a specialization in higher education administration, school administration, or school administration with ESOL endorsement.

Undergraduate degree programs include business administration, criminal justice administration, and psychology. An online post-baccalaureate certificate in emergency planning and administration rounds out the available courses of study.

Credit Options

Most online courses are 3 credits each. Courses with labs are 4 credits. Courses offered with less than 3 credits are identified in the Academic Catalog, which can be found online at http://www.lynn.edu/pm.

Lynn University accepts transfer credits from most regionally accredited schools. Specific information about transfer credits may be found in the catalog. Credits earned in the online program can be combined with credits earned on campus to complete a degree.

Faculty

The faculty members at Lynn University are highly qualified and committed to providing high-quality instruction and learning opportunities for self-directed learners. Along with excellent academic credentials, many faculty members are practitioners in their fields of expertise, thus providing the theoretical context for the practical applications of the subject matter.

Admission

To enroll in an undergraduate degree program, students must have earned a high school diploma or GED certificate.

Attendees of foreign schools are required to submit an international transcript evaluation and course equivalency report. International students whose first language is not English must submit official test results of the Test of English as a Foreign Language (TOEFL) or IELTS. Applicants with TOEFL scores of 470–499 (paper based) or 150–170 (computer- based) are placed in the English for Academic Purposes Program. Applicants with TOEFL scores of 500 or higher (paper-based) or 173 (computer-based) are considered for regular admission.

Graduate students must have earned a college diploma from a regionally accredited or internationally listed college or university. Applicants whose undergraduate grade point average (GPA) was less than 3.0 must also submit the appropriate entrance examination score from the GRE, GMAT, or MAT. All graduate degree program applicants must submit two recommendation letters, a resume, and a statement of professional goals. Other admission requirements vary by degree program and are outlined in the Academic Catalog.

Tuition and Fees

All new students pay a one-time nonrefundable $50 application fee. The tuition fees and registration fees follow the pricing established for the respective colleges and noncredit programs. For the 2007–08 academic year, the fees were $280 per undergraduate credit hour and $525 per graduate credit hour. Noncredit tuition varies with the individual courses. There is a registration fee of $50 at the beginning of each term enrolled. More information and specific details regarding fees are available in the Academic Catalog on the University's Web site, http://www.lynn.edu.

Financial Aid

The Financial Aid Office is committed to tailoring a financial package to meet students' individual needs. For those who take advantage of available financial aid (federal, state, and institutional), private higher education is affordable. Students should visit the "Resources for Future Students" section of the Web site for tools that will help them calculate costs and for detailed information on financial aid.

Applying

Students may apply online or download a printable application at http://www.lynn.edu/pm. To obtain an application by mail, students should call the Admissions Office at 800-888-LYNN (5966) (toll-free in the United States) or 561-237-7900 (outside the U.S.).

CONTACT

Mary L. Tebes, Ph.D.
Director, Institute for Distance Learning
Lynn University
3601 North Military Trail
Boca Raton, Florida 33431
Phone: 561-237-7902
E-mail: mtebes@lynn.edu
Web site: http://www.lynn.edu

NAROPA UNIVERSITY

Boulder, Colorado

Naropa University is a private, nonprofit, nonsectarian liberal arts institution dedicated to advancing contemplative education. This approach to learning integrates the best of Eastern and Western educational traditions, helping students know themselves more deeply and engage constructively with others. Accredited by the Higher Learning Commission of the North Central Association of Colleges and Schools, the University comprises a four-year undergraduate college and graduate degree programs in the arts, education, environmental leadership, psychology, and religious studies, as well as a study-abroad program in Prague, Czech Republic.

Distance Learning Program

In addition to its many in-residence programs, Naropa University offers four low-residency graduate degree programs: an M.A. in contemplative education, an M.A. in transpersonal psychology (MATP), an M.A. in transpersonal psychology with a concentration in ecopsychology, and an M.F.A. in creative writing.

Delivery Media

Courses are offered from the heart of Naropa University's liberal arts curriculum. They are taught by experienced Naropa faculty members and translated and refined for delivery through state-of-the-art Internet technology. Naropa utilizes the latest interactive Internet technologies, with private, password-secure Web pages for the exclusive use of the students and instructors of each class. Communication tools include audio lectures, multimedia, chat rooms, threaded discussion groups, private online journals, written lectures, local assignments, and group projects in a dynamic online learning community. Enrolled students have access to 24/7 technical support.

Programs of Study

The Master of Arts in contemplative education is a two-year, 36-credit degree program for practicing teachers from all levels of instruction and for others interested in a nonsectarian, contemplative approach to teaching and learning. This professional development program joins together the wisdom and skillful means of Eastern meditative traditions with Western holistic educational methods and insights. Based on the principles and practices of mindfulness and awareness primarily from Tibetan contemplative traditions, the curriculum offers a path of personal nourishment and effective pedagogy. The program begins in late June with a 3½-week residential program, which is followed by two online courses in each of the fall and spring semesters. Online semesters apply contemplative approaches to each student's classroom as well as extend academic studies of spiritual approaches to teaching, learning, and human emotional development. The second year repeats this sequence, except the Thesis Seminar is the only spring online course. The program is completed during the third summer with a weekend thesis presentation. Summer programs focus on the contemplative transformation of the teacher. For further information, students should contact Richard Brown, Chair, M.A. in Contemplative Education Program (phone: 303-545-4765; e-mail: rbrown@naropa.edu).

The low-residency Master of Arts in transpersonal psychology is a two-year, 36-credit program that integrates intellectual rigor, contemplative practice, personal development, and applications of transpersonal psychology. The curriculum includes required courses on foundations, theories and applications of transpersonal psychology, and meditation practice. Two 1-week summer intensives on the campus provide community building and exploration of transpersonal practices and issues. The transpersonal psychology program does not result in a clinical degree. Those who already have professional clinical or counseling training and credentials may use this degree to expand their understanding and practice. Prospective students should contact John Davis, Director, M.A. in Transpersonal Psychology Program (phone: 303-245-4654; e-mail: jdavis@naropa.edu).

The Master of Arts in transpersonal psychology with a concentration in ecopsychology integrates psychology and ecology in the study of human/nature relationships. At Naropa University, contemplative practice and transpersonal psychology provide a foundation for this integration, and the result is a unique contemplative and transpersonal orientation. Following the general format of the MATP program, the ecopsychology program is a two-year, 38-credit program that begins in the summer. Students also attend a three-day intensive course in Boulder each winter. Course work integrates theory, experience, and contemplative practice in the study of ecopsychology, ecology, transpersonal psychology, and meditative practices. The ecopsychology concentration does not result in a clinical degree. Additional information is available from Jed Swift, Director, Ecopsychology Program (phone: 303-245-4837 or 614-921-1997; e-mail: jedscottswift@earthlink.net).

The Master of Fine Arts in creative writing is a 49-credit degree program.

Courses are taken online during the regular academic year, and 16 credit hours of the Summer Writing Program (spread out over two or three summers) are completed at Naropa University's Boulder campus. The curriculum balances online writing workshops and literature seminars. This reflects the department's conviction that creative writing, reading, and critical analysis must be involved in a writer's growth. The contact person for the program is Junior Burke, Chair, Department of Writing and Poetics, and Director, M.F.A. in Creative Writing Program (phone: 303-245-4820; e-mail: jrburke@naropa.edu).

Faculty

The Naropa University faculty is distinguished by a wealth of experience in the professional, artistic, and scholastic applications of their disciplines. In addition to the outstanding ranked faculty members, an international community of scholars and artists is consistently drawn to Naropa because of its strong vision and leadership in contemplative education. The average class size is 14, and Naropa's student-teacher ratio is 10:1.

Admission

In keeping with its philosophy of contemplative education, Naropa University's graduate school values and seeks to foster an individual's aspiration to contribute to the world with understanding and compassion. The academic departments' admissions committees consider inquisitiveness and engagement with the world as well as previous academic achievement when making acceptance decisions. A student's transcript, statement of interest, interview, letters of recommendation, and supplemental application materials play important roles in the admissions process. GRE scores are not required.

Tuition and Fees

Beginning in summer 2008, graduate tuition is $726 per credit hour, plus a registration fee ($120 for summer, $250 for fall, $250 for spring). In addition, the technology fee for a 3-credit class is $120.

Financial Aid

Naropa University makes every attempt to assist students who do not have the financial resources to accomplish their educational objectives. Approximately 70 percent of Naropa's degree-seeking students receive some form of financial aid. Awards are based on financial need and are offered in the form of scholarships, grants, loans, student employment, and graduate assistantships. Naropa also offers a payment plan that breaks tuition into four monthly payments with no interest charges.

Applying

The suggested deadline for receiving completed applications for the summer and fall semesters is January 15 and for the spring semester, October 15. Any applications received after the suggested deadline are reviewed on a space-available basis.

CONTACT

Office of Admissions
Naropa University
2130 Arapahoe Avenue
Boulder, Colorado 80302
Phone: 303-546-3572
      800-772-6951 (toll-free)
E-mail: admissions@naropa.edu
Web site: http://www.naropa.edu

THE NEW SCHOOL: A UNIVERSITY

Bachelor's Degree Program for Adults

New York, New York

The New School was founded in New York City nearly a century ago as a bastion of intellectual and artistic freedom. Today, it is a leading urban university containing some of the nation's most respected programs in design, liberal arts, the performing arts, and social and political thought. Artists, scholars, and students from across the country and around the world attend The New School's diverse programs, enjoying small class sizes, superior resources, and a renowned faculty of artists, scholars, and professionals who practice what they teach. The New School's founding mission was to create a place where global peace and justice were more than theoretical ideals. To this day, New School students participate in programs that strive for academic excellence, technical mastery, and engaged world citizenship.

In addition to offering seventy graduate and undergraduate degrees, the University offers certificate programs and more than 1,000 continuing education courses to 25,000 adult learners every year. The University began offering online courses and programs in 1994 with the support of grants from FIPSE, ATT, Citibank, and the Alfred P. Sloan Foundation. The New School and its degree programs are fully accredited by the Commission on Higher Education of the Middle States Association of Colleges and Schools. Its credits and degrees are recognized and accepted by other accredited colleges, universities, and professional schools throughout the United States.

Distance Learning Program

The New School offers online degrees, certificates, and individual courses to more than 1,110 students. More than 200 Web-based classes taught by New School professors are available annually and can be taken for degree credit, general credit (courses for transfer to other institutions), or no credit. In March 2007, Crain's New York Business noted that The New School's seminar style of teaching translated especially well to the Web and that the University's online program was "fast becoming a national model."

All online courses are drawn from the University's curriculum and are designed to integrate with the rest of the student's program of study. A recent issue of *ComputerLife* magazine cited The New School as having "one of the best and most extensive course offerings in the field of liberal arts online."

Delivery Media

Students must have a computer and an Internet connection in order to access MyNewSchool.edu, where the University's online classes "meet." Similar to any class taken on campus, the professor presents the material and then leads a discussion. However, instead of speaking, students post comments using the My Courses feature of MyNewSchool. The experience is much like that of a traditional class—in fact, the conversation is sometimes more in depth, because the posting mechanism makes it easier for all students to participate. Online classes meet asynchronously, meaning that students can read materials, join discussions, and post responses at any time. Although each class is different, it is strongly recommended that students log in to the class a minimum of three times each week.

Programs of Study

Students from across the country and around the globe turn to The New School for General Studies to complete their bachelor's degrees—online or on campus in Greenwich Village—in an innovative liberal arts program tailored specifically to the needs of adults. With the assistance of a faculty adviser, each student selects a program of study based on intellectual interests and professional goals. The New School requires a total of 120 credits for the bachelor's degree, with at least 30 credits of course work as a matriculated student. However, the credit requirement may be waived for students age 24 or older.

The following areas of study are currently available to bachelor's degree students: cinema and media studies, the city, creative writing, democracy and cultural pluralism, literature, media production, psychology, visual arts, and visual studies. Classes are also available in food studies and business. For detailed information on the courses within these areas, students should visit http://www.newschool.edu/ba.

Special Programs

The New School Bachelor's Program online offers non–liberal arts credit for internships arranged through the degree program office. To apply for an internship, students should have earned at least 12 credits in residence at The New School and have an internship in mind that contributes to their overall plan of study. Students are allowed to take up to two internships while matriculated in the Bachelor's Program. Credit for independent study courses can be arranged through the degree program office in conjunction with the academic departments.

Student Services

The same student services that are available to those who take classes on campus—advising, admissions, registration, tuition payment, and enrollment—are also available to the University's online students. Online students have the advantage of being able to arrange everything online or by phone, fax, mail, or e-mail—all without having to visit the campus.

Through an online student orientation, students learn how to navigate the online classroom, gain familiarity with online communication, and get a sense of the dynamics of online interaction before a course begins. The orientation remains available for reference throughout the semester. Technical support and student service professionals are available by phone or e-mail 24 hours a day, seven days a week.

Credit Options

The New School awards up to 6 credits for college-level learning comparable to the courses offered at the University. Students considering applying for credit for prior learning should discuss their options with their adviser.

Faculty

Instructors at the New School come from diverse fields within and outside the field of education. They all share one common motivation—teaching what they are most interested in and what they consider most valuable to know. In addition to academic scholars, many are working professionals who bring to the classroom the benefit of their experience.

Admission

The New School Bachelor's Program online welcomes applications from individuals with at least 33 credits toward a bachelor's degree (the credit requirement may be waived for students age 24 or older) who have the maturity to be in charge of their own learning process and can demonstrate their ability to work successfully in an intellectually challenging academic environment. The New School seeks students who are inquisitive, independent, and self-directed. Applicants should have strong verbal skills (spoken and written) and a capacity for clear, critical thinking.

Tuition and Fees

Tuition for 2008–09 is $890 per credit plus $115 in University fees, which covers the registration and technology fee, as well as a Student Activity Fee of $15. New tuition and fee schedules are published several months in advance of each academic year.

Financial Aid

Financial aid is granted on the basis of need and merit, with financial need determined in accordance with federal regulations. Packages awarded are based on estimated total educational costs for the academic year. Most forms of financial aid require recipients to take a minimum of 6 credits each semester, and some require full-time study (12 credits or more). To maintain eligibility for federal and state financial aid, students must be in good academic standing and must be making satisfactory progress toward their baccalaureate degree.

Applying

Students must submit the completed application form, the nonrefundable $50 application fee, official transcripts from each college or university attended, a resume, and three essays (Educational Objective, New Way of Thinking, and Course Plan). An interview may be required. Additional information can be found on the link for Admissions at http://adultba.newschool.edu/.

For the fall semester, the priority deadline is June 1 and the final deadline is July 1. The deadline for spring admission is November 1.

CONTACT

Office of Admissions
The New School
66 West 12th Street, Room 401
New York, New York 10011
Phone: 212-229-5630
Fax: 212-989-3887
E-mail: nsadmissions@newschool.edu
Web site: http://www.newschool.edu/ba

THE NEW SCHOOL: A UNIVERSITY

M.A. in Teaching English to Speakers of Other Languages
New York, New York

The New School was founded in New York City nearly a century ago as a bastion of intellectual and artistic freedom. Today, it is a leading urban university containing some of the nation's most respected programs in design, liberal arts, the performing arts, and social and political thought. Artists, scholars, and students from across the country and around the world attend The New School's diverse programs, enjoying small class sizes, superior resources, and a renowned faculty of artists, scholars, and professionals who practice what they teach. The New School's founding mission was to create a place where global peace and justice were more than theoretical ideals. To this day, New School students participate in programs that strive for academic excellence, technical mastery, and engaged world citizenship.

In addition to offering seventy graduate and undergraduate degrees, the University offers certificate programs and nearly 1,000 continuing education courses to 15,000 adult learners every year. The University began offering online courses and programs in 1994 with the support of grants from FIPSE, ATT, Citibank, and the Alfred P. Sloan Foundation. The New School and its degree programs are fully accredited by the Commission on Higher Education of the Middle States Association of Colleges and Schools. Its credits and degrees are recognized and accepted by other accredited colleges, universities, and professional schools throughout the United States.

Distance Learning Program

The New School offers degrees, certificates, and individual courses online to more than 1,110 students. Over 200 Web-based classes taught by New School professors are available annually and can be taken for degree credit, general credit (courses for transfer to other institutions), or no credit. In March 2007, *Crain's New York Business* noted that The New School's seminar style of teaching translated especially well to the Web and that the University's online program was "fast becoming a national model."

All online courses are drawn from the University's curriculum and are designed to integrate with the rest of the student's program of study. A recent issue of *ComputerLife* magazine cited The New School as having "one of the best and most extensive course offerings in the field of liberal arts online."

Delivery Media

Students must have a computer and an Internet connection in order to access MyNewSchool.edu, where the University's online classes "meet." As in any classes taken on campus, the professor presents the material and then leads a discussion. However, instead of speaking, students post comments using the My Courses feature of MyNewSchool. The experience is much like that of a traditional class—in fact, the conversation is sometimes more in depth, because the posting mechanism makes it easier for all students to participate. Online classes meet asynchronously, meaning that students can read materials, join discussions, and post responses at any time. Although each class is different, it is strongly recommended that students log in to the class a minimum of three times each week.

Programs of Study

The New School's 30-credit Master of Arts in Teaching English to Speakers of Other Languages (MATESOL) program is designed to raise the standards of trained professionals in the TESOL field and consequently to raise the standards of the profession itself. Some elements that make the New School MATESOL distinctive include its esteemed international faculty, political and cultural orientation, flexible scheduling, and emphasis on theory leading to practical, hands-on training. A thesis is not required.

The MATESOL program offers concentrations in teaching and curriculum development. The program provides students with the practical, relevant training they will need to advance in careers in teaching or designing curriculum in the public or private sector. The goal of the program is to produce well-trained, culturally and politically aware professionals who are proficient in their specialties and knowledgeable about crucial issues in language teaching and learning in the evolving global environment.

Students who take six courses online and four courses during the summer in New York City can complete the MATESOL in one calendar year or three semesters. Students generally need four semesters to complete the entire program online.

Special Programs

A six-week intensive summer program at The New School in Greenwich Village in New York City gives MATESOL students the option of completing 12 credits of course work while experiencing one of the most exciting cities in the world. Students also have the chance to do internships at well-known ESOL publishers or in ESL programs at some of the best teaching sites in the city. Housing is available in university dormitories.

Student Services

The same student services that are available to those who take classes on campus—advising, admissions, registration, tuition payment, and enrollment—are also available to the University's online students. Online students have the advantage of being able to arrange everything online or by phone, fax, mail, or e-mail, without the need to schedule a campus visit.

Through an online student orientation, students have the opportunity to learn how to navigate the online classroom, gain familiarity with online communication, and get a sense of the dynamics of online interaction before a course begins. The orientation remains available for reference throughout the semester. Technical support and student service professionals are available by phone or e-mail 24 hours a day, seven days a week.

Faculty

Instructors at The New School come from diverse fields within and outside education. In addition to academic scholars, many are working professionals who bring to the classroom the benefit of their experience. The MATESOL faculty members and course developers have been chosen from among the best, most experienced, and most respected TESOL professionals around the world, including teacher educators, publishers, writers, curriculum designers, and program administrators.

Admission

The MATESOL program welcomes applications from individuals interested in preparing for careers in teaching English to adults and from ESL or EFL professionals with two or more years of teaching experience. Proficiency in a language other than English is assumed for all applicants. Applications are reviewed and admission decisions are made by a faculty committee.

Tuition and Fees

Tuition for the 2008–09 academic year is $1076 per credit plus $115 per semester in University fees, which cover the registration and technology fee, as well as a Student Activity Fee of $15. New tuition and fee schedules are published several months in advance of each academic year.

Financial Aid

Financial aid is granted on the basis of need and merit, with financial need determined in accordance with federal regulations. Packages awarded are based on estimated total educational costs for the academic year. Most forms of financial aid require recipients to take a minimum of 6 credits each semester, and some require full-time study (12 credits or more). To maintain eligibility for federal and state financial aid, students must be in good academic standing.

The MATESOL program gives scholarship consideration to all applicants as part of the admissions review process. Strong academic and professional achievements identify those candidates for admission who, in the estimation of the admissions committee, merit special recognition. Scholarship amounts vary and cover partial costs of tuition. A student must register for a minimum of 6 credits to maintain the scholarship.

Applying

Applicants must hold a bachelor's degree from an accredited university. Students must submit the completed application, the $50 application fee, official transcripts from every institution attended for undergraduate and graduate studies, a resume, a statement of purpose, and two letters of recommendation. In addition, applicants for the concentrations in publishing and writing, program development and management, or curriculum development must have completed a minimum of 100 hours of English language teacher training as well as two years of English language teaching and must submit a lesson plan, an essay on the philosophy of teaching, and one recommendation from a teaching supervisor.

The deadline for fall admission is March 15. All applicants are encouraged to submit applications well in advance of the stated deadline. Only completed applications received by the deadline are considered for the upcoming academic term.

CONTACT

Office of Admissions
The New School
66 West 12th Street, Room 401
New York, New York 10011
Phone: 212-229-5630
Fax: 212-989-3887
E-mail: nsadmissions@newschool.
edu
Web site: http://www.newschool.
edu/matesol

THE NEW SCHOOL: A UNIVERSITY

Master of Arts in Media Studies Program

New York, New York

THE NEW SCHOOL
A UNIVERSITY

The New School was founded in New York City nearly a century ago as a bastion of intellectual and artistic freedom. Today, it is a leading urban university containing some of the nation's most respected programs in design, liberal arts, the performing arts, and social and political thought. Artists, scholars, and students from across the country and around the world attend The New School's diverse programs, enjoying small class sizes, superior resources, and a renowned faculty of artists, scholars, and professionals who practice what they teach. The New School's founding mission was to create a place where global peace and justice were more than theoretical ideals. To this day, New School students participate in programs that strive for academic excellence, technical mastery, and engaged world citizenship.

In addition to offering seventy graduate and undergraduate degrees, the University offers certificate programs and nearly 1,000 continuing education courses to 15,000 adult learners every year. The University began offering online courses and programs in 1994 with the support of grants from FIPSE, ATT, Citibank, and the Alfred P. Sloan Foundation. The New School and its degree programs are fully accredited by the Commission on Higher Education of the Middle States Association of Colleges and Schools. Its credits and degrees are recognized and accepted by other accredited colleges, universities, and professional schools throughout the United States.

Distance Learning Program

The New School offers degrees, certificates, and individual courses online to more than 1,110 students. Over 200 Web-based classes taught by New School professors are available annually and can be taken for degree credit, general credit (courses for transfer to other institutions), or no credit. In March 2007, Crain's New York Business noted that The New School's seminar style of teaching translated especially well to the Web and that the University's online program was "fast becoming a national model."

All online courses are drawn from the University's curriculum and are designed to integrate with the rest of the student's program of study. A recent issue of *ComputerLife* magazine cited The New School as having "one of the best and most extensive course offerings in the field of liberal arts online."

Delivery Media

Students must have a computer and an Internet connection in order to access MyNewSchool.edu, where the University's online classes "meet." As in any class taken on campus, the professor presents the material and then leads a discussion. However, instead of speaking, students post comments using the My Courses feature of MyNewSchool. The experience is much like that of a traditional class—in fact, the conversation is sometimes more in depth, because the posting mechanism makes it easier for all students to participate. Online classes meet asynchronously, meaning that students can read materials, join discussions, and post responses at any time. Although each class is different, it is strongly recommended that students log in to the class a minimum of three times each week.

Program of Study

In an era defined by rapidly changing information and communication technologies, The New School's Master of Arts (M.A.) in Media Studies program can give students the competitive edge they need to advance or change their careers in various fields of media. The New School's Media Studies program is one of the few in the country that allows students to integrate course work in media theory, media production, and media management. The program helps students put theory into practice, guided by a faculty of media professionals from all walks of academic, artistic, and commercial life, who strive to be humane and thoughtful citizens in an increasingly mediated world.

Students must successfully complete a minimum of 36 credits (thesis option) or 39 credits (nonthesis option) to fulfill degree requirements. All degree candidates are required to take Foundations of Media Theory, Foundations of Media Design, Media Research Methods, and two courses in a production sequence (video, audio, film, digital design, or multimedia). The online program of study provides an opportunity for students to satisfy all the requirements for the M.A. degree. Required theory and research courses and a full complement of electives are offered online over two academic years.

The New School M.A. in Media Studies program reflects a commitment to a number of core values: an emphasis on the essential relationship between media theory and practice in the belief that a conceptual understanding of media is necessary for creating discerning productions and, in turn, that producing media messages grounds an understanding of theory; a respect for both aesthetic and pragmatic dimensions of communication; a recognition of the integrity and potential contribution of all media formats; an awareness of the ethical imperatives of communication throughout the "global village;" an appreciation of the ways in which media theory and practice can contribute to intercultural understanding; an acknowledgment of the challenging marketplace conditions facing today's graduates; and a belief in the importance of openness to change and innovation.

Special Programs

Each semester the students in Media Studies create videos, films, and multimedia as part of their requirements for the degree. These showcases, which highlight selected group projects and special events, include the Critical Themes in Media Studies Student Conference, Mixed Messages, the Hirshon Film Festival, and Immediacy, an online journal.

Media studies students have held internships over the past years at such organizations as Showtime, MTV, Oxygen Television, NBC, Children's Television Workshop, Bloomberg Television, *POV, 60 Minutes,* Polygram Records, and the United Nations.

Student Services

The same student services that are available to those who take classes on campus—advising, admissions, registration, tuition payment, and enrollment—are also available to online students. Online students have the advantage of being able to access these services online or by phone, fax, mail, or e-mail, without the need to schedule a campus visit.

Through an online student orientation, students have the opportunity to learn how to navigate the online classroom, gain familiarity with online communication, and get a sense of the dynamics of online interaction before a course begins. The orientation remains available for reference throughout the semester. Technical support and student service professionals are available by phone or e-mail 24 hours a day, seven days a week.

Credit Options

Admitted degree candidates may apply for transfer of up to 9 credits to be used toward the elective requirement.

Faculty

Instructors at the New School come from diverse fields within and outside education. They all share one common motivation—teaching what they are most interested in and what they consider most valuable to know. In addition to academic scholars, many are working professionals who bring to the classroom the benefit of their experience.

Admission

The Media Studies Program takes an inclusive view of media and communication studies, and welcomes strong applicants from all undergraduate majors, especially in the liberal arts. The program seeks mature and motivated individuals who demonstrate a clear vision and potential for original thinking and work. For more information and/or to arrange a class visit, prospective students should contact an admissions counselor at 212-229-5630.

Tuition and Fees

In 2008–09, students pay $1076 per credit plus $115 per semester in University fees, which cover the registration and technology fee, as well as a Student Activity Fee of $15. New tuition and fee schedules are published several months in advance of each academic year.

Financial Aid

Media Studies scholarships are awarded to those who demonstrate academic merit. To apply for assistantships, students must complete an application form that is available from the Media Studies Student Services Office. Students must be registered for a minimum of 6 credits during the fall and spring semesters. Candidates eligible for college work-study may work hours in addition to, but not combined with, award hours. Awards are available to degree candidates only. All awards are for the academic year, not the semester. Students are invited to apply for more than one award.

All applications should be submitted to the Media Studies Scholarship Committee, Department of Media Studies and Film, The New School, 70 Fifth Avenue, New York, New York 10011.

Applying

An applicant must hold a bachelor's degree from an accredited college or university. A completed application (available online), the $50 application fee, a statement of purpose, official transcripts of all undergraduate and graduate studies, and one academic and one professional letter of recommendation should be submitted. International students must submit a minimum TOEFL score of 230 (570 on the paper-based test) and official transcripts of all undergraduate and graduate studies translated into English as well as a WES credential evaluation.

The application deadline for the fall semester is February 15; the spring semester deadline is October 15.

CONTACT

Office of Admissions
The New School
66 West 12th Street, Room 401
New York, New York 10011

Phone: 212-229-5630
Fax: 212-989-3887
E-mail: nsadmissions@newschool.edu
Web site: http://www.newschool.edu/mediastudies

NORTH DAKOTA STATE UNIVERSITY

Division of Distance and Continuing Education

Fargo, North Dakota

Founded in 1890, North Dakota State University (NDSU) affirms its heritage as the land-grant institution of North Dakota. Located on the state's eastern border in Fargo, North Dakota's largest city, the University is a leader in information systems technology, economic development, and lifelong learning. It encompasses a broad spectrum of curriculum offerings, scholarly activity, and services. NDSU is one of two major research institutions in the state university system and is accredited by the North Central Association of Colleges and Schools (NCA).

Distance Learning Program

Many of the distance learning opportunities offered by NDSU are administered through the Office of Distance and Continuing Education. NDSU provides courses for undergraduate students, graduate students, and those seeking professional development. Courses are delivered through an array of distance delivery systems, including online, correspondence, video, video conferencing, and any combination of these technologies. NDSU provides a high-quality, convenient, and user-friendly environment for all of its distance education opportunities. A number of specialty courses and programs are in development. For the most current information, students should visit the Web site at http://www.ndsu.edu/dce.

Delivery Media

NDSU supports a variety of distance delivery systems, including online, video- and print-based individual study, video conferencing, and any combination of these technologies. Technological support is available to individuals participating in courses. Students may interact with instructors via mail, telephone, e-mail, or fax. Students should have reasonably current computers, software, and browsers.

Programs of Study

In 1974, NDSU offered its first distance learning course. Today, NDSU offers more than 100 distance learning courses. Courses are available for undergraduate credit, graduate credit, or professional development.

Special Programs

In conjunction with several regional universities, NDSU offers master's degrees through online courses in the disciplines of family and consumer sciences education, family financial planning, gerontology, and merchandising. These unique collaborative degrees allow students to take at least one class from each university and choose the university they wish to receive their degree from. Students have the opportunity to experience many universities through each university's online environment.

NDSU offers a master's degree in communication. This degree is offered completely online, with two to three courses offered each semester.

Student Services

Students taking courses from a distance have access to a wide array of electronic library material.

Credit Options

The Office of Registrar determines all credits transferred into NDSU. Students may transfer credits from another institution or may earn credits through examinations, portfolio assessment, military training, or business training. NCA accreditation makes transfer of credits to other institutions easier. For questions, students should contact NDSU's Office of Registration and Records at 701-231-7981, 800-608-6378 (toll-free), or http://www.ndsu.edu/registrar.

Faculty

NDSU faculty members are very experienced in their fields and are dedicated to teaching distance education. Approximately 75 percent of Distance and Continuing Education faculty members who teach distance education hold a doctoral degree; the remaining hold an advanced degree.

Admission

Prior to enrolling in a distance education course, students must be admitted to the University, as either a degree-seeking or a non-degree-seeking student. Requirements differ, so students should contact NDSU for more information.

For any questions, students should contact NDSU's Office of Admission at 701-231-8643, 800-488-NDSU, or http://www.ndsu.edu/prospective_students. For graduate studies, students should contact the Graduate School at 701-231-7033 or http://www.ndsu.edu/grad-school/.

Tuition and Fees

Generally, distance education courses carry one fee. For current prices, students should visit http://www.ndsu.edu/business_office. There is also an application fee of $35 for undergraduate students and $45 for graduate students. All fees are subject to change without notice.

Financial Aid

Students may apply for federal financial aid by submitting the Free Application for Federal Student Aid (FAFSA). Other forms of financial aid may come from scholarships, loans, grants, and/or the student's employer. For questions regarding financial aid, students should contact NDSU's Financial Aid Office at http://bisonconnection.ndsu.edu/sfs.

Applying

Students are encouraged to contact North Dakota State University's Office of Admission to obtain application materials and/or assistance. If students have any questions, they are invited to contact the Office of Admission by

telephone at 701-231-8643 or 800-488-NDSU (toll-free) or online at http://www.ndsu.edu/prospective_students. For graduate studies, students should contact the Graduate School at 701-231-7033 or http://www.ndsu.edu/grad-school/.

CONTACT

Distance and Continuing Education
North Dakota State University
P.O. Box 5819
Fargo, North Dakota 58105
Phone: 701-231-7015
Phone: 800-726-1724 (toll-free)
Fax: 701-231-7016
E-mail: ndsu.dce@ndsu.edu
Web site: http://www.ndsu.edu/dce

NOVA SOUTHEASTERN UNIVERSITY
Graduate School of Computer and Information Sciences
Fort Lauderdale, Florida

A major force in educational innovation, the Graduate School of Computer and Information Sciences (GSCIS) provides educational programs of distinction to prepare students for leadership roles in its disciplines. Its strengths include a distinguished faculty, a cutting-edge curriculum, and flexible online formats for its six M.S. and four Ph.D. programs and for its graduate certificate program in information security. All programs enable working professionals to earn their degrees without interrupting their careers. Online master's degree programs require no campus attendance and are available to part-time or full-time students worldwide. A unique online doctoral program requires only four weekends or two weeklong campus visits each year. The school has online students living in every state in the United States and in more than twenty-five countries. Ranked by Forbes magazine as one of the nation's top twenty cyber universities and listed in the Princeton Review's The Best Distance Learning Graduate Schools, the School currently offers more than 300 online classes annually. A leader in online graduate education, the School began offering online programs in 1983 and created the first electronic classroom in 1985.

In addition to its regional accreditation by the Commission on Colleges of the Southern Association of Colleges and Schools, Nova Southeastern University (NSU) has been designated a National Center for Academic Excellence in Information Assurance Education by the U.S. National Security Agency and the Department of Homeland Security. Its curriculum in information security has been certified by the NSA for compliance with CNSS standards. Collaborative programs include DANTES, the U.S. Army's eArmyU initiative, and the Southern Regional Education Board's Electronic Campus. The school has a chapter of Upsilon Pi Epsilon (UPE), the International Honor Society for the Computing and Information Disciplines, and a student chapter of the Institute of Electrical and Electronic Engineers (IEEE), the largest in Florida.

Located on a beautiful 300-acre campus in Fort Lauderdale, Florida, NSU has more than 25,000 students and is the largest independent institution of higher education in the southeast United States. The sixth-largest private university in the United States, it awards associate, bachelor's, master's, educational specialist, doctoral, and first-professional degrees in more than 90 disciplines. It has a college of arts and sciences, as well as schools of medicine, dentistry, pharmacy, allied health, optometry, law, computer and information sciences, psychology, education, business and entrepreneurship, oceanography, and humanities and social sciences.

Distance Learning Program
All of the school's graduate programs are offered in distance learning formats. Online master's programs require no on-campus classroom attendance. Students may complete the M.S. degree in twelve to eighteen months. Doctoral programs use one of two formats: cluster or institute. Cluster students attend four cluster meetings per year, held quarterly over an extended week-end (Friday, Saturday, and half-day Sunday) at the University. Cluster terms start in September and March. Cluster weekends take place in September, December, March, and June. Institute students attend a weeklong institute twice a year at the University. Institutes are held in mid-January and mid-July at the start of each five-month term. Clusters and institutes bring together students and faculty members for participation in courses, workshops, and dissertation counseling. Doctoral courses also have an online component. Between meetings, students complete assignments, research papers, and projects and participate in a range of online activities.

Delivery Media
Online students use the Web to access course materials, announcements, e-mail, distance library services, the Electronic Library, and other information and for interaction with faculty and fellow students. Online, interactive learning methods are used throughout the instructional sequence based on the use of WebCT as a course management system. Online activities facilitate frequent student-to-faculty and student-to-student interaction. They are supported by threaded discussion boards, white boards, chat rooms, and e-mail. In addition, WebCT enables students to submit assignments online in multimedia formats and to receive their professor's reviews of assignments online in the same formats.

Programs of Study
The School offers distance programs leading to the M.S. in computer information systems (including an optional concentration in information security), computer science, computing technology in education (including an optional concentration in information security), information security, information technology (including optional concentrations in software development, information systems security, educational technology, information security management, and information technology management), and management information systems (including an optional concentration in information security); the Ph.D. in computer information

systems (including an optional concentration in information security), computer science, computing technology in education, and information systems, (including optional concentrations in information security and information science); and a graduate certificate in information security.

The School's M.S. students may apply for early admission into the doctoral program, which provides the opportunity to earn the Ph.D. in a shorter time. The M.S. requires 36 credit hours (thesis optional). Terms are twelve weeks long, and there are four terms each year. To earn the M.S. in twelve months, the student must enroll in three courses each term. To complete the M.S. in eighteen months, the student must enroll in two courses each term. Master's terms start in September, January, April, and July.

Doctoral programs require 64 credits, including eight 4-credit courses, two research 4-credit projects, and the dissertation. It may be completed in three years. The Ph.D. in computer information systems and computer science are offered only in cluster format. Doctoral programs in computing technology in education and information systems are offered in cluster and institute formats. Students attend clusters or institutes during their first two years of the program while completing course work.

Special Programs

All of the School's programs are offered through the Southern Regional Education Board's Electronic Campus and the U.S. Army's eArmyU program.

Credit Options

Up to 6 graduate credits from a regionally accredited institution may be transferred to one of the master's degree program. Courses proposed for transfer must have received grades of at least B. Credit is not awarded for life or work experience.

Faculty

GSCIS has 23 full-time and 29 part-time faculty members. All faculty members teaching at the graduate level have doctoral degrees.

Admission

The master's applicant must have an undergraduate degree with a GPA of at least 2.5 in an appropriate major. The doctoral applicant must have a master's degree with an appropriate major and a GPA of at least 3.25. Degrees must be from regionally accredited institutions. Master's applicants must submit a summary of professional experience or score report of the GRE. All doctoral applicants must submit a summary of professional experience. English proficiency is a requirement for admission.

Tuition and Fees

Tuition is $450 per credit for master's students; for doctoral students, tuition is $550 per credit hour for course work and $492 per credit hour for the dissertation.

Financial Aid

To qualify for financial assistance, a student must be admitted, must be a U.S. citizen or an eligible permanent resident, and must plan on registering for a minimum of 6 credit hours per term. A prospective student who requires financial assistance should apply for it while still a candidate for admission. For financial assistance information or application forms, students should call 800-806-3680 (toll-free).

Applying

Admission decisions are made on a rolling basis. To ensure evaluation for the desired starting term, reviewable applications must be received at least one month prior to the start of that term. The application fee is $50. Late applications that cannot be processed in time for the desired starting term are considered for the next term. Applicants may be granted provisional admission status pending completion of the application process. Admission forms, brochures, and the graduate catalog may be downloaded from the School's Web site. Master's terms start in September, January, April, and July. Doctoral cluster terms start in September and March. Doctoral institute terms start in January and July.

CONTACT

Graduate School of Computer and Information Sciences
Nova Southeastern University
Carl DeSantis Building, Fourth Floor
3301 College Avenue
Fort Lauderdale, Florida 33314-9918

Phone: 954-262-2000
      800-986-2247 (toll-free)
E-mail: scisinfo@nova.edu
Web site: http://www.scis.nova.edu

OREGON STATE UNIVERSITY
Extended Campus
Corvallis, Oregon

Founded in 1868 and accredited by the Northwest Commission on Colleges and Universities, Oregon State University (OSU) is one of a select number of schools nationwide to receive the Carnegie Foundation's highest rating for education and research. A land-grant, sea-grant, space-grant, and sun-grant university, Oregon State serves the state of Oregon, the nation, and the world through its teaching, research, and outreach efforts. Today, OSU is the home of 19,753 students who are pursuing their degrees in one of more than 200 undergraduate and graduate academic degree programs. The American Productivity and Quality Center recently named Oregon State a top university for providing electronic services to students.

Distance Learning Program

During fall term 2007, more than 2,500 individuals throughout Oregon and the world were enrolled in Oregon State University courses off campus. Each year, through OSU Extended Campus (Ecampus), students have access to more than 400 distance and online courses in more than sixty subjects. Subject areas are as diverse as education, fisheries and wildlife, history, math, chemistry, and psychology. Courses are designed as part of bachelor's completion programs, undergraduate minors, certificate programs, and some graduate-level degrees and course work.

Delivery Media

Oregon State offers the majority of its distance courses via the Web, DVDs, videotapes, and streaming media. Courses often entail a combination of delivery methods, such as a video course with class interaction through an electronic listserv or Web site. Students communicate with instructors and administrative staff members via e-mail, phone, fax, or regular mail. Certain courses and programs are also delivered through face-to-face instruction or interactive television broadcasting (ITV) at statewide locations.

Programs of Study

Oregon State University is one of a handful of universities nationwide pioneering the field of online education. The majority of the more than 400 distance courses offered through Ecampus each year are delivered partially or entirely on the Web. The remainder of distance courses involve some online requirement, such as e-mail communication with faculty members or discussion board communication with peers.

Degree partnership programs are available through many Oregon community colleges; however, many students work with Ecampus Student Services staff to utilize past college experiences and to plan individual programs. Students can complete their degree from anywhere in the world by taking upper-division course work through OSU Extended Campus. Students may select from a Bachelor of Arts/Bachelor of Science (B.A./B.S.) in liberal studies (a preprofessional elementary education option is available statewide), a B.S. in environmental sciences, a B.S. in general agriculture, and a B.S. in natural resources. Students in bachelor's programs must accumulate a minimum of 180 quarter credit hours to graduate.

Undergraduate minors in anthropology, environmental sciences, fisheries and wildlife, German, natural resources, political science, psychology, sociology, U.S. history, and writing are available worldwide. Minors usually include at least 27 quarter credit hours of study and can be pursued as part of a bachelor's program or added to a transcript after graduation.

OSU Ecampus also offers online graduate degrees in education and in radiation health physics. An online graduate certificate in sustainable natural resources, an online/on-site health management and policy graduate certificate, and an online professional certificate in geographic information science are also available.

Special Programs

Web-based graduate-level course work in education is available through Ecampus for teachers, trainers, and other professional educators who wish to pursue an advanced degree or simply gain skills in advanced teaching strategies or teaching course work online. The School of Education offers an on-site/online hybrid program for those seeking to earn their Oregon Continuing Teaching License. The Master of Arts in Teaching (M.A.T.) in early childhood/elementary education and the ESOL bilingual endorsement programs are also delivered online and on-site. In these programs, students may enroll in Web courses and related practicums at a rate based on their individual needs, tailoring their education to meet both time and financial constraints. Students should visit the program's Web site for specific contact information on these and other graduate-level programs, including an online Ed.M. and graduate degrees in adult and higher education leadership.

OSU's Workforce and Noncredit programs in Ecampus operate as an outreach to corporations, public agencies, organizations, and professionals seeking to upgrade their skill level and increase their employability and productivity. These programs offer a variety of online noncredit programs, such as management and human resource skills for pharmacists. They also offer online short skill-building courses that fit the busy adult's lifestyle and pocketbook.

OSU Extended Campus also offers OSU K–12 Online, a top-quality high school curriculum that is available to homeschooled students or high school students seeking courses that may not be available through their district. These online courses can be taken for elective credit and/or high school graduation completion.

Student Services

Oregon State makes it a priority to provide excellent student services to distance learners via e-mail, a toll-free phone number, and a comprehensive Web site that includes live chat, online forums, and a searchable knowledge base. Students have access to online library services, online tutoring, a toll-free hotline for computer consulting, online writing support, step-by-step assistance with procedures, and an online schedule of classes. Students can subscribe to *OSU E-News,* a free electronic newsletter that provides timely course and program information, student and faculty member profiles, and technical tips.

Credit Options

All credits earned through OSU distance or online education are recorded identically on the Oregon State University transcript as courses that are taken on campus. Each course falls under the same accreditation ratings of the individual department from which it originates. Transfer students enrolled in academic programs must have previous credits evaluated by an OSU adviser to ensure that program requirements are met. Forty-five of the last 75 credit hours for bachelor's completion programs must be from Oregon State University.

Faculty

Oregon State has more than 2,700 faculty members, with nearly 1,100 in the tenure system. Eighty-five percent of faculty members in professorial ranks have doctoral degrees. OSU distance education faculty members must adhere to the same quality standards as any faculty member teaching on campus.

Admission

Students taking distance or online courses to meet OSU degree requirements must be admitted to the University through the regular admission process and must meet the requirements for admission. Nondegree enrollment requires no formal admission and can be attained by contacting the Office of Admissions. For more information on regular or nondegree admission, students can visit the Office of Admissions Web site at http://oregonstate.edu/admissions.

Tuition and Fees

Tuition for undergraduate distance degree courses is $204 per quarter credit hour for most courses. Graduate-level courses are generally $418 per quarter credit, depending upon the program. Additional fees may be assessed for tape rental or other course materials. Students may check the Ecampus Web site for additional information.

Financial Aid

Distance learners are eligible for financial aid programs according to the same rules as on-campus students. Generally, to be considered, a student must be taking at least 6 quarter hours. Some scholarships are open to part-time distance learning students. Students can consult specific information on the Web site at http://oregonstate.edu/admin/finaid.

Applying

Online or distance learners seeking an OSU degree should apply through the regular application process. Some of the distance programs at the graduate level are cohort based and require admission prior to fall quarter. The undergraduate distance degree programs accept students year-round. It is recommended that students seek initial advising prior to the application process. Registration for individual courses generally requires no application other than to contact the registrar for admission as a nondegree or part-time student.

CONTACT

OSU Extended Campus
Attention: Student Services Center
4943 The Valley Library
Oregon State University
Corvallis, Oregon 97331-4504

Phone: 541-737-9204
      800-667-1465 (toll-free)
Fax: 541-737-2734
E-mail: ecampus@oregonstate.edu
Web site: http://ecampus.oregonstate.edu

PARK UNIVERSITY
College for Distance Learning
Parkville, Missouri

> *Park University was founded in 1875 and is accredited by the Higher Learning Commission of the North Central Association of Colleges and Schools. Park's College for Distance Learning offers Bachelor of Science (B.S.) and Master of Science (M.S.) degrees. Numerous undergraduate courses and degrees are offered through the Internet. Graduate programs in public affairs, education, and business administration are also offered.*
>
> *Park University is a nonprofit entrepreneurial institution of learning that is devoted to providing access to academic excellence to prepare learners to think critically, communicate effectively, and engage in lifelong learning while serving a global community.*

Distance Learning Program

Hectic schedules are the biggest reason most adults fail to complete their college education. With busy schedules, family responsibilities, and travel obligations, it is often impossible for many adults to attend regularly scheduled classes.

The Online learning environment at Park University allows course participants to go to class when and where their schedule permits. Commuting time disappears, travel conflicts no longer matter, and childcare issues disappear.

The Online learning programs offered by Park University represent more than thirty years of experience in extended learning—experience honed through operating forty-one satellite "campus centers" on military bases where course work needs to be compact and mobile. As a result of this experience, Park developed, and now offers, accelerated eight-week courses as well as standard sixteen-week offerings. Online courses, first developed in 1996, now number more than 225 different courses. Virtually all in-person courses that are taught at Park University are also taught Online, along with other unique course offerings that were developed specifically for Online delivery or a combination of on-ground activities with online interaction.

Surveys of Online students indicate a higher degree of satisfaction for the general learning experience. In traditional classroom settings, people are often treated according to others' preconceived perceptions of age, gender, ethnicity, and even income level. In Park University's Online learning program, students are judged only by the caliber of their thoughts and the quality of their contributions. This learning environment is active and student-centered. Some students find the online format particularly effective for certain types of courses. In fact, the level of interactivity is actually higher in Park University's Online courses. Online learning requires extensive work—including much reading and writing—but many Online students actually learn better through the Online format than they do in traditional, face-to-face classes.

Delivery Media

Park University offers more than 225 Online courses at five entry points—terms—during each year. Most courses are in accelerated eight-week format. Some courses follow sixteen-week formats. All courses require minimum computer-system capabilities.

To ensure the highest degree of success, prospective Online students need a basic level of computer literacy. Learners will be asked to open and transfer files and have a working knowledge of the use of e-mail within a course environment. Online students will do well if they have access to a Windows-capable computer with at least a 56.6 kbps modem; Netscape Navigator, Internet Explorer, or an equivalent, reliable Internet browser. Students should not borrow someone else's account, use a public-access account (such as a public library terminal), or use a temporary free account when taking the Online courses.

Courses are offered in a variety of subject areas, and learners can take many courses without enrolling in a degree program.

Each undergraduate course is concluded with a proctored exam.

Programs of Study

Park University has provided degree completion programs via distance learning for more than thirty years. The goal of Park's degree completion program is to provide students with the opportunity and assistance to enable them to complete the last two years of their undergraduate degrees. In addition, students can enter Park their freshman year and complete a degree entirely online. Current fields of study include the Bachelor of Science degree in computer information systems, criminal justice, health care, human resources, management, marketing, and social psychology.

Graduate Online degree programs include the Master of Arts in communication and leadership; Master of Business Administration with an emphasis in entrepreneurship, health care/health services management, international business, and management of information services; Master of Healthcare Leadership; Master of Public Affairs with an emphasis in government/business relations, health care, management of information services, nonprofit and community services management, and public management; and Master of Education with an emphasis in arts in teaching, educational administration, and special education.

Online learning is a dynamic, growing program at Park University. New courses continue to be developed on an on-going basis.

Special Programs
Online students have access to an Online bookstore and library and all traditional student services, such as academic advising, online application, registration, and financial aid.

Credit Options
Park University Online courses are transferable to programs at other regionally accredited institutions. In turn, Park accepts credit from other regionally accredited institutions. Specifically, the University accepts up to 75 hours of course completion with a grade of C or better from two-year schools. Official transcripts from previous colleges or universities; official test reports or transcripts from CLEP, USAFI, or DANTES; and ACT/PEP documentation can accompany an application. Up to 24 hours of credit may be awarded for military service and for Validated Learning Equivalency.

Faculty
Park University has hundreds of Internet faculty instructors, all of whom have advanced degrees and have taught previously. In addition, each Online instructor has completed an intensive eight-week training program to develop the skills necessary for meeting the challenges of teaching Online. This course, which is taught Online, of course, enables instructors to learn firsthand the challenges of being an Online student.

Admission
Park's Online undergraduate programs are open to students who have earned a high school diploma, a GED certificate, or the equivalent; have a minimum 2.0 cumulative GPA in all previous college study; have completed the online Application for Admission; and have paid the application fee. To receive a degree from Park University, students must complete at least 30 semester hours through the University, with 12 hours in their major.

For admission to graduate programs, students must have a bachelor's degree from a regionally accredited U.S. institution of higher learning or four years of equivalent full-time college work from an accredited foreign institution. They must also have a 2.75 minimum GPA on a 4.0 scale. Individual programs may require appropriate entrance test scores, such as the GRE or GMAT. Although entrance test scores, by themselves, do not constitute the sole or final criterion for granting or denying admission to any student, each program that uses test scores will consider them, in combination with other criteria, as an essential part of the requirements for granting full admission.

Students are required to meet course and program standards to remain in the Online program.

Tuition and Fees
For the 2007–08 academic year, undergraduate Online tuition is $260 per credit hour, with an Internet fee of $15 per credit hour. Graduate Online tuition is $360 per credit hour, with a $18 per credit hour Internet fee.

Financial Aid
Financial assistance may be awarded to full-time and part-time students who qualify.

Applying
Undergraduate degree-seeking students must meet all admission standards for Park University and pay a one-time $25 application fee. Graduate degree-seeking students must also meet all admissions standards for Park University and pay a one-time $50 application fee.

For more information, students should contact Park University at the telephone number listed below or visit the Web site at the address listed below.

CONTACT

For undergraduate online programs:
College for Distance Learning
Park University
8700 Northwest River Park Drive
Parkville, Missouri 64152-3795
Phone: 866-505-1059 (toll-free)
E-mail: online@park.edu
Web site: http://www.park.edu/online

For graduate online programs:
Graduate School
Park University
8700 Northwest River Park Drive
Parkville, Missouri 64152-3795
Phone: 816-842-6182 Ext. 5525
E-mail: gradschool@park.edu
Web site: http://www.park.edu/grad

PEIRCE COLLEGE

Peirce Online

Philadelphia, Pennsylvania

Founded in 1865, Peirce is a private, four-year, specialized institution providing practical, leading-edge curricula to primarily working adult learners. The College has been offering online programs since 2000 through Peirce Online.

Peirce is accredited by the Commission on Higher Education of the Middle States Association of Colleges and Schools and the Pennsylvania Department of Education to award bachelor's and associate degrees. The business administration program is accredited by the Association of Collegiate Business Schools and Programs (ACBSP). The American Bar Association (ABA) approves the paralegal studies program.

Distance Learning Program

Peirce Online offers students high-quality programs from an accredited college, the flexibility to fit higher education into their busy lifestyles, and the personalized attention from faculty and staff members needed to successfully complete their degrees.

Peirce Online courses are seven weeks in length, with new courses starting every month. Students can earn an associate degree in eighteen months and a bachelor's degree in thirty-six months.

Delivery Media

Peirce Online students must have access to the Internet and an e-mail account.

Courses and degree programs can be completed entirely online, with no residency requirement. While there are weekly deadlines, students complete course work at their own pace. As part of each course, students submit homework assignments, papers, and exams online and participate in asynchronous online discussions. Through the online courseware, students can join with classmates in threaded conversations, privately correspond with instructors, and review their progress with the online grade book.

Program of Study

Peirce College offers bachelor's and associate degrees in business administration, information technology, and paralegal studies. Degrees in business administration and information technology can be completed entirely online. A minimum of 61 credits is required for an associate degree and 121 credits for a bachelor's degree.

In business administration, students can choose from concentrations in accounting, business law, entrepreneurship/small business management, human resource management, management, marketing, or real estate management.

In information technology, students can select from concentrations in application programming with .NET technology, desktop applications for business, information security, networking, network security, or technology management.

In paralegal studies, students can complete most courses online. After taking four initial courses in a traditional classroom setting at Peirce's Philadelphia campus, or from other accredited paralegal programs, students can conveniently complete the remainder of their degree online.

Peirce maintains strong business community relationships and continually upgrades courses to reflect hiring trends. In all degree programs, students take general education core courses in English, communication, social sciences, mathematics, and science. Supervised cooperative education is available in all programs. Most of the bachelor's degree programs include a capstone course in the last term of the program.

Student Services

Peirce offers student services in an online format, including academic advising, workshops, and tutoring; career development counseling and workshops; and services for students with disabilities. Library services include an extensive collection of online databases incorporating full-text periodicals, e-books, industry and financial reports, legal research, and reference materials. All Peirce College students are welcome to request a free copy of Microsoft Office Professional.

Credit Options

Peirce College reserves the right, in its sole discretion, to allow students to earn 90 credits toward a bachelor's degree and 30 credits toward an associate degree through any combination of transfer credits, credit by examination, work experience, and portfolio assessment. Students wishing to receive a degree or certificate from Peirce must complete 15 credits in their concentration through courses offered by Peirce College.

Faculty

Peirce Online emphasizes personal attention from faculty and staff members. Small classes and convenient online courseware ensure that faculty members are readily available to offer professional guidance to individual students. Faculty members also serve as career and academic advisers.

Peirce College employs full-time and adjunct faculty members with diverse professional backgrounds. Most faculty members have advanced degrees and are practitioners in their field. Attorneys, certified public accountants, psychologists, market analysts, computer experts, health-care professionals, business managers, and other professionals are among the teaching staff members at Peirce.

Admission

Peirce College is an Equal Opportunity Institution. The College is committed to ensuring equal opportunity in all educational programs and activities (including but not limited to recruitment, admissions, programs and course offerings, counseling, financial aid and scholarships, employment, facilities, and College-sponsored extracurricular activities). The College does not engage in or tolerate unlawful discrimination, harassment, or retaliation on account of age, sex, race, color, religion, creed, national origin, ancestry, citizenship, disability, sexual orientation, gender identity, marital status, veteran status, military status, or membership in any other group protected under local, state, or federal law.

Inquiries or complaints relating to equal opportunity for prospective or current students may be directed to the Manager, Employee Relations/Equal Opportunity Representative, who is a member of the Human Resources Department and is available at 3R Alumni Hall (215-670-9328).

Prospective or current students requiring reasonable accommodation or who have questions regarding educational services, activities, programs, or facilities that are accessible to or usable by students with disabilities should contact the Facilitator, Perkins Grant/Student Disability Services Coordinator, who is available at the Mary W. Walker '33 Center for Academic Excellence, 2 Alumni Hall (215-670-9251).

Applicants for a degree program must submit the following official documents for consideration: a completed application for admission with application fee, an official transcript documenting high school graduation or a copy of the GED or state equivalency diploma and scores, official college transcripts for college transfer credit, and evaluation of transfer credits for final admission and acceptance into the College.

Complete admissions requirements are available in the Peirce *Student Handbook,* which is posted at the College Web site http://www.peirce. edu.

Tuition and Fees

For the 2007–08 academic year, tuition and fees were $425 per credit hour for day, evening, and online courses plus a $100 technology fee. Books and supplies average about $100 per course. Costs are subject to change.

Financial Aid

Financial assistance includes scholarships, grants, loans, and on-campus employment. Peirce College participates in most federal and state aid programs. Approximately 70 percent of students receive financial aid. Applicants for aid must submit the Free Application for Federal Student Aid (FAFSA).

Applying

The Peirce Online application process is convenient and flexible. When students apply to Peirce Online, they can register and begin their studies while transcripts and other documents are being processed. There is no long wait—the initial application should take only 15 minutes. The application/registration process can be completed online at http://www.peirce.edu. There is a $50 fee due at time of application.

CONTACT

Online Programs
Peirce College
1420 Pine Street
Philadelphia, Pennsylvania 19102-4699

Phone: 888-GO-PEIRCE Ext. 9800 (toll-free)
Fax: 215-670-9101
E-mail: online@peirce.edu
Web site: http://www.peirce.edu
          http://www.peirceonline.net (Online Learning)

PENN STATE WORLD CAMPUS

University Park, Pennsylvania

The Pennsylvania State University, founded in 1855, is a land-grant institution that offers undergraduate and graduate programs. The University has more than 4,500 faculty members and offers degrees in about 160 baccalaureate and 150 graduate programs. Penn State regularly ranks among the nation's top fifteen public research universities, with yearly research expenditures of more than $500 million. Penn State is a member of the Association of American Universities, and it is accredited by the Middle States Association of Colleges and Schools.

Distance Learning Program

In 1998, Penn State launched its twenty-fifth campus of the University, Penn State World Campus. The World Campus is "Penn State Online," delivering close to sixty distance education programs to learners around the world. The World Campus carries on Penn State's proud tradition of more than a century of delivering distance education programs designed to meet the educational goals of a diverse set of learners.

As one of the nation's leading public research universities, Penn State has a longstanding commitment to reach beyond its traditional campuses and to engage in helping to solve the needs of the individuals and communities it serves. From its pioneering innovation with correspondence study—the first generation of distance education—in 1892 to its leadership in online learning in the twenty-first century, Penn State has made creative use of technology to address the changing nature of work, home life, and learning.

The World Campus provides adult learners worldwide (all fifty states, more than forty countries, and all seven continents) with some of Penn State's most highly regarded graduate, undergraduate, and continuing professional education degrees, certificates, and courses available anytime, anywhere. As part of Penn State's global learning community, World Campus students interact with faculty members and exchange ideas and expertise with one

another in the same high-quality, academically challenging courses as those taught in the classroom, as they strive to meet their educational and career goals. Credits earned through the World Campus are identical to those earned at Penn State's traditional campuses.

Delivery Media

Students enrolled in online group and online individual classes must have access to the Web; Internet access for independent learners is optional. In online groups, students interact with their instructors and other students, and group work and/or student-student interaction may be required. In online individual courses, students interact one-on-one with their instructors, with no student interaction required. For independent learners, an optional Web site and e-mail lesson submission may be included.

Programs of Study

Penn State's World Campus offers fifty-nine programs, 691 courses, seventeen graduate/postbaccalaureate certificates, and fifteen undergraduate certificates.

Thirteen undergraduate degree programs are offered through the World Campus, including the Associate in Arts (A.A.) in letters, arts, and sciences; the Associate in Science (A.S.) in business administration; the A.S. in hotel, restaurant, and institutional management; the A.S. in human development and family

studies; the A.S. in information sciences and technology; the Bachelor of Arts (B.A.) in letters, arts, and sciences; the B.A. in law and society; the B.A. in psychology; the Bachelor of Science (B.S.) in criminal justice; the B.S. in nursing (RN to B.S.); the B.S. in organizational leadership; the B.S. in psychology; and the B.S. in turfgrass science.

Twelve graduate degrees are offered; they are the Master of Business Administration (iMBA), which is accredited by AACSB International; the Master of Education, with concentrations in adult education, curriculum and instruction–children's literature, curriculum and instruction–teacher leadership, earth science, and instructional systems–educational technology; the Master of Geographic Information Systems; the Master of Homeland Security in Public Health Preparedness; the Master of Professional Studies, with concentrations in community and economic development, human resources and employment relations, and supply chain management; and the Master of Project Management.

Student Services

Penn State World Campus programs are supported by a full range of student services. Support services, such as library access, advising, and assessment, are structured to meet students' needs while providing support that is often lacking in more traditional distance education programs. The World Campus HelpDesk offers technical support resources to ensure that students have a successful online learning experience. Staff members can answer questions regarding the online learning environment; software, Web browsers, and operating systems; and computer hardware and Internet issues. Online resources include tutorials, news/alerts, and additional training resources. More information is available at http://www.worldcampus.psu.edu/StudentServices.shtml.

Credit Options
Penn State accepts only certain types of professional experience for credit toward fulfilling degree requirements, determined by a process called Credit by Portfolio Evaluation, which is typically restricted to students with particular types of formal professional training such as nurses or police officers. Some aspects of military training may also result in transfer credits if officially documented. Other types of professional training are considered on a case-by-case basis, but the review is costly and rarely results in credit conferral.

Students who wish to earn their degrees from Penn State must complete a minimum number of credits through World Campus—for an associate degree, at least 18 of the student's last 30 credits earned must be from Penn State, and for a bachelor's degree, at least 36 of the last 60 credits.

In order to transfer college credits to Penn State, the college must be accredited by one of the following accrediting agencies: Middle States Association of Colleges and Schools, Northwest Association of Schools and Colleges, New England Association of Schools and Colleges, Southern Association of Schools and Colleges, North Central Association of Colleges and Schools, and the Western Association of Schools and Colleges.

Each Penn State academic unit has its own requirements for accepting transfer credits. General information about applying as a graduate transfer student can be found on the Web site for The Graduate School at Penn State at http://www.gradsch.psu.edu/.

Faculty
The Penn State World Campus faculty consists of the same faculty members teaching courses at the Penn State campuses. Recognizing that a primary key to the success of an online teaching and learning program is a skilled and competent faculty, Penn State's World Campus has sponsored a faculty development initiative since 1995. The main goal of the Faculty Development Program is to build a teaching and learning community of faculty and staff members who can effectively author, design, develop, and deliver distance education courses via Penn State's World Campus. In addition, members of the Instructional Design and Development (ID&D) unit of the World Campus work closely with faculty members to produce high-quality distance education courses.

Admission
Application requirements vary by program. In general, students must submit an application, the application fee, and official transcripts. Additional materials, such as test scores or letters of recommendation, may be required.

Students should visit the Web page for the World Campus program of interest and click on the "Apply Now" button for specific instructions.

Tuition and Fees
Graduate tuition ranges between $550 and $1000 per credit hour, depending on the program. Upper-division undergraduate tuition is $454 per credit hour; lower-division undergraduate tuition is $423 per credit hour for online groups and $250 per credit hour for individuals and for independent learners. An information technology fee is assessed each semester. At this time, the World Campus online iMBA program is the only program that offers a payment plan.

Financial Aid
Penn State World Campus degree students who take at least 6 credits per semester and who meet all other federal eligibility requirements may be eligible to receive federal student aid. The University offers some scholarships for which distance-learning students are eligible, including the Fischer Family Scholarship Program, the World Campus Student Fund, and the Trustee Scholarship Program. More information is available online at http://www.worldcampus.psu.edu/StudentServices_Paying.shtml.

Applying
Program deadlines vary. Students should check online for more detailed information.

CONTACT
Penn State World Campus
128 Outreach Building
The Pennsylvania State University
University Park, Pennsylvania 16802
Phone: 814-865-5403
        800-252-3592 (toll-free within the United States)
Fax: 814-865-3290
E-mail: psuwd@psu.edu
Web site: http://www.worldcampus.psu.edu/

Pennsylvania College
of Technology

PENNSTATE

PENNSYLVANIA COLLEGE OF TECHNOLOGY
An Affiliate of The Pennsylvania State University
Distance Learning
Williamsport, Pennsylvania

The mission of distance learning at Pennsylvania College of Technology (Penn College)—a special mission affiliate of Penn State, committed to applied technology education—is to provide educational opportunities, using a variety of media, as an alternative to traditional classroom-based learning. Distance learning courses are accessible to students both off and on campus and are intended to meet the needs of students who desire an alternative to traditional face-to-face courses due to work schedules, geographical distance from the campus, or other special needs.

Distance Learning Program

The Penn College distance learning program was founded on the central principle of providing excellence in instruction and appropriate educational opportunities to students. Serving approximately 500 students per semester, the College offers an average of forty-five distance courses per semester across a range of academic disciplines as well as five bachelor's degree–completion programs that are available entirely via distance learning.

Delivery Media

Penn College operates on the WebCT Campus Edition 4.1 instructional platform. In addition, supported applications include Microsoft Office, Adobe Photoshop, Adobe Acrobat, Macromedia Director, Flash, Apple QuickTime, Windows Media Player, and Respondus. Certain discipline-specific software programs also are employed.

Programs of Study

The Bachelor of Science in technology management allows students who enter with an associate degree in a technical/professional area to obtain a baccalaureate degree, with the last two years emphasizing the development of business management skills. Technical/professional associate degrees include those with a concentrated area of study in a technical/professional area.

The Bachelor of Science in applied health studies is a 129-credit major for individuals who are certified, licensed, or registered in a health-care profession or for students enrolled in the College's occupational therapy assistant studies, emergency medical services, radiography, physical fitness specialist studies, or surgical technology majors who wish to earn a bachelor's degree. Students acquire the advanced-level core knowledge that guides all health-care practitioners. This degree allows the student to increase knowledge in management and administrative issues; assist in planning, problem solving, and evaluating health-care delivery methods and systems; and establish a more marketable, multiskilled background.

The Bachelor of Science in dental hygiene is designed to prepare licensed dental hygienists to contribute to the improvement of oral health in a rapidly changing health-care environment. This program enables hygienists to build upon their current knowledge base and assume positions of responsibility in a variety of alternate-care settings as well as in positions created to meet future health-care needs.

The Bachelor of Science in nursing is designed for the registered nurse who wishes to earn a degree on a full- or part-time basis. The curriculum builds on the knowledge and skills possessed by RNs who have graduated from diploma and associate-degree nursing programs. This program prepares licensed registered nurses to contribute to the quality provision of nursing care in a rapidly changing health-care environment. This major enables nurses to build upon their knowledge base and assume positions of responsibility in a variety of health-care settings, from promoting health and facilitating adaptation to increasingly complex health-care problems/needs.

The Bachelor of Science in automotive technology management is structured to meet the needs of the automotive service and manufacturing industries. The curriculum provides an in-depth study of technical skills, technical knowledge, and management skills as applied in the automotive industry. It emphasizes supervision and personnel management, financial analysis and accounting principles, sales promotion and market planning, problem-solving methods, and organization and planning techniques as well as communications and mathematics, which are essential for a management career.

Special Programs

The Distance Learning Office assists in scheduling and determining each semester's class offerings in concert with the academic deans. Courses are offered on a regular and predictable basis to ensure academic progress and adequate course selection for those learning at a distance.

To accommodate the needs of distance learners, selected enrollments are restricted at the start of each semester scheduling period. Resident students also may enroll in distance courses on a space-available basis.

Student Services

Penn College distance learners have full student standing and are entitled to all the privileges and services of a Penn College student. The Financial Aid Office, Counseling and Career Services, the Advisement Center, and the College Store all have a Web presence and respond to student inquiries via telephone or e-mail. Distance students may order textbooks via the Web site. The library catalog and other references, periodical abstracts, and full-text databases are available through the Penn College Library Web site. An electronic reserve system is provided for assigned readings and supplemental assignments. A College librarian is assigned to each distance learning course to address distance learning and library instruction needs.

Credit Options

Transfer credits, advanced placement, credit for military experience, professional certifications, and credit by exam may be considered during transcript review. Acceptance of credits varies by major.

Faculty

Approximately 55 faculty members teach distance learning courses; 92 percent are full-time faculty members.

Admission

Distance learners are accepted to Penn College and the academic school that houses their major. There is no separate admission process for distance learning students.

Tuition and Fees

Tuition and fee rates for 2007–08 were $375 per credit hour for in-state students and $471 per credit hour for out-of-state students.

Financial Aid

As students in full standing, distance learners may be eligible for financial aid, including federal aid programs.

Applying

Students should submit an application for admission online at http://www.pct.edu/forms or contact the Admissions Office at the College's toll-free number.

CONTACT

Paula Neal
Distance Learning Services Assistant
Pennsylvania College of Technology
One College Avenue
Williamsport, Pennsylvania 17701
Phone: 570-320-8019
         800-367-9222 (toll-free)
Fax: 570-321-5559
E-mail: distancelearning@pct.edu
Web site: http://www.pct.edu/away

PRESCOTT COLLEGE
Adult Degree, Master of Arts, and Ph.D. Programs
Prescott, Arizona

Prescott College's mission is to educate students of diverse ages and backgrounds to understand, thrive in, and enhance the world community and environment. Prescott regards learning as a continuing process and strives to provide an education that enables students to live productive lives while achieving a balance between self-fulfillment and service to others. Students are encouraged to think critically and act ethically, with sensitivity to both the human community and the biosphere. The College's philosophy stresses experiential learning and self-direction within an interdisciplinary curriculum.

Prescott College is an independent liberal arts college that grants Bachelor of Arts (B.A.), Master of Arts (M.A.), and Ph.D. degrees. The College is accredited by the Higher Learning Commission of the North Central Association of Colleges and Schools. The teacher education program is approved by the Arizona State Board of Education and the Arizona State Directors of Teacher Education and Certification. The Association of Experiential Education also accredits the College.

Distance Learning Program

The Prescott College distance learning programs consist of the Adult Degree Program (ADP), a B.A. completion program; a Master of Arts program (MAP); and a Ph.D. in education program. In all programs, students maintain their personal and professional lives while earning a degree. The programs are self-designed (with the assistance of faculty members), student-centered, and flexible. The programs require very limited residencies in Prescott, Arizona. The College offers ongoing support from faculty members and other students.

Delivery Media

The Adult Degree Program: Students in the B.A. Adult Degree Program work with mentors (local professionals) in their home communities along with core faculty members at Prescott College on an individualized course of study. Students study with these mentors one-on-one in their home communities and at times and places that are convenient to them. It is not an online program. Students are required to be in Arizona for just one 3-day weekend during their program.

The Master of Arts Program: Faculty-chosen graduate advisers assist students in the Master of Arts program in planning, executing, and evaluating their graduate study programs. These faculty members are recruited from everywhere in the U.S. and are selected based upon the student's spe-cific area of interest. Students and graduate advisers send material via postal or electronic mail to one another. Master's students must attend two 3-day colloquia per semester. Program length varies depending upon the degree sought and ranges from 1½ to 2½ years.

The Ph.D. in Education Program: In this program, with a concentration in sustainability education, Ph.D. students are guided by committees that consist of a core faculty member and 3 affiliate faculty members. Doctoral students attend approximately thirty-five days of residency (seven trips to Arizona) over the course of the four-year program.

Programs of Study

The Adult Degree Program: B.A. students can complete degrees in adventure education, education, environmental studies, human development, human services, humanities, and management. Working with faculty members, students design concentrations in individualized areas within each of these degrees. Within each degree area, students have developed a wide range of concentrations.

Adventure education: adventure-based tourism, ecotourism, outdoor education, outdoor program administration, recreation management, and wilderness leadership.

Education: Teacher education students may complete all courses leading to Ari-zona teaching credentials in elementary, secondary, or special education while earning their bachelor's degree. Students may also complete post-bachelor's teacher certification. Other areas of concentration within education include adult education and alternative education.

Environmental studies: agroecology, appropriate technologies and assessment, biology, bioregional studies, botany, conservation biology, Earth sciences, ecological design, ecological economics, ecology, environmental education, environmental policy, global studies, international sustainable development, natural resource assessment and management, permaculture, restoration ecology, rural planning, sustainable communities and agriculture, sustainable community development, urban planning, and wildlife studies.

Human development/human services: advocacy, border studies, child development, community health education, counseling, criminal justice, ecopsychology, expressive arts therapy, family and community services, family studies, gender studies, gerontology, healing arts, holistic health, human development, human relations, leadership, political science, psychology, social justice, social science, sociology, somatic psychology, spiritual studies, transpersonal psychology, and wilderness therapy.

Humanities: anthropology, art (performance, studio, visual), art history, comparative religion, creative writing, cultural studies, dance, drama, expressive arts, English, film studies, geography, history, independent media studies, journalism, language studies (e.g., Spanish, Ute), literature, mathematics, museum studies, music, peace studies, philosophy, photo journalism, photography, and theater arts.

Management: accounting, business management, communications, computer information systems, ecological economics, environmental planning, environmental resource conservation, finance, human resource management, leadership for change, legal studies, marketing, nonprofit management, organizational development, public administration, safety and risk management, small business management, and technologies studies.

The Master of Arts Program Students may design programs in five broadly defined programs of study—adventure education, counseling and psychology, education, environmental studies, and the humanities. Within these degree areas, the possibilities for areas of concentration are extensive. Students propose their area of study during the application process and further refine and develop it with the assistance of their graduate advisers.

Adventure education: adventure-based tourism, community recreation programs, corrections and outfitting, Earth-based studies, ecotourism, guiding and outfitting, integral adventure education, outdoor education, outdoor program administration, recreation management, school and college curricula, therapeutic applications of adventure education, and wilderness leadership.

Counseling and psychology: Students may prepare for certification or licensure in professional counseling or marriage and family therapy or in a nonclinical, more theoretical, aspect of the field. Counseling and psychology students focus on specialties such as adventure-based psychotherapy, child development, equine-assisted mental health, expressive arts therapies, grief counseling, and somatic psychology.

Education: curriculum design, English as a second language, pedagogy, literacy, school guidance counseling, school renewal, and bilingual, elementary, environmental, experiential, global, international, multicultural, secondary, and special education.

Environmental studies: agroecology, conservation biology, Earth sciences, ecological design, ecological restoration, ecology, environmental education, environmental ethics and philosophy, environmental history, ethnobotany, marine studies, natural history, natural resource management, social ecology, sustainability education, sustainability science and practice, sustainable community development, and wildlife conservation.

Humanities: Concentrations within the humanities fall within four academic areas.

The traditional humanities (arts and letters): art education, art history, art theory, communication, creative non-fiction, creative writing, dance, environmental writing, journalism, literature, painting, photojournalism, photography, poetry sculpture, technical writing, theater, and video or film theory or production.

Cultural studies: African-American studies, class studies, conflict resolution, gender studies, geography, historic preservation, history of the Southwest, international studies, justice and activism studies, languages (e.g., Spanish, Navajo), literature, men's studies, peace studies, political science, queer studies, social ecology, social sustainability, solidarity studies, and women's studies.

Business and management: business administration, economics, globalism and economics, health-care administration, healthcare management, human resources, international development, management, marketing, organizational development, public administration, and sustainable business practices.

Other social sciences: anthropology, archaeology, cosmology, depth psychology, dialogical ecology, eco-feminism, ecopsychology, forensic psychology, mythology, philosophy, psychology of women, religious studies, spirituality, theology, and wellness.

The Ph.D. Program Students design their own studies within the area of sustainability education. Areas of concentration have been in the areas of community activism, economics, education, environmental studies, and social justice.

Admission

For admission requirements and to contact the admission counselors, students should visit the Prescott College Web site at http://www.prescott.edu/admissions.

Tuition and Fees

For 2008–09, tuition for the B.A. program is $9864 per year, tuition for the M.A. program is $13,608, and tuition for the Ph.D. program is $17,904. Tuition increases may occur in July of each year.

Financial Aid

The types of financial aid available are Federal Pell Grants, Prescott College grants and scholarships, Arizona State Student Incentive Grants, Federal Supplemental Educational Opportunity Grants, the Arizona Voucher Program, the Postsecondary Education Grant, Federal Stafford Student Loans, and student employment. Students seeking any form of financial assistance are encouraged to speak with the Financial Aid Office. The financial aid process begins with filling out the Free Application for Federal Student Aid (FAFSA), which is available online at http://www.fafsa.ed.gov. The Prescott College school code is 013659.

Applying

Application requirements vary by program (B.A., M.A., and Ph.D.) and are available in the program catalogs or online at Prescott's Web site. Applicants may apply online or use the application from the College's catalogs. Students in Tucson and southern Arizona who are interested in the B.A. or M.A. programs should contact the Tucson office. All other geographic areas may work with the Prescott admissions office.

The Admissions Office strongly encourages applicants to submit all required application materials by the priority filing date. Files that are received after the priority filing date are still considered on a rolling basis.

CONTACT

Admissions Office
Prescott College
220 Grove Avenue
Prescott, Arizona 86301

Phone: 928-350-2112
    877-350-2100 Ext. 2112 (toll-free)
Fax: 928-776-5242
E-mail: admissions@prescott.edu
Web site: http://www.prescott.edu

Admissions
Prescott College Tucson Center
2233 East Speedway Boulevard
Tucson, Arizona 85719

Phone: 888-797-4680 (toll-free)
Fax: 520-319-1032

ROOSEVELT UNIVERSITY
RU Online Distance Learning Program
Chicago, Illinois

Roosevelt is a national leader in educating socially conscious citizens for active and dedicated lives as leaders in their professions and their communities. Deeply rooted in practical scholarship and principles of social justice expressed as ethical awareness, leadership development, economic progress, and civic engagement, Roosevelt University encourages community partnerships and prepares its diverse graduates for responsible citizenship in a global society. Founded in 1945 in Chicago, the University was one of the first institutions of higher learning to admit all qualified students, regardless of race, religion, or gender. Since then, Roosevelt opened a second campus in northwest suburban Schaumburg, Illinois, and, more recently, began an online distance learning program, RU Online.

Distance Learning Program

RU Online is Roosevelt University's fully online learning program. Students around the globe join in engaging, interactive, and enriching learning experiences. RU Online offers master's and bachelor's degree programs as well as certificates and courses. The program has been recognized for academic integrity by Blackboard and the American Society for Training and Development. In addition, the program has received full accreditation by the Higher Learning Commission of the North Central Association of Colleges and Schools.

Delivery Media

RU Online is focused more on the learner and the teaching/learning process than on the technology used to operate it. As long as students have access to a computer and the Internet, they are eligible to enroll in RU Online. The courses are twelve weeks in length and have weekly learning modules. The courses have real instructors, students, and course materials, but the courses themselves provide more flexibility than face-to-face classes. Although students have greater freedom, they also have the security of knowing that classmates are learning along with them at the same pace. All fully online

courses are taught in cohort groups (classmates go through the course together at the same time), and they are offered within the same semester or session time frame as on-campus courses. In addition, students can interact with the instructor and fellow classmates by e-mail, online discussion forums, and telephone.

Programs of Study

Roosevelt offers several programs that students can take completely through RU Online without attending classes at either the Chicago or the Schaumburg campus. There are fully online bachelor's degree programs in organizational leadership, psychology, and criminal justice leadership. These are part of Roosevelt's Bachelor of Professional Studies (B.P.S.) program, which has been a nationally recognized leader in accelerated studies for working adults since 1966.

There are fully online master's degree programs in training and development (M.A.T.D.) and teacher leadership (M.A.T.L.), both of which can provide a career boost in the corresponding fields.

In addition, RU Online includes fully online undergraduate certificate programs in criminal justice leadership, meeting coordinator studies, organiza-

tional leadership, and teaching writing-intensive courses. There are also graduate certificate programs in e-learning, instructional design, online teaching, performance consulting, and training and development.

RU Online provides numerous courses in subjects from four of the University's five colleges: College of Arts and Sciences, College of Education, Evelyn T. Stone College of Professional Studies, and Walter E. Heller College of Business Administration (classes in the Chicago College of Performing Arts are not typically given online). To earn their degrees from these colleges, students have the flexibility of enrolling in some classes online while taking others in traditional classrooms. Students interested in continuing education find a wide variety of online courses from which to choose.

Student Services

RU Online provides training for students and faculty and staff members via online and face-to-face workshops. Students have full access to the Roosevelt University library via its Web services and embedded course librarians. They also have full access to the 24/7 information technology help center, an online adviser, and the Student Writing Center.

Credit Options

Roosevelt University awards credit for successful completion of many CLEP examinations as well as for satisfactory scores on Advanced Placement tests and International Baccalaureate course work.

For adult students who have completed an associate degree, there is a series of options designed to streamline the education process to make the transition easier from community college to Roosevelt University.

In many cases, the University has made special arrangements with community colleges to accept transfer credits from A.A.S. degrees. Students from some of Roosevelt's undergraduate programs are eligible to enter the online graduate programs upon graduation, through the Transitions to Graduate Study Program. For specific details, students should visit http://faculty.roosevelt.edu/ruonline/ or contact the RU Online program.

Faculty

Most of the faculty members who teach in Roosevelt's online program also teach traditional classroom courses on campus or teach blended courses, which have both online and classroom components. Roosevelt University has 216 full-time faculty members, 84 percent of whom hold terminal degrees, and 413 adjunct faculty members.

Roosevelt University is proud of its faculty, whose members are equally serious at teaching and at pursuing scholarship and research in their respective fields. They are committed to student success and are focused on helping each student achieve his or her goals. In addition, they are experienced and creative online teachers.

The 2007 Illinois Professor of the Year, Steven A. Meyers, is one of the instructors for RU Online psychology courses. Meyers, who teaches developmental and clinical psychology, was presented with an award from the Carnegie Foundation for the Advancement of Teaching, the only national program to recognize excellence in undergraduate teaching and mentoring.

Admission

There are no admission requirements for enrolling in individual courses. Students who wish to enroll in a degree or certificate program must meet the requirements of the specific program. For information about individual program requirements, students should visit http://faculty.roosevelt.edu/ruonline (toll-free).

Tuition and Fees

For information about Roosevelt's schedule of tuition and fees, students should visit http://www.roosevelt.edu/financialaid/tuition.htm or call 866-421-0935 (toll-free).

Financial Aid

Payment for online courses can be arranged in the same manner as traditional courses at Roosevelt University. Payment options include financial aid, employer tuition reimbursement, deferred-payment plans, and full payment. For financial aid information, students should visit http://www.roosevelt.edu/financialaid or call 866-421-0935 (toll-free).

Applying

For information about the application process, students should contact the Admissions Office (Web site: http://www.roosevelt.edu/admission; telephone: 877-APPLY RU (toll-free); or e-mail: applyRU@roosevelt.edu).

CONTACT

Linda Gunden
Program/Admission Specialist
Roosevelt University
430 South Michigan Avenue
Chicago, Illinois 60605
Phone: 312-341-2602
        866-885-3823 (toll-free)
E-mail: ruonline@roosevelt.edu
Web site: http://www.roosevelt.edu/admission

SAINT JOSEPH'S COLLEGE OF MAINE
Graduate & Professional Studies
Standish, Maine

Saint Joseph's College is a Roman Catholic liberal arts college that nurtures intellectual, spiritual, and social growth in students of all faiths and all ages. Saint Joseph's was founded in 1912 by the Sisters of Mercy and chartered by the Maine Legislature in 1915. It is the Catholic college of Maine. Saint Joseph's grants degrees in fulfillment of the educational ideals of the Sisters of Mercy, founded by Mary Catherine McAuley in Dublin, Ireland, in 1831. The College's 350-acre campus is situated on the shore of Sebago Lake in Standish, Maine, a half hour from Portland, Maine's largest city, and 2 hours north of Boston. Approximately 1,000 young adults reside at the College's campus, where they pursue their undergraduate studies.

In 1976, distance education was introduced at Saint Joseph's to serve the needs of nontraditional adult learners in the U.S. and abroad. The distance education program at Saint Joseph's College, the Division of Graduate & Professional Studies, is known for its high-quality education geared to working professionals and is one of the most established in the country. With more than three decades of experience providing distance education to adult students, the College has the procedures and polices that work for busy professionals who are interested in furthering their education for career advancement and for personal growth.

Saint Joseph's College is accredited by the New England Association of Schools and Colleges to award baccalaureate and master's degrees. The nursing program is approved by the Maine State Board of Nursing, Augusta, Maine, and accredited by the Commission on Collegiate Nursing Education. The long-term-care administration program is accredited by the National Association of Boards of Examiners of Long-Term Care Administrators.

Distance Learning Program

Saint Joseph's College offers the adult learner an opportunity to integrate formal education in the liberal arts tradition with professional experience. The Graduate & Professional Studies Program provides academic options in a variety of disciplines leading to undergraduate and graduate certificates and to associate, baccalaureate, and graduate degrees. Students may also choose individual courses for personal goals and/or industry continuing education requirements. Each option is designed to reflect the special nature of Saint Joseph's commitment to its students. Approximately 8,800 Saint Joseph's alumni have earned their degrees through the distance program.

Delivery Media

Students can complete their course work virtually anywhere in the world at their convenience with St. Joseph's online programs. Distance education courses through the Division of Graduate & Professional Studies and the Department of Nursing are available online via the World Wide Web, using WebCT. This integrated online platform is a flexible learning system through which students have access to course content, study tips, resources tailored to the individual course, and various communication tools.

Instructors use asynchronous instruction, so students enjoy a highly flexible, accessible mode of education that allows them to complete their programs of study where they reside, completely on their individual schedules. Upon enrollment, students receive the necessary texts and materials for their courses, including course access instructions. All online courses require a computer with Internet access. Faculty members assist each student with their studies through a combination of written feedback on assignments, telephone consultations, and e-mail. An academic adviser is assigned to work with each student from enrollment through graduation.

Programs of Study

Saint Joseph's College offers the following degree programs at the graduate level: a Master of Arts in Pastoral Theology, which is designed for those involved with parishes, diocesan agencies, hospitals, retreat/spiritual centers, or social service agencies; a Master of Science in Education (33 credits), with specializations in teaching and learning and administrative management, which is intended for teachers and/or administrators who are interested in initiating or enhancing a career in K–12 education, community college, or adult education; a Master of Health Administration (42 credits) for senior management roles in complex health-care organizations; a Master of Science in Nursing (39 credits), with specializations in nursing administration and nursing education; and a Master of Business Administration (42 credits), with a specialization in leadership. Graduate certificates (18 credits) include programs in nursing and health-care education and nursing administration and leadership.

At the undergraduate level, Saint Joseph's College offers the following degrees through distance learning: the Bachelor of Science (128 credits), offering majors in business administration, with specializations in banking through a joint venture with the Center for Financial Training, and management; general studies (a degree-completion program for adult students), with specializations in adult education and training, business administration, criminal justice, human services, and psychology; health administration; long-term-care administration; and radiologic science (a postcertification baccalaureate degree for radiology technicians).

A Bachelor of Arts in theological studies (128 credits) is also available at the undergraduate level. In addition, a Bachelor of Science in Nursing (129 credits) is available for RNs; it can also be earned in the RN to M.S.N. program, a curriculum that allows students to more rapidly progress through the B.S.N. and M.S.N. requirements and earn both degrees. Students can also choose from six majors within the Associate of Science degree (66 credits), including adult education and training, business administration, criminal justice, general studies, human services, and psychology.

Undergraduate certificate programs (18 credits) are available in adult education and training, business administration, health-care management, and long-term-care administration. Students who would like to take individual courses at either the graduate or undergraduate level may enroll as continuing education students.

Special Programs

The Division of Graduate & Professional Studies has developed partnerships with numerous organizations and corporations to provide educational opportunities to their employees throughout the country at multiple locations. (For more information, students should contact the Admissions Office.) Saint Joseph's College is also a member of Servicemembers Opportunity Colleges (SOC), which guarantees transfer of credit for military personnel completing courses from other SOC schools. The Division is also a member of eArmyU, the Navy College Program Distance Learning Partnership, and Troops to Teachers and assists active and nonactive military personnel in their educational pursuits.

Credit Options

The Graduate & Professional Studies Program acknowledges the value of certain formal learning and career-based experience. For most programs, the College follows the American Council on Education (ACE) guidelines in granting transfer credit for courses of study from accredited colleges or universities with a grade of C or better; ACE/PONSI-approved credit; ACE-approved military training and experience credit; CEUs earned through professional seminars, workshops, internships, and in-service education classes as elective credit; and CLEP, ACT/PEP, and DANTES exams. The total number of credits that can be awarded varies depending on the program.

Faculty

Nearly 200 full-time and part-time faculty members serve students in the Graduate & Professional Studies Program. Many teach in the residential program at Saint Joseph's College as well as in distance education. Each online instructor is required to complete a comprehensive five-week online training program to develop and refine the necessary skills to teach in an online environment. All instructors excel in their fields and have substantial experience with nontraditional students. Students communicate with faculty members via e-mail, phone, fax, and/or regular postal mail.

Admission

Admission requirements vary by program of study. Prospective students should contact the Admissions Office for the Graduate & Professional Studies Program at 800-752-4723 (toll-free) with specific questions about admission requirements. Information can also be obtained online at http://www.sjcme.edu/pg.

Tuition and Fees

For the 2007–08 academic year, tuition was $275 per credit ($825 per 3-credit course) at the undergraduate level. Graduate course tuition varies depending on the program and ranged from $300 to $375 per credit ($900 to $1125 per 3-credit course). Application fees are $50 for degree programs and $25 for certificate programs and continuing education. A complete fee schedule is available at the College's Web site.

Financial Aid

Students may be eligible for the Federal Pell Grant and/or Federal Stafford Student Loan. Applying for financial aid is an individualized process requiring consultation and evaluation. For more information and assistance, students should call the Financial Aid Office at 800-752-1266 (toll-free).

Applying

Applicants for all programs and all courses are required to submit an application and a nonrefundable application fee. Application fees are $50 for degree programs and $25 for certificate programs and continuing education. For many programs, students are accepted on a rolling admissions basis and, therefore, can apply and begin their studies at any time during the year. Students may download the application forms online or apply online at the College's Web site. For further information, students may contact the Admissions Office.

CONTACT

Admissions Office
Division of Graduate & Professional
   Studies
Saint Joseph's College
278 Whites Bridge Road
Standish, Maine 04084-5263

Phone: 800-752-4723 (toll-free)
Fax: 207-892-7480
E-mail: info@sjcme.edu
Web site:
   http://www.sjcme.edu/pg

ST. LOUIS COMMUNITY COLLEGE SYSTEM

Telelearning Services

St. Louis, Missouri

St. Louis Community College (SLCC) is a public coeducational college supported by local taxes, state funds, and student fees. Created by area voters in 1962, the College offers freshman- and sophomore-level career and college transfer, developmental, and continuing education programs at its four campuses, three education centers, and numerous other locations throughout St. Louis city and county. Nearly 130,000 students enroll each year in credit and noncredit courses. The College also serves the business community by offering St. Louis area business stakeholders performance improvement, consulting, and training services. St. Louis Community College and its campuses are accredited by the Higher Learning Commission of North Central Association of Colleges and Schools. The College is also a founding member of the League for Innovation in the Community College, serving on the League's Board of Directors and as a Board member of Project SAIL

Distance Learning Program

St. Louis Community College offers instruction via the World Wide Web, videotapes, CD-ROMs, DVDs, e-mail, live interactive video, and streaming video in addition to face-to-face classroom instruction. Since 1973, St. Louis Community College has offered distance education to students locally, nationally, and internationally. Approximately 6,000 students annually enroll in distance learning courseware through SLCC.

Delivery Media

Web-based courses and TeleWEB-courses: Course orientation and exams may be administered via the Web or held on campus or at instructor-approved sites, depending on the specific course. Assignments, announcements, projects, tutorials, e-mail, student discussion forums, essay submission and retrieval, operating instructions, bulletins, and library research are accomplished via asynchronous communication in distance learning courses.

Telecourses: Video lessons—televised, videocassette, or CD/DVD—accompany related readings and assignments, discussions, and examinations. When students need help, instructors are just a phone call or e-mail away.

Special print materials (textbooks, study guides, and student manuals) have been prepared to accompany each course.

Programs of Study

SLCC offers an Associate in Applied Science (A.A.S.) in hospitality studies and in information reporting technology as well as certificates of proficiency in funeral directing, information reporting technology, and business administration.

Hospitality Studies: Graduates of the Associate of Applied Science degree program are prepared to enter the hospitality industry at an entry-level management level and perform management functions and duties. Students with a Certificate of Proficiency in hotel and restaurant management are prepared for entry-level positions such as front office management, guest services, bar and beverage management, and restaurant or facility management.

Funeral Directing: This certificate of proficiency program prepares the student for licensure as a funeral director and entry-level employment in a funeral establishment. This is a nontechnical certificate geared toward the business and public relations aspects of operating a funeral home. There are no courses in embalming.

Graduates are eligible to take the licensing examinations for Missouri or for any other states with similar licensing requirements.

Information Reporting Technology: CART and Captioning Reporting: An Associate in Applied Science degree and a certificate of proficiency are offered through the Information Reporting Technology program. Communication Access Realtime Translation (CART), also referred to as realtime captioning, is a word-for-word speech-to-text interpreting service for people who need communication access. For students who are fascinated with words and have good English skills, manual dexterity, keyboarding experience, and the ability to hear the spoken word, CART and captioning reporting may be the perfect career. This program prepares the student for entry-level positions in realtime captioning.

Business Administration: This program, which offers a certificate of proficiency and a certificate of specialization, addresses the educational and occupational needs of several groups of people in the business field. Students can enroll in short-term, intensive training for job opportunities, or they can complete specific undergraduate requirements toward an advanced degree in business.

Special Programs

St. Louis Community College offers an honors program; students are admitted based on their high school GPA and SAT or ACT scores. Students who earn 15 hours of honors credit receive the designation of Honors Program Scholar on their diplomas and transcripts.

In recognition of the importance of the United States' position within the international community, SLCC offers transcultural and international study.

This includes semesters abroad and study tours. The International Education Office (314-539-5176) has additional information.

Student Services
Students can access many SLCC student services via the Web, including admissions, registration, financial aid, library services, and the 24/7 HelpDesk.

Credit Options
Students may be eligible for credit for academic knowledge gained outside the classroom. The number of credits earned through examination is limited; College policy states that 15 of the final 25 semester hours earned toward an associate degree must be earned at St. Louis Community College. Students should get official transcripts mailed to the College and request an evaluation of previously earned credits by the campus admission/registration office.

Faculty
Faculty members specialize in teaching at the undergraduate level and hold advanced degrees—master's or doctoral—or advanced licensing degrees in technical fields. Career instructors have worked in business and industry and keep current with changes in their fields. Of the College's 1,469 faculty members, 423 are full-time.

Admission
St. Louis Community College has an open-admissions policy in keeping with its original purpose to provide a high-quality, low-cost education to area residents. Although admission to the College is not based on minimum academic qualifications, certain programs have required standards for admission and retention.

Tuition and Fees
Maintenance fees are $81 per credit hour for students in the SLCC service area, $118 per credit hour for out-of-district students, $148 per credit hour for out-of-state students, and $158 per credit hour for international students.

Financial Aid
St. Louis Community College provides a comprehensive financial aid program funded by federal, state, and private agencies. Aid awards fall into four categories—grants, scholarships, loans, and work. Although superior ability and talent are recognized through College and other scholarship programs, most aid is awarded on the basis of financial need. Students are encouraged to apply for aid as early as possible (by April 1 for the fall semester). Students who wish to know more about their financial aid eligibility should contact the College's financial aid office.

Applying
Students can apply online, by mail or fax, or in person. Applicants must submit an official high school transcript or GED score. International students must also submit TOEFL scores and certification of finances.

CONTACT

Daniel A. Bain, Ph.D., Director
Telelearning Services
St. Louis Community College System
300 South Broadway
St. Louis, Missouri 63102

Phone: 314-539-5056
Fax: 314-539-5125
E-mail: dbain@stlcc.edu
Web site: http://www.stlcc.edu/distance

SAVANNAH COLLEGE OF ART AND DESIGN

SCAD-eLearning Program

Savannah, Georgia

Savannah College of Art and Design (SCAD) exists to prepare talented students for professional careers, emphasizing learning through individual attention in a positively oriented university environment. SCAD is a private, coeducational institution with locations in Atlanta and Savannah, Georgia. Online programs are offered through SCAD-eLearning. A balanced fine arts and liberal arts curriculum has attracted students from every state and from more than ninety countries, making SCAD one of the largest art and design colleges in the United States.

Distance Learning Program

The Savannah College of Art and Design offers individual courses and degree and certificate programs at the undergraduate and graduate levels through SCAD-eLearning. SCAD, a member of the Sloan Consortium of institutions, is an award-winning, recognized leader in online course design, instructional technology, and online education. SCAD-eLearning is committed to academic excellence, technology integration, and twenty-first-century design practices. Its distance education programs give students the flexibility to further their creative talents online in order to suit their locations, schedules, and preferences.

SCAD, including SCAD-eLearning, is regionally accredited by the Commission on Colleges of the Southern Association of Colleges and Schools (1866 Southern Lane, Decatur, Georgia 30033-4097; 404-679-4500) to award bachelor's and master's degrees. SCAD-eLearning students earn a SCAD degree, with no distinction made between degree requirements met on campus and online.

Delivery Media

Courses are delivered via the Internet and are offered year-round; each is organized into ten units, usually one per week. Courses adhere to a ten-week quarter with start and end dates but are not held at scheduled times. Instead, students attend class when it is convenient for them. Students are expected to complete course work according to a schedule that stipulates due dates, assessments, and discussions. Student participation is expected in all assignments, examinations, and field trips or other activities. Attendance is determined by active login time and participation.

SCAD-eLearning provides a secure and user-friendly way for faculty members and students to communicate with one another. Regular online discussions, live chat sessions with professors and peers, assessments, and feedback help students maximize their experience. Students have access to an extensive range of online services and resources.

Instructional designers and technologists, media designers, and e-services staff members collaborate with faculty members to ensure that all courses are fully ADA compliant and adhere to the same high standards as SCAD's on-site course offerings.

SCAD-eLearning students must possess basic computer skills and have regular access to appropriate hardware, software, and Internet connectivity. SCAD-eLearning courses are designed to run on a variety of computers and operating systems and may be accessed with a 56K modem connection or better. Prospective students may find specific technical requirements online at http://www.scadelearning.org.

Programs of Study

SCAD-eLearning programs include Bachelor of Arts (B.A.) degrees in digital media and visual communications; Master of Arts degrees in broadcast design and motion graphics, digital photography, graphic design, historic preservation, illustration design, interactive design and game development, interior design, and painting; a Master of Fine Arts degree in graphic design; an undergraduate certificate in digital publishing; and graduate certificates in historic preservation, interactive design, digital publishing management, and typeface design.

The four-year Bachelor of Arts degree program incorporates fine arts foundation studies, general education courses, an area of concentration, and electives. The majority of the B.A. curriculum consists of fine arts, humanities, general education, and liberal arts courses. An area of study concentration complements the course work. Students pursuing a B.A. degree in digital media may choose a concentration in game development or interactive design; those interested in a visual communication degree may concentrate in graphic design or sequential art.

The Master of Arts degree in broadcast design and motion graphics is a mixture of graphic design in motion and experimental animation. The program combines taught and self-directed studies, critical approaches to spatial and material culture, project management, design methodology, research, communication, and design theory.

The Master of Arts degree in digital photography allows students to gain a thorough knowledge of the medium and the photographic applications of digital technology. Students achieve a mastery of craft, technology, and aesthetics by exploring creative possibilities, developing a personal vision, and studying the history and criticism of the medium.

The eLearning certificates and degree programs in graphic design prepare students for careers in a variety of fields, including publishing, education, advertising, and new media. In the certificate programs, students learn to produce a broad range of materials, including newsletters, brochures, and Web sites, with industry-standard computer applications. The undergraduate certificate in digital publishing features an emphasis on production, while the graduate certificate in digital publishing management emphasizes management of content, design and development processes, and creative teams. With the graduate certificate in typeface design, students pursue historical and practical research opportunities and a comprehensive understanding of the nature of typeface design processes. Students invent, develop, and promote their own typeface solutions. The Master of Arts program in graphic design is professionally oriented and allows a broad course of study; the Master of Fine

Arts program includes a field or teaching internship and a thesis component.

The graduate certificate in historic preservation is designed for individuals working in historic preservation or related fields and those with an interest in historic preservation who would like to expand their knowledge or prepare to enter the field or enhance their careers. The Master of Arts program includes courses in building assessment and preservation planning and requires a final project.

The Master of Arts degree in illustration design allows students to create a substantial body of work, producing comprehensive portfolios in preparation for a career in freelance illustration. Students are introduced to the practical side of the illustration business, from portfolio presentation to marketing and invoicing. Course work parallels professional practice and sometimes involves actual clients.

The graduate certificate and Master of Arts degree in interactive design and game development prepare students for careers in interactive art and design, particularly with large design firms, advertising agencies, product manufacturers, and education. The online method of course delivery is compelling, as students are educated in the electronically mediated environment in which they typically work or plan to work. Students are prepared for or may enhance their careers in interactive design, art direction, creative technology, exhibit design, and projection media.

The Master of Arts degree in interior design prepares students for advanced professional practice, teaching, or research. The curriculum includes commercial, residential, and institutional projects, both large and small, that address a wide range of behavioral, environmental, decorative, and technical issues.

Painting students in the Master of Arts degree program develop their work through informed, individual instruction and a curriculum that promotes exploration based on practical knowledge and awareness of historical and contemporary factors. The program begins with a five-week residency in Savannah, continues online, and finishes with a five-week residency in Atlanta.

All courses may be credited toward other applicable degree programs upon successful application and acceptance to the program.

Student Services

SCAD-eLearning provides a forum for students to participate in College events and discussions through Webcasts, online forums, and other digital-programming outlets. Through the College's MySCAD Intranet, students may access comprehensive e-campus services, including course registration, peer tutoring, career services, Writing Center instruction, and SCAD's Jen Library online services. Students are encouraged to communicate with their peers through course discussions, e-mail, quarterly online chats, and the eLearning Club, which holds regular meetings online in real time.

Credit Options

Through SCAD-eLearning, the Savannah College of Art and Design offers students the option of taking courses without enrolling in a degree or certificate program. Depending on their admission status, students may take courses for credit. Course offerings change quarterly; students should consult the SCAD-eLearning Web site for an updated course listing.

Faculty

SCAD-eLearning courses are taught by highly qualified professors, who guide students toward academic and professional success. Seventy-four percent of SCAD faculty members hold terminal degrees, and 81 percent are full-time. Every SCAD professor offers the professional experience, academic credentials, expertise, and passion for teaching that are characteristic of SCAD faculty members. Professors actively teach, publish academic papers, work as professional artists and designers, and exhibit their work in museums and galleries.

Admission

Application and admission policies and procedures for SCAD-eLearning are the same as for all undergraduate and graduate programs offered by the College. New students may enter for the fall, winter, spring, or summer quarter. Applicants are encouraged to submit their applications online and to apply as early as possible. Students applying for federal or state financial aid should plan to complete their application file and submit all financial aid information at least six months prior to their intended entry quarter. Students who wish to be considered for institutional scholarships must indicate this on the application for admission and must submit all required materials as requested. Scholarship funds are limited and are awarded to the earliest qualifiers.

As a general rule, applications for fall quarter should be completed no later than March 1 in order for admission decisions to be rendered by April 1. This same time frame applies with corresponding dates for students entering for the winter, spring, or summer quarters. Applications received less than one month prior to the intended entry date are considered only on a space-available basis.

Tuition and Fees

Undergraduate tuition for 2008–09 is $2885 per 5-credit-hour course; graduate tuition is $2935 per 5-credit-hour course. All degree-seeking students pay a one-time, non-refundable matriculation fee of $500. Non-degree-seeking students pay a tuition deposit of $200.

Financial Aid

Qualified SCAD-eLearning students are eligible to receive scholarships, fellowships, and federal and state financial aid. Only degree-seeking and certificate students who are enrolled at least half-time (two classes) may be eligible for federal financial aid. For application requirements and detailed information about scholarships, fellowships, and financial aid, prospective students should visit http://www.scadelearning.org. Students enrolling less than half-time and non-degree-seeking students should contact an alternative lender for financial assistance. Alternative lender information may be found on the College Web site at http://www.scad.edu. Aid programs offered by the state of Georgia may be available to Georgia students who are enrolled full-time (three classes). Non-Georgia students are encouraged to research their states' incentive program scholarships.

Applying

To apply for admission, learn more about online programs, or take the SCAD-eLearning self-assessment test, students should visit SCAD's Web site at http://www.scadelearning.org.

CONTACT

SCAD-eLearning
Savannah College of Art and Design
P.O. Box 2072
Savannah, Georgia 31402-2072
Phone: 912-525-5100
         800-869-7223 (toll-free)
E-mail: elearn@scad.edu
Web site: http://www.scadelearning.
         org

SAYBROOK GRADUATE SCHOOL AND RESEARCH CENTER
Graduate Programs in Psychology, Human Science, and Organizational Systems
San Francisco, California

Saybrook Graduate School and Research Center, accredited by the Western Association of Schools and Colleges (WASC), is a nonprofit distance learning graduate institution. Grounded in the humanistic tradition, Saybrook offers master's and doctoral degrees in psychology, human science, and organizational systems. Valuable certificate programs are also offered.

Saybrook now offers several new programs. The Doctor of Psychology (Psy.D.), a five-year program designed for students who aspire to make a difference in the practice of psychology, offers the opportunity for students to specialize in life-span development phases (such as adolescence, midlife, or late adult life) or other areas that include forensic psychology and integrative and alternative approaches to health. The degree programs in Jungian studies are for clinicians and other students who wish to explore the work of Carl Jung. The M.A. in leadership of sustainable systems is a program for the visionary leaders of the future in the public, corporate, and nonprofit sectors who want to help build a humane and sustainable future. The M.A. in social transformative change is a specialization that prepares students to respond to social, cultural, and political challenges in a unique way: as scholar-practitioner-activists who are able to create transformative changes in social systems that embody deeply humanistic values.

Saybrook students come from forty-six states and fourteen countries and represent a broad range of career and educational experience in the social sciences, education, business, humanities, and the arts.

Saybrook provides a premier learning environment rooted in humanistic values. Saybrook's mentored distance education model blends scholarship, practice, and service to support students in pursuing their life's work.

Distance Learning Program

Saybrook Graduate School and Research Center offers a distance education model that blends mentored courses, virtual-classroom participation, and face-to-face learning and gives working professionals the opportunity to complete a degree program wherever they live.

Programs begin with a Residential Orientation that introduces students to their program, faculty members, classmates, and the online learning environment. They are paired with an academic adviser who assists with mapping the unique path of their programs.

Twice a year, students reunite in person with faculty members and the other students during Residential Conferences in San Francisco. The Residential Conferences offer intensive classroom time where faculty members and students delve deeper into selected topics of interest.

Between Residential Conferences, students complete course work in virtual-classroom settings, where they interact with their professors and classmates through threaded discussions. Courses are also offered in an individually mentored format in which students work directly with a faculty member who provides guidance and critique to hone the student's writing and research skills. Each course and interaction contributes to the student's research, final project, or thesis.

The 98-unit Psy.D. cohort program offers a residential component that is conveniently clustered in three weeklong and seven weekend intensives during the first academic year, two weeklong and four weekend intensives during the second academic year, and two weeklong and two weekend intensives during the third year. The fourth and fifth years are dedicated to internship and dissertation.

Students of the new M.A. or Ph.D. programs in psychology, Jungian studies specialization, are provided with more significant residential components. They attend the San Francisco Residential Orientation and seven seminars each year that are held in Houston, Texas, at the Jung Center.

Saybrook offers a distance learning format that provides academic rigor, strong community, and network opportunities within a structure that won't interfere with family and career obligations.

Saybrook students have the flexibility to move at their own pace and may progress more rapidly through some programs by completing 12 to 15 units per semester.

Delivery Media

In addition to the residential component, students are engaged in individually mentored courses in which they set the pace for their own programs of study, completing assignments with supervision by a Saybrook faculty member. Faculty mentors provide guidance and critique, working with students to hone writing and research skills and to encourage students to go deeper into their inquiry. Mentors can also help students expand the meaning of their individual work within the overarching humanistic vision. A Learning Guide serves as a map of the course, outlining learning objectives and expectations such as required texts, writing assignments, and research activities.

Students also participate in virtual-classroom courses, online classes that offer a formal class structure as well as an interactive learning experience. Students begin and end the course together as a group and typically participate in the class by viewing streamed video presentations, posting research work, and contributing to threaded discussions. Assignments are completed as scheduled throughout the semester.

Programs of Study

Saybrook offers three degrees, the M.A., Ph.D., and Psy.D., and a variety of options that allow students to structure their studies to meet their career goals within three program areas: psychology, organizational systems, and human science.

Saybrook's psychology degree programs are based in humanistic philosophy, grounded in the teachings of Rollo May, Carl Rogers, Erich Fromm, and others. They prepare students to create health and wholeness as scholar-practitioners to address the urgent needs of human beings in all stages of development.

Students who are interested in applied practice and clinical careers may wish to consider the M.A. specialization in psychology, marriage, and family therapy; the Ph.D. in psychology specialization in clinical psychology; or the new Doctor of Clinical Psychology (Psy.D.). Those interested in careers in teaching, research, or publishing may wish to consider specializations in the new M.A. or Ph.D. in psychology, Jungian studies, or the M.A. in psychology, creativity. Psychology students may also choose to pursue a concentration in consciousness and spirituality, humanistic and transpersonal psychology, integrative health studies, organizational systems, or social transformation.

Innovative M.A. and Ph.D. programs in organizational systems are action- and systems-oriented to educate professionals to assume leadership roles and address urgent issues of sustainability and human resource development. The programs train students to develop their leadership skills; create new structures, processes, values, and beliefs; support humanistic and sustainable practices; and engage in participative management. Programs include the M.A. or Ph.D. in organizational systems and the new M.A. in leadership of sustainable systems.

Human science programs foster an interdisciplinary focus on the human condition to offer a unique perspective on contemporary life by learning about social problems from multiple perspectives. These programs prepare students for new or enhanced careers as leaders and activists in governmental and nongovernmental social action and community service organizations and networks and as teachers in higher education institutions. Programs include the M.A. and Ph.D. in human science and the new M.A. in transformative social change. Human science students may choose to pursue concentrations in consciousness and spirituality, humanistic and transpersonal psychology, integrative health studies, organizational systems, or social transformation.

Saybrook students have the opportunity to complete certificate programs as well. Certificates provide valuable integrative and multidisciplinary training for professionals in areas such as creativity, dream studies, expressive arts, organizational consulting, and peace and conflict resolution.

Whether students' career goals are to shape the future of clinical practice to promote health and wholeness or to be visionary leaders seeking transformative change in social and organizational systems, Saybrook offers graduate degrees for professionals working toward a more humane and sustainable future.

Student Services
Resources offered in person and at a distance throughout a student's progress at Saybrook include student support services through the Dean of Students and Saybrook enrollment coordinators; an electronic library composed of extensive database resources that contain electronic books, articles, and complete journals; and a lifetime connection to the Saybrook community.

Credit Options
In the Saybrook M.A. to Ph.D. Option, students who complete a Saybrook master's degree can transfer 31 units toward their 76-unit Ph.D. program, condensing the Ph.D. completion time by up to two years. If they have already begun their graduate career at another institution, they may transfer up to 12 units toward Saybrook's master's degrees and up to 18 units toward Saybrook's doctoral degrees.

Saybrook also offers transfer options for students who have completed Saybrook course work on a nondegree basis.

Faculty
All Saybrook Graduate School and Research Center faculty members have earned doctorates and are respected authors and leaders recognized for their cutting-edge research, clinical practice, activist pursuits, and publications. They support and mentor students as they progress in their programs and foster an environment where the highest and best expression of the human spirit is possible for all.

Admission
All applicants seeking admission into a master's program must hold a bachelor's degree from a regionally accredited institution. The minimum expected grade point average (GPA) requirement is 3.0.

Doctoral degree applicants must have a master's degree from a regionally accredited institution. If they wish to earn a doctoral degree and have not already earned a master's degree, students are encouraged to complete a Saybrook master's degree and transfer 31 units to the 76-unit Ph.D. pro-

gram, condensing the Ph.D. completion time by up to two years.

Tuition and Fees
For 2008–09, annual tuition is $18,900 for M.A. and Ph.D. programs and $22,000 for the Psy.D. program. Most programs require the Residential Orientation, which costs $650, and the twice-a-year Residential Conferences, which cost $950 each

Financial Aid
Students' educations at Saybrook are affordable investments in themselves and their futures. Saybrook offers a number of scholarships, including the New Student Scholarship, Community Leadership Scholarship, Leir Charitable Trusts Scholarship, and the Saybrook Psy.D. Scholar Program. In addition, students are eligible to apply for federal financial aid, and they have access to a variety of alternative loan resources.

All master's and doctoral students are eligible for master's project or thesis and dissertation grants. For the 2008–09 academic year, the doctoral research grants are 37 percent of annual tuition.

Applying
Students are welcome to apply at any time. Priority is given to applications received by May 1 for fall-semester enrollment and December 1 for spring-semester enrollment. A complete application includes the online application found at https://mars.saybrook.edu/SMS/MainAdmissionsLogin.jsp; the $50 application fee; an academic writing sample; a personal statement; official, sealed transcripts from all postsecondary institutions attended; two letters of recommendation; and a resume.

In addition, applications for the Psy.D. program require a GRE score, and applications for the Jungian studies program require an additional personal essay that addresses the student's interest in studying the works of C. G. Jung.

Interested students should feel free to contact Saybrook for assistance.

CONTACT

Saybrook Graduate School and Research Center
747 Front Street, 3rd Floor
San Francisco, California 94111-1920
Phone: 415-433-9200
        800-825-4480 (toll-free)
Fax: 415-433-9271
E-mail: admissions@saybrook.edu
Web site: http://www.saybrook.edu

SCHILLER INTERNATIONAL UNIVERSITY

Online Degree Programs

Largo, Florida

Schiller International University (SIU), a leader in global education, with seven campuses in six countries, was founded in 1964. SIU is a licensed and accredited institution offering a curriculum of more than 300 courses in sixteen areas of study that lead to associate, bachelor's, and master's degrees. The mission of SIU is to prepare students, personally and professionally, for future leadership roles in an international setting. Schiller students have the unique opportunity to transfer among SIU's campuses without losing any credits while continuing their chosen program of study. SIU's campuses are in Largo, Florida; London, England; Paris, France; Strasbourg, France; Heidelberg, Germany; Leysin, Switzerland; and Madrid, Spain.

Schiller is a university where personal initiative is encouraged and where faculty members know students by name. The close attention paid to each individual student is one of the hallmarks of an SIU education. SIU is accredited by the Accrediting Council for Independent Colleges and Schools (ACICS) and is licensed by the Florida Commission for Independent Education (http://www.fldoe.org) to award associate, bachelor's, and master's degrees. The accreditation and licensing apply to both traditional and online programs.

Distance Learning Program

Distance learning is a natural extension of the University's high-quality education, on both the graduate and undergraduate levels, for students from all over the world. The development of this program has leveraged Schiller's network of campuses to furnish and equip learners with the tools and resources needed to compete in this global marketplace. The creative use of modern education technology makes selected SIU programs available anytime, anywhere, through the World Wide Web. Students may complete their entire degree program online, or online courses may be combined with one or more terms in residence at an SIU campus in the United States or in Europe.

Delivery Media

Schiller's online programs are available to all students who have access to a Pentium-based computer, a 28.8-Kbps (or faster) modem, the usual office software, and an Internet connection. (Students in the management of IT program may need additional software packages.) All courses are Web based and are delivered via the Internet, using the eCollege.com platform. Technical support is provided 24 hours a day, seven days a week, by eCollege's help desk. The course Web site contains a home page with the most essential information about the course, e-mail links to the instructor and other students taking the course, a discussion forum that allows the instructor and students to communicate with the group as a whole, Web links, and glossaries. Each course utilizes a textbook and the Web-based course materials, which also provide the medium of interaction. Most courses also include an online study guide. Although most interaction is asynchronous, chat rooms are available for student and faculty use.

Programs of Study

Completion of an online M.B.A. requires 36 credit hours. However, students who are interested in pursuing an M.B.A. with a further concentration need to complete 45 credit hours. The curriculum for the international business degree concentrates on the more detailed aspects of international marketing, management, finance, and economics. For the concentrations in financial planning, international hotel and tourism management (IHTM), or management of information technology (MIT), students complete seven core M.B.A. courses, two elective courses, and six concentrated courses in either financial planning, IHTM, or MIT. The Master of International Management (M.I.M.) in international business degree requires 36 credit hours for completion. The course work spans a variety of topics relating to business administration, including management, marketing, accounting, communications, business law, and economics. Students whose undergraduate background does not include preparation in accounting/finance, economics, or statistics are required to take additional preparatory courses, which are available online. At the undergraduate level, Schiller offers online the B.B.A. in international business and international hotel and tourism management, the B.A. in interdepartmental studies, and the B.A. in international relations and diplomacy. The degree requirements are designed to provide practical knowledge and training for future business executives. SIU online programs promote a professional academic environment without borders in which world-class education is offered in worldwide classrooms online. More information about all programs can be accessed from SIU's Web site (http://www.schiller.edu).

Student Services

The University has developed a number of methods to assist students in distance learning programs. A Student Services Representative is available to guide and assist students, and academic advising is also available. Specially trained faculty mentors are always available by e-mail for consultation, and the Web-based host for the courses offers technical assistance 24 hours a day. Students in the distance learning programs have access to the full range of support services, including the Library and Information Resource Network (LIRN) and NET Library, that are used by all Schiller students. Each online course has its own library of study aids and resources. Lecture notes, sample quizzes, assignment checks, and hyperlinks to other interesting sites are available for viewing and downloading.

Credit Options

For the master's program, up to 12 semester credits toward a 36-credit-hour master's degree and up to 18 semester credits toward an M.B.A. degree with concentration may be accepted for transfer if the graduate course has been completed with a grade B or above. Bachelor's degree candidates may transfer in a maximum of 91 credits, and associate degree candidates may transfer in a maximum of 29 credits. Credit is granted for undergraduate work completed with a grade of C or above, provided it is applicable to Schiller degree programs. Credits and/or advanced placement may be awarded to students who receive appropriate scores in CLEP subject examinations, ACT Proficiency Examinations (PEP), USAFI, and DANTES College Level Examinations, as well as on the College Board Advanced Placement Exams.

Faculty

All online courses are taught by instructors with advanced degrees and extensive practical experience in their fields. The faculty members' ability to teach in both online and ground-based formats ensures consistency across the programs. All courses in the distance learning program are Web based. An online course has learning objectives identical to those of a ground-delivered course, incorporating both asynchronous and the possibility of synchronous technology to facilitate learning. Each course has a syllabus describing the course content, assignments, and grading policy. The faculty members choose from many course-delivery technologies, including journals and e-mail for assignment submission and correspondence and discussion forums and chat rooms for ongoing questions and answers. The instructor uses these technologies to enhance the learning experience.

Admission

Admission to the online graduate degree programs requires completion of a B.B.A. degree or equivalent; a bachelor's degree or equivalent, with a major in business studies or economics, provided that core courses have been completed in economics, statistics, business law, marketing, management, and accounting; or a bachelor's degree or equivalent in a nonbusiness field, provided that course work in the areas listed above has been completed. Nonnative English speakers must provide TOEFL scores of at least 550 (paper-based), 133 (computer-based), or 79 (Internet-based) taken within the past three years.

For undergraduate admission, applicants must have completed the secondary level of education, generally twelve years, or have five GCE O-levels at Grade C or above. Undergraduate students who have a TOEFL score received during the past three years of at least 500 (paper-based), 173 (computer-based), or 61 (Internet-based) can be accepted into university studies without further EFL requirements. Test scores should be sent directly to the University.

A completed application form must be sent to the SIU Office of Admissions together with a $65 application fee, payable by check, credit card, or international money order. Applicants must also request that official transcripts of academic work be sent via airmail to the Office of Admissions. Graduate-level applicants must submit transcripts of all college courses attended as well as proof of an earned degree and TOEFL scores, if applicable. Undergraduate applicants must submit proof of high school graduation as well as TOEFL scores, if applicable. Original documents or certified copies must be submitted, along with a certified English translation of those documents not in English.

Tuition and Fees

Distance learning students pay the same tuition as on-campus students. Tuition for the 2008–09 academic year is $520 per graduate credit and $500 per undergraduate credit. It is payable by check, credit card, or international money order. Tuition includes all instruction and faculty-produced materials. Students are responsible for the additional cost of textbooks, and information about online booksellers is provided. Room and board fees vary by campus. Students wishing to complete a portion of their degree in residence should contact the individual campus. Additional fees include a $65 application fee, a $100 graduation fee, a $100 technology fee per online course, and a late-registration fee of $200, which is applicable only after classes commence.

Financial Aid

SIU participates in Title IV programs and is eligible to participate in the Veteran's Training Program. Both programs are for U.S. citizens and residents who qualify. Students should e-mail the Office of Financial Aid for further information.

Applying

Applications for admission are accepted year-round. Classes begin in September, January, and June. Students interested in online courses must complete two surveys, which are found on the distance learning page of the SIU Web site. Students can visit this site or contact the Office of Admissions for further information. Skype users may contact the Office of Admissions at Schiller.admissions.info.

CONTACT

Office of Admissions
Schiller International University
300 East Bay Drive
Largo, Florida 33770
Phone: 727-736-5082
      877-748-4338 (toll-free in the U.S. and Canada)
Fax: 727-734-0359
E-mail: admissions@schiller.edu
      financial_aid@schiller.edu
Web site: http://www.schiller.edu

SETON HALL UNIVERSITY

M.A. in Counseling
South Orange, New Jersey

Founded in 1856, Seton Hall is a private coeducational Catholic institution—the nation's oldest diocesan institution of higher education in the United States. One of the region's most prestigious academic institutions and a recognized leader in online education, Seton Hall University enrolls approximately 10,000 undergraduate and graduate students. Seton Hall University is accredited by the Middle States Commission on Higher Education.

Distance Learning Program
SetonWorldWide, Seton Hall's online campus, provides learners with the opportunity to earn a Seton Hall University degree in an e-learning environment that allows the working professional to fit their education into their busy lifestyle.

Delivery Media
Learners access their online course rooms using an Internet connection—anytime, anywhere. This 24/7 access allows course study and interaction in a flexible user-friendly environment.

Programs of Study
Seton Hall University's online counseling degrees follow a predetermined set of courses and are designed to expertly train students of diverse backgrounds, providing them with a solid, general knowledge base and clinical preparation for advanced work in the mental-health field or in the field of school counseling. The program's primary goal is to provide students with a thorough grounding in the theories, skills, and models of interventions essential to function effectively as counselors in a variety of settings.

The 48-credit curriculum provides students with a thorough background in individual counseling and group counseling skills and theory; clinical practice and ethical, professional, and legal issues in counseling; social and cultural factors in counseling; human development across the life span; work,

leisure, and career development theories and interventions; appraisal and assessment issues in counseling; the application of research methodology and statistics to understand mental-health issues; and the role and function of community mental-health agencies.

Seton Hall University's 48-credit online Master of Arts in School Counseling program prepares students for work in educational settings as school guidance counselors and may lead to certification as a school counselor in certain states. The program in school counseling emphasizes the development of competence, social consciousness, and reflection. Students are trained to work in ethnically, geographically, and socially diverse K–12 settings. This program promotes three major counseling functions within the context of school settings: prevention and intervention of personal and interpersonal concerns, fostering of optimal human development, and coordination of care services for students within school systems. Students begin the program learning the basics of counseling skills and foundational theories, and they end the program transitioning from a three-semester applied clinical experience.

Special Programs
A clinical experience is a part of the master's degree. Students receive individual counseling, guidance, and support from dedicated faculty members throughout this aspect of the program

to ensure the most professional experience possible during the practicum and internship.

The program curriculum meets many state requirements for licensure. For students requiring an additional number of courses, Seton Hall University offers a 12-credit sequence of courses or a post-masters licensure program online.

Students who are completing the M.A. in Counseling program can also enroll in the 12-credit post-master's School Counselor Certificate program that meets many state requirements for certification as a school counselor in grades K–12, and they can enroll in a post-masters licensing sequence if additional courses are needed.

Student Services
Seton Hall provides online support and assistance throughout the program and learners have online access to Seton Hall University's extensive library resources.

Credit Options
This program is open only to those who are matriculating as new students. Transfer credits are accepted on a selective individual basis.

Faculty
The program uses Seton Hall University faculty members as well as qualified adjunct professors who are leading experts and practitioners in the field of counseling. Faculty members also engage in traditional classroom teaching and learning. Students have a variety of instructors, all highly qualified. All course facilitators meet requirements as instructors.

Admission

All applicants must have a bachelor's degree from an accredited college or university and submit three letters of recommendation, a personal statement, and a resume. GRE or MAT scores may be waived in individual cases.

Tuition and Fees

The total cost of the 48-credit program is $34,000. This includes all fees, except for the application fee, and all expenses, including books and other materials and room and meals for the short on-campus residencies. Computer equipment, software, Internet access, and travel expenses to the residencies are not covered.

Financial Aid

There are various options for financing a degree from Seton Hall University. In order to be eligible for financial aid, a student must be accepted into a degree program. Financial aid for graduate students is available in the form of a FFELP/Stafford Loan, an alternative loan, or a personal loan. Another option available to students is a budget plan that divides tuition costs into monthly payments. Students are encouraged to check with their human resources departments to determine what educational assistance or tuition reimbursement programs may be available.

To be considered for any federal, state or University financial aid programs administered by Seton Hall, students must fill out the Free Application for Federal Student Aid (FAFSA). This free form is used to determine a student's eligibility for all financial aid programs. The FAFSA application can be completed online at http://www. fafsa.ed.gov. The Seton Hall University school code for FAFSA is 002632.

Applying

Applicants must submit the completed online application, the $50 nonrefundable application fee, transcripts from all undergraduate or graduate institutions attended, GRE or MAT scores (may be waived in individual cases), TOEFL scores (if applicable), three letters of recommendation, a resume, and a personal statement.

CONTACT

Rosalie Maiorella, Program Administrator
Presidents Hall, Room 324
Seton Hall University
400 South Orange Avenue
South Orange, New Jersey 07079

Phone: 973-313-6239
Fax: 973-761-9325
E-mail: maiorero@shu.edu
Web site: http://www.setonworldwide.net

SETON HALL UNIVERSITY

M.A. in Educational Leadership, Management, and Policy
South Orange, New Jersey

Founded in 1856, Seton Hall is a private coeducational Catholic institution—the nation's oldest diocesan institution of higher education. One of the region's most prestigious academic institutions and a recognized leader in online education, the University enrolls about 10,000 students.

Seton Hall University and its associated online programs are accredited by the National Council for Accreditation of Teacher Education (NCATE) and the Middle States Association of Colleges and Schools.

Distance Learning Program

SetonWorldWide, Seton Hall's online campus, provides learners with the opportunity to earn a Seton Hall University degree in an e-learning environment that allows the working professional to fit their education into their busy lifestyle.

Delivery Media

Learners access their online course rooms using an Internet connection—anytime, anywhere. This 24/7 access allows course study and interaction in a flexible user-friendly environment. The student-professor ratio is kept at 10:1 to ensure a timely response from the professor to each student.

Programs of Study

The M.A. in Education, Leadership, Management, and Policy (ELMP) program provides students with extensive knowledge of educational administration, including academic theories, skills, and techniques. This graduate degree concentration can lead to a supervisor certification with the New Jersey State Department of Education, and course work can be applied toward similar certification in other states. Students also train for the principal certification, which is built into this degree program.

The two-year program consists of thirteen 3-credit courses and 6-credit principal internship for a total of 39 credits. All candidates take a comprehensive written examination at the end of the sixth semester.

The Department of Education Leadership, Management, and Policy holds two mandatory on-campus residency weekends. These weekend residencies usually begin in mid-July. Each weekend begins on Friday afternoon and runs through noon on Sunday. Residencies provide learning team members the opportunity to meet face-to-face, share experiences, continue discussions, provide feedback on program progress, and meet with instructors.

Special Programs

SetonWorldWide and Seton Hall University's College of Education and Human Services have teamed up to create an online supervisor's certificate program for teachers who have a master's degree but require additional credits to obtain the certificate. Successful completion of the 12-credit program enables students to be eligible for a supervisor of instruction position.

Student Services

Seton Hall provides online support and assistance throughout the program, and learners have access to Seton Hall University's extensive library resources.

Credit Options

Transfer credits are accepted on a selective, individual basis.

Faculty

All courses are taught by Seton Hall University faculty members with expertise in education, leadership, and management and policy as well as in online teaching and learning. There are 13 faculty members in the department.

Admission

Applicants must have a bachelor's degree from an accredited institution and at least a 3.0 GPA.

Tuition and Fees

The cost for the entire program is $22,500 and includes all fees and expenses, tuition, books and other materials, room and meals for the on-campus residencies, and graduation costs. Travel expenses to the residencies, the nonrefundable application fee, computer equipment, software, and Internet access are not included. Tuition for teachers in Catholic schools is $14,000, according to Seton Hall University policy.

Financial Aid

Most applicants who are American citizens are eligible for low-interest federal loans.

Applying

Interested students should apply online at http://www.setonworldwide.net, following the online instructions. A toll-free number and e-mail are available if questions arise. Applicants must submit the completed application, the nonrefundable $50 application fee, transcripts from all undergraduate institutions attended, a letter of intent that explains the reasons for applying to the program, a current resume, scores from the GRE or MAT, and three letters of recommendation from academic and/or professional references.

CONTACT

Mel Klein, Assistant Academic Director
Jubilee Hall, Room 357
Seton Hall University
400 South Orange Avenue
South Orange, New Jersey 07079
Phone: 888-738-6699 Ext. 2469
     (toll-free)
Fax: 973-761-9325
E-mail: kleinmel@shu.edu

Al Galloway, Program Director
Jubilee Hall, Room 357
Seton Hall University
400 South Orange Avenue
South Orange, New Jersey 07079
Phone: 888-738-6699 Ext. 2469
     (toll-free)
Fax: 973-761-9325
E-mail: gallowal@shu.edu
Web site:
     http://www.setonworldwide.net

SETON HALL UNIVERSITY

M.A. in Strategic Communication and Leadership

South Orange, New Jersey

Founded in 1856, Seton Hall is a private coeducational Catholic institution—the nation's oldest diocesan institution of higher education in the United States. One of the region's most prestigious academic institutions and a recognized leader in online education, Seton Hall University enrolls approximately 10,000 undergraduate and graduate students. Seton Hall University is accredited by the Middle States Commission on Higher Education.

Distance Learning Program

SetonWorldWide, Seton Hall's online campus, provides learners with the opportunity to earn a Seton Hall University degree in a highly interactive e-learning environment that allows the working professional to fit their education into their busy lifestyle.

Delivery Media

Learners access their online courses using an Internet connection—anytime, anywhere. This 24/7 access allows course study and interaction in a flexible user-friendly environment.

Programs of Study

A basic building block for success in today's highly competitive world is the manager who can lead, communicate, and manage change effectively. Executives, managers, professionals, and military command personnel are increasingly expected to bring to their organizations these unique competencies. The Master of Arts in Strategic Communication and Leadership (MASCL) program has been designed to meet the leadership development needs of today's busy professional. Through a highly interactive curriculum that allows for significant discussion of strategies and solutions to current issues

in effective leadership and communication, the program provides an opportunity to network and study with colleagues and experts in specialized disciplines. Using state-of-the-art online learning technologies, this rigorous program is aimed at helping the high-potential individual earn a Seton Hall University degree in a convenient format.

A serious program for the serious learner, MASCL requires 36 credits and takes eighteen months to complete. Students interact with a learning team of their peers (successful executives, managers, and professionals), experienced instructors, and other experts in an anytime, anyplace e-learning environment. Three on-campus weekend-long residencies, five 12-week modules, and an ongoing leadership and communication skills enhancement program combine to develop the superior abilities required for dynamic leadership. Faculty members mentor participants throughout the program to polish interpersonal, presentation, and writing skills.

The three on-site weekends—Orientation, Mid-Program Residency, and Final Residency—include sessions for students to practice their communication and leadership skills. Individual coaching is provided during all of the residencies. The Orientation Weekend prepares the

learning team for the program. Students meet one another, faculty members, and administrators. They learn how to access and use the online learning technologies, and they make a presentation and receive feedback and coaching. At the Mid-Program residency, students give group and individual presentations, and they also take part in a mock press conference. During the Final Residency, students present their strategic-communication plan, with an emphasis on how they intend to communicate it to their organization's stakeholders. The weekend concludes with commencement exercises.

Student Services

Seton Hall provides online support and assistance throughout the program, and learners have access to Seton Hall University's extensive library resources.

Faculty

The Department of Communication faculty members combine practical experience with academic preparation. Each curricular area utilizes faculty members who have impressive professional records and those with doctoral degrees for a blend of the academic and practical.

Admission

Applicants should have a baccalaureate degree from an accredited college or university. The ideal candidate has significant professional work experience in a corporate, military, governmental, association, or nonprofit organization. Candidates are ready for increased workplace responsibilities or a new executive position and seek to develop and enhance their leadership communication skills in preparation for these challenges and opportunities. They typically do not have the time to attend an on-campus program and seek a rigorous online program in communication, leadership, business strategy, and organizational development.

Tuition and Fees

The cost for the entire program is $28,656 and includes all fees and expenses, tuition, room and meals for the on-campus residencies, and graduation costs. Travel expenses to the on-campus residencies, the application fee, computer equipment, software, and Internet access are not included in this figure.

Financial Aid

Financial aid for graduate students is available in the form of a FFELP/Stafford Loan, an alternative loan, or a personal loan. Students are encouraged to check with their human resources departments to determine what educational assistance or tuition reimbursement programs may be available.

Applying

Students must submit the completed online application, the $50 nonrefundable application fee, official transcripts from all colleges and universities attended, two letters of recommendation (preferably one each from a present and a former supervisor), a current resume, a work sample in any medium that demonstrates the candidate's excellence in his or her field, and a short (about 500 words) essay that states the candidate's goals for engaging in the MASCL learning experience.

CONTACT

Jennifer Vallario, Assistant Program Director
A&S Hall 228
Seton Hall University
400 South Orange Avenue
South Orange, New Jersey 07079
Phone: 973-275-2419
Fax: 973-761-9325
E-mail: vallarje@shu.edu
Web site: http://www.shu.edu/academics/setonworldwide/
ma-communication/index.html

SETON HALL UNIVERSITY

Master of Healthcare Administration

South Orange, New Jersey

Founded in 1856, Seton Hall is a private coeducational Catholic institution—the oldest diocesan institution of higher education in the United States. One of the nation's most prestigious academic institutions and a recognized leader in online education, the University enrolls about 10,000 students.

Seton Hall University is accredited by the Middle States Commission on Higher Education. A member of the Association of University Programs in Health Administration (AUPHA), a national association of university-based educational programs dedicated to continuously improving the field of health management and practice, the Seton Hall University Master of Healthcare Administration Program is ranked thirteenth in Modern Healthcare's survey of the nation's twenty-five largest M.H.A. programs in the nation.

Distance Learning Program

SetonWorldWide, Seton Hall's online campus, provides learners with the opportunity to earn a Seton Hall University degree in an e-learning environment that allows the working professional to fit their education into their busy lifestyle.

Delivery Media

Learners access their online course rooms using any Internet connection—anytime, anywhere. This 24/7 access allows course study and interaction in a flexible user-friendly environment.

Programs of Study

The Seton Hall University Online Master of Healthcare Administration (M.H.A.) program and the online Graduate Certificate in Healthcare Administration program help prepare managers for leadership roles within the health-care industry. Providing a rigorous and thorough understanding of the health-care environment, the programs address real-world strategies and skills that help health-care managers make significant contributions to their organizations.

Using state-of-the-art learning technologies in a highly interactive learning environment, the M.H.A. program is designed around an applied-focused, rigorous curriculum. The 42-credit program consists of six competency areas—Understanding the Environment, Managing Change, Financial Competencies, Decision Making, Strategic Leadership, and Analysis—and a capstone project. All course work is completed online. There are three required on-campus weekend residencies. Learners begin the program with an orientation residency, followed by a midprogram residency, and a final residency at the end of the program.

Special Programs

The 15-credit online Graduate Certificate Program in Healthcare Administration is designed for individuals who might wish to pursue a career in health-care administration, those who already have a graduate degree but need to develop specific management skills, or individuals who would like to enroll in a selected set of graduate health-care administration courses but choose not to commit to an entire graduate degree program.

Student Services

Seton Hall provides online support and assistance throughout the program, and learners have access to Seton Hall University's extensive library resources.

Credit Options

Learners enroll in a cohort class and follow a prescribed sequential course of study. In most cases previously earned academic course credits are not accepted toward fulfilling the degree requirements.

Faculty

The faculty is composed of full-time Seton Hall faculty members and experienced practitioners with extensive knowledge in their respective fields. The SetonWorldWide Online M.H.A. program faculty members provide an in-depth theoretical and real-world practice knowledge base.

Admission

Candidates must have a baccalaureate degree from an accredited college or university with an undergraduate GPA of at least 3.0 or equivalent and health-care managerial experience.

Tuition and Fees

The cost for the six-semester program is $31,000 and includes all tuition, room and meals for the on-campus residencies, and graduation costs. Travel expenses to the residencies, the application fee, computer equipment, software, and Internet access are not included in this figure.

Financial Aid

Many learners fund their tuition through employer tuition-reimbursement benefits or through federal and private institutional loan programs. The University does not offer financial aid in the form of scholarships or grants for online M.H.A. students.

Applying

Application to the program can be submitted online. The application process includes submission of a completed online application, a $50 nonrefundable application fee, transcripts from all universities attended, a letter of intent, a current resume, and three letters of recommendation from academic or professional references.

CONTACT

Susan Spencer, Ph.D., Program Director
SetonWorldWide Online Master of Healthcare Administration Program
A&S Hall, Room 224
Seton Hall University
400 South Orange Avenue
South Orange, New Jersey 07079

Phone: 973-313-6236
Fax: 973-761-9325
E-mail: spencesu@shu.edu
Web site: http://www.shu.edu/academics/setonworldwide

SETON HALL UNIVERSITY
Programs in Nursing
South Orange, New Jersey

Founded in 1856, Seton Hall is a private coeducational Catholic institution—the nation's oldest diocesan institution of higher education in the United States. One of the region's most prestigious academic institutions and a recognized leader in online education, the University enrolls about 10,000 students. Seton Hall University and its associated online programs are accredited by the Middle States Association of Colleges and Schools.

Distance Learning Program

SetonWorldWide, Seton Hall's online campus, offers degree programs and certificates designed for professionals who have demonstrated achievement in their respective fields and have the ability, desire, and dedication to accept the rigors of a fast-paced, challenging curriculum. Working professionals can benefit from "anytime, anywhere" education. As learning team members, students and faculty members have extensive interaction, and these relationships provide a rich and dynamic online learning experience. All SetonWorldWide degree program graduates receive an accredited Seton Hall University degree.

Delivery Media

Online learning takes advantage of different methods of presentation, but the educational objectives are the same as traditional, in-classroom learning at Seton Hall University. SetonWorldWide provides for student-teacher interaction through a discussion section for each unit, which poses questions and comments initiated by the instructor. Students then respond both to the instructor and to each other with answers that show critical thinking and synthesis of course content. E-mail is used for individual and small-group interactions. Instructors review student material submitted electronically, and students receive feedback via e-mail or telephone.

Programs of Study

The Bachelor of Science in Nursing (B.S.N.) program is designed for the busy RN who wants to balance career and personal commitments with a flexible educational program of study. The five-semester program offers the required 34 credits of nursing (nine courses) online, and students may complete their clinical requirements within their respective geographical locations.

The nationally ranked Master of Science in Nursing (M.S.N.)–Nurse Practitioner program provides highly interactive online multimedia programs in five clinical specialty areas: adult, gerontological, pediatric, women's health, and acute-care nurse practitioner. Students complete the didactic portion of the program online in their home or office at their convenience. The required clinical practice component is fulfilled within the students' geographical location. All nurse practitioner graduates are eligible to apply for advanced-practice certification.

The 33-credit M.S.N. in health systems administration is designed to prepare nurse managers, directors, and executives with the needed leadership skills demanded by today's complex health-care industry. Students become knowledgeable about the business and financial operations necessary to effectively manage large patient-care departments. Nurses looking to bring their career to a new level in management are ideal candidates.

Three on-campus weekend residencies enable students to meet their classmates and the faculty in person. On Orientation Weekend, students participate in hands-on training in accessing their online courses and resources, tour the Seton Hall campus, and meet other online learning teams. For the Mid-Program Weekend Residency, clinical assessment skills are refined and role development sessions are scheduled. The Final Residency Weekend is the culminating event of the program, with scheduled final student project presentations and graduation activities. The health systems administration students attend only the first and last weekend residencies.

Student Services

Students find everything they need online, including admission information, academic assistance, financial aid assistance, career guidance, and other services. The Help Desk's technical support staff has the knowledge and experience to help make every student's transition into the virtual classroom a smooth one. All SetonWorldWide participants have access to Seton Hall University library resources. During the orientation, students meet the librarians and technical staff members who provide assistance throughout the program. Students can use the library's ASK ME service to request and receive assistance from a fully qualified librarian.

Credit Options

Graduate credits earned recently at another accredited college or university may be accepted in partial satisfaction of graduate credit requirements. A total of 6 credits may be approved for transfer.

Faculty

The College of Nursing faculty includes distinguished educators and prolific researchers who bring real-world management perspectives to the learning environment. Students receive truly individualized personal attention as well as supportive career direction and guidance. The College has about 60 full- and part-time faculty members.

Admission

In addition to having a diploma or an associate degree from a nursing program, applicants to the B.S.N. program must have a minimum overall GPA of 3.0 and RN licensure. M.S.N. applicants must have graduated from an NLN- or CCNE-accredited baccalaureate pro-gram in nursing and have earned at least a B average in nursing courses and overall. GRE or MAT testing is required.

Tuition and Fees

The all-inclusive tuition includes all fees, except for the application fee and room and meals for the short on-campus residencies. Computer equipment, software, Internet access, and travel expenses to the residencies are not covered. The cost for tuition for the 2007–08 academic year was $797 per credit for undergraduate courses and $826 per credit for graduate courses.

Financial Aid

Almost 90 percent of the students who entered Seton Hall in 2005 received some form of financial aid, and 75 percent of these students received money directly from the University. The four types of financial aid include scholar-ships, grants and discounts, loans, and part-time jobs on campus. In addition, many working RNs use tuition remission through their places of employment. Specific nursing scholarships are available for nursing students during the clinical portion of the curriculum.

Applying

B.S.N. applicants must submit the completed application, the $45 nonrefundable application fee, all official high school and college transcripts, two letters of recommendation from academic and professional references, and a resume or curriculum vitae. M.S.N. applicants must submit the completed application, the $50 nonrefundable application fee, a typewritten statement of goals, a curriculum vitae or resume, all official college transcripts, two letters of recommendation, and scores from the Miller Analogies Test.

CONTACT

Mary Jo Bugel, Director of Recruitment
Schwartz Hall
Seton Hall University
400 South Orange Avenue
South Orange, New Jersey 07079

Phone: 973-275-9306
Fax: 973-761-9607
E-mail: nursing@shu.edu
Web site: http://www.setonworldwide.net

SKIDMORE COLLEGE
University Without Walls
Saratoga Springs, New York

University Without Walls (UWW) is the degree completion program for adults at Skidmore College. UWW was in the vanguard in establishing a program for distance learners. The program began in 1971 as an experiment in nontraditional education jointly funded by the Ford Foundation and the U.S. Department of Education. When the funding for this experiment ended in 1975, Skidmore College took over the program as its own. Over the years, UWW has evolved to serve adult students pursuing baccalaureate degrees in a variety of liberal arts, performing arts, and preprofessional fields.

The UWW program is characterized by its flexibility and the high quality of education students receive. The unique advising system at UWW guarantees that each program meets the student's individual needs and the high standards of Skidmore College.

Distance Learning Program

UWW serves 200 full- and part-time undergraduate students from as near as the city of Saratoga Springs and as far away as Europe, Africa, and Asia. The UWW program does not require its students to be in residence on campus. Student programs may include UWW online courses, independent study with Skidmore faculty members, courses at other accredited institutions, internships, and distance learning courses from major universities. Every program incorporates 12 credits of Skidmore course work, which includes a final project in the area of the student's focus.

Delivery Media

With support from an Alfred P. Sloan Foundation grant in 2001–04, UWW has created a rich offering of online courses designed to meet the educational needs of its students. Students can also take on-site or online courses through other accredited institutions. Independent study with Skidmore faculty members or faculty members at other institutions takes place through telephone, mail, and e-mail communications.

Programs of Study

UWW offers Bachelor of Arts degrees in most traditional liberal arts fields, including American studies, anthropology, art history, classics, computer science, economics, English, French, geology, government, history, mathematics, philosophy, psychology, religion, sociology, and Spanish. Bachelor of Science degrees are available in art, business, dance, human services, and theater. Students can also combine fields to create an interdisciplinary program, such as arts management, Asian studies, communications, environmental studies, health studies, human behavior, international affairs, Latin American studies, management information systems, nonprofit management, organizational behavior, public administration, and religion and culture. Individually designed majors are welcomed.

All degrees are 120-credit programs. Programs are expected to include at least 12 credits in the humanities, 6 credits in history, 12 credits in the social sciences, and 9 credits in math or science, including laboratory experience. Professional programs must include at least 60 credits in the liberal arts. Courses taken prior to enrollment in UWW may be considered in satisfaction of these requirements.

Special Programs

UWW's flexibility allows many students to take advantage of unusual learning opportunities. Recent UWW students have studied abroad in Austria, Canada, Costa Rica, the Czech Republic, Germany, India, Ireland, Poland, Spain, and Switzerland, among other locations. Business students often have the opportunity to include professional management and banking seminars in satisfaction of their degree requirements.

UWW students are often able to participate in programs sponsored by Skidmore College and the Office of Special Programs, including a summer study program in Florence, the New York State Writers Institute, the Skidmore Jazz Institute, the Summer Dance Workshop, and the SITI Summer Theater Workshop. UWW students are eligible for substantial discounts on courses offered by Skidmore Summer Academic Sessions and the Summer Six Art Program.

Student Services

UWW is a small, personal program, and the staff members are happy to assist students in any way possible. Typical services include academic advising, registration assistance, and financial aid counseling. Local students also enjoy library privileges, career counseling, access to recreational facilities, and access to computer labs.

Credit Options

UWW accepts transfer credit for courses completed at an accredited institution with a grade of C or better. There is no limit to the number of credits transferred or the age of the work, provided that the course is appropriate to a liberal arts curriculum. Credit is also available for experiential learning and internships. In addition, students may document knowledge through CLEP, ACT-PEP, DANTES, and Regents examinations. Many college-level courses offered through the military are accepted. Credit from international universities is usually accepted.

Faculty

Skidmore has approximately 200 full- and part-time faculty members. Most participate as advisers and instructors in the UWW program. Ninety-three percent of the Skidmore faculty members have a terminal degree.

Admission

UWW considers any applicant able to succeed at demanding college-level work. However, the program works best for students who have had some college experience. Applicants must have a high school diploma or the equivalent.

Tuition and Fees

Tuition is determined by the number of credits the student is taking. In general, semester costs range from $6300 for a full-time program (12–16 credits per semester) to $3500 for less than half-time (fewer than 6 credits). These fees include full access to UWW online courses and independent study with Skidmore faculty members. UWW reimburses students for courses taken at other institutions ($250 per credit hour, with a semester cap that varies depending on the student's total number of credits). A different fee schedule applies to summer courses, and a fee of $1000 is charged for experiential credit review.

Financial Aid

Students are eligible for Federal Pell Grants, New York State TAP awards, and all federal loan programs. A small amount of scholarship assistance is available.

Applying

Application forms are available from UWW or can be downloaded from the UWW Web site. All applicants are required to attend a personal admissions interview on the Skidmore campus.

CONTACT

University Without Walls
Skidmore College
815 North Broadway
Saratoga Springs, New York 12866
Phone: 518-580-5450
866-310-6444 (toll-free)
Fax: 518-580-5449
E-mail: uww@skidmore.edu
Web site: http://www.skidmore.edu/uww

SOUTHERN METHODIST UNIVERSITY

School of Engineering

Dallas, Texas

Founded in 1911, SMU is a private, comprehensive university. SMU comprises six degree-granting schools: the School of Engineering, Dedman College of Humanities and Sciences, Meadows School of the Arts, the Edwin L. Cox School of Business, the Dedman School of Law, and Perkins School of Theology. Southern Methodist University is accredited by the Commission on Colleges of the Southern Association of Colleges and Schools.

For more than forty years, the School of Engineering has been a national pioneer in offering distance education courses for graduate study. In 1964, the School of Engineering established one of the first two regional closed-circuit TV distance learning networks in the nation. In 1978, it instituted its own for-credit videotape program for students living outside the Dallas/Ft. Worth area. Today, the program is delivered via distance learning and students are enrolled nationally from coast to coast and is now available to international applicants.

Distance Learning Program

The School of Engineering's distance learning program serves more than 600 graduate students. Master of Science degree programs are offered nationally via distance learning. No campus attendance is required to complete the degree programs. Twenty M.S. degrees can be earned via distance learning.

Delivery Media

Distance learning students are enrolled in classes that are given on the SMU campus. The lectures are recorded and loaded to a server within 24 hours. Distance learning students log in to the secured server to download the recorded on-campus lectures.

Distance learning students interact with their professors via phone, fax, e-mail, or the Internet. Many professors make course materials available to the student via the School of Engineering's Web site.

Programs of Study

Engineering schools have an obligation to be responsive to challenges and opportunities in a technological society. As a private university, SMU can respond quickly to engineering needs with high-quality academic programs.

The School of Engineering offers the following Master of Science degree programs via distance learning: civil engineering, computer engineering, computer science, electrical engineering, engineering management, environmental engineering, environmental science, environmental science (major in environmental systems management), environmental science (major in hazardous and waste materials management), facilities management, information engineering and management, manufacturing systems management, mechanical engineering, operations research, packaging of electronic and optical devices, security engineering, software engineering, systems engineering, and telecommunications.

The Master of Science degree requires 30 semester credit hours for completion, with a minimum 3.0 grade point average on a 4.0 scale. Distance learning students may meet the credit requirement entirely by course work or have the option of preparing a thesis for 6 semester hours of credit in specific programs.

A number of certificate programs are also available. Interested students should contact SMU Engineering for details.

Credit Options

Generally, up to 6 semester hours of graduate courses may be transferred from an institution approved by the School of Engineering's Graduate Division, provided that such course work was completed in the five years prior to matriculation, that the transferred courses carried graduate credit, that those courses were not used to meet the requirements of an undergraduate degree, and that grades of B– or higher were received in the courses to be transferred.

Faculty

Of the 45 full-time faculty members, 100 percent hold the doctorate or terminal professional degree in their fields. In addition, in the professional degree programs, the School of Engineering utilizes outstanding adjunct faculty members to bring into the classroom valuable experience from industry and government.

Admission

Admission to a Master of Science degree program requires the bachelor's degree appropriate to the program to which the student is applying, as well as a minimum grade point average of 3.0 (on a 4.0 scale) in previous undergraduate and graduate study. Scores on the Graduate Record Examinations (GRE) are required for the M.S. programs in civil engineering, computer engineering, computer science, electrical engineering, environmental engineering, environmental science, and mechanical engineering.

Tuition and Fees

Tuition for distance learning students is $1063 per credit hour or $3189 for a 3-credit-hour course.

Financial Aid

Financial aid opportunities are available to distance learning students, including Federal Stafford Student Loans. SMU's distance learning programs are approved for Veterans Administration educational benefits.

Applying

Distance learning students must complete an application for admission to the Graduate Division of the School of Engineering and submit transcripts of all previous undergraduate and graduate work. Application deadline dates are as follows: for the fall semester, July 1; for the spring semester, November 15; and for the summer semester, April 15.

CONTACT

Teresa Harvey, Assistant Director
Graduate Student Experience and Enrollment Management
School of Engineering
Southern Methodist University
P.O. Box 750335
Dallas, Texas 75275-0335

Phone: 214-768-4661
       800-601-4040 (toll-free)

Fax: 214-768-3778

E-mail: tharvey@engr.smu.edu

Web site: https://engr.smu.edu

OSWEGO
STATE UNIVERSITY OF NEW YORK

STATE UNIVERSITY OF NEW YORK AT OSWEGO

B.A. in Broadcasting and Mass Communication
B.A. in Public Justice
B.S. in Vocational Teacher Preparation
Oswego, New York

The State University of New York at Oswego was founded in 1861 as the Oswego Normal School. The institution became Oswego State Teachers College and one of SUNY's charter members in 1948. While maintaining its high standards as a center for teacher education, the college began to broaden its academic perspective in 1962 when it became one of the colleges of arts and science of the State University of New York.

Today, Oswego is one of thirteen university colleges in the SUNY system. About 8,000 students enroll annually. Oswego offers more than 100 academic programs leading to bachelor's degrees, master's degrees, and certificates of advanced study. The college is accredited by the Middle States Association of Colleges and Schools and by the Commission on Higher Education. The School of Education is accredited by the National Council for Accreditation of Teacher Education.

Distance Learning Program

The Bachelor of Arts (B.A.) in broadcasting and mass communication, the Bachelor of Arts in public justice, and the Bachelor of Science (B.S.) in six majors in vocational teacher preparation (agricultural, business and marketing, family and consumer sciences, health careers, technical, and trade education) are available to students with two-year degrees in appropriate disciplines. Degrees in vocational teacher preparation are offered in the following areas: agriculture education, business education, family and consumer sciences, health occupations subjects education, technical subjects education, and trade subjects education. All required courses, cognates, and electives as well as courses in other disciplines to fulfill general education requirements are offered online. Students also have the opportunity to complete an economics minor online.

Delivery Media

All courses are taught via the World Wide Web in asynchronous mode through the SUNY Learning Network (SLN) (http://sln.suny.edu). Students are required to have reliable access to computers connected to the Internet.

Courses use texts/reading materials and involve substantial writing assignments. Students may be required to arrange laboratory experiences with colleges or universities close to home, with credits transferred to Oswego.

Students taking VTP 312 online must attend a one-week summer residency in Oswego.

Students taking PBJ 401 online must attend a weekend residency in Oswego during the semester in which the course is offered.

Programs of Study

Some required courses may be transferred into the program through substitution or through articulation agreements with two-year and four-year colleges. A transfer evaluation of credit assigns previously earned credits to the appropriate program and to general education and college requirements. Students must complete a total of 122 credit hours for broadcasting and 127 credit hours for vocational teacher preparation to graduate, with a minimum of 30 credit hours taken from SUNY Oswego. At least 60 hours must be from a four-year college. General education requirements also apply.

Specific requirements in the broadcasting major, the public justice major, and the vocational teacher preparation major, including cognates and electives, are available at the Oswego State Web site. Students can find requirements for broadcasting at http://www.oswego.edu/ODP/. Requirements for public justice can be found at http://www.oswego.edu/academics/colleges_and_departments/departments/public_justice/. Vocational teacher preparation requirements can be found at http://www.oswego.edu/vtp/.

Special Programs

Some degree program students may benefit from internship opportunities arranged through the Office of Experience-Based Education. Up to 15 hours of internship credit may be applied as electives both in the major and under the general studies curriculum. Past students have performed internships in network television, local and regional media, advertising, media research, and government. Such experiences often lead to job offers and referrals.

Student Services

Some of the campus services and resources that are available online include certain resources in Penfield Library, the Registrar's Office, Student Accounts, the Financial Aid Office, and the Career Services Center. The State University of New York at Oswego Web site is http://www.oswego.edu. Advisement options include e-mail and telephone consultation for all students.

Credit Options

Up to 62 transfer credits from a two-year school may be applied toward the broadcasting and public justice degrees, and up to 67 transfer credits from a two-year school and 97 transfer credits from a four-year school may be applied toward the vocational teacher preparation degree. The public justice programs may accept up to 92 transfer credits from a four-year school. The College-Level Examination Program (CLEP) is offered and accepted. Up to 32 credits may be earned through CLEP, which is considered transfer credit.

Faculty

Approximately 40 full-time and 30 part-time faculty and professional staff members currently teach distance courses at SUNY Oswego. Of these, 70 percent have doctoral degrees. The student-teacher ratio is 20:1.

Admission

Applicants must submit official transcripts indicating that they have graduated with a two-year degree appropriate for their program. Students may enroll full-time or part-time and must become matriculated after completing 22 credit hours of study at Oswego.

Tuition and Fees

Part-time undergraduate tuition (in-state) is $181 per credit hour. Part-time undergraduate tuition (out-of-state) is $429 per credit hour. Full-time undergraduate tuition (in-state) is $2175 per semester. Full-time undergraduate tuition (out-of-state) is $5150 per semester.

Part-time fees (in-state and out-of-state) are $25.39 per credit hour.

Tuition and fee amounts are subject to change.

Financial Aid

Students should contact the Office of Financial Aid for information regarding income, credit hours, and other guidelines. In most instances, students must be enrolled in at least 6 credit hours to be eligible for financial aid.

Applying

A SUNY application needs to be submitted for all programs. The programs have an additional application that must be obtained by contacting the applicable department. Students are notified in writing if and when they are accepted into the program. An orientation session is optional.

CONTACT

For information on broadcasting and mass communication:

Dr. Michael S. Ameigh, Assistant Provost and Coordinator, Online Degree Program
35A Lanigan Hall
State University of New York at Oswego
Oswego, New York 13126
Phone: 315-312-3500
Fax: 315-312-3195
E-mail: ameigh@oswego.edu
Web site: http://www.oswego.edu/ODP/

For information on vocational teacher preparation:

Dr. Margaret Martin, Chair, Vocational Teacher Preparation Department
307 Park Hall
State University of New York at Oswego
Oswego, New York 13126
Phone: 315-312-2480
Fax: 315-312-3062
E-mail: mmartin4@oswego.edu
Web site: http://www.oswego.edu/vtp/

For information on vocational public justice:

Dr. Margaret Ryniker, Chair, Public Justice Department
307 Park Hall
State University of New York at Oswego
Oswego, New York 13126
Phone: 315-312-2480
Fax: 315-312-3062
E-mail: pubjust@oswego.edu
Web site: http://www.oswego.edu/publicjustice

STATE UNIVERSITY OF NEW YORK EMPIRE STATE COLLEGE
Center for Distance Learning
Saratoga Springs, New York

Empire State College, of the State University of New York, is an internationally recognized innovator in adult education and a pioneer in distance learning. Since 1971, the College has served students who need alternatives to campus-based education because of work, family, or other responsibilities. Providing flexible degree programs at the associate, bachelor's, and master's levels, Empire State College features a number of student-focused study methods, such as one-to-one instruction, online courses, intensive mentoring by a faculty adviser, and undergraduate credit for college-level learning gained from life experience.

The College currently enrolls more than 17,000 students per year at thirty-five locations in New York State. Through its Center for Distance Learning (CDL), the College also serves students across the nation and around the world. Empire State College was the first public, nontraditional institution to receive regional accreditation by the Middle States Association of Colleges and Schools.

Distance Learning Program

More than 6,000 students are served annually by the College's Center for Distance Learning (CDL). Established in 1979, CDL offers full degrees as well as individual courses entirely online. As a founding member of the SUNY Learning Network, the College was among the first in the State University of New York to offer online courses. It was also the first within the University to offer an entire degree (in business, management, and economics) online. Today, students may earn degrees online in all undergraduate areas of study offered by the College.

Delivery Media

The Center for Distance Learning makes use of the latest distance learning technology on the World Wide Web. Empire State College's online courses can be accessed at any time of the day, allowing students and faculty members to share ideas and concepts at times that are convenient to them. In addition, all student services, such as registration, academic advising, career and library services, and peer support, are available on the Internet.

Programs of Study

The Center for Distance Learning offers both two- and four-year degrees: Associate in Arts, Associate in Science, Bachelor of Arts, Bachelor of Science, and Bachelor of Professional Studies.

One of the strengths of the Empire State College distance learning program is that students are assigned a faculty adviser, also called a mentor, who guides them through all phases of their degree program, from academic planning to graduation. With their adviser, undergraduate students design individualized degree programs in any of eleven areas of study: the arts; business, management, and economics; community and human services; cultural studies; educational studies; historical studies; human development; interdisciplinary studies; labor studies; science, mathematics, and technology; and social theory, social structure, and change. Within these degree programs, a number of concentrations can be developed. Some examples of these are fire service administration, criminal justice, emergency management, health services administration, and information systems.

To earn an associate degree, a student must successfully complete 64 credits, with at least 24 earned through study with Empire State College. A bachelor's degree requires successful completion of 128 credits, with at least 32 being earned through the College.

Special Programs

The Center for Distance Learning is one of a select number of institutions of higher education to offer online degree programs to the United States Army, the United States Navy, the United States Coast Guard, and the Army National Guard. Through eArmyU, soldiers may take part in portable learning that suits the requirements of military life. The College also participates in the Navy College Program Distance Learning Partnership (NCPDLP) for sailors who need maximum flexibility in the ways they study. Many other organizations and corporations work with CDL to sponsor educational options for their employees, including a number of telecommunications companies and unions. A complete list is available at http://www.esc.edu/CDL.

Credit Options

Students can transfer credits earned at other regionally accredited institutions to Empire State College and can receive credit for college-level learning gained through work and life experience and through the College-Level Examination Program (CLEP), standardized tests, or individualized evaluation. A total of 40 prior learning credits may be granted in the associate degree program; 96 credits may be applied to a bachelor's degree program.

Faculty

There are 875 full- and part-time faculty members at Empire State College, including adjunct faculty. Ninety-six percent of full-time faculty members and nearly half of part-time faculty members have doctoral or other terminal academic degrees.

Admission

There are two principal requirements for admission to Empire State College: possession of a high school diploma or its equivalent and the ability of the College to meet the applicant's educational needs and objectives.

Tuition and Fees

In 2007–08, undergraduate tuition was $181 per credit. A per-term telecommunications development and support fee of $75 was also charged, which provided access to electronic mail, computer conferencing, the Internet, and other information sources. Other fees also apply. Students should visit the College's Web site at http://www.esc.edu for further details

Financial Aid

More than $30 million in financial aid was awarded to Empire State College students in 2005–06, with more than 50 percent of the enrolled students receiving some form of financial assistance. General financial aid programs available through Empire State College include the Federal Pell Grant, Federal Supplemental Educational Opportunity Grant, Federal Perkins Loan, and the Federal Work-Study Program. New York State financial aid programs include the Tuition Assistance Program (TAP), Aid for Part-Time Study (APTS), and the SUNY Supplemental Tuition Award. The Empire State College Foundation awards more than $241,982 in scholarships and grants annually.

Applying

Empire State College reviews applications in order of date received, and students may apply online. The number of new students accepted depends on available space. There are five deadlines per year posted on the Web site (address listed below). Nonmatriculated students can take up to 16 credits without applying to the College.

CONTACT

Shelley Dixon
Center for Distance Learning
Empire State College
111 West Avenue
Saratoga Springs, New York 12866-6048

Phone: 800-847-3000 Ext. 2300 (toll-free)
Fax: 518-587-2660
E-mail: cdl@esc.edu
Web site: http://www.esc.edu/CDL

STEVENS INSTITUTE OF TECHNOLOGY
Graduate School Distance Learning Programs
Hoboken, New Jersey

Stevens Institute of Technology, one of the world's premier technical universities, offers an array of Web-based distance learning graduate programs from WebCampus. Stevens is ranked among the top twenty-five schools with entrepreneurial programs. Optimize magazine selected Stevens as one of the five schools that prepare technology managers. Stevens is one of only fourteen schools accredited by the Project Management Institute. Stevens has won the Sloan Consortium's top award for best "institution-wide online teaching and learning programming," the US Distance Learning Association's "21st Century Award for Best Practices in Distance Learning," and the "2006 Best Practices in Programming" award. Stevens offers fifteen master's degree programs and thirty-four graduate certificate programs in engineering, management, and science online.

Students are instructed by noted faculty members who deliver the same superior courses taught on the main campus. Blended-learning programs (with online and conventional classroom components) are also available, as well as conveniently located off-campus courses at corporate sites. Many classes include a real-time Web conferencing component. Stevens is accredited by the Middle States Commission on Higher Education of the Middle States Association of Colleges and Schools. WebCampus is cosponsored by the Association of Computing Machinery (ACM), the Institute of Electrical and Electronics Engineers (IEEE), the American Society for Mechanical Engineers (ASME), the Society of Naval Architects and Marine Engineers (SNAME), the American Society of Civil Engineers (ASCE), and the National Exchange Carrier Association (NECA).

Distance Learning Program

Graduate certificates and master's degrees for professionals seeking advanced knowledge in science, engineering, and management are available online through WebCampus. In addition, a wide range of off-campus graduate degree programs in engineering, management, and information technology, among other disciplines, are taught at corporate sites.

Delivery Media

Stevens has been at the forefront of distance learning for a number of years, offering instructor-led courses that take advantage of the benefits of Web conferencing and other net applications. WebCampus online graduate students use rich Web features such as real-time and recorded lectures, threaded discussions, chat rooms, bulletin boards, e-mail, file sharing, whiteboards, and work groups for in-depth online participation. Students also have online library privileges, with instant search and retrieval of important databases such as the IEEE Electronic Library and Hoovers Company Records.

Programs of Study

Master's degree and certificate programs include biomedical engineering, construction management, cybersecurity, database systems, digital signal processing, engineering management, environmental engineering, financial engineering, information systems and management, microelectronics, multimedia technology, networked information systems, pharmaceutical management, pharmaceutical manufacturing, photonics, professional communications, project management, software engineering, systems engineering, technology management, and telecommunications management.

Graduate certificate programs offer students the opportunity to focus on a specific area of study without having to complete a master's degree program. Credits earned toward a graduate certificate at Stevens may also be applied to a master's degree should students wish to continue their studies. Specialized graduate certificate programs include atmospheric research, business process management, logistics and supply chain management, maritime engineering, and space systems engineering.

Off campus, at corporate and other sites, graduate students may enroll as part of company-sponsored programs, some of which are delivered using Web conferencing. Employees at some of the nation's most progressive and prominent companies, including Boeing, Johnson & Johnson, Con Ed, Verizon, and dozens of others, may take graduate certificate courses and master's degree courses in a number of disciplines at corporate sites. These include computer engineering, computer science, electrical engineering, management, mechanical engineering, project management, technology management, and telecommunications management.

For high school seniors who wish to get a head start on their college studies, Stevens created the Euclid Program of Online Courses. The Euclid Program covers the following areas: calculus and advanced math, computer science, and physics.

Student Services

Online learning graduate students access the entire range of Stevens' student services online, including faculty advising, books and materials ordering, admissions, registration, and financial aid. Graduate students also have instant online access to the school's digital library. A cyberlibrarian is available via e-mail and telephone to guide students in the use of electronic databases and other research tools and media. Technical and other help desk support services are also available online. Stevens' Student Information System allows distance learners to access course schedules, grades, account statements, and other documents entirely online.

Credit Options

All graduate courses are worth 3 credits. Most graduate certificates are awarded after students have completed four courses online, on campus, or both. To earn a master's degree in engineering and science, students are required to complete ten courses. Students must complete twelve courses for a master's degree in management.

Faculty

An impressive graduate faculty teaches courses at Stevens, providing the same superior instruction online and on and off campus. WebCampus faculty members are required to participate in teaching and learning colloquia, which are held periodically during each semester, in order to share their experiences and to demonstrate their online teaching capabilities. Faculty members who teach online are also trained in how to exploit the technological and pedagogical benefits of Web-based courseware applications.

Admission

To be admitted to an online learning program at Stevens, students are required to satisfy the same qualifications as those who wish to enroll in Stevens' conventional courses. Prospective graduate students need to have completed an undergraduate degree at an accredited institution. Applicants may either apply by mail or complete an application form online at https://apply.embark. com/grad/stevens/14/. Two letters of recommendation are required. Applicants must also provide official transcripts in English for each college or university attended. Transcripts translated into English must be prepared by the school attended or by an official translator with a recognized seal. Applicants must provide official confirmation of the degree earned if it was awarded by a non-U.S. institution. The applicant's name, Social Security number, or date of birth must be on all submitted documents. All documents must be in English or have attested English translations.

Tuition and Fees

Each semester, students are required to pay nominal enrollment and technology fees. Tuition for management courses is $885 per credit hour. Tuition for engineering and science courses is $985 per credit hour. Other fees may apply for late enrollment and late payment, among other services.

Financial Aid

Stevens has a strong commitment to assisting and investing in talented students. The school offers a number of scholarships, many of which are made available through generous friends and successful alumni. Many graduate students receive tuition reimbursement from their companies. Members of the WebCampus cosponsoring professional societies receive a 10 percent discount upon successful completion of the course.

Applying

Before applying to the online or off-campus distance learning programs, it is recommended that students review the Graduate School Web site or Stevens' WebCampus site in order to obtain information, instructions, and online application forms.

CONTACT

Online programs:
Wendy Pate
Stevens Institute of Technology
Castle Point on Hudson
Hoboken, New Jersey 07030
Phone: 201-216-5015
           800-494-4935 (toll-free)
Fax: 201-216-5011
E-mail: webcampus@stevens.edu
Web site: http://www.webcampus.
               stevens.edu

Off-campus programs:
Stephanie Robinson
Stevens Institute of Technology
Castle Point on Hudson
Hoboken, New Jersey 07030
Phone: 201-216-5510
Fax: 201-216-5011
E-mail: srobins2@stevens.edu
Web site: http://gradschool.stevens-
               tech.edu/home/

 # STRAYER UNIVERSITY

Over 60 Campuses and Online

> *Established in 1892, Strayer University was designed to answer the educational needs of working students. To do this, Strayer University offers a real-world education in the areas of accounting, business, information systems, management, public administration, health services administration, and education in a format that allows students to balance college classes with their jobs and personal lives. In addition, Strayer University supports their students' success with individualized instruction and personalized support services, from enrollment through graduation and beyond. By continuously updating and expanding the curricula, Strayer University ensures that its students are well equipped to excel in today's dynamic workplace.*
>
> *Today, Strayer University is one of the largest and most respected accredited universities in the United States. With more than sixty campuses in twelve states and Washington, D.C., as well as online instruction offered around the world, Strayer University currently helps 36,000 working students achieve their goals.*
>
> *Strayer University is regionally accredited by the Middle States Commission on Higher Education, an institutional accrediting agency recognized by the U.S. Department of Education.*

Distance Learning Program

Strayer University understands that its students' schedules are demanding. That's why it offers two distance learning formats to make getting to class more practical: **online synchronous** and **online asynchronous**. Both formats are designed to provide a quality education in the most convenient way possible.

Synchronous classes meet online on the same day and time every week. With this format, students hear live audio from the professor, supported by a "virtual blackboard". They can also use real-time text messaging to ask questions or interact with their professors and classmates.

Asynchronous classes provide the maximum scheduling flexibility, allowing students to attend class any time, 24 hours a day, seven days a week. With this format, they access recorded audio lectures, video presentations, and other instructional materials via the Internet. They also have the option to participate in real time chats, which permit more interaction among the students.

Delivery Media

The only equipment that students need to take online classes at Strayer University is a computer with access to the Internet. The necessary software is available free from the Web site or through Web site links. Strayer University's virtual classrooms use RealAudio. More detailed system requirements can be found at http://www.strayer.edu.

Programs of Study

When time and money are invested into an education, quality and value are very important. Students want the best instructors, the most relevant curriculum, and the most effective learning methods. Strayer University offers the highest caliber of education, in a proven educational format. By continuously updating and expanding its curricula, Strayer University ensures that its students are well prepared to excel in today's dynamic workplace. Strayer University's instructors combine impressive academic credentials with years of practical work experience, and they are committed to the success of their students. In addition, Strayer University supports its students with the highest level of academic and administrative services.

Strayer University offers a wide variety of graduate and undergraduate degree programs in today's high-demand career fields.

Some of the most popular disciplines include accounting, business, information systems, health services administration, public administration, and education. Students should visit Strayer University's Web site, http://www.strayer.edu, to learn more about the academic programs. Program availability varies by state and by campus. All classes within a program may not be available at every campus location. A student may be required to take courses in an online format in order to complete a degree program.

Student Services

As experienced professionals, Strayer University's faculty advisers help students design the appropriate plan to achieve their objectives and career goals. In addition, tutoring is available on campus and online for many introductory-level courses.

Credit Options

Students who have attended other educational institutions may receive transfer credit or advanced standing in Strayer University's degree and diploma programs. College credit may be awarded for CLEP and DSST tests, certain training received in the military, or prior work/life learning. The required number of credits taken in residence, online, or on campus is 36 for a master's degree, 54 for a bachelor's degree, 27 for an associate degree, and 31.5 for a diploma.

Faculty

Strayer University has more than 150 full-time and more than 1,540 part-time faculty members. Of these, more 500 than teach classes online.

Admission

Students who apply to undergraduate degree programs must provide certification of high school graduation or the equivalent. For admission to graduate degree programs, students must have graduated from an accredited college or university with a U.S. baccalaureate degree.

Tuition and Fees

For the 2008 academic year, tuition for graduate courses is $408 per credit hour. Full-time undergraduate students (13.5 credits or more) pay $301 per credit hour, and part-time undergraduate students pay $318 per credit hour.

Financial Aid

In today's business world, a college education is one of the best investments that can be made in one's career. To make education more affordable, Strayer University's Business Office can help identify and understand a wide variety of financing and financial aid options. Among these options are the following:

Federal Grants and Loans. Federal grants do not have to be repaid; federal loans are available that offer funds at a reduced interest rate or with deferred payment. Applications can be submitted online via links to the U.S. Department of Education.

Private Loans. Low cost, private loans are available to undergraduate and graduate students. These loans can also fill the financial gap not covered by federal student aid programs.

The Bailey Family Foundation Scholarship. The Bailey Family Foundation, founded in 1996 by Strayer University past President Ron K. Bailey, offers scholarship programs to high school seniors as well as current college students of any age with demonstrated scholastic achievement and financial need. A limited number of these scholarships are reserved for Strayer University students. To qualify, a current student must be in good standing with the University, and a new student must be accepted into one of Strayer University's programs. Scholarship applications and additional information are available online at http://www.bailey-family.org/.

Active-Duty Military Scholarship. Strayer University is a GoArmyEd, NCP-DLP, and Air University ABC School, as well as a member of the Servicemembers Opportunity Colleges. Under its scholarship program, active duty military students will be responsible for $0 per class for all undergraduate courses and $375 per class for all graduate courses. Interested students should contact Strayer University for further details about its military scholarship programs.

Veterans Educational Benefits. Veterans' educational benefits are available for eligible programs at the University. Strayer University remains in contact with the Department of Veterans Affairs and can advise students about current requirements and regulations.

Employer Tuition Assistance. Many companies provide tuition benefits to their employees in the form of either direct payment to the school or reimbursing tuition expenses directly to the employee/student. Strayer University encourages all students to check with their employer's human resources or training and education department for more information about educational benefits.

Applying

Applications are accepted on an ongoing basis and can be accessed online at http://www.strayer.edu. There is a $50 application fee.

CONTACT

Strayer University Information
  Processing
P.O. Box 1310
Newington, Virginia 22122

Phone: 866-344-3286 (toll-free)
Fax: 703-339-4948
E-mail: info@strayer.edu
Web site: http://www.strayer.edu

SYRACUSE UNIVERSITY
Master of Social Science Degree Program
Syracuse, New York

Founded in 1870, Syracuse University (SU) is a major private research university of 14,400 residential students and an additional 3,700 part-time adult students located in central New York State. Organized into twelve separate schools and colleges, each offering a variety of baccalaureate, master's, and doctoral degrees, Syracuse has excellent research facilities, including sophisticated computer networks and a library containing more than 2.8 million volumes. Syracuse is one of the select group of American and Canadian universities chosen for membership in the prestigious Association of American Universities. Syracuse has a long-standing commitment to adult education. The University's innovative distance education degree programs are a form of nontraditional education in which Syracuse was a pioneer. Offered through five of the University's academic units, SU's distance programs make up one of the three oldest external degree programs in the United States. The programs have been active since 1966 and reflect the University's response to the demands for creative educational techniques and programs in a constantly changing society.

Distance Learning Program

Syracuse's distance education degree programs have a limited-residency structure: they combine short periods of intensive on-site instruction with longer periods of home study, during which students and faculty members communicate online. There are currently about 1,000 adults actively enrolled in twelve different degree programs through distance education, approximately one sixth of whom are international students or Americans living abroad. Syracuse degrees earned through distance study are the same as those earned by traditional Syracuse students in comparable campus programs and have the same accreditation.

Program of Study

University College grants a 30-credit Master of Social Science (M.S.Sc.) with an international relations emphasis. The program offers an interdisciplinary, international, and multicultural approach to complex global issues. An internationally renowned faculty teaches

courses for the degree from Syracuse University's Maxwell School of Citizenship and Public Affairs.

The degree is state and regionally accredited. Students may initially enroll on a nonmatriculated basis.

Student Services

All distance education students are provided with free computer accounts and have access to the Syracuse University library and computer facilities. Online students have access to a help desk for technical problems. All distance students at Syracuse have access to a full range of online student services, including academic advising, financial aid, assistance, and registration.

Faculty

M.M.Sc. courses are taught by full-time Syracuse University faculty members from the Maxwell School who participate in the distance education programs in addition to their full-time campus responsibilities.

Admission

Applicants whose primary language is a language other than English must take the TOEFL.

Applicants must submit official transcripts of prior academic work, three letters of recommendation, and a personal statement that accompanies the application form.

Tuition and Fees

For 2008–09, the graduate tuition rate is $1069 per credit. Additional expenses for room and board during the on-site residences vary depending upon the choice of facility, and book charges average $150 per course.

Financial Aid

Distance education students who are U.S. citizens are eligible for all the standard federal grants and loans available to part-time students. Selective institutional aid is available; detailed information is available upon request. Syracuse University awards more than $100,000 to distance education students each year. International students (non-U.S. citizens) are not eligible for financial aid.

Applying

Applicants should request application materials from the address below. The programs admit students on a continuous basis, and students can begin in the fall, spring, or summer terms. In-person interviews are not required, although they can be arranged on request.

CONTACT

Marketing Department
Syracuse University/University College
700 University Avenue
Syracuse, New York 13244-2530

Phone: 315-443-3480
　　　　800-442-0501　(toll-free, U.S. only)
Fax: 315-443-4174
E-mail: parttime@uc.syr.edu
Web site: http://YeSU.syr.edu/mssc

THOMAS EDISON STATE COLLEGE

Trenton, New Jersey

Thomas Edison State College specializes in providing flexible, high-quality, collegiate learning opportunities for self-directed adults. One of New Jersey's twelve senior public institutions of higher education, the College offers associate, baccalaureate, and master's degrees in more than 100 areas of study. Students earn degrees through a wide variety of rigorous and high-quality academic methods that can by customized to meet their individual needs. Identified by Forbes magazine as one of the top twenty colleges and universities in the nation in the use of technology to create learning opportunities for adults, Thomas Edison State College is a national leader in the assessment of adult learning and a pioneer in the use of educational technologies. Founded in 1972, Thomas Edison State College is regionally accredited by the Commission on Higher Education of the Middle States Association of Colleges and Schools.

Distance Learning Program

Thomas Edison State College offers one of the most highly regarded, comprehensive distance learning programs in the United States. Adults may choose from more than 430 distance learning courses, including online classes. Students also take tests and submit portfolios to demonstrate and earn credit for college-level knowledge they already have and may transfer credits earned at other accredited institutions.

Delivery Media

Distance education courses are provided through several options, including Thomas Edison State College courses offered through the mail and online. Also available are online credit-by-examination *e*-Pack® courses, which allow students to prepare for a comprehensive final examination by taking a series of chapter quizzes delivered via the Internet.

Programs of Study

Thomas Edison State College offers associate, baccalaureate, and master's degrees in more than 100 areas of study. Undergraduate degrees offered include the Associate in Applied Science; Associate in Arts; Associate in Science in Applied Science and Technology; Associate in Science in Business Administration; Associate in Science in Natural Sciences and Mathematics; Associate in Science in Public and Social Services; Bachelor of Arts; Bachelor of Science in Applied Science

and Technology; Bachelor of Science in Business Administration; Bachelor of Science in Health Sciences, a joint-degree program with the University of Medicine and Dentistry of New Jersey (UMDNJ) School of Health Related Professions (SHRP); Bachelor of Science in Human Services; Bachelor of Science in Organizational Leadership; and Bachelor of Science in Nursing.

Each undergraduate degree requires work in general education, the area of study, and elective subjects. Students are encouraged to work in conjunction with one of the College's program advisers to develop an individual program plan.

In addition, the College offers five online master's programs. The Master of Science in Human Resources Management degree serves human resources professionals who wish to become strategic partners in their organizations. This program uses a cohort model and is designed to position human resources professionals as leaders within their organizations. The 36-semester-hour program provides practitioners with technical human resources skills in staffing, providing professional development, managing organizational culture, and measuring and rewarding performance. The Master of Science in Management degree program serves employed adults with professional experience in management. It integrates the theory and practice of management as it applies to diverse organizations. The Col-

lege's Master of Arts in Liberal Studies degree program provides working professionals an opportunity to study the liberal arts from an applied perspective. The Master of Arts in Educational Leadership is designed to prepare teachers and administrators to become educational leaders serving in the complex environment of elementary and secondary education. The Master of Science in Nursing RN–B.S.N./M.S.N.) degree program is designed for experienced RNs who want a quality education with the convenience and flexibility that an online program can provide.

Special Programs

Thomas Edison State College's Military Degree Completion Program (MDCP) serves military personnel worldwide and was developed to accommodate the special needs of military personnel whose location, relocation, and time constraints make traditional college attendance difficult, if not impossible. The program allows students to engage in a degree program wherever they may be stationed and receive maximum credit for military training and education. Thomas Edison State College is a partner college for the Navy College Program Distance Learning Partnership (NCPDLP) and the Navy College Program Afloat College Education (NCPACE) and is a participant in the Army Continuing Education System (GoArmy Ed/eArmyU) program.

The College's unique program allows students to transfer previously earned credits that have been awarded by regionally accredited colleges and universities. Graduates of regionally accredited community colleges may transfer up to 80 credits earned through their two-year institution. Students may transfer up to 120 credits earned at regionally accredited four-year institutions.

The College's School of Professional and continuing Studies offers a broad array of high-quality professional certificates, seminars, workshops, and other noncredit programs specifically designed for the working adult to develop and enhance knowledge, skills, and competencies in the workplace.

Student Services

Academic advisement is provided to enrolled students by the College's Advisement Center, which assists students in integrating their learning style, background, and educational goals with the credit-earning methods and programs available. Students may access advisement through in-person appointments or through the Advisement Phone Center. They also have 24-hour access through fax and e-mail.

Credit Options

Students have the opportunity to earn degrees through traditional and nontraditional methods and use several convenient methods of meeting degree requirements, depending upon their individual learning styles and preferences. Once a student has applied and chosen a specific degree program, an evaluator determines the number of credits the student has already earned and fits those into the degree program requirement.

Credit-earning options for nondegree students benefit individuals who would like to earn credit through examinations, prior learning assessment, and Thomas Edison State College courses. Students may do so by paying the appropriate fee for these programs. An application to the College is not required to take advantage of these nondegree, credit-earning options.

Credit Banking is for students who wish to document college-level learning and consolidate college-level work into a Thomas Edison State College transcript. Credits transcribed under the Credit Banking program may or may not apply to a degree program at Thomas Edison State College.

Thomas Edison State College grants credit for current professional licenses or certificates that have been approved for credit by the American Council on Education (ACE) and the College's Academic Council. Students must submit notarized copies of their license or certificate and current renewal card, if appropriate, to receive credit. A list of licenses and certificates approved for credit may be found in the College's *Undergraduate Prospectus*.

Faculty

There are approximately 300 mentors at Thomas Edison State College. Drawn from other highly regarded colleges and universities, mentors provide many services, including assessment of prior knowledge and advisement.

Admission

Adults 21 years of age or older who are seeking an associate, baccalaureate, or master's degree and are high school graduates are eligible to become Thomas Edison State College students. Because Thomas Edison State College delivers high-quality education directly to students wherever they live or work, students may complete degree requirements at their convenience. A computer is required to complete graduate degrees and to take undergraduate online courses.

Tuition and Fees

Tuition is payment for all costs directly associated with the academic delivery of a Thomas Edison State College education. Fees are designated as payment for administrative services and for materials used by students for courses and other activities. Thomas Edison State College offers

one annual tuition plan, the Comprehensive Tuition Plan, for students who want access to all components of the tuition package. For those students who have determined that their particular situation is one where only components of the Comprehensive Tuition Plan are required, the College offers the Enrolled Options Plan. A complete listing of tuition and fees is included in the College's information packet and is available by calling the Office of Admissions or by visiting the College Web site.

Financial Aid

Thomas Edison State College participates in a number of federal and state aid programs. Eligible students may receive Federal Pell Grants or federal education loans such as the Federal Stafford Student Loan (subsidized and unsubsidized). Eligible New Jersey residents may also tap a variety of state grant and loan programs. Students may use state aid to meet all or part of their college costs, provided they are taking at least 12 credits per semester. Detailed information about the financial aid process may be found in the financial aid packet, which is available from the Office of Financial Aid & Veterans' Affairs or on the College Web site. To receive this information, students should contact the office at 609-633-9658 or finaid@tesc.edu.

Applying

Students may apply to Thomas Edison State College by mail or fax or online at http://www.tesc.edu. The Office of Admissions assists potential applicants in determining whether Thomas Edison State College suits their particular academic goals.

CONTACT

David Hoftiezer
Acting Director of Admissions
Thomas Edison State College
101 West State Street
Trenton, New Jersey 08608-1176

Phone: 888-442-8372 (toll-free)
Fax: 609-984-8447
E-mail: info@tesc.edu
Web site: http://www.tesc.edu

TUI UNIVERSITY
Distance Learning Program
Cypress, California

TUI University, located in southern California, is regionally accredited by the Commission for Senior Colleges and Universities of the Western Association of Schools and Colleges.

TUI University offers affordable degree programs on the Internet, using the latest technology and innovative live interactive delivery methodology.

TUI University is committed to sustaining the high quality of its pedagogical model, its faculty, and its support services. A worldwide university operating 24 hours a day, 365 days a year, TUI University offers students an excellent learning experience accessed from their own homes, while allowing them to maintain their work and family responsibilities.

Distance Learning Program

TUI University offers high-quality education utilizing online Internet instruction as its primary means of delivery. There is no residency requirement and no need for campus visits. The student-centered teaching model has two major elements: modular case-based learning and the cyber classroom. These essential elements are part of every module of every course.

Delivery Media

The cyber classroom approach includes the use of multimedia for academic transactions and interactive collaboration (live exchange with professors and peers). The multimedia approach includes audio and video on demand, Internet links, PowerPoint presentations, and live conferences among students and between professors and students. This allows students to work as a team with fellow students from around the world. Case-based learning provides real-world application to each topic.

Programs of Study

TUI University consists of the College of Business Administration, the College of Education, the College of Health Sciences, and the College of Information Systems. The College of Business

Administration offers three degree programs: the Bachelor of Science in Business Administration (120 semester credits), with concentrations in criminal justice, finance, general management, human resources management, information technology management, logistics management, and degree completion specially designed for students with an A.A. or A.S. degree; the Master of Science in Business Administration (44 semester credits), with concentrations in conflict and negotiations management, criminal justice administration, entrepreneurship, finance, general management, human resource management, information technology management, international business, logistics management, public management, and strategic leadership; and the Doctor of Philosophy in Business Administration (44 semester credits of course work plus a research dissertation). The concentration depends on the candidate's specific research interests.

The College of Education offers two degree programs: the Master of Arts in Education (36 semester credits), with concentrations in teaching and instruction, educational leadership and administration, higher education, and e-learning, and the Doctor of Philosophy in Educational Leadership (48 semester

credits of course work plus a research dissertation), with specializations in K–12 leadership, higher education leadership, and e-learning leadership.

The College of Health Sciences offers three degree programs: the Bachelor of Science in Health Sciences (124 semester credits), with concentrations in health education, health-care management, and professional degree completion; the Master of Science in Health Sciences (40 semester credits), with specializations in clinical research administration, emergency and disaster management, health-care management, health-care informatics, health education, international health, law and expert witness studies, and public health, and graduate certificates in clinical research administration, emergency and disaster management, environmental health science, health-care administration, health informatics, law and expert witness studies, and quality assurance; and the Doctor of Philosophy in Health Sciences (44 semester credits in course work plus a research dissertation), with specializations in international health and options in educator/researcher/practitioner studies and health-care administration.

The College of Information Systems offers three degree programs: the Bachelor of Science in Computer Science (120 semester credits), the Bachelor of Science in Information Technology Management (120 semester credits), and the Master of Science in Information Technology Management (36 semester credits).

Student Services

TUI University maintains five specific student services. Preadmission advisement assists students with enrollment procedures and any other student concerns. Preadmission English competency evaluation is provided for stu-

---

dents whose first language is not English, who do not meet TUI University's English competency requirements, or who feel that they do not possess adequate English skills. Post-admission advisement assists students with course selection and sequencing, developing good study habits, and other student concerns. Information technology assistance is provided to ensure that students have access to all information technology features of TUI University courses. The Information Technology department also assists students with installation and configuration. Library resource assistance is provided via e-mail in the use of all cyber library holdings.

TUI University provides financial assistance under three federal programs that are available to citizens and eligible noncitizens of the United States.

Faculty

All TUI University faculty members hold doctoral degrees and have experience in their respective fields in addition to having sound academic teaching, research, and dissertation advisement records. Exceptional full-time faculty members teach nearly all TUI University classes. The highest level of faculty expertise in each field is also available through guest lecturers and visiting faculty members via the cyber classroom delivery mode.

Admission

TUI University offers four sessions per year, beginning in April, July, October, and January, with each session lasting twelve weeks. All TUI University courses are valued at 4 semester credits. A full-time load is two courses per session, whereby students can earn 32 semester credits per year while continuing with family and work responsibilities.

The Office of Admissions assists potential students in determining their compatibility with the program based on past academic performance and educational goals. For specific details about each degree program, students may visit the Web site.

Tuition and Fees

TUI University's tuition is one of the most affordable in the nation. Tuition is $250 per semester credit for bachelor's-level courses, $300 per semester credit for master's-level courses, and $500 per semester credit for Ph.D.-level courses. Students may contact TUI University registration for information about scholarships and financial aid.

Active-duty military, retired military, military dependents, and civilian military employees receive special tuition rates through TUI University's DANTES agreement. Students should contact their base or post education officer or TUI University for details.

Applying

Applications may be completed online at http://www.tuiu.edu and are accepted year-round. A complete application package must be received by TUI University two weeks prior to the start of the first session. TUI University will respond within 24 business hours of receiving the complete package of application materials.

CONTACT

College of Business Administration
TUI University
5665 Plaza Drive, 3rd Floor
Cypress, California 90630
Phone: 714-816-0366
        800-375-9878 (toll-free)
Fax: 714-816-0367
E-mail: infocba@tuiu.edu
Web site: http://www.tuiu.edu

College of Education
TUI University
5665 Plaza Drive, 3rd Floor
Cypress, California 90630
Phone: 714-226-9840
        800-375-9878 (toll-free)
Fax: 714-226-9844
E-mail: infocoe@tuiu.edu
Web site: http://www.tuiu.edu

College of Health Sciences
TUI University
5665 Plaza Drive, 3rd Floor
Cypress, California 90630
Phone: 714-226-9840
        800-375-9878 (toll-free)
Fax: 714-226-9844
E-mail: infochs@tuiu.edu
Web site: http://www.tuiu.edu

College of Information Systems
TUI University
Cypress, California 90630
Phone: 714-816-0366
        800-375-9878 (toll-free)
Fax: 714-816-0367
E-mail: infocis@tuiu.edu
Web site: http://www.tuiu.edu

For program information:
Phone: 800-375-9878 (toll-free)
E-mail: infoDEV@tuiu.edu

THE UNIVERSITY OF ALABAMA

College of Continuing Studies
Division of Academic Outreach

Tuscaloosa, Alabama

> *Founded in 1831, the University of Alabama has been selected repeatedly as one of the top fifty public universities in the country. By using technology and flexible formats, the Division of Academic Outreach provides diverse and convenient academic programs to students pursuing educational and personal development.*

Distance Learning Program

The Division of Academic Outreach accommodates distance and adult learners who are limited by time, geography, work schedules, or personal obligations. Degrees and courses are available via the Internet, DVD, and videoconferencing.

Delivery Media

Online: Academic Outreach delivers high school and college courses over the Internet directly to the student's computer. Students are instructed through a secure Internet site, and they interact with their professors and complete lessons through the online course-management system.

DVD: Academic Outreach delivers undergraduate and graduate courses via DVD to students who cannot attend classes on campus. Courses are filmed as they occur, and DVDs are mailed to students the same week. Students take proctored exams at convenient locations. Video courses are semester based. Interested students should visit http://www.BamaByDistance.ua.edu for registration information or call 800-452-5971 (toll-free).

Videoconferencing: The Intercampus Interactive Telecommunication System (IITS) is a network of conference rooms connected to Vianet, a statewide videoconferencing network. Approximately 120 sites throughout Alabama are equipped with cameras, monitors, and other devices that allow teachers and students to interact as if they were in the same room. Interested students should visit http://www.BamaByDistance.ua.edu for registration information or call 800-452-5971 (toll-free).

Programs of Study

Online bachelor's programs comprise the B.S. in consumer sciences (concentration in consumer affairs), B.S. in consumer sciences (concentration in family financial planning and counseling), B.S. in human environmental sciences (general studies), B.S. in Nursing (RN to B.S.N.), B.S./M.S. Nursing (RN to B.S.N./M.S.N.), B.S. in restaurant and hospitality management (executive restaurant and hospitality management), and B.S. in restaurant and hospitality management (restaurant, hotel, and meetings management).

Online master's programs include the M.A. in health studies (health promotion), M.A. in management (global business management), Master of Law and Taxation, Master of Library and Information Studies, M.S. in human environmental sciences (general studies), M.S. in human environmental sciences (general studies with a certificate in family financial planning and counseling), M.S. in human environmental sciences (general studies with a concentration in consumer quality management), M.S. in human environmental sciences (general studies with a specialization in interactive technology), M.S. in human environmental sciences (human nutrition), M.S. in human environmental sciences (restaurant and hospitality management), M.S. in nursing (case management for rural populations/clinical nurse leader), and M.S. in operations management.

Online Education Specialist programs are offered in counselor education and in secondary education (science concentration).

A minor is available in online computing technology and applications.

Blended programs that use multiple delivery methods include the B.S. in early childhood education, B.S. in human development and family studies, B.S. in mechanical engineering (available in Dothan, Alabama), M.A. in counselor education (Alabama only), and M.S. in aerospace engineering.

Special programs offered through distance learning are B.A. and B.S. external degree programs in interdisciplinary studies and a nondegree program in Japanese.

Special Programs

The External Degree Program is an interdisciplinary undergraduate distance learning program. Students may apply previously earned academic credits transferred from regionally accredited colleges or earned through national tests such as the College-Level Examination Program (CLEP), independent study, out-of-class learning contracts, correspondence studies, classroom work, and demonstrated prior learning toward a B.A. or a B.S. in interdisciplinary studies.

Applicants must have high school diplomas or General Educational Development (GED) equivalency scores of at least 50 if the test was taken prior to January 2002 or at least 500 if the test was taken after January 2002, be 25 years of age or older, have cumulative GPAs of 2.0 or higher on all previous college work, and have educational goals that are attainable through the program. As with most of the University's distance programs, applicants need not be Alabama residents.

Credit Options

Applicability of credit toward an undergraduate degree refers to the prerogative of the respective academic divisions to count specific credit toward a student's degree requirements. A maximum of 64 semester hours of two-year college credit may be applied toward graduation requirements. At the graduate level, a maximum of 12 semester hours of work taken as a nondegree student may be applied to the credit-hour requirements for a degree. Responsibility rests with the student to observe the limitations imposed on credit hours, course work, and transfer of credit. Procedures and forms are furnished upon request.

Faculty

At The University of Alabama, distinguished faculty members require the same level of academic excellence from their distance students as they do from on-campus students. Faculty members receive special training in facilitating distance learning, and students receive high-quality degree programs from an accredited, world-class institution.

Admission

Admission policies and procedures for degree programs and courses offered through Academic Outreach vary. Students are responsible for reading and understanding admissions polices and procedures for the degree program and courses in which they plan to enroll. For more information, students should visit the Web site at http://BamaByDistance.ua.edu and click on the Prospective Student tab.

The Division of Academic Outreach provides services to assist students with the admission process, registration, advising and schedule building, and financial aid. Students should contact Nina Smith for assistance (telephone: 205-348-0089 or 800-467-0227 (toll-free); e-mail: nsmith@ccs.ua.edu or AOinfo@ccs.ua.edu).

Tuition and Fees

Tuition varies by program and format. Students should visit the Division of Academic Outreach Web site at http://BamaByDistance.ua.edu for current tuition rates.

Financial Aid

Loans are administered through the Office of Student Financial Services. Academic Outreach offers several scholarships for adult students each academic year. Applications are generally available in the fall semester, and the deadline is usually in early December.

Applying

Students may obtain information on admission and registration by contacting the Division of Academic Outreach online at http://www.BamaByDistance.ua.edu, by e-mail at aoinfo@ccs.ua.edu, or by telephone at 205-348-0089 or 800-467-0227 (toll-free).

CONTACT

Division of Academic Outreach
College of Continuing Studies
The University of Alabama
Box 870388
Tuscaloosa, Alabama 35487-0388
Phone: 205-348-0089
          800-467-0227 (toll-free)
Fax: 205-348-0249
E-mail: AOinfo@ccs.ua.edu
Web site: http://www.BamaByDistance.ua.edu

UNIVERSITY OF ALASKA FAIRBANKS
Center for Distance Education and Independent Learning
Fairbanks, Alaska

> *From its start in 1917 as a mining and agricultural school, UAF has become America's arctic university and flagship of the state's university system. A land-, sea-, and space-grant university, UAF's range of teaching and research is as diverse as Alaska itself. From physics to foreign languages, supercomputers to sociology, UAF helps people learn more about their world.*
>
> *UAF currently offers baccalaureate, master's, and doctoral degree programs. All courses are approved and meet the accreditation standards of the Northwest Commission on Colleges and Universities. UAF is an Affirmative Action/Equal Opportunity employer and educational institution.*

Distance Learning Program

UAF developed a Correspondence Study Program in the late 1950s, but the current Center for Distance Education and Independent Learning (CDE) was created in 1987. CDE is part of the College of Rural and Community Development, with branch campuses in Bethel, Dillingham, Interior-Aleutians (Fairbanks), Kotzebue, and Nome, as well as participating with extended campuses of the University of Alaska Anchorage and University of Alaska Southeast.

The Center for Distance Education offers more than 135 courses in nearly forty disciplines, with approximately 6,000 student enrollments throughout the world each year.

Most of the independent learning courses are open for enrollment with the option of either yearlong or semester-based enrollment. Yearlong students have up to one year from the date of enrollment to finish course work but have the option of completing the work earlier than the one-year timeframe. CDE also supports close to 150 distance-delivered courses offered on a semester basis.

Some courses have prerequisites that must be met before students are eligible to register in the course. These requirements are used as a guideline so that the student is prepared for the intended course. It is up to the student to make sure that he or she has fulfilled these requirements. Prerequisites are listed in the individual course descriptions. Some courses require placement exams for all students intending to register in these courses beginning September 2008. Students should contact CDE for additional information.

Delivery Media

A wide range of media, including course guides, textbooks, other books and manuals, and DVDs and CDs, is utilized to deliver instruction. Many courses are available online, most utilizing the Blackboard Learning System. Not all modes of delivery are available for every course, and students must have access to the appropriate equipment as specified in individual course descriptions. Most interaction between students and instructors is asynchronous in nature and may be via written communication, e-mail, or by phone interview.

Programs of Study

Approximately 150 CDE (independent learning) courses can be used to fulfill degree program requirements within the University of Alaska's statewide system or at any other university that accepts the credits. The Center for Distance Education and Independent Learning is not a degree-granting organization. Future plans include delivery of certificates and degrees online.

Special Programs

The Center for Distance Education and Independent Learning participates in the Defense Activity for Non-Traditional Education Support (DANTES) programs; information is available from base personnel or education officers. Veterans' educational benefits are also applicable. DANTES students must complete a UAF enrollment form as well as the DANTES forms.

People interested in being certified to teach in Alaska find courses available that fulfill teacher certificate and recertification requirements for the State of Alaska Department of Education. Students may choose among several courses that satisfy the Alaska studies and multicultural requirements.

Student Services

Students have access to the state library system and the UAF Rasmuson Library either in person or through the online Statewide Library System. All students can obtain accounts on the University of Alaska computer network, which also gives access to the wider Internet and the World Wide Web. The UAF Writing Center offers free tutoring for student use. A toll-free UAF math hotline for problem solving and math help is also available for student use. Available hours may vary each semester.

Faculty

The CDE Independent Learning Program includes approximately 90 faculty members, about half of whom are also full-time members of the UAF faculty and have terminal academic degrees. Adjunct faculty members and discipline professionals are hired to supplement the University's full-time faculty.

Admission

Students may enroll in individual courses any time during the year and have one year to complete the course. There are no admissions requirements or procedures, since the Center for Distance Education and Independent Learning is not a degree-granting organization.

Tuition and Fees

All students enrolled in UAF Independent Learning courses are charged the same tuition whether they are Alaska residents or not. Tuition for 100- to 200-level courses is $134 per credit, 300- to 400-level courses are $151 per credit, and 600-level courses are $301

per credit. There is an additional UA Network fee, which is assessed at 2 percent of tuition. The only other costs for courses are materials fees that vary by course and a $25 service fee per course. Students outside the U.S. must submit payment in U.S. dollars and are charged an extra $55 per course plus any additional shipping charges for the delivery of materials. Actual costs of delivery are determined upon registration.

Financial Aid

Alaska students who are full-time (enrolled in at least 12 credits per semester) and are taking independent learning courses on a semester basis are eligible for all the types of financial aid available to other students, including Federal Pell Grants, Federal Supplemen-

tal Educational Opportunity Grants, State Educational Incentive grants, Bureau of Indian Affairs grants, Federal Stafford Student Loans, and State of Alaska student loans. Students enrolled in regular yearlong courses are not eligible to receive financial aid, and the courses will not contribute to a full-time or part-time enrollment status.

Applying

No application is required of students taking CDE courses. Completion of a UAF enrollment form and payment of fees are all that are required of students to take courses. Verification of enrollment and course materials are mailed to the students outside of the local Fairbanks area.

CONTACT

Curt Madison, Director
Center for Distance Education and Independent Learning
P.O. Box 756700
University of Alaska Fairbanks
Fairbanks, Alaska 99775-6700

Phone: 907-479-3444
         800-277-8060 (toll-free)
Fax: 907-479-3443
E-mail: distance@uaf.edu
Web site: http://distance.uaf.edu

UNIVERSITY OF CENTRAL MISSOURI

Office of Extended Campus–Distance Learning
Department of Nursing

Warrensburg, Missouri

Founded in 1871, the University of Central Missouri (UCM) (formerly Central Missouri State University) is a state university offering approximately 150 areas of study to 11,100 undergraduate and graduate students. In 2007, UCM was named one of "America's Best Colleges" by U.S. News and World Report. The Princeton Review also named UCM a "2008 Best College in the Midwestern Region." As Missouri's lead institution for professional technology, an area long recognized as one of the University's greatest strengths. The new mission has expanded this commitment and means that Central Missouri will continue to integrate the latest technologies into every level of its comprehensive liberal arts curriculum. Central Missouri is committed to acquiring, disseminating, and utilizing technology to enhance the University's comprehensive educational mission. Central Missouri is accredited by the North Central Association of Colleges and Schools.

Distance Learning Program

Central Missouri's main distance learning program provides undergraduate and graduate-level courses through two-way interactive television and Internet-based courses. The online program currently includes one doctoral degree, four master's degrees, two graduate certificates, three undergraduate completion programs, and numerous graduate and undergraduate courses. From fall 1994 through fall 2006, Central Missouri provided instruction to more than 40,000 graduate, undergraduate, and high school students in a distance learning environment.

Institutional and financial information about the University of Central Missouri can be accessed via the Web, http://www.ucmo.edu/rsearch/ir/toc.htm.

Delivery Media

Central Missouri uses a variety of technologies to deliver its distance learning courses. These include two-way interactive television and Internet technologies, including video and audio streaming. UCM links to the Missouri Research and Educational Network (MOREnet) statewide backbone, which connects all of Missouri's public higher education institutions and many K–12

schools, to provide Internet-based and interactive television programming. Central Missouri's complement of six 2-way videoconferencing facilities, which are capable of ISDN, H.323, T.120, and audioconferencing, allow Central Missouri to provide distance learning content anywhere in the world.

Programs of Study

There are two degrees offered by the Department of Nursing through distance learning technologies. The RN completion program resulting in a baccalaureate degree is delivered through online courses, as well as the Master of Science in rural family nursing.

The Bachelor of Science in Nursing degree is designed for the registered nurse who wants to upgrade to a bachelor's degree. The bachelor's degree provides more flexibility and leads to more career opportunities in nursing. Employment opportunities increase as the level of education increases. A baccalaureate degree provides many more options in the areas of public health, home health, nursing management, program planning, and health teaching. Registered nurses face increasingly complex demands that require a broad-based bachelor's-degree

preparation. The program enhances a nurse's ability to think critically, teaches more effective communication skills, broadens the scope of nursing into areas of wellness, and provides a deeper understanding of professional nursing leadership.

The program features flexible scheduling that allows students to start any semester and set their own pace for completion. Full-time students can complete the course work in one year; part-time students can take up to four years to complete the program. The program allows the transfer of up to 64 credit hours of university studies and nursing prerequisites from other institutions. Students receive credit for courses completed within another nursing program and for professional experience. Nursing faculty members understand the needs of working professionals who are students. The program is accredited by the Commission on Collegiate Nursing Education (CCNE). More information is available online in the undergraduate catalog at http://www.ucmo.edu/catalogs/.

The Master of Science in rural family nursing online degree program is designed for nurses with a baccalaureate degree who seek advanced practice as a specialist. Central Missouri, with more than forty-five years of experience providing high-quality nursing education, uses state-of-the-art technology to deliver the program. Students specialize in one of two professional tracks: family nurse practitioner or nurse educator.

There are many benefits for students earning a Master of Science in rural family nursing degree at Central Missouri. All professional tracks offer flexibility at an affordable cost. The online classes provide "anytime, anywhere" access, and the online format eliminates travel time and expense.

Online classes expand the student's technical skills, increasing valuable workplace skills. Classes are student centered and user friendly, providing individual attention from the instructors. Earning this degree provides students with the foundation for advanced practice, specialty practice, and advanced study at the doctoral level. More information can be found in the graduate catalog online, http://www.ucmo.edu/catalogs/.

Special Programs

Central Missouri's distance learning program builds on the existing curriculum offerings at UCM as well as offerings that address special distance learning needs. Central Missouri's distance learning students are eligible to participate in the same opportunities as on-campus students. These include study tours and internships in many disciplines. The Office of Career Services reports a 94 percent placement rate for UCM graduates within six months of graduation.

Student Services

The toll-free University number, 877-729-8266, allows access to offices involved with student services: Extended Campus and Distance Learning, Admissions, Student Financial Services, University Housing, and the Graduate School. All students enrolled at Central Missouri are issued a network account to access University resources. The Help Desk is available to Central Missouri students needing technical computer assistance. A Web site dedicated to distance learning students provides access to course information, the UCM library, career services, the online writing lab (OWL) for writing assistance, as well as links to other resources that take the distance out of learning. The University Bookstore provides students the ability to order textbooks online.

Credit Options

Upon approval, a student may transfer a maximum of 9 semester hours of graduate credit from another institution to a UCM master's degree program.

Faculty

Faculty members at Central Missouri exemplify the goals of the institution as they balance personal attention with expertise in their respective fields. Approximately 68 percent of the 449 full-time faculty members hold doctoral degrees. The student-faculty ratio is 16:1.

Admission

Students interested in pursuing graduate degree through Central Missouri's Department of Nursing should contact the Graduate School for application information, 877-729-8266 Ext. 3 or visit the Web site, http://www.ucmo.edu/graduate. The Graduate School should receive all application materials at least three weeks prior to the beginning of the semester in which the student wishes to register.

Applicants must be admitted to the Graduate School before enrolling in a nursing program. If this is a student's first enrollment at Central Missouri, a $30 nonrefundable application fee (international students, $50) must accompany the application and official transcripts of all undergraduate and graduate course work. Admission to the Graduate School, which permits enrollment in classes, is not equivalent to admission to a particular program or degree.

Tuition and Fees

For 2007–08, graduate tuition was $271 per credit hour for Internet-based courses. Undergraduate tuition was $230 per credit hour for Internet-based programs. Prospective students should note that tuition rates may be changed at any time by action of the Board of Governors.

Financial Aid

Central Missouri recognizes a student's continuing need for financial assistance. Federal grant and loan funds are available for eligible students who have been accepted for regular degree programs at UCM. Application eligibility information may be obtained by contacting the Office of Student Financial Services, 660-543-8266 or 877-729-8266 (toll-free). Students who are veterans may also be considered for VA educational benefits to help with tuition costs.

The University participates in all federal student financial aid grant, loan, and employment programs. Visiting and non-degree-seeking students are not eligible to receive federal student aid.

Applying

Undergraduate students should call 660-543-4290/4677 or 877-729-8266 Ext. 1 (toll-free). Graduate students should call 660-543-4621 or 877-729-8266 Ext. 3 (toll-free).

CONTACT

Barbara Carder
Assistant Director for Distance Learning
Office of Extended Campus and Distance Learning
Humphreys 410
University of Central Missouri
Warrensburg, Missouri 64093
Phone: 660-543-8480
       877-729-8266 Ext. 21
       (toll-free)
Fax: 660-543-8333
E-mail: bcarder@ucmo.edu
Web site: http://www.ucmo.edu/ucmonline

UNIVERSITY OF CENTRAL MISSOURI

Office of Extended Campus–Distance Learning
Master of Science in Criminal Justice

Warrensburg, Missouri

Founded in 1871, the University of Central Missouri (UCM) (formerly Central Missouri State University) is a state university offering approximately 150 areas of study to 11,100 undergraduate and graduate students. In 2007, UCM was named one of "America's Best Colleges" by U.S. News and World Report. The Princeton Review also named UCM a "2008 Best College in the Midwestern Region." As Missouri's lead institution for professional technology, an area long recognized as one of the University's greatest strengths. The new mission has expanded this commitment and means that Central Missouri will continue to integrate the latest technologies into every level of its comprehensive liberal arts curriculum. Central Missouri is committed to acquiring, disseminating, and utilizing technology to enhance the University's comprehensive educational mission. Central Missouri is accredited by the North Central Association of Colleges and Schools.

Distance Learning Program

Central Missouri's main distance learning program provides undergraduate and graduate-level courses through two-way interactive television and Internet-based courses. The online program currently includes one doctoral degree, four master's degrees, two graduate certificates, three undergraduate completion programs, and numerous graduate and undergraduate courses. From fall 1994 through fall 2006, Central Missouri provided instruction to more than 40,000 graduate, undergraduate, and high school students in a distance learning environment.

Institutional and financial information about the University of Central Missouri can be accessed via the Web, http://www.ucmo.edu/rsearch/ir/toc.htm.

Delivery Media

Central Missouri uses a variety of technologies to deliver its distance learning courses. These include two-way interactive television and Internet technologies, including video and audio streaming. UCM links to the Missouri Research and Educational Network (MOREnet) statewide backbone, which connects all of Missouri's public higher education institutions and many K–12 schools, to provide Internet-based and interactive television programming. Central Missouri's

complement of six 2-way videoconferencing facilities, which are capable of ISDN, H.323, T.120, and audioconferencing, allow Central Missouri to provide distance learning content anywhere in the world.

Programs of Study

The Master of Science in Criminal Justice program is designed to provide the requisite knowledge, skills, and abilities for those students who intend to enter and/or advance in the criminal justice fields of law enforcement, corrections, and juvenile justice or who seek leadership, professional specialization, research, or teaching positions in criminal justice. Course work emphasizes leading justice system issues, including legal aspects; organization, administration, management, and leadership; and information acquisition, analysis, and interpretation. Distance delivery of the Master of Science in Criminal Justice includes complete online delivery of the degree program.

The graduate with a Master of Science in Criminal Justice can use the knowledge and skills obtained in the program to articulate knowledge of the major issues facing the criminal justice system in the nation and world; conduct and present an independent research project; communicate and interact profession-

ally in scholarly, academic settings; and delineate the ethical principles of human subject protection in social science research.

First offered in 1962, the program is one of the most respected criminal justice programs in the world. Among Central Missouri's criminal justice alumni are members of numerous police and corrections agencies, national and state government officials, judges, attorneys, professors, and approximately 400 chief administrators in all parts of the world.

To be accepted into the program of study for the Master of Science in Criminal Justice, a student must have an undergraduate degree in criminal justice or a related field and have earned a minimum grade point average of 2.75 on all undergraduate course work and 3.0 on all graduate course work. A student without a criminal justice degree may be required to complete up to 15 hours of background courses in criminal justice prior to taking graduate-level courses. The requirement to take background courses may be waived by the department's graduate coordinator based on previous courses taken and/or relevant professional experience. Students not meeting program admission requirements may request that the department's graduate committee admit them provisionally to the program. GRE scores are generally not required.

The 36-hour Master of Science in Criminal Justice program allows for 6 semester hours of departmentally approved electives under the thesis option and 9 hours under the nonthesis or comprehensive examination option.

Special Programs

Central Missouri's distance learning program builds on the existing curriculum offerings at UCM as well as offerings that address special distance learning needs.

Central Missouri's distance learning students are eligible to participate in the same opportunities as on-campus students. These include study tours and internships in many disciplines.

The Office of Career Services reports a 94 percent placement rate for UCM graduates within six months of graduation.

Student Services

A toll-free University number, 877-729-8266, allows access to offices involved with student services: Extended Campus and Distance Learning, Admissions, Student Financial Services, University Housing, and the Graduate School. All students enrolled at Central Missouri are issued a network account to access University resources. The Help Desk is available to Central Missouri students needing technical computer assistance. A Web site dedicated to distance learning students provides access to course information, the UCM library, career services, the online writing lab (OWL) for writing assistance, as well as links to other resources that take the distance out of learning. The University Bookstore provides students the ability to order textbooks online.

Credit Options

Upon approval, a student may transfer a maximum of 9 semester hours of graduate credit from another institution to a UCM master's degree program.

Faculty

Faculty members at Central Missouri exemplify the goals of the institution as they balance personal attention with expertise in their respective fields. Approximately 68 percent of the 449 full-time faculty members hold doctoral degrees. The student-faculty ratio is 16:1.

The criminal justice faculty has a unique blend of academic credentials and field experience, with all members holding terminal degrees. In addition, 90 percent of the faculty members had significant experience with a criminal justice agency prior to joining the faculty of the University of Central Missouri.

Admission

Individuals interested in pursuing a graduate degree at the University of Central Missouri should contact the Graduate School for application information at 877-729-8266 Ext. 3 (toll-free) or visit the Web site, http://www.ucmo.edu/graduate. The Graduate School should receive all application materials at least three weeks prior to the beginning of the semester in which the student wishes to register.

All degree-seeking student applicants must submit a formal application for admission to the Graduate School and official transcripts of all undergraduate/graduate course work. If this is a student's first enrollment at Central Missouri, a $30 nonrefundable application fee is required (international students must re-

mit $50). Admission to the Graduate School, which permits enrollment in classes, is not equivalent to admission to a particular program or degree.

Tuition and Fees

For 2007–08, graduate tuition was $271 per credit hour for Internet-based courses. Prospective students should note that tuition rates may be changed at any time by action of the Board of Governors.

Financial Aid

Central Missouri recognizes a student's continuing need for financial assistance. Federal grant and loan funds are available for eligible students who have been accepted for regular degree programs at UCM. Application eligibility information may be obtained by contacting the Office of Student Financial Services, 660-543-8266 or 877-729-8266 Ext. 6 (toll-free). Students who are veterans may also be considered for VA educational benefits to help with tuition costs.

The University participates in all federal student financial aid grant, loan, and employment programs. Visiting and non-degree-seeking students are not eligible to receive federal financial aid.

Applying

Graduate students should contact the Graduate School, 660-543-4621 or toll-free at 877-729-8266 Ext. 3.

CONTACT

Dr. Gene Bonham
Faculty Graduate Coordinator
University of Central Missouri
Humphreys 302 D
Warrensburg, Missouri 64093
Phone: 660-543-4669
E-mail: lbonham@ucmo.edu
Web site: http://www.ucmo.edu/
    criminaljustice

Barbara Carder
Assistant Director for Distance Learning
Office of Extended Campus and
    Distance Learning
Humphreys 410
University of Central Missouri
Warrensburg, Missouri 64093
Phone: 660-543-8480
    877-729-8266 Ext. 21 (toll-free)
Fax: 660-543-8333
E-mail: bcarder@ucmo.edu
Web site: http://www.ucmo.edu/
    ucmonline

UNIVERSITY OF CENTRAL MISSOURI

Office of Extended Campus–Distance Learning
Master of Science in Industrial Management

Warrensburg, Missouri

Founded in 1871, the University of Central Missouri (UCM) (formerly Central Missouri State University) is a state university offering approximately 150 areas of study to 11,100 undergraduate and graduate students. In 2007, UCM was named one of "America's Best Colleges" by U.S. News and World Report. The Princeton Review also named UCM a "2008 Best College in the Midwestern Region." As Missouri's lead institution for professional technology, an area long recognized as one of the University's greatest strengths. The new mission has expanded this commitment and means that Central Missouri will continue to integrate the latest technologies into every level of its comprehensive liberal arts curriculum. Central Missouri is committed to acquiring, disseminating, and utilizing technology to enhance the University's comprehensive educational mission. Central Missouri is accredited by the North Central Association of Colleges and Schools.

Distance Learning Program

Central Missouri's main distance learning program provides undergraduate and graduate-level courses through two-way interactive television and Internet-based courses. The online program currently includes one doctoral degree, four master's degrees, two graduate certificates, three undergraduate completion programs, and numerous graduate and undergraduate courses. From fall 1994 through fall 2006, Central Missouri provided instruction to more than 40,000 graduate, undergraduate, and high school students in a distance learning environment.

Institutional and financial information about the University of Central Missouri can be accessed via the Web, http://www.ucmo.edu/rsearch/ir/toc.htm.

Delivery Media

Central Missouri uses a variety of technologies to deliver its distance learning courses. These include two-way interactive television and Internet technologies, including video and audio streaming. UCM links to the Missouri Research and Educational Network (MOREnet) statewide backbone, which connects all of Missouri's public higher education institutions and many K–12 schools, to provide Internet-based and interactive television programming. Finally, Central Missouri's complement of six 2-way videoconferencing facilities, which are capable of ISDN, H.323, T.120, and audioconferencing, allow Central Missouri to provide distance learning content anywhere in the world.

Programs of Study

The Master of Science in industrial management is designed for students who are preparing for upward mobility in supervisory or management positions in business and industry, manufacturing, quality control or quality systems management, or related positions.

In a recent survey of graduates from this degree, the average response age was 40 years old, with a mean salary of $65,000 per year. Some occupational titles include vice president of operations, production manager, shift supervisor, quality systems manager, and plant manager.

Participants in the Master of Science degree in industrial management develop skills useful to business and industry. The program provides a balanced curriculum focusing on the human element of the workplace as well as a variety of industrial systems.

Specific skills are developed in the fields of leadership, problem solving, and decision making.

The graduate with a Master of Science degree in industrial management can use the knowledge and skills obtained in the program to apply management skills and concepts to specific situations, plan and implement a project, analyze and develop a human relations strategy, demonstrate the ability to communicate effectively, explain and apply the basic concepts of an industrial economy, introduce and adapt technical expertise to a given process or product, and perform, interpret, and explain research.

The Master of Science in industrial management is a 33-hour degree program. Complete online delivery of the program began in fall 2002. Students may enter the course cycle at the beginning of any semester. Courses are scheduled with the capability of completing the degree program in two calendar years, including one summer session. Degree information is available on the Web, http://www.ucmo.edu/msim.

A strength of this program is the flexibility built into the cognate course work and culminating experience. The program allows several curricular paths leading to graduation and facilitates articulation to a cooperative doctoral program in technology management.

To be accepted into this program, a student shall have a minimum GPA of 2.6 in the undergraduate major. A student not meeting this requirement may petition the department for admittance on a conditional basis. GRE or GMAT scores are not required.

Special Programs

Central Missouri's distance learning program builds on the existing curriculum offerings at UCM as well as offerings that address special distance learning needs.

Central Missouri's distance learning students are eligible to participate in the same opportunities as on-campus students. These include study tours and internships in many disciplines.

The Office of Career Services reports a 94 percent placement rate for UCM graduates within six months of graduation.

Student Services

A toll-free University number, 877-729-8266, allows access to offices involved with student services: Extended Campus and Distance Learning, Admissions, Student Financial Services, University Housing, and the Graduate School. All students enrolled at Central Missouri are issued a network account to access University resources. The Help Desk is available to Central Missouri students needing technical computer assistance. A Web site dedicated to distance learning students provides access to course information, the UCM library, career services, the online writing lab (OWL) for writing assistance, as well as links to other resources that take the distance out of learning. The University Bookstore provides students the ability to order textbooks online.

Credit Options

Upon approval, a student may transfer a maximum of 9 semester hours of graduate credit from another institution to a UCM master's degree program.

Faculty

Faculty members at Central Missouri exemplify the goals of the institution as they balance personal attention with expertise in their respective fields. Approximately 68 percent of the 449 full-time faculty members hold doctoral degrees. The student-faculty ratio is 16:1.

Admission

Individuals interested in pursuing a graduate degree at the University of Central Missouri should contact the Graduate School for application information at 877-729-8266 Ext. 3 (toll-free) or visit the Web site, http://www.ucmo.edu/graduate. The Graduate School should receive all application materials at least three weeks prior to the beginning of the semester in which the student wishes to register.

All degree-seeking student applicants must submit a formal application for admission to the Graduate School and official transcripts of all undergraduate/graduate course work. If this is a student's first enrollment at Central Missouri, a $30 nonrefundable application fee is required (international students must remit $50). Admission to the Graduate School, which permits

enrollment in classes, is not equivalent to admission to a particular program or degree.

Tuition and Fees

For 2007–08, graduate tuition was $271 per credit hour for Internet-based courses. Prospective students should note that tuition rates may be changed at any time by action of the Board of Governors.

Financial Aid

Central Missouri recognizes a student's continuing need for financial assistance. Federal grant and loan funds are available for eligible students who have been accepted for regular degree programs at UCM. Application eligibility information may be obtained by contacting the Office of Student Financial Services, 660-543-8266 or 877-729-8266, Ext. 6 (toll-free). Students who are veterans may also be considered for VA educational benefits to help with tuition costs.

The University participates in all federal student financial aid grant, loan, and employment programs. Visiting and non-degree-seeking students are not eligible to receive federal financial aid.

Applying

Graduate students should contact the Graduate School, 660-543-4621 or toll-free at 877-729-8266 Ext 3.

CONTACT

Dr. Ronald Woolsey
Faculty Coordinator
University of Central Missouri
Warrensburg, Missouri 64093
Phone: 660-543-4340
E-mail: woolsey@ucmo.edu
Web site: http://www.ucmo.edu/msim

Barbara Carder
Assistant Director for Distance Learning
Office of Extended Campus and
    Distance Learning
Humphreys 410
University of Central Missouri
Warrensburg, Missouri 64093
Phone: 660-543-8480
    877-729-8266 Ext. 21 (toll-free)
Fax: 660-540-8333
E-mail: bcarder@ucmo.edu
Web site: http://www.ucmo.edu/
    ucmonline

UNIVERSITY OF CENTRAL MISSOURI

Office of Extended Campus–Distance Learning
Master of Science in Physical Education, Exercise, and Sport
Science

Warrensburg, Missouri

Founded in 1871, the University of Central Missouri (UCM, formerly Central Missouri State University) is a state university offering approximately 150 areas of study to 11,100 undergraduate and graduate students. In 2007, UCM was named one of "America's Best Colleges" by U.S. News and World Report. The Princeton Review also named UCM a "2008 Best College in the Midwestern Region." As Missouri's lead institution for professional technology, an area long recognized as one of the University's greatest strengths, Central Missouri will continue to integrate the latest technologies into every level of its comprehensive liberal arts curriculum. Central Missouri is committed to acquiring, disseminating, and utilizing technology to enhance the University's comprehensive educational mission. Central Missouri is accredited by the North Central Association of Colleges and Schools.

Distance Learning Program

Central Missouri's main distance learning program provides undergraduate and graduate-level courses through two-way interactive television and the Internet. The online program currently includes one doctoral degree, four master's degrees, two graduate certificates, three undergraduate completion programs, and numerous graduate and undergraduate courses. From fall 1994 through fall 2006, Central Missouri provided instruction to more than 40,000 graduate, undergraduate, and high school students in a distance learning environment.

Institutional and financial information about the University of Central Missouri can be accessed via the Web (http://www.ucmo.edu/rsearch/ir/toc.htm).

Delivery Media

Central Missouri uses a variety of technologies to deliver its distance learning courses. These include two-way interactive television and Internet technologies, including video and audio streaming. UCM links to the Missouri Research and Educational Network (MOREnet) statewide backbone, which connects all of Missouri's public higher education institutions and many K–12 schools, to provide Internet-based and interactive television programming. Central Missouri's complement of six 2-way videoconferencing facilities, which are capable of

ISDN, H.323, T.120, and audioconferencing, allow Central Missouri to provide distance learning content to anywhere in the world.

Programs of Study

The Master of Science in physical education, exercise, and sport science, specializing in athletics and sports business administration, is designed to train competent professionals and well-trained administrators in the field. Where athletics, fitness, wellness, and sports industries represent billions of dollars annually, competent and effective leadership and administration are essential to realizing organizational goals in this growing marketplace.

Through course work, internships, and/or research, graduates demonstrate creative thinking, problem solving, and independent study skills. They also demonstrate and apply an understanding of current technology available in athletics and sports. Students explore appropriate interdisciplinary relationships within and between athletics, sports, and associated disciplines (fitness, wellness, health promotion) and examine the nature and effects of administrative knowledge and skills applied to athletics and sports.

Individuals with a background in physical education, athletics, coaching, business, health promotion, athletic training

and sports medicine, fitness/wellness, intramurals, or recreation, to name a few, can enroll in and benefit from this online Master of Science degree.

To be accepted into this program, a student should have an undergraduate major in physical education or exercise science or have appropriate background courses. A minimum undergraduate GPA of 2.5 or a GPA of 3.0 in 8 semester hours of earned graduate credit is required.

The student's program must be planned with the advice and consent of a department adviser. The elective hours must be an integrated and related group of advanced courses fulfilling the department's and student's objectives.

Special Programs

Central Missouri's distance learning program builds upon the existing curriculum offerings at UCM as well as offerings that address special distance learning needs.

Central Missouri's distance learning students are eligible to participate in the same opportunities as on-campus students. These include study tours and internships in many disciplines.

The Office of Career Services reports a 94 percent placement rate for UCM graduates within six months of graduation.

Student Services

A toll-free University number (877-729-8266) allows access to offices involved with student services: Extended Campus and Distance Learning, admissions, Student Financial Services, University Housing, and the Graduate School. All students enrolled at Central Missouri are issued a network account to access University resources. The Help Desk is available to Central Missouri students needing technical computer assistance. A Web site dedicated to UCM's distance learning students provides access to course information, the UCM library, career services, and Central Missouri's online writing lab (OWL, for writing assistance), as well as links to other resources that take the distance out of learning. The University Bookstore provides students the ability to order textbooks online.

Credit Options

Upon approval, a student may transfer a maximum of 9 semester hours of graduate credit from another institution to a UCM master's degree program.

Faculty

Faculty members at Central Missouri exemplify the goals of the institution as they balance personal attention with expertise in their respective fields. Approximately 68 percent of the 449 full-time faculty members hold doctoral degrees. The student-faculty ratio is 16:1.

Admission

Individuals interested in pursuing a graduate degree at the University of Central Missouri should contact the Graduate School for application information (877-729-8266 Ext. 3) or visit the Web site (http://www.ucmo.edu/graduate).

The Graduate School should receive all application materials at least three weeks prior to the beginning of the semester in which the student wishes to register.

All degree-seeking student applicants must submit a formal application for admission to the Graduate School and official transcripts of all undergraduate/graduate course work. If this is a student's first enrollment at Central Missouri, a $30 nonrefundable application fee is required (international students must remit $50). Admission to the Graduate School, which permits enrollment in classes, is not equivalent to admission to a particular program or degree.

Tuition and Fees

For 2007–08, graduate tuition was $271 per credit hour for Internet-based courses. Prospective students should note that tuition rates may be changed at any time by action of the Board of Governors.

Financial Aid

Central Missouri recognizes a student's continuing need for financial assistance. Federal grant and loan funds are available for eligible students who have been accepted for regular degree programs at UCM. Application eligibility information may be obtained by contacting the Office of Student Financial Services (660-543-8266 or 877-729-8266 Ext. 6). Students who are veterans may also be considered for VA educational benefits to help with tuition costs.

The University participates in all federal student financial aid grant, loan, and employment programs. Visiting and non-degree-seeking students are not eligible to receive federal financial aid.

Applying

Graduate students should contact the Graduate School, 660-543-4621 or toll-free at 877-729-8266 Ext. 3.

CONTACT

Dr. H. Scott Strohmeyer
Faculty Graduate Coordinator
University of Central Missouri
Warrensburg, Missouri 64093
Phone: 660-543-8191
E-mail: strohmeyer@ucmo.edu
Web site: http://www.ucmo.edu/exsci

Barbara Carder
Assistant Director for Distance Learning
Office of Extended Campus and
    Distance Learning
Humphreys 410
University of Central Missouri
Warrensburg, Missouri 64093
Phone: 660-543-8480
    800-729-8266 Ext. 21 (toll-free)
Fax: 660-543-8333
E-mail: bcarder@ucmo.edu
Web site: http://www.ucmo.edu/
    ucmonline

UNIVERSITY OF COLORADO DENVER

CU Online

Denver, Colorado

The University of Colorado Denver (UCD) is one of three institutions in the University of Colorado system and the only public university in the Denver metropolitan area. Ranked among America's best graduate schools, UCD features a 15:1 student-faculty ratio, respected academic programs, and a collaborative community relationship. With the Denver skyline as its backdrop, three major sports arenas within walking distance, and numerous outdoor activities at its doorstep, UCD is quickly growing into the model for metro campuses. But with CU Online, UCD's virtual campus, that doorstep has been extended globally. CU Online was among the first fully accredited online programs in the country. It has grown and evolved to be a respected and renowned institution and continues in that tradition. The University of Colorado Denver was founded in 1965 and is accredited by the North Central Association of Colleges and Schools.

Distance Learning Program

CU Online allows students the opportunity to attend the University of Colorado Denver on their time schedule and at their convenience, while also providing the recognition and respect that only a brick and mortar university can offer.

CU Online offers not just one or two courses; there are over 350 courses. Students can actually complete an entire degree—or ten—all online, without setting a foot on campus. CU Online allows students to enjoy the same stimulating courses, top-notch faculty members, and dedicated resources as the on-campus students—but with the freedom and convenience that online courses naturally provide.

That is only the beginning. CU Online is well on its way to achieving its initial goal of providing students with the most compressive set of online courses, services, and resources of any institution of higher education in the world. Whether students are looking to start a degree, finish one, or just take the occasional course or two, CU Online provides them the opportunity to tailor courses around their lives—rather than tailor life around their courses.

Delivery Media

CU Online courses run on a traditional semester schedule. Although courses are not self-paced, they are flexible. Students are able to log into their courses on a regular basis, at their convenience. They are assigned a homepage to access courses, find lectures and assignments, and contribute to threaded discussions and real-time course chat rooms.

Each course is developed to offer everything students would expect from UCD, but it is online instead of on-campus, so instructors deliver course content and lectures through cutting-edge technologies such as streaming audio, video, Web conferencing, virtual animations, and multimedia slide shows.

Programs of Study

CU Online offers courses in liberal arts and science, arts and media, business, education, engineering, public affairs, and architecture and planning. A variety of degrees and certificates can be obtained exclusively through online courses.

Fully online degree programs include the Bachelor of Arts (B.A.) in English writing; Bachelor of Arts (B.A.) in sociology; the Master of Arts (M.A.) in early childhood education; the Master of Arts (M.A.) in information and learning technologies (ILT), with an emphasis in e-learning design and implementation or in school library; Master of Business Administration (M.B.A.); Master of Engineering (M. Eng.), with an emphasis in geographic information systems; Master of Public Administration (M.P.A.); Master of Science (M.S.) in information systems; and Master of Science (M.S.) in management.

Other online programs include certificates in designing and implementing Web-based learning environments, and early literacy.

Online licensing modules are offered in early childhood special education specialist and special education generalist.

All online courses may be applied to a degree program at UCD or may be transferred to a student's home institution, pending approval.

Credits and degrees earned through CU Online courses are identical to credits and degrees earned through traditional on-campus courses. UCD is a fully accredited institution making credits easily transferable to other universities.

Special Programs

A hybrid course is just like it sounds: half on-campus and half online. Hybrid courses might be what students are looking for if they are taking online courses and enjoy the scheduling flexibility, but feel they are missing out on some of the intangibles of being in a classroom. Hybrid courses meet approximately 50 percent of the normal classroom hours on campus, and the remainder is completed online.

Student Services

An online education wouldn't be complete without support and services dedicated exclusively to online students. To make the online experience more integrated and beneficial, CU Online students can do the following online: search the University catalog, register for courses, buy textbooks, receive guided advising, apply for financial aid, receive tutoring, view academic records, visit the virtual library (which has online journals, books and subject guides), and more. If students ever have problems or issues with their online courses, they can contact the 24/7 support staff.

Credit Options

Credit, noncredit, and continuing and professional education courses are all available. Most online courses are measured by traditional letter grades. Some courses also offer the pass/fail option.

Faculty

The professors and faculty members of traditional classes are the same ones teaching the online courses. Four out of five full-time faculty members hold doctoral degrees and have many years of teaching experience, and most are actively engaged in their fields outside the classroom. Not only do they have real-world experience, but many are consultants, advisers, and partners to the leading organizations that frequently hire CU Online graduates.

Admission

A smooth transition to UCD is a primary goal. Students currently living in the state of Colorado must apply and be admitted as either a degree-seeking or a non-degree-seeking student. Students living outside of Colorado do not need to be admitted to the University to take CU Online courses; however, if they wish to complete their degree through CU Online, they need to apply and be formally admitted to the University.

Tuition and Fees

Tuition rates vary depending on the specific college students are interested in and the students' residency status. For residents, most undergraduate courses cost from $201 to $290 per credit hour. There is also a standard $100 course fee for the online technology and 24-7 customer service—out-of-state students pay $125. However, regardless of how many online courses are taken—one course or four—the fee is still just $100 (or $125 for out-of-state students). Any student that registers strictly for online courses is only responsible for the IT Fee and the Student Information System Fee. All other traditional fees are waved, including the incidental fees associated with driving, mass transit, and parking. Students should visit the CU Online Web site at http://www.cuonline.edu/stu_htm/online_tuition_fees.shtml for current cost information.

Financial Aid

UCD firmly believes that finances should never stand in the way of motivated, talented individuals. As a result, the financial aid programs are strong and well established. To be eligible for financial aid, students must be enrolled as a degree-seeking student at UCD. Students who have any questions or who would like to request further information about financial aid should contact the financial aid office (303-556-2886; finaid@carbon.cudenver.edu).

Applying

Students can apply to the University online at http://www.cuonline.edu/petersons or by paper application. Admission requirements vary by college and school. To find specific information about applying to the University of Colorado Denver, students can visit the CU Online Web site at http://cuonline.edu.

CONTACT

For more information about CU Online, students should contact:

CU Online, Campus Box 198
University of Colorado Denver
P.O. Box 173364
Denver, Colorado 82017-3364
Phone: 303-315-3700
Fax: 303-315-3711
E-mail: help@cuonline.edu
Web site: http://www.cuonline.edu/petersons

UNIVERSITY OF CONNECTICUT
Center for Continuing Studies
Storrs, Connecticut

Founded in 1881, the University of Connecticut (UConn) is categorized by the Carnegie Foundation among the Doctoral/Research Universities–Extensive, a distinction shared by fewer than 4 percent of America's higher education institutions that confer the widest number and range of degrees. UConn is the only public institution in New England with its own Schools of Law, Social Work, Medicine, and Dental Medicine. The University is accredited by the New England Association of Schools and Colleges.

The Center for Continuing Studies (CCS) offers a master's degree that is available online. The Center identifies, develops, and provides high-quality, research-based interdisciplinary, academic, professional, and enrichment programs as well as appropriate support services to diverse communities of learners in a fiscally responsible manner. Working with academic and student support units across the University, the Center for Continuing Studies provides a gateway linking the University with individuals as well as with corporate and public service sectors statewide, nationally, and internationally. CCS is dedicated to engaging learners in a lifelong academic partnership with the University of Connecticut.

Distance Learning Program

Based on educational demand and market research, the Center for Continuing Studies provides a variety of learning opportunities that utilize the most effective and efficient mode of delivery, given the course/program content and the intended learners. Individuals in CCS programs achieve relevant academic, professional, and technical competence and/or the personal enrichment they seek through a student-centered approach that reflects a high-quality education. Students may take individual courses or enroll in one of the online graduate programs. The asynchronous course format allows students to take courses from anywhere in the world. Faculty members are a key component of the online courses and programs and ensure that online students receive a high-quality education and personalized attention.

Delivery Media

All online courses are offered completely through the Internet using WebCT Vista in a paced, asynchronous environment. The asynchronous format allows access to courses seven days a week, 24 hours a day, including holidays. Discussion and interactivity among the students and the instructor are a key component of all of the online courses. Much of this interactivity is accomplished using an asynchronous threaded discussion tool within the course. An e-mail system that is internal to the course is used for private communication. Some assignments have been designed for students working in groups. Online programs offered through the Center for Continuing Studies are geared toward working adults who need the flexibility to juggle work, family, and academic responsibilities. Courses are accessible using either a PC or a Macintosh. Prospective students are encouraged to review the list of frequently asked questions located at http://continuingstudies.uconn. edu/onlinecourses/faqs./index.html.

Programs of Study

The Center for Continuing Studies offers a Master of Professional Studies (M.P.S.) and a Bachelor of General Studies (B.G.S.). The online M.P.S. degree offers three fields of study: homeland security leadership, human resource management and humanitarian services administration. The M.P.S. degree is specifically designed for individuals and practitioners who are developing marketable skills to meet evolving workforce demands, seeking professional development or expanded promotional opportunities, or interested in changing careers. The M.P.S. requires 36 graduate-level credits, including 30 credits of course work and 6 credits of a capstone project toward the end of the program. The M.P.S. also includes an issues-based two-week on-site residency requirement.

The M.P.S. in homeland security leadership is designed to meet the professional development need of individuals who are U.S. citizens and have experience in law enforcement, emergency management, corporate security, transportation security, fire service, public safety, public health preparedness, and the military.

The M.P.S. in human resource management is designed to meet the professional development needs of individuals who are currently working in the field of human resource management or who are interested in pursuing a career in human resource management. Interested individuals who do not have human resource management or supervisory experience are strongly encouraged to participate in an internship, which may be taken for course credit. Students may select a career track in either labor relations or personnel or may select a program combining electives from both tracks, depending upon their career interests.

The M.P.S. in humanitarian services administration is designed to meet the educational needs of individuals involved or interested in humanitarian assistance programs, whether in disaster relief or sustainability programs. Students develop theoretical and professional knowledge to operate and conduct humanitarian response missions with nongovernmental, governmental, and international organizations. Students can choose courses related to disaster relief or sustainability, or they may select courses from both areas, depending on their interests.

The B.G.S. program, established in 1977, is an interdisciplinary major designed for returning adults. Some of the courses may be completed online. A student needs at least 60 college credits or an associate degree from a regionally accredited college to be admitted to the program. B.G.S. students work one on one with the same academic adviser through graduation. The adviser and student work together to develop an academic program that suits the student's educational and career goals through an individualized major. B.G.S. alumnae have been accepted into graduate programs at Yale, Princeton, Columbia, MIT, Berkeley, and William and Mary in such fields as medicine, dentistry, law, ministry, and business.

Students may enroll in a degree program, or they may take individual courses. Online noncredit programs are offered in health-care information technology.

Special Programs

Students can take individual courses as nondegree students, allowing working adults to enroll in University of Connecticut graduate courses and earn academic credit without being formally admitted to a degree program. Nondegree study allows college graduates of all ages to return to college to complete a graduate course at their own pace and gain the confidence they need to complete their education. If students later choose to apply for a degree program, it is likely that these credits can be applied toward their degree. Taking a course as a nondegree student at UConn is also a convenient way for students from other colleges and universities to take credit courses at UConn and then transfer the credits to their own university. Students in the online programs can take on-campus courses. If students are degree students, they need permission from their advisers. Nondegree students do not need to see an adviser before registering.

Student Services

All major student services are available to online students, including registration services, advising, bookstore ordering, library, e-mail, and tutoring. Technical support is available to all students in online courses.

Credit Options

Students in the B.G.S. program may transfer up to 90 credits that they have earned through other regionally accredited institutions.

Faculty

The Center for Continuing Studies employs full-time and adjunct faculty members. Faculty members who teach online are approved by the department and also teach on-campus courses. All full-time faculty members and all faculty members teaching in the graduate program have earned doctorates. Adjunct faculty members are accomplished practitioners and have the requisite educational experience to make them effective online instructors.

Admission

Applicants to the M.P.S. program must have completed a baccalaureate degree from a regionally accredited college or university. For further admission information for the M.P.S. program, students should visit http://continuingstudies. uconn.edu/mps/academicinfo.html. Applicants to the B.G.S. degree must have an associate degree from a regionally accredited college or university or must have completed at least 60 college credits from a regionally accredited college or university. For further admission information for the B.G.S. program, students should visit http://continuingstudies. uconn.edu/bgs/admissions.html. Students may register for individual courses without matriculating into a program, provided they meet specific course requirements. For course registration information, students should visit http:// continuingstudies.uconn.edu/overview/ register.html.

Tuition and Fees

Undergraduate course fees are $1086 per 3-credit course. Graduate course fees are $1668 per 3-credit course. There is a $48 infrastructure maintenance fee for undergraduate and graduate courses. Course fees are calculated on a per-credit basis; current fees are subject to change. Students who enroll in the center's online courses pay the same fees as in-state students. Students should visit the Web site for current fees.

Financial Aid

Financial aid is available to online students who have matriculated into a degree program. For further information, students should contact the Office of Student Financial Aid Services at 860-486-2819 or visit the Web site at http://www. financialaid.uconn.edu.

Applying

Application to the M.P.S. degree program is available online at http://continuingstudies.uconn.edu/mps/academicinfo. html. Application to the B.G.S. degree program is available online at https:// continuing studies.uconn.edu/bgs/admissions.html.

CONTACT

Dr. Judy Buffolino, Director
Distance Education Office
Center for Continuing Studies
University of Connecticut
One Bishop Circle, Unit 4056
Storrs, Connecticut 06269-4056

Phone: 860-486-1080
Fax: 860-486-0756
E-mail: ccsonline@uconn.edu
Web site: http://continuingstudies.
    uconn.edu/onli-
    necourses

UNIVERSITY OF DALLAS

Graduate School of Management
Center for Distance Learning

Irving, Texas

The University of Dallas' Graduate School of Management (GSM) is a professional school whose primary purpose is to prepare its students to become competent, ethical practitioners in the profession of management. GSM's academic programs do not emphasize theoretical courses; instead, they offer highly pragmatic programs, both on campus and online, that focus on the practical realities of managerial life and success.

The Harvard Business Review *recently published an article about how business schools have lost their way by hiring professors who are qualified to teach but have never engaged in the actual practice of running a business. The Graduate School of Management at the University of Dallas was one of only four business schools that the article cited in a favorable light. Its professors are scholar-practitioners, which means they have done what they teach, so they bring practical, real-world experiences to the classroom. Online courses are taught by the same professors who teach the on-campus courses. Students get the benefit of faculty experience along with the flexibility of completing any core course or concentration online or combining online courses with on-campus courses to complete degree requirements.*

The University of Dallas was founded in 1956 as an independent Catholic university dedicated to excellence in its educational programs. The Graduate School of Management is the largest M.B.A. program in the Southwest. GSM was founded in 1966 with a distinctive mission—to create an M.B.A. program for working professionals; more than 80 percent of GSM students work full-time. With a comprehensive online campus and three on-ground campuses in the Dallas–Fort Worth area, the program is designed to meet the needs of busy professionals. The program attracts students from all over the world.

The Graduate School of Management is accredited by the Commission on Colleges of the Southern Association of Colleges and Schools (SACS), the International Assembly for Collegiate Business Education (IACBE), and the Association of Collegiate Business Schools and Programs (ACBSP).

Distance Learning Program

GSM began its online campus in 1997 with three courses and 30 students. Today, GSM offers the entire M.B.A. core curriculum and thirteen concentrations completely online. The online campus is ideal for students who live outside of the Dallas–Fort Worth area, travel frequently for business, or prefer the convenience of taking classes online.

There are three areas that distinguish GSM from more traditional management schools. (1) GSM faculty members have professional experience in the area in which they teach. Each professor has extensive business experience, engages regularly in consulting projects, and is an active member of their respective professional organizations. (2) Curriculum is based on real-world situations and issues. Students receive pertinent instruction and projects designed to prepare them to be leaders in today's dynamic, global business environment. (3) Students participate in consulting and applied research projects. Through the Capstone Experience, students conduct full-scale projects by applying what they have learned to help actual organizations solve real-world business issues. Unlike other business schools, GSM's Capstone Experience is required for all students in the M.B.A. and M.M. programs. Capstone consulting teams have completed classroom-based projects for more than 600 clients in the past thirty years.

Because the online courses are taught by the same professors and follow the same curriculum, there is no distinction made on the transcript between classroom and online courses. Whether a student's ambition is to earn an M.B.A. or enhance knowledge and skills in a specialized area, GSM helps design and complete a program specifically tailored to fit each student's lifestyle and goals.

Delivery Media

The virtual campus was created with the understanding that students need the ability to organize their class schedules without being confined to a certain time, campus, or even country. Students access the online campus using a standard Internet connection and Web browser. The courses use an instructor-led, asynchronous method of teaching, which means that students and their professors do not have to be online at the same time. This allows flexibility for those students who travel or have other obligations. Classes fit into everyday life. However, both professors and students are expected to be online multiple times during the weekly sessions.

For additional information on the online campus, students should visit http://www.thedallasmba.com/imba.cfm.

Programs of Study

The University of Dallas offers Master of Business Administration (M.B.A.), Master of Science (M.S.), Master of Management (M.M.), and Graduate Certificate programs.

The M.B.A. is a 41-credit-hour program (depending on previous course work, students may be responsible for satisfying additional requirements) that provides a management education covering both the functional areas of business and critical knowledge and skills required of managers.

The curriculum is divided into three components: the value creation core, 17 credit hours (eight courses); concentration/electives, 15 credit hours (five courses); and the integrative core, 9 credit hours (three courses).

Students may select from one of the twenty-one M.B.A. concentrations, with ten available fully online: corporate finance, health services management, information assurance, information technology, interdisciplinary (custom curriculum), marketing management, not-for-profit management, project management, sports and entertainment management, and supply chain management.

On GSM's twelve-week trimester system, most full-time M.B.A. students can complete their degree requirements in less than two years; part-time students typically complete their degree in 2½ to 3 years. For more details, students should visit http://www.udallas.edu/gsm/academics/overview.cfm.

The Master of Science is a 31-credit-hour program (depending on previous course work, students may be responsible for satisfying additional requirements) designed for students who seek in-depth practical and technical knowledge in a specific field. For more information, students should visit http://www.udallas.edu/gsm/academics/overview.cfm.

The Graduate School of Management also offers an M.S./M.B.A. dual degree (http://www.udallas.edu/gsm/msmba.cfm).

The Master of Management is a 30-credit-hour program that provides profession-specific education to those who already hold an M.B.A. from a regionally accredited U.S. college or university or a comparable international degree. Students can select from six concentrations available fully online (http://www.udallas.edu/gsm/academics/overview.cfm).

The Graduate Certificate program is a 15- to 18-credit-hour program (depending on previous course work, students may be responsible for satisfying additional requirements) for individuals looking to acquire specialized knowledge without completing a graduate degree. Each Graduate Certificate consists of five or six graduate-level courses, with seven concentration areas available fully online (http://www.udallas.edu/gsm/academics/overview.cfm).

Special Programs
GSM has partnerships with Fortune 500 corporations to provide classes to their employees through the online campus. Inquiries are welcomed from other organizations that may be interested in offering graduate business studies to their employees.

Student Services
Student services at the Graduate School of Management are tailored to provide support and service for prospective, current, and past students. Admission Executives are assigned to each concentration area and help answer students' questions, address unique concerns, and guide them through the application, admissions, and registration process. Students are assigned an adviser, who assists them in selecting classes and helps answer questions.

Staff members in the Online Learning Department are available to address questions unique to distance learning. A help desk that operates 24 hours a day handles Web- and PC-based questions.

Credit Options
The M.B.A. Degree Completion Program allows a student who has already started M.B.A. course work in another accredited program to complete the requirements for an M.B.A. through the Graduate School of Management. This program allows for a larger number of transfer credits (up to 18 credit hours) to qualified applicants. M.B.A. Degree Completion students at the University of Dallas are required to complete at least 50 percent plus 1 credit hour through the GSM program. In addition, the student must have successfully completed at least five 3-credit-hour courses in their previous M.B.A. program.

Faculty
GSM professors who teach the on-campus courses also teach the online courses, ensuring the same level of relevance and rigor while providing students with the convenience and choice they need to complete their degree. All GSM professors are scholar-practitioners with real-world experience in their area of teaching expertise and ongoing involvement in their field.

The professors have business experience in addition to their academic qualifications. They have held positions ranging from entrepreneur to senior-level executive in large companies. Full-time faculty members engage in consulting within their field, while adjunct professors hold jobs in their area of teaching, thus keeping the classes current and relevant.

Admission
Admission to the Dallas M.B.A. program is competitive. The program seeks highly motivated individuals demonstrating potential for management and leadership responsibility and possessing the intellectual ability, initiative, and creativity to excel in its programs as well as in the globally competitive marketplace.

Success in the M.B.A. program depends on a number of factors ranging from motivation to practical knowledge to academic ability. The primary purpose of the School's admission criteria and application process is to determine a prospective student's potential to successfully complete the requirements for the M.B.A. degree.

Although an undergraduate degree is a prerequisite, no specific undergraduate major or concentration is required to pursue the Dallas M.B.A. program in any concentration.

Because the Graduate School of Management enrolls full-time, part-time, and international students, a variety of paths are available to students seeking admission.

Prospective students may apply for admission to the Graduate School of Management; for more information, students should visit http://www.udallas.edu/gsm/admissions/index.cfm.

Tuition and Fees
Graduate tuition is $541 per credit hour for the 2008–09 academic year for residents and nonresidents.

Financial Aid
U.S. graduate students may obtain financial assistance through various loan programs. The University's Financial Aid Office (telephone: 972-721-5266; Web site: http://www.udallas.edu/gsm/fa/index.cfm) has information and application forms for loans.

Applying
Those interested are encouraged to contact GSM at the address in the Contact section or visit the Web site for additional information. Students can apply online from anywhere in the world.

CONTACT

Office of Admissions
Graduate School of Management
University of Dallas
1845 East Northgate Drive
Irving, Texas 75062-4799
Phone: 972-721-5174
          800-832-5622 (toll-free)
E-mail: admiss@gsm.udallas.edu
Web site:
    http://www.thedallasmba.com

UNIVERSITY OF DENVER

University College
Denver, Colorado

The University of Denver (DU), the oldest independent university in the Rocky Mountain region, is a premier liberal arts university founded in 1864. In addition to its rich history, DU is known for its research and high-quality teaching. To augment the traditional undergraduate and graduate programs, this outstanding institution offers innovative graduate programs through its division for professional and continuing studies—University College. University College was founded in 1983. With more than forty national awards and many other distinctions from its peers, University College of the University of Denver is recognized as one of the very best providers of adult education in the nation. University College offered its first online master's degree program in 1996. Today, it offers master's degrees in ten different areas, more than thirty Certificates of Advanced Study, and numerous individual courses in a variety of subject areas. In fall 2006, University College added a Bachelor of Arts Completion Program for students who have started their bachelor's degree, but for some reason have not finished. University College is accredited by the North Central Association of Colleges and Schools.

Distance Learning Program

The University College distance learning program provides the same premier, internationally recognized University of Denver program quality to students who, because of geographic location, work schedule, or personal commitments, would otherwise not have the opportunity to attend DU. The learning experience for the distance student goes beyond the traditional classroom by capitalizing on the advantages of distance learning technology. University College provides an anytime, anywhere support service as well as consistent high-quality instruction. University College has more than 600 students actively taking courses online from a wide list of states and countries.

Delivery Media

All of the University College distance learning bachelor's degrees, master's degrees, and Certificates of Advanced Study can be taken entirely online. A wide array of learning techniques is used to help students develop their knowledge, understanding, and problem-solving skills. University College has an entire team dedicated to utilizing emerging technologies and understanding individualized learning styles to enhance the educational experience. University College uses eCollege® as its courseware management tool. The system is interactive, allows students to work collaboratively in

lively discussion boards and chat rooms, and promotes the exchange of ideas and the development of a learning community. This interaction includes extensive communication with faculty members over the Internet, virtual teams, individual and group assignments, online projects, and online papers and connects students to experts from around the world.

Programs of Study

The University College online programs offer master's degrees in twelve different program areas and more than thirty graduate Certificates of Advanced Study. There are no on-campus requirements for any of the distance learning programs. The on-campus and online master's degree programs require 48 credit hours of study to be completed in five years or less. Typically, a program can be completed in less than two years. Certificates are 24 quarter credit hours and typically take twelve to eighteen months to complete. A bachelor's degree is required for a certificate, and certificate course credits may be applied toward a master's degree.

Professionals with at least one year of transferable undergraduate credits can now complete their degrees online and earn a Bachelor of Arts in communication arts, global studies, leadership and organization studies, public policy and social services, or science and technology in a program

that provides a dynamic new experience. Designed with the input of business and civic leaders, the program focuses on developing the talents needed for success in the information age: effective communication, problem solving, creative thinking, multi-tasking, decision making, technology utilization, and teamwork. These talents are approached from an interdisciplinary perspective, providing the most balanced and well-rounded experience possible.

The Applied Communication master's degree program is designed to teach the real-time and practical knowledge and skills that provide the specific industry expertise required for career success in a wide range of communication professions. The program's curriculum emphasizes a balance of theory, principles, and practice combined with professional experience to generate focused outcomes that are not offered in generic communication degree programs. Concentrations are available online in alternative dispute resolution, public relations and marketing, and training and development.

The Computer Information Systems program is designed for computer professionals as well as for those planning a new career in the computer industry. This flexible program keeps current with today's changing technology and how it relates to new technologies, existing systems, and customers' needs. In addition to the master's degree program, five online certificate programs of advanced study are offered: computer information systems, database administration, distributed object-oriented analysis and design, information systems security, and Web design and development technologies.

The Environmental Policy and Management program provides a seamlessly blended graduate education that emphasizes ethical management, science-based environmental policies, and professional applications of technical knowledge. Six certificate programs of advanced study are offered in environmental, health, and safety management; environmental information management; environmental management;

environmental policy; environmental project management; and natural resource management.

The Geographic Information Systems (GIS) program provides great job opportunities for those interested in managing physical facilities, providing services, analyzing markets, and managing information in public agencies or private organizations. The master's degree, designed in conjunction with DU's Department of Geography, allows students in the University College GIS certificate program to transfer up to 24 quarter hours from their certificate. The certificate program, also designed in conjunction with the DU's Department of Geography, offers working professionals the opportunity to acquire the background information and hands-on-expertise necessary to capitalize on the emerging technology.

The Human Resource Administration program offers a Master of Professional Studies (M.P.S.) in human resource administration. It provides a comprehensive examination of the HR profession and positions graduates for career advancement in a variety of organizational settings that include business, government, and not-for-profit organizations.

University of Denver University College, in collaboration with the Library and Information Science Program in the College of Education, now offers the Master's of Applied Science in knowledge and information technologies. This program is the first of its kind in the Rocky Mountain region. An engaging learning environment filled with professionals who value their educational experience ensures the development of effective critical and creative thinking, strategic and tactical decision making, and global awareness. Degree tracks are available in computer information systems, geographic information systems, and technology management.

The Organizational Leadership program is a flexible management and leadership degree presenting both the analytic and interpersonal skills necessary to be an effective manager in a variety of enterprises. The degree is structured around a core of management and leadership courses. Students select from a wide range of specializations, such as project management, leadership, alternative dispute resolution, environmental policy and management, telecommunications, computer information systems, and others. Most of the concentrations offered in other University College degrees are potential concentrations in the M.P.S.

The Security Management degree is designed for business and organizational security management professionals. The program provides students with the latest skills for effectively leading and managing security operations and addressing personnel, property, facility, information, and business-continuity security. The program provides the management skills and technical knowledge required to function as a chief security officer, director of loss prevention, director of security, security consultant, investigator, firefighter, or police officer.

The Technology Management program is designed for those who understand the power of leveraging technology in business to create their own competitive advantage. Career opportunities are limitless for those who can create, manage, and use emerging technology. In addition, five certificate programs of advanced study are offered in international markets, leadership, project management, research and development management, and twenty-first century strategic management.

The Telecommunications program fosters an integration of telecommunications technologies and effective management. In an industry driven by new technology, new applications, and an increasing demand for services, professionals need to maintain a current understanding of fundamental issues surrounding those technologies and the regulations which govern them. The telecommunications offerings at University College are designed to help students keep abreast of changes and take advantage of the opportunities change offers. Certificate programs of advanced study are offered in four areas: broadband, telecommunications management and policy, telecommunications technology, and wireless networks.

Student Services
University College is dedicated to providing complete student services online. This includes admissions, registration, student advising, online resources through the library, access to the bookstore, and an individualized career counselor. There is a complete support team for technical issues as well as student support and training for eCollege.

Credit Options
Students may be able to transfer credit earned at other accredited graduate colleges and universities. The credit hours for the certificates may apply toward the related master's degree.

Faculty
University College has 300 faculty members, all with advanced degrees, who are practicing professionals in the areas in which they teach. At any given time there are 20 to 30 faculty members teaching online. University College engages in advanced and continual training for its faculty members in the methods and application of distance learning.

Admission
Entrance examinations are not required. Students who are applying for admission to the master's degree programs must have a bachelor's degree from a regionally accredited institution and a minimum 3.0 undergraduate GPA. Applicants must also submit an essay, a career goal statement, and letters of recommendation.

Tuition and Fees
Tuition is $380 per credit hour for on-campus classes and $417 per credit hour for online classes. There is also a technology fee of $4 per credit hour.

Financial Aid
Some financial aid programs are available to assist University College students. The University of Denver's Office of Student Financial Services handles all financial aid applications (http://www.du.edu/sfs/).

Applying
To apply for admission to University College, students must complete a full application, including a degree plan. Registration is available on the University College Web site at http://www.universitycollege. du.edu/registernow/registerinstructions. asp# online. For more information or an application, students should visit the University College Web site.

CONTACT
Enrollment Manager
University College
University of Denver
2211 South Josephine
Denver, Colorado 80208

Phone: 303-871-3315
          800-347-2042 (toll-free)
Fax: 303-871-3070
E-mail: ucolinfo@du.edu
Web site: http://www.university
          college.du.edu

UF | UNIVERSITY of FLORIDA **UNIVERSITY OF FLORIDA**

College of Engineering UF EDGE (Electronic Delivery of Graduate Engineering)

Gainesville, Florida

The University of Florida (UF) is a major, public, comprehensive, land-grant, research university. Founded in 1853, it is the state's oldest, largest, and most comprehensive university, and it is among the nation's most academically diverse public universities. With more than 48,000 students, Florida is now the fourth-largest university in the nation. Florida has a 2,000-acre campus and more than 900 buildings (including 170 with classrooms and laboratories). The northeast corner of the campus is listed as a Historic District on the National Register of Historic Places.

UF is accredited by the Southern Association of Colleges and Schools (SACS; 1866 Southern Lane, Decatur, Georgia 30033-4097; telephone: 404-679-4501), and the College of Engineering is accredited by ABET.

Distance Learning Program

The College of Engineering distance learning program, the UF EDGE, serves more than 250 graduate students. UF EDGE programs have been delivered to practicing engineers in Florida and throughout the world since 1982. Master of Science degrees are offered via streaming video. No campus attendance is required to complete the degree programs.

Delivery Media

Distance learning students are enrolled in classes that are given on the UF campus. The lectures are recorded and are available via streaming video at the close of business on that same day at the course's WebCT Vista course site. Distance learning students interact with their professors via phone, fax, e-mail, or the Internet. Professors also make course materials available to their students via course Web sites.

Programs of Study

The College of Engineering offers the following Master of Science (M.S.) degree programs via distance learning: civil engineering; computer engineering/computer science; computer engineering/computer science, with a bioinfor-

matics track; electrical and computer engineering, with a communications track; environmental engineering, with a specialization in water resources planning and management; environmental engineering, with a specialization in water, wastewater, and stormwater engineering; environmental engineering, with a specialization in systems ecology and ecological engineering; mechanical and aerospace engineering, with a specialization in fundamentals of thermal fluids transport; mechanical and aerospace engineering, with a specialization in solid mechanics; mechanical and aerospace engineering, with a specialization in dynamics and control; and material science engineering. The Master of Science degree requires 30 semester credit hours for completion, with a minimum 3.0 grade point average on a 4.0 scale. Distance learning students may meet the credit requirement entirely by course work.

Special Programs

The College of Engineering offers graduate certificate programs in the areas of environmental policy and management. Each certificate program requires the completion of three to five 3-semester-hour courses. The curricu-

lum consists of required courses and two or more electives chosen from a specified list.

Student Services

Library service is provided via remote access to all internal holdings and to several electronic databases through http://www.uflib.ufl.edu. Access is provided to currently registered students via a personal identification number and password for certain restricted databases.

Academic advising is provided through e-mail, fax, and telephone contact on a request basis. Distance learning students are also eligible to use the University's career placement services.

Credit Options

Students earn credit toward their degree by registering for and completing courses delivered via distance learning. Requirements for each course are the same as for on-campus students enrolled in the course.

Only graduate-level work to the extent of 9 semester credits, earned with a grade of A, B+, or B, may be transferred from an institution approved by the Graduate School or 15 semester credits from postbaccalaureate work at the University of Florida. Credits transferred from other universities are applied toward meeting the degree requirement, but the grades earned are not computed in the student's grade point average. Acceptance of transfer of credit requires approval from the student's department and the Dean of the Graduate School.

Faculty

There are 2,685 full-time faculty members at the University, with 319 in the College of Engineering. In the College of Engineering, 126 faculty members (39 percent) have taught in the distance learning program.

Admission

Admission decisions are made by the individual departments based on GRE or Fundamentals of Engineering (FE) score, GPA, and letters of reference.

Tuition and Fees

Tuition and fees for the 2007–08 academic year were $368 per credit hour for in-state students and $600 per credit hour for out-of-state students. Costs are subject to change each year. Students must purchase their own textbooks.

Financial Aid

As a general rule, a graduate student must be enrolled half-time (at least 5 semester hours per term) as a regular student in a degree program and must be a United States citizen or an eligible non-U.S. citizen to qualify for federal and/or state financial aid. Specific information is available through the Office of Student Financial Affairs. Although students may apply for Federal Direct Stafford/Ford Loans throughout the year, they must observe the deadlines set each semester for applying for loans for the following semester and should always apply as early as possible. Many employers have programs that can help students pay for courses.

Applying

Application materials can be obtained from the school to which the student is applying. For specific program information, prospective students should visit http://www.admissions.ufl.edu/grad/gradegreeprograms.html#engineering. Application information is available online through http://www.admissions.ufl.edu/start.html. Official transcripts are required from all colleges or universities attended. Admission decisions are made by the individual departments.

CONTACT

UF EDGE Registrar
College of Engineering
E-117, CSE
University of Florida
P.O. Box 116100
Gainesville, Florida 32611-6100

Phone: 352-392-9670
E-mail: ufedge@ufl.edu
Web site: http://ufedge.eng.ufl.edu

UNIVERSITY OF HOUSTON-VICTORIA

School of Business Administration

Victoria, Texas

The University of Houston-Victoria (UH-Victoria) is an upper-level institution that offers more than thirty undergraduate and graduate degree programs and concentrations to citizens in the Coastal Bend region. For three decades, UH-Victoria has proudly served the higher-education needs of the region through the School of Arts and Sciences, the School of Business Administration (SoBA), and the School of Education. UH-Victoria and the UH System Centers in Sugar Land and Cinco Ranch (Katy) are home to an outstanding faculty and staff, whose members serve to enhance students' studies and University experience. The University emphasizes student learning, related research, responsiveness to student needs, and collaboration in the development and delivery of academic programs.

Distance Learning Program

SoBA is accredited by AACSB International–The Association to Advance Collegiate Schools of Business. An integrated curriculum blends theoretical concepts with practical applications to ensure that students receive the knowledge and skills to successfully manage organizations in a dynamic environment. SoBA primarily serves nontraditional, working professional students. Online programs serve the fastest-growing segment of SoBA's student population. Online courses are taught by the same faculty members who teach face-to-face courses, with the same textbooks and comparable syllabi. Success in these programs requires scholastic aptitude, strong written English and reading comprehension, and the maturity and discipline to keep up with assignments. All online students are required to participate in asynchronous online discussions at least weekly so that students may benefit from this interaction with other students and the instructor. Course syllabi communicate specific discussion board requirements. All courses are entirely online, with the exception of the M.B.A. Conference for students enrolled in the Strategic M.B.A. program. There is no residency requirement.

Delivery Media

All courses are delivered via WebCT Vista, a course management and communications application. This online collabora-tion tool allows students and faculty members to easily maintain contact and share information across time zones. WebCT allows students to send e-mail, post and read messages from other students and instructors on the course bulletin board, chat with others, access course syllabi and read lecture notes and lessons, take quizzes online, and post group projects.

Programs of Study

For undergraduates, SoBA offers the Bachelor of Business Administration (B.B.A.) online in general business, health-care administration, management, and marketing. The B.B.A. prepares students for entry-level and professional positions in business. Program graduates comprehend the business environment and functions, demonstrate effective communication skills, demonstrate computer usage skills, employ ethical principles in all business situations, and demonstrate the ability to work effectively on teams in diverse organizations.

UH-Victoria is a leader in online course delivery and offers graduate students the Strategic M.B.A., the Global M.B.A., and the Master of Science (M.S.) in Economic Development and Entrepreneurship. Offered online, each program has flexible scheduling and accommodates complex personal and professional commitments.

The programs include real-world applied learning, case studies, and team projects. Specifically, the programs seek to develop a student's capacity to understand and adapt to the changing business, political, and social environments; evaluate and respond to emerging threats and opportunities; interact with and effectively lead diverse groups; analyze and evaluate business operations and processes; and synthesize and apply cross-functional approaches to organizational issues.

The Strategic M.B.A., designed for current and future managers, is a cross-disciplinary program focusing on strategy and leadership. The strategic-planning model/process is integrated throughout the program, which features a cross-disciplinary approach to complex business problems. This 48-hour program, comprising twelve required core courses and four elective courses, can be completed part-time in under three years or full-time in eighteen months. A concentration, made up of the 12 credit hours of electives, can be in accounting, finance, general business, international business, management, or marketing. With the exception of the one-day M.B.A. Conference, all courses are offered completely online. During the conference, held in the Houston area, students participate in a team-case competition as part of the Seminar in Strategic Management course.

The Global M.B.A. program is management-based, relevant, and highly integrated. Designed for current and future members of the international business community, it provides students with the knowledge and skills needed to function as managers in the global marketplace. Students from around the world connect with one another as they learn to solve company-wide problems that transcend national borders. The program requires 30 to 54 credit hours of work beyond the bachelor's—recent B.B.A. graduates may qualify for waivers of up to 24 credit hours based on evaluation—and provides concentrations in either finance or management. Full-time students can complete the program in two years; part-time students usually take three years.

The M.S. in Economic Development and Entrepreneurship, the only program of its kind, combines training in traditional economic development (attracting businesses) with entrepreneurship (starting businesses). Designed for economic development professionals and current and/or future owners of small businesses, the program focuses on starting, growing, and attracting new businesses. Its 36-credit-hour curriculum that includes two elective courses, can be completed part-time in two years.

Special Programs

Through the Office of International Programs and Special Projects, study-abroad programs are available in the United Kingdom, Mexico, Spain, and the Czech Republic, among other countries.

Student Services

Professional staff members are available by phone and e-mail to help online students with technical questions. Services for on-campus students, such as advising and use of the library, are also offered to online students.

Credit Options

Students who have completed a B.B.A. degree in the last five years may qualify for up to 24 credit hours of foundation course waivers. Transfer credits are accepted. Students can check online at http://www.uhv.edu/bus/admission/transfer.asp for details.

Faculty

The faculty ensures that graduates possess the knowledge and skills necessary for successful careers in business and society, fostering intellectual contributions that emphasize the application of knowledge to improve management practices. UH-Victoria has 154 faculty members, 53 percent of whom are full-time. The student-to-faculty ratio is 16:1.

Admission

To be eligible for unconditional undergraduate admission to UH–Victoria, a student must have earned a minimum of 54 semester hours in nonremedial college-level course work from an accredited institution.

Applicants to the M.B.A. and M.S. programs must have at least a four-year bachelor's degree in any field, with a minimum GPA of 2.5 (cumulative or last 60 hours, whichever is higher) and a GMAT score of at least 450 (verbal and quantitative scores combined). Students who do not meet the GMAT requirement may be eligible for temporary or conditional admission and may take up to 12 credit hours of courses. Under certain circumstances, conditional admission may be granted without the GMAT to applicants who have an undergraduate GPA of 3.0 or higher and at least two years of relevant professional and/or management/supervisory experience. Conditional admission is subject to earning a B or better in the QMS6351 and MGT6351 courses.

In addition, international students must have a minimum TOEFL score of 550 (213 on the computer-based test, 79 on the Internet-based test) and are not eligible for conditional admission.

Fourth-Year Bridge Strategic M.B.A. and Global M.B.A. programs are available for students who have earned the equiva-

lent of a three-year bachelor's degree from an accredited university with a minimum GPA of 2.5 and have a GMAT score of 450 or higher. Temporary graduate student admission is not available to Fourth-Year Bridge students.

Tuition and Fees

The bachelor's programs were $10,252 a year for Texas residents and $27,210 a year for nonresidents. The 2007–08 graduate tuition for residents was $194 per semester credit hour, while nonresidents paid $409.50 per semester credit hour. In addition to tuition, all graduate students paid $101.50 per semester credit hour in additional fees. Fees for 2008–09 are not yet available.

Financial Aid

Students may apply for financial aid in the form of grants, scholarships, and loans. Students are notified of any award or missing documents through "Awards by Web," which sends notices to the student's University e-mail address. There are limited opportunities for graduate assistantship positions within SoBA.

Applying

Applications are submitted online at http://www.uhv.edu. Supporting materials should be submitted to the Office of Admissions, University of Houston–Victoria, 3007 North Ben Wilson Street, Victoria, Texas 77901. There is no application fee. With the exception of international student admissions, there are no specific deadlines for applications for admission; however, credentials should be received as early as possible to ensure time for processing before registration. For international students, the admission deadline is eight weeks prior to the first day of class.

CONTACT

Jifu Wang, Ph.D., Interim Dean
School of Business Administration
University of Houston–Victoria
3007 North Ben Wilson Street
Victoria, Texas 77901

Phone: 800-687-4293 (toll-free)
Fax: 361-570-4229
E-mail: busadvisor@uhv.edu
Web site: http://www.uhv.edu/bus/future.asp

UNIVERSITY OF MARYLAND, COLLEGE PARK

Online Studies

College Park, Maryland

The University of Maryland is the flagship institution among the University System of Maryland's eleven state public colleges and universities. Founded in 1856 as the original land-grant institution in Maryland, the University is the top public research institution in the mid-Atlantic region and one of the nation's best. Sixty-nine of its programs are ranked in the top twenty-five in the country, with fifty Maryland programs ranked in the top fifteen. The University of Maryland is accredited by the Middle States Association of Colleges and Schools and is a member of the Association of American Universities.

In 2000, the University of Maryland Office of Professional Studies introduced a University-wide online-learning strategy and launched its first program: Master of Life Sciences. The Web-based Master of Life Sciences is a content-rich, interdisciplinary program, with options in biology and chemistry, that focuses on the most current issues in modern science. Designed to enable practicing teachers to conveniently pursue an advanced degree, the program has attracted students worldwide. In 2007, the University launched an online Graduate Certificate in Food Safety Risk Analysis, one of a few food science programs in the country to include risk analysis in the curriculum.

Distance Learning Program

The University of Maryland is dedicated to increasing the visibility and reputation of its high-quality professional and graduate programs, measured not only by advances in research but also by innovations in the delivery of programs to a worldwide audience. The University's online studies program provides the platform for conveniently delivering educational solutions to students anywhere, at any time.

Delivery Media

Courses are delivered asynchronously through the Internet using a range of technologies, including chat rooms, threaded discussions, and links to campus libraries and academic resources. Faculty members are available in person, through e-mail, and by prescribed phone appointments.

Programs of Study

Online Studies at the University of Maryland offers three completely Web-based graduate programs: a 30-credit Master of Life Sciences, a 12-credit Graduate Certificate in Food Safety Risk Analysis, and a 12-credit Graduate Certificate in Public Health Informatics.

Master of Life Sciences. The Master of Life Sciences provides in-depth knowledge of current research areas in the chemical, biological, biochemical, and biomedical sciences. Courses cover modern biology, chemistry, modern molecular genetics, transmission genetics, human physiology, biodiversity and conservation biology, chemical ecology, principles of chemical biology, biochemistry, natural products chemistry, electrochemical cells, evolutionary biology and behavior, and experimental biology. Students may follow concentrations in chemistry or biology.

Graduate Certificate in Food Safety Risk Analysis. While risk analysis has been used for hundreds of years in the insurance industry and engineering fields, its application to food production and distribution is a recent phenomenon. In the past decade, federal agencies responsible for food safety have adopted risk analysis as the official

science-based paradigm for decision making. However, few food science academic programs include risk analysis in their curricula. The new professional studies Graduate Certificate in Food Safety Risk Analysis from the University of Maryland is one of the few such programs in the United States.

Offered by the University of Maryland's Office of Professional Studies, in conjunction with the Department of Nutrition and Food Science and the Joint Institute for Food Safety and Applied Nutrition (JIFSAN), the graduate certificate can be completed entirely online in only one year. Through a series of four 10-week online courses, students will be instructed in the three basic components of risk analysis: risk management and risk communication.

Graduate Certificate in Public Health Informatics. The Graduate Certificate in Public Health Informatics offers online, graduate-level courses in applied health informatics. The curriculum supports the emerging international movement toward evidence-based approaches to health information management, including evaluation and integration of health information systems for health data collection, analysis, and presentation. It familiarizes students with the most recent technologies and computer applications in public health education and practice. The course work provides students with a thorough understanding of the theory and practice of health informatics in the real world. Additionally, students are required to demonstrate the ability to use scientific and population health principles to evaluate and implement health information systems for their organizations. They learn how to use qualitative and quantitative methods for conducting health surveillance activities and enhancing public health preparedness, as well as use computer models to measure and present health outcomes. There is no research component required and the courses can be completed entirely online in 10 weeks. This intensive program has been approved to award continuing education contact hours (CECHs) to meet requirements for health educators who are certified health education specialists through the Society for Public Health Education (SOPHE). The credits earned may also meet the degree requirements for the M.P.H. and Ph.D. degrees.

Student Services

Through Single Point of Contact (SPOC), listed in the Contact section, students may inquire about the programs, apply for admission, register, pay their bills, and purchase textbooks. Students also have access to equipment and software specifications needed for successful completion of course work, online library resources, and technical support.

Faculty

The Master of Life Sciences program has 11 full-time University of Maryland faculty members with doctoral degrees. The Graduate Certificate in Food Safety

Risk Analysis and the Graduate Certificate in Public Health Informatics programs are taught by faculty members with outstanding teaching and research credentials.

Admission

The Master of Life Sciences program requires an undergraduate degree in biological science, chemistry, biochemistry, or science education; one year of teaching experience or the equivalent; letters of recommendation from a school principal and a science supervisor; and successful completion of a gateway review class, LFSC510 Concepts of Modern Biology or LFSC520 Concepts of Modern Chemistry, or acceptable performance on an admission exam based on LFSC510 or LFSC520.

The Graduate Certificate In Food Safety Risk Analysis requires an earned bachelor's degree with a GPA of 3.0 or better from an accredited institution. Applicants with an undergraduate GPA of less than 3.0 may be admitted on a provisional basis if they have demonstrated satisfactory performance in another graduate program and/or salutary work experience.

The Graduate Certificate In Public Health Informatics is open to qualified applicants with an earned bachelor's

degree, GPA of 3.0 or better, from an accredited institution. Applicants with foreign credentials must submit academic records in the original language with literal English translations. Allow at least three months for evaluation. TOEFL scores are required for all international applicants.

Tuition and Fees

The Master of Life Sciences program costs $379 per credit hour, and there are a $60-per-term technology/distance learning fee and an admission exam fee of $20.

The Graduate Certificate in Food Safety Risk Analysis program costs $600 per credit hour, and there is a $60-per-term technology/distance learning fee.

The Graduate Certificate Public Health Informatics program costs $425 per credit hour. There is a $60-per-term technology/distance learning fee.

All tuition and fees are subject to change. All graduate students pay a one-time $60 application fee.

Financial Aid

Information regarding financial assistance may be obtained online at http://www.onlinestudies.umd.edu/financialaid.html.

CONTACT

Single Point of Contact (SPOC)
Mitchell Building, First Floor
University of Maryland
College Park, Maryland 20742-5231

Phone: 301-314-3572
        877-989-SPOC (toll-free)
Fax: 301-314-1282
E-mail: onlinestudies@umd.edu
Web site: http://www.onlinestudies.umd.edu

UNIVERSITY OF MINNESOTA, TWIN CITIES CAMPUS

Independent and Distance Learning, College of Continuing Education

Saint Paul, Minnesota

The University of Minnesota, with its four campuses, is one of the most comprehensive universities in the United States and ranks among the most prestigious. It is both a land-grant university with a strong tradition of education and public service and a major research institution. It was founded as a preparatory school in 1851 and was reorganized as a university in 1869, benefiting from the Morrill (or Land-Grant) Act of 1862.

The University of Minnesota has campuses in the Twin Cities (Minneapolis and St. Paul), Duluth, Morris, Rochester, and Crookston, Minnesota. The Twin Cities campus, home of the College of Continuing Education, is a classic Big Ten campus with comprehensive academic programs offering unlimited opportunities for students and faculty.

Distance Learning Program

Independent and Distance Learning (IDL) offers outstanding University credit courses using mail and electronic technologies. In a recent year, the department received approximately 5,000 registrations from 3,600 students throughout the United States and abroad. The 175 courses are fully accredited each year by approximately sixty different academic departments in fifteen colleges at the University. IDL is part of the College of Continuing Education (CCE), the division of the University of Minnesota that serves adult and part-time learners.

Delivery Media

Most courses are delivered online either in a nine-month, self-paced format or in a semester-based format with assignment deadlines. Other courses are offered as printed packets by mail (which provide assignment exchange via e-mail and postal mail with faculty members). The program is continually adding more online courses that are fully interactive. All students who register in an Independent and Distance Learning course receive a University of Minnesota e-mail and Internet account.

Programs of Study

Independent and Distance Learning courses are known for their high academic quality and variety of topics. Approximately 175 credit courses are offered in such varied subjects as applied business, child psychology, ecology, English literature and writing courses, foreign languages, management, math, and physics. Most courses are at the undergraduate level.

Although no bachelor's degrees can be completed entirely through IDL, an online upper-level undergraduate certificate in applied business is available. Students interested in the certificate program should visit http://www.cce.umn.edu/certificates for more details.

Student Services

The Continuing Education Information Center offers a complete array of help, including sharing information about desired courses, explaining how to register, providing academic advising, and counseling students about financial aid resources.

University of Minnesota libraries fully support distance learners with reference services, research assistance, and home delivery of documents.

If students have a disability, Independent and Distance Learning coordinates efforts to provide accommodations that remove academic and physical barriers to earning credits. Such accommodations may include more time to complete exams or an alternate format for an exam, a separate testing room, audiotaping required materials, and taped rather than written comments from an instructor. Requests for such accommodations should be made well in advance of when they are needed so that necessary documentation may be obtained and accommodations facilitated.

Faculty

IDL has more than 100 faculty members. Approximately 40 percent are University of Minnesota professors, 30 percent are graduate student teaching assistants, and 30 percent are adjunct faculty members, lecturers, or others. All instructors hold advanced degrees.

Admission

There is no admission process and no application is necessary in order to register in IDL courses.

Tuition and Fees

Students who are not admitted to a University of Minnesota certificate or degree program receive in-state tuition rates, regardless of location of their residence. Tuition for 2008–09 is $326.92 per undergraduate semester credit. A University-wide fee of $55 per credit is assessed. An administrative fee of up to $255 per semester is assessed. Textbooks and other materials can be purchased directly from the University of Minnesota bookstore. For some courses, IDL also provides supplementary materials, free of charge.

Financial Aid

Financial aid is limited. Eligibility requirements may vary, but most aid programs place restrictions on some types of IDL enrollment and require admission to a University of Minnesota, Twin Cities, degree program or eligible certificate program. Non-admitted students who reside in Minnesota may be eligible for College of Continuing Education grants or scholarships, which have more flexible eligibility criteria. Employer assistance may also be an option for some students.

Applying

No application is needed to register in individual courses. For most courses, students can register any day of the year and have nine months to complete the course.

CONTACT

College of Continuing Education Information Center
20 Classroom Office Building
University of Minnesota
1994 Buford Avenue
Saint Paul, Minnesota 55108

Phone: 612-624-4000
      800-234-6564 (toll-free)
Fax: 612-625-1511
E-mail: cceinfo@umn.edu
Web site: http://www.cce.umn.edu/petersons

THE UNIVERSITY OF NORTH CAROLINA AT CHAPEL HILL
The William and Ida Friday Center for Continuing Education
Chapel Hill, North Carolina

As the nation's first state university, the University of North Carolina (UNC) at Chapel Hill was chartered in 1789 and opened to students in 1795. UNC–Chapel Hill was the only public university to award degrees to students in the eighteenth century. Today, there are more than 3,200 faculty members and 27,000 students at UNC. Carolina's academic offerings span a broad range of fields, including seventy-one bachelor's, 107 master's, and seventy-four doctoral degree programs as well as professional degrees in dentistry, medicine, pharmacy, and law. Distance learning has been available since 1913. The University is accredited by the Southern Association of Colleges and Schools.

Distance Learning Program

The Friday Center for Continuing Education offers a variety of credit programs for part-time students. Carolina Courses Online and Self-paced Courses are college-level distance courses that enable students to earn college credit without having to be admitted to UNC or travel to the campus. The Friday Center administers courses from eight institutions of the University of North Carolina: Appalachian State University, East Carolina University, Elizabeth City State University, North Carolina State University, UNC–Chapel Hill, UNC–Greensboro, Western Carolina University, and Winston-Salem State University. Approximately 5,000 students enroll in distance education courses through the Friday Center each year.

Delivery Media

The Self-paced Courses program offers correspondence and online courses. Students enrolled in print-based Self-paced Courses receive a printed course manual that contains all lessons, assignments, and instructions. Students enrolled in online Self-paced Courses receive information on how to access the Web pages containing this information.

Students work through the course at their own pace. Each course has an instructor who grades assignments and answers questions. The minimum completion time for a Self-paced Course is twelve weeks, and students have nine months to complete the course. Students may take two courses at a time. More than 90 Self-paced Courses are available, and most courses are offered for credit at the undergraduate college level.

The Carolina Courses Online program follows the UNC calendar. Students enrolled in a Carolina Courses Online course receive information on how to access the Web pages that contain all lessons, assignments, and instructions. They communicate with classmates and their instructor via e-mail and discussion forums and are encouraged to use the vast resources available through the Internet as they complete their course work. More than seventy Carolina Courses Online courses are available, and most courses are offered for credit at the undergraduate college level.

Programs of Study

The Friday Center offers a variety of courses in more than thirty subjects, including accounting, African and Afro-American studies, art, biology, business, chemistry, classics, criminal justice, communication studies, drama, economics, education, English, environmental sciences, French, geography, geology, history, hospitality management, Italian, journalism, Latin, law, mathematics, music, nursing, nutrition, philosophy, physics, political science, psychology, recreation administration, religious studies, Russian, sociology, Spanish, and statistics. Credit earned in courses offered through the Friday Center can be applied toward degree requirements at UNC–Chapel Hill and other institutions.

Special Programs

Credit courses offered by the Friday Center may be used for teacher license renewal at the discretion of the local district. Students should visit the Friday Center Web site listed in the Contact section for more information.

Student Services

Friday Center staff members are available to answer questions, provide academic advising, and process enrollments. Online library services are available through the UNC–Chapel Hill library system.

Credit Options

Most courses are offered for credit at the undergraduate college level. Credit earned in these courses may be applied toward a degree, if the course is applicable to the requirements of the particular degree program.

Faculty

Faculty members are appointed by the department or school offering the course. Approximately 120 faculty members teach in the program at any given time.

Admission

Carolina Courses Online and Self-paced Courses are open to anyone who wishes to enroll; there are no admission requirements.

Tuition and Fees

Tuition must be paid in full at the time of enrollment. The 2007 tuition and fees were $126 per credit hour for North Carolina residents and $257 per credit hour for nonresidents. Most courses are 3 credit hours. Tuition and other charges are subject to change without notice. Textbooks must be purchased separately.

Financial Aid

Financial aid may be available through VA benefits, vocational rehabilitation grants, local education agencies, and Defense Activity for Non-Traditional Education Support (DANTES).

Applying

Enrollments in Self-paced Courses are accepted at any time by mail, fax, in person, or online. Carolina Courses Online enrollments must be received by specified deadlines. Students should visit the Friday Center Web site for more information.

CONTACT

Student Services Manager
CB #1020
University of North Carolina at
    Chapel Hill
Chapel Hill, North Carolina 27599-
    1020
Phone: 919-962-1134
        800-862-5669 (toll-free)
Fax: 919-962-5549
E-mail: ceinfo@unc.edu
Web site: http://fridaycenter.unc.
    edu

The University of Oklahoma
OUTREACH

THE UNIVERSITY OF OKLAHOMA

University Outreach
College of Continuing Education
College of Liberal Studies
Norman, Oklahoma

The University of Oklahoma's (OU) College of Continuing Education (CCE) is a lifelong learning organization dedicated to helping individuals, businesses, groups, and communities transform themselves through knowledge. Formally organized in 1913, CCE is the outreach arm of the University of Oklahoma. Nationally recognized for its pioneering efforts in continuing education, CCE extends the educational resources of the University through more than thirty different program formats, including undergraduate and graduate degree programs, correspondence and other distance programs, and on- and off-campus courses as well as through a wide variety of programs conducted under the auspices of federal and state grants and contracts. On the Norman campus, adult and other learners attend programs at the Oklahoma Center for Continuing Education, one of eleven W. K. Kellogg Foundation–funded, University-based residential conference centers in the world. Annually, CCE offers some 2,000 courses and activities to more than 250,000 nontraditional learners in Oklahoma and in locations all over the world.

The mission of the College of Liberal Studies is to provide the highest-quality interdisciplinary education to nontraditional undergraduate and graduate students through innovative delivery formats. By combining independent study with weekend classes or brief seminars on campus or 100 percent online study, adult students can earn a Bachelor of Arts in liberal studies or Master of Arts in liberal studies degree. The College of Liberal Studies is a fully accredited, academic division of the University of Oklahoma. Additional information is available at http://www.CLS.OU.edu

Distance Learning Program

In carrying out its mission to help nontraditional learners transform themselves through knowledge, CCE offers a variety of credit and noncredit distance learning courses and programs within the state of Oklahoma and beyond. University Outreach/CCE now offers the opportunity to earn a high school diploma, bachelor's degree, or master's degree 100 percent online, anywhere in the world. Each year, CCE extends the educational resources of the University of Oklahoma through more than thirty different program formats. Annually, CCE offers some 2,000 courses and activities to more than 600,000 nontraditional learners in Oklahoma and worldwide.

Delivery Media

Courses are delivered via television, videotapes, videoconferencing, interactive television, audiotapes, audioconferencing, computer software, CD-ROM, computer conferencing, World Wide Web, e-mail, and print. Students and faculty members may meet in person or interact via videoconferencing, audioconferencing, mail, telephone, fax, e-mail, interactive television, or World Wide Web. The following equipment may be required: audiocassette player, fax machine, television, cable television, videocassette player, computer, modem, Internet access, e-mail, and CD-ROM.

Programs of Study

A variety of programs are available in various distance formats. Independent study courses (credit and noncredit)—some of which are offered online—are available in the following subjects: anthropology, astronomy, business administration, business communication, chemistry, Chinese, classical culture, communication, drama, economics, education, engineering, English, finance, French, geography, geology, German, Greek, health and sport sciences, history, human relations, journalism and mass communication, Latin, library and information studies, management, marketing, mathematics, modern languages, music, philosophy, political science, psychology, Russian, sociology, and Spanish. Master's degree programs in the following areas are presented on-site at military and civilian locations around the world: communication, economics, human relations (including a human resource development emphasis and a community services emphasis), public administration, and social work. In addition, a doctorate in organizational leadership is available at some overseas sites. (These programs combine on-site course delivery with online and correspondence study.) In addition, students in Oklahoma have access to telecourses and OneNet courses.

Special Programs

CCE offers a number of distance learning special programs. Among these are the DHS/SATTRN (Satellite Training Network) programs held for Oklahoma Department of Human Services and other state employees. CCE's Independent Study Department works closely with the DANTES program and the Navy College PACE program. In addition, this department offers a number of noncredit writing courses and more than seventy-five high school courses, many of them available online.

Credit Options

CCE's Independent Study Department provides students various options to earn credit through testing. Among these are the College-Level Examination Program (CLEP), DANTES, and institutionally developed advanced-standing examinations.

Faculty

The faculty for distance programs includes regular University of Oklahoma faculty members, adjunct faculty members, and instructors with special appointments. All are experienced and highly qualified instructional professionals who are knowledgeable about the needs, concerns, and capabilities of distance education students.

Admission

Admission to the University of Oklahoma is necessary for credit courses other than those offered through Independent Study. Independent Study students need not be first admitted to OU. To participate in graduate programs, admission to OU's Graduate College is required. For more information, prospective students should use the information listed in the Contact section.

Tuition and Fees

Tuition and fees vary based on the chosen program. Prospective students are encouraged to inquire about the costs associated with the program in which they are interested. Expenses relating to continuing education courses taken to maintain and improve professional skills may be tax deductible (Treas. Reg. 1.162-5, Coughlin v. Commissioner, 203f.2d 307). A tax adviser can make this determination based on the particular facts relating to one's professional situation. All tuition and fees at the University of Oklahoma are subject to changes made by the State Regents for Higher Education.

Financial Aid

Financial aid is available for many of the semester-based programs offered through CCE. Financial aid is not available to Independent Study students. Each program has different eligibility requirements. Interested students are encouraged to use the contact information below. They will then be put in touch with the appropriate CCE department that can fully answer their financial aid questions.

Applying

Distance learners interested in credit and noncredit programs may enroll by telephone (800-522-0772 Ext. 2248) or by fax (405-325-7164). Prospective students should use the contact information below to determine the appropriate telephone number.

CONTACT

Larry Hayes
College of Continuing Education
The University of Oklahoma
1700 Asp Avenue
Norman, Oklahoma 73072-6400

Phone: 405-325-4414
Fax: 405-325-7196
E-mail: lhayes@ou.edu
Web site: http://www.outreach.ou.edu

THE UNIVERSITY OF TEXAS SYSTEM

UT TeleCampus (UTTC)—Online Courses and Degrees

Austin, Texas

The University of Texas (UT) System offers online courses and degree programs via the award-winning UT TeleCampus (UTTC). The UT TeleCampus is the central support center for online learning within UT System institutions. Students can access virtual classrooms, links to University services and offices, a UT TeleCampus digital library, and many other service features. Launched in May 1998, the UT TeleCampus gives students the assurance of accredited universities, expert faculty members, and high-quality online education, along with the support services students need to succeed. The UT TeleCampus has received numerous national and regional awards since its development. All UT academic institutions participating in UT TeleCampus–based programs are Southern Association of Colleges and Schools (SACS) accredited. To learn more about online degrees or courses, prospective students should visit the UTTC Web site.

Distance Learning Program

UT TeleCampus–based programs and courses are composed of the same rigorous content found on-site at the UT System's fifteen institutions. From application to graduation, students face the same general expectations and receive the same high-quality courses on-site or online. Online courses follow a semester schedule, allowing flexibility during the week for study and participation in Web-based group discussions. An online syllabus maps out test and project deadlines.

The majority of the courses offered through the UT TeleCampus can be taken entirely online. Students can learn from anywhere in the world with access to the Internet.

Delivery Media

The UT TeleCampus uses Internet technologies for course delivery and student support via the World Wide Web. Courses may also utilize additional distance education tools, including CDs, audiotapes and videotapes, streaming video and audio, e-mail, discussion groups, and chat rooms.

Programs of Study

The UT TeleCampus offers online master's degrees, bachelor's degree-

completion programs, and various graduate, undergraduate, and professional development courses and certificate programs.

The M.B.A. in general management is a 48-hour program that received the 2001 U.S. Distance Learning Association's Excellence in Distance Learning Programming award.

The Master of Public Administration is a 36-hour nonthesis program designed to provide students with the skills needed for effective public leadership.

The Master of Science in human resource development is a 36-hour nonthesis program that is ideal for corporate trainers, HR directors, and administrators in education as well as others with an interest in technology for human resource development. Certification programs in office education, trade and industrial, and health science technology are available with this degree plan.

Designed for individuals with significant ability in a science discipline as well as a serious commitment to teaching, the online Master of Arts in teaching science education prepares educators in research and pedagogy focused on science content.

Physical educators, athletics directors, wellness trainers, and coaches can earn their master's degree in kinesiology online from their choice of four UT institutions. This 36-hour program received the 2002 U.S. Distance Learning Association's Excellence in Distance Learning Programming award.

The 36-hour M.Ed. in educational technology is designed for teachers, technology coordinators, administrators, and corporate trainers who want to excel at integrating technology into their curriculum.

The 36-hour M.Ed. in curriculum and instruction with a literacy emphasis includes a Master Reading Teacher (MRT) certification program, a reading specialist certification program, and a four-course English as a second language (ESL) endorsement program. Certificate and endorsement course work can also be taken separately.

A bilingual Master of Fine Arts in creative writing program is offered to prepare writers for the publishing marketplace and teaching and editing careers in both the United States and Latin America.

A four-course superintendent certification program, UTOPS, prepares candidates for superintendent certification in Texas.

An alternative teacher certification program (ATCP) is available to individuals with bachelor's degrees in areas other than education who want to become fully certified teachers.

A postprofessional certificate program, Improved Training of Physical Therapists in Early Intervention Settings (IMPRINTS), prepares physical therapists to provide services to infants and toddlers with disabilities.

Online nursing programs include an RN-to-B.S.N. program, which offers the five required nursing courses for registered nurse students to complete their

B.S. in nursing degree, and a graduate certificate in nursing education, a three-course program designed for registered nurses who are interested in pursuing the role of a nurse educator.

A bachelor's degree-completion program in criminology and criminal justice is available entirely online. The program consists of 66 hours of upper-level course work.

A bachelor's degree-completion program in applied technology health services technology is offered for graduates of Associate of Applied Science degrees in the allied health and nursing fields.

Other areas of academic study include most general undergraduate curriculum required in Texas, an undergraduate track in management information systems, a chess in education program, a blood bank technology program, and border studies and border administration certificates.

Special Programs
The UT TeleCampus also facilitates the delivery of professional development training in a wide range of topics, including paralegal studies, blood bank technology, and border studies certificates. Interested students should visit the UTTC Web site and follow the links

to Professional Development Online (PDO) to view the catalog.

Student Services
The UT TeleCampus was designed with the online student in mind. It provides all of the services students need to succeed, including technical support available 24/7, an extensive digital library, and free online academic support that provides students with tutorials and writing labs. In addition, department liaisons are available at each campus to aid online students with questions about the library, registration, financial aid, and veteran's affairs.

Credit Options
Transfer credit toward online courses and programs is generally the same as comparable on-site programs. Students should contact the program advisers listed on the UT TeleCampus Web site for specifics.

Faculty
The same expert faculty members who teach on-campus courses at the University of Texas campuses teach online academic courses offered through the UT TeleCampus. Courses are designed

and developed by these faculty members, with production support and faculty development provided by the institutions and the UT TeleCampus.

Admission
Admission criteria and processes for online offerings are generally the same as on-site courses. It is advisable to start the initial application process at least ninety days prior to the beginning of a semester.

Tuition and Fees
The amount of tuition and fees charged by each UT System institution varies and is based on residency status. Students should access the UT TeleCampus Web site for links to campus tuition and fee information.

Financial Aid
Financial aid opportunities are available for students enrolled in UT TeleCampus courses.

Applying
Prospective students need to apply and be admitted to the UT System institution offering their course or degree program. Depending on the program of interest, different institutions participate.

CONTACT
Student Services
UT TeleCampus
The University of Texas System
702 Colorado Street, Suite 4.100
Austin, Texas 78701
Phone: 888-TEXAS-16 (toll-free)
Fax: 512-499-4715
E-mail: telecampus@utsystem.edu
Web site: http://www.telecampus.utsystem.edu

UNIVERSITY OF THE INCARNATE WORD

Universe Online
San Antonio, Texas

University of the Incarnate Word (UIW) was founded in 1881 as an outgrowth of the original mission of the Sisters of Charity of the Incarnate Word, who settled in San Antonio, Texas, in 1869. The school maintains the mission of the founders by providing high-quality educational opportunities to all students, developing graduates who are concerned and enlightened citizens. UIW is accredited by a variety of regional and national associations but most notably by the regional accrediting body of the Commission on Colleges of the Southern Association of Colleges and Schools. Through its College of Professional Studies, UIW is nationally accredited by the Association of Collegiate Business Schools and Programs. Universe Online is accredited by the Association of Accredited Online Programs International.

Distance Learning Program

Universe Online is a natural extension of the mission and the entrepreneurial nature of UIW. By utilizing personal computers and asynchronous instruction, the program addresses the changing needs of adult learners. Maintaining the quality for which it is known, UIW allows students to complete a degree program totally online.

Delivery Media

Students accepted into the program use computer-conferencing software that allows for asynchronous interaction, in an eight-week-term format. Students interact throughout the week in both private and group discussions. Students are required to have an Internet service provider (ISP) to connect and upload/download assignments.

Programs of Study

Universe Online offers a variety of undergraduate degree programs and graduate programs.

Understanding the needs of the transfer student, UIW has developed a variety of degree programs that accept transfer credit and use it to complete the degree program. This allows students to finish faster and not lose credit for their past work.

The Bachelor of Arts in organizational development and the Bachelor of Arts in human resources combine courses that are relevant to today's business world and the specialty with the opportunity for students to include transfer work or a minor.

The Bachelor of Arts degree in applied science is designed for the person who has an associate degree in a specialized field or up to 60 credits in a concentration area. This degree then allows students to complete a professional sequence, giving them a tailored degree that will meet the needs of the business community using the student's specific skill set.

The Bachelor of Arts in administration has been designed especially for the transfer student. It contains a professional sequence of business courses that provide students the necessary background in administration for entry-level positions. This degree permits students to customize their plans by incorporating at least 12 hours of previous work with a large elective area that is very useful for transferring students.

The Bachelor of Business Administration (B.B.A.) prepares the student for today's changing business climate. The required core and choice of specialization prepare students for positions of leadership in the business world. Areas of specialization include accounting, information systems, international business, management, and marketing.

The Master of Business Administration (M.B.A.) degree program seeks to develop in each student a broad understanding of how the elements and processes of business organizations relate to one another and to the external environment. Degree requirements are designed to develop students' proficiency and confidence in all of the functional areas of business. Students can elect the general or international focus.

The Master of Arts in Administration (M.A.A.) degree program provides participants with the knowledge and skills required for managers, administrators, and supervisors to function more effectively in all types of organizations, plus the specialized managerial expertise needed for management positions within or related to the organizational development profession. Concentrations are communication arts, organizational development, and urban administration.

Students must complete both the course work in their major field of study and the University's general studies core as required in all courses. A minimum of 128 credits of course work is required to graduate in all undergraduate programs. All classes, including graduate classes, are 3 credits (semester hours). Students must complete 36 semester hours to graduate from the graduate programs.

Student Services

All students at UIW, including Universe Online students, have a wide variety of student service options. Online students have access to academic and financial aid advising, library and bookstore services, and online admission application and registration. In addition, students have access to career planning services.

Credit Options

Universe Online welcomes transfer students. UIW accepts all transfer work, requiring students to complete a minimum of 45 semester hours to receive the UIW degree.

Upon acceptance as a degree-seeking student at the University, a student must obtain prior written approval to transfer any additional credits from other institutions.

Faculty

Given the stringent requirements of national/regional accreditation, faculty members must meet a very exacting set of requirements; this has led to a high-quality educational program delivered by highly credentialed and dedicated faculty members.

Admission

Undergraduate students must possess a high school diploma or its equivalent. Students having previous college work must have a GPA of 2.5 or better. Students must have worked for three years prior to application, in or outside of the home. Students who have not completed English composition I and II and college algebra must take these courses early in their program of study and may be tested for level.

International student transcripts and course descriptions must be translated.

Tuition and Fees

Undergraduate tuition is $395 per credit and graduate tuition is $605 per credit. There is a one-time transcript fee of $30. There are no other fees assessed.

Active duty military are charged $250 an hour for both undergraduate and graduate work. This is the "cap" for tuition assistance. Active duty military

family members, DOD civilian employees, and military retirees qualify for a rate of $275 an hour for both undergraduate and graduate classes.

Financial Aid

Financial aid and payment plans are available for all qualified students. Military benefits, as well as employer reimbursement benefits, may be used for online courses.

Applying

To apply for admission, students can fill out an application for admission through the University's Web site. In order to be considered for admission, students must fill out an application online at the school Web site and submit official high school or postsecondary school transcripts from all institutions attended. Students are notified of application decisions via e-mail and U.S. mail.

CONTACT

Universe Online
University of the Incarnate Word
CPO #324
4301 Broadway
San Antonio, Texas 78209

Phone: 877-827-2702 (toll-free)
Fax: 210-829-2756
E-mail: virtual@uiwtx.edu
Web site: http://www.uiw.edu/online

THE UNIVERSITY OF TOLEDO
Distance and eLearning
Toledo, Ohio

Established in 1872, the University of Toledo (UT) has a diverse enrollment of more than 20,000 students representing nearly ninety countries. Located in the heart of Toledo in northwest Ohio, the University plays an important role in the region. Faculty members participate in research, are involved in the community, and are committed to teaching. The Colleges of Arts and Sciences, Business, Education, Engineering, Health Science and Human Service, Nursing, Medicine, Pharmacy, Law, and University College offer a variety of certificate, associate, bachelor's, master's, and doctoral degree programs. UT is regionally accredited by the Higher Learning Commission and a member of the North Central Association of Colleges and Schools and is authorized to offer degrees online.

Distance Learning Program

Distance and eLearning was established in June 1995 to meet the distance learning mission of the University of Toledo (UT). The University is the leader in distance learning among Ohio's four-year public universities and colleges, offering more than 950 courses and forty academic programs online.

Delivery Media

Student-faculty interaction is accomplished through e-mail, chat room discussions, bulletin board postings, CD-ROM, and phone. Most courses are offered via the Internet in an asynchronous environment.

Programs of Study

Distance learning at the University of Toledo provides a flexible environment to fit its students' busy lifestyles for a variety of undergraduate and graduate degree and certificate programs as well as an array of individual courses.

Accounting for Health Care and Nonprofit Certificate Program This program focuses on the unique aspects of accounting for the health care industry and the nonprofit sector.

Accounting Software Applications Certificate Program This program provides a solid foundation in the most popular accounting software programs.

Accounting Technology Certificate Program This program provides participants with the skills necessary to prepare financial statements and record business transactions and offers a foundation in the current technology pertaining to the profession.

Applied Organizational Technology Certificate Program This program offers a broad background that assists people who are interested in or have experience with technical support and managerial training. It concentrates on workplace applications such as supervision, leadership, marketing, and law.

Business Management Technology Certificate Program The program gives participants a solid foundation in the skills necessary to manage/own a business. Acquired skills include general knowledge of all aspects of organizations, including human resources, economics, and management, marketing, and workplace diversity.

Computer Software Specialist Certificate Program This program gives students the necessary skills to organize and perform activities related to the office environment. Graduates are prepared to sit for the Microsoft certification examination.

Diversity Management Certificate Program Participants in this program learn how to create a bias-free workplace, develop diversity training for all types of organizations, and set up mentorship programs and diversity councils.

Health Information Administration Certificate Program This program prepares students with bachelor's degrees for administrative positions in the health-care industry. The program is accredited by CAHIM and students are eligible to sit for the national certification examination of the AHIMA.

Information Services and Support Certificate Program This certificate prepares students for careers as software and hardware support professionals, operating-systems experts, information technologists, and computer technicians.

Legal Secretarial Certificate Program This program prepares students for positions in law offices. In addition, the program also prepares participants for the Microsoft Office Specialist (MOS) certification test.

Management Accounting Certificate Program This program offers an accounting foundation for managers in a wide-range of workplace environments.

Marketing and Sales Technology Certificate Program This program prepares students for careers in new product development, merchandising, advertising, and wholesale/retail trade management.

Nursing Education Graduate Certificate Program This program is designed for registered nurses with a baccalaureate degree or higher degree and provides an opportunity for current and potential nurse educators in academic and health-care settings to develop and refine the practice of teaching.

Programming and Software Development Certificate Program This certificate prepares students to work in the computer industry as programmers, software developers, data managers, and information system designers.

Psychiatric–Mental Health Clinical Nurse Specialist Graduate Certificate Program The program is for individuals with a master's degree in nursing and who desire to obtain specialized knowledge to seek certification as an adult psychiatric and mental health NCS. Graduates are qualified to take national certification examinations.

Associate Degree in Accounting Technology Program Students receive a well-rounded education in all areas of accounting, including payroll, accounts receivable/payable, purchasing, and taxation, and are prepared for careers in the public and private sectors.

Associate Degree in Business Management Technology Program This program explores aspects of human resources, computer technology, marketing, accounting, and workplace diversity.

Associate Degree in Business Management Technology Program—Fast-Track Option This degree can be completed in fifteen months or less. Cohort groups provide supportive, interactive distance-learning experiences. Courses are presented in either eight- or sixteen-week sessions.

Associate Degree in Computer Software Specialist Program This program teaches skills necessary to organize and perform activities related to the office environment. Graduates are prepared to sit for the Microsoft certification examination.

Associate Degree in Information Services and Support Program This program prepares students for careers as software and hardware support professionals, operating-systems experts, information technologists, and computer technicians.

Associate Degree in Interdisciplinary Technical Studies Program In this program, students develop a program to meet their unique interests and career goals.

Associate Degree in Marketing and Sales Technology Program This program enables students to develop the business skills necessary to recognize changes in the marketplace and technology; students can specialize in the process of bringing raw materials from the producer to the final customer.

Associate Degree in Programming and Software Development Program This program prepares students to work in the computer industry as programmers, software developers, data managers, and information system designers.

Bachelor of Applied Organizational Technology This bachelor's degree-completion program includes a broad liberal arts background, a general core of business courses, and a specific area of specialization.

Bachelor of Arts in Liberal Studies Program Students complete topical seminars in humanities, natural sciences, and social sciences along with an individualized component of traditional courses.

Bachelor of Science in Criminal Justice The program prepares graduates to work in the field of criminal justice or related fields, attend graduate school in criminal justice or a related discipline, and attend law school.

Bachelor of Science in Engineering Technology Program This degree completion program provides the last two years of the computer science and engineering technology program curriculum, focusing on aspects of computer networking and Web-based programming. Appli-

cants must have an associate degree in electrical engineering technology or a closely related field.

Bachelor of Science in Health Information Management Program Graduates play a critical role in maintaining, collecting, and analyzing data that health-care providers need to deliver high-quality health care. An associate degree in health information technology or a closely related field may be applied to this degree. Graduates are eligible to sit for the national certification examination to become registered health administrators (RHIA).

Bachelor of Science in Information Technology This program prepares students for positions as information technologists providing operational and infrastructure support for computer and information systems in business, manufacturing, and institutional organizations.

Bachelor of Science in Nursing Program (for current RNs): Graduates provide theory-based nursing care in diverse health-care settings, including hospitals, clinics, nursing homes, schools, and outpatient facilities. Students can take many of the general education, liberal arts, and science courses online as well as College of Nursing courses.

Master of Liberal Studies Program In this flexible, customized College of Arts and Sciences program, students complete seminars in humanities, natural and social sciences, and visual and performing arts and a master's thesis.

Master of Science in Engineering Program This part-time, cross-disciplinary program, with a concentration in engineering practice, integrates engineering, business, and elective courses. The program, designed for students with a bachelor's degree in engineering, engineering technology, or a closely related area, combines study in business management and engineering.

M.S.N., Nurse Educator Program This program is for nurses with a bachelor's degree and clinical nursing experience who want to teach undergraduate nursing students in classroom and clinical settings. This program focuses on curriculum development, teaching-learning processes, classroom and clinical teaching strategies, and evaluation principles.

M.S.N., Psychiatric–Mental Health Clinical Nurse Specialist Program This is a two-year, full-time program with part-time options. The curriculum prepares advanced practice nurses to work in a wide variety of community and hospital-based psychiatric settings, and includes theoretically based and clinically focused courses.

Student Services

Distance and eLearning provides comprehensive student services to enable students to become involved participants in the online learning process. Students have access to a number of services, including online applications, applications for financial aid, registration, academic advising, software information, the UT Bookstore, Career Services, UT's online library, and the eWriting Center. The University has been awarded the designation of meeting Best Practices in Student Services by the Ohio Learning Network.

Credit Options

College credits earned through distance learning courses are recorded on a University of Toledo transcript in the same manner as credits earned in on-campus courses. There is no special designation on the transcript. Students who have attended a regionally accredited college or university may be able to transfer credits.

Admission

All distance learners must be admitted to the University and meet the same requirements as traditional students. Special-status admission is available for non-degree-seeking students.

Tuition and Fees

Tuition and fees for online courses are the same as for on-campus courses. Students who are not Ohio residents are eligible for the Distance Learning scholarship, which covers the out-of-state tuition surcharge and the admission application fee. University scholarships are available for both in-state and out-of-state students.

Applying

Prospective students should submit an official application along with the admission fee, an official high school transcript, GED scores, or official transcripts from all previous colleges or universities. Applications are available online or by mail.

CONTACT

Gary Carr, Director, eLearning
 Student Services Management
eLearning and Academic Support
The University of Toledo
M.S. 516
2801 Bancroft Street
Toledo, Ohio 43606-3390
Phone: 866-886-5336 (toll-free)
Fax: 419-530-8835
E-mail: utdl@utoledo.edu
Web site: http://www.utoledo.edu/dl

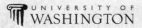

UNIVERSITY OF WASHINGTON

UW Extension
Seattle, Washington

Founded in 1861, the University of Washington (UW) is one of the oldest state-supported institutions of higher education on the Pacific coast. The University comprises three campuses: the Seattle campus, which is made up_of seventeen schools and colleges offering educational opportunities to students ranging from first-year undergraduates through doctoral-level candidates; the Bothell campus; and the Tacoma campus.

The primary mission of the University of Washington is the preservation, advancement, and dissemination of knowledge. UW advances new knowledge through many forms of research, inquiry, and discussion. Accreditation is by the Northwest Association of Schools and Colleges.

Distance Learning Program

The University of Washington offers twelve degree programs, twenty-five certificate programs, and hundreds of courses online, making it one of the leading public institutions in the online field. The UW online program has been rated among the top ten online learning education offerings available through U.S. universities. Distance learning courses at UW are developed by a team of online learning designers working with UW faculty members and academic departments. They create courses that are academically rigorous, suitable for a distance format, and convenient. Several courses have won the prestigious Helen Williams Award for Excellence in Collegiate Independent Study from the well-respected American Association for Collegiate Independent Study (AACIS) as well as awards from the University Continuing Education Association (UCEA). The distance learning program at UW has 4,074 students enrolled.

Delivery Media

Most programs rely on the Internet and e-mail to access instruction and to communicate with teachers and fellow students. Some classes start and finish at set times; others enable students to start according to their own schedule.

Students can contact their instructors at any time with questions about the courses. Many courses use online discussion, and some courses incorporate chats into their curriculum.

Programs of Study

UW offers a Master in Strategic Planning for Critical Infrastructures degree program that was developed in partnership with the Washington National Guard for leaders who are responsible for ensuring the reliability and security of critical infrastructures and emergency services. This program was developed for officials in public and private infrastructure, emergency management, and homeland security.

Master's degrees in engineering are available through UW's Education at a Distance for Growth and Excellence (UW/EDGE), with four areas of specialization: aeronautics and astronautics, aerospace engineering, manufacturing engineering, and mechanical engineering.

The master's in construction engineering is designed for professionals in the heavy construction industry, combining courses in construction management and civil engineering.

The Master of Science in applied mathematics is designed for profession-

als in scientific fields who cannot attend classes on campus.

The Master of Library and Information Science degree was established to meet the high demand for library and information professionals. Delivery of instruction is primarily Internet based, with on-campus three-day residencies at the beginning of each quarter.

Twenty-five certificate programs are offered, with each requiring three to nine intensive courses. Certificate programs include Brain Research in Education, Business Foundations, C++ Programming, Construction Management, Curriculum Integration in Action, Data Resource Management, E-learning Design and Development, Facility Management, Gerontology, Heavy Construction Project Management, Infrastructure Construction, Internet Programming, Java 2 Programming, Object-Oriented Analysis and Design Using UML, Paralegal Studies, Project Management, Quantitative Construction Management, School Library Media Professional, Site Planning, Web Administration, Web Consultant for Small Business, Web Technology Essentials, and Writers' Program: Literary Fiction Writing and Nonfiction Writing.

More than 200 courses are available in architecture and urban planning, arts and sciences, business and management, computing, engineering and technology, education, health sciences, languages, and library and information science. The OpenUW program at UW offers twelve free noncredit classes.

Student Services

Academic advising is available via e-mail and telephone and, for those who are able to come to the campus, in person. Advisers can answer questions about prerequisites and course content. Students enrolled in online learning courses receive student numbers and have library checkout privileges at UW libraries. Distance learning students living outside the Seattle area may request specific library materials by mail. Technical support for courses is provided. Textbooks may be ordered online.

Credit Options

Credit earned by taking a distance learning course can be applied to an undergraduate degree or can help students prepare for UW admission. Online learning credits are not considered residence credits. It is not possible to earn an undergraduate degree from the University of Washington through online learning alone. However, nine master's degrees may be completed solely through online learning.

Faculty

Most UW online learning courses are designed and taught by faculty members who teach the same courses on the UW campus. The instructors are familiar with student questions and needs. With the help of instructional designers, they have developed the appropriate methods and materials, interactive strategies, and online activities to help students achieve the course objectives in a distance learning format.

Admission

It is not necessary to be admitted to the University of Washington before taking distance learning courses. (There are prerequisites for some courses, and TOEFL scores are required for international students.) Certificate and graduate degree programs have an application process.

Tuition and Fees

All registrants pay a nonrefundable $30 registration fee. Fees for credit courses through distance learning are $176 per credit for undergraduate students and $387 per credit for Tier 1 graduate and graduate courses. Prices for graduate instruction vary by degree program.

Financial Aid

UW distance learning students are ineligible for the University's financial aid programs in most cases. For information about alternative funding, students should visit http://www.outreach. washington.edu/extinfo/loan_sources. asp.

Applying

Prospective students can register online for courses. Application forms for certificates and degree programs can be downloaded.

CONTACT

University of Washington Online Learning
4311 11th Avenue, NE
Seattle, Washington 98105-4608

Phone: 206-897-8936
 800-506-1338 (toll-free)
E-mail: extnadvising@extn.washington.edu
Web site: http://www.onlinelearning.washington.edu

UNIVERSITY OF WISCONSIN–SUPERIOR

Distance Learning Center
Superior, Wisconsin

The Distance Learning Center (formerly known as the Extended Degree Program) at the University of Wisconsin–Superior (UW–Superior) was established in 1978. UW–Superior is part of the highly acclaimed University of Wisconsin System.

The Distance Learning Program is a nationwide program with one tuition for all students. It is accredited by the North Central Association of Colleges and Schools and serves adults who do not have access to a four-year institution because of where they live or because of career and/or family responsibilities.

UW–Superior recognizes that adults are dedicated to achieving educational goals but must also address other priorities. By enrolling in UW–Superior's Distance Learning Program, students can obtain a degree without having to come to the campus. The individually designed major is designed by the student to fit his or her career goals and educational needs. Elementary education is an option for the student who wants to teach in Wisconsin. Communications is the third major offered by the Distance Learning Center.

Distance Learning Program

The Distance Learning Program is a semester-based program. The three enrollment periods include fall, spring, and summer. Each class is taught by a UW–Superior faculty member to ensure that students are receiving the best instruction possible, with an up-to-date curriculum. At any given time, more than 200 students are enrolled in the program. Advisers work closely with students as they complete their degrees.

Delivery Media

Courses are delivered mainly via online format, although a few courses are print-based. Access to the Desire 2 Learn software is provided through the UW–Superior network system. Students are encouraged to utilize e-mail and message boards while enrolled in the online courses. Print-based course materials can be mailed or faxed to the Distance Learning Office.

Programs of Study

The Distance Learning Program offers three bachelor's degree options: communications, elementary education, and the individually designed major.

The communications degree is the newest major offered. Students work with faculty members who specialize in improving communications. It not only allows students to dig deeper into the communications discipline but also gives students a wide range of communication venues to explore—interpersonal, conflict, persuasion, organizational, and intercultural communication.

The individualized major allows students to plan a major using both past and new learning experiences. It is designed by students to meet their educational and career goals. Examples of individualized majors include human services, child development, and health management.

The elementary education degree at a distance has been in existence for more than twenty-five years. It provides preparation for Wisconsin licensure for birth through ages 11–12 or ages 6 through 12–13. UW–Superior's Teacher Education Department has an excellent reputation for quality and innovation.

Credit Options

Credit for prior learning is made possible through credit by exam, credit for military service, and credit for non-university programs. Students also have the option to petition for technical college credit and to seek credit through portfolio development.

Admission

Students seeking admission to the Distance Learning Program can apply online at the University's Web site (http://www.uwsuper.edu). They can also request admission information via e-mail.

Tuition and Fees

All distance learning students pay the same tuition regardless of residency. An additional course fee is charged for each course.

Financial Aid

Financial aid is available to distance learning students.

CONTACT

Distance Learning Program
University of Wisconsin–Superior
Belknap and Catlin Avenues
Superior, Wisconsin 54880
Phone: 877-528-6597 (toll-free)
E-mail: dlc@uwsuper.edu
Web site: http://www.uwsuper.edu/distancelearning

UNIVERSITY OF WYOMING
New Thinking

THE UNIVERSITY OF WYOMING
Outreach School
Division of Outreach Credit Programs
Laramie, Wyoming

The University of Wyoming (UW), a land-grant university founded in 1886, is accredited by the Higher Learning Commission and is a member of the North Central Association of Colleges and Schools. The University of Wyoming was the first university west of the Missouri River to offer correspondence courses. In its outreach mission, the University of Wyoming is guided by the following vision: the state of Wyoming is the campus of the University of Wyoming. The University has one faculty and staff, one student body, and one set of academic programs. Teaching, research, and service are the missions of the University, regardless of location. The University recognizes that its "one student body" is composed of a wide variety of students whose needs differ.

Distance Learning Program

The UW Outreach School's Outreach Credit Programs division delivers the University's distance learning programs. The mission of the Outreach School is to extend the University of Wyoming's educational programs and services to people in the state of Wyoming and beyond. The School delivers more than 300 University courses and complete degree and certificate programs to approximately 4,000 students per semester through Outreach Credit Programs and the other academic division of the Outreach School, UW/CC Center, the University's largest location of onsite courses outside the main campus..

Delivery Media

Outreach Credit Programs launched Online UW in the spring of 1999 in cooperation with eCollege to serve students interested in learning online. In addition, Outreach Credit Programs delivers programs via correspondence study, audio-teleconference, videoconference, onsite instruction, and streaming video. Additional courses also are offered through Web-based instruction.

For a list of audio, video, Web-based, onsite, streaming video, and correspondence study courses, students should visit http://outreach.uwyo.edu/ocp. All correspondence study courses, all Web-based courses, all streaming video courses, and a limited number of audio-teleconference courses are available to students outside the state of Wyoming.

Programs of Study

Degrees, certificates, and endorsements are available to students through distance education. For a complete list of programs, requirements, tuition charges, and academic advising contacts, students should visit the Web at http://outreach.uwyo.edu/ocp/degrees&programs.asp.

Certificate programs include land surveying (offered nationwide through audio-teleconference with videotaped lectures), family and consumer sciences/early childhood program director's certificate (available online), and real estate (available online).

Endorsement programs include early childhood birth to 5 endorsement, early childhood special education endorsement, principal endorsement, and Wyoming reading endorsement literacy program, all available statewide through a combination of delivery media.

Graduate programs include an Executive M.B.A. (available online); an M.S. in education, with a specialization in instructional technology (available online); an M.S. in kinesiology and health (statewide, some courses nationwide); an M.S. in nursing, with an advanced practice in rural health/nurse educator option (online); an M.S. in speech-language pathology (available nationwide through audio-teleconference with videotaped lectures); and an M.S.W. in social work (statewide).

Other available distance degrees are baccalaureate completion degrees in business administration and family and consumer science (online), criminal justice, psychology, and social science (statewide, some courses nationwide) and an RN/B.S.N. completion program (online).

Special Programs

Outreach Credit Programs currently delivers more than 100 University courses and ten degrees and certificates completely online. Courses are available worldwide in the areas of adult learning, astronomy, biochemistry, business administration, child development, directing preschool and day-care programs, economics, education, engineering, family and consumer sciences, human resources management, instructional technology, nutrition, physics, psychology, real estate, religion, and statistics. Students should visit http://outreach.uwyo.edu/ocp/degrees&programs.asp for a list of programs offered.

Student Services

All student services (such as admission, enrollment, tuition payment, grade reporting, financial aid, bookstore, and library outreach) are available to distance learning students. The library outreach service is available at http://www.lib.uwyo.edu. Students can purchase textbooks and course packets online at the University Bookstore at http://www.uwyobookstore.com. In addition, services from the Center for Advising and Career Services, Disability Support Services, Educational Opportunity Center, Testing Center, Writing Center, and Student Affairs are also available to distance students. A complete list of all services is available at http://outreach.uwyo.edu/ocp/resources.asp.

Credit Options

Students may transfer courses from accredited institutions of higher education to the University of Wyoming. Credit is also available through AP, CLEP, portfolio assessment, and departmental examinations. Degrees require a minimum of 48 hours of upper-division credit, with a minimum of 30 credits from the University of Wyoming. Most degree programs require 120–124 credits for graduation.

Faculty

The majority of those who teach through Outreach Credit Programs are full-time faculty members at the University of Wyoming. A limited number of adjunct faculty members, who are approved by the University's academic departments, teach distance courses. In any given semester, approximately 75 regular full-time faculty members and 15 part-time adjunct faculty members teach distance courses through the Outreach School. The programs offered at a distance are academically challenging, and the requirements for enrollment, admission, and completion are the same as for the programs offered on the main University campus in Laramie, Wyoming.

Admission

All students interested in enrolling in UW courses through Outreach Credit Programs must first be admitted to the University. Students should check with the appropriate academic departments for their study plan requirements.

Students who decide to pursue UW undergraduate degrees must apply and be admitted to a specific degree program at the University. A maximum of 12 UW credit hours can be applied to a UW degree program prior to admission. Undergraduate admission generally requires completion of at least 13 high school units in a precollege curriculum, a cumulative high school grade point average of at least 2.75, and an ACT score of at least 20 or an SAT score of at least 960. Conditional admission is available for adult learners who do not meet these criteria.

Students who decide to pursue UW graduate degrees must apply and be admitted to a specific degree program at the University. Credits taken prior to admission may or may not apply to a graduate program of study. Graduate programs require a Graduate Record Examinations (GRE) combined verbal and quantitative score of at least 900. The University offers GRE testing through the University of Wyoming Testing Center. For more information, students can visit the Web site at http://www.uwyo.edu/ucc/utc/.

Tuition and Fees

All outreach students are charged tuition at an in-state rate. Undergraduate tuition for outreach courses is $94 per credit hour, with an $15-per-credit-hour delivery fee or a $40-per-credit-hour delivery fee for Online UW courses. Graduate tuition for outreach courses is $174 per credit hour, with an $15-per-credit-hour delivery fee or a $40-per-credit-hour delivery fee for Online UW courses. Tuition for the Executive M.B.A. program is $550 per credit hour plus a $40-per-credit-hour delivery fee, and tuition for the land surveying program is $208 per credit hour.

Financial Aid

All forms of federal financial aid and other scholarship aid are available to Outreach students. Outreach Credit Programs also has a number of scholarships available to Outreach students. Information describing available aid and award criteria is available on the Web at http://www.uwyo.edu/sfa or from the Office of Student Financial Aid, Department 3335, University of Wyoming, 1000 East University Avenue, Laramie, Wyoming 82071.

Applying

Non-degree-seeking and degree-seeking students should apply through the Admissions Office (telephone: 800-DIAL-WYO (toll-free) or 307-766-2287; Web site: http://www.uwyo.edu) or Graduate Admissions (telephone: 307-766-2287; Web site: http://www.uwyo.edu/uwgrad).

CONTACT

Outreach School
Division of Outreach Credit
  Programs
Department 3274
University of Wyoming
1000 East University Avenue
Laramie, Wyoming 82071
Phone: 307-766-4300
        800-448-7801 (toll-free)
Fax: 307-766-4048
E-mail: ocp@uwyo.edu
Web site: http://outreach.uwyo.
        edu/ocp

UPPER IOWA UNIVERSITY
Established in 1857™

UPPER IOWA UNIVERSITY
Extended University
Fayette, Iowa

Upper Iowa University (UIU) was established in 1857 and has since become the largest private university in the state of Iowa. Unlike some of the newer schools offering distance learning programs, UIU has a beautiful residential campus on 90 acres with eight academic buildings and three residence halls. Upper Iowa also has seventeen sports teams, known as the Peacocks, who compete in the NCAA Division II. As a nonprofit, rapidly growing, four-year liberal arts institution of higher learning, UIU offers a wide range of high-quality degree programs to nearly 6,000 students worldwide. UIU provides educational opportunities to the global community, focusing on the future while preserving the traditions of the past. Upper Iowa University is accredited by the Higher Learning Commission and is a member of the North Central Association of Colleges and Schools (Web site: http://www.ncahigherlearningcommission.org; telephone: 312-263-0456).

Distance Learning Program

The Extended University's distance learning programs are offered through two primary modes of delivery. Its External Degree program offers Associate of Arts and Bachelor of Science degree programs with seventeen majors through independent study/ correspondence, and its Online program currently offers a Bachelor of Science (B.S.) with seven business majors, criminal justice, emergency and disaster management, health-services administration, interdisciplinary studies, public administration, a Master of Business Administration (M.B.A.) and a Master of Public Administration (M.P. A.). Courses offered through both External Degree and Online formats meet the same standards as courses offered through the residential University in Fayette, Iowa. The External Degree program, which began in 1972, has been successfully delivered to more than 10,000 learners. Upper Iowa's External Degree program was one of the first and most successful in the United States. Both the External Degree and Online programs continue to be vital components in serving both civilian and military learners worldwide.

Delivery Media

In the External Degree program, students communicate with instructors via e-mail, fax, and regular mail. Classes are self-paced with no minimum completion time. Upper Iowa's Online program is noted for its e-mail–like feel. Online students log on (via the Internet) just long enough to send and receive materials, anytime, anywhere, day or night. Most work is accomplished off-line, or through asynchronous communication. Online students may also communicate with their instructors through course software, e-mail, fax, or phone.

Programs of Study

Upper Iowa University has a long history of offering high-quality degree programs through distance learning.

In the External Degree program, associate and bachelor's degree programs are available in a wide range of academic areas, including accounting, business administration, criminal justice, emergency and disaster management, finance, health-services administration, human resources management, human services, interdisciplinary stud-

ies, management, marketing, psychology, public administration (general, law enforcement, or fire science), social science, and technology and information management.

Upper Iowa's Online program offers a Bachelor of Science degree with fifteen majors to choose from: accounting, business administration, criminal justice, emergency and disaster management, finance, health-services administration, human resources management, human services, interdisciplinary studies, management, marketing, psychology, public administration (general, law enforcement, or fire science), and technology and information management.

The M.B.A. offers six areas of emphasis: accounting, corporate financial management, global business, human resources management, organizational development, and quality management.

The M.P.A. offers four areas of emphasis: health and human services, homeland security, justice administration, and public personnel management. The course work focuses on the theories and skills that are the foundation for tomorrow's organizations, including organizational design, total quality management, self-managed teams, employee empowerment, change management, facilitation skills, high-performance work systems, and more.

Special Programs

Each summer, the External Degree program sponsors the Institute for Experiential Learning (IEXL) for undergraduate students. During an intensive weeklong session held on the Fayette campus, students have the opportunity to earn 3 semester hours of undergraduate credit while visiting the residential campus and networking with other learners from around the world.

Student Services

External Degree and Online students are provided with one-on-one academic advising via U.S. mail, e-mail, telephone, fax communication, and through use of a special software/courseware package (for Online program students). In addition to local university libraries, undergraduate and graduate students and faculty members have access to the Henderson Wilder Library holdings through Upper Iowa University's Web site.

Credit Options

Full credit is given to students for college-level courses completed at regionally accredited colleges and universities. Students can transfer a maximum of 45 semester hours for an associate degree, 90 semester hours for a bachelor's degree, and 12 semester hours for a master's degree. Other sources of credit include the American Council on Education (ACE), the College-Level Examination Program (CLEP), Dantes Subject Standardized Test (DSST) subject exams, and experiential learning.

Faculty

Upper Iowa University's distance learning program has more than 100 adjunct faculty members, many of whom have doctoral or terminal degrees. Faculty members are experienced in the areas in which they teach.

Admission

Admission criteria for undergraduate degrees include graduation from an accredited public or private high school or completion of the GED test or its equivalent. For the graduate program, prospective students must hold an undergraduate degree from a regionally accredited college or university. More information regarding grade point requirements, TOEFL scores for international students, and transfer credit is available upon request or on the UIU Web site.

Tuition and Fees

Associate- and baccalaureate-level tuition for courses taken through External Degree (independent study/correspondence) for 2007–08 was $762 per 3-semester-credit course. Undergraduate and graduate online (Internet-based) courses were $897 and $1107 respectively, per 3-semester-credit course.

Financial Aid

Financial aid in the form of Federal Stafford Student Loans, Federal Pell Grants, Iowa Tuition Grants (Iowa residents only), Veterans Assistance, and Military Tuition Assistance is available.

Applying

Students may enroll in UIU distance learning programs at any time. In the External Degree program, students may start courses at any time. In the Online program, eight-week terms begin six times a year. Students should send official transcripts (including CLEP, DSST, or DD-214), GRE/GMAT score reports (if required), and a completed Application for Admission form (available online or by contacting the school via telephone or e-mail) directly to Upper Iowa University.

CONTACT

Extended University
Upper Iowa University
605 Washington Street
P.O. Box 1857
Fayette, Iowa 52142-1857

Phone: 877-366-0581 (toll-free)
Fax: 563-425-5771
E-mail: moreinfo@uiu.edu
Web site: http://www.uiu.edu

UTAH STATE UNIVERSITY

Regional Campuses and Distance Education

Logan, Utah

Utah State University (USU) was founded in 1888 as part of the public educational system of Utah and operates under the constitution and laws of the state. It belongs to the family of institutions known as land-grant universities, which had their origin in 1862. USU is governed by the State Board of Regents and accredited by Northwest Association of Accredited Schools.

USU integrates teaching, research, extension, and service to meet its unique role as Utah's land-grant university.

Distance Learning Program

USU Distance Education is an integral part of USU's outreach mission. USU Distance Education provides educational opportunities for time- and place-bound students who are not able to come to the campus to attend classes.

Distance Education offers several bachelor's and master's degree programs via interactive broadcast and a master's degree over the Internet. Many other interactive broadcast, Internet-based, and independent-study CD-ROM courses are offered.

USU is one of the leading institutions in the United States for its off-campus programs.

Delivery Media

Distance Education is made up of three program delivery units: interactive broadcast (satellite, video teleconferencing), online, and independent study.

Interactive broadcast degree programs are offered at USU education centers and are only available to Utah students. Online courses are designed for access any time of the day or night. Online students submit assignments electronically and interact with their instructors and classmates via e-mail and online discussions.

Students who register for independent-study courses receive a CD-ROM or printed course outline at registration. Independent-study students mail in assignments, take proctored examinations, and may contact their instructors by phone or e-mail.

Programs of Study

Complete degree and certificate programs can be earned entirely through Regional Campuses and Distance Education (RCDE). For a detailed list, interested students should visit http://distance.usu.edu.

Student Services

Student services available to distance learners include access to the University bookstore, Library Support System for Distance Learners, and the Academic Resource Center. For more information on student services available to distance learners, prospective students should visit the Web site at http://distance.usu.edu.

Credit Options

Credit earned through USU Distance Education is measured in semester units and is transferable to most colleges and universities in the U.S. Students who plan to transfer credit should make arrangements with the transfer institution prior to registration.

Faculty

The majority of Distance Education instructors are USU faculty members; many are leading researchers in their field. Distance Education faculty members recognize that the needs of individuals are of major importance; programs have been established to give students optimal individual attention.

Admission

Non-degree-seeking students do not need to be admitted to enroll in Distance Education courses. Degree-seeking students must apply for admission. Admission requirements are program specific and may be obtained by contacting the Admissions Office at 435-797-1079. Prospective students may complete an application for admission online at http://www.usu.edu/admissions.

Tuition and Fees

For tuition and fee information, prospective students should visit the Web site at http://distance.usu.edu.

Financial Aid

Financial aid is available for distance education students. Utah State University participates in the following financial aid programs: Federal Pell Grants, Federal Supplemental Educational Opportunity Grants (FSEOG), LEAAP Grants, Federal Perkins Loans, Federal Work-Study Program, Federal Stafford Student Loans, Federal PLUS loans, scholarships, and emergency loans. For more information, prospective students should contact the financial aid office at 435-797-0173 or visit the Web site at http://www.usu.edu/finaid/.

Applying

Students working toward any of the degree programs offered through Independent and Distance Education must be admitted to the University. Prospective students may complete an application for admission online at http://www.usu.edu/admissions or request a printed application by contacting the Admissions Office at 435-797-1129 or toll-free at 800-488-8108.

CONTACT

Regional Campuses and Distance Education
5055 Old Main Hill
Utah State University
Logan, Utah 84322-5055

Phone: 800-233-2137 (toll-free)
Fax: 435-797-1399
E-mail: distance.info@usu.edu
Web site: http://distance.usu.edu

VIRGINIA POLYTECHNIC INSTITUTE AND STATE UNIVERSITY
Institute for Distance and Distributed Learning
Blacksburg, Virginia

Founded in 1872 as a land-grant college named Virginia Agricultural and Mechanical College, Virginia Tech is now a comprehensive, innovative research university with the largest number of degree offerings in Virginia, more than 100 campus buildings, a 2,600-acre main campus, off-campus educational facilities in six regions, a study-abroad site in Switzerland, and a 1,700-acre agriculture research farm near the main campus. Through a combination of its three missions of teaching and learning, research and discovery, and outreach and engagement, Virginia Tech enrolls more than 29,000 undergraduate and graduate students from all fifty states and more than 100 countries in over 180 academic degree programs.

The University's growing reputation for excellence includes national recognition as a leader in distance and distributed learning. Virginia Tech's eLearning enrollments (including credit and noncredit) celebrated a significant milestone in the fall 2007 semester, having surpassed the 100,000 mark since summer 1998. During that time, more than 3,500 different courses were offered to eLearners with over 700 different faculty members engaged in delivering courses at a distance. Virginia Tech is helping to meet the changing needs of undergraduate and graduate students with online and distance-delivered master degree programs, certificates, and licensures as well as noncredit offerings for personal and professional growth. Innovative use of technology is transforming the educational process, while making it more accessible and learner-centered. Virginia Tech is fully accredited by the Commission on Colleges of the Southern Association of Colleges and Schools.

Distance Learning Program

As part of the Office of the University Provost and Vice President and Dean for Undergraduate Education, Virginia Tech's Institute for Distance and Distributed Learning (IDDL) provides leadership, coordination, management, and support to the distance and distributed learning (eLearning) activities of Virginia Tech. Through these activities, Virginia Tech extends its campus to communities throughout the world and provides an open campus environment that allows individuals to engage in learning at anytime and from anywhere. In addition, Virginia Tech shares the practical application of the University's knowledge and expertise in support of economic development, increases the University's access to the world and the world's access to the University, and researches new teaching and learning environments through the application of technology.

The 2006–07 academic year accounted for close to 16,000 enrollments representing 740 courses. Virginia Tech Online—Virginia Tech's student gateway to eLearning—features an academic portfolio of thirty graduate degree, certificate, and licensure programs; a program of fifty-five undergraduate core courses; an undergraduate concentration in humanistic traditions; and five noncredit professional or personnel development programs. Virginia Tech actively participates in the Electronic Campus of Virginia and collaboratively delivers courses and degree programs at a distance with other Virginia colleges and universities through the Commonwealth Graduate Engineering Program and Virginia Consortium of Engineering and Science Universities. Virginia Tech also participates in the Southern Region

Electronic Campus and the Natural Resources Distance Learning Consortium.

Programs of Study

Virginia Tech offers twelve graduate certificate programs in business information systems, communication, computer engineering, decision support systems, liberal arts, natural resources, networking, political science, and software development.

Teacher licensures are available in alternative licensure professional studies and in career and technical education.

Programs leading to a Master of Arts degree are available in instructional technology and political science.

Master of Science degrees can be earned in agriculture and life sciences, career and technical education, civil and environmental engineering, civil infrastructure engineering, computer engineering, electrical and computer engineering, engineering administration, health promotion, information technology, ocean engineering, and systems engineering.

An undergraduate concentration in humanistic traditions is offered both in an online and a face-to-face environment.

A wide variety of credit and noncredit courses is also offered through distance learning in the areas of accounting, architecture, art, biology, black studies, building construction, business, communications, computer science, economics, education, engineering, English, entomology, finance, geography, history, hotel management, horticulture, information science, landscape architecture, management, marketing, math, music, philosophy, physics, psychology, science and technology, sociology, Spanish, statistics, women's studies, and more.

Student Services

Recognizing the diverse needs of distance learners, Virginia Tech employs a holistic approach to distance learning in which the student's total educational experience is considered. A dedicated eLearning Student Services Coordinator within IDDL is charged with ensuring that all University eLearners have the services they need to successfully engage in a high quality educational experience. These efforts include collaboration and partnerships with student services and student affairs units (such as tutoring and academic support services) as well as establishing new services that meet the specific needs of eLearners. A current initiative in development is the creation of a Virtual Student Center, which will serve as a virtual space where students can go to meet online with other students; obtain academic, career, or financial services; have "coffee" with faculty members; attend presentations by speakers; and engage in other University-sponsored events.

Credit Options

Distance learners can transfer credits earned at other accredited postsecondary institutions to Virginia Tech following the established University policies. Students admitted to the University who have been certified by the Virginia Community College System or Richard Bland College as completing the trans-

fer module are deemed to have completed the University core curriculum components and receive 35 total credits for the module.

Faculty

The faculty is the foundation of Virginia Tech's distance learning programs and assures its academic excellence. The same faculty members, including some of the most highly honored faculty at the University, who teach traditional classroom-based campus courses also teach distance learning courses. Currently, 88 percent of Virginia Tech's academic teaching departments are involved in teaching distance learning courses. Over 280 faculty members were engaged in developing and delivering eLearning courses in 2006–07, an increase of 15 percent over the previous year

Admission

To become undergraduate or graduate degree candidates at Virginia Tech, students must apply formally for admission. Students' records at Virginia Tech and all other colleges and universities attended are reviewed within the context of current admission policies. Virginia Tech allows qualified students at other Virginia universities and colleges to enroll in its courses as non-degree-seeking or Commonwealth Campus students. For more information on undergraduate admission, students

should visit the IDDL Web site http://www.iddl.vt.edu; those interested in graduate programs should visit http://www.grads.vt.edu.

Tuition and Fees

For the latest information, students should visit http://www.bursar.vt.edu.

Financial Aid

Virginia Tech is a direct lending institution and awards financial aid from federally funded and state-funded programs as well as privately funded sources. Financial aid sources include the Federal Direct Stafford Loan, Federal Perkins Loan, Federal Direct PLUS Loan, Federal Pell Grant, Federal Work-Study, Virginia Guaranteed Assistance Program, Commonwealth Award, and the College Scholarship Assistance Program.

Applying

Students applying for undergraduate admission can access current information at http://www.admiss.vt.edu. Students applying for graduate admission can access current information at http://www.grads.vt.edu. Students can register for Internet-based courses at http://www.vto.vt.edu.

There is a nonrefundable fee ($50 undergraduate, $25 graduate) for non-degree-seeking students.

CONTACT

Angie Starr
Enrollment Services Coordinator
Office of Distance Learning and Summer Sessions
University Gateway Center, Suite 120 (0392)
902 Prices Fork Road
Virginia Tech (0445)
Blacksburg, Virginia 24061

Phone: 540-231-1264
Fax: 540-231-2079
E-mail: vto@vt.edu
Web site: http://www.iddl.vt.edu
        http://www.vto.vt.edu (online catalog)

WALDEN UNIVERSITY
A higher degree. A higher purpose.

WALDEN UNIVERSITY
Distance Education
Minneapolis, Minnesota

Walden University's online doctoral, master's, and bachelor's programs are designed to help students achieve their goals of personal enrichment and professional advancement and make a difference in the lives of others. Walden combines high-quality curricula, expert faculty members, and innovative distance learning models to offer highly applied, rigorous programs that allow adult learners to pursue advanced degrees while maintaining their personal and professional commitments.

Founded in 1970, Walden University offers master's and doctoral degrees in education, health and human services, management, psychology, and public policy and administration; master's degrees in engineering and IT; and bachelor's degrees in business administration, psychology, child development, and computer information systems. Walden University is accredited by The Higher Learning Commission and is a member of the North Central Association, http://www.ncahlc. org; 312-263-0456.

Distance Learning Program
With a global network of peers and faculty mentors, Walden's students collaborate with a diverse range of professionals to gain the critical insights and skills that are relevant to the work they do every day.

Delivery Media
Students and faculty members exchange ideas and collaborate through e-mail, online courses, study teams, and, in some programs, face-to-face residency sessions. Individual mentoring, online courses, and progress based on demonstrations of knowledge are among the components of Walden's programs. Students who enroll in a Walden program should be comfortable using e-mail, the Internet, and common desktop productivity software.

Programs of Study
The Ph.D. in Applied Management and Decision Sciences program offers an interdisciplinary approach that prepares students to advance the knowledge and practice of management and leadership. Students can complete a general program; specialize in accounting, engineering management, finance, information systems management, knowledge management, leadership and organizational change, learning management, or operations research; or pursue a self-designed program.

The Ph.D. in Education program produces leaders who can address the nation's most pressing educational chal-

lenges. Options include a general program; specializations in adult education leadership, community college leadership, early childhood education, educational technology, higher education, K–12 educational leadership, and special education; and a self-designed program.

The Ph.D. in Health Services program examines both the theoretical and practical aspects of health-care services, based on a learning model that encourages original research and real-world application of knowledge. A general program is available as are specializations in community health promotion and education and health management and policy.

The Ph.D. in Human Services program prepares students to participate in the design and delivery of cutting-edge public and private services. Students can complete a general program; specialize in clinical social work, counseling, criminal justice, family studies and intervention strategies, human services administration, or social policy analysis and planning; or pursue a self-designed program.

The Ph.D. in Public Health program focuses on seeking solutions to significant public health problems and applying and integrating new knowledge into public health research and practice settings. Specializations are available in community health promotion and education and in epidemiology.

The Ph.D. in Psychology program follows a scholar-practitioner model that prepares psychology professionals to excel in a wide range of careers in health-care settings, private practices, and global industries. Specializations include clinical psychology (licensure), counseling psychology (licensure), general psychology (with tracks in educational psychology and research and evaluation), health psychology, organizational psychology, and school psychology (licensure). The clinical, counseling, and school psychology specializations are designed to meet the academic licensure requirements of several state psychology boards. (Students are encouraged to consult the appropriate agency to determine specific licensing requirements.)

The Ph.D. in Public Policy and Administration program prepares students to meet the challenges of governance and effective service delivery. A general program is available as are specializations in criminal justice, health services, homeland security policy and coordination, international nongovernmental organizations (NGOs), knowledge management, nonprofit management and leadership, public management and leadership, public policy, and public safety management.

The Doctor of Education (Ed.D.) program has three specializations. Teacher leadership and administrator leadership for teaching and learning are both designed for K–12 educators who want to continue their practice while assuming leadership roles. The track in higher education and adult learning is designed to improve the competencies and expand the knowledge of professionals interested in teaching adult learners in a variety of settings.

The Master of Business Administration (M.B.A.) program offers students comprehensive cross-disciplinary skills to meet the complex issues and challenges of the global economy. Students may choose a general program or select from specializations in entrepreneurship, finance, human resource management, leadership, marketing, project management, risk management, or technology.

The Master of Public Administration (M.P.A.) prepares professionals to excel across the public, private, and governmental sectors. Students may choose a general program or specialize in health policy, homeland security policy, interdisciplinary policy studies, law and public policy, local government and management for sustainable communities, nonprofit management and leadership, or policy analysis.

The Master of Science in Nonprofit Management and Leadership program gives students the opportunity to gain the management and organizational skills needed to lead diverse and complex nonprofit organizations and to serve as social change agents in local and global communities.

In the M.S. in Psychology program, students learn to apply psychological theories and scientific methods in a variety of work settings to help prepare them for a career in a wide range of industries. The program includes a general program as well as specializations in crisis management and response, leadership development and coaching, media psychology, and organizational psychology and development.

The M.S. in Mental Health Counseling Program, through a mix of research, fieldwork, and courses taught by national experts, prepares students to address and treat behavioral disorders knowledgeably, ethically, and with respect for diversity.

The M.S. in Education program develops scholar-practitioners among educators serving students in pre-K–12 classrooms. The program offers specializations in curriculum, instruction, and assessment (grades K–12); educational leadership (K–12); elementary reading and literacy (pre-K–6); elementary reading and mathematics (K–6); integrating technology in the classroom (K–12); literacy and learning in the content areas (6–12); mathematics (K–5); mathematics (6–8); middle level education (5–8); science (K–8), and a teacher leadership specialization (K–12).

The Master of Public Health (M.P.H.) program features a practice-oriented approach using real-world examples and case studies and addresses the growing need for well-prepared public health professionals. Graduates are provided with the credentials to serve as an advocate for the development for healthy individuals, organizations, and communities.

The Master of Healthcare Administration (M.H.A.) program provides both current and future administrators with a strong background in health-care management, giving them the specialized, targeted knowledge and skills required to assume leadership positions across the spectrum of health-care delivery organizations.

The M.S. in Nursing program is accredited by the Commission on Collegiate Nursing Education (CCNE). Graduates gain the knowledge, skills, and influence to affect more lives and to make an even greater contribution through specializations in nursing education, leadership and management, and nursing informatics.

The M.S. in Software Engineering program helps students become experts in the latest software development theories and the engineering principles that support progressive software design.

The M.S. in Systems Engineering program provides the necessary processes and tools to define and validate system requirements, develop effective designs, and ensure those designs are safe and meet customer requirements.

The Master of Information Systems Management (M.I.S.M.) program helps prepare students for leadership in the creation and management of information systems, processes, and services that meet organizational needs. Specializations include business information management, customer relationship marketing, enterprise information security, IT strategy and governance, and managing global software and service supply chains.

The B.S. in Business Administration program is specifically designed for motivated adults with career experience and provides students with a strong foundation for a meaningful career in a variety of fields. Options include a general program and concentrations in finance, human resource management, information systems, management, and marketing.

The B.S. in Child Development program is a nonlicensure program for professionals interested in the field of early childhood education and development who want to continue to work and balance personal commitments. This program offers three concentrations: preschool, infant/toddler, and a dual concentration (preschool and infant/toddler).

The Bachelor of Science in Computer Information Systems program is designed to prepare students with the technical and business skills to advance their careers in information technology. Options include concentrations in educational computing, health-care informatics, human-computer interaction, information systems management, information systems security, and online work and communities and self-designed programs.

The B.S. in Psychology provides students with a broad understanding of psychology and its relevance in a diverse and global society. Concentrations include psychology applied to everyday life, psychology applied to the helping professions, psy-chology applied to the workplace, and preparation for graduate studies.

Walden University also offers a state-approved postbaccalaureate teacher preparation program and a state-approved special education endorsement program.

Student Services

Student services include academic advising, course management, financial aid, technical assistance, orientation, disability services, tutoring, the Writing Center, and a career center. Walden University partners with a national research library to provide reference, search, catalog, and distribution services to its students.

Credit Options

Transfer of credit from other institutions is permitted in most programs.

Faculty

Walden attracts esteemed scholars, researchers, and distinguished professionals as faculty members. The online learning model allows students to fully benefit from the diverse talents and experiences of the finest faculty members, regardless of where they reside.

Admission

Walden University has a long-standing commitment to providing educational opportunities to a diverse population of learners. To learn more, students should contact a Walden enrollment adviser.

Tuition and Fees

Tuition and fees vary by program.

Financial Aid

Walden offers students a variety of options to assist in funding their educational expenses. More information can be found at http://www.WaldenU.edu.

Applying

A completed and signed online application, a $50 application fee, and a personal/professional statement of purpose are required. Applicants must also send a resume, official transcripts from the institution that conferred their bachelor's or master's degree, and, for some programs, two completed recommendation forms.

CONTACT

Walden University
155 Fifth Avenue South, Suite 100
Minneapolis, Minnesota 55401

Phone: 866-492-5336 (toll-free)
Web site: http://www.WaldenU.edu

WASHINGTON STATE UNIVERSITY

WSU Center for Distance and Professional Education
Pullman, Washington

Washington State University (WSU), the state's land-grant institution, is dedicated to the preparation of students for productive lives and professional careers, to basic and applied research, and to the dissemination of knowledge. Founded in 1890, the University is a statewide institution with a main campus in Pullman, three branch campuses, ten community learning centers, and numerous Cooperative Extension and research facilities throughout the state. WSU is accredited by the Northwest Association of Schools and Colleges. In addition, the University is an acknowledged leader in developing and delivering distance education programs. Since 1992, WSU's Office of Distance Degree Programs (DDP) has served students in Washington, across the nation, and around the world and continues to expand online credit and noncredit options as the Center for Distance and Professional Education (CDPE). The University's undergraduate core curriculum, including world civilization courses and expanded writing requirements, is nationally recognized. Money magazine has called WSU a "public ivy" and rated the honors program as one of the nation's best.

Distance Learning Program

WSU's Center for Distance and Professional Education offers degree-completion programs leading to a Bachelor of Arts (B.A.) in business administration (with majors in entrepreneurship, management information systems (MIS), or management and operations), criminal justice, human development, humanities, social sciences, or women's studies; a Bachelor of Science in Nursing (B.S.N.); and a Master of Science (M.S.) in agriculture and in engineering and technology management. The undergraduate degree programs are designed primarily for students who have completed the equivalent of the first two years of college. They are the same degrees offered on three WSU campuses; requirements are the same, but students can complete their degrees without attending WSU in person.

Four credit certificate programs are offered online: Early Childhood Development and Care, Instructional Design (graduate level), Organic Agriculture, and Professional Writing, as well as three online noncredit certificate programs, Business Planning for Protected Areas, Forensic Ecology for Law Enforcement, and Internet Safety for Educators.

Delivery Media

Courses are delivered directly to students via the Internet. Students must have Internet access and e-mail to fulfill course requirements. Courses may also incorporate multimedia resources (DVDs, CDs, videotapes), lab kits, library resources, and print materials available through the DDP office.

Programs of Study

WSU's online B.A. in business administration with a major in entrepreneurship builds on business fundamentals and offers a curriculum that develops the unique skill set necessary for successful entrepreneurship. Graduates are prepared to lead innovation at businesses ranging from start-ups to well-established corporations. The programs is fully accredited by AACSB International—the Association to Advance Collegiate Schools of Business.

The online B.A. in business administration with a major in management information systems is designed to enable graduates to enter the working world as programmer-analysts, systems project managers, or Web masters. The program is also fully accredited by AACSB International.

The online B.A. in business administration with a major in management and operations provides a broad foundation for employment in the world of business, either at a large corporation or in the student's own business. The program is also fully accredited by AACSB International.

WSU's online B.A. in criminal justice offers a broad exposure in the social sciences through a policy-focused curriculum that prepares students for positions in the criminal justice system, other government agencies, and the private sector.

The online B.A. in human development is especially effective for individuals who work in child- or elder-care programs or in direct-service roles with a variety of special-needs clients. The degree program includes an internship component supervised by a WSU faculty member.

The B.A. in humanities is a broad-based, interdisciplinary liberal arts degree program with no set list of required courses. The program focuses on the humanities as it develops skills in communication, writing, problem solving, and critical thinking.

WSU's online B.A. in social sciences is a liberal arts degree that offers students multiple options and emphases in the social sciences and provides a broad background applicable to a variety of careers through an interdisciplinary approach.

The online B.A. in women's studies is the interdisciplinary study of gender and how class, race, ethnicity, nationality, sexual orientation, age, and ability shape the female and male experience. Students learn how female and male social roles affect personal lives and world-wide issues. They also develop an understanding of how a wide variety of inequalities were created and are reproduced and learn the manner in which societal change has addressed problems of discrimination and marginalization.

A B.S.N. degree program is available for registered nurses. The Intercollegiate College of Nursing/WSU College of Nursing offers nine theory courses using Web-based software and two clinical courses, which, in some circumstances, may be taken close to home. Out-of-state students may be required to complete the two clinical courses in Washington, which are scheduled based on negotiations between the student and faculty. RNs work with B.S.N.-prepared preceptors; nursing faculty members supervise the course. RN students must meet specific criteria prior to application to this program.

The online M.S. in agriculture program is designed for students who wish to prepare for or further their careers in agriculture without having to relocate or interfere with their current employment. A student can concentrate in one or two fields or otherwise tailor the curriculum to fit their particular needs. They may choose a thesis or no thesis program.

The online M.S. in engineering and technology management program provides engineers and professionals in technology management with formal academic experience in managing projects, people, organizations, operations, and quality. The program often results in immediate on-the-job improvements and provides graduates the ability to gain management responsibility.

The online certificate program in early childhood development and care addresses the complex ways in which child development is influenced and how this knowledge can be applied to designing innovative and effective programs for young children and their families. The program is ideal for students pursuing a degree in human development who would like to specialize in early childhood, individuals who already hold a bachelor's degree in another discipline, and persons currently working in the field of early childhood education who have at least 27 semester credits of college course work.

The online graduate certificate program in instructional design is designed for working professionals, educators, Web designers, and corporate trainers to strengthen their traditional face-to-face education and training skills and improve their ability to work in alternative learning environments. The 12-credit graduate program incorporates courses in constructivist learning design, educational technology and media, and leadership.

WSU's online organic agriculture certificate program, the first in the nation, develops a solid background in the agricultural sciences, including an understanding of complex agriculture and food systems. The program is designed for professionals working in agriculture or related fields that require an in-depth knowledge of organic systems, those wanting to pursue a career in organic agriculture, anyone interested in beginning a community-supported agriculture (CSA) farm, and home gardeners.

WSU's Professional Writing Certificate program allows students to develop a base of skills and knowledge of effective communication (including editorial and technical skills and the broader skills of analysis and synthesis) useful in the professional world. The certificate requires completion of 15 credits (made up of five courses taken in a specific order), with a grade of B (3.0) or better in each course.

Noncredit professional education options include Business Planning for Pro-

tected Areas, Forensic Ecology for Law Enforcement, and Internet Safety for Educators certificate programs, with requirements differing from credit and degree programs; students should visit http://professionaleducation.wsu.edu for details.

Nearly 200 courses are available to the students. Courses are also available from the National Universities Degree Consortium (NUDC), a group of eight land-grant and state universities formed to address the needs of adult and part-time learners.

A bachelor's degree at WSU requires the completion of at least 120 semester credits (40 at the upper-division level), with at least 30 credits taken through WSU. Courses must meet WSU general education requirements. Graduate credit programs require admission to the WSU Graduate School.

Student Services

Academic advising is available to all currently enrolled degree-seeking students. The WSU Office of Admissions prepares an official evaluation of a student's transcript when he or she is admitted to the University. A Distance Degree Programs (DDP) adviser assists DDP students in developing a study plan based on the program options and University requirements. A student services coordinator is available to help students with logistical details.

Students register online or with support from DDP student services. Students may order textbooks and course guides from the WSU Students Book Corporation online or via the toll-free telephone number.

All DDP students have access to the WSU libraries. The DDP librarian is available via toll-free telephone to assist students with database searches, checking out materials, and copying.

The ASWSU-DDP Career Counselor is available to WSU DDP students to discuss career-related concerns ranging from developing a school-to-career identity to finding a graduate school program.

Credit Options

Undergraduate students may transfer to WSU a maximum of 60 semester credits of lower-division credit and up to 30 credits from other four-year institutions. The exact number of transfer credits accepted by WSU may vary depending upon an individual's choice of degree.

The University accepts credit by examination, including Advanced Placement (AP), College-Level Examination Program (CLEP), and American Council on Education (ACE). Interested students should check with their advisers for details.

Faculty

There are 1,131 full-time and 231 part-time instructional faculty members in the WSU system, with 84 percent having terminal academic degrees.

Admission

Admission to the Center for Distance and Professional Education degree programs requires at least 27 semester or 40 quarter credits of transferable college course work from an accredited community or four-year college, with at least a 2.5 cumulative GPA. Applicants with a 2.0 to 2.49 cumulative GPA are given consideration.

Tuition and Fees

In 2008–09, semester-based tuition for undergraduates is $336 per credit for Washington residents and $492 for nonresidents. Semester-based graduate tuition is $403 per credit for residents and $593 for nonresidents. DVD, CD, and videotape rental charges vary by course.

Financial Aid

A financial aid adviser is available to all DDP students. WSU students receive aid from all federal programs. Washington residents are eligible for institutional and state need grants. In 2005–06, WSU awarded approximately $190 million in financial aid. Approximately 61 percent of all WSU students receive financial aid.

Applying

WSU degree-seeking students must submit an admissions form, have official copies of transcript(s) sent directly from the postsecondary institution(s) attended, and pay the $50 undergraduate application fee. Graduate requirements differ, so students should visit http://www.gradsch.wsu.edu/howtoapply.htm for information on WSU Graduate School admission requirements.

CONTACT

Student Support Services
Center for Distance and Professional Education
Van Doren 104
Washington State University
P.O. Box 645220
Pullman, Washington 99164-5220
Phone: 509-335-3557
       800-222-4978 (toll-free)
Fax: 509-335-4850
E-mail: distance@wsu.edu
Web site: http://www.online.wsu.edu

WEBER STATE UNIVERSITY
Distance Learning
Ogden, Utah

Weber State University (WSU) provides lifelong opportunities for diverse learners on and off campus. It offers degrees through seven colleges and forty departments via distance learning options, including online and independent study courses. Students may earn their Associate of Science in general studies or receive specialized training in health professions or criminal justice. WSU's academic programs prepare students for immediate employment or further study and equip them with liberal education concepts and skills to support their lifelong learning.

WSU serves as Utah's premier public undergraduate university. The institution was founded in 1889, became a state junior college in 1933, and added upper-division courses and began bachelor's degree programs in 1959. On January 1, 1991, Weber State further expanded its offerings and was granted university status.

Weber State University is accredited by the Northwest Association of Schools and Colleges. In addition, professional agencies such as the Commission on Accreditation for Allied Health Education Programs and the Association of University Programs in Health Administration accredit specific disciplines.

Distance Learning Program

The WSU Distance Learning Program serves students who cannot attend college classes in person. During the 2007–08 academic year, more than 25,000 students enrolled in print- and Internet-based courses. Students use distance learning to earn general education credits, as well as degrees and professional credentials in manufacturing, criminal justice, and health science areas.

Delivery Media

Students follow study guides, read textbooks, view videotapes/DVDs, hear cassettes, and/or participate in online courses. They interact with other students, instructors, and advisers by using mail, telephone, e-mail, and online discussion groups. Exams are delivered online or through the mail and are administered by approved proctors. Access to a videocassette/DVD player, audiocassette player, word processor, or a computer with browser software and an Internet service provider may be required.

Programs of Study

The WSU Distance Learning degree program evolved from a commitment to providing education for health-care professionals and other working adults regardless of location. Combining independent study with Internet courses, a bachelor's degree requires 120 semester hours (40 upper-division, 30 through WSU) with a minimum GPA of at least a 2.0 (or C).

Bachelor's degrees are available in clinical laboratory science, diagnostic medical sonography (medical-vascular), health information management, health promotion, health services administration, nuclear medicine, radiation therapy, and radiologic science (emphases in advanced radiography, cardiovascular-interventional technology, computed tomography, magnetic resonance imaging, mammography, and quality management).

An Associate of Science degree is available in health information technology, and an Associate of Applied Science degree is available in clinical laboratory science.

The associate degree in general studies serves the needs of students who want to individualize the first two years of their academic programs, students who want to obtain a broad liberal education, and students who want to lay broad foundations for continued higher education.

The Weber State University Distance Learning Associate of Science degree program in criminal justice and the professional certificate programs in production and inventory management are designed for professionals whose work and travel schedules and remote locations make it difficult for them to participate in classroom course work.

Law enforcement and security professionals can register online with the Utah Electronic College (UEC) and take courses through Weber State University or one of its six collaborating institutions, completing their training on their home or work computers.

Weber State University works in partnership with the 70,000-member APICS (The Association for Operations Management) to offer its certification program through WSU Online for people who work in production and resource management.

WSU certificate programs include health-care coding and classification and radiologic sciences. Radiologic sciences classes can be used toward continuing education units (CEU).

Special Programs

WSU Online, the award-winning extension of the University on the Internet, allows students to take online courses, use online support services, and participate in online discussions and activities with faculty and staff members and other students. WSU Online makes it possible for students with busy schedules and/or long commutes to take advantage of the convenience of online courses with support services and interpersonal experiences that are essential to their success. For current course listings and additional information, students can visit the WSU Web site at http://wsuonline.weber.edu.

Courses from a wide range of academic disciplines are available through Weber State University's independent study program, allowing students to complete their course work at their convenience. Each year, more than 10,000 students enroll in these Internet or print-based courses and take advantage of this self-paced, individualized mode of study.

Student Services

WSU recognizes that most of its students have work, family, and other responsibilities that limit their participation in traditional classroom college courses; therefore, convenience is a major factor in the design of the Distance Learning Program.

Students receive guidance from distance learning staff and faculty members. Degree-seeking students are assigned academic advisers who review transcripts and past learning experiences. This information is used to design individualized programs of study.

Students may access Stewart Library's catalog, interlibrary loan, reference help, document delivery, and other services electronically at http://library.weber.edu. Textbooks can be purchased directly from the WSU bookstore, by telephone (800-848-7770

Ext. 6352), or online (http://bookstore.weber.edu) for a small handling charge.

Credit Options

WSU may grant credit for active military, National Guard, or reserve experience; 38 or more credits to registered radiographers; a maximum of 45 credits to diploma nursing school graduates; and varying credits to registered respiratory therapy technicians and graduates of accredited therapy/specialty programs. Official transcripts should be sent directly from universities and colleges attended. WSU also recognizes College-Level Examination Program (CLEP) credits.

Faculty

WSU Distance Learning currently employs 200 full-time university faculty members and 50 adjunct faculty members. Nearly all faculty members hold terminal degrees in their respective fields.

Admission

Degree-seeking Distance Learning applicants must meet WSU admission requirements. The programs in health professions require separate applications and information specific to their academic areas. Students not seeking to complete a degree at WSU may be eligible for simplified, nonmatriculated admission.

Tuition and Fees

Distance Learning tuition averages $180 per semester hour. Additional materials

may include course study guides ($3–$40) and audiotape, videotape, or DVD deposits of $60 to $100, with a $40 refund upon their return.

Tuition fees for online courses are $180 per semester hour for non-Utah residents. Utah residents pay regular on-campus tuition and fees. All fees are subject to change. Students can consult the current catalog or visit the Web site at http://www.weber.edu/distancelearning/ for more information.

Financial Aid

Eligible students may apply for federal financial aid such as Pell Grants, Supplemental Educational Opportunity Grants (SEOG), Perkins Loans, and Stafford Student Loans. Students can contact the office of financial aid toll-free at 800-848-7770 Ext. 7569.

Veterans may also be considered for VA educational benefits (office of Veteran Affairs telephone: 800-848-7770 Ext. 6039, toll-free). Health professions degree programs are approved by DANTES.

Applying

Students should apply online at http://weber.edu/admissions/ and send an individual program application (if required); official transcripts from previous colleges; and an application fee of $30 (may be paid online by credit card) to the contact address. Distance Learning students need not attend an orientation.

CONTACT

Office of Distance Learning
Weber State University
4005 University Circle
Ogden, Utah 84408-4005
Phone: 801-626-6600
        800-848-7770 Ext. 6600 (toll-free)
Fax: 801-626-8035
E-mail: dist-learn@weber.edu
Web site: http://wsuonline.weber.edu
        http://weber.edu/distancelearning

WESTWOOD COLLEGE–DENVER NORTH ONLINE PROGRAMS

Westwood College Online
Denver, Colorado

Westwood College has been providing fast-track, career-focused education since 1953. In addition to online degree programs, Westwood College operates seventeen campuses, with locations in Anaheim, Inland Empire (Upland), South Bay, and Los Angeles, California; Atlanta, Georgia; DuPage, O'Hare Airport, River Oaks, and Chicago–Loop, Illinois; Denver–North and Denver–South, Colorado; Dallas, Fort Worth, and Houston, Texas; and the Washington, D.C., area.

Westwood's fast-track programs enable a student to complete an associate degree in as little as twenty months and a bachelor's degree in as little as three years. By offering year-round classes focused on the most critical skills needed to advance your career, you can complete your course work in less time than students at traditional schools.

Online degree programs are offered through Westwood College–Denver North Online Programs and are accredited by the Accrediting Commission of Career Schools and Colleges of Technology (ACCSCT).

Distance Learning Program

Westwood College started offering online degree programs in May 2002. Westwood College Online is an excellent option for students who are outside of the metro areas served by Westwood campuses or students whose work or family obligations do not allow time to attend scheduled classes on campus.

Delivery Media

The online courses are instructor led, not self-paced. Assignments are due weekly. The online courses may include the use of threaded discussions simulating in-class discussion and interaction; group projects; student-to-student, student-to-instructor, and instructor-to-student e-mails; chat rooms; short online audio and video lectures; and graphical demonstrations of concepts.

Programs of Study

Westwood College Online offers twenty degree programs ranging from business administration to criminal justice to game art and design. The curriculum provides hands-on projects incorporating some of the latest skills and technologies students learn during course work. Education at Westwood College Online challenges students, enriches them, and helps launch them into a successful career.

Westwood College Online's programs include the following:

School of Business: Business administration, with concentrations in accounting and marketing and sales; e-business management; fashion merchandising; health-care management; technical management; and Master of Business Administration.

School of Design: Animation, game art and design, graphic design and multimedia, interior design, visual communications, and Web design and multimedia.

School of Justice: Criminal justice and paralegal.

School of Technology: Computer network engineering, computer network management, game software development, information systems security, and software engineering.

For a complete overview of each program as well as program topics, details, and career opportunities, students should visit http://www.westwoodonline.edu for an up-to-date listing and information.

Special Programs

Alumni retraining is a special program at Westwood. All Westwood alumni are entitled to tuition-free graduate retraining in the program they completed at Westwood. Graduates are able to audit classes to update their skills as curriculum changes in their field of study. Charges for books and student fees may apply.

Student Services

Westwood distance learning students receive online access to the same student services that are provided to on-campus students. With its academic advising, Westwood is dedicated to helping students remove obstacles to success. There are several programs that provide students with the opportunity to solve problems, share ideas, and set goals with members of the college staff. Westwood has a free tutoring program that provides online help. There is a full research library that is available online to students 24 hours a day, seven days a week. Distance learning students also have access to technical assistance 24 hours a day, seven days a week.

The primary objective of the Career Development Services Office is to help students achieve their career goals. At Westwood, successful job-search assistance begins long before graduation. In fact, Westwood's unique approach to career planning and job-placement assistance begins at registration and continues beyond graduation.

Credit Options

There are four ways to achieve advanced academic standing at Westwood College: with transfer credits from accredited colleges or universities, through articulation agreements with selected high schools and colleges, through Westwood College Proficiency Exams, and through Advanced Placement (AP) exams, College Level Examination Program (CLEP) exams, or nationally recognized certification exams.

Faculty

Westwood instructors bring a wealth of real-world experience in their fields and eagerly share that knowledge in the classroom. They are also experts in online teaching and consistently receive high marks from their students: according to Westwood College Online's survey, 96 percent of Westwood College Online graduates said they would recommend their teacher to other students.

Admission

Admission into any program requires that the applicant meet certain admissions requirements. Applicants must provide documentation of prior educa-

tion and must demonstrate proficiency in basic college-level skills. Applicants from countries where English is not the primary language spoken and applicants whose native language is not English must demonstrate English language proficiency. For a complete list of admissions requirements found in the Colorado catalog, students should visit http://www.westwood.edu/pdf/catalogs/default.asp.

Tuition and Fees

A complete listing of tuition and charges is contained in a catalog addendum. The College reserves the right to adjust tuition rates at the beginning of any academic term, but such increases are announced at least sixty days in advance. Students should visit http://www.westwood.edu/pdf/catalogs/default.asp for a list of the catalogs.

Financial Aid

Tuition assistance is available for those who qualify. In order to help guide applicants through the tuition assis-

tance application process, Westwood provides a step-by-step guide as well as links to all of the forms that can be filled out online.

Applying

To qualify for admission, students must submit an application fee of $25 and a registration fee of $75, provide proof of a high school diploma or GED completion, and provide passing test scores from college-level exams outlined in the Admission section.

CONTACT

Westwood College Online
Westwood College–Denver
    North–Online Programs
7350 North Broadway
Denver, Colorado 80221

Phone: 888-996-6546 (toll-free)
Fax: 303-426-1832
E-mail: wolinternet@westwood.edu
Web site:
    http://www.westwoodonline.
    edu

Consortium In-Depth Description

The organization listed in this section represents a consortium of institutions offering distance learning programs. Consortia are formed so that an expanded set of distance learning options can be offered beyond the resources available through any single member institution. They do not have a central application process and/or do not directly award credits and degrees. The application process, credits, or conferred degrees are awarded through one of the member institutions. Further, consortia generally are not directly granted accreditation; rather, credits and degrees reflect the accreditation of the awarding institution. The reader should obtain specific information directly from the consortium itself.

SREB'S ELECTRONIC CAMPUS

Atlanta, Georgia

In February 2004, the Southern Regional Education Board (SREB) launched a more robust Electronic Campus, recreating it as a regional "learning network for the South", with improved levels of function. The Electronic Campus Web site (http://www.ElectronicCampus.org) is the gateway to e-learning opportunities and online services designed to meet the unique needs of the adult learners who want to start, continue, or complete their education. It provides a one-stop place for adults to learn about and understand educational opportunities, to select campuses and/or e-learning opportunities that best match their needs, and to apply online and enroll in courses or programs. While the Electronic Campus is an online resource for all students, it is targeted at the unique needs of adult and e-learners to help them get the education they need to meet the demands of the twenty-first-century workforce.

Established in 1998, SREB's Electronic Campus has grown from 104 courses to more than 20,000 courses and over 650 degree programs from colleges and universities from the sixteen member states. New courses and programs are added continually.

The Southern Regional Education Board, the nation's first interstate compact for education, was created in 1948 at the request of southern business, education, and governmental leaders. It is designed to help leaders in government and education work together to advance education and thus improve the social and economic life of the region. SREB's member states are Alabama, Arkansas, Delaware, Florida, Georgia, Kentucky, Louisiana, Maryland, Mississippi, North Carolina, Oklahoma, South Carolina, Tennessee, Texas, Virginia, and West Virginia.

Distance Learning Program

The *Electronic Campus* provides detailed common and comparable information about distance learning courses and programs offered by participating colleges and universities. The goal is to provide enhanced educational opportunities for adult e-learners as well as traditional and nontraditional students by removing many of the barriers that have long hindered access to higher education.

Delivery Media

Courses and programs are available in a variety of delivery formats. The predominant delivery method is the World Wide Web. Courses and programs are available via the Web in both synchronous and asynchronous modes. Other delivery formats are videotapes, satellite, CD-ROMs, compressed video, and open broadcast. Information on the delivery formats for each course and program is available on the *Electronic Campus* Web site (http://www.ElectronicCampus.org).

Programs of Study

The *Electronic Campus* provides access to more than 650 academic programs from regionally accredited public and private colleges and universities. Programs are available in a variety of disciplines and majors at the associate, bachelor's, master's, and doctoral levels. Certificate programs at various levels are also available. More than 20,000 credit courses at the undergraduate and graduate levels, all offered electronically, are available and fully searchable on the Web site.

All courses and programs available at the *Electronic Campus* meet SREB's

Principles of Good Practice and have undergone a review at the institutional, state, and regional levels. The Principles are the quality cornerstone of the *Electronic Campus*. Institutions offering courses and programs must meet a variety of requirements: the course or program must provide appropriate interaction between faculty members and students and among students, high-quality faculty members must provide appropriate supervision of the program or course that is offered electronically, and academic standards for all programs or courses offered electronically must be the same as those for other courses or programs delivered at the institution from which they originate.

Special Programs

The *Electronic Campus* also offers specialized portals to help individuals meet their professional development needs in specific career areas. The first is The Teacher Center (http://www.TheTeacherCenter.org), a site that links teachers, administrators, counselors, librarians, teacher aides, and aspiring teachers to a comprehensive set of services. Educators can search for and enroll in online courses and programs that are offered at the undergraduate and graduate level and that provide either college credit or continuing education units. The portal also provides information about scholarships and financial aid; information about the federal No Child Left Behind Act and each state's requirements for highly qualified teachers; information about each SREB state's licensure, certification, and alternative routes to teaching; career opportunities; and numerous other online services.

The Academic Common Market/ *Electronic Campus* program enables a student in the SREB states to get a waiver of out-of-state tuition if certain conditions are met. Those conditions include the following: no public college or university in a student's home state (state of residence) offers a degree program in the chosen field of study; the program is available in another SREB state participating in the Academic Common Market; the program is available through the *Electronic Campus;* the home state adopts/accepts the program for its residents; the student meets admissions requirements; and the student can be certified as a resident in their home state to participate. More than sixty degree programs are now available through the Academic Common Market/*Electronic Campus*.

Faculty

Many of the SREB region's most respected professors teach courses and programs on the *Electronic Campus.* The faculty members respond to students' questions online and often list times that they can be reached by telephone and e-mail in their campus offices. Students say communication with online professors is as effective as or even more effective than in a classroom setting.

Admission

Each college or university handles admission to its degree programs offered on the *Electronic Campus.* Students can access this information directly from the *Electronic Campus* Web site. Many institutions allow potential students to complete the application for admission online with just a few mouse clicks. Students who wish to enroll in a specific course may be able to do so without formal application and admission. The enrollment procedure and requirements for all colleges and universities participating in the *Electronic Campus* are outlined on the Web site.

Tuition and Fees

Each college or university offering courses and programs sets its tuition and fees. Tuition and fee charges are available at the *Electronic Campus* site.

A growing number of colleges and universities participating in the *Electronic Campus* are offering courses at a single or "electronic rate." These rates apply to students enrolling in courses irrespective of their residence. These courses are clearly marked to help

more students gain access and afford these learning opportunities.

Financial Aid

Participating colleges and universities coordinate financial aid. Specific information on financial aid is available from the institutions. General information is available on the *Electronic Campus* site.

Applying

Anyone with Internet access may search courses and programs available through the *Electronic Campus.* There is no charge for accessing or using the services available at the site. A simple registration can be completed when visiting. Creating a free *Electronic Campus* or Teacher Center account allows users to use (and reuse) data to complete online applications for colleges and universities and financial aid, save course and program information, establish e-mail and personal calendars, and take advantage of other services at the *Electronic Campus.*

CONTACT

Mary Agnes Larson
Associate Director
Student Access Programs and Services
Southern Regional Education Board
592 10th Street, NW
Atlanta, Georgia 30318-5776

Phone: 404-875-9211
Fax: 404-872-1477
E-mail: electroniccampus@sreb.org
Web site: http://www.ElectronicCampus.org

Indexes

INSTITUTIONS OFFERING DEGREE AND CERTIFICATE PROGRAMS

Index of degree and certificate programs offered by institutions. A=Associate degree; B=Bachelor's degree;
GC=Graduate certificate; M=Master's degree; UC=Undergraduate certificate

A+ CERTIFICATION AND COMPUTER TECHNOLOGY

Cleveland Institute of Electronics (UC)

AAS NURSING, HEALTH CARE PROVIDER TO RN ARTICULATION

St. Clair County Community College (A)

ACADEMIC ADVISING

Kansas State University (GC,M)

ACCELERATED CERTIFICATION FOR TEACHING

Wheeling Jesuit University (GC)

ACCELERATED MASTER OF TOURISM ADMINISTRATION

The George Washington University (M)

ACCELERATED PROGRAM

California State University, San Marcos (B)

ACCOMPLISHED TEACHING

Columbus State University (M)

ACCOUNTANCY

Auburn University (M)
National University (B)
State University of New York Institute of Technology (M)
State University of New York Institute of Technology (M)
University of Phoenix (M)

ACCOUNTANT

Lake Superior College (A)

ACCOUNTING

AIB College of Business (A,B)
Athabasca University (B,UC)
Bellevue University (B)
Blackhawk Technical College (A)
Brenau University (M)
Chemeketa Community College (A)
City University of Seattle (B,UC)
Colorado Technical University Colorado Springs (A,B)
Darton College (UC)
DeVry University Online (A)
Dickinson State University (B)
Excelsior College (B)
Florida Institute of Technology (B)
Florida Tech University Online (B)

Franklin Pierce University (UC)
Franklin University (A,B)
Gateway Technical College (A)
Golden Gate University (M,GC,M,B)
IIA College (A)
Indiana Wesleyan University (A)
Ivy Tech Community College–Bloomington (A)
Ivy Tech Community College–Central Indiana (A)
Ivy Tech Community College–Columbus (A)
Ivy Tech Community College–East Central (A)
Ivy Tech Community College–Kokomo (A)
Ivy Tech Community College–Lafayette (A)
Ivy Tech Community College–North Central (A)
Ivy Tech Community College–Northeast (A)
Ivy Tech Community College–Northwest (A)
Ivy Tech Community College–Southeast (A)
Ivy Tech Community College–Southern Indiana (A)
Ivy Tech Community College–Southwest (A)
Ivy Tech Community College–Wabash Valley (A)
Ivy Tech Community College–Whitewater (A)
Kaplan University Online (A,B)
Kaskaskia College (A)
Keiser University (A,B)
Lakeland College (B)
Liberty University (M,A,B)
Mercy College (A)
Middlesex Community College (A)
Minnesota School of Business–Richfield (B)
Montgomery County Community College (A)
Mountain Empire Community College (A)
Myers University (B)
New Jersey City University (M)
Northampton County Area Community College (A)
Northeastern University (A)
Northern Virginia Community College (A)
Northwest Missouri State University (B)
Northwest Technical College (A)
Nova Southeastern University (M)
Piedmont Community College (UC)
Randolph Community College (A)
Saint Leo University (B)
Saint Mary-of-the-Woods College (A,B)
San Diego Community College District (A)
Seminole Community College (A)
Southern New Hampshire University (GC,A,B,UC)
Southwestern College (B)
Strayer University (A,B,UC)
Sullivan University (A)
Thomas Edison State College (B)
University of Dallas (M)
The University of Maine at Augusta (B)
University of Maryland University College (GC,B)
University of Northwestern Ohio (B)

University of Phoenix (M,A)
Upper Iowa University (B)
Utah State University (B)
Vincennes University (A)
Western Wyoming Community College (A,UC)

ACCOUNTING (BACHELOR COMPLETION)

Indiana Wesleyan University (B)

ACCOUNTING (UNDERGRADUATE)

Golden Gate University (UC)

ACCOUNTING AND BUSINESS ADMINISTRATION

Lake Region State College (A)

ACCOUNTING AND BUSINESS LEADERSHIP

AIB College of Business (A)

ACCOUNTING AND COMPUTING

Illinois Eastern Community Colleges, Olney Central College (A)

ACCOUNTING AND FINANCE CONCENTRATION (10-MONTH PROGRAM)

American InterContinental University Online (M)

ACCOUNTING AND FINANCE CONCENTRATION (COMPLETION PROGRAM)

American InterContinental University Online (B)

ACCOUNTING AND FINANCE SPECIALIZATION

Florida Tech University Online (M)

ACCOUNTING AND FINANCIAL MANAGEMENT

DeVry University Online (M)
University of Maryland University College (M)

ACCOUNTING AND FINANCIAL SERVICES

AIB College of Business (A)

ACCOUNTING AND INFORMATION TECHNOLOGY

AIB College of Business (A)
University of Maryland University College
  (GC,M)

ACCOUNTING AND TAX SPECIALIST

Minnesota School of Business–Richfield (A)

ACCOUNTING APPLICATIONS

Seminole Community College (UC)

ACCOUNTING CLERK

Northwest Technical College (UC)

ACCOUNTING CONCENTRATION

Colorado Technical University Colorado
  Springs (M)
Saint Leo University (M)
Sullivan University (B)

ACCOUNTING FOR HEALTH CARE AND NON-PROFIT

The University of Toledo (UC)

ACCOUNTING INFORMATION SYSTEMS

Saint Mary-of-the-Woods College (B)

ACCOUNTING NYS CPA TRACK

Excelsior College (B)

ACCOUNTING ONLINE

Bryant and Stratton Online (A)

ACCOUNTING SOFTWARE APPLICATIONS

The University of Toledo (UC)

ACCOUNTING TECHNICIAN

Minot State University–Bottineau Campus (A)

ACCOUNTING TECHNOLOGY

Broward Community College (A)
The University of Toledo (A,UC)

ACCOUNTING–ASSOCIATE OF BUSINESS

York Technical College (A)

ACCOUNTING–GENERAL ACCOUNTING TRACK (BBS)

University of Windsor (B)

ACCOUNTING–HEALTHCARE ACCOUNTING AND FINANCIAL MANAGEMENT

Indiana University System (UC)

ACCOUNTING, ADVANCED

Athabasca University (UC)
College of Southern Maryland (UC)

ACCOUNTING, BASIC

College of Southern Maryland (UC)

ACCOUNTING, FINANCE, INFORMATION SYSTEMS, MARKETING

Old Dominion University (B)

ACCOUNTING/FINANCE

Southern New Hampshire University (M,B)

ACCOUNTING/INFORMATION SYSTEMS

Southern New Hampshire University (B)

ACQUISITION AND CONTRACT ADMINISTRATION (MSA)

University of West Florida (M)

ACQUISITION AND CONTRACT MANAGEMENT

Bellevue University (M)
Florida Institute of Technology (M)
Strayer University (A,B,UC)

ACQUISITION AND CONTRACTING CONCENTRATION OR PROJECT MANAGEMENT CONCENTRATION

American Graduate University (M)

ACQUISITION MANAGEMENT

University of Management and Technology
  (M,UC)

ACQUISITION MANAGEMENT– MASTER OF ACQUISITION MANAGEMENT

American Graduate University (M)

ACUTE CARE NURSE PRACTITIONER

Drexel University (M,)
Vanderbilt University (M)

ADDICTION STUDIES

University of Cincinnati (B)

ADDICTIONS COUNSELING

Darton College (UC)

ADDICTIONS COUNSELING CERTIFICATION PROGRAM

Fort Hays State University (UC)

ADMINISTRATION

Athabasca University (UC)
University of the Incarnate Word (B)

ADMINISTRATION OF JUSTICE

Arizona Western College (A)
Cerro Coso Community College (A)
Thomas Edison State College (A,B)
University of Louisville (M,B)

ADMINISTRATION OF JUSTICE AND SECURITY

University of Phoenix (M)

ADMINISTRATION OF JUSTICE– LAW ENFORCEMENT

West Hills Community College (A)

ADMINISTRATION–BUILDING CODE ADMINISTRATION

Central Michigan University (B)

ADMINISTRATION– COMMUNICATION ARTS

University of the Incarnate Word (M)

ADMINISTRATION–GENERAL ADMINISTRATION CONCENTRATION

Central Michigan University (M)

ADMINISTRATION–HEALTH SERVICES ADMINISTRATION CONCENTRATION

Central Michigan University (M)

ADMINISTRATION–HUMAN RESOURCE ADMINISTRATION

Central Michigan University (M)

ADMINISTRATION–INFORMATION RESOURCE MANAGEMENT CONCENTRATION

Central Michigan University (M)

ADMINISTRATION–LEADERSHIP CONCENTRATION

Central Michigan University (M)

ADMINISTRATION– ORGANIZATIONAL ADMINISTRATION

Central Michigan University (B)

ADMINISTRATION–PUBLIC ADMINISTRATION CONCENTRATION

Central Michigan University (M)

ADMINISTRATIVE ASSISTANT

Minot State University–Bottineau Campus (A)
North Dakota State College of Science (A)
Northwest Technical College (A)

ADMINISTRATIVE ASSISTANT–ACCOUNTING OPTION

Williston State College (A)

ADMINISTRATIVE ASSISTANT–FRONT OFFICE OPTION

Williston State College (UC)

ADMINISTRATIVE ASSISTANT–HEALTH INFORMATION MANAGEMENT OPTION

Williston State College (A)

ADMINISTRATIVE ASSISTANT–INFORMATION PROCESSING OPTION

Williston State College (A,UC)

ADMINISTRATIVE ASSISTANT–MEDICAL BILLING AND CODING OPTION

Williston State College (UC)

ADMINISTRATIVE COMMUNICATIONS–LIBERAL STUDIES

Washburn University (B)

ADMINISTRATIVE INFORMATION TECH

Illinois Eastern Community Colleges, Frontier Community College (A)
Illinois Eastern Community Colleges, Lincoln Trail College (A)
Illinois Eastern Community Colleges, Olney Central College (A)
Illinois Eastern Community Colleges, Wabash Valley College (A)

ADMINISTRATIVE MEDICAL SPECIALIST WITH MEDICAL BILLING AND CODING CERTIFICATE

California State University, Dominguez Hills (GC)

ADMINISTRATIVE SERVICES CERTIFICATE

National University (UC)

ADMINISTRATIVE STUDIES

Missouri State University (M)
St. John's University (B)
Thomas Edison State College (A)
York University (B)

ADMINISTRATIVE STUDIES/HEALTH SERVICES ADMINISTRATION

The University of South Dakota (M)

ADMINISTRATIVE STUDIES/INTERDISCIPLINARY STUDIES

The University of South Dakota (M)

ADMINISTRATIVE STUDIES/LONG-TERM CARE ADMINISTRATION

The University of South Dakota (M)

ADMINISTRATIVE STUDIES/ORGANIZATIONAL LEADERSHIP

The University of South Dakota (M)

ADMINISTRATIVE SUPPORT

Northwest Technical College (UC)
Rappahannock Community College (UC)

ADMINISTRATIVE SUPPORT TECHNOLOGY

Mountain Empire Community College (A)

ADMINISTRATIVE SUPPORT TECHNOLOGY MEDICAL OFFICE SPECIALIST

Mountain Empire Community College (A)

ADMINISTRATIVE/MANAGEMENT STUDIES

Excelsior College (A)

ADULT AND CONTINUING EDUCATION

Kansas State University (M)

ADULT DEVELOPMENT AND AGING SERVICES

Penn State University Park (UC)

ADULT EDUCATION

Bellevue University (B)
Brock University (UC)
Buffalo State College, State University of New York (GC,M)
Indiana University System (M)
Northwestern State University of Louisiana (M)
Oregon State University (M)
Penn State University Park (M)
University of Southern Maine (M)
University of Wisconsin–Platteville (M)

ADULT EDUCATION (BED IN ADULT EDUCATION)

Brock University (B)

ADULT EDUCATION AND LEADERSHIP

Jones International University (M)

ADULT EDUCATION AND TRAINING

Saint Joseph's College of Maine (A,UC)

ADULT EDUCATION AND TRAINING (AET)

Colorado State University (M)

ADULT LEARNING

University of Calgary (UC)

ADULT LEARNING AND DEVELOPMENT

Cleveland State University (GC,M)

ADULT LIBERAL STUDIES

The University of Toledo (B)

ADULT NURSE PRACTITIONER

Clarkson College (M,)
East Carolina University (M,)
Vanderbilt University (M)

ADULT PSYCHIATRIC MENTAL HEALTH NURSE PRACTITIONER

Drexel University (M,)

ADULT RELIGIOUS EDUCATION

Saint Joseph's College of Maine (B)

ADVANCED BUSINESS

Fort Hays State University (GC)

ADVANCED CATECHIST CERTIFICATE

The Catholic Distance University (UC)

ADVANCED CODING FOR THE PHYSICIAN'S OFFICE

California State University, Dominguez Hills (GC)

ADVANCED COMMUNITY PUBLIC HEALTH PRACTICE

University of Illinois at Chicago (UC)

ADVANCED HOSPITAL CODING AND CCS PREP

California State University, Dominguez Hills (GC)

ADVANCED IMAGING SCIENCES (WITH UMDNJ)

Thomas Edison State College (B)

ADVANCED NURSING LEADERSHIP

University of Illinois at Chicago (UC)

ADVANCED PARALEGAL CERTIFICATE

California State University, Dominguez Hills (GC)

ADVANCED PRACTICE FORENSIC NURSE

University of Illinois at Chicago (UC)

ADVANCED PRACTICE PALLIATIVE CARE

University of Illinois at Chicago (UC)

ADVANCED PROGRAMS

University of Oklahoma (D,M)

ADVANCED PROJECT MANAGEMENT

University of Wisconsin–Platteville (GC)

ADVENTURE EDUCATION

Prescott College (M,B)

ADVERTISING

Academy of Art University (M,A,B)

ADVERTISING AND MARKETING

Minot State University–Bottineau Campus (A,UC)

ADVERTISING AND PUBLIC RELATIONS

Seminole Community College (A)

ADVERTISING DESIGN

Syracuse University (M)

ADVERTISING MANAGEMENT

Bellevue University (B)

AERONAUTICAL SCIENCE

Embry-Riddle Aeronautical University (M)

AERONAUTICS AND ASTRONAUTICS

Stanford University (M)
University of Washington (M)

AEROSPACE

The University of Tennessee (M)

AEROSPACE AND MECHANICAL ENGINEERING (COMPUTATIONAL FLUID AND SOLID MECHANICS)

University of Southern California (M)

AEROSPACE AND MECHANICAL ENGINEERING (DYNAMICS AND CONTROL)

University of Southern California (M)

AEROSPACE ENGINEERING

Auburn University (M)
Georgia Institute of Technology (M)
North Carolina State University (M)
The University of Alabama (M)
University of Colorado at Boulder (M)
University of Southern California (M)
University of Washington (M)

AFRICAN AMERICAN MINISTRY LEADERSHIP MODULE

Defiance College (UC)

AFRICANA STUDIES

University of Michigan–Flint (UC)

AGRIBUSINESS

Kansas State University (M)
University of Northwestern Ohio (A)

AGRICULTURAL AND EXTENSION EDUCATION

The University of Tennessee (M)

AGRICULTURAL AND EXTENSION EDUCATOR

New Mexico State University (M)

AGRICULTURAL AND LIFE SCIENCES

Virginia Polytechnic Institute and State University (M)

AGRICULTURAL AND RESOURCE ECONOMICS

Colorado State University (B)

AGRICULTURAL BUSINESS ECONOMICS

West Texas A&M University (M)

AGRICULTURAL EDUCATION

Texas Tech University (D,M)
University of Illinois at Urbana–Champaign (M)

AGRICULTURAL EXTENSION EDUCATION SPECIALIZATION

Colorado State University (M)

AGRICULTURAL SALES AND SERVICES–EQUINE OPTION

Dickinson State University (A)

AGRICULTURAL SYSTEMS TECHNOLOGY, FAMILY AND CONSUMER SCIENCES EDUCATION AND EXTENSION EMPHASIS

Utah State University (M)

AGRICULTURAL SYSTEMS TECHNOLOGY, SECONDARY/ POST-SECONDARY AGRICULTURAL EDUCATION EMPHASIS

Utah State University (M)

AGRICULTURAL TEACHER EDUCATION

North Carolina State University (M)

AGRICULTURAL, FOOD, AND LIFE SCIENCES NON-THESIS (FOOD SAFETY EMPHASIS)

University of Arkansas (M)

AGRICULTURE

Texas Tech University (M)
Washington State University (M)

AGRICULTURE AND NATURAL RESOURCES SYSTEMS MANAGEMENT

The University of Tennessee at Martin (M)

AGRICULTURE BUSINESS

Northeast Iowa Community College (A)

AGRICULTURE, GENERAL

Oregon State University (B)

AIR TRAFFIC CONTROL

Thomas Edison State College (A,B)

AIRCRAFT MAINTENANCE

Embry-Riddle Aeronautical University (A)

ALCOHOL AND DRUG ABUSE STUDIES

The University of South Dakota (GC,UC)

ALLIED DENTAL EDUCATION (WITH UMDNJ)

Thomas Edison State College (B)

ALLIED HEALTH

Independence University (A)
National University (B)
Widener University (B)

ALLIED HEALTH LEADERSHIP–BS COMPLETION PROGRAM

East Tennessee State University (B)

ALLIED HEALTH MANAGEMENT

Oregon Institute of Technology (B)

ALTERNATIVE DISPUTE RESOLUTION–CERTIFICATE OF ADVANCED STUDY

University of Denver (UC)

ALTERNATIVE EDUCATION

Lock Haven University of Pennsylvania (M)

ALTERNATIVE ENERGY SYSTEMS

Prescott College (M)

ALTERNATIVE TEACHER

The University of Texas System (UC)

ALTERNATIVE TEACHERS CERTIFICATION PROGRAM

The University of Texas at El Paso

AMERICAN STUDIES

Coastline Community College (A)
Columbia College (B)

ANGLICAN STUDIES

Trinity Episcopal School for Ministry (UC)

ANIMAL SCIENCE AND INDUSTRY

Kansas State University (B)

ANIMATION

Regent University (B)
Westwood Online (B)

ANIMATION AND VISUAL EFFECTS

Academy of Art University (M,A,B)

ANTHROPOLOGY

Prescott College (M)
Thomas Edison State College (B)
University of North Texas (M)

ANTHROPOLOGY (3 YEAR)

Athabasca University (B)

ANTHROPOLOGY (4 YEAR)

Athabasca University (B)

ANTHROPOLOGY PRE-MAJOR

Seminole Community College (A)

APPAREL AND MERCHANDISING

Colorado State University (M,UC)

APPAREL AND MERCHANDISING (GRADUATE)

Colorado State University (UC)

APPLICATION SOFTWARE SPECIALIST

Minot State University (GC)

APPLIED ARTS AND SCIENCES (BAAS)

University of the Incarnate Word (B)

APPLIED ARTS AND SCIENCES DEGREE

Texas A&M University–Commerce (B)

APPLIED BEHAVIOR ANALYSIS FOR SPECIAL EDUCATION

Penn State University Park (GC)

APPLIED BUSINESS INFORMATION TECHNOLOGY

Minot State University (B)

APPLIED COMMUNICATION–MASTER OF PROFESSIONAL STUDIES IN APPLIED COMMUNICATION

University of Denver (M)

APPLIED COMPUTER SCIENCE

Northwest Missouri State University (M)

APPLIED COMPUTER STUDIES

Thomas Edison State College (A)

APPLIED ELECTRONIC STUDIES

Thomas Edison State College (A)

APPLIED GEOTECHNICS

University of Idaho (UC)

APPLIED GERONTOLOGY

University of North Texas (M)

APPLIED HEALTH STUDIES

Pennsylvania College of Technology (B)
Thomas Edison State College (A)

APPLIED INFORMATION MANAGEMENT

University of Oregon (M)

APPLIED INFORMATION TECHNOLOGY, TELECOMMUNICATIONS DEGREE

Pace University (A)

APPLIED MANAGEMENT

Central Texas College (A)
Franklin University (B)
Minot State University (B)

APPLIED MANAGEMENT AND DECISION SCIENCES

Walden University (D)

APPLIED MANAGEMENT WITH COMPUTER APPLICATIONS (NON-TEXAS STUDENTS ONLY)

Central Texas College (A)

APPLIED MATHEMATICS

New Jersey Institute of Technology (M)

APPLIED NUTRITION

Northeastern University (M)

APPLIED ORGANIZATIONAL MANAGEMENT

University of St. Francis (B)

APPLIED ORGANIZATIONAL TECHNOLOGY

The University of Toledo (UC)

APPLIED PHYSICS

Columbia University (M)

APPLIED RESEARCH AND EVALUATION METHODS

University of Southern Maine (UC)

APPLIED SCIENCE

Nashville State Technical Community College (A)

APPLIED SCIENCE IN TECHNOLOGY

Dickinson State University (B)

APPLIED SCIENCE IN TECHNOLOGY (BAST)

Dickinson State University (B)

APPLIED SCIENCE–BACHELOR OF APPLIED SCIENCE

East Tennessee State University (B)
The University of Maine at Augusta (B)

APPLIED SCIENCE–DIPLOMA IN APPLIED SCIENCE AND ASSOCIATE IN APPLIED SCIENCE

Central Carolina Community College (A)

APPLIED STATISTICAL METHODS

New Jersey Institute of Technology (GC)

APPLIED STATISTICAL STRATEGIES

The University of Tennessee (GC)

APPLIED STATISTICS

Kansas State University (GC)
New Jersey Institute of Technology (M)
Penn State University Park (GC)
Rochester Institute of Technology (M)

APPLIED STATISTICS AND DATA ANALYSIS

Colorado State University (UC)

APPLIED STUDIES

Athabasca University (B)
California State University, Dominguez Hills (B)

APPLIED TECHNOLOGY

Central Texas College (A)

APPLIED TECHNOLOGY AND PERFORMANCE IMPROVEMENT

University of North Texas (B)

APPLIED TECHNOLOGY, ALLIED HEALTH SERVICES OPTION

Granite State College (B)

APPLIED TECHNOLOGY, EDUCATION AND TRAINING OPTION

Granite State College (B)

APPLIED TECHNOLOGY, MANAGEMENT OPTION

Granite State College (B)

APPLIED TECHNOLOGY, TRAINING, AND DEVELOPMENT

University of North Texas (M)

ARABIC STUDIES

National University (B)

ARCHITECTURAL DESIGN

Thomas Edison State College (A,B)

ARCHITECTURAL DRAFTING AND ESTIMATING TECHNOLOGY

North Dakota State College of Science (A)

ARCHITECTURAL STUDIES

New Jersey Institute of Technology (M)
University of Missouri–Columbia (D,M)

ARCHITECTURE

Texas Tech University (B)

ARCHITECTURE MANAGEMENT

Lawrence Technological University (GC)

ART

Northwestern State University of Louisiana (M)
Prescott College (B)
Thomas Edison State College (B)

ART EDUCATION

East Carolina University (M)
Mansfield University of Pennsylvania (M)
Texas Tech University (M)

ART HISTORY

Mansfield University of Pennsylvania (B)
Prescott College (M)

ART THERAPY

Prescott College (M)
Saint Mary-of-the-Woods College (M)

ARTIFICIAL INTELLIGENCE

Stanford University (GC)

ARTS

Athabasca University (UC)

ARTS ADMINISTRATION

Goucher College (M)

ARTS AND HUMANITIES

Coastline Community College (A)

ARTS AND LITERATURE–CERTIFICATE OF ADVANCED STUDY

University of Denver (UC)

ARTS AND SCIENCE

Athabasca University (B)

ARTS AND SCIENCE DEGREE PROGRAM

Southwest Virginia Community College (A)

ARTS AND SCIENCE–APPLIED ARTS AND SCIENCE

Rochester Institute of Technology (B)

ARTS AND SCIENCE–APPLIED ARTS AND SCIENCES

Midwestern State University (B)

ARTS AND SCIENCES

Clarion University of Pennsylvania (A)
College of Southern Maryland (A)
Mountain View College (A)
Northeastern University (A)

ARTS AND SCIENCES–APPLIED SCIENCE AND TECHNOLOGY

College of Southern Maryland (A)

ARTS AND SCIENCES–ARTS AND HUMANITIES

College of Southern Maryland (A)

ARTS AND SCIENCES–SOCIAL SCIENCES

College of Southern Maryland (A)

ARTS MANAGEMENT

Prescott College (M)
University of Windsor (UC)

AS TO BS APPLIED SCIENCES

University of South Florida (B)

ASIAN STUDIES

University of Maryland University College (B)

ASSET MANAGEMENT

The American College (GC)

ASSISTIVE TECHNOLOGY

California State University, Dominguez Hills (UC)
East Carolina University (GC)

ASSISTIVE TECHNOLOGY SPECIALIZATION

Bowling Green State University (M)

ASSOCIATE IN GENERAL STUDIES (AGS)

Northwestern Michigan College (A)

ASSOCIATE IN INDUSTRIAL TECHNOLOGY, MAJOR IN INDUSTRIAL ELECTRONICS TECHNOLOGY

Piedmont Technical College (A)

ASSOCIATE OF ARTS AND BACHELOR OF GENERAL STUDIES

Indiana University–Purdue University Fort Wayne (B)

ASSOCIATE OF BIBLICAL STUDIES

Dallas Baptist University (A)

ASTRONAUTICAL ENGINEERING

University of Southern California (GC,M)

AT-RISK YOUTH SPECIALIZATION

Central Texas College (A,UC)

ATHLETIC ADMINISTRATION

Jacksonville State University (M)

ATHLETIC COACHING

West Virginia University (M)

ATMOSPHERIC AND ENVIRONMENTAL SCIENCE AND ENGINEERING

Stevens Institute of Technology (GC)

AUTISM

Penn State University Park (GC)
Texas Tech University (GC)

AUTISTIC SPECTRUM DISORDERS

University of North Dakota (GC)

AUTOMOTIVE ENGINEERING

University of Michigan (M)

AUTOMOTIVE MANAGEMENT

University of Northwestern Ohio (A)

AUTOMOTIVE SYSTEMS ENGINEERING

University of Michigan–Dearborn (M)

AUTOMOTIVE TECHNOLOGY MANAGEMENT

Pennsylvania College of Technology (B)

AVIATION (BACCALAUREATE DEGREE TRANSFER)

Utah Valley State College (A)

AVIATION ADMINISTRATION/ MANAGEMENT

Utah Valley State College (B)

AVIATION FLIGHT TECHNOLOGY

Thomas Edison State College (A,B)

AVIATION JOB READY DEGREE

Utah Valley State College (A)

AVIATION MAINTENANCE MANAGEMENT

Embry-Riddle Aeronautical University (B)
St. Cloud State University (B)

AVIATION MAINTENANCE TECHNOLOGY

Thomas Edison State College (A,B)

AVIATION MANAGEMENT

Lynn University (M)

AVIATION PROFESSIONAL PILOT

Utah Valley State College (B)

AVIATION SCIENCE

Utah Valley State College (B)

AVIATION STUDIES

Excelsior College (A)

AVIATION SUPPORT

Thomas Edison State College (A)

BACHELOR OF APPLIED HEALTH

University of Minnesota, Crookston (B)

BACHELOR OF APPLIED SCIENCE

Siena Heights University (B)

BACHELOR OF APPLIED SCIENCE IN TECHNOLOGY MANAGEMENT (TWO-YEAR COMPLETION)

Missouri State University (B)

BACHELOR OF APPLIED SCIENCE, ORGANIZATIONAL LEADERSHIP CONCENTRATION

University of Wyoming (B)

BACHELOR OF APPLIED TECHNOLOGY

The University of Texas at Brownsville (B)

BACHELOR OF ARTS COMPLETION PROGRAM

University of Denver (B)

BACHELOR OF HEALTH SCIENCES

Huntington College of Health Sciences (B)

BACHELOR OF MANUFACTURING MANAGEMENT ONLINE

University of Minnesota, Crookston (B)

BANKING

Strayer University (B)

BANKING AND FINANCIAL MANAGEMENT

New England College (M)

BASIC COMMUNITY PUBLIC HEALTH PRACTICE

University of Illinois at Chicago (UC)

BASIC GROUNDS WORK SKILLS

Minot State University–Bottineau Campus (UC)

BEHAVIOR ANALYSIS

St. Cloud State University (M)
University of North Texas (GC)

BEHAVIORAL INTERVENTION IN AUTISM

University of Massachusetts Lowell (GC)

BEHAVIORAL LEADERSHIP AND MANAGEMENT

Amridge University (M)

BEHAVIORAL SCIENCE

Bellevue University (B)
Granite State College (A)
Mercy College (B)

BEHAVIORAL SCIENCE– SUBSTANCE ABUSE CERTIFICATE

Vincennes University (UC)

BEHAVIORAL SCIENCES

Community College of Denver (A)
Vincennes University (A)

BIBLE AND THEOLOGY

Crossroads College (GC)
Global University (B)

BIBLE/THEOLOGY

Global University (A)

BIBLICAL AND CULTURAL LEADERSHIP

Taylor University (UC)

BIBLICAL AND THEOLOGICAL STUDIES

Covenant Theological Seminary (GC)

BIBLICAL MINISTRY

Baptist Bible College of Pennsylvania (M)

BIBLICAL STUDIES

Amridge University (D,M,B)
The Baptist College of Florida (B)
Dallas Baptist University (B)
Hope International University (A,UC)
Life Pacific College (A)
Regent University (M)
Southern California Seminary (M,A,B)
Taylor University (A,UC)

BIBLICAL STUDIES–BROAD FIELD PLAN

Global University (M)

BIBLICAL STUDIES–NEW TESTAMENT CONCENTRATION

Global University (M)

BILINGUAL EDUCATION

Prescott College (M)

BIODESIGN

Stanford University (GC)

BIOETHICS

Cleveland State University (GC,UC)

BIOINFORMATICS

Stanford University (GC)
University of Illinois at Chicago (UC)
University of Maryland University College (GC)

BIOLOGICAL AND AGRICULTURAL ENGINEERING

North Carolina State University (GC,M)

BIOLOGICAL AND AGRICULTURAL ENGINEERING (WATER MANAGEMENT EMPHASIS)

University of Idaho (M)

BIOLOGY

Community College of Denver (A)
Thomas Edison State College (A,B)
University of Nebraska at Kearney (M)

BIOLOGY EDUCATION

Western Kentucky University (M)

BIOMEDICAL ELECTRONICS

Thomas Edison State College (A,B)

BIOMEDICAL ENGINEERING

Columbia University (M)
University of Southern California (M)

BIOMEDICAL ENGINEERING (MEDICAL IMAGING AND IMAGING INFORMATICS)

University of Southern California (M)

BIOMEDICAL ENGINEERING SPECIALIZATION

Colorado State University (M)

BIOMEDICAL INFORMATICS

Stanford University (M)

BIOMEDICAL QUALITY SYSTEMS

San Diego State University (M)

BIOMEDICAL WRITING

University of the Sciences in Philadelphia (M)

BIOMEDICAL/PHARMACEUTICAL (MSA)

University of West Florida (M)

BIOSTATISTICS ESSENTIALS

New Jersey Institute of Technology (GC)

BIOTECHNOLOGY

University of Maryland University College (M)

BIOTECHNOLOGY LABORATORY TECHNICIAN

California State University, San Marcos (UC)

BIOTECHNOLOGY MANAGEMENT

University of Maryland University College (GC)

BIOTERRORISM PREPAREDNESS

Penn State University Park (GC)

BIRTH–KINDERGARTEN EDUCATION

East Carolina University (M)

BLOOD BANK TECHNOLOGY

The University of Texas System (UC)

BOOKKEEPING

Kirtland Community College (UC)
Minot State University–Bottineau Campus (UC)

BOOKKEEPING– PARAPROFESSIONAL ACCOUNTING PROGRAM

Bellevue Community College (UC)

BOOKKEEPING–PROFESSIONAL BOOKKEEPER

Lake Superior College (UC)

BOOKKEEPING/ACCOUNTING

Rappahannock Community College (UC)

BORDER ADMINISTRATION

The University of Texas System (UC)

BORDER STUDIES

The University of Texas System (UC)

BRAIN RESEARCH IN EDUCATION

University of Washington (UC)

BRIDGE DOCTOR OF PHYSICAL THERAPY

Simmons College (D)

BROADBAND–CERTIFICATE OF ADVANCED STUDY

University of Denver (UC)

BROADCAST DESIGN AND MOTION GRAPHICS

Savannah College of Art and Design (M)

BROADCAST ENGINEERING

Cleveland Institute of Electronics (UC)

BROADCASTING

Southwestern Adventist University (B)

BSAS IN ALLIED HEALTH

Youngstown State University (B)

BSAS IN CRIMINAL JUSTICE

Youngstown State University (B)

BSAS IN PUBLIC HEALTH

Youngstown State University (B)

BSIS-EC4

The University of Texas at Tyler (B)

BUILDING A SUSTAINABLE WORLD

Saybrook Graduate School and Research Center (GC)

BUILDING CODE ENFORCEMENT

Red Rocks Community College (A)

BUISNESS MANAGEMENT

Baltimore City Community College (A)

BUSINESS

Bellevue University (B)
Buena Vista University (B)
Capella University (M,B)
Chemeketa Community College (A)
Clinton Community College (A)
Columbia Southern University (A)
Dallas County Community College District (A)
Drexel University (M)
Excelsior College (M,A)
Fort Hays State University (GC)
Granite State College (A)
IIA College (A)
Independence University (A)
Indiana Wesleyan University (A)
Judson College (B)
Kaplan University Online (B)
Liberty University (A,B)
Mercy College (A)
New Jersey Institute of Technology (B)
New York Institute of Technology (M)
Northeast State Technical Community College (A)
Prescott College (B)
Red Rocks Community College (A)
Regent University (A)
Rose State College (A)
St. John's University (A)
Spring Arbor University (M)
Trine University (B)
University of Phoenix (A)
University of the Incarnate Word (A)
Utah State University (B)

BUSINESS & COMPUTING

New Jersey Institute of Technology (GC)

BUSINESS (TRANSFER PROGRAM)

St. Clair County Community College (A)

BUSINESS ADMINISTRATION

Adams State College (B)
AIB College of Business (A,B)
American Public University System (M,B)
Arizona Western College (A)
Athabasca University (M)
Auburn University (M)
Baker College of Flint (M,A,B)
Ball State University (M)
Bellevue University (M,B)
Benedictine University (M)
Berkeley College (A,B)
Bethel College (M)
Brenau University (M,B)
Broward Community College (A)
Bryant and Stratton Online (B)
California National University for Advanced Studies (M,B)
California State University, Dominguez Hills (M)

Cardinal Stritch University (M)
Cayuga County Community College (A)
Central New Mexico Community College (A)
Central Texas College (A)
Cerro Coso Community College (A)
Chadron State College (M)
Clarion University of Pennsylvania (M)
Clinton Community College (A)
Coastline Community College (A)
College of Southern Maryland (A)
College of The Albemarle (A)
Colorado State University (M)
Colorado Technical University Colorado Springs (A)
Columbia College (M,A,B)
Columbia Southern University (D,M,B)
Community College of Denver (A)
Concordia University, St. Paul (M)
Concordia University Wisconsin (M)
Culver-Stockton College (B)
Dallas Baptist University (B)
Daniel Webster College (A)
Darton College (A)
Delaware County Community College (A)
DeVry University Online (M,B)
Dickinson State University (B)
Drexel University (M)
East Carolina University (M,B)
Eastern Oregon University (B)
Eastern Wyoming College (A)
Fitchburg State College (M)
Florida Gulf Coast University (M)
Florida Institute of Technology (M,A,B)
Florida State University (M)
Florida Tech University Online (A)
Franklin University (A,B)
Gadsden State Community College (A)
Genesee Community College (A)
Golden Gate University (M,B)
Grantham University (M,A,B)
Harford Community College (A)
Harrisburg Area Community College (A)
Haywood Community College (A)
Herkimer County Community College (A)
Hodges University (M)
Independence University (M)
Indiana State University (B)
Indiana Tech (A,B)
Indiana Wesleyan University (M)
Ivy Tech Community College–Bloomington (A)
Ivy Tech Community College–Central Indiana (A)
Ivy Tech Community College–Columbus (A)
Ivy Tech Community College–East Central (A)
Ivy Tech Community College–Kokomo (A)
Ivy Tech Community College–Lafayette (A)
Ivy Tech Community College–North Central (A)
Ivy Tech Community College–Northeast (A)
Ivy Tech Community College–Northwest (A)
Ivy Tech Community College–Southeast (A)
Ivy Tech Community College–Southern Indiana (A)
Ivy Tech Community College–Southwest (A)
Ivy Tech Community College–Wabash Valley (A)
Ivy Tech Community College–Whitewater (A)
Jacksonville State University (M)
James A. Rhodes State College (A)
Jefferson Community College (A)

Jones International University (D,M,A,B)
J. Sargeant Reynolds Community College (A)
Kansas State University (GC)
Kaplan University Online (M)
Keiser University (M,B)
Lakeland College (M,B)
Lake Superior College (A)
Lawrence Technological University (M)
Lehigh Carbon Community College (A)
Lehigh University (M)
Liberty University (M)
Limestone College (A)
Lynn University (B)
Marist College (M)
Mayville State University (B)
Memorial University of Newfoundland (B,UC)
Mercy College (M,B)
Metropolitan State University (M,B)
Miami Dade College (A)
Middle Georgia College (A)
Midstate College (B)
Minnesota School of Business–Richfield (M,A,B)
Mississippi State University (GC,M)
Missouri State University (M)
Missouri State University–West Plains (M)
Missouri University of Science and Technology (M)
Monroe Community College (A)
Montgomery Community College (A)
Montgomery County Community College (A)
Mountain Empire Community College (A)
Mount Wachusett Community College (A)
National University (M,B)
New York Institute of Technology (B)
Northampton County Area Community College (A)
Northcentral University (D,M,B)
Northeastern University (A)
Northeast Iowa Community College (A)
Northern Virginia Community College (A)
Northwestern Michigan College (A)
Northwestern State University of Louisiana (A)
Nova Southeastern University (M,B)
The Ohio State University (M)
Ottawa University (M)
Park University (M)
Patrick Henry Community College (A)
Penn State University Park (A)
Piedmont Community College (A,UC)
Randolph Community College (A)
Regent University (M)
Regis University (M,B)
St. Cloud State University (M)
Saint Joseph's College of Maine (A,B,UC)
Saint Leo University (A)
Saint Mary-of-the-Woods College (B)
San Diego Community College District (A)
San Joaquin Valley College–Online (A)
Schiller International University (M)
Shippensburg University of Pennsylvania (M)
Siena Heights University (B)
Sinclair Community College (A)
Southeast Community College Area (A)
Southeastern Community College (A)
Southern Arkansas University Tech (A)
Southern New Hampshire University (A,B)
Southwestern Adventist University (B)
Southwestern College (M,B)

State University of New York Empire State College (M)
Strayer University (M,,A,UC)
Taft College (A)
Taylor University (B)
Texas A&M University–Commerce (M)
Texas Woman's University (M)
TUI University (D,M,B)
Union County College (A)
University of Colorado at Colorado Springs (M)
University of Colorado Denver (M)
The University of Findlay (M)
University of Houston–Victoria (M)
University of Illinois at Springfield (B)
University of La Verne (M)
The University of Maine at Augusta (A)
University of Management and Technology (A)
University of Maryland University College (M,B)
University of Massachusetts Lowell (M)
University of Michigan–Flint (M,B)
University of North Dakota (M)
University of Northwestern Ohio (B)
University of Phoenix (D,M)
University of St. Francis (M)
The University of South Dakota (M)
The University of Tennessee at Martin (M)
The University of Texas at Brownsville (M)
The University of Texas at Tyler (M,B)
The University of Texas of the Permian Basin (M)
University of the Incarnate Word (B)
University of Windsor (UC)
University of Wisconsin–Platteville (B)
University of Wisconsin–Platteville (B)
University of Wyoming (B)
Upper Iowa University (B)
Vincennes University (A)
Walden University (M,B)
Washington State University (B)
Wayne State College (M)
Webster University (M)
Western Wyoming Community College (A)
West Texas A&M University (M)
West Virginia University (M)
West Virginia University at Parkersburg (A)
Westwood Online (M)

BUSINESS ADMINISTRATION (ASBA)

Thomas Edison State College (A)

BUSINESS ADMINISTRATION (BACHELOR COMPLETION)

Indiana Wesleyan University (B)

BUSINESS ADMINISTRATION (BACHELOR OF APPLIED SCIENCE)

Mayville State University (B)

BUSINESS ADMINISTRATION (GENERAL BUSINESS)

University of Wisconsin–Whitewater (B)

BUSINESS ADMINISTRATION (HUMAN RESOURCE MANAGEMENT CONCENTRATION)

Southern New Hampshire University (B)

BUSINESS ADMINISTRATION (IN STATE)

Daytona State College (A)

BUSINESS ADMINISTRATION (INFORMATION SYSTEMS/ TECHNOLOGY EMPHASIS)

City University of Seattle (B)

BUSINESS ADMINISTRATION (MARKETING EMPHASIS)

City University of Seattle (B)

BUSINESS ADMINISTRATION (ORGANIZATIONAL LEADERSHIP CONCENTRATION)

Southern New Hampshire University (B)

BUSINESS ADMINISTRATION (OUT OF STATE)

Daytona State College (A)

BUSINESS ADMINISTRATION (PROJECT MANAGEMENT EMPHASIS)

City University of Seattle (B)

BUSINESS ADMINISTRATION (SMALL BUSINESS MANAGEMENT CONCENTRATION)

Southern New Hampshire University (B)

BUSINESS ADMINISTRATION AND BUSINESS EDUCATION CONCENTRATIONS

Parkland College (A)

BUSINESS ADMINISTRATION AND FINANCIAL SERVICES

AIB College of Business (A)

BUSINESS ADMINISTRATION AND LEADERSHIP

AIB College of Business (A)

BUSINESS ADMINISTRATION AND MANAGEMENT

The University of Texas System (M)

BUSINESS ADMINISTRATION AND ONLINE MASTERS OF BUSINESS ADMINISTRATION

University of Wisconsin–Whitewater (M)

BUSINESS ADMINISTRATION CAREER

Middlesex Community College (A)

BUSINESS ADMINISTRATION FOUNDATION COURSES

Missouri State University (M)

BUSINESS ADMINISTRATION IN AVIATION

Embry-Riddle Aeronautical University (M)

BUSINESS ADMINISTRATION MANAGEMENT

Ball State University (A)

BUSINESS ADMINISTRATION TRANSFER

Anne Arundel Community College (A)
Middlesex Community College (A)

BUSINESS ADMINISTRATION– ACCELERATED DEGREE COMPLETION

Tiffin University (B)

BUSINESS ADMINISTRATION– ACCOUNTING

Limestone College (B)

BUSINESS ADMINISTRATION– ACCOUNTING CONCENTRATION

Peirce College (A,B)
Westwood Online (B)

BUSINESS ADMINISTRATION– ADMINISTRATIVE SUPPORT TECHNOLOGY SPECIALIZATION

Northern Virginia Community College (A)

BUSINESS ADMINISTRATION– APPLIED MANAGEMENT

Tompkins Cortland Community College (A)

BUSINESS ADMINISTRATION– BUSINESS LAW CONCENTRATION

Peirce College (A,B,UC)

BUSINESS ADMINISTRATION– COMPUTER PROGRAMMING

Limestone College (B)

BUSINESS ADMINISTRATION–COMPUTER SOFTWARE APPLICATIONS

Limestone College (B)

BUSINESS ADMINISTRATION–DISTANCE MBA PROGRAM

Colorado State University (M)

BUSINESS ADMINISTRATION–E-COMMERCE EMPHASIS (BULGARIA)

City University of Seattle (B)

BUSINESS ADMINISTRATION–E. MBA

Pace University (M)

BUSINESS ADMINISTRATION–ECONOMIC CRIME AND FRAUD MANAGEMENT

Utica College (M)

BUSINESS ADMINISTRATION–EN ESPANOL (IN THE SPANISH LANGUAGE)

Keiser University (B)

BUSINESS ADMINISTRATION–ENTREPRENEURSHIP/SMALL BUSINESS MANAGEMENT CONCENTRATION

Peirce College (A,B)

BUSINESS ADMINISTRATION–GENERAL BUSINESS

Limestone College (B)

BUSINESS ADMINISTRATION–GENERAL BUSINESS ADMINISTRATION AND ACCOUNTING

University of Hawaii–West Oahu (B)

BUSINESS ADMINISTRATION–GENERAL MANAGEMENT EMPHASIS

City University of Seattle (B)

BUSINESS ADMINISTRATION–HONOURS BUSINESS ADMINISTRATION

University of Windsor (B)

BUSINESS ADMINISTRATION–HUMAN RESOURCE EMPHASIS

City University of Seattle (B)

BUSINESS ADMINISTRATION–HUMAN RESOURCE MANAGEMENT CONCENTRATION

Peirce College (A,B)

BUSINESS ADMINISTRATION–INDIVIDUALIZED STUDY EMPHASIS

City University of Seattle (B)

BUSINESS ADMINISTRATION–INFORMATION SYSTEMS MANAGEMENT

Berkeley College–New York City Campus (A,B)
Berkeley College–Westchester Campus (A,B)

BUSINESS ADMINISTRATION–INTERNATIONAL OPTION

Montgomery County Community College (A)

BUSINESS ADMINISTRATION–MANAGEMENT

Berkeley College–New York City Campus (A,B)
Berkeley College–Westchester Campus (A,B)
Limestone College (B)

BUSINESS ADMINISTRATION–MANAGEMENT CONCENTRATION

Peirce College (A,B)

BUSINESS ADMINISTRATION–MARKETING

Berkeley College–New York City Campus (A,B)
Berkeley College–Westchester Campus (A,B)

BUSINESS ADMINISTRATION–MARKETING AND SALES CONCENTRATION

Westwood Online (B)

BUSINESS ADMINISTRATION–MARKETING CONCENTRATION

Peirce College (A,B)

BUSINESS ADMINISTRATION–OFFERED IN THE SPANISH LANGUAGE

Keiser University (B)

BUSINESS ADMINISTRATION–ONLINE MBA

Franklin University (M)
Temple University (M)

BUSINESS ADMINISTRATION–ONLINE MBA PROGRAM

University of North Alabama (M)

BUSINESS ADMINISTRATION–PROFESSIONAL ACCOUNTANCY

Utica College (M)

BUSINESS ADMINISTRATION–PROFESSIONAL MASTER OF BUSINESS ADMINISTRATION

Florida Institute of Technology (M)

BUSINESS ADMINISTRATION–REAL ESTATE MANAGEMENT CONCENTRATION

Peirce College (B)

BUSINESS ADMINISTRATION–SALES AND MARKETING

AIB College of Business (A)

BUSINESS ADMINISTRATION–TECHNICAL MANAGEMENT

College of Southern Maryland (A)

BUSINESS ADMINISTRATION, ACCOUNTING CONCENTRATION

Saint Leo University (B)

BUSINESS ADMINISTRATION, ACCOUNTING SPECIALIZATION

Florida Tech University Online (B)

BUSINESS ADMINISTRATION, COMPUTER INFORMATION SYSTEMS SPECIALIZATION

Florida Tech University Online (B)

BUSINESS ADMINISTRATION, HEALTH SERVICES MANAGEMENT CONCENTRATION

Saint Leo University (B)

BUSINESS ADMINISTRATION, HEALTHCARE MANAGEMENT SPECIALIZATION

Florida Tech University Online (B)

BUSINESS ADMINISTRATION, MANAGEMENT CONCENTRATION

Saint Leo University (B)

BUSINESS ADMINISTRATION, MANAGEMENT SPECIALIZATION

Florida Tech University Online (B)

BUSINESS ADMINISTRATION, MARKETING SPECIALIZATION

Florida Tech University Online (B)

BUSINESS ADMINISTRATION/ GENERAL BUSINESS

Amridge University (B)

BUSINESS ADMINISTRATION/ HEALTH CARE MANAGEMENT

University of Phoenix (M)

BUSINESS ADMINISTRATION/ INFORMATION COMMUNICATION

Amridge University (B)

BUSINESS ADMINISTRATION/ INFORMATION SYSTEMS MANAGEMENT

Amridge University (B)

BUSINESS ADMINISTRATION/ MANAGEMENT

Chadron State College (B)
Kaplan University Online (A)

BUSINESS ADMINISTRATION/ MANAGEMENT INFORMATION SYSTEMS

Chadron State College (B)

BUSINESS ADMINISTRATION/ MARKETING

Chadron State College (B)
University of Phoenix (M)

BUSINESS AND ECONOMICS

Eastern Oregon University (B)

BUSINESS AND INFORMATION SYSTEMS IMPLEMENTATION

New Jersey Institute of Technology (GC)

BUSINESS AND MANAGEMENT

Daniel Webster College (B)

BUSINESS AND MARKETING EDUCATION

University of Missouri–Columbia (M)

BUSINESS AND ORGANIZATIONAL SECURITY MANAGEMENT

Webster University (M)

BUSINESS AND TECHNOLOGY

Columbia University (UC)

BUSINESS ASPECTS OF PUBLISHING

Pace University (GC)

BUSINESS COMMUNICATION

Fort Hays State University (B)
Jones International University (M,B)

BUSINESS COMPLETION

Presentation College (B)

BUSINESS CONCENTRATION

American InterContinental University Online (A)

BUSINESS ECONOMICS

York University (B)

BUSINESS EDUCATION

Darton College (A)
East Carolina University (M)
Southern New Hampshire University (M)

BUSINESS ENGLISH

Northeastern University (UC)

BUSINESS FORENSICS

Franklin University (B)

BUSINESS FOUNDATIONS

University of Washington (UC)

BUSINESS HOSPITALITY MANAGEMENT

University of Phoenix (B)

BUSINESS IN GENERAL BUSINESS

Independence University (A)

BUSINESS INFORMATION SYSTEMS

Bellevue University (B)
Fort Hays State University (UC)
Southern New Hampshire University (UC)
Utah State University (M)

BUSINESS INFORMATION SYSTEMS (BACHELOR COMPLETION)

Indiana Wesleyan University (B)

BUSINESS INTELLIGENCE

Saint Joseph's University (M)

BUSINESS INTELLIGENCE ANALYST

Bellevue Community College (UC)

BUSINESS INTELLIGENCE DEVELOPER

Bellevue Community College (UC)

BUSINESS MANAGEMENT

Anne Arundel Community College (A)
Burlington County College (A)
Central Texas College (A,UC)
Columbus State Community College (A)
Concordia University Wisconsin (B)
Dawson Community College (A)
Granite State College (B)
Grantham University (A,B)
Lehigh Carbon Community College (A,UC)
Malone College (B)
Minnesota School of Business–Richfield (B)
Montgomery County Community College (UC)
Northampton County Area Community College (A)
Northern Virginia Community College (A)
Northwest Missouri State University (B)
Parkland College (A)
Southwestern Adventist University (B)
Sullivan University (A)
Tyler Junior College (A)
Union County College (A)
The University of Findlay (B)
Vincennes University (A)

BUSINESS MANAGEMENT ASSOCIATE OF SCIENCE

Utah Valley State College (A)

BUSINESS MANAGEMENT CERTIFICATE

Montgomery County Community College

BUSINESS MANAGEMENT CONCENTRATION

Colorado Technical University Colorado Springs (M)

BUSINESS MANAGEMENT FOR ENGINEERS

University of Illinois at Urbana–Champaign (GC)
University of Illinois at Urbana–Champaign (GC)

BUSINESS MANAGEMENT MARKETING AND SALES

Central Texas College (UC)

BUSINESS MANAGEMENT MARKETING AND SALES MANAGEMENT

Central Texas College (A)

BUSINESS MANAGEMENT ONLINE

Westfield State College (B)

BUSINESS MANAGEMENT TECHNOLOGY

The University of Toledo (A,UC)

BUSINESS MANAGEMENT TECHNOLOGY–FASTTRACK OPTION

The University of Toledo (A)

BUSINESS MANAGEMENT–EBUSINESS EMPHASIS

North Dakota State College of Science (A)

BUSINESS MANAGEMENT–PUBLIC MANAGEMENT SPECIALIZATION

Northern Virginia Community College (A)

BUSINESS MINISTRY CONCENTRATION

Dallas Baptist University (M)

BUSINESS ONLINE

Bryant and Stratton Online (A)
University of Minnesota, Crookston (B)

BUSINESS QUALITY MANAGEMENT

Southwestern College (B)

BUSINESS SOFTWARE

Chemeketa Community College (UC)

BUSINESS SOFTWARE SPECIALIST–BUSINESS TECHNOLOGY SYSTEMS

Bellevue Community College (UC)

BUSINESS SPECIALIST

Northeast Iowa Community College (A)

BUSINESS STUDIES (ACCOUNTING CONCENTRATION)

Southern New Hampshire University (B)

BUSINESS STUDIES (BUSINESS ADMINISTRATION CONCENTRATION)

Southern New Hampshire University (B)

BUSINESS STUDIES (BUSINESS FINANCE CONCENTRATION)

Southern New Hampshire University (B)

BUSINESS STUDIES (HUMAN RESOURCE MANAGEMENT CONCENTRATION)

Southern New Hampshire University (B)

BUSINESS STUDIES (INFORMATION TECHNOLOGY CONCENTRATION)

Southern New Hampshire University (B)

BUSINESS STUDIES (INTERNATIONAL MANAGEMENT CONCENTRATION)

Southern New Hampshire University (B)

BUSINESS STUDIES (MARKETING CONCENTRATION)

Southern New Hampshire University (B)

BUSINESS STUDIES (ORGANIZATIONAL LEADERSHIP CONCENTRATION)

Southern New Hampshire University (B)

BUSINESS STUDIES (SMALL BUSINESS MANAGEMENT CONCENTRATION)

Southern New Hampshire University (B)

BUSINESS SUCCESSION PLANNING

The American College (GC)

BUSINESS TECHNOLOGY

Motlow State Community College (A)
West Virginia University at Parkersburg (A)

BUSINESS–ACCOUNTING

Herkimer County Community College (A)

BUSINESS–ASSOCIATE IN BUSINESS, GENERAL BUSINESS MAJOR

Piedmont Technical College (A)

BUSINESS–ASSOCIATE IN BUSINESS, OFFICE SYSTEMS TECHNOLOGY MAJOR

Piedmont Technical College (A)

BUSINESS–BACHELOR OF SCIENCE IN BUSINESS

Murray State University (B)

BUSINESS–BUSINESS ADMINISTRATION

Erie Community College (A)
Erie Community College, North Campus (A)
Erie Community College, South Campus (A)
Herkimer County Community College (A)

BUSINESS–BUSINESS ADMINISTRATION (TRANSFER OPTION)

Erie Community College (A)
Erie Community College, North Campus (A)
Erie Community College, South Campus (A)

BUSINESS–BUSINESS AND ORGANIZATIONAL LEADERSHIP

Corban College (B)

BUSINESS–FASHION MERCHANDISING

Westwood Online (B)

BUSINESS–HEALTH SERVICES MANAGEMENT TECHNOLOGY

Herkimer County Community College (A)

BUSINESS–HUMAN RESOURCE MANAGEMENT

Herkimer County Community College (A)

BUSINESS–MARKETING

Herkimer County Community College (A)

BUSINESS–OFFICE MANAGEMENT

Erie Community College (A)
Erie Community College, North Campus (A)
Erie Community College, South Campus (A)

BUSINESS–SMALL BUSINESS MANAGEMENT

Herkimer County Community College (A)

BUSINESS, GENERAL

Berkeley College–New York City Campus (B)
Berkeley College–Westchester Campus (B)
Chadron State College (B)
Excelsior College (B)
Independence University (B)
Kansas State University (B)
Saint Mary-of-the-Woods College (A)
Seminole Community College (A)
Taft College (A)
University of Houston–Victoria (B)
Upper Iowa University (A)

BUSINESS, MANAGEMENT, AND ECONOMICS

State University of New York Empire State College (A,B)

BUSINESS/ACCOUNTING

University of Phoenix (B)

BUSINESS/BUSINESS ADMINISTRATION

University of Phoenix (B)

BUSINESS/COMMUNICATION

University of Phoenix (B)

BUSINESS/E-BUSINESS

University of Phoenix (B)

BUSINESS/FINANCE

University of Phoenix (B)

BUSINESS/GLOBAL BUSINESS MANAGEMENT

University of Phoenix (B)

BUSINESS/INFORMATION SYSTEMS

University of Phoenix (B)

BUSINESS/INTEGRATED SUPPLY CHAIN AND OPERATIONS MANAGEMENT

University of Phoenix (B)

BUSINESS/MANAGEMENT

University of Phoenix (B)

BUSINESS/MARKETING

University of Phoenix (B)

BUSINESS/ORGANIZATIONAL INNOVATION

University of Phoenix (B)

BUSINESS/PUBLIC ADMINISTRATION

University of Phoenix (B)

BUSINESS/RETAIL MANAGEMENT

University of Phoenix (B)

CANADIAN STUDIES

Western Kentucky University (UC)

CANADIAN STUDIES (3 YEAR)

Athabasca University (B)

CANADIAN STUDIES (4 YEAR)

Athabasca University (B)

CANCER INFORMATION MANAGEMENT

Eastern Iowa Community College District (A)

CARDIOVASCULAR BIOENGINEERING

Stanford University (GC)

CAREER AND TECHNICAL EDUCATION

Ball State University (M)
Indiana State University (B)
University of Central Florida (M)
University of South Florida (M)
University of Wisconsin–Stout (M,B)
Virginia Polytechnic Institute and State
  University (M,UC)

CAREER AND TECHNICAL EDUCATION (CTE)

University of West Florida (M)

CAREER AND TECHNICAL STUDIES EDUCATION–VOCATIONAL PROGRAM DEVELOPMENT

University of West Florida (B)

CAREER AND TECHNICAL STUDIES EDUCATION–VOCATIONAL TEACHER EDUCATION

University of West Florida (B)

CAREER DEVELOPMENT

Athabasca University (UC)
Memorial University of Newfoundland (UC)

CAREER STUDIES CERTIFICATE–ACCOUNTING

Mountain Empire Community College (UC)

CAREER STUDIES CERTIFICATE–CHILD DEVELOPMENT

Mountain Empire Community College (UC)

CAREER STUDIES CERTIFICATE–COMPUTER SOFTWARE SPECIALIST

Mountain Empire Community College (UC)

CAREER STUDIES CERTIFICATE–GEOGRAPHICAL INFORMATION SYSTEMS

Mountain Empire Community College (UC)

CAREER STUDIES CERTIFICATE–HEALTH INFORMATION TECHNOLOGY

Mountain Empire Community College (UC)

CAREER STUDIES CERTIFICATE–LEGAL OFFICE ASSISTING

Mountain Empire Community College (UC)

CAREER STUDIES CERTIFICATE–MEDICAL RECORDS CLERK

Mountain Empire Community College (UC)

CAREER STUDIES CERTIFICATE–MEDICAL TRANSCRIPTIONIST

Mountain Empire Community College (UC)

CAREER STUDIES CERTIFICATE–OFFICE AUTOMATION SPECIALIST

Mountain Empire Community College (UC)

CAREER STUDIES CERTIFICATE–PERSONAL COMPUTING FOR HOME AND OFFICE

Mountain Empire Community College (UC)

CAREER STUDIES CERTIFICATE–POLYSOMNOGRAPHY

Mountain Empire Community College (UC)

CAREER STUDIES CERTIFICATE–WASTEWATER PLANT OPERATOR

Mountain Empire Community College (UC)

CAREER STUDIES CERTIFICATE–WATER PLANT OPERATOR

Mountain Empire Community College (UC)

CAREER STUDIES CERTIFICATE–WORD PROCESSING

Mountain Empire Community College (UC)

CAREER STUDIES–ALLIED HEALTH

Patrick Henry Community College (UC)

CAREER STUDIES–MANAGEMENT ASSISTANT

Patrick Henry Community College (UC)

CAREER STUDIES–MEDICAL TRANSCRIPTIONIST

Patrick Henry Community College (UC)

CAREER STUDIES–OFFICE ASSISTING

Patrick Henry Community College (UC)

CAREER STUDIES–WELLNESS

Patrick Henry Community College (UC)

CAREGIVER SERVICES–ADULT

Minot State University–Bottineau Campus (A)

CAREGIVER SERVICES–CHILD

Minot State University–Bottineau Campus (A)

CATECHETICAL DIPLOMA

The Catholic Distance University (UC)

CATHOLIC SCHOOL LEADERSHIP

Marymount University (M)

CERTIFICATE IN WEB APPLICATIONS

Ball State University (UC)

CERTIFICATE OF MASTERY IN PRIOR LEARNING ASSESSMENT

DePaul University (UC)

CERTIFIED INFORMATION SYSTEMS SECURITY PROFESSIONAL (CISSP)

Peirce College (UC)

CERTIFIED MEDICATION AIDE UPDATE

Johnson County Community College (UC)

CERTIFIED NURSE AIDE

Johnson County Community College (UC)

CFP(R) CERTIFICATION CURRICULUM

The American College (UC)

CHARITABLE PLANNING

The American College (GC)

CHARTERED ADVISOR FOR SENIOR LIVING (CASL) DESIGNATION

The American College (UC)

CHARTERED ADVISOR IN PHILANTHROPY(R)(CAP) DESIGNATION

The American College (GC)

CHARTERED FINANCIAL CONSULTANT (CHFC(R)) DESIGNATION

The American College (UC)

CHARTERED LEADERSHIP FELLOW(R) (CLF(R)) DESIGNATION

The American College (UC)

CHARTERED LIFE UNDERWRITER (CLU(R)) DESIGNATION

The American College (UC)

CHEMICAL DEPENDENCY SPECIALIZATION

Central Texas College (A,UC)

CHEMICAL DEPENDENCY STUDIES COUNSELING

Tompkins Cortland Community College (A)

CHEMICAL ENGINEERING

Auburn University (M)
Columbia University (M)
Kansas State University (M)
Lehigh University (M)
North Carolina State University (M)
University of North Dakota (M)
University of Southern California (M)
University of South Florida (M)

CHEMICAL ENGINEERING CONTINUING EDUCATION/ BRIDGING PROGRAM

Michigan State University (UC)

CHEMISTRY

Community College of Denver (A)
Lehigh University (M)

CHESS IN EDUCATION ONLINE

The University of Texas System (UC)

CHIEF INFORMATION OFFICER (CIO)

University of Maryland University College (GC)

CHILD AND FAMILY STUDIES

University of Southern Mississippi (M)

CHILD CARE TRAINING

Colorado State University (UC)

CHILD CARE–FAMILY CHILD CARE

Northampton County Area Community College (UC)

CHILD CARE–SCHOOL AGE CHILD CARE

Northampton County Area Community College (UC)

CHILD DEVELOPMENT

Concordia University, St. Paul (B)
Walden University (B)

CHILD DEVELOPMENT SERVICES

Thomas Edison State College (A,B)

CHILDHOOD MINISTRY CONCENTRATION

Dallas Baptist University (M)

CHILDREN'S LITERATURE

Penn State University Park (GC)

CHILDREN'S MENTAL HEALTH

University of South Florida (GC)

CHILDREN, YOUTH, AND FAMILY SERVICES

Penn State University Park (UC)

CHRISTIAN EDUCATION– CHILDHOOD MINISTRY

Dallas Baptist University (M)

CHRISTIAN LEADERSHIP

Hope International University (GC)
Liberty University (M)

CHRISTIAN MINISTRIES

Anderson University (M)
Crown College (A)
Dallas Baptist University (B)
Shasta Bible College (M)

CHRISTIAN MINISTRY

Amridge University (D)
Crown College (B)
Hope International University (A,B)
Trinity Episcopal School for Ministry (UC)
Wayland Baptist University (M)

CHRISTIAN OUTREACH

Concordia University, St. Paul (M)

CHRISTIAN PROFESSIONAL STUDIES

Shasta Bible College (B)

CHRISTIAN SCHOOL EDUCATION

Baptist Bible College of Pennsylvania (M)

CHRISTIAN SCHOOL PROGRAM

Regent University (M)

CHRISTIAN STUDIES

Crown College (M)
Regent University (A)

CHRISTIAN STUDIES, GENERAL

Hobe Sound Bible College (B)

CHRISTIAN TRADITION

Saint Joseph's College of Maine (B,UC)

CHRISTIAN WORKER

Taylor University (UC)

CHURCH EDUCATION

Defiance College (UC)

CHURCH MINISTRIES

Global University (A)

CHURCH PLANTING

Hope International University (GC)

CINEMA ARTS

Regent University (M)

CINEMA STUDIES

Burlington College (B)

CINEMA-TELEVISION

Regent University (B)

CISCO NETWORKING

Minnesota State Community and Technical
  College–Fergus Falls (UC)

CIVIL AND CONSTRUCTION ENGINEERING TECHNOLOGY

Thomas Edison State College (A)

CIVIL AND ENVIRONMENTAL ENGINEERING

University of South Florida (M)
Virginia Polytechnic Institute and State
  University (M)

CIVIL ENGINEERING

Auburn University (M)
Colorado State University (M)
Columbia University (M,UC)
Kansas State University (M)
Missouri University of Science and
  Technology (M)
North Carolina State University (M)
Southern Methodist University (M)
University of Florida (M)
University of Idaho (M)
University of North Dakota (B)

CIVIL ENGINEERING (CONSTRUCTION ENGINEERING)

University of Southern California (M)

CIVIL ENGINEERING (STRUCTURAL ENGINEERING)

University of Southern California (M)

CIVIL ENGINEERING AND SURVEYING TECHNOLOGY

North Dakota State College of Science (A)

CIVIL ENGINEERING TECHNOLOGY

Old Dominion University (B)
Thomas Edison State College (B)

CIVIL ENGINEERING– CONSTRUCTION ENGINEERING AND MANAGEMENT

Columbia University (M)

CIVIL ENGINEERING– TRANSPORTATION ENGINEERING SPECIALIZATION

University of Louisville (M)

CIVIL INFRASTRUCTURE ENGINEERING

Virginia Polytechnic Institute and State
  University (M)

CLERICAL ASSISTANT

Mountain Empire Community College (UC)

CLERICAL STUDIES

Patrick Henry Community College (UC)

CLIENT-SERVER APPLICATION DEVELOPMENT

Daniel Webster College (UC)

CLINICAL COUNSELING

Bellevue University (M)

CLINICAL GENETICS

Simmons College (GC)

CLINICAL HEALTH SCIENCES

The George Washington University (M)

CLINICAL INFORMATICS

Stanford University (GC)

CLINICAL INVESTIGATION

MGH Institute of Health Professions (GC)
University of South Florida (GC)

CLINICAL INVESTIGATIONS

MGH Institute of Health Professions (M)

CLINICAL LAB SCIENCE

Thomas Edison State College (A,B)

CLINICAL LABORATORY SCIENCE

University of Cincinnati (B)

CLINICAL LABORATORY SCIENCES

Weber State University (B)

CLINICAL LABORATORY SCIENCES (ADVANCED AND CATEGORICAL)

Rosalind Franklin University of Medicine and
  Science (M)

CLINICAL LABORATORY SCIENCES (ENTRY-LEVEL)

Rosalind Franklin University of Medicine and
  Science (M)

CLINICAL LABORATORY TECHNICIAN

Weber State University (A)

CLINICAL MANAGEMENT

Vanderbilt University (M)

CLINICAL MANAGEMENT AND LEADERSHIP

The George Washington University (M)

CLINICAL MEDICAL ASSISTING

San Joaquin Valley College–Online (A)

CLINICAL NUTRITION

University of Medicine and Dentistry of New
  Jersey (M)

CLINICAL NUTRITION (DCN)

University of Medicine and Dentistry of New
  Jersey (D)

CLINICAL NUTRITION/NUTRITION EDUCATION

Rosalind Franklin University of Medicine and
  Science (M)

CLINICAL PATHOLOGY

University of Massachusetts Lowell (GC)

CLINICAL PSYCHOLOGY

Fielding Graduate University (D)

CLINICAL RESEARCH ADMINISTRATION

The George Washington University (M)

CLINICAL RESEARCH DESIGN AND MANAGEMENT

University of Southern California (GC)

CLINICAL RESEARCH MANAGEMENT

Vanderbilt University (M)

CLINICAL RESEARCH ORGANIZATION AND MANAGEMENT

Drexel University (M)

CLINICAL SPECIALIST

University of St. Francis (M)

CLINICAL TRIALS RESEARCH

Drexel University (M,UC)

COACHING EDUCATION

Michigan State University (UC)

COACHING–NATIONAL COACHING CERTIFICATION

United States Sports Academy (UC)

COACHING–NEW YORK STATE COACHING CERTIFICATION

Monroe Community College (UC)

COLLABORATIVE LEARNING AND TEACHING

Graceland University (M)

COLLABORATIVE TEACHER AND EARLY CHILDHOOD EDUCATION

Auburn University (M)

COLLEGE STUDENT PERSONNEL

Arkansas Tech University (M)

COLLEGE TRANSFER

Randolph Community College (A)
Southeastern Community College (A)

COMMERCE AND BUSINESS ADMINISTRATION (GENERAL BUSINESS)

The University of Alabama (B)

COMMERCE AND BUSINESS ADMINISTRATION (MANAGEMENT)

The University of Alabama (B)

COMMERCE–BACHELOR OF COMMERCE PROGRAM FOR UNIVERSITY GRADUATES

University of Windsor (B)

COMMISSIONED LAY PASTOR

University of Dubuque (UC)

COMMUNICATING ARTS, SPEECH COMMUNICATION CONCENTRATION

University of Wisconsin–Superior (B)

COMMUNICATION

Dallas Baptist University (B)
Drexel University (B)
Indiana Wesleyan University (UC)
Kaplan University Online (B)
North Dakota State University (M)
Regent University (D)
Spring Arbor University (M)
University of Louisville (B)
Utah Valley State College (A)

COMMUNICATION AND LEADERSHIP STUDIES

Gonzaga University (M)

COMMUNICATION ARTS (BA OR BS)

Austin Peay State University (B)

COMMUNICATION DISORDERS

Western Kentucky University (M)

COMMUNICATION DISORDERS AND SCIENCE–CEUS IN COMMUNICATION DISORDERS AND SCIENCE

California State University, Northridge (GC)

COMMUNICATION DISORDERS AND SCIENCES

California State University, Northridge (M)

COMMUNICATION STUDIES

Athabasca University (B)
Regent University (M)
University of Maryland University College (B)

COMMUNICATION STUDIES–PROFESSIONAL COMMUNICATION STUDIES

Pace University (B)

COMMUNICATION SYSTEMS

University of Idaho (UC)

COMMUNICATION–ORGANIZATIONAL COMMUNICATION AND LEADERSHIP

Marist College (M)

COMMUNICATION–PROFESSIONAL COMMUNICATION

East Carolina University (GC)

COMMUNICATION/PUBLIC RELATIONS/JOURNALISM CONCENTRATION

East Carolina University (B)

COMMUNICATIONS

Indiana Wesleyan University (UC)
Prescott College (B)
Regent University (B)
Southern New Hampshire University (B)
State University of New York at Oswego (B)
Thomas Edison State College (B)
University of Phoenix (A)

COMMUNICATIONS AND APPLIED TECHNOLOGY

Drexel University (B)

COMMUNICATIONS MANAGEMENT

Southern Polytechnic State University (GC)
Syracuse University (M)
Webster University (M)

COMMUNICATIONS–PROFESSIONAL COMMUNICATIONS

Stevens Institute of Technology (GC)

COMMUNICATIVE DISORDERS AND DEAF EDUCATION (POST-BACHELORS)

Utah State University (B)

COMMUNITY AND ECONOMIC DEVELOPMENT

Penn State University Park (GC,M)

COMMUNITY AND HUMAN SERVICES

State University of New York Empire State College (A,B)

COMMUNITY AND PUBLIC HEALTH, SCHOOL NURSE OPTION

The University of North Carolina at Charlotte (M)

COMMUNITY CHANGE AND CIVIC LEADERSHIP

Antioch University McGregor (M)

COMMUNITY COLLEGE EDUCATION

University of Central Florida (GC)

COMMUNITY COLLEGE LEADERSHIP

Mississippi State University (D,M)
Old Dominion University (D)

COMMUNITY COLLEGE LEADERSHIP (CCL)

Colorado State University (D)

COMMUNITY COLLEGE LEADERSHIP CONCENTRATION

Oregon State University (D)

COMMUNITY COLLEGE MANAGEMENT

Antioch University McGregor (M)

COMMUNITY COLLEGE TEACHING

California State University, Dominguez Hills (UC)
East Carolina University (GC)
North Carolina State University (GC)

COMMUNITY COLLEGE TEACHING AND LEARNING

University of Illinois at Urbana–Champaign (GC)

COMMUNITY COLLEGE TEACHING AND LEARNING (ED.M)

University of Illinois at Urbana–Champaign (M)

COMMUNITY COUNSELING

St. Mary's University (M)

COMMUNITY DEVELOPMENT

Fort Hays State University (UC)
Kansas State University (M)
North Dakota State University (M)

COMMUNITY DEVELOPMENT, COMMUNITY SERVICES MAJOR

Central Michigan University (B)

COMMUNITY DEVELOPMENT, HEALTH SCIENCES MAJOR

Central Michigan University (B)

COMMUNITY DEVELOPMENT, PUBLIC ADMINISTRATION MAJOR

Central Michigan University (B)

COMMUNITY HEALTH

Old Dominion University (M)

COMMUNITY HEALTH AND DEVELOPMENT

Saybrook Graduate School and Research Center (GC)

COMMUNITY HEALTH PROMOTION

University of Arkansas at Little Rock (B)

COMMUNITY LEADERSHIP

Duquesne University (M)

COMMUNITY MENTAL HEALTH

New York Institute of Technology (B)

COMMUNITY PSYCHOLOGY

St. Cloud State University (B)

COMMUNITY REHABILITATION

University of Calgary (B)
Vincennes University (UC)

COMMUNITY SERVICES

Thomas Edison State College (A,B)

COMMUNITY STUDIES COMPLETER PROGRAM

University of Massachusetts Boston (B)

COMMUNITY, MEDIA, AND TECHNOLOGY

University of Massachusetts Boston (UC)

COMMUNITY-BASED DEVELOPMENT

Colorado State University (UC)

COMPLEMENTARY AND INTEGRATIVE THERAPIES

Drexel University (UC)

COMPLETION PROGRAM

American InterContinental University Online (A)

COMPOSITE SOCIAL SCIENCE

Dickinson State University (B)

COMPUTATIONAL FLUID DYNAMICS

The University of Tennessee (GC)

COMPUTATIONAL SCIENCE AND ENGINEERING (CSE)

Georgia Institute of Technology (M)

COMPUTER AND INFORMATION SCIENCE

University of Maryland University College (B)

COMPUTER AND INFORMATION SCIENCES

Knowledge Systems Institute (M)

COMPUTER AND INFORMATION SYSTEMS

University of Michigan–Flint (M)

COMPUTER AND NETWORK SECURITY

University of Colorado at Boulder (GC)

COMPUTER AND NETWORK TECHNOLOGY

Minnesota State Community and Technical College–Fergus Falls (A,UC)

COMPUTER APPLICATIONS FOR THE OFFICE

Erie Community College (UC)
Erie Community College, North Campus (UC)
Erie Community College, South Campus (UC)

COMPUTER APPS/OFFICE PROCEDURES

Montgomery County Community College (A)

COMPUTER ARCHITECTURE

Stanford University (GC)

COMPUTER ARTS/NEW MEDIA

Academy of Art University (M,A,B)

COMPUTER ASSISTED DRAFTING (CAD)

Chemeketa Community College (UC)

COMPUTER EDUCATION

Fontbonne University (M)

COMPUTER EDUCATION AND COGNITIVE SYSTEMS

University of North Texas (M)

COMPUTER ENGINEERING

Southern Methodist University (M)
State University of New York at Binghamton (M)
University of Idaho (M)
University of Michigan–Dearborn (M)
University of Southern California (M)
Virginia Polytechnic Institute and State University (GC,M)

COMPUTER ENGINEERING (BIOINFORMATICS TRACK)

University of Florida (M)

COMPUTER ENGINEERING (GENERAL TRACK)

University of Florida (M)

COMPUTER ENGINEERING TECHNOLOGY

DeVry University Online (B)
Grantham University (A,B)

COMPUTER GRAPHICS

Stevens Institute of Technology (GC)

COMPUTER HARDWARE AND VLSI DESIGN

Stanford University (GC)

COMPUTER HELP DESK TECHNICIAN

Minnesota State Community and Technical College–Fergus Falls (A)

COMPUTER INFORMATION SYSTEM

Capital Community College (A)
University of Houston–Victoria (M)

COMPUTER INFORMATION SYSTEMS

Bellevue University (M,B)
Cerro Coso Community College (A)
Darton College (A)
DeVry University Online (B)
Florida Institute of Technology (B)
Florida Tech University Online (B)
Ivy Tech Community College–Bloomington (A)
Ivy Tech Community College–Central Indiana (A)
Ivy Tech Community College–Columbus (A)
Ivy Tech Community College–East Central (A)
Ivy Tech Community College–Kokomo (A)
Ivy Tech Community College–Lafayette (A)
Ivy Tech Community College–North Central (A)
Ivy Tech Community College–Northeast (A)
Ivy Tech Community College–Northwest (A)
Ivy Tech Community College–Southeast (A)
Ivy Tech Community College–Southern Indiana (A)
Ivy Tech Community College–Southwest (A)
Ivy Tech Community College–Wabash Valley (A)
Ivy Tech Community College–Whitewater (A)
Jamestown Community College (A)
Kaplan University Online (A)
Mercy College (B)
Missouri State University (M)
Mount Wachusett Community College (A)
Nova Southeastern University (D,M)

Prescott College (B)
Regis University (B)
Saint Leo University (B)
Saint Mary-of-the-Woods College (B)
Southwestern Adventist University (A,B)
Thomas Edison State College (B)
Walden University (B)
Western Wyoming Community College (A)

COMPUTER INFORMATION SYSTEMS (BACHELOR OF APPLIED SCIENCE)

Mayville State University (B)

COMPUTER INFORMATION SYSTEMS IN BUSINESS

Bellevue University (B)

COMPUTER INFORMATION SYSTEMS NETWORK ADMINISTRATION

Tyler Junior College (A)

COMPUTER INFORMATION SYSTEMS–CERTIFICATE OF ADVANCED STUDY

University of Denver (UC)

COMPUTER INFORMATION SYSTEMS–MASTER OF APPLIED SCIENCE IN COMPUTER INFORMATION SYSTEMS

University of Denver (M)

COMPUTER INFORMATION SYSTEMS–WEB DESIGN

North Dakota State College of Science (UC)

COMPUTER INFORMATION SYSTEMS/COMPUTER PROGRAMMING

Bristol Community College (A)

COMPUTER INFORMATION SYSTEMS/MULTIMEDIA AND INTERNET

Bristol Community College (A)

COMPUTER INFORMATION TECHNOLOGY

Franklin Pierce University (B)
Moberly Area Community College (A)
Regis University (M)
University of Maryland University College (B)
Western Kentucky University (B)

COMPUTER INFORMATION TECHNOLOGY AND SYSTEMS MANAGEMENT

Cleveland Institute of Electronics (A)

COMPUTER LANGUAGES AND OPERATING SYSTEMS

Stanford University (GC)

COMPUTER NETWORK ENGINEERING

Westwood Online (A)

COMPUTER NETWORK MANAGEMENT

Westwood Online (B)

COMPUTER NETWORK PROFESSIONAL

East Carolina University (GC)

COMPUTER NETWORKING

George Mason University (GC)
Regis University (B,UC)

COMPUTER NETWORKING AND SECURITY MANAGEMENT

Keiser University (A)

COMPUTER OPERATIONS TECHNOLOGY

Southwestern College (B)

COMPUTER PROGRAMMING

Bristol Community College (UC)
College of Southern Maryland (A)
Minnesota State Community and Technical College–Fergus Falls (A)
North Carolina State University (UC)
Seminole Community College (UC)

COMPUTER PROGRAMMING AND ANALYSIS

Seminole Community College (A)

COMPUTER PROGRAMMING AND ANALYSIS (C++ PROGRAMMING SPECIALIZATION)

Seminole Community College (A)

COMPUTER PROGRAMMING AND ANALYSIS VISUAL BASIC PROGRAMMING SPECIALIZATION

Seminole Community College (A)

COMPUTER PROGRAMMING TECHNOLOGY

Southwestern College (B)

COMPUTER PROGRAMMING WITH JAVA AND C#

Cleveland Institute of Electronics (UC)

COMPUTER PROGRAMMING–C PROGRAMMING

University of Washington (UC)

COMPUTER PROGRAMMING–C++ PROGRAMMING

University of Washington (UC)

COMPUTER PROGRAMMING–C/UNIX PROGRAMMING

Daniel Webster College (UC)

COMPUTER PROGRAMMING–JAVA 2 PROGRAMMING

University of Washington (UC)

COMPUTER PROGRAMMING–JAVA PROGRAMMING

Regis University (UC)

COMPUTER PROGRAMMING–MS WINDOWS PROGRAMMING

Daniel Webster College (UC)

COMPUTER PROGRAMMING–UNIX (SOLARIS)

Regis University (UC)

COMPUTER PROGRAMMING–UNIX SYSTEMS ADMINISTRATION

Daniel Webster College (UC)

COMPUTER SCIENCE

California National University for Advanced Studies (B)
California State University, Chico (M,B)
Colorado State University (M)
Columbia University (GC,M)
DePaul University (M)
Dickinson State University (B)
Drexel University (M)
Franklin University (A,B)
George Mason University (M)
Grantham University (A,B)
Hofstra University (M)
Jamestown Community College (A)
Lakeland College (B)
Mercy College (B)
Missouri University of Science and Technology (M)
Montgomery County Community College (A)
National University (M,B)
New Jersey Institute of Technology (M,B)
North Carolina State University (M)
Nova Southeastern University (D,M)
Old Dominion University (B)
Regis University (B)
Southern Methodist University (M)
Southwestern Adventist University (B)
Stanford University (M)
State University of New York at Binghamton (M)
Stevens Institute of Technology (M)

Texas Tech University (D,M)
Thomas Edison State College (A,B)
TUI University (B)
Union County College (A)
University of Bridgeport (B)
University of Colorado at Boulder (M)
University of Idaho (M)
University of Illinois at Springfield (M,B)
University of Illinois at Urbana–Champaign (M)
University of Louisville (M)
University of Management and Technology (M,A,B)
University of Maryland University College (B)
University of Southern California (M)
Utah State University (M,B)

COMPUTER SCIENCE (COMPUTER NETWORKING)

University of Southern California (M)

COMPUTER SCIENCE (COMPUTER SECURITY)

University of Southern California (M)

COMPUTER SCIENCE (MULTIMEDIA AND CREATIVE TECHNOLOGIES)

University of Southern California (M)

COMPUTER SCIENCE (SOFTWARE ENGINEERING)

University of Southern California (M)

COMPUTER SCIENCE AND ENGINEERING

Auburn University (M)

COMPUTER SCIENCE AND ENGINEERING TECHNOLOGY

The University of Toledo (B)

COMPUTER SCIENCE INFORMATION TECHNOLOGY

Limestone College (B)

COMPUTER SCIENCE INTERNET MANAGEMENT

Limestone College (A)

COMPUTER SCIENCE INTERNET MANAGEMENT–DATABASE

Limestone College (B)

COMPUTER SCIENCE INTERNET MANAGEMENT–E-COMMERCE

Limestone College (B)

COMPUTER SCIENCE INTERNET MANAGEMENT–OPERATIONS MANAGEMENT

Limestone College (B)

COMPUTER SCIENCE INTERNET MANAGEMENT–WEB DEVELOPMENT

Limestone College (B)

COMPUTER SCIENCE INTERNET MANAGEMENT, GENERAL

Limestone College (B)

COMPUTER SCIENCE MANAGEMENT INFORMATION SYSTEMS

Limestone College (A)

COMPUTER SCIENCE PROGRAMMING

Limestone College (A,B)

COMPUTER SCIENCE TECHNOLOGY

Thomas Edison State College (A,B)

COMPUTER SCIENCE–APPLIED COMPUTER SCIENCE

Columbus State University (M)

COMPUTER SCIENCE–CISCO CERTIFIED NETWORK ASSOCIATE PREPARATION, ACCELERATED

Fort Hays State University (UC)

COMPUTER SCIENCE–CISCO CERTIFIED NETWORK ASSOCIATE PREPARATION, MILITARY

Fort Hays State University (UC)

COMPUTER SCIENCE–CYBERSECURITY CONCENTRATION

Stevens Institute of Technology (M)

COMPUTER SCIENCE–ELEMENTS OF COMPUTER SCIENCE

Stevens Institute of Technology (GC)

COMPUTER SCIENCE–FOUNDATIONS IN COMPUTER SCIENCE

Stanford University (GC)

COMPUTER SCIENCE–INFORMATION SYSTEMS

Austin Peay State University (B)
University of Management and Technology (B)

COMPUTER SCIENCE–INFORMATION TECHNOLOGY

Central Texas College (A)
University of Management and Technology (B)

COMPUTER SCIENCE–MASTER OF COMPUTER SCIENCE

University of Illinois at Urbana–Champaign (M)

COMPUTER SCIENCE–MICROSOFT CERTIFIED SYSTEMS ADMINISTRATOR

Seminole Community College (UC)

COMPUTER SCIENCE–MICROSOFT CERTIFIED SYSTEMS ENGINEER

Seminole Community College (UC)

COMPUTER SCIENCE–PC NETWORKING

Daniel Webster College (UC)

COMPUTER SCIENCE–SOFTWARE ENGINEERING

University of Management and Technology (B)

COMPUTER SCIENCE, COMPUTER AND INFORMATION SYSTEMS SECURITY

Limestone College (B)

COMPUTER SCIENCE/COMPUTER SECURITY

University of Illinois at Urbana–Champaign (GC)

COMPUTER SCIENCE/INFORMATION SYSTEMS

University of Illinois at Urbana–Champaign (GC)

COMPUTER SCIENCE/NETWORKS AND DISTRIBUTED SYSTEMS

University of Illinois at Urbana–Champaign (GC)

COMPUTER SCIENCE/SOFTWARE ENGINEERING

University of Illinois at Urbana–Champaign (GC)

COMPUTER SCIENCE/SYSTEM SOFTWARE

University of Illinois at Urbana–Champaign (GC)

COMPUTER SECURITY

University of Illinois at Urbana–Champaign (GC)

COMPUTER SKILLS FOR MANAGERS

College of Southern Maryland (UC)

COMPUTER SOFTWARE

Excelsior College (A)

COMPUTER SOFTWARE SPECIALIST

The University of Toledo (A,UC)

COMPUTER STUDIES

University of Maryland University College (B)

COMPUTER SUPPORT ESSENTIALS

Minnesota State Community and Technical College–Fergus Falls (UC)

COMPUTER SUPPORT SPECIALIST

Three Rivers Community College (A)

COMPUTER SYSTEMS (NETWORKING/TELECOMMUNICATIONS EMPHASIS)

City University of Seattle (B)

COMPUTER SYSTEMS AND SOFTWARE DESIGN

Jacksonville State University (M)

COMPUTER SYSTEMS MANAGEMENT

University of Maryland University College (M)

COMPUTER TECHNOLOGY

Broome Community College (A)
Excelsior College (B)
New England Institute of Technology (A)

COMPUTER TECHNOLOGY MANAGEMENT

Dickinson State University (B)

COMPUTER, INFORMATION, AND NETWORK SECURITY

DePaul University (M)

COMPUTER/TECHNOLOGY

Cleveland State University (UC)

COMPUTERS AND MANAGEMENT INFORMATION SYSTEMS

Athabasca University (UC)

COMPUTING

Pace University (D)

COMPUTING AND INFORMATION SYSTEMS

Athabasca University (B,UC)

COMPUTING AND INFORMATION SYSTEMS–POST-DIPLOMA

Athabasca University (B)

COMPUTING AND SECURITY TECHNOLOGY

Drexel University (B)

COMPUTING TECHNOLOGY IN EDUCATION

Nova Southeastern University (D,M)

CONFLICT RESOLUTION

Antioch University McGregor (M)
Kansas State University (GC)
The University of North Carolina at Greensboro (M,UC)

CONFLICT RESOLUTION AND RECONCILIATION

Abilene Christian University (M,UC)

CONSTRUCTION

Thomas Edison State College (B)

CONSTRUCTION AND FACILITY SUPPORT

Thomas Edison State College (A)

CONSTRUCTION ENGINEERING

National University (B)
University of Washington (M)

CONSTRUCTION MANAGEMENT

East Carolina University (M)
New Jersey Institute of Technology (GC)
North Dakota State University (M)
San Joaquin Valley College–Online (A)
University of Southern California (M)
University of Washington (UC)

CONSTRUCTION SCIENCE AND MANAGEMENT

Clemson University (M)

CONSTRUCTION SUPERVISION

California State University, San Marcos (UC)

CONSTRUCTION TECHNOLOGY

University of Southern Mississippi (B)

CONSTRUCTION TECHNOLOGY–CONSTRUCTION ELECTRICIAN EMPHASIS

Red Rocks Community College (A)

CONSTRUCTION TECHNOLOGY–POWER TECHNOLOGY EMPHASIS

Red Rocks Community College (A)

CONSUMER AND FAMILY SCIENCES, CHILD STUDIES EMPHASIS

Western Kentucky University (B)

CONSUMER SCIENCES (CONSUMER AFFAIRS)

The University of Alabama (B)

CONSUMER SCIENCES (FAMILY FINANCIAL PLANNING AND COUNSELING)

The University of Alabama (B)

CONTEMPLATIVE EDUCATION

Naropa University (M)

CONTEMPORARY COMMUNICATIONS

University of Massachusetts Lowell (UC)

CONTEMPORARY NURSING FACULTY

Drexel University (M,,UC)

CONTENT DEVELOPMENT

Southern Polytechnic State University (GC)

CONTINUING TEACHING LICENSURE

Oregon State University (UC)

CONTRACT MANAGEMENT–MASTER OF CONTRACT MANAGEMENT

American Graduate University (M)

CONTROL AND SYSTEM ENGINEERING

Stanford University (GC)

CORE BUSINESS COMPETENCIES

Colorado State University (UC)

CORPORATE COMMUNICATION

Austin Peay State University (M)
Bellevue University (B)

CORPORATE COMMUNICATIONS

Southwestern Adventist University (B)

CORPORATE FINANCE

University of Dallas (M)

CORPORATE MANAGEMENT

Myers University (B)

CORRECTIONAL SERVICES

Mountain Empire Community College (A)

CORRECTIONS

Herkimer County Community College (UC)
Indiana State University (UC)
James A. Rhodes State College (A)
Kaplan University Online (UC)

CORRECTIONS ADMINISTRATION AND MANAGEMENT

Bellevue University (B)

CORRECTIONS AND JUVENILE JUSTICE

Eastern Kentucky University (M,B)

CORRECTIONS OFFICER ACADEMIC PROGRAM

Alpena Community College (UC)

CORRECTIONS PRE-CERTIFICATION

Tunxis Community College (UC)

COSMETOLOGY BUSINESS

Minnesota School of Business–Richfield (A)

COTA TO MOT

Texas Woman's University (M)

COUNSELING

Athabasca University (M,)
Liberty University (D)
Mercy College (M)
Oregon State University (D)
Seton Hall University (M)
University of North Dakota (M)
The University of Tennessee at Martin (M)

COUNSELING (MENTAL HEALTH)

University of the Southwest (M)

COUNSELING AND PSYCHOLOGY

Prescott College (M)

COUNSELING EDUCATION AND SUPERVISION

Regent University (D)

COUNSELING MINISTRIES

Baptist Bible College of Pennsylvania (M)

COUNSELING PSYCHOLOGY

Memorial University of Newfoundland (M)

COUNSELING PSYCHOLOGY/HUMAN SERVICES

Prescott College (B)

COUNSELING WOMEN

Athabasca University (UC)

COUNSELING–FAMILY THERAPY TRACK

University of Massachusetts Boston (M)

COUNSELING–MENTAL HEALTH COUNSELING TRACK

University of Massachusetts Boston (M)

COUNSELING–REHABILITATION COUNSELING TRACK

University of Massachusetts Boston (M)

COUNSELING–SCHOOL COUNSELING, ADVANCED

The University of North Carolina at Greensboro (GC)

COUNSELING–SCHOOL GUIDANCE COUNSELING

Prescott College (M)

COUNSELING–SCHOOL GUIDANCE TRACK

University of Massachusetts Boston (M)

COUNSELING/COMMUNITY COUNSELING

University of Phoenix (M)

COUNSELING/MARRIAGE AND FAMILY COUNSELING

University of Phoenix (M)

COUNSELING/MARRIAGE, FAMILY, AND CHILD THERAPY

University of Phoenix (M)

COUNSELING/MENTAL HEALTH COUNSELING

University of Phoenix (M)

COUNSELING/SCHOOL COUNSELING

University of Phoenix (M)

COUNSELOR EDUCATION

The University of Alabama

COUNSELOR EDUCATION (REHABILITATION)

The University of Alabama (M)

CPA EXAM ELIGIBILITY PROGRAM

Clarion University of Pennsylvania (UC)

CREATIVE NONFICTION

Goucher College (M)

CREATIVE STUDIES

Buffalo State College, State University of
New York (GC,M)

CREATIVE WRITING

Chatham University (M)
Naropa University (M)
National University (M)
Prescott College (B)
Saint Mary-of-the-Woods College (B)
The University of Texas at El Paso (M)

CREATIVITY STUDIES

Saybrook Graduate School and Research
Center (GC)

CRIME ANALYSIS

Tiffin University (M)

CRIME SCENE TECHNICIAN

Kaplan University Online (UC)

CRIMINAL BEHAVIOR

Tiffin University (M)

CRIMINAL JUSTICE

American Public University System (M,B)
Athabasca University (B)
Bowling Green State University (M)
Bryant and Stratton Online (A)
California State University, San Bernardino
(M)
Centralia College (A)
Central Texas College (A)
College of The Albemarle (A)
Colorado Technical University Colorado
Springs (A,B)
Columbia College (A,B)
Columbia Southern University (A)

Concordia University, St. Paul (B)
Darton College (A)
East Carolina University (M)
Eastern Wyoming College (A)
Excelsior College (B)
Florida Gulf Coast University (B)
Florida Institute of Technology (B)
Florida Tech University Online (B)
Franklin Pierce University (A,B)
Genesee Community College (A)
Golden West College (A)
Granite State College (B)
Grantham University (A,B)
Herkimer County Community College (A)
Hodges University (M,B)
Indiana Wesleyan University (A,UC)
Ivy Tech Community College–Bloomington
(A)
Ivy Tech Community College–Central Indiana
(A)
Ivy Tech Community College–Columbus (A)
Ivy Tech Community College–East Central
(A)
Ivy Tech Community College–Kokomo (A)
Ivy Tech Community College–Lafayette (A)
Ivy Tech Community College–North Central
(A)
Ivy Tech Community College–Northeast (A)
Ivy Tech Community College–Northwest (A)
Ivy Tech Community College–Southeast (A)
Ivy Tech Community College–Southern
Indiana (A)
Ivy Tech Community College–Southwest (A)
Ivy Tech Community College–Wabash Valley
(A)
Ivy Tech Community College–Whitewater (A)
Jefferson Community College (A)
Judson College (B)
Kaplan University Online (M,A,B)
Keiser University (M,A,B)
Lakeland College (B)
Liberty University (A,B)
Limestone College (B)
Lynn University (B)
Mercy College (B)
Michigan State University (M)
Monroe Community College (A)
Montgomery Community College (A)
Montgomery County Community College (A)
New Mexico State University (M,B)
New York Institute of Technology (B)
Northampton County Area Community
College (A)
Northeast Iowa Community College (A)
Northwestern State University of Louisiana
(A,B)
Old Dominion University (B)
Ouachita Technical College (A)
Peninsula College (A)
Penn State University Park (B)
Prescott College (B)
Randolph Community College (A)
St. John's University (A,B)
Saint Joseph's College of Maine (A)
Saint Leo University (M,B)
Saint Mary-of-the-Woods College (B)
San Antonio College (A)
Southwestern Adventist University (B)
Southwestern College (B)
Thomas Edison State College (B)
Tunxis Community College (A)
The University of Alabama (B)

University of Arkansas at Little Rock (M,B)
University of Central Florida (M)
University of Central Missouri (M)
University of Cincinnati (M)
University of Houston–Victoria (B)
University of Management and Technology
(M,A,B)
University of Maryland University College
(B)
University of Massachusetts Lowell (M)
University of Phoenix (A)
The University of Texas at Brownsville (B)
The University of Texas of the Permian Basin
(B)
University of the Southwest (B)
The University of Toledo (B)
University of Wisconsin–Platteville (GC)
University of Wisconsin–Platteville (GC)
University of Wisconsin–Platteville (M)
University of Wisconsin–Platteville (M)
University of Wisconsin–Platteville (B)
University of Wisconsin–Platteville (B)
University of Wyoming (B)
Upper Iowa University (B)
Utah Valley State College (A)
Washburn University (B)
Washington State University (B)
Weber State University (A)
Westwood Online (B)

CRIMINAL JUSTICE (BACHELOR COMPLETION)

Indiana Wesleyan University (B)

CRIMINAL JUSTICE (COMPLETION DEGREE)

The University of Texas System (B)

CRIMINAL JUSTICE ADDICTIONS

Central Texas College (UC)

CRIMINAL JUSTICE ADMINISTRATION

Bellevue University (B)
Columbia College (M)
Columbia Southern University (M,B)
Lynn University (M)
Mountain State University (B)
Myers University (B)
National University (B)
Park University (B)
Taft College (A)
The University of Findlay (B)
University of Management and Technology
(B)
University of Phoenix (B)

CRIMINAL JUSTICE ADMINISTRATION (MSA)

University of West Florida (M)

CRIMINAL JUSTICE ADMINISTRATION CONCENTRATION

American InterContinental University Online
(A)

CRIMINAL JUSTICE AND CRIMINOLOGY

Mount Olive College (B)

CRIMINAL JUSTICE CONCENTRATION

Colorado Technical University Colorado Springs (M)
Saint Leo University (M)

CRIMINAL JUSTICE CORRECTIONS SPECIALIZATION

Central Texas College (A,UC)

CRIMINAL JUSTICE LEADERSHIP

Roosevelt University (B,UC)

CRIMINAL JUSTICE MANAGEMENT

Darton College (UC)
Saint Leo University (GC)

CRIMINAL JUSTICE STUDIES

St. Cloud State University (M,B)

CRIMINAL JUSTICE STUDIES SPECIALIZATION

Central Texas College (UC)

CRIMINAL JUSTICE TECHNOLOGY

Haywood Community College (A)

CRIMINAL JUSTICE–ADMINISTRATION OPTION

Middlesex Community College (A)

CRIMINAL JUSTICE–COMPUTER SCIENCE

Grantham University (A,B)

CRIMINAL JUSTICE–CYBERSECURITY

Herkimer County Community College (A)

CRIMINAL JUSTICE–ECONOMIC CRIME

Herkimer County Community College (A)

CRIMINAL JUSTICE–HOMELAND SECURITY

Austin Peay State University (B)
Grantham University (A,B)

CRIMINAL JUSTICE–LAW ENFORCEMENT OPTION

Middlesex Community College (A)

CRIMINAL JUSTICE, ADMINISTRATION OPTION

Granite State College (B)

CRIMINAL JUSTICE, CRITICAL INCIDENT MANAGEMENT CONCENTRATION

Saint Leo University (M)

CRIMINAL JUSTICE, ECONOMIC CRIME INVESTIGATION

Utica College (B)

CRIMINAL JUSTICE, SPECIAL POPULATIONS CONCENTRATION

American InterContinental University Online (B)

CRIMINAL JUSTICE/CORRECTIONS

Cayuga County Community College (A)

CRIMINAL JUSTICE/POLICE

Cayuga County Community College (A)

CRIMINOLOGY

Indiana University of Pennsylvania (M)
Memorial University of Newfoundland (UC)

CRIMINOLOGY AND CRIMINAL JUSTICE

Indiana State University (M,B)

CRIMINOLOGY, CRIMINAL JUSTICE STUDIES MAJOR

Florida State University (M)

CRITICAL AND CREATIVE THINKING (FOCUS ON CREATIVITY AT WORK)

University of Massachusetts Boston (GC)

CROP PROTECTION

Texas Tech University (GC)

CROP SCIENCE

Texas Tech University (M)

CROP SCIENCES

University of Illinois at Urbana–Champaign (M,UC)

CROSS CULTURAL TEACHING

National University (M)

CROSS-CATEGORICAL SPECIAL EDUCATION

Regent University (M)

CULINARY ARTS

Bellevue University (B)

CULTURAL AND REGIONAL STUDIES

Prescott College (B)

CULTURAL STUDIES

Prescott College (M)
State University of New York Empire State College (A,B)

CURRICULUM AND INSTRUCTION

Abilene Christian University (M)
Black Hills State University (GC)
The College of St. Scholastica (M)
Concordia University Wisconsin (M)
North Carolina State University (M)
University of Arkansas
University of Massachusetts Lowell (M)
The University of North Carolina at Greensboro (M)
The University of Texas System (M)
University of the Southwest (M)

CURRICULUM AND INSTRUCTION (FOR HEALTH CARE PROFESSIONALS)

University of Cincinnati (M)

CURRICULUM AND INSTRUCTION CONCENTRATION (10-MONTH PROGRAM)

American InterContinental University Online (M)

CURRICULUM AND INSTRUCTION IN MEDICAL EDUCATION FOR HEALTHCARE PROFESSIONALS

University of Cincinnati (UC)

CURRICULUM AND INSTRUCTION K-12

University of Nebraska at Kearney (M)

CURRICULUM AND INSTRUCTION–ADULT EDUCATION

University of Phoenix (M)

CURRICULUM AND INSTRUCTION–BILINGUAL

University of the Southwest (M)

CURRICULUM AND INSTRUCTION–CHILDREN'S LITERATURE

Penn State University Park (M)

CURRICULUM AND INSTRUCTION–EDUCATIONAL LEADERSHIP

University of Colorado at Colorado Springs (M)

CURRICULUM AND INSTRUCTION–EDUCATIONAL TECHNOLOGY

La Sierra University (M)

CURRICULUM AND INSTRUCTION–EFFECTIVE TEACHING AND INSTRUCTIONAL LEADERSHIP EMPHASIS

Buena Vista University (M)

CURRICULUM AND INSTRUCTION–INSTRUCTIONAL TECHNOLOGY CONCENTRATION

University of South Florida

CURRICULUM AND INSTRUCTION–READING

University of the Southwest (M)

CURRICULUM AND INSTRUCTION–SECONDARY EDUCATION, TESOL SPECIALIZATION

University of South Florida (M)

CURRICULUM AND INSTRUCTION–SPECIAL EDUCATION AND READING

University of Nebraska at Kearney (M)

CURRICULUM AND INSTRUCTION–TEACHING ENGLISH AS A SECOND LANGUAGE EMPHASIS

Buena Vista University (M)

CURRICULUM AND INSTRUCTION–TESOL

University of the Southwest (M)

CURRICULUM AND INSTRUCTION-LEARNING TECHNOLOGIES EMPHASIS

New Mexico State University (D)

CURRICULUM AND INSTRUCTIONAL TECHNOLOGY

Framingham State College (M)

CURRICULUM INTEGRATION IN ACTION

University of Washington (UC)

CURRICULUM TEACHING AND LEARNING STUDIES

Memorial University of Newfoundland (M)

CURRICULUM, TECHNOLOGY, AND EDUCATION REFORM

University of Illinois at Urbana–Champaign (M)

CURRICULUM, TECHNOLOGY, AND EDUCATION REFORM (CTER)

University of Illinois at Urbana–Champaign (M)

CYBER SECURITY

Stevens Institute of Technology (GC)

CYBERSECURITY AND INFORMATION ASSURANCE

Utica College (B)

CYTOTECHNOLOGY

Thomas Edison State College (B)

DAIRY SCIENCE

University of Illinois at Urbana–Champaign (UC)

DANCE EDUCATION

The University of North Carolina at Greensboro (M)

DATA MINING

Central Connecticut State University (M)
New Jersey Institute of Technology (GC)
University of Louisville (GC)

DATA MINING AND APPLICATIONS (STATISTICS)

Stanford University (GC)

DATA RESOURCE MANAGEMENT

University of Washington (UC)

DATA/TELECOMMUNICATIONS

University of Massachusetts Lowell (UC)

DATABASE ADMINISTRATION (MSA)

University of West Florida (M)

DATABASE ADMINISTRATION–CERTIFICATE OF ADVANCED STUDY

University of Denver (UC)

DATABASE MANAGEMENT

University of Washington (UC)

DATABASE SPECIALIST

Union County College (UC)

DATABASE SYSTEMS

Stevens Institute of Technology (GC)

DATABASE SYSTEMS TECHNOLOGIES

University of Maryland University College (GC)

DATABASE TECHNOLOGIES (MSCIT)

Regis University (GC)

DATABASE TECHNOLOGY AND MANAGEMENT (UNDERGRADUATE)

Golden Gate University (UC)

DATABASES

Stanford University (GC)

DEAF AND HARD OF HEARING

Texas Tech University (UC)

DEAF EDUCATION

Texas Woman's University (M)

DECISION ANALYSIS

Stanford University (GC)

DECISION SUPPORT SYSTEMS

Webster University (GC)

DEGREE COMPLETION

Duquesne University (B)

DENTAL ASSISTING

Monroe Community College (UC)

DENTAL HYGIENE

Pennsylvania College of Technology (B)
Thomas Edison State College (B)

DENTAL HYGIENE (THROUGH UMDNJ)

Thomas Edison State College (A)

DENTAL HYGIENE ONLINE (DEGREE COMPLETION PROGRAM)

University of Bridgeport (B)

DENTAL HYGIENE–BS COMPLETION PROGRAM

East Tennessee State University (B)

DENTAL HYGIENE–DENTAL HYGIENE DEGREE COMPLETION

Oregon Institute of Technology (B)

DESIGN FOR CUSTOMER VALUE AND MARKET SUCCESS

Stanford University (GC)

DESIGN TECHNOLGY

Ivy Tech Community College–East Central (A)

DESIGN TECHNOLOGY

Ivy Tech Community College–Bloomington (A)
Ivy Tech Community College–Central Indiana (A)
Ivy Tech Community College–Columbus (A)
Ivy Tech Community College–Kokomo (A)
Ivy Tech Community College–Lafayette (A)
Ivy Tech Community College–North Central (A)
Ivy Tech Community College–Northeast (A)
Ivy Tech Community College–Northwest (A)
Ivy Tech Community College–Southeast (A)
Ivy Tech Community College–Southern Indiana (A)
Ivy Tech Community College–Southwest (A)
Ivy Tech Community College–Wabash Valley (A)
Ivy Tech Community College–Whitewater (A)

DESIGNING AND IMPLEMENTING WEB-BASED LEARNING ENVIRONMENTS

University of Colorado Denver (UC)

DESKTOP PUBLISHING TECHNOLOGY

Bristol Community College (UC)

DEVELOPMENTAL DISABILITIES

Minot State University (A,UC)

DIETARY MANAGEMENT

Auburn University (UC)

DIETETIC SCIENCES (WITH UMDNJ)

Thomas Edison State College (B)

DIETETIC TECHNICIAN

Baltimore City Community College (A)

DIETETICS

Eastern Michigan University (B)
Kansas State University (B)
North Dakota State University (M)

DIFFERENTIATED CURRICULUM FOR GIFTED STUDENTS

University of Southern California (UC)

DIFFERENTIATED INSTRUCTION

Concordia University, St. Paul (M)

DIGITAL ARTS AND COMMUNICATIONS

Academy of Art University (A,B)

DIGITAL CINEMA

National University (M)

DIGITAL COMMUNICATION

Stanford University (GC)

DIGITAL INFORMATION MANAGEMENT

The University of Arizona (GC)

DIGITAL LIBRARIES

Syracuse University (GC)

DIGITAL MEDIA

Jones International University (A)
Savannah College of Art and Design (B)

DIGITAL MEDIA ARTS

Cerro Coso Community College (A)

DIGITAL MEDIA COMMUNICATION

Saint Mary-of-the-Woods College (B)

DIGITAL MUSIC EDUCATION

University of South Florida (GC)

DIGITAL PHOTOGRAPHY

Savannah College of Art and Design (M)

DIGITAL PRINT AND PUBLISHING

Rochester Institute of Technology (GC)

DIGITAL PUBLISHING

Savannah College of Art and Design (UC)

DIGITAL PUBLISHING MANAGEMENT

Savannah College of Art and Design (GC)

DIGITAL SIGNAL PROCESSING

Stevens Institute of Technology (GC)

DIRECT MARKETING CERTIFICATE

Columbus State Community College (GC)

DIRECT TRANSFER

Everett Community College (A)

DISASTER AND EMERGENCY MANAGEMENT

Park University (M)
Rochester Institute of Technology (UC)

DISASTER MANAGEMENT

University of South Florida (GC)

DISASTER MEDICINE AND MANAGEMENT

Philadelphia University (M)

DISASTER PREPAREDNESS

Penn State University Park (GC)

DISASTER PREPAREDNESS AND EMERGENCY MANAGEMENT

University of Hawaii–West Oahu (UC)

DISPUTE RESOLUTION SPECIALIST

Sullivan University (UC)

DISTANCE DOCTORATE

Utah State University (D)

DISTANCE EDUCATION

Athabasca University (M)
Indiana University System (UC)
Penn State University Park (GC)
University of Maryland University College (M)

DISTANCE EDUCATION (TECHNOLOGY)

Athabasca University (GC)

DISTANCE EDUCATION LEADERSHIP

University of Maryland University College (GC)

DISTANCE EDUCATION–ONLINE TEACHING AND LEARNING

Appalachian State University (GC)

DISTANCE EDUCATION, GLOBALIZATION, AND DEVELOPMENT

University of Maryland University College (GC)

DISTANCE INSTRUCTION

East Carolina University (GC)

DISTANCE LEARNING

Utah State University (UC)

DISTANCE LEARNING DESIGN AND DEVELOPMENT

University of Washington (UC)

DISTANCE M.DIV.

University of Dubuque (M)

DISTANCE MBA

Colorado State University (M)

DISTRIBUTED OBJECT-ORIENTED ANALYSIS AND DESIGN–CERTIFICATE OF ADVANCED STUDY

University of Denver (UC)

DIVERSITY AND EQUITY ISSUES IN EDUCATION EMPHASIS

University of Illinois at Urbana–Champaign (M)

DIVERSITY MANAGEMENT

The University of Toledo (UC)

DIVINITY

The Baptist College of Florida (A)
Global University (M)
Liberty University (M)

DOCTOR OF PHYSICAL THERAPY (DPT)—TRANSITION

Temple University

DOING BUSINESS IN CHINA

Thunderbird School of Global Management

DOING BUSINESS IN INDIA

Thunderbird School of Global Management

DOMESTIC VIOLENCE PREVENTION

University of Massachusetts Lowell (GC)

DREAM STUDIES

Saybrook Graduate School and Research Center (GC)

DRIVER EDUCATION INSTRUCTOR

Indiana State University (UC)

DSJS–DOCTOR OF SCIENCE IN JEWISH STUDIES

Spertus Institute of Jewish Studies

DUAL IMPAIRMENTS

Texas Tech University (GC)

DUAL MACE/MBA

Dallas Baptist University (M)

DUAL MBA/MACE

Dallas Baptist University (M)

DUKE ENVIRONMENTAL LEADERSHIP MASTER OF ENVIRONMENTAL MANAGEMENT

Duke University (M)

E-BUSINESS

Dallas Baptist University (M,UC)

E-BUSINESS

Rochester Institute of Technology (UC)
Strayer University (B)

E-BUSINESS

University of Maryland University College (GC)

E-BUSINESS MANAGEMENT

Westwood Online (B)

E-BUSINESS SOFTWARE (DATABASE TRACK)

Seminole Community College (UC)

E-BUSINESS SOFTWARE (WEB DESIGN TRACK)

Seminole Community College (UC)

E-BUSINESS TECHNOLOGY (MICROSOFT TRACK)

Seminole Community College (UC)

E-BUSINESS TECHNOLOGY (SECURITY SPECIALIZATION)

Seminole Community College (A)

E-BUSINESS TECHNOLOGY (SOFTWARE SPECIALIZATION)

Seminole Community College (A)

E-BUSINESS TECHNOLOGY (TECHNOLOGY SPECIALIZATION)

Seminole Community College (A)

E-COMMERCE

Athabasca University (B,UC)
University of Maryland University College (M)
University of North Texas (UC)

E-COMMERCE AND WEBMASTER TECHNOLOGY

Rose State College (A)

E-COMMERCE ENGINEERING (MSCIT)

Regis University (GC)

E-COMMERCE TECHNOLOGY

DePaul University (M)

E-COMMERCE WEB DEVELOPMENT

Fort Hays State University (UC)

E-FINANCIAL PLANNING

DePaul University (UC)

E-LEARNING

George Mason University (GC)
Roosevelt University (GC)
University of Calgary (UC)

E-LEARNING AND ONLINE TEACHING GRADUATE CERTIFICATE

University of Wisconsin–Stout (GC)

E-LEARNING PROFESSIONAL DEVELOPMENT

University of Central Florida (GC)

EARLY CHILDHHOOD DEVELOPMENT AND CARE

Washington State University (UC)

EARLY CHILDHOOD

Broome Community College (A)
Concordia University, St. Paul (M)
Southeast Community College Area (A)

EARLY CHILDHOOD ASSOCIATE

Lake Region State College (A)

EARLY CHILDHOOD ASSOCIATE–SPECIAL EDUCATION

Haywood Community College (A)

EARLY CHILDHOOD ASSOCIATE–TEACHER ASSOCIATE

Haywood Community College (A)

EARLY CHILDHOOD BIRTH TO FIVE ENDORSEMENT

University of Wyoming (UC)

EARLY CHILDHOOD DEVELOPMENT

J. Sargeant Reynolds Community College (A)
National University (B)

EARLY CHILDHOOD DIRECTORS CREDENTIAL PROGRAM

Clarion University of Pennsylvania (UC)

EARLY CHILDHOOD EDUCATION

Arkansas Tech University (A,B)
Brenau University (M)
Clarion University of Pennsylvania (A)
College of the Siskiyous (A)
Darton College (A)
Eugenio María de Hostos Community College of the City University of New York (A)
Haywood Community College (A)
Independence University (A)
Ivy Tech Community College–Bloomington (A)
Ivy Tech Community College–Central Indiana (A)
Ivy Tech Community College–Columbus (A)
Ivy Tech Community College–East Central (A)
Ivy Tech Community College–Kokomo (A)
Ivy Tech Community College–Lafayette (A)
Ivy Tech Community College–North Central (A)
Ivy Tech Community College–Northeast (A)
Ivy Tech Community College–Northwest (A)
Ivy Tech Community College–Southeast (A)
Ivy Tech Community College–Southern Indiana (A)
Ivy Tech Community College–Southwest (A)
Ivy Tech Community College–Wabash Valley (A)
Ivy Tech Community College–Whitewater (A)
Kansas State University (B)
Lehigh Carbon Community College (A,UC)
Mayville State University (B)
Montgomery County Community College (A)
Northampton County Area Community College (A)
South Piedmont Community College (A)
Taft College (A)
The University of Alabama (B)
University of Cincinnati (A,B)
University of Colorado Denver (M)
University of Missouri–Columbia (M)
University of North Dakota (M)
University of the Southwest (M)

EARLY CHILDHOOD EDUCATION ASSISTANT

San Joaquin Delta College (UC)

EARLY CHILDHOOD EDUCATION ASSOCIATE

Mayville State University (A)

EARLY CHILDHOOD EDUCATION PRE-K-3 (NON-LICENSURE)

The University of Toledo (M)

EARLY CHILDHOOD EDUCATION–HOME-BASED EARLY CHILDHOOD EDUCATION

Northampton County Area Community College (UC)

EARLY CHILDHOOD EDUCATION, ELEMENTARY EDUCATION, SECONDARY EDUCATION, SPECIAL EDUCATION, AND MASS COMMUNICATION (INTEGRATED) CONCENTRATIONS

Parkland College (A)

EARLY CHILDHOOD INTERVENTION

Auburn University (M)

EARLY CHILDHOOD SPECIAL EDUCATION

National University (UC)
University of Missouri–Columbia (M)
University of Wyoming (UC)

EARLY CHILDHOOD SPECIAL EDUCATION, SPECIALIST

University of Colorado Denver (UC)

EARLY CHILDHOOD UNIFIED

Fort Hays State University (B)

EARLY CHILDHOOD/CHILD DEVELOPMENT

Saint Mary-of-the-Woods College (A)

EARLY CHILDHOOD/ELEMENTARY EDUCATION

Oregon State University (M)

EARLY CHILDHOOD/MIDDLE CHILDHOOD

University of Wisconsin–Stout (UC)

EARLY LITERACY

University of Colorado Denver (UC)

EARTH AND ENVIRONMENTAL ENGINEERING

Columbia University (M)

EARTH LITERACY

Saint Mary-of-the-Woods College (M)

EARTH SCIENCE EDUCATION

Eastern Michigan University (M)

EARTH SCIENCES

Penn State University Park (M)

EARTH SYSTEMS SCIENCE

Michigan Technological University (M)

ECOLOGY

Prescott College (M)

ECOMMERCE

Franklin Pierce University (GC)

ECONOMIC CRIME INVESTIGATION

Genesee Community College (A)

ECONOMIC CRIME MANAGEMENT

Utica College (M)

ECONOMIC DEVELOPMENT

University of Southern Mississippi (M)

ECONOMIC DEVELOPMENT AND ENTREPRENEURSHIP

University of Houston–Victoria (M)

ECONOMICS

Coastline Community College (A)
Community College of Denver (A)
Darton College (A)
Foothill College (A)
Strayer University (A,B)
Thomas Edison State College (B)
University of Illinois at Springfield (B)
Western Wyoming Community College (A)

ECONOMICS (BUSINESS TRACK)

Seminole Community College (A)

ECONOMICS (LIBERAL ARTS TRACK)

Seminole Community College (A)

ECONOMICS OF DEVELOPMENT

Mississippi State University (GC)

EDUCATION

Arizona Western College (A)
Athabasca University (D)
Capella University (D,M)
Cardinal Stritch University (M)
Central Michigan University (M)
Columbia College (M)
Drexel University (B)
Fort Hays State University (M)
Hope International University (M)
Indiana Wesleyan University (M)
Judson College (B)
Kaplan University Online (M)
Keiser University (M)
Lehigh Carbon Community College (A)
Liberty University (D,M)
Michigan State University (M)
New Mexico State University (M)
New River Community College (A)
Northcentral University (D,M)
Oregon State University (M)
Prescott College (M,B)
Regent University (GC)
Regis University (M)
Saint Joseph's College of Maine (M)
Saint Mary-of-the-Woods College (M)
Saint Mary-of-the-Woods College (M)
Spring Arbor University (M)
Strayer University (M)
TUI University (M)
University of Phoenix (M,B)
The University of Tennessee at Martin (M)
University of Wisconsin–Stout (M)
Walden University (D,M)
Wayland Baptist University (M)

EDUCATION ADMINISTRATION

Concordia University Wisconsin (M)

EDUCATION ADMINISTRATION AND SUPERVISION

The University of Tennessee at Martin (M)

EDUCATION AND HUMAN RESOURCE STUDIES (ORGANIZATIONAL PERFORMANCE AND CHANGE–OPC)

Colorado State University (M)

EDUCATION AND SCHOOL ADMINISTRATION

The University of North Carolina at Charlotte (M)

EDUCATION AND TRAINING MANAGEMENT SUBSPECIALTY/ HUMAN PERFORMANCE TECHNOLOGY

University of West Florida (M)

EDUCATION AND TRAINING MANAGEMENT SUBSPECIALTY/ INSTRUCTIONAL TECHNOLOGY

University of West Florida (M)

EDUCATION COUNSELING

Concordia University Wisconsin (M)

EDUCATION DOCTORATE

Regent University (D)

EDUCATION LEADERSHIP

University of North Dakota (M)

EDUCATION LEADERSHIP (MSA)

University of West Florida (M)

EDUCATION LEADERSHIP– PACIFIC COHORTS

San Diego State University (M)

EDUCATION LEADERSHIP, MANAGEMENT, AND POLICY (ELMP)

Seton Hall University (M)

EDUCATION OF TWICE EXCEPTIONAL STUDENTS

University of Southern California (UC)

EDUCATION SPECIALIST

Liberty University
Utah State University

EDUCATION SPECIALIST AND SCHOOL SUPERINTENDENT

University of Nebraska at Kearney

EDUCATION–ADAPTING CURRICULUM FRAMEWORKS FOR ALL LEARNERS

University of Massachusetts Boston (GC)

EDUCATION–ADMINISTRATION AND SUPERVISION SPECIALIZATION

University of Phoenix (M)

EDUCATION–ADULT AND POST-SECONDARY EDUCATION

University of Wyoming (M)

EDUCATION–ATHLETIC ADMINISTRATION

Nova Southeastern University (M)

EDUCATION–BIRTH-KINDERGARTEN EDUCATION

East Carolina University (B)

EDUCATION–BIRTH-KINDERGARTEN TEACHER LICENSURE

The University of North Carolina at Greensboro (B)

EDUCATION–CAREER AND TECHNICAL EDUCATION (EVOC)

California State University, San Bernardino (M)

EDUCATION–CHARTER SCHOOL EDUCATION AND LEADERSHIP

Nova Southeastern University (M)

EDUCATION–COGNITIVE AND BEHAVIORAL DISABILITIES

Nova Southeastern University (M)

EDUCATION–COMPREHENSIVE MASTERS IN EDUCATION

University of West Florida (M)

EDUCATION–COMPUTER EDUCATION

University of Phoenix (M)

EDUCATION–COMPUTER SCIENCE EDUCATION

Nova Southeastern University (M)

EDUCATION–CURRICULUM AND INSTRUCTION

University of Phoenix (M)

EDUCATION–EARLY CHILDHOOD EDUCATION SPECIALIZATION

University of Phoenix (M)

EDUCATION–EARLY LITERACY AND READING EDUCATION

Nova Southeastern University (M)

EDUCATION–EDUCATIONAL LEADERSHIP

University of Wyoming (M)

EDUCATION–EDUCATIONAL MEDIA

Nova Southeastern University (M)

EDUCATION–ELEMENTARY EDUCATION

Dickinson State University (B)
Nova Southeastern University (M)

EDUCATION–ENGLISH EDUCATION

Nova Southeastern University (M)

EDUCATION–EXCEPTIONAL STUDENT EDUCATION

Nova Southeastern University (M)

EDUCATION–GIFTED EDUCATION

Nova Southeastern University (M)

EDUCATION–GRADUATE INTERN TEACHING CERTIFICATE

Drexel University (UC)

EDUCATION–GRADUATE PA SECONDARY TEACHER CERTIFICATION PROGRAM

Clarion University of Pennsylvania (UC)

EDUCATION–HEALTH CARE EDUCATION

Nova Southeastern University (D)

EDUCATION–HIGHER EDUCATION

Nova Southeastern University (D)

EDUCATION–HUMAN RESOURCE DEVELOPMENT STRAND

The University of Findlay (M)

EDUCATION–HUMAN SERVICES ADMINISTRATION

Nova Southeastern University (D)

EDUCATION–INSTRUCTIONAL LEADERSHIP

Nova Southeastern University (D)

EDUCATION–INSTRUCTIONAL TECHNOLOGY

University of Wyoming (M)

EDUCATION–INSTRUCTIONAL TECHNOLOGY (ETEC)

California State University, San Bernardino (M)

EDUCATION–INSTRUCTIONAL TECHNOLOGY AND DISTANCE EDUCATION

Nova Southeastern University (D)

EDUCATION–INTERDISCIPLINARY ARTS

Nova Southeastern University (M)

EDUCATION–K-12 EDUCATORS AND ADMINISTRATION

Jones International University (M)

EDUCATION–KINDERGARTEN-ELEMENTARY EDUCATION

Saint Mary-of-the-Woods College (B)

EDUCATION–LEVEL I EDUCATION SPECIALIST CREDENTIAL: MILD/MOD

National University (UC)

EDUCATION–MASTER OF EDUCATION

University of Calgary (M)

EDUCATION–MATHEMATICS EDUCATION

Nova Southeastern University (M)

EDUCATION–MIDDLE SCHOOL EDUCATION

Buena Vista University (UC)

EDUCATION–MIDDLE SCHOOL/HIGH SCHOOL SPECIAL EDUCATION

Saint Mary-of-the-Woods College (B)

EDUCATION–MISSOURI VISUAL IMPAIRMENT PERSONNEL PREPARATION PROGRAM

Missouri State University (UC)

EDUCATION–ORGANIZATIONAL LEADERSHIP

Nova Southeastern University (D)

EDUCATION–POST-BACCALAUREATE DIPLOMA IN EDUCATION PROGRAM

University of Manitoba (GC)

EDUCATION–POST-BACHELOR'S TEACHING CERTIFICATE

Drexel University (UC)

EDUCATION–PRE-K THROUGH 6

Old Dominion University (M)

EDUCATION–PREKINDERGARTEN AND PRIMARY EDUCATION

Nova Southeastern University (M)

EDUCATION–PRESCHOOL-GRADE 3 EDUCATION/MILD INTERVENTION

Saint Mary-of-the-Woods College (B)

EDUCATION–READING EDUCATION

Nova Southeastern University (M)

EDUCATION–READING EDUCATION (ERDG)

California State University, San Bernardino (M)

EDUCATION–SCIENCE EDUCATION

Nova Southeastern University (M)

EDUCATION–SECONDARY EDUCATION

Buena Vista University (UC)
Judson College (B)
University of North Texas (M)

EDUCATION–SOCIAL STUDIES EDUCATION

Nova Southeastern University (M)

EDUCATION–SPANISH LANGUAGE EDUCATION

Nova Southeastern University (M)

EDUCATION–SPECIAL EDUCATION

Nova Southeastern University (D)
University of Wyoming (M)

EDUCATION–SPECIAL EDUCATION—LEVEL II CREDENTIAL ESPE

California State University, San Bernardino (M)

EDUCATION–SPEECH-LANGUAGE PATHOLOGY

Nova Southeastern University (D)

EDUCATION–SUSTAINABILITY EDUCATION

Prescott College (D)

EDUCATION–TEACHER PREPARATION

Old Dominion University (B)

EDUCATION–TEACHING AND LEARNING

University of Wyoming (M)

EDUCATION–TEACHING ENGLISH AS A FOREIGN LANGUAGE

Nova Southeastern University (M)

EDUCATION–TEACHING ENGLISH TO SPEAKERS OF OTHER LANGUAGES (TESOL)

Nova Southeastern University (M)

EDUCATION–TED MULTIPLE OR SINGLE SUBJECT TEACHING CREDENTIAL

National University (UC)

EDUCATION, ACADEMICALLY OR INTELLECTUALLY GIFTED ADD-ON TEACHER LICENSURE

The University of North Carolina at Charlotte (GC)

EDUCATION, CHILD DEVELOPMENT CONCENTRATION

Nova Southeastern University (B)

EDUCATION, GENERAL

Ouachita Technical College (A)
Park University (M)

EDUCATION, GENERAL TRANSFER

Northwestern Michigan College (A)

EDUCATION, MIDDLE AND SECONDARY EDUCATION TEACHER LICENSURE

The University of North Carolina at Charlotte (GC)

EDUCATION, MIDDLE GRADES

The University of North Carolina at Charlotte (M)

EDUCATION/ADULT EDUCATION AND TRAINING

University of Phoenix (M)

EDUCATION/CROSS-CATEGORICAL SPECIAL EDUCATION

University of Phoenix (M)

EDUCATION/CURRICULUM AND INSTRUCTION–ENGLISH AND LANGUAGE EDUCATION

University of Phoenix (M)

EDUCATION/CURRICULUM AND INSTRUCTION–MATHEMATICS EDUCATION

University of Phoenix (M)

EDUCATION/ELEMENTARY TEACHER EDUCATION

University of Phoenix (M)

EDUCATION/ESL

University of Phoenix (M)

EDUCATION/SECONDARY TEACHER EDUCATION

University of Phoenix (M)

EDUCATIONAL ADMINISTRATION

California State University, Northridge (M)
Fort Hays State University (M)
Hope International University (M)
Kansas State University (M)
Missouri State University–West Plains (M)
New Mexico State University (M)
Prescott College (M)
St. Cloud State University (M)
The University of Alabama (D)
University of Massachusetts Lowell (M)
University of North Texas (M)
University of South Alabama (UC)
University of the Southwest (M)

EDUCATIONAL ADMINISTRATION (EDUCATIONAL LEADERSHIP)

New Mexico State University (D)

EDUCATIONAL ADMINISTRATION AND ADMINISTRATIVE SERVICES

National University (M)

EDUCATIONAL ADMINISTRATION AND SUPERVISION

Ball State University (M)
University of North Texas (M)

EDUCATIONAL ADMINISTRATION–COLLABORATIVE LEADERSHIP

Drexel University (M)

EDUCATIONAL ADMINISTRATION–SCHOOL ADMINISTRATION

The University of North Carolina at Greensboro (M)

EDUCATIONAL ADMINISTRATION–WEBPLUS! MPA PROGRAM

University of Michigan–Flint (M)

EDUCATIONAL ADMINISTRATION/ ADULT AND HIGHER EDUCATION

The University of South Dakota (M)

EDUCATIONAL ADMINISTRATION/ ELEMENTARY SCHOOL PRINCIPAL

The University of South Dakota (M,)

EDUCATIONAL ADMINISTRATION/ PRE-K-12 PRINCIPAL

The University of South Dakota (M,)

EDUCATIONAL ADMINISTRATION/ SCHOOL DISTRICT SUPERINTENDENT

The University of South Dakota (M,)

EDUCATIONAL ADMINISTRATION/ SECONDARY SCHOOL PRINCIPAL

The University of South Dakota (M,)

EDUCATIONAL ADMINISTRATIVE LICENSURE

New Mexico State University (UC)

EDUCATIONAL AND INSTRUCTIONAL TECHNOLOGY

National University (M)

EDUCATIONAL ASSESSMENT AND EVALUATION CONCENTRATION (10-MONTH PROGRAM)

American InterContinental University Online (M)

EDUCATIONAL COMPUTING, DESIGN, AND ONLINE LEARNING/ CLASSROOM TECHNOLOGY

Kansas State University (GC,M)

EDUCATIONAL DIAGNOSTICIAN

Texas Tech University (UC)
University of the Southwest (M)

EDUCATIONAL LEADERSHIP

Bridgewater State College (M)
Clemson University (D)
Crown College (M)
Dallas Baptist University (M)
LeTourneau University (M)
Midwestern State University (M)
Nova Southeastern University (D)
Regent University (M)
Saint Leo University (M)
Texas Tech University (D)
TUI University (D)
The University of Alabama (M)
University of Cincinnati (M)
University of Missouri–Columbia (M)
University of North Dakota (D)

University of Phoenix (D)
University of South Alabama (M)
The University of Texas at Tyler (M)

EDUCATIONAL LEADERSHIP (CERTIFICATION)

The University of Alabama

EDUCATIONAL LEADERSHIP (MAEDL)

Thomas Edison State College (M)

EDUCATIONAL LEADERSHIP (NON-CERTIFICATION)

The University of Alabama

EDUCATIONAL LEADERSHIP AND CHANGE

Fielding Graduate University (D)

EDUCATIONAL LEADERSHIP AND INSTRUCTION

Northwestern State University of Louisiana (GC)

EDUCATIONAL LEADERSHIP AND POLICY EMPHASIS

University of Illinois at Urbana–Champaign (M)

EDUCATIONAL LEADERSHIP AND PRINCIPAL PROFESSIONAL CERTIFICATION PREPARATION

Texas Tech University (M)

EDUCATIONAL LEADERSHIP STUDIES

Memorial University of Newfoundland (M)

EDUCATIONAL LEADERSHIP WITH PRINCIPAL CERTIFICATION

Stephen F. Austin State University (M)

EDUCATIONAL LEADERSHIP, CHARTER SCHOOL ADMINISTRATION EMPHASIS

Central Michigan University (M)

EDUCATIONAL LEADERSHIP, CURRICULUM AND INSTRUCTION SPECIALIZATION

University of Phoenix (D)

EDUCATIONAL LEADERSHIP, HIGHER EDUCATION ADMINISTRATION SPECIALIZATION

Lynn University (M)

EDUCATIONAL LEADERSHIP, RENEWAL, AND CHANGE

Colorado State University (D,M)

EDUCATIONAL LEADERSHIP, SCHOOL ADMINISTRATION SPECIALIZATION

Lynn University (M)

EDUCATIONAL LEADERSHIP, SCHOOL ADMINISTRATION WITH ESOL ENDORSEMENT SPECIALIZATION

Lynn University (M)

EDUCATIONAL LEADERSHIP/ ADMINISTRATION

Florida State University (M)

EDUCATIONAL LEADERSHIP/ EDUCATION TECHNOLOGY

University of Phoenix (D)

EDUCATIONAL MEDIA

University of Central Florida (GC)

EDUCATIONAL MEDIA (LIBRARY MEDIA)

University of South Alabama (M,UC)

EDUCATIONAL MEDIA AND TECHNOLOGY

The College of St. Scholastica (M)
Eastern Michigan University (GC,M)

EDUCATIONAL MEDIA, NEW MEDIA AND GLOBAL EDUCATION

Appalachian State University (M)

EDUCATIONAL PSYCHOLOGY

Texas A&M University–Commerce (D)
University of North Texas (M)

EDUCATIONAL SPECIALIST/ EDUCATION LEADERSHIP

East Carolina University

EDUCATIONAL STUDIES

State University of New York Empire State College (A,B)

EDUCATIONAL TECHNOLOGY

Azusa Pacific University (M)
Boise State University (M)
Chadron State College (M)
Cleveland State University (M)
The College of St. Scholastica (UC)
Dakota State University (M)
DeVry University Online (M)

Michigan State University (M)
Michigan State University (M)
Michigan State University (UC)
National University (M)
New Jersey City University (M)
Northwestern State University of Louisiana (M)
San Diego State University (M)
The University of Texas at Brownsville (M)
The University of Texas System (M)
Webster University (M)
Western Michigan University (M)

EDUCATIONAL TECHNOLOGY INTEGRATION

Penn State University Park (GC)

EDUCATIONAL TECHNOLOGY LEADERSHIP

The George Washington University (M)

EDUCATIONAL TECHNOLOGY– MASTER OF EDUCATIONAL TECHNOLOGY

The University of British Columbia (M)

ELEARNING DESIGN AND IMPLEMENTATION

University of Colorado Denver (M)

ELECTRIC MACHINES AND DRIVES

University of Idaho (UC)

ELECTRICAL AND COMPUTER ENGINEERING

Northeastern University (M)
University of Colorado at Boulder (M)
University of Florida (M)
Virginia Polytechnic Institute and State University (M)

ELECTRICAL AND COMPUTER ENGINEERING (TELECOMMUNICATIONS)

Colorado State University (M)

ELECTRICAL ENGINEERING

Clemson University (M)
Columbia University (GC,M)
DeVry University Online (M)
Drexel University (M)
Georgia Institute of Technology (M)
Kansas State University (M)
Michigan Technological University (M)
Southern Methodist University (M)
Stanford University (M)
State University of New York at Binghamton (M)
University of Idaho (M)
University of North Dakota (B)
University of Southern California (M)
University of South Florida (M)
University of Washington (M)

ELECTRICAL ENGINEERING (COMPUTER NETWORKS)

University of Southern California (M)

ELECTRICAL ENGINEERING (MULTIMEDIA AND CREATIVE TECHNOLOGIES)

University of Southern California (M)

ELECTRICAL ENGINEERING (VLSI DESIGN)

University of Southern California (M)

ELECTRICAL ENGINEERING TECHNOLOGY

Old Dominion University (B)
The University of North Carolina at Charlotte (B)

ELECTRICAL TECHNOLOGY

Thomas Edison State College (A,B)

ELECTRICAL/COMPUTER ENGINEERING

Utah State University (M)

ELECTRICAL/MECHANICAL ENGINEERING TECHNOLOGY

Rochester Institute of Technology (B)

ELECTRICAL/MECHANICAL SYSTEMS AND MAINTENANCE

Thomas Edison State College (A)

ELECTROMAGNETICS TECHNOLOGY CAMPUS CERTIFICATE

University of Illinois at Chicago (UC)

ELECTRONIC BUSINESS

National University (M)

ELECTRONIC CIRCUITS

Stanford University (GC)

ELECTRONIC COMMERCE

Finger Lakes Community College (A)
Southeastern Community College (A)

ELECTRONIC DEVICES AND TECHNOLOGY

Stanford University (GC)

ELECTRONIC ENGINEERING TECHNOLOGY

Cleveland Institute of Electronics (A)
Thomas Edison State College (A,B)

ELECTRONICS AND COMPUTER TECHNOLOGY

DeVry University Online (A)
Indiana State University (M)

ELECTRONICS ENGINEERING

Cleveland Institute of Electronics (UC)

ELECTRONICS ENGINEERING TECHNOLOGY

DeVry University Online (B)
Excelsior College (B)
Grantham University (A,B)

ELECTRONICS TECHNOLOGY

Excelsior College (A)
Indiana State University (B)

ELECTRONICS TECHNOLOGY AND ADVANCED TROUBLESHOOTING

Cleveland Institute of Electronics (UC)

ELECTRONICS TECHNOLOGY WITH DIGITAL MICROPROCESSOR LAB

Cleveland Institute of Electronics (UC)

ELECTRONICS TECHNOLOGY WITH FCC LICENSE PREPARATION

Cleveland Institute of Electronics (UC)

ELECTRONICS TECHNOLOGY WITH LABORATORY

Cleveland Institute of Electronics (UC)

ELEMENTARY EDUCATION

Ball State University (M)
Buena Vista University (B)
Fitchburg State College (M)
Fort Hays State University (B)
Kansas State University (B)
Mayville State University (B)
Mississippi State University (B)
Missouri State University (M,B)
Missouri State University–West Plains (M,B)
Montgomery County Community College (A)
New Mexico State University (B)
Nova Southeastern University (B)
Prescott College (B)
Southwestern Adventist University (B)
The University of Alabama (M,)
The University of North Carolina at Charlotte (M,B)
University of North Dakota (M)
University of Phoenix (A)
University of Wisconsin–Superior (B)
Utah State University (M)
West Virginia University (M)

ELEMENTARY EDUCATION (POST-BACCALAUREATE CERTIFICATION)

Stephen F. Austin State University (UC)

ELEMENTARY EDUCATION WITH ESOL ENDORSEMENT

Nova Southeastern University (B)

ELEMENTARY EDUCATION/ READING

University of Arkansas (M)

ELEMENTARY LICENSURE (POST-BA)

New Mexico State University (UC)

ELEMENTARY OR SECONDARY EDUCATION

Marshall University (M)

ELEMENTARY, MIDDLE GRADES, AND SPECIAL EDUCATION

Southeastern Community College (A)

ELEMENTS OF HEALTH CARE LEADERSHIP

Rochester Institute of Technology (GC)

EMARKETING

Franklin University (B)

EMBA

Western Kentucky University (M)

EMBEDDED AND REAL-TIME SYSTEMS PROGRAMMING

University of Washington (UC)

EMERGENCY ADMINISTRATION AND MANAGEMENT

Arkansas Tech University (B)

EMERGENCY AND DISASTER MANAGEMENT

American Public University System (M,B)
Lynn University (GC,UC)
Upper Iowa University (B,UC)

EMERGENCY DISASTER SERVICES

Thomas Edison State College (A,B)

EMERGENCY HEALTH SERVICES

The George Washington University (M)

EMERGENCY MANAGEMENT

Jacksonville State University (GC,M)
Millersville University of Pennsylvania (M)

New Jersey Institute of Technology (GC)
University of Maryland University College
  (B)

EMERGENCY MANAGEMENT (HOMELAND SECURITY MINOR)

Jacksonville State University (B)

EMERGENCY MANAGEMENT (PUBLIC SAFETY COMMUNICATIONS MINOR)

Jacksonville State University (B)

EMERGENCY MANAGEMENT AND PLANNING

Red Rocks Community College (A)

EMERGENCY MEDICAL SERVICE PROFESSIONS (PARAMEDIC OPTION)

Tyler Junior College (A)

EMERGENCY MEDICAL SERVICES PROGRAM

James A. Rhodes State College (A)

EMERGENCY PLANNING AND ADMINISTRATION

Lynn University (M)

EMERGENCY PREPAREDNESS AND CONTINUITY PLANNING

University of Illinois at Chicago (UC)

EMERGING NETWORK TECHNOLOGIES

Franklin Pierce University (GC)

EMPLOYEE RELATIONS SPECIALIST

Sullivan University (UC)

END-USER COMPUTING

Union County College (UC)

ENERGY ELECTIVE

Athabasca University (M)

ENERGY MANAGEMENT

New York Institute of Technology (M)

ENERGY SYSTEMS

University of Michigan (M)

ENERGY UTILITY TECHNOLOGY

Thomas Edison State College (B)

ENGINEERING

California National University for Advanced
  Studies (M,B)
Eastern Michigan University (M)
Texas Tech University (M)
The University of Arizona (M)
University of Illinois at Chicago (M)
The University of Toledo (M)
University of Virginia (M)
University of Wisconsin–Platteville (M)
University of Wisconsin–Platteville (M)

ENGINEERING ADMINISTRATION

Virginia Polytechnic Institute and State
  University (M)

ENGINEERING AND MANAGEMENT SYSTEMS

Columbia University (M)

ENGINEERING GRAPHICS

Thomas Edison State College (A,B)

ENGINEERING LAW AND MANAGEMENT CAMPUS CERTIFICATE

University of Illinois at Chicago (UC)

ENGINEERING MANAGEMENT

California National University for Advanced
  Studies (M)
California State University, Northridge (M)
Drexel University (GC,M)
Kansas State University (M)
Kettering University (M)
Missouri University of Science and
  Technology (M)
National University (M)
New Jersey Institute of Technology (M)
Old Dominion University (M)
Southern Methodist University (M)
Stevens Institute of Technology (M)
The University of Alabama in Huntsville (M)
University of Colorado at Boulder (GC,M)
University of Colorado at Colorado Springs
  (M)
University of Michigan–Dearborn (M)
University of Southern California (M)
University of South Florida (M)
The University of Tennessee (GC,M)
University of Wisconsin–Platteville (GC)
University of Wisconsin–Platteville (GC)

ENGINEERING MECHANICS–MATHEMATICAL FOUNDATIONS AND APPLICATIONS

Stanford University (GC)

ENGINEERING ONLINE

North Carolina State University (M)

ENGINEERING TECHNOLOGY

University of Central Florida (B)

ENGINEERING TECHNOLOGY COMMERCIALIZATION

University of Southern California (GC)

ENGINEERING TECHNOLOGY MANAGEMENT

University of South Florida (GC)

ENGINEERING TECHNOLOGY, GENERAL

Old Dominion University (B)

ENGINEERING–COMPUTATIONAL AND MATHEMATICAL ENGINEERING

Stanford University (M)

ENGINEERING–ELECTRICAL AND COMPUTER ENGINEERING CONCENTRATION

Kettering University (M)

ENGINEERING–MANUFACTURING ENGINEERING CONCENTRATION

Kettering University (M)

ENGINEERING–MECHANICAL DESIGN CONCENTRATION

Kettering University (M)

ENGINEERING, INDUSTRIAL ENGINEERING CONCENTRATION

Mississippi State University (D)

ENGINEERING/ENGINEERING MANAGEMENT CERTIFICATES

Walden University (UC)

ENGLISH

American Public University System (B)
Bowling Green State University (M)
Buena Vista University (B)
Darton College (A)
Dickinson State University (B)
Judson College (B)
Mercy College (B)
National University (M,B)
Northeastern University (B)
Regent University (B)
Rose State College (A)
Saint Mary-of-the-Woods College (B)
Southwestern Adventist University (B)
Thomas Edison State College (B)
University of Illinois at Springfield (B)
University of Maryland University College
  (B)
University of Waterloo (B)

ENGLISH (3 YEAR)

Athabasca University (B)

ENGLISH (4 YEAR)

Athabasca University (B)

ENGLISH AS A SECOND LANGUAGE

Murray State University (UC)

ENGLISH AS A SECOND LANGUAGE (ESL)

The University of Texas System (UC)

ENGLISH AS A SECOND LANGUAGE EDUCATION PROGRAM

University of Colorado at Colorado Springs (M)

ENGLISH AS A SECOND LANGUAGE–ESL

University of Nebraska at Kearney (UC)

ENGLISH LANGUAGE AND LITERATURE

Southern New Hampshire University (B)

ENGLISH LANGUAGE LEARNER/ ENGLISH AS A SECOND LANGUAGE

University of North Dakota (UC)

ENGLISH LANGUAGE STUDIES

Athabasca University (UC)

ENGLISH LITERATURE

Eastern Oregon University (B)
Mercy College (M)

ENGLISH SPEAKERS OF OTHER LANGUAGES ENDORSEMENT

Fort Hays State University (UC)

ENGLISH–PROFESSIONAL AND TECHNICAL COMMUNICATION CONCENTRATION

East Carolina University (M)

ENGLISH–SINGLE SUBJECT PREPARATION IN ENGLISH

National University (B)

ENGLISH–WRITING

University of Colorado Denver (B)

ENGLISH, TECHNICAL COMMUNICATION TRACK

University of Central Florida (M)

ENGLISH/LITERATURE

Community College of Denver (A)

ENGLISH/TECHNICAL WRITING SPECIALIZATION ONLINE

Utah State University (M)

ENTREPRENEURSHIP

Genesee Community College (A)
Kirtland Community College (UC)
Thomas Edison State College (B)
University of South Florida (GC)
Utah State University (B)
Williston State College (A,UC)

ENVIRONMENTAL AND REGULATORY SCIENCE

NorthWest Arkansas Community College (A)

ENVIRONMENTAL AND TECHNOLOGICAL STUDIES

St. Cloud State University (M)

ENVIRONMENTAL AND WATER RESOURCES ENGINEERING

University of Illinois at Urbana–Champaign (GC)
University of Illinois at Urbana–Champaign (GC)

ENVIRONMENTAL EDUCATION

Prescott College (M)

ENVIRONMENTAL ENGINEERING

Georgia Institute of Technology (M)
Missouri University of Science and Technology (M)
Southern Methodist University (M)
The University of Tennessee (M)
Worcester Polytechnic Institute (GC,M)

ENVIRONMENTAL ENGINEERING (SYSTEMS ECOLOGY AND ECOLOGICAL ENGINEERING TRACK)

University of Florida (M)

ENVIRONMENTAL ENGINEERING (WATER RESOURCES PLANNING AND MANAGEMENT TRACK)

University of Florida (M)

ENVIRONMENTAL ENGINEERING (WATER, WASTEWATER, AND STORMWATER ENGINEERING TRACK)

University of Florida (M)

ENVIRONMENTAL HEALTH

East Carolina University (M)

ENVIRONMENTAL HEALTH AND SAFETY MANAGEMENT

Rochester Institute of Technology (M)

ENVIRONMENTAL HEALTH INFORMATICS CAMPUS CERTIFICATE

University of Illinois at Chicago (UC)

ENVIRONMENTAL INFORMATION MANAGEMENT–CERTIFICATE OF ADVANCED STUDY

University of Denver (UC)

ENVIRONMENTAL MANAGEMENT

Columbia Southern University (B)
University of Calgary (UC)
University of Maryland University College (GC,M,B)
Webster University (M)

ENVIRONMENTAL MANAGEMENT–CERTIFICATE OF ADVANCED STUDY

University of Denver (UC)

ENVIRONMENTAL POLICY AND MANAGEMENT

American Public University System (M)

ENVIRONMENTAL POLICY AND MANAGEMENT–MASTER OF APPLIED SCIENCE IN ENVIRONMENTAL POLICY AND MANAGEMENT

University of Denver (M)

ENVIRONMENTAL POLICY– CERTIFICATE OF ADVANCED STUDY

University of Denver (UC)

ENVIRONMENTAL PROJECT MANAGEMENT–CERTIFICATE OF ADVANCED STUDY

University of Denver (UC)

ENVIRONMENTAL SCIENCE

Southern Methodist University (M)

ENVIRONMENTAL SCIENCE (ENVIRONMENTAL SYSTEMS MANAGEMENT MAJOR)

Southern Methodist University (M)

ENVIRONMENTAL SCIENCE (HAZARDOUS AND WASTE MATERIALS MANAGEMENT MAJOR)

Southern Methodist University (M)

ENVIRONMENTAL SCIENCE AND MANAGEMENT

Duquesne University (M)

ENVIRONMENTAL SCIENCES

New Jersey Institute of Technology (M)
Oregon State University (B)
Thomas Edison State College (A,B)

ENVIRONMENTAL STUDIES

American Public University System (B)
Columbia College (A)
Northeastern University (B)
Prescott College (M,B)
Thomas Edison State College (B)

ENVIRONMENTAL STUDIES IN CONSERVATION BIOLOGY

Green Mountain College (M)

ENVIRONMENTAL STUDIES–NATURAL RESOURCES AND SUSTAINABLE DEVELOPMENT CONCENTRATION

University of Illinois at Springfield (M)

ENVIRONMENTAL SUSTAINABILITY

New Jersey Institute of Technology (GC)

ENVIRONMENTAL, HEALTH, AND SAFETY MANAGEMENT–CERTIFICATE OF ADVANCED STUDY

University of Denver (UC)

ENVIRONMENTAL, SAFETY, AND HEALTH MANAGEMENT

The University of Findlay (M,B)

ENVIRONMENTAL, SAFETY, AND SECURITY TECHNOLOGY

Thomas Edison State College (A)

EPIDEMIOLOGY AND BIOSTATISTICS

Drexel University (UC)

EQUINE ASSISTED MENTAL HEALTH

Prescott College (M)

ERGONOMICS, BASIC

Colorado State University (UC)

ESL ENDORSEMENT IN ELEMENTARY AND SECONDARY EDUCATION

Kansas State University (UC)

ESOL

University of South Florida (GC)

ESOL/BILINGUAL EDUCATION

Oregon State University (UC)

ESR ACCESS

Earlham School of Religion (M)

ESSENTIALS OF BUSINESS APPLICATION DESIGN

New Jersey Institute of Technology (UC)

ESSENTIALS OF INFORMATION SECURITY

New Jersey Institute of Technology (UC)

ESSENTIALS OF INFORMATION SYSTEMS MANAGEMENT

New Jersey Institute of Technology (UC)

ESSENTIALS OF WEB APPLICATION DEVELOPMENT

New Jersey Institute of Technology (UC)

ESTATE PLANNING

Golden Gate University (GC)

ESTATE PLANNING AND TAXATION

The American College (GC)

ETUDES FRANCAISES (EN DEVELOPPEMENT)

Laurentian University (B)

EVANGELISM AND CHURCH PLANTING

Liberty University (M)

EVENT MANAGEMENT

The George Washington University (UC)

EVIDENCE BASED COACHING

Fielding Graduate University (UC)

EVIDENCE-BASED PRACTICE

The University of Texas System (UC)

EXCEPTIONAL AND SECONDARY EDUCATION–MIDDLE GRADES ENGLISH

Saint Leo University (M)

EXCEPTIONAL AND SECONDARY EDUCATION–MIDDLE GRADES MATHEMATICS

Saint Leo University (M)

EXCEPTIONAL AND SECONDARY EDUCATION–MIDDLE GRADES SCIENCE

Saint Leo University (M)

EXCEPTIONAL AND SECONDARY EDUCATION–MIDDLE GRADES SOCIAL STUDIES

Saint Leo University (M)

EXCEPTIONAL EDUCATION

University of Central Florida (M)
Western Kentucky University (M)

EXCEPTIONAL NEEDS WITH MILD INTERVENTIONS (SPECIAL ED)

Indiana Wesleyan University (UC)

EXCEPTIONAL STUDENT EDUCATION

Nova Southeastern University (B)
Saint Leo University (GC)
University of West Florida (B)

EXCEPTIONAL STUDENT EDUCATION CONCENTRATION

Saint Leo University (M)

EXCEPTIONAL STUDENT EDUCATION WITH ESOL ENDORSEMENT

Nova Southeastern University (B)

EXECUTIVE

The University of Tennessee (M)

EXECUTIVE ASSISTANT

Central Texas College (A)

EXECUTIVE INTERNATIONAL MANAGEMENT (MSM)

Regis University (GC)

EXECUTIVE LEADERSHIP (MSM)

Regis University (GC)

EXECUTIVE MASTER OF BUSINESS ADMINISTRATION

Bellevue University (M)
Colorado Technical University Colorado
  Springs (M)
University of Wyoming (M)

EXECUTIVE MASTER OF BUSINESS ADMINISTRATION (SPANISH VERSION)

National University (M)

EXECUTIVE MASTER OF ORGANIZATION DEVELOPMENT

Bowling Green State University (M)

EXECUTIVE MASTER OF PUBLIC ADMINISTRATION

Golden Gate University (M)

EXECUTIVE MINISTRY

Hope International University (M)

EXPRESSIVE ARTS FOR HEALING AND SOCIAL CHANGE

Saybrook Graduate School and Research
  Center (GC)

FACILITIES MANAGEMENT

Southern Methodist University (M)

FACILITY MANAGEMENT

Rochester Institute of Technology (M)
University of Washington (UC)

FAMILY AND CONSUMER SCIENCE EDUCATION

North Dakota State University (M)

FAMILY AND CONSUMER SCIENCES (EARLY CHILDHOOD PROGRAM DIRECTOR'S CERTIFICATE)

University of Wyoming (UC)

FAMILY AND CONSUMER SCIENCES (FAMILY AND COMMUNITY SERVICES OPTION)

University of Wyoming (B)

FAMILY AND CONSUMER SCIENCES (PROFESSIONAL CHILD DEVELOPMENT OPTION)

University of Wyoming (B)

FAMILY AND CONSUMER SCIENCES EDUCATION TEACHER EDUCATION

Texas Tech University (UC)

FAMILY AND CONSUMER SCIENCES, CHILD DEVELOPMENT CONCENTRATION

Jacksonville State University (B)

FAMILY AND HUMAN DEVELOPMENT

Utah State University (M)

FAMILY DEVELOPMENT

American Public University System (B)

FAMILY DEVELOPMENT CREDENTIAL

Kansas State University (UC)

FAMILY FINANCIAL PLANNING

North Dakota State University (GC,M)

FAMILY LIFE EDUCATION

Concordia University, St. Paul (B)

FAMILY LIFE STUDIES AND HUMAN SEXUALITY

Laurentian University (UC)

FAMILY LITERACY

Penn State University Park (GC,UC)

FAMILY NURSE PRACTITIONER

Clarkson College (M,)
Graceland University (GC,M)
Indiana State University
University of Missouri–Columbia (M)
University of Phoenix (M)

FAMILY NURSE PRACTITIONER TRACK

Fort Hays State University (M)

FAMILY STUDIES

Texas Woman's University (M)

FAMILY STUDIES AND CONSUMER SCIENCE EDUCATION

Texas Tech University (M)

FAMILY THERAPY

Amridge University (D)

FASHION

Academy of Art University (M,A,B)

FIBERS AND TEXTILES

Texas Tech University (GC)

FICTION WRITING

University of Washington (UC)

FILM AND CINEMA STUDIES

Prescott College (M)

FINANCE

Dallas Baptist University (M)
Dickinson State University (B)
Excelsior College (B)
Golden Gate University (GC,M)
LeTourneau University (M)
Myers University (B)
Northeastern University (A)
Nova Southeastern University (M)
Regis University (B)
Strayer University (B)
Thomas Edison State College (B)
University of Maryland University College
  (B)
Upper Iowa University (B)
Webster University (M)

FINANCE AND ACCOUNTING MANAGEMENT

Northeastern University (B)

FINANCE CONCENTRATION

Colorado Technical University Colorado
  Springs (M,B)
Sullivan University (B)

FINANCE CONCENTRATION (10 MONTH PROGRAM)

American InterContinental University Online
  (M)

FINANCE FOR MANAGERS

New Jersey Institute of Technology (GC)

FINANCE–CORPORATE FINANCE CONCENTRATION

Golden Gate University (M)

FINANCE–METHODS IN FINANCE

Columbia University (M)

FINANCE/ECONOMICS

Southern New Hampshire University (B)

FINANCIAL CRIME INVESTIGATION

Utica College (UC)

FINANCIAL CRIME INVESTIGATION CERTIFICATE PROGRAM

Utica College

FINANCIAL ENGINEERING

Columbia University (UC)
Stevens Institute of Technology (GC,M)

FINANCIAL INSTITUTION MANAGEMENT

Thomas Edison State College (B)

FINANCIAL MANAGEMENT

City University of Seattle (GC)
Franklin University (A,B)
Immaculata University (B)
National University (B)

FINANCIAL MANAGEMENT AND INFORMATION SYSTEMS

University of Maryland University College (M)

FINANCIAL MANAGEMENT IN ORGANIZATIONS

University of Maryland University College (GC)

FINANCIAL PLANNING

Golden Gate University (GC,M)
Schiller International University (M)

FINANCIAL PLANNING AND TAXATION

Golden Gate University (M)

FINANCIAL PLANNING–GRADUATE FINANCIAL PLANNING TRACK

The American College (GC)

FINANCIAL SERVICE

Athabasca University (B)

FINANCIAL SERVICES

The American College (M)
Athabasca University (UC)
Berkeley College (A)
Labette Community College (A)
Nipissing University (B)
University of Phoenix (A)

FINANCIAL VALUATION AND INVESTMENT MANAGEMENT

Lynn University (M)

FINE ART

Academy of Art University (M,A,B)

FINE ARTS

Burlington College (B)

FIRE ADMINISTRATION, FIRE PREVENTION AND TECHNOLOGY

Cogswell Polytechnical College (B)

FIRE AND EMERGENCY SERVICES ADMINISTRATION

Colorado State University (B)

FIRE AND EMERGENCY SERVICES ADMINISTRATION (FESA)

Colorado State University (UC)

FIRE AND SAFETY ENGINEERING TECHNOLOGY

Eastern Kentucky University (B)

FIRE PROTECTION

Middlesex Community College (A)

FIRE PROTECTION ENGINEERING

Worcester Polytechnic Institute (GC,M)

FIRE PROTECTION SCIENCE

Thomas Edison State College (A,B)

FIRE PROTECTION TECHNOLOGY–FIRE PREVENTION

Chemeketa Community College (A)

FIRE PROTECTION TECHNOLOGY–FIRE SUPPRESSION

Chemeketa Community College (A)

FIRE SCIENCE

Columbia Southern University (A,B)
Keiser University (A)
Prescott College (M)
University of Maryland University College (B)
The University of North Carolina at Charlotte (B)

FIRE SCIENCE ADMINISTRATION

Columbia College (A)

FIRE SCIENCE MANAGEMENT

American Public University System (B)
Red Rocks Community College (A)

FIRE SCIENCE TECHNOLOGY

Pikes Peak Community College (A)
University of Cincinnati (A,B)

FIRE SERVICES ADMINISTRATION

Eastern Oregon University (B)

FITNESS AND WELLNESS SERVICES

Thomas Edison State College (A)

FOLKLORE ET ETHNOLOGIE DE L'AMERIQUE FRANCAISE

Laurentian University (B,UC)

FOOD AND NUTRITION

Bowling Green State University (GC)

FOOD PROTECTION

North Dakota State University (GC)

FOOD SAFETY

Michigan State University (M)
University of Southern California (GC)

FOOD SAFETY AND DEFENSE

Kansas State University (GC)
University of Missouri–Columbia (GC)

FOOD SCIENCE

Kansas State University (GC,UC)

FOOD SCIENCE AND INDUSTRY

Kansas State University (M,B)

FOOD SCIENCE, NUTRITION, AND HEALTH PROMOTION

Mississippi State University (M)

FOOD SERVICE TRAINING PROGRAM

Southeast Community College Area (UC)

FOOD SYSTEMS ADMINISTRATION (NUTRITION AND FOOD SCIENCES)

Texas Woman's University (M)

FOREIGN LANGUAGE

Auburn University (M)
Darton College (A)
Thomas Edison State College (B)

FOREIGN LANGUAGES

Prescott College (M)

FORENSIC ACCOUNTING

Franklin University (A,B)
Myers University (B)
Northeastern University (GC)

FORENSIC CRIMINOLOGY

University of Massachusetts Lowell (GC)

FORENSIC NURSING

Cleveland State University (M)

FORENSIC PSYCHOLOGY

University of North Dakota (M)

FORENSIC SCIENCE–FORENSIC ANALYSIS TRACK

University of Central Florida (M)

FORENSIC SCIENCE–FORENSIC BIOCHEMISTRY TRACK

University of Central Florida (M)

FORENSIC SCIENCES–MASTER OF FORENSIC SCIENCES

National University (M)

FORESTRY

Thomas Edison State College (A,B)

FOUNDATIONS OF BUSINESS

University of Massachusetts Lowell (GC)

FOUNDATIONS OF DISTANCE EDUCATION

University of Maryland University College (GC)

FOUNDATIONS OF HOLISTIC HEALTH

University of Southern Maine (UC)

FOUNDATIONS OF HUMAN RESOURCE MANAGEMENT

University of Maryland University College (GC)

FOUNDATIONS OF INFORMATION TECHNOLOGY

University of Maryland University College (GC)

FRANK J. MANNING CERTIFICATE IN GERONTOLOGY

University of Massachusetts Boston (UC)

FRENCH (3 YEAR)

Athabasca University (B)

FRENCH (4 YEAR)

Athabasca University (B)

FRENCH LANGUAGE PROFICIENCY

Athabasca University (UC)

FRENCH TRANSLATION

University of Illinois at Urbana–Champaign (GC)

FUNDAMENTALS OF INFORMATION TECHNOLOGY

University of Massachusetts Boston (UC)

FUNERAL SERVICE EDUCATION

Vincennes University (A)

GAME AND SIMULATION PROGRAMMING

DeVry University Online (B)

GAME ART AND DESIGN

Westwood Online (B)

GAME SOFTWARE DEVELOPMENT

Westwood Online (B)

GAMING AND SIMULATION

Bellevue University (B)

GAMING MANAGEMENT

University of Wisconsin–Stout (UC)

GAY AND LESBIAN STUDIES

Prescott College (M)

GENDER STUDIES

Burlington College (B)
Prescott College (M)

GENERAL AGRICULTURE

Missouri State University–West Plains (B)

GENERAL AVIATION FLIGHT TECHNOLOGY

Indiana State University (A)

GENERAL BIOLOGY–TEACHERS IN BIOLOGY

Mississippi State University (M)

GENERAL BUSINESS

Kirtland Community College (A)
Missouri State University–West Plains (B)
New Mexico State University (B)
Nichols College (B)
Northwest Technical College (UC)

GENERAL BUSINESS (COMPLETION DEGREE)

Missouri State University (B)

GENERAL BUSINESS ADMINISTRATION

Prairie View A&M University (M)

GENERAL CONCENTRATION

Dallas Baptist University (M)

GENERAL CONCENTRATION

Kettering University (M)

GENERAL DEGREE

Arkansas State University–Mountain Home (A)
Barton County Community College (A)
Dallas Baptist University (A)
Edison State Community College (A)
Fairfield University (A)
Gulf Coast Community College (A)
Hibbing Community College (A)
Lakeland Community College (A)
Marshalltown Community College (A)
Nashville State Technical Community College (A)
Northeast Iowa Community College (A)
St. Clair County Community College (A)
Wake Technical Community College (A)
West Virginia University at Parkersburg (A)
York Technical College (A)

GENERAL DEGREE STUDIES–3-YEAR GENERAL DEGREE

University of Manitoba (B)

GENERAL EDUCATION

Columbia Southern University (A)
Hope International University (A)
Pulaski Technical College (A)
St. Clair County Community College (A)
Wake Technical Community College (A)

GENERAL EDUCATION REQUIREMENTS

Adams State College (A)

GENERAL EDUCATION STUDIES

Henry Ford Community College (A)

GENERAL MANAGEMENT

City University of Seattle (GC)
Darton College (UC)
Thomas Edison State College (B)
Tiffin University (M)

GENERAL MANAGEMENT OPTION

Southeast Missouri State University (M)

GENERAL PROGRAM

Ball State University (A)
Dickinson State University (A)
Saint Mary-of-the-Woods College (A,B)
Seattle Central Community College (A)
University of the Incarnate Word (M)

GENERAL SCIENCE

University of Windsor (B)

GENERAL STUDIES

American Public University System (A)
Baker College of Flint (B)
Ball State University (B)
Baltimore City Community College (A)
Barton County Community College (A)
Belhaven College (A)
Bellevue Community College (A)
Black Hills State University (A)
Cape Fear Community College (A)
Capital Community College (A)
Central Carolina Community College (A)
Central Texas College (A)
Charter Oak State College (A,B)
Chemeketa Community College (A)
City University of Seattle (A,B)
College of Southern Maryland (A,UC)
Colorado Technical University Colorado
  Springs (A)
Columbia College (A,B)
Columbus State Community College (A)
Dakota State University (A)
Dallas County Community College District
  (A)
Daniel Webster College (A)
Darton College (A)
Dawson Community College (A)
Delaware County Community College (A)
Eastern Illinois University (B)
Everett Community College (A)
Fort Hays State University (A,B)
Franklin Pierce University (A,B)
Gadsden State Community College (A)
Garrett College (A)
Genesee Community College (A)
Granite State College (A)
Grantham University (A,B)
Gulf Coast Community College (A)
Harford Community College (A)
Illinois Eastern Community Colleges, Frontier
  Community College (A)
Illinois Eastern Community Colleges, Lincoln
  Trail College (A)
Illinois Eastern Community Colleges, Olney
  Central College (A)
Illinois Eastern Community Colleges, Wabash
  Valley College (A)
Indiana Tech (A)
Indiana University System (A)
Indiana Wesleyan University (A,B)
Ivy Tech Community College–Bloomington
  (A)
Ivy Tech Community College–Central Indiana
  (A)
Ivy Tech Community College–Columbus (A)
Ivy Tech Community College–East Central
  (A)
Ivy Tech Community College–Kokomo (A)
Ivy Tech Community College–Lafayette (A)
Ivy Tech Community College–North Central
  (A)
Ivy Tech Community College–Northeast (A)
Ivy Tech Community College–Northwest (A)
Ivy Tech Community College–Southeast (A)
Ivy Tech Community College–Southern
  Indiana (A)
Ivy Tech Community College–Southwest (A)

Ivy Tech Community College–Wabash Valley
  (A)
Ivy Tech Community College–Whitewater (A)
Johnson County Community College (A)
Labette Community College (A)
Liberty University (A)
Luzerne County Community College (A)
Marshall University (A)
Minot State University (B)
Montgomery County Community College (A)
Mountain Empire Community College (A)
Mount Wachusett Community College (A)
Nashville State Technical Community College
New River Community College (A)
Northampton County Area Community
  College (A)
Northern Virginia Community College (A)
North Seattle Community College (A)
Northwestern State University of Louisiana
  (A,B)
Palm Beach Community College (A)
Parkland College (A)
Patrick Henry Community College (A)
Rappahannock Community College (A)
Reading Area Community College (A)
Regent University (A)
Saint Joseph's College of Maine (A,B)
Seminole Community College (A)
Southeast Missouri State University (B)
Southern Arkansas University Tech (A)
Southwest Virginia Community College (A)
Strayer University (A)
Texas Tech University (B)
Texas Woman's University (B)
Three Rivers Community College (A)
Triton College (A)
Tyler Junior College (A)
University of Bridgeport (B)
University of Management and Technology
  (A,B)
University of Maryland University College
  (B)
University of North Dakota (B)
University of North Texas (B)
University of Phoenix (A)
The University of South Dakota (A)
Utah State University (A)
Utah Valley State College (A)
Vincennes University (A)
Weber State University (A)
Western Wyoming Community College (A)
West Shore Community College (A)
West Texas A&M University (B)
Widener University (A)
Wilfrid Laurier University (B)
Yuba College (A)

GENERAL STUDIES (SECONDARY EDUCATION)

University of North Dakota (M)

GENERAL STUDIES DEGREE PROGRAM

Indiana University System (B)

GENERAL STUDIES–ASSOCIATE OF ARTS

National University (A)

GENERAL STUDIES–BACHELOR OF GENERAL STUDIES

East Tennessee State University (B)

GENERAL STUDIES–BUSINESS STUDIES

Vincennes University (A)

GENERAL STUDIES–CUSTOMIZED CERTIFICATE

Vincennes University (UC)

GENERAL STUDIES–INDIVIDUALIZED STUDIES

Drexel University (B)

GENERAL STUDIES–SURGICAL TECHNOLOGY DEGREE COMPLETION

Vincennes University (A)

GENERAL STUDIES, BUSINESS MINOR

Drexel University (B)

GENERAL STUDIES, CRIMINAL JUSTICE SEQUENCE

University of Maine at Fort Kent (A)

GENERAL STUDIES/LIBERAL ARTS

Tunxis Community College (A)

GENERAL STUDIES/SOCIAL SCIENCE

Foothill College (A)

GENERAL TECHNOLOGY

Anne Arundel Community College (A)

GENERAL TRACK

Saint Leo University (M)

GENERALIST

Community College of Denver (A)

GEOGRAPHIC INFORMATION SCIENCE

Northwest Missouri State University (M)

GEOGRAPHIC INFORMATION SCIENCE AND TECHNOLOGY

University of Southern California (GC,M)

GEOGRAPHIC INFORMATION SCIENCES

Oregon State University (UC)
University of North Dakota (GC)

GEOGRAPHIC INFORMATION SYSTEMS

Columbus State Community College (GC)
Eastern Michigan University (GC)
North Carolina State University (GC)
Penn State University Park (GC,M)
Roosevelt University (UC)

GEOGRAPHIC INFORMATION SYSTEMS (GIS)

Fort Hays State University (UC)
University of Colorado Denver (M)

GEOGRAPHIC INFORMATION SYSTEMS–CERTIFICATE OF ADVANCED STUDY

University of Denver (UC)

GEOGRAPHY

University of Manitoba (B)

GEOLOGICAL ENGINEERING

University of Idaho (M)

GEOSCIENCES

Mississippi State University (B)

GEOSCIENCES, BROADCAST METEOROLOGY

Mississippi State University (UC)

GEOSCIENCES, OPERATIONAL METEOROLOGY

Mississippi State University (UC)

GEOSCIENCES, TEACHERS IN GEOSCIENCE

Mississippi State University (M)

GEOSPATIAL AND REMOTE SENSING

Mississippi State University (GC,UC)

GEOSPATIAL INTELLIGENCE

Penn State University Park (GC)

GEOTECHNICAL ENGINEERING

University of Wisconsin–Platteville (GC)
University of Wisconsin–Platteville (GC)

GEOTECHNICS

Missouri University of Science and Technology (M)

GERIATRIC RECREATIONAL THERAPY

Florida Gulf Coast University (M)

GERIATRIC REHABILITATION AND WELLNESS

Sacred Heart University (M)

GERONTOLOGICAL NURSE PRACTICIONER

Illinois State University (M)

GERONTOLOGICAL NURSE PRACTITIONER

University of Missouri–Columbia (M)

GERONTOLOGY

Appalachian State University (GC)
Coastline Community College (A)
Kansas State University (GC,M)
Laurentian University (B,UC)
North Dakota State University (GC,M)
Texas Tech University (GC)
Thomas Edison State College (A,B)
The University of Arizona (GC)
University of Maryland University College (B)
University of Phoenix (M)
University of Southern California (GC,M)
University of South Florida (GC)
University of Washington (UC)

GERONTOLOGY (HUMAN DEVELOPMENT AND FAMILY STUDIES)

University of Missouri–Columbia (M)

GERONTOLOGY–MANAGEMENT OF AGING SERVICES TRACK

University of Massachusetts Boston (GC,M)

GERONTOLOGY–MASTER OF ARTS IN GERONTOLOGY (MAG)

Chatham University

GIFTED AND TALENTED

Murray State University (UC)

GIFTED AND TALENTED EDUCATION

Ball State University (UC)
University of North Texas (UC)

GIFTED AND TALENTED GRADUATE TEACHING ENDORSEMENT

Western Kentucky University (UC)

GIFTED EDUCATION

University of Central Florida (GC)
University of Missouri–Columbia (M)
University of North Texas (GC)
University of South Florida (GC,M)

GIFTED GRADUATE ENDORSEMENT

University of Nebraska at Kearney (UC)

GLOBAL AND INTERNATIONAL EDUCATION

Drexel University (M)

GLOBAL AUTOMOTIVE AND MANUFACTURING ENGINEERING

University of Michigan (M)

GLOBAL BUSINESS

Excelsior College (B)
Regent University (B)
University of Dallas (M)

GLOBAL BUSINESS AND PUBLIC POLICY

University of Maryland University College (B)

GLOBAL HUMAN RESOURCE DEVELOPMENT

University of Illinois at Urbana–Champaign (M)

GLOBAL MANAGEMENT

University of Phoenix (M)

GLOBAL MASTER OF BUSINESS ADMINISTRATION FOR LATIN AMERICAN MANAGERS

Thunderbird School of Global Management (M)

GLOBAL MASTER OF BUSINESS ADMINISTRATION ON-DEMAND

Thunderbird School of Global Management (M)

GLOBAL MBA

Southern New Hampshire University (M)
University of Houston–Victoria (M)

GLOBAL MBA ON-LINE

The University of Texas at Dallas (M)

GLOBAL STUDIES

National University (B)

GLOBAL STUDIES IN EDUCATION

University of Illinois at Urbana–Champaign (M)

GLOBAL TRAVEL AND HOSPITALITY MANAGEMENT

Kaplan University Online (A)

GOLF ENTERPRISE MANAGEMENT

University of Wisconsin–Stout (B)

GOVERNANCE, LAW, AND MANAGEMENT

Athabasca University (B)

GOVERNMENT

Regent University (M)

GOVERNMENT CONTRACTING

Webster University (GC)

GOVERNMENT MANAGEMENT

Walden University (GC)

GOVERNMENT–BUSINESS RELATIONS

Park University (M)

GRADUATE CERTIFICATE IN PUBLIC HEALTH INFORMATICS

University of Maryland, College Park (GC)

GRADUATE TEACHING LICENSURE

The College of St. Scholastica (M,UC)

GRANT PROPOSAL WRITING AND PROGRAM EVALUATION

Fort Hays State University (UC)

GRAPHIC DESIGN

Academy of Art University (M,A,B)
Savannah College of Art and Design (M)

GRAPHIC DESIGN AND MULTIMEDIA

Westwood Online (A)

GREENHOUSE TECHNOLOGY

Minot State University–Bottineau Campus (UC)

GUIDANCE AND CONTROL (AERONAUTICS AND ASTRONAUTICS)

Stanford University (GC)

GUIDANCE AND COUNSELING–SCHOOL GUIDANCE AND COUNSELING

Buena Vista University (M)

HACCP/FOOD SAFETY MANAGERS

North Carolina State University (UC)

HEALTH ADMINISTRATION

Athabasca University (B)
University of North Dakota (GC)
University of Phoenix (A,B)
University of Southern Indiana (M)

HEALTH ADMINISTRATION INFORMATICS

University of Maryland University College (M)

HEALTH ADMINISTRATION POST-DIPLOMA

Athabasca University (B)

HEALTH ADMINISTRATION–DOCTOR OF HEALTH ADMINISTRATION (DHA)

University of Phoenix (D)

HEALTH ADMINISTRATION–MASTER OF HEALTH ADMINISTRATION

University of Phoenix (M)

HEALTH ADMINISTRATION/HEALTH INFORMATION SYSTEMS

University of Phoenix (B)

HEALTH ADMINISTRATION/LONG-TERM CARE

University of Phoenix (B)

HEALTH ADMINISTRATIVE SERVICES

Weber State University (B)

HEALTH AND HUMAN PERFORMANCE

Fort Hays State University (M)
Northwestern State University of Louisiana (M)

HEALTH AND NUTRITION COUNSELING

Thomas Edison State College (B)

HEALTH AND SAFETY (OCCUPATIONAL SAFETY MANAGEMENT SPECIALIZATION)

Indiana State University (M)

HEALTH AND SOCIAL SERVICES

New Mexico State University (B)

HEALTH AND WELLNESS

Kaplan University Online (B)

HEALTH CARE

Independence University (M)

HEALTH CARE ADMINISTRATION

Columbia Southern University (B)
Independence University (M)
National University (A)
Saint Joseph's College of Maine (B)
University of Hawaii–West Oahu (UC)
University of Maryland University College (GC,M)
University of Northwestern Ohio (B)
The University of Toledo (B)

HEALTH CARE ADMINISTRATION (MSA)

University of West Florida (M)

HEALTH CARE ADMINISTRATION CONCENTRATION

Saint Leo University (M)

HEALTH CARE ADMINISTRATION–MEDICAL RECORDS

University of Phoenix (A)

HEALTH CARE ADMINISTRATION–PHARMACY PRACTICE

University of Phoenix (A)

HEALTH CARE BUSINESS LEADERSHIP

Clarkson College (M)

HEALTH CARE BUSINESS–HEALTH INFORMATION MANAGEMENT MAJOR

Clarkson College (B)

HEALTH CARE BUSINESS–INFORMATICS MAJOR

Clarkson College (B)

HEALTH CARE BUSINESS–MANAGEMENT MAJOR

Clarkson College (B)

HEALTH CARE CODING

Lehigh Carbon Community College (UC)

HEALTH CARE CODING AND CLASSIFICATION

Weber State University (UC)

HEALTH CARE LEADERSHIP

University of St. Francis (B)

HEALTH CARE MANAGEMENT

Dallas Baptist University (B)
East Carolina University (GC)
Franklin University (B)
Graceland University (B)
Immaculata University (B)
Minnesota School of Business–Richfield (B)
Saint Joseph's College of Maine (UC)

HEALTH CARE MANAGEMENT CONCENTRATION

Colorado Technical University Colorado Springs (M,B)

HEALTH CARE MANAGEMENT, ADVANCED

Saint Joseph's College of Maine (UC)

HEALTH CARE MANAGER CERTIFICATE

Columbus State Community College (GC)

HEALTH CARE SERVICES

University of Phoenix (B)

HEALTH CARE SYSTEMS MANAGEMENT

Loyola University New Orleans (M)

HEALTH CARE/HEALTH SERVICES MANAGEMENT

Park University (M)

HEALTH DEVELOPMENT ADMINISTRATION

Athabasca University (UC)

HEALTH EDUCATION

East Carolina University (M)

HEALTH INFORMATICS

University of Illinois at Chicago (M,,UC)

HEALTH INFORMATICS (EXECUTIVE PROGRAM)

University of Missouri–Columbia (M)

HEALTH INFORMATION ADMINISTRATION

Dakota State University (B)

HEALTH INFORMATION MANAGEMENT

Clarkson College (A)
The College of St. Scholastica (M)
Darton College (A)
East Carolina University (B)
University of Cincinnati (B)
The University of Toledo (B)
Vincennes University (A)

Weber State University (B)

HEALTH INFORMATION MANAGEMENT (BS OR BPS)

State University of New York Institute of Technology (B)

HEALTH INFORMATION MANAGEMENT DEGREE COMPLETION

The College of St. Scholastica (B)

HEALTH INFORMATION MANAGEMENT TECHNOLOGY

Quinebaug Valley Community College (UC)

HEALTH INFORMATION MANAGEMENT–FOUNDATIONS

Clarkson College (UC)

HEALTH INFORMATION MANAGEMENT–HIM

Clarkson College (UC)

HEALTH INFORMATION RESOURCES

Rochester Institute of Technology (GC)

HEALTH INFORMATION TECHNICIAN

North Dakota State College of Science (A)

HEALTH INFORMATION TECHNOLOGY

Dakota State University (A)
Darton College (A)
DeVry University Online (A)
Eastern Iowa Community College District (A)
Edgecombe Community College (A)
Hodges University (A)
Minnesota State Community and Technical College–Fergus Falls (A)
Northeast Iowa Community College (A)
Passaic County Community College (A)
Tyler Junior College (A)
Weber State University (A)

HEALTH MANAGEMENT AND POLICY

Oregon State University (GC)

HEALTH POLICY AND MANAGEMENT

University of Southern Maine (UC)

HEALTH PRACTICE MANAGEMENT

Franklin Pierce University (GC,M)

HEALTH PROFESSION EDUCATION EMPHASIS

University of Illinois at Urbana–Champaign (M)

HEALTH PROFESSIONS

The University of Texas at Tyler (B)

HEALTH PROFESSIONS AND RELATED SCIENCES

University of Southern Indiana (B)

HEALTH PROFESSIONS EDUCATION

Simmons College (GC)
University of Illinois at Chicago (M)

HEALTH PROMOTION

Weber State University (B)

HEALTH PROMOTIONS

Virginia Polytechnic Institute and State University (M)

HEALTH SCIENCE

Chatham University (M)
Cleveland State University (M)
Florida Gulf Coast University (M,B)
The George Washington University (M)
Kaplan University Online (B)
Mercy College (B)

HEALTH SCIENCE OCCUPATIONS

University of Wisconsin–Stout (UC)

HEALTH SCIENCE TECHNOLOGY TEACHER

The University of Texas System (UC)

HEALTH SCIENCES

Excelsior College (B)
Keiser University (B)
Old Dominion University (B)
TUI University (D,M,B)
University of Medicine and Dentistry of New Jersey (D,M,B)
University of South Florida (GC)

HEALTH SCIENCES, ALLIED HEALTH

University of West Florida (B)

HEALTH SCIENCES, HEALTH CARE PROFESSIONAL

University of West Florida (B)

HEALTH SCIENCES, MEDICAL INFORMATION TECHNOLOGY

University of West Florida (B)

HEALTH SERVICE

University of St. Thomas (M)

HEALTH SERVICE ADMINISTRATION

Austin Peay State University (M)
Keiser University (A)

HEALTH SERVICE TECHNOLOGY

Thomas Edison State College (B)

HEALTH SERVICES

Thomas Edison State College (B)
Walden University (D)

HEALTH SERVICES ADMINISTRATION

Berkeley College (A)
Berkeley College–New York City Campus (A,B)
Berkeley College–Westchester Campus (A)
Drexel University (B)
Keiser University (B)
Saint Joseph's College of Maine (M)
State University of New York Institute of Technology (M)
State University of New York Institute of Technology (M)
Strayer University (M)
Thomas Edison State College (B)
University of Central Florida (B)
University of St. Francis (M)
Upper Iowa University (B)

HEALTH SERVICES ADMINISTRATION AND NURSING DUAL DEGREE

Saint Joseph's College of Maine (M)

HEALTH SERVICES ADMINISTRATION SPECIALIZATION

The University of South Dakota (M)

HEALTH SERVICES ADMINISTRATION–MEDICAL INSURANCE, BILLING, AND CODING

Berkeley College (A)
Berkeley College–New York City Campus (A)
Berkeley College–Westchester Campus (A)

HEALTH SERVICES ADMINISTRATION/HEALTH SERVICES ADMINISTRATION AND MEDICAL IMAGING

Washburn University (B)

HEALTH SERVICES COMMUNITY HEALTH

Independence University (M)

HEALTH SERVICES EDUCATION AND MANAGEMENT (WITH UMDNJ)

Thomas Edison State College (B)

HEALTH SERVICES MANAGEMENT

Berkeley College–Westchester Campus (B)
East Carolina University (B)
Herkimer County Community College (A)
Independence University (B)
Mercy College (M)
Myers University (B)
University of Dallas (GC,M)

HEALTH SERVICES MANAGEMENT (EXECUTIVE PROGRAM)

University of Missouri–Columbia (M)

HEALTH SERVICES TECHNOLOGY (BAT)

The University of Texas System (B)

HEALTH SERVICES WELLNESS PROMOTION

Independence University (M)

HEALTH STUDIES

Texas Woman's University (M,B)

HEALTH STUDIES (HEALTH PROMOTION)

The University of Alabama (M)

HEALTH STUDIES–MASTER OF HEALTH STUDIES

Athabasca University (M)

HEALTH SYSTEM MANAGEMENT

Vanderbilt University (M)

HEALTH SYSTEMS

University of Medicine and Dentistry of New Jersey (M)

HEALTH SYSTEMS ADMINISTRATION

Rochester Institute of Technology (M,UC)

HEALTH SYSTEMS FINANCE

Rochester Institute of Technology (GC)

HEALTH TECHNOLOGY MANAGEMENT, MEDICAL ASSISTANT SPECIALIZATION

IIA College (A)

HEALTH TECHNOLOGY MANAGEMENT, PATIENT CARE TECHNICIAN SPECIALIZATION

IIA College (A)

HEALTH, PHYSICAL EDUCATION, AND RECREATION

Utah State University (M)

HEALTH, SAFETY, AND ENVIRONMENTAL TECHNOLOGY

Eastern Iowa Community College District (A)

HEALTH/TEACHER EDUCATION

East Carolina University (M)

HEALTHCARE ADMINISTRATION

Bellevue University (M)
Central Michigan University (D)
New England College (B)
Seton Hall University (M)
Walden University (M)

HEALTHCARE ADMINISTRATION AND MANAGEMENT

Rosalind Franklin University of Medicine and Science (GC,M)

HEALTHCARE ADMINISTRATION CONCENTRATION

American InterContinental University Online (A)

HEALTHCARE ETHICS

Rush University (GC)

HEALTHCARE INFORMATICS

The College of St. Scholastica (UC)
Drexel University (UC)

HEALTHCARE LEADERSHIP

Wheeling Jesuit University (B)

HEALTHCARE MANAGEMENT

Bellevue University (B)
Brenau University (M)
Jefferson College of Health Sciences (B)

HEALTHCARE MANAGEMENT CONCENTRATION (10-MONTH PROGRAM)

American InterContinental University Online (M)

HEALTHCARE MANAGEMENT CONCENTRATION (COMPLETION PROGRAM)

American InterContinental University Online (B)

HEALTHCARE SPECIALIZATION

Florida Tech University Online (M)

HEARING SPECIALIST–EARLY INTERVENTION

University of South Florida (GC)

HEATING, VENTILATION, AND AIR CONDITIONING (HVAC) SYSTEMS

University of Idaho (UC)

HEAVY CONSTRUCTION PROJECT MANAGEMENT

University of Washington (UC)

HEMODIALYSIS PATIENT CARE TECHNICIAN

Lake Superior College (UC)

HERITAGE RESOURCES MANAGEMENT

Athabasca University (GC,UC)

HIGHER EDUCATION

Abilene Christian University (M)
Dallas Baptist University (M)
Drexel University (M)
Kaplan University Online (M)
University of Louisville (M)
University of North Dakota (D)

HIGHER EDUCATION ADMINISTRATION

Northeastern University (GC)
Prescott College (M)
St. Cloud State University (M)
The University of Alabama (D,M)
University of Phoenix (D)

HIGHER EDUCATION ADMINISTRATION (EXECUTIVE COHORT)

The University of Alabama (D)

HIGHER EDUCATION LEADERSHIP PROFESSIONAL FOCUS

Quinnipiac University (M)

HIGHER EDUCATION–SCHOOL ADMINISTRATION

Union University (D)

HISTOLOGIC TECHNOLOGY

Darton College (A)

HISTOLOGY

Darton College (UC)

HISTORIC PRESERVATION

Goucher College (M)
Savannah College of Art and Design (GC,M)

HISTORICAL STUDIES

State University of New York Empire State College (A,B)

HISTORY

American Public University System (M,B)
Buena Vista University (B)
Butler Community College (A)
Coastline Community College (A)
Columbia College (B)
Darton College (A)
Dickinson State University (B)
Foothill College (A)
Judson College (B)
Mercy College (B)
National University (B)
Northeastern University (B)
Prescott College (B)
Rose State College (A)
Southwestern Adventist University (B)
Thomas Edison State College (B)
University of Houston–Victoria (B)
University of Illinois at Springfield (B)
University of Maryland University College (B)

HISTORY (3 YEAR)

Athabasca University (B)

HISTORY (4 YEAR)

Athabasca University (B)

HISTORY (IN DEVELOPMENT)

Laurentian University (B)

HISTORY AND POLITICAL STUDIES

Saint Mary-of-the-Woods College (B)

HISTORY, LIBERAL ARTS AND SCIENCES, MASS COMMUNICATIONS (ADVERTISING/PUBLIC RELATIONS; JOURNALISM), POLITICAL SCIENCE, AND PSYCHOLOGY CONCENTRATIONS

Parkland College (A)

HIT–MEDICAL CODING

North Dakota State College of Science (UC)

HOLOCAUST STUDIES

Gratz College (GC)

HOMELAND SECURITY

American Public University System (M,B)
Keiser University (A,B)

University of Maryland University College (B)
University of South Florida (GC)

HOMELAND SECURITY ADMINISTRATION

Tiffin University (M)

HOMELAND SECURITY AND EMERGENCY MANAGEMENT

Central Texas College (A,UC)

HOMELAND SECURITY AND SAFETY ENGINEERING

National University (M)

HOMELAND SECURITY IN PUBLIC HEALTH PREPAREDNESS

Penn State University Park (M)

HOMELAND SECURITY LEADERSHIP

University of Connecticut (M)

HOMELAND SECURITY MANAGEMENT

University of Maryland University College (GC)

HOMELAND SECURITY STUDIES

Michigan State University (UC)

HORTICULTURAL AND TURFGRASS SCIENCES

Texas Tech University (M,B)

HORTICULTURAL LANDSCAPE MANAGEMENT

Texas Tech University (GC)

HORTICULTURE

Thomas Edison State College (A,B)
University of Illinois at Urbana–Champaign (UC)

HORTICULTURE SCIENCE

North Carolina State University (GC)

HOSPITAL HEALTH CARE ADMINISTRATION

Thomas Edison State College (B)

HOSPITALITY AND TOURISM

Columbia Southern University (B)

HOSPITALITY AND TOURISM MANAGEMENT

Strayer University (B)

HOSPITALITY MANAGEMENT

American Public University System (B)
Central Texas College (A)
Chemeketa Community College (A,UC)
East Carolina University (B)
Excelsior College (B)
Lynn University (M)
Middlesex Community College (A)
New York Institute of Technology (B)
Penn State University Park (UC)
Thomas Edison State College (B)
University of North Texas (GC,M)

HOSPITALITY MANAGEMENT CONCENTRATION

Sullivan University (B)

HOSPITALITY MANAGEMENT–FOOD AND BEVERAGE MANAGEMENT

Central Texas College (A,UC)

HOSPITALITY MANAGEMENT–PROPERTY MANAGEMENT ADVANCED

Central Texas College (UC)

HOSPITALITY MANAGEMENT–ROOMS DIVISION

Central Texas College (UC)

HOSPITALITY, TRAVEL, AND TOURISM

University of Phoenix (A)

HOTEL AND RESTAURANT MANAGEMENT

Auburn University (M)
Tompkins Cortland Community College (A)

HOTEL, RESTAURANT, AND INSTITUTIONAL MANAGEMENT

Penn State University Park (A,UC)
University of Minnesota, Crookston (UC)

HOTEL, RESTAURANT, AND TOURISM MANAGEMENT

New Mexico State University (B)

HUMAN AND ORGANIZATIONAL DEVELOPMENT

Fielding Graduate University (D)

HUMAN AND SOCIAL SERVICES ADMINISTRATION

Bellevue University (B)

HUMAN BEHAVIOR

National University (M)

HUMAN CAPITAL DEVELOPMENT

University of Southern Mississippi (D)

HUMAN CAPITAL MANAGEMENT

Bellevue University (M)

HUMAN DEVELOPMENT

Amridge University (B)
California State University, East Bay (B)
Hope International University (B)
Pacific Oaks College (M,B)
State University of New York Empire State
  College (A,B)
Washington State University (B)

HUMAN DEVELOPMENT AND FAMILY STUDIES

Colorado State University (B)
Penn State University Park (A)
The University of Alabama (B)

HUMAN DEVELOPMENT AND FAMILY STUDIES (GERONTOLOGY EMPHASIS)

Texas Tech University (M)

HUMAN ENVIRONMENTAL SCIENCES (CONSUMER QUALITY MANAGEMENT)

The University of Alabama (M)

HUMAN ENVIRONMENTAL SCIENCES (FAMILY FINANCIAL PLANNING AND COUNSELING)

The University of Alabama (M)

HUMAN ENVIRONMENTAL SCIENCES (GENERAL STUDIES)

The University of Alabama (M)

HUMAN ENVIRONMENTAL SCIENCES (HUMAN NUTRITION)

The University of Alabama (M)

HUMAN ENVIRONMENTAL SCIENCES (INTERACTIVE TECHNOLOGY)

The University of Alabama (M)

HUMAN ENVIRONMENTAL SCIENCES (RESTAURANT AND HOSPITALITY MANAGEMENT)

The University of Alabama (M)

HUMAN ENVIRONMENTAL SCIENCES–FOOD AND NUTRITION

The University of Alabama (M)

HUMAN ENVIRONMENTAL SCIENCES–GENERAL STUDIES OPTION

The University of Alabama (B)

HUMAN ENVIRONMENTAL SCIENCES–RESTAURANT AND HOSPITALITY MANAGEMENT

The University of Alabama (B)

HUMAN ENVIRONMENTAL STUDIES (GENERAL STUDIES)

The University of Alabama (B)

HUMAN NUTRITION

Eastern Michigan University (M)
University of Bridgeport (M)

HUMAN PERFORMANCE MANAGEMENT

Immaculata University (B)

HUMAN PERFORMANCE TECHNOLOGY

Boise State University (GC)

HUMAN PERFORMANCE TECHNOLOGY (MSA)

University of West Florida (M)

HUMAN RELATIONS AND BUSINESS

Amberton University (M)

HUMAN RESOURCE ADMINISTRATION

San Joaquin Valley College–Online (A)

HUMAN RESOURCE ADMINISTRATION–CERTIFICATE OF ADVANCED STUDY

University of Denver (UC)

HUMAN RESOURCE ADMINISTRATION–MASTER OF PROFESSIONAL STUDIES IN HUMAN RESOURCE ADMINISTRATION

University of Denver (M)

HUMAN RESOURCE DEVELOPMENT

Buffalo State College, State University of
  New York (GC)
Clemson University (M)
Drexel University (M)
Indiana State University (GC,M,B)
Limestone College (B)
Southwestern College (B)

University of Arkansas (B)
The University of Texas System (M)

HUMAN RESOURCE EDUCATION

University of Louisville (M)

HUMAN RESOURCE LEADERSHIP

Amridge University (B)
Sullivan University (M,B)

HUMAN RESOURCE LEADERSHIP PROFESSIONAL FOCUS

Quinnipiac University (M)

HUMAN RESOURCE MANAGEMENT

Columbia Southern University (B)
Concordia University, St. Paul (B)
Dallas Baptist University (M)
DeVry University Online (M)
Dickinson State University (B)
Eastern Michigan University (GC)
Fort Hays State University (UC)
Franklin Pierce University (GC,M)
Franklin University (B)
Golden Gate University (GC,M,UC)
LeTourneau University (M)
Mercy College (M)
Myers University (B)
Nova Southeastern University (M)
Saint Mary-of-the-Woods College (B)
Southern New Hampshire University (GC,UC)
Strayer University (B)
University of Calgary (UC)
University of Connecticut (M)
University of Maryland University College (B)
University of Phoenix (M)
University of Wisconsin–Platteville (UC)
University of Wisconsin–Platteville (UC)
University of Wisconsin–Stout (UC)

HUMAN RESOURCE MANAGEMENT AND ORGANIZATIONAL DEVELOPMENT

National University (M)

HUMAN RESOURCE MANAGEMENT CONCENTRATION

Colorado Technical University Colorado Springs (M,B)

HUMAN RESOURCE MANAGEMENT CONCENTRATION (10-MONTH PROGRAM)

American InterContinental University Online (M)

HUMAN RESOURCE MANAGEMENT CONCENTRATION (COMPLETION PROGRAM)

American InterContinental University Online (B)

HUMAN RESOURCE MANAGEMENT PRACTICE

California National University for Advanced Studies (UC)

HUMAN RESOURCES

California National University for Advanced Studies (M)
Indiana Tech (B)
Minnesota State Community and Technical College–Fergus Falls (A)
Ottawa University (M)
St. Joseph's College, Long Island Campus (UC)
St. Joseph's College, New York (UC)
University of the Incarnate Word (B)

HUMAN RESOURCES ADMINISTRATION CONCENTRATION

Saint Leo University (M)

HUMAN RESOURCES AND EMPLOYMENT RELATIONS

Penn State University Park (M)

HUMAN RESOURCES AND LABOUR RELATIONS

Athabasca University (B,UC)

HUMAN RESOURCES CONCENTRATION

American InterContinental University Online (A)

HUMAN RESOURCES DEVELOPMENT

Webster University (M)

HUMAN RESOURCES MANAGEMENT

Florida Institute of Technology (M)
Golden Gate University (B)
Northeastern University (A)
Stevens Institute of Technology (GC)
Thomas Edison State College (M)
University of Management and Technology (B)
Upper Iowa University (B,UC)
Webster University (M)

HUMAN RESOURCES MANAGEMENT/MARKETING (3 YEAR)

Athabasca University (B)

HUMAN RESOURCES MANAGEMENT/MARKETING (4 YEAR)

Athabasca University (B)

HUMAN RESOURCES MANAGEMENT/ ORGANIZATIONAL MANAGEMENT

Thomas Edison State College (B)

HUMAN RESOURCES SPECIALIST

Bryant and Stratton Online (A)

HUMAN SCIENCE

Athabasca University (B)
Saybrook Graduate School and Research Center (D,M)

HUMAN SCIENCE–POST-DIPLOMA

Athabasca University (B)

HUMAN SCIENCES

Stephen F. Austin State University (M)

HUMAN SERVICES

Athabasca University (B)
Bellevue University (M)
Broome Community College (A)
Burlington College (B)
Capella University (D,M)
Coastline Community College (A)
Columbia College (A,B)
Dawson Community College (A)
Franklin Pierce University (A,B,UC)
Herkimer County Community College (A)
Indiana Wesleyan University (UC)
Ivy Tech Community College–Bloomington (A)
Ivy Tech Community College–Central Indiana (A)
Ivy Tech Community College–Columbus (A)
Ivy Tech Community College–East Central (A)
Ivy Tech Community College–Kokomo (A)
Ivy Tech Community College–Lafayette (A)
Ivy Tech Community College–North Central (A)
Ivy Tech Community College–Northeast (A)
Ivy Tech Community College–Northwest (A)
Ivy Tech Community College–Southeast (A)
Ivy Tech Community College–Southern Indiana (A)
Ivy Tech Community College–Southwest (A)
Ivy Tech Community College–Wabash Valley (A)
Ivy Tech Community College–Whitewater (A)
Liberty University (M)
Mount Wachusett Community College (A)
Northeastern University (B)
Old Dominion University (B)
Saint Joseph's College of Maine (A)
Saint Mary-of-the-Woods College (B)
University of Phoenix (B)
Upper Iowa University (B)
Walden University (D)
Washburn University (B)

HUMAN SERVICES COUNSELING

Regent University (M)

HUMAN SERVICES MANAGEMENT

University of Phoenix (A)

HUMAN SERVICES SHORT-TERM CERTIFICATE

Sinclair Community College (UC)

HUMAN SERVICES–CRIMINAL JUSTICE LEADERSHIP EMPHASIS

Concordia University, St. Paul (M)

HUMAN SERVICES–FAMILY LIFE EDUCATION EMPHASIS

Concordia University, St. Paul (M)

HUMAN SERVICES–SOCIAL SERVICES ADMINISTRATION CONCENTRATION

University of Illinois at Springfield (M)

HUMAN SERVICES/MANAGEMENT

University of Phoenix (B)

HUMANE AND ENVIRONMENTAL STUDIES (MNM)

Regis University (GC)

HUMANE LEADERSHIP

Duquesne University (B)

HUMANITARIAN ASSISTANCE

University of South Florida (GC)

HUMANITARIAN SERVICES ADMINISTRATION

University of Connecticut (M)

HUMANITIES

American Public University System (M)
California State University, Dominguez Hills (M)
Cerro Coso Community College (A)
Prescott College (M,B)
Saint Mary-of-the-Woods College (A,B)
Santa Rosa Junior College (A)
Thomas Edison State College (B)
Tiffin University (M)
University of Maryland University College (B)
University of Waterloo (B)
Washington State University (B)

HUMANITIES (3 YEAR)

Athabasca University (B)

HUMANITIES (4 YEAR)

Athabasca University (B)

HUMANITIES OPTION

Passaic County Community College (A)

I-MBA

Penn State University Park (M)

I.T. CONCENTRATION

Kettering University (M)

IIT NETWORKING AND TELECOMMUNICATIONS WITH E-LEARNING SYSTEMS

University of West Florida (B)

ILLUSTRATION

Academy of Art University (M,A,B)
Syracuse University (M)

ILLUSTRATION DESIGN

Savannah College of Art and Design (M)

IMAGING SCIENCE

Rochester Institute of Technology (M)

IMBA

Syracuse University (M)
Syracuse University (M)

IMS ACCOUNTING

Syracuse University (M)

INCLUSIVE EDUCATION

Athabasca University (UC)

INDEPENDENT BUSINESS MANAGEMENT

Parkland College (UC)

INDEPENDENT STUDIES– BACHELOR OF INDEPENDENT STUDIES/GENERAL STUDIES

Murray State University (B)

INDIVIDUAL STUDIES

Jamestown Community College (GC,A)
Jefferson Community College (A)

INDIVIDUALIZED DEGREE PROGRAM

Regent University (M)

INDIVIDUALIZED LIBERAL AND PROFESSIONAL STUDIES (VARIOUS SELF-DESIGNED TOPICS)

Antioch University McGregor (M)

INDIVIDUALIZED MAJOR

University of Wisconsin–Superior (B)

INDIVIDUALIZED MAJOR/ INTERDISCIPLINARY STUDIES

Burlington College (B)

INDIVIDUALIZED OCCUPATIONAL PREPARATION

Northwest Technical College (A,UC)

INDIVIDUALIZED STUDIES

Metropolitan State University (B)

INDIVIDUALIZED TRANSFER STUDIES

Northampton County Area Community College (A)

INDIVIDUALLY DESIGNED FOCUS AREA

DePaul University (B)

INDUSTRIAL AND SYSTEMS ENGINEERING

Auburn University (M)
Georgia Institute of Technology (M)
The University of Alabama in Huntsville (D)
University of Michigan–Dearborn (M)
University of Southern California (M)

INDUSTRIAL DESIGN

Academy of Art University (M,A,B)

INDUSTRIAL ELECTRONICS WITH PLC TECHNOLOGY

Cleveland Institute of Electronics (UC)

INDUSTRIAL ENGINEERING

Columbia University (UC)
Mississippi State University (M)
New Mexico State University (M)
State University of New York at Binghamton (M)
The University of Alabama in Huntsville (M)
University of South Florida (M)

INDUSTRIAL ENGINEERING AND OPERATIONS RESEARCH

Columbia University (GC)

INDUSTRIAL ENGINEERING TECHNOLOGY

James A. Rhodes State College (A)

INDUSTRIAL ENVIRONMENTAL MANAGEMENT

Rochester Institute of Technology (UC)

INDUSTRIAL HYGIENE

Montana Tech of The University of Montana (M)

INDUSTRIAL MANAGEMENT

Myers University (B)
University of Central Missouri (M)

INDUSTRIAL TECHNOLOGY

Southeast Missouri State University (B)

INDUSTRIAL TECHNOLOGY–BIOPROCESS MANUFACTURING

East Carolina University (B)

INDUSTRIAL TECHNOLOGY–INDUSTRIAL DISTRIBUTION AND LOGISTICS

East Carolina University (B)

INDUSTRIAL TECHNOLOGY–INDUSTRIAL SUPERVISION

East Carolina University (B)

INDUSTRIAL TECHNOLOGY–INFORMATION AND COMPUTER TECHNOLOGY

East Carolina University (B)

INDUSTRIAL TECHNOLOGY–MANUFACTURING SYSTEMS

East Carolina University (B)

INDUSTRIAL/ORGANIZATIONAL PSYCHOLOGY

Kansas State University (M)

INFANT MENTAL HEALTH

Chatham University (GC)

INFECTION CONTROL

University of South Florida (GC)

INFORMATICS

Northeastern University (M)
University of Maryland University College (GC)
University of Phoenix (M)

INFORMATION AND COMMUNICATION TECHNOLOGIES

University of Wisconsin–Stout (B)

INFORMATION AND COMMUNICATION TECHNOLOGY

New Mexico State University (B)

INFORMATION AND LEARNING TECHNOLOGIES, SCHOOL LIBRARY

University of Colorado Denver (M)

INFORMATION AND SYSTEMS ENGINEERING (MS OR MENG)

Lehigh University (M)

INFORMATION ASSURANCE

East Carolina University (GC)
Kaplan University Online (UC)
New Jersey Institute of Technology (GC)
University of Dallas (GC,M)
University of Maryland University College (GC,B)

INFORMATION ASSURANCE AND COMPUTER SECURITY

Dakota State University (M)

INFORMATION ASSURANCE AND SECURITY

Mercy College (M,B)

INFORMATION CENTER SPECIALIST

Central Texas College (UC)

INFORMATION COMMUNICATION TECHNOLOGIES

University of Wisconsin–Stout (M)

INFORMATION DESIGN AND TECHNOLOGY

State University of New York Institute of Technology (M)

INFORMATION ENGINEERING AND MANAGEMENT

Southern Methodist University (M)

INFORMATION ENGINEERING TECHNOLOGY

University of West Florida (B)

INFORMATION MANAGEMENT

Buena Vista University (B)
Grantham University (M)
Syracuse University (M)

INFORMATION MANAGEMENT FOR MANAGERS

New Jersey Institute of Technology (GC)

INFORMATION MANAGEMENT TECHNOLOGY

Grantham University (M)

INFORMATION MANAGEMENT–PROJECT MANAGEMENT

Grantham University (M)

INFORMATION MEDIA

St. Cloud State University (M)

INFORMATION NETWORKING AND TELECOMMUNICATIONS (COMPUTER NETWORKING AND TELECOMMUNICATIONS CONCENTRATION)

Fort Hays State University (B)

INFORMATION NETWORKING AND TELECOMMUNICATIONS (WEB DEVELOPMENT CONCENTRATION)

Fort Hays State University (B)

INFORMATION SCIENCE AND TECHNOLOGY

Drexel University (GC)
Missouri University of Science and Technology (M)
Penn State University Park (UC)

INFORMATION SCIENCES

University of North Texas (M)
The University of Tennessee (M)

INFORMATION SCIENCES AND TECHNOLOGY

Penn State University Park (A)

INFORMATION SECURITY

James Madison University (M)
Nova Southeastern University (M)

INFORMATION SECURITY AND PRIVACY

The University of North Carolina at Charlotte (GC)

INFORMATION SECURITY MANAGEMENT

Northeastern University (GC)
Saint Leo University (GC)
Syracuse University (GC)

INFORMATION SECURITY MANAGEMENT CONCENTRATION

Saint Leo University (M)

INFORMATION SECURITY–CERTIFICATE OF ADVANCED STUDY

University of Denver (UC)

INFORMATION SERVICES AND SUPPORT

The University of Toledo (A,UC)

INFORMATION SERVICES TECHNOLOGY

College of Southern Maryland (A,UC)

INFORMATION SERVICES TECHNOLOGY–WEB DEVELOPER

College of Southern Maryland (A)

INFORMATION STUDIES

Florida State University (M)

INFORMATION SYSTEMS

Athabasca University (M)
Baker College of Flint (M)
City University of Seattle (GC)
Columbia University (UC)
Dakota State University (D,M)
DePaul University (M)
Drexel University (M)
Eugenio María de Hostos Community College of the City University of New York (GC)
Minot State University (M)
National University (M,B)
New Jersey Institute of Technology (M,B)
Northeastern University (M)
Nova Southeastern University (D)
Piedmont Community College (A,UC)
Randolph Community College (A)
Shippensburg University of Pennsylvania (M)
Stevens Institute of Technology (M)
Strayer University (M,,A,B,UC)
University of Colorado Denver (M)
University of Illinois at Urbana–Champaign (GC)
University of Phoenix (M)
University of the Incarnate Word (A)

INFORMATION SYSTEMS (3 YEAR)

Athabasca University (B)

INFORMATION SYSTEMS (4 YEAR)

Athabasca University (B)

INFORMATION SYSTEMS AND TELECOMMUNICATIONS MANAGEMENT

Syracuse University (GC)

INFORMATION SYSTEMS CONCENTRATION

American InterContinental University Online (A)

INFORMATION SYSTEMS MANAGEMENT

DeVry University Online (M)
Hodges University (M,B)
University of Maryland University College (B)

INFORMATION SYSTEMS SECURITY

Westwood Online (B)

INFORMATION SYSTEMS SECURITY CONCENTRATION

Colorado Technical University Colorado Springs (M)

INFORMATION SYSTEMS SECURITY–CERTIFICATE OF ADVANCED STUDY

University of Denver (UC)

INFORMATION SYSTEMS TECHNOLOGY

Patrick Henry Community College (A)
Union County College (A)
University of Central Florida (B)
University of Northwestern Ohio (A)

INFORMATION TECHNOLOGIES

East Carolina University (B)

INFORMATION TECHNOLOGY

Bellevue University (B)
Capella University (D,M,B)
Colorado Technical University Colorado Springs (A)
Columbia Southern University (B)
Columbus State University (B)
DePaul University (M)
Eastern Iowa Community College District (A)
Excelsior College (B)
Florida Institute of Technology (M)
Florida Institute of Technology (M)
Florida Tech University Online (M)
Franklin University (A,B)
Golden Gate University (GC,M,B,UC)
Grantham University (M)
Jamestown Community College (GC,A)
Kaplan University Online (M,B)
Keiser University (A)
Kettering University (M)
Lawrence Technological University (B)
Memorial University of Newfoundland (M)
Minnesota School of Business–Richfield (A,B)
Myers University (B)
New England Institute of Technology (A)
New Jersey Institute of Technology (B)
Northeastern University (B)
Northern Virginia Community College (A)
Southern New Hampshire University (A,B)
Southern Polytechnic State University (B)
University of Dallas (GC,M)
University of Management and Technology (A,B,UC)
University of Maryland University College (M)
University of Massachusetts Lowell (A,B,UC)
University of Phoenix (A,B)
The University of Toledo (B)
Vincennes University (A)
Virginia Polytechnic Institute and State University (M)

INFORMATION TECHNOLOGY AND BACHELOR OF INFORMATION TECHNOLOGY (BIT), COMPUTER FORENSICS CONCENTRATION (COMPLETION PROGRAM)

American InterContinental University Online (B)

INFORMATION TECHNOLOGY AND BACHELOR OF INFORMATION TECHNOLOGY (BIT), INTERNET SECURITY CONCENTRATION (COMPLETION PROGRAM)

American InterContinental University Online (B)

INFORMATION TECHNOLOGY AND INFORMATION SERVICES LIBRARY PARAPROFESSIONAL

Belmont Technical College (A)

INFORMATION TECHNOLOGY CONCENTRATION

Colorado Technical University Colorado Springs (B)

INFORMATION TECHNOLOGY COORDINATOR

New Mexico State University (UC)

INFORMATION TECHNOLOGY FLUENCY

Bristol Community College (UC)

INFORMATION TECHNOLOGY LEADERSHIP

The College of St. Scholastica (M,UC)

INFORMATION TECHNOLOGY LEADERSHIP PROFESSIONAL FOCUS

Quinnipiac University (M)

INFORMATION TECHNOLOGY MANAGEMENT

American Public University System (B)
Concordia University, St. Paul (B)
Franklin Pierce University (M)
Keiser University (B)
National University (B)
Saint Joseph's College of Maine (A,UC)
TUI University (M,B)
University of Management and Technology (B)
Webster University (M)

INFORMATION TECHNOLOGY MANAGEMENT CONCENTRATION

Colorado Technical University Colorado Springs (M)

INFORMATION TECHNOLOGY ONLINE

Bryant and Stratton Online (A)
Oregon Institute of Technology (B)

INFORMATION TECHNOLOGY PATHWAY

Kaplan University Online (UC)

INFORMATION TECHNOLOGY– .NET TECHNOLOGY CONCENTRATION

Peirce College (UC)

INFORMATION TECHNOLOGY– BACHELOR OF INFORMATION TECHNOLOGY (BIT)–COMPUTER SYSTEMS CONCENTRATION (COMPLETION PROGRAM)

American InterContinental University Online (B)

INFORMATION TECHNOLOGY– BACHELOR OF INFORMATION TECHNOLOGY (BIT)–NETWORK ADMINISTRATION CONCENTRATION (COMPLETION PROGRAM)

American InterContinental University Online (B)

INFORMATION TECHNOLOGY– BACHELOR OF INFORMATION TECHNOLOGY (BIT)– PROGRAMMING CONCENTRATION (COMPLETION PROGRAM)

American InterContinental University Online (B)

INFORMATION TECHNOLOGY– BUSINESS INFORMATION SYSTEMS MODULE

Virginia Polytechnic Institute and State University (GC)

INFORMATION TECHNOLOGY– COMMUNICATIONS MODULE

Virginia Polytechnic Institute and State University (GC)

INFORMATION TECHNOLOGY– DECISION SUPPORT SYSTEMS

Virginia Polytechnic Institute and State University (GC)

INFORMATION TECHNOLOGY– DESKTOP APPLICATIONS FOR BUSINESS CONCENTRATION

Peirce College (A,B)

INFORMATION TECHNOLOGY– HELP DESK TECHNICIAN CONCENTRATION

Peirce College (UC)

INFORMATION TECHNOLOGY– INFORMATION SECURITY CONCENTRATION

Peirce College (B)

INFORMATION TECHNOLOGY–IT MANAGEMENT

University of Management and Technology (M)

INFORMATION TECHNOLOGY–IT PROJECT MANAGEMENT

University of Management and Technology (M)

INFORMATION TECHNOLOGY– MANAGEMENT INFORMATION SYSTEMS

University of Management and Technology (M)

INFORMATION TECHNOLOGY– NETWORK SECURITY CONCENTRATION

Peirce College (A,B)

INFORMATION TECHNOLOGY– NETWORKING

Virginia Polytechnic Institute and State University (GC)

INFORMATION TECHNOLOGY– NETWORKING CONCENTRATION

Peirce College (A,B)

INFORMATION TECHNOLOGY– PROGRAMMING AND APPLICATION DEVELOPMENT CONCENTRATION

Peirce College (B)

INFORMATION TECHNOLOGY– PROGRAMMING APPLICATION AND DEVELOPMENT CONCENTRATION

Peirce College (A)

INFORMATION TECHNOLOGY– TECHNOLOGY MANAGEMENT CONCENTRATION

Peirce College (A,B)

INFORMATION TECHNOLOGY– WEB ANALYST/PROGRAMMER

Wisconsin Indianhead Technical College (A)

INFORMATION TECHNOLOGY– WINDOWS NETWORK OPERATING SYSTEM CONCENTRATION

Peirce College (UC)

INFORMATION TECHNOLOGY, BUSINESS MINOR

University of Massachusetts Lowell (B)

INFORMATION TECHNOLOGY, NETWORK MANAGEMENT CONCENTRATION

Colorado Technical University Colorado Springs (B)

INFORMATION TECHNOLOGY, SECURITY CONCENTRATION

Colorado Technical University Colorado Springs (B)

INFORMATION TECHNOLOGY, SOFTWARE SYSTEMS ENGINEERING CONCENTRATION

Colorado Technical University Colorado Springs (B)

INFORMATION TECHNOLOGY/ BUSINESS SYSTEMS ANALYSIS

University of Phoenix (B)

INFORMATION TECHNOLOGY/ INFORMATION SYSTEMS SECURITY

University of Phoenix (B)

INFORMATION TECHNOLOGY/ MULTIMEDIA AND VISUAL COMMUNICATION

University of Phoenix (B)

INFORMATION TECHNOLOGY/ NETWORKING

University of Phoenix (A)

INFORMATION TECHNOLOGY/ NETWORKING AND TELECOMMUNICATIONS

University of Phoenix (B)

INFORMATION TECHNOLOGY/ SOFTWARE ENGINEERING

University of Phoenix (B)

INFORMATION TECHNOLOGY/ VISUAL COMMUNICATION

University of Phoenix (B)

INFORMATION TECHNOLOGY/ VISUAL COMMUNICATIONS

University of Phoenix (A)

INFRASTRUCTURE CONSTRUCTION

University of Washington (UC)

INITIAL TEACHER PROFESSIONAL PREPARATION

University of Central Florida (GC)

INSTITUTIONAL FOOD SERVICE SUPERVISOR

Northeast Iowa Community College (UC)

INSTITUTIONAL RESEARCH

Penn State University Park (GC)

INSTRUCTIONAL AND PERFORMANCE TECHNOLOGY

Boise State University (M)

INSTRUCTIONAL ASSISTANT

Gateway Technical College (A)

INSTRUCTIONAL DESIGN

Roosevelt University (GC)
Saint Leo University (M)
Southern Polytechnic State University (GC)
University of Massachusetts Boston (M)

INSTRUCTIONAL DESIGN & TECHNOLOGY

University of North Dakota (GC)

INSTRUCTIONAL DESIGN AND DEVELOPMENT

Bellevue University (M)
University of South Alabama (M)

INSTRUCTIONAL DESIGN AND TECHNOLOGY

University of North Dakota (M)

INSTRUCTIONAL DESIGN FOR SIMULATIONS

University of Central Florida (GC)

INSTRUCTIONAL LEADERSHIP

The University of Alabama (D)

INSTRUCTIONAL LEADERSHIP CONCENTRATION

Saint Leo University (M)

INSTRUCTIONAL LEADERSHIP FOR NURSE EDUCATORS

The University of Alabama (D,M)

INSTRUCTIONAL SPECIALIST (BILINGUAL EDUCATION OR EARLY CHILDHOOD EDUCATION)

The University of Texas System (M)

INSTRUCTIONAL SYSTEMS– EDUCATIONAL TECHNOLOGY

Penn State University Park (M)

INSTRUCTIONAL SYSTEMS–OPEN AND DISTANCE LEARNING MAJOR

Florida State University (M)

INSTRUCTIONAL SYSTEMS– PERFORMANCE IMPROVEMENT AND HUMAN RESOURCE DEVELOPMENT MAJOR

Florida State University (M)

INSTRUCTIONAL TECHNOLOGY

Cardinal Stritch University (M)
East Carolina University (M)
Fort Hays State University (M)
Saint Joseph's University (M)
San Diego State University (UC)
University of Maryland University College (M)
University of Nebraska at Kearney (M)
University of the Incarnate Word (M)
University of West Florida (M)
Virginia Polytechnic Institute and State University (M)
West Texas A&M University (M)

INSTRUCTIONAL TECHNOLOGY (DISTANCE EDUCATION EMPHASIS)

Texas Tech University (M)

INSTRUCTIONAL TECHNOLOGY (WEBIT)

The University of Tennessee (M)

INSTRUCTIONAL TECHNOLOGY AND DISTANCE EDUCATION

Nova Southeastern University (M)

INSTRUCTIONAL TECHNOLOGY CONCENTRATION (10-MONTH PROGRAM)

American InterContinental University Online (M)

INSTRUCTIONAL TECHNOLOGY DESIGN

University of Massachusetts Boston (GC)

INSTRUCTIONAL TECHNOLOGY EDUCATION SPECIALIST

Bloomsburg University of Pennsylvania (M)

INSTRUCTIONAL TECHNOLOGY FOR EDUCATORS

University of Massachusetts Boston (GC)

INSTRUCTIONAL TECHNOLOGY SPECIALIST

Clarion University of Pennsylvania (UC)
Drexel University (UC)
Missouri State University (GC)

INSTRUCTIONAL TECHNOLOGY SYSTEMS

DePaul University (M)

INSTRUCTIONAL TECHNOLOGY– DISTANCE EDUCATION

University of South Florida (GC)

INSTRUCTIONAL TECHNOLOGY– EDUCATIONAL TECHNOLOGY EMPHASIS

Utah State University (M)

INSTRUCTIONAL TECHNOLOGY– WEB DESIGN

University of South Florida (GC)

INSTRUCTIONAL TECHNOLOGY/ MEDIA E-LEARNING OR INSTRUCTIONAL SYSTEMS

University of Central Florida (M)

INSTRUCTIONAL TECHNOLOGY/ MEDIA-EDUCATIONAL MEDIA TRACK

University of Central Florida (M)

INSTRUCTIONAL TECHNOLOGY/ MEDIA-EDUCATIONAL TECHNOLOGY TRACK

University of Central Florida (M)

INSTRUCTIONAL/EDUCATIONAL TECHNOLOGY

University of Central Florida (GC)

INSURANCE AND RISK MANAGEMENT

Indiana State University (B)

INSURANCE AND RISK MANAGEMENT CONCENTRATION

Colorado Technical University Colorado Springs (M)

INSURANCE LEADERSHIP PROFESSIONAL FOCUS

Quinnipiac University (M)

INTEGRAL STUDIES

Fielding Graduate University (UC)

INTEGRATED DIRECT MARKETING

University of Maryland University College (GC)

INTEGRATED MARKETING COMMUNICATIONS

Eastern Michigan University (M)
Golden Gate University (GC,M)
Southern New Hampshire University (GC)
West Virginia University (M,UC)

INTEGRATED RESOURCE MANAGEMENT (IRM)

Colorado State University (M)

INTEGRATED STUDIES

Athabasca University (M)

INTEGRATIVE SUPPLY CHAIN MANAGEMENT

University of Maryland University College (GC)

INTELLIGENT SYSTEMS

Columbia University (UC)

INTER-AMERICAN STUDIES

Burlington College (B)

INTERACTIVE DESIGN

Savannah College of Art and Design (GC)

INTERACTIVE DESIGN AND GAME DEVELOPMENT

Savannah College of Art and Design (M)

INTERCULTURAL CONFLICT MANAGEMENT

Antioch University McGregor (M)

INTERCULTURAL STUDIES

Crown College (M)
Hope International University (GC,B)

INTERDEPARTMENTAL STUDIES

Schiller International University (B)

INTERDISCIPLINARY (CUSTOM CURRICULUM)

University of Dallas (M)

INTERDISCIPLINARY EARLY CHILDHOOD EDUCATION

Western Kentucky University (A)

INTERDISCIPLINARY PROGRAM IN TECHNICAL STUDIES

The University of Toledo (A)

INTERDISCIPLINARY SCIENCES

Mississippi State University (M)

INTERDISCIPLINARY SOCIAL SCIENCE

Florida State University (B)

INTERDISCIPLINARY SOCIAL SCIENCES

Kansas State University (B)

INTERDISCIPLINARY STUDIES

Adams State College (B)
Central Texas College (A)
Eastern Wyoming College (A)
Governors State University (B)
Grantham University (A,B)
Hodges University (A,B)
Kaplan University Online (A)
Mississippi State University (B)
New York Institute of Technology (B)
Regent University (B)
Southeast Missouri State University (B)
State University of New York Empire State College (A,B)
The University of Alabama (B)
University of Central Florida (B)
Upper Iowa University (B)

INTERDISCIPLINARY STUDIES (BA OR BS)

The University of Toledo (B)

INTERDISCIPLINARY STUDIES EC-6, 4-8

Stephen F. Austin State University (B)

INTERDISCIPLINARY STUDIES–8 CONCENTRATIONS

Dallas Baptist University (B)

INTERDISCIPLINARY STUDIES–ACTION FOR A VIABLE FUTURE

Sonoma State University (M)

INTERDISCIPLINARY STUDIES–EARLY CHILDHOOD THROUGH GRADE FOUR (EDUCATION)

The University of Texas at Tyler (B)

INTERIOR ARCHITECTURE AND DESIGN

Academy of Art University (M,A,B)

INTERIOR DESIGN

Savannah College of Art and Design (M)

INTERNATIONAL

University of Phoenix (M)
University of the Incarnate Word (M)

INTERNATIONAL AFFAIRS

Southwestern Adventist University (B)
Tufts University (M)

INTERNATIONAL BUSINESS

Berkeley College (A)
Berkeley College–New York City Campus (A,B)
Berkeley College–Westchester Campus (A,B)
Dallas Baptist University (M)
Dickinson State University (B)
Golden Gate University (M)
LeTourneau University (M)
Lynn University (M)
Park University (M)
Schiller International University (M,A,B)
Southern New Hampshire University (GC,B)
Strayer University (B)
Thomas Edison State College (B)
University of Wisconsin–Platteville (UC)
University of Wisconsin–Platteville (UC)

INTERNATIONAL BUSINESS ADMINISTRATION–MASTER OF INTERNATIONAL BUSINESS ADMINISTRATION

Nova Southeastern University (M)

INTERNATIONAL BUSINESS CONCENTRATION

Colorado Technical University Colorado Springs (B)

INTERNATIONAL BUSINESS CONCENTRATION (10-MONTH PROGRAM)

American InterContinental University Online (M)

INTERNATIONAL BUSINESS CONCENTRATION (COMPLETION PROGRAM)

American InterContinental University Online (B)

INTERNATIONAL COMMERCE

New Jersey Institute of Technology (GC)

INTERNATIONAL COMMERCE CERTIFICATE

Columbus State Community College (GC)

INTERNATIONAL DEVELOPMENT

Hope International University (GC,M)

INTERNATIONAL FOOD LAW

Michigan State University (UC)

INTERNATIONAL HOTEL AND TOURISM MANAGEMENT

Schiller International University (M,B)

INTERNATIONAL LOGISTICS AND TRANSPORTATION MANAGEMENT

Rochester Institute of Technology (UC)

INTERNATIONAL MANAGEMENT

Thunderbird School of Global Management
University of Management and Technology (B)
University of Maryland University College (M)

INTERNATIONAL MARKETING

Thunderbird School of Global Management
University of Maryland University College (GC)

INTERNATIONAL PUBLIC HEALTH–COMMUNITY ORIENTED PRIMARY CARE OPTION

The George Washington University (UC)

INTERNATIONAL REGULATORY AFFAIRS

Northeastern University (GC)

INTERNATIONAL RELATIONS

American Public University System (B)
St. Mary's University (M)
Webster University (M)

INTERNATIONAL RELATIONS AND CONFLICT RESOLUTION

American Public University System (M)

INTERNATIONAL RELATIONS AND DIPLOMACY

Schiller International University (B)

INTERNATIONAL SCIENTIFIC AND TECHNICAL COMMUNICATION

Bowling Green State University (GC)

INTERNATIONAL SECURITY

Stanford University (GC)

INTERNATIONAL SPORT DIPLOMA

United States Sports Academy (UC)

INTERNATIONAL STUDENT SERVICES

Western Kentucky University (UC)

INTERNATIONAL STUDIES

Montgomery County Community College (UC)

INTERNATIONAL TAXATION

Golden Gate University (GC)

INTERNATIONAL TRADE

University of Maryland University College (GC)

INTERNET AND WEBSITE DEVELOPMENT

Kaplan University Online (UC)

INTERNET APPLICATIONS DEVELOPMENT

New Jersey Institute of Technology (GC)

INTERNET BUSINESS SYSTEMS

Mercy College (M)

INTERNET PROGRAMMING

University of Washington (UC)

INTERNET SECURITY CONCENTRATION (10-MONTH PROGRAM)

American InterContinental University Online (M)

INTERNET TECHNOLOGIES

Pace University (GC)

INTERNET TECHNOLOGY

Pace University (GC)

INTERNET TECHNOLOGY FOR E-COMMERCE

Pace University (M)

INTERNETWORKING

Fort Hays State University (UC)

INTERPERSONAL COMMUNICATIONS

Seminole Community College (A)

INTERPRETER EDUCATION MASTER MENTOR

Northeastern University (GC)

INTERPRETER PEDAGOGY

Northeastern University (M)

INTERPROFESSIONAL HEALTHCARE STUDIES

Rosalind Franklin University of Medicine and Science (D)

INTRODUCTION TO COMPUTER PROGRAMMING LANGUAGE

Kaplan University Online (UC)

INTRODUCTION TO HOME AUTOMATION INSTALLATION

Cleveland Institute of Electronics (UC)

INTRODUCTORY C++ PROGRAMMING

Bellevue Community College (UC)

INVESTIGATIONS

Bellevue University (B)

INVESTIGATIVE FORENSICS

University of Maryland University College (B)

IRISH STUDIES

Regis University (UC)

IT PROJECT MANAGEMENT CONCENTRATION (10 MONTH PROGRAM)

American InterContinental University Online (M)

JEWISH EARLY CHILDHOOD EDUCATION

Gratz College (GC)

JEWISH EDUCATION

Gratz College (GC,M)

JEWISH EDUCATION–MASTER OF SCIENCE IN JEWISH EDUCATION (MSJE)

Spertus Institute of Jewish Studies (M)

JEWISH MUSIC

Gratz College (GC)

JEWISH NON-PROFIT MANAGEMENT

Gratz College (GC)

JEWISH STUDIES

Gratz College (GC,M,B)
Hebrew College (M)
Spertus Institute of Jewish Studies (D,M)

JOURNALISM

Prescott College (B)
Regent University (M,B)
Saint Mary-of-the-Woods College (B)
Seminole Community College (A)
Southwestern Adventist University (B)
Thomas Edison State College (B)

JOURNALISM (MEDIA MANAGEMENT)

University of Missouri–Columbia (M)

JOURNALISM (STRATEGIC COMMUNICATIONS)

University of Missouri–Columbia (M)

JOURNALISM EDUCATION

University of Missouri–Columbia (M)

JUDICIAL ADMINISTRATION GRADUATE SPECIALIZATION

Michigan State University (UC)

JUSTICE ADMINISTRATION

IIA College (A)
Tiffin University (M,B)

JUSTICE ADMINISTRATION–MINISTRY CONCENTRATION

Taylor University (A)

JUSTICE ADMINISTRATION–PUBLIC POLICY CONCENTRATION

Taylor University (A)

JUSTICE AND MINISTRY

Taylor University (UC)

JUSTICE STUDIES

Fort Hays State University (B)
Southern New Hampshire University (M)

JUSTICE STUDIES–CRIMINAL JUSTICE

Berkeley College (A,B)

K-12 EDUCATION LEADERSHIP

Jones International University (D)

K-12 SPECIALIZATION

Northeastern University (M)

KELLEY DIRECT MBA/M-GM DUAL DEGREE–THUNDERBIRD AND INDIANA UNIVERSITY

Thunderbird School of Global Management (M)

KINESIOLOGY

California State University, San Marcos (B)
Texas Woman's University (M)
The University of Texas at Tyler (M)
The University of Texas of the Permian Basin (M)
The University of Texas System (M)

KINESIOLOGY AND HEALTH

University of Wyoming (M)

KNOWLEDGE AND INFORMATION TECHNOLOGIES–MASTER OF APPLIED SCIENCE IN KNOWLEDGE AND INFORMATION TECHNOLOGIES

University of Denver (M)

KNOWLEDGE MANAGEMENT

Minot State University (GC)

LABOR STUDIES

State University of New York Empire State College (A,B)
Thomas Edison State College (B)

LABOR STUDIES AND INDUSTRIAL RELATIONS

Penn State University Park (UC)

LABORATORY ANIMAL SCIENCE

Thomas Edison State College (A,B)

LABOUR STUDIES

Athabasca University (UC)
University of Windsor (UC)

LABOUR STUDIES (3 YEAR)

Athabasca University (B)

LABOUR STUDIES (4 YEAR)

Athabasca University (B)

LAND SURVEYING

University of Wyoming (UC)

LAND USE PLANNING

Prescott College (M)

LANDSCAPE TECHNOLOGY

Minot State University–Bottineau Campus (UC)

LAW AND JUSTICE

Laurentian University (B,UC)

LAW AND SOCIETY

Penn State University Park (B)
University of Connecticut (B)

LAW ENFORCEMENT

Baltimore City Community College (A)
Dawson Community College (A)
Indiana State University (UC)

LAW ENFORCEMENT STUDIES

Vincennes University (A)

LAW FIRM MANAGEMENT

The George Washington University (M)

LAW–SCHOOL LAW

Park University (M)

LEADERSHIP

The American College (M)
Bellevue University (M,B)
City University of Seattle (M)
Fort Hays State University (M,UC)
Franklin Pierce University (M)
Northeastern University (GC,M,B)
Nova Southeastern University (M)
Regent University (GC)
Southwestern College (M)

LEADERSHIP (MNM)

Regis University (GC)

LEADERSHIP (MSA)

University of West Florida (M)

LEADERSHIP AND BUSINESS ETHICS

Duquesne University (M)

LEADERSHIP AND ETHICAL DECISION MAKING

University of Colorado at Boulder (GC)

LEADERSHIP AND HUMAN PERFORMANCE

University of Wisconsin–Platteville (UC)
University of Wisconsin–Platteville (UC)

LEADERSHIP AND INFORMATION TECHNOLOGY–MASTERS OF LEADERSHIP AND INFORMATION TECHNOLOGY

Duquesne University (M)

LEADERSHIP AND LIBERAL STUDIES

Duquesne University (M)

LEADERSHIP AND MANAGEMENT

Amridge University (M)

LEADERSHIP AND MINISTRY

Williamson Christian College (B)

LEADERSHIP AND SUPERVISION

St. Joseph's College, Long Island Campus (UC)
St. Joseph's College, New York (UC)

LEADERSHIP CONCENTRATION

Tiffin University (M)

LEADERSHIP DEVELOPMENT

Saint Mary-of-the-Woods College (M)
Taylor University (UC)

LEADERSHIP IN NURSING AND HEALTHCARE SYSTEMS

University of Missouri–Columbia (M)

LEADERSHIP IN THE PUBLIC SECTOR

North Carolina State University (B)

LEADERSHIP OF EDUCATIONAL ORGANIZATIONS CONCENTRATION (10-MONTH PROGRAM)

American InterContinental University Online (M)

LEADERSHIP OF LEARNING

Abilene Christian University (M)

LEADERSHIP–CERTIFICATE OF ADVANCED STUDY

University of Denver (UC)

LEADING ORGANIZATIONAL TRANSFORMATION

Saybrook Graduate School and Research Center (GC)

LEAN SIX SIGMA

East Carolina University (GC)

LEARNING AND KNOWLEDGE MANAGEMENT SYSTEMS

Rochester Institute of Technology (GC,M)

LEARNING SYSTEMS DESIGN AND DEVELOPMENT

University of Missouri–Columbia (M)

LEARNING SYSTEMS DESIGN AND DEVELOPMENT (EDUCATIONAL SPECIALIST)

University of Missouri–Columbia

LEARNING SYSTEMS TECHNOLOGY

University of Arkansas at Little Rock (M)

LEARNING TECHNOLOGIES

Drexel University (M)

LEEP–LIBRARY AND INFORMATION SCIENCE

University of Illinois at Urbana–Champaign (M)

LEGAL ADMINISTRATIVE ASSISTANT

Minnesota State Community and Technical College–Fergus Falls (A)

LEGAL AND JUSTICE STUDIES

Burlington College (B)

LEGAL ASSISTANT (PARALEGAL)

Lake Region State College (A)

LEGAL ASSISTING

University of Northwestern Ohio (A)

LEGAL SECRETARIAL CERTIFICATE

The University of Toledo (UC)

LEGAL SECRETARY

Kaplan University Online (UC)

LEGAL SECRETARY TECHNOLOGY

Minnesota State Community and Technical College–Fergus Falls (UC)

LEGAL SERVICES

Thomas Edison State College (A,B)

LEGAL STUDIES

American Public University System (B)
Bellevue University (B)
Florida Gulf Coast University (B)
Kaplan University Online (M,B)
Keiser University (B)
Strayer University (B)
University of Illinois at Springfield (M)
University of Maryland University College (B)
West Virginia University (M)

LEGAL STUDIES (MLS)

West Virginia University

LETTERS, ARTS, AND SCIENCES

Penn State University Park (A,B)

LIBERAL AND PROFESSIONAL STUDIES

University of Windsor (B)

LIBERAL ARTS

Austin Peay State University (A)
Broward Community College (A)
Burlington County College (A)
Butler Community College (A)
Cabrillo College (A)
Cerro Coso Community College (A)
Colorado State University (B)
Community College of Denver (A)
Eastern Iowa Community College District (A)
Excelsior College (A,B)
Florida Institute of Technology (A)
Florida Tech University Online (A)
Lake Region State College (A)
Lehigh Carbon Community College (A)
Lock Haven University of Pennsylvania (M)
Minot State University–Bottineau Campus (A)
Monroe Community College (A)
Mountain Empire Community College (A)
The New School: A University (B)
Northampton County Area Community College (A)
Northern Virginia Community College (A)
Peninsula College (A)
Piedmont Technical College (A)
Rose State College (A)
St. Cloud State University (A)
Saint Leo University (A)
Seattle Central Community College (A)
Southern New Hampshire University (A)
Southwestern Community College (A)
Syracuse University (A)
Taft College (A)
University of Arkansas at Little Rock (B)
University of Wisconsin Colleges (A)
Upper Iowa University (A)
Virginia Polytechnic Institute and State University (GC)
West Hills Community College (A)
Widener University (A)

LIBERAL ARTS (BLA)

University of Massachusetts Lowell (B)

LIBERAL ARTS (IN STATE)

Daytona State College (A)

LIBERAL ARTS (OUT OF STATE)

Daytona State College (A)

LIBERAL ARTS AND GENERAL STUDIES

Dallas County Community College District (A)

LIBERAL ARTS AND HUMANITIES

Cayuga County Community College (A)

LIBERAL ARTS AND SCIENCE

San Joaquin Delta College (GC)

LIBERAL ARTS AND SCIENCE/ HUMANITIES AND SOCIAL SCIENCE

Erie Community College (A)
Erie Community College, North Campus (A)
Erie Community College, South Campus (A)

LIBERAL ARTS AND SCIENCES

Burlington County College (A)
Mercy College (A)
Middlesex Community College (A)
Minnesota State Community and Technical College–Fergus Falls (A)
Northland Community and Technical College–Thief River Falls (A)
Sinclair Community College (A)

LIBERAL ARTS AND SCIENCES– GENERAL STUDIES

Herkimer County Community College (A)

LIBERAL ARTS AND SCIENCES– HUMANITIES

Herkimer County Community College (A)

LIBERAL ARTS AND SCIENCES– SOCIAL SCIENCE

Herkimer County Community College (A)

LIBERAL ARTS AND SCIENCES/ MATHEMATICS AND SCIENCES

Cayuga County Community College (A)

LIBERAL ARTS WITH BUSINESS MINOR

Northeastern University (B)

LIBERAL ARTS–ASSOCIATE OF ARTS IN LIBERAL ARTS

Arkansas State University–Beebe (A)

LIBERAL ARTS–GENERAL STUDIES

Broome Community College (A)

LIBERAL ARTS–HISTORY CONCENTRATION

Taylor University (A)

LIBERAL ARTS–HUMANITIES AND SOCIAL SCIENCE

Jefferson Community College (A)

LIBERAL ARTS– INTERDISCIPLINARY CONCENTRATION

Taylor University (A)

LIBERAL ARTS–MASTER OF LIBERAL ARTS

Texas Christian University (GC)

LIBERAL ARTS–SOCIAL SCIENCE CONCENTRATION

Taylor University (A)

LIBERAL ARTS, GENERAL

DePaul University (B)

LIBERAL ARTS/ SOCIAL SCIENCE CONCENTRATION

Vincennes University (A)

LIBERAL ARTS/GENERAL STUDIES

Thomas Edison State College (A)

LIBERAL ARTS/HUMANITIES

Westchester Community College (A)

LIBERAL ARTS/HUMANITIES AND SOCIAL SCIENCE

Clinton Community College (A)

LIBERAL ARTS/SOCIAL SCIENCE

Westchester Community College (A)

LIBERAL EDUCATION

Lake Superior College (A)

LIBERAL SCIENCE

Laurentian University (B)

LIBERAL STUDIES

Amridge University (A,B)
Bellevue University (B)
California State University, Chico (B)
Clarion University of Pennsylvania (B)
Coastline Community College (A)
Eastern Oregon University (B)
East Tennessee State University (M)
Excelsior College (M,B)
Fort Hays State University (M)
Limestone College (A,B)
Middlesex Community College (A,UC)
Middle Tennessee State University (B)
Montgomery County Community College (A)
Mount Wachusett Community College (A)
Neumann College (A)
Northeastern University (B)
Oregon State University (B)
St. John's University (M,A,B)
Sonoma State University (B)
State University of New York Empire State College (M)
Syracuse University (B)
Thomas Edison State College (M,B)
Union County College (A)
University of Illinois at Springfield (B)
The University of Maine at Augusta (A,B)
The University of North Carolina at Greensboro (M)
University of Northern Iowa (B)
University of Oklahoma (M,B)
University of Pittsburgh at Bradford (A)
University of the Incarnate Word (A)
The University of Toledo (M)
University of Waterloo (B)
University of Wisconsin–Whitewater (B)
Widener University (B)

LIBERAL STUDIES (HUMANITIES CONCENTRATION)

The University of North Carolina at Greensboro (B)

LIBERAL STUDIES–BACHELOR OF LIBERAL STUDIES ONLINE DEGREE PROGRAM

Bowling Green State University (B)

LIBERAL STUDIES–MASTER OF LIBERAL STUDIES

University of Denver (M)

LIBERAL STUDIES, LIBRARY SCIENCE CONCENTRATION

Clarion University of Pennsylvania (B)

LIBRARY AND INFORMATION SCIENCE

Drexel University (M)
Syracuse University (M)
The University of Alabama (M)
University of Illinois at Urbana–Champaign (GC)
University of Illinois at Urbana–Champaign (GC)

University of Illinois at Urbana–Champaign (M)
University of South Florida (M)
University of Washington (M)

LIBRARY AND INFORMATION SCIENCE IN SCHOOL MEDIA

Syracuse University (M)

LIBRARY AND INFORMATION SCIENCE K-12

University of Illinois at Urbana–Champaign (UC)

LIBRARY AND INFORMATION SCIENCES

University of North Texas (GC)

LIBRARY AND INFORMATION SERVICES

The University of Maine at Augusta (A,B)

LIBRARY AND INFORMATION STUDIES

The University of North Carolina at Greensboro (M)

LIBRARY AND INFORMATION STUDIES–MASTER OF LIBRARY AND INFORMATION STUDIES

The University of Alabama (M)

LIBRARY AND INFORMATION TECHNOLOGIES–SCHOOL LIBRARY AND INFORMATION TECHNOLOGIES

Mansfield University of Pennsylvania (M)

LIBRARY ASSISTANT

Ivy Tech Community College–Bloomington (A)
Ivy Tech Community College–Central Indiana (A)
Ivy Tech Community College–Columbus (A)
Ivy Tech Community College–Southeast (A)
Ivy Tech Community College–Southern Indiana (A)
Ivy Tech Community College–Southwest (A)
Ivy Tech Community College–Wabash Valley (A)
Ivy Tech Community College–Whitewater (A)

LIBRARY INFORMATION MANAGEMENT

Chadron State College (B)

LIBRARY INFORMATION SCIENCE

University of Southern Mississippi (M)

LIBRARY MEDIA EDUCATION

Western Kentucky University (M)

LIBRARY MEDIA GRADUATE ENDORSEMENT

University of Nebraska at Kearney (UC)

LIBRARY MEDIA SPECIALIST

Fort Hays State University (UC)

LIBRARY MEDIA TEACHING

Azusa Pacific University (UC)

LIBRARY SCIENCE

Clarion University of Pennsylvania (M)
East Carolina University (M)
Texas Woman's University (M)
University of Missouri–Columbia (M)
University of North Texas (M)

LIBRARY SCIENCE–SCHOOL LIBRARIANSHIP

Azusa Pacific University (M)

LIBRARY STUDIES

Memorial University of Newfoundland (UC)

LIBRARY TECHNICAL ASSISTANT

Ivy Tech Community College–East Central (A)
Ivy Tech Community College–Kokomo (A)
Ivy Tech Community College–Lafayette (A)
Ivy Tech Community College–North Central (A)
Ivy Tech Community College–Northeast (A)
Ivy Tech Community College–Northwest (A)
Rose State College (A)

LIBRARY TECHNICAL SERVICES

Northampton County Area Community College (UC)

LICENSED PRACTICAL NURSE TO BACHELOR OF SCIENCE IN NURSING

University of Phoenix (B)

LICENSED VOCATIONAL NURSE TO BACHELOR OF SCIENCE IN NURSING

University of Phoenix (B)

LIFE ISSUES

Fort Hays State University (UC)

LIFE SCIENCES

University of Maryland, College Park (M)

LINGUISTICS–APPLIED LINGUISTICS, ESL CONCENTRATION

University of Massachusetts Boston (M)

LITERACY

University of Missouri–Columbia (M)

LITERACY PROGRAM (WYOMING READING ENDORSEMENT)

University of Wyoming (UC)

LOCAL CHURCH MINISTRY

Grace College (M)

LOGISTICS AND DISTRIBUTION MANAGEMENT

Sullivan University (A)

LOGISTICS AND DISTRIBUTION MANAGEMENT CONCENTRATION

Sullivan University (B)

LOGISTICS AND SUPPLY CHAIN MANAGEMENT CONCENTRATION

Colorado Technical University Colorado Springs (M)

LOGISTICS MANAGEMENT

Bellevue University (B)
Florida Institute of Technology (M)

LONG TERM CARE ADMINISTRATION

Bellevue University (B)

LONG-TERM CARE ADMINISTRATION

Saint Joseph's College of Maine (B,UC)
University of Southern California (M)

LONG-TERM CARE ADMINISTRATION, ADVANCED

Saint Joseph's College of Maine (UC)

LONG-TERM CARE MANAGEMENT

The University of South Dakota (GC)

LOSS PREVENTION AND SAFETY

Eastern Kentucky University (M)

LPN/RN TO BSN

North Dakota State University (B)

LUTC FELLOW DESIGNATION

The American College (UC)

LVN TO BACHELOR OF SCIENCE IN NURSING

The University of Texas at Tyler (B)

MANAGEMENT

Amberton University (M,B)
American Public University System (M,B)
Athabasca University (GC)
Austin Peay State University (M)
Belhaven College (B)
Bellevue University (M,B)
Berkeley College (B)
Cerro Coso Community College (A)
Chemeketa Community College (A)
Dallas Baptist University (M,B)
Darton College (A)
Embry-Riddle Aeronautical University (M)
Florida Institute of Technology (M)
Fort Hays State University (B,UC)
Franklin Pierce University (A,B,UC)
Franklin University (B)
Golden Gate University (M,B)
Hodges University (M,B)
Hope International University (M,B)
IIA College (B)
Indiana Tech (B)
Indiana Wesleyan University (M)
Kaplan University Online (M)
LeTourneau University (M)
Liberty University (M)
Metropolitan State University (B)
Minot State University (M,B)
Montgomery County Community College (A)
National University (M,B)
New Jersey Institute of Technology (M)
Northeastern University (B)
Northwest Technical College (UC)
Old Dominion University (B)
Park University (B)
Prescott College (B)
Regis University (M)
Saint Joseph's College of Maine (A)
Southwestern College (M)
Stevens Institute of Technology (M)
Strayer University (B)
Texas A&M University–Commerce (M)
Thomas Edison State College (M)
The University of Alabama (M)
University of Arkansas at Little Rock (B)
University of Houston–Victoria (B)
The University of Maine at Augusta (B)
University of Management and Technology (M,B)
University of Maryland University College (D,M)
University of North Texas (M)
University of Phoenix (M,B)
University of St. Francis (M)
University of Wisconsin–Stout (B)
Upper Iowa University (B)
Wayland Baptist University (M)
Worcester Polytechnic Institute (GC,M)

MANAGEMENT (BACHELOR COMPLETION)

Indiana Wesleyan University (B)

MANAGEMENT (GLOBAL BUSINESS MANAGEMENT)

The University of Alabama (M)

MANAGEMENT ACCOUNTING

Minnesota School of Business–Richfield (A)
The University of Toledo (UC)

MANAGEMENT AND ETHICS

Williamson Christian College (B)

MANAGEMENT AND HUMAN RESOURCE SKILLS FOR PHARMACISTS

Oregon State University (UC)

MANAGEMENT AND LEADERSHIP

Judson University (B)
Webster University (M)

MANAGEMENT AND MARKETING

Darton College (UC)
DeSales University (B)

MANAGEMENT AND ORGANIZATION

University of Colorado Denver (M)

MANAGEMENT AND ORGANIZATIONAL BEHAVIOR

Silver Lake College (M)

MANAGEMENT AND ORGANIZATIONAL DEVELOPMENT

Bethel College (B)
Spring Arbor University (B)

MANAGEMENT AND SUPERVISION (IN STATE)

Daytona State College (B)

MANAGEMENT AND SUPERVISION (OUT OF STATE)

Daytona State College (B)

MANAGEMENT COMMUNICATION

Amridge University (B)

MANAGEMENT CONCENTRATION

Colorado Technical University Colorado Springs (B)
Sullivan University (B)

MANAGEMENT CONCENTRATION (10-MONTH PROGRAM)

American InterContinental University Online (M)

MANAGEMENT CONCENTRATION (COMPLETION PROGRAM)

American InterContinental University Online (B)

MANAGEMENT DEVELOPMENT

College of Southern Maryland (A,UC)

MANAGEMENT DEVELOPMENT– MARKETING

College of Southern Maryland (UC)

MANAGEMENT ESSENTIALS

New Jersey Institute of Technology (GC)

MANAGEMENT IN COMPUTER SCIENCE/TELECOM WITH SECURITY MANAGEMENT AND FORENSICS

Stevens Institute of Technology (M)

MANAGEMENT INFORMATION SCIENCES

Franklin University (B)

MANAGEMENT INFORMATION SYSTEMS

Auburn University (M)
Bellevue University (B)
Culver-Stockton College (B)
Dakota State University (B)
Dallas Baptist University (M,B)
Excelsior College (B)
Florida State University (M)
Fort Hays State University (B)
Liberty University (A,B)
Minot State University (B)
Montgomery County Community College (A)
Myers University (B)
Northeastern University (A)
Northwest Missouri State University (B)
Nova Southeastern University (M)
Regis University (UC)
Seminole Community College (A)
Stevens Institute of Technology (GC)
University of Illinois at Springfield (M)

MANAGEMENT OF HEALTH INFORMATICS

Bellevue University (B)

MANAGEMENT OF HEALTH SERVICES

Ottawa University (B)

MANAGEMENT OF HUMAN RESOURCES

Bellevue University (B)
Excelsior College (B)

MANAGEMENT OF INFORMATION SYSTEMS

Bellevue University (M)
Keiser University (B)

MANAGEMENT OF INFORMATION TECHNOLOGY

Schiller International University (M)

MANAGEMENT OF TECHNOLOGY

New Jersey Institute of Technology (GC)
The University of Texas at San Antonio (M)

MANAGEMENT OF TECHNOLOGY (MSCIT)

Regis University (GC)

MANAGEMENT POST-DIPLOMA (3 YEAR)

Athabasca University (B)

MANAGEMENT POST-DIPLOMA (4 YEAR)

Athabasca University (B)

MANAGEMENT SCIENCE

Neumann College (M)

MANAGEMENT SCIENCE AND ENGINEERING

Stanford University (GC,M)

MANAGEMENT SCIENCES– MASTER OF MANAGEMENT SCIENCES ONLINE (MMSC)

University of Waterloo (M)

MANAGEMENT SPECIALIZATION

Florida Tech University Online (M)

MANAGEMENT STUDIES

University of Maryland University College (B)

MANAGEMENT STUDIES, ADVANCED

Brenau University (M)

MANAGEMENT–HUMAN RESOURCES CONCENTRATION

Fort Hays State University (B)

MANAGEMENT, GENERAL

Dallas Baptist University (M)
University of Calgary (UC)

MANAGEMENT/COMPUTER INFORMATION SYSTEMS

Park University (B)

MANAGEMENT/HUMAN RESOURCES

Park University (B)

MANAGEMENT/MARKETING

Park University (B)

MANAGING APPLIED RESEARCH IN TECHNOLOGY

University of Colorado at Boulder (GC)

MANAGING INNOVATION

University of Colorado at Boulder (GC)

MANUFACTURING ENGINEERING

Columbia University (UC)
Missouri University of Science and Technology (M)
University of Michigan (M)
University of Washington (M)
University of Wisconsin–Stout (M)

MANUFACTURING ENGINEERING (INDUSTRIAL AND MANUFACTURING ENGINEERING CONCENTRATION)

Kettering University (M)

MANUFACTURING ENGINEERING TECHNOLOGY

Thomas Edison State College (A,B)

MANUFACTURING MANAGEMENT

Kettering University (M)
Missouri State University (UC)

MANUFACTURING OPERATIONS

Kettering University (M)

MANUFACTURING SYSTEMS ENGINEERING

Lehigh University (M)

MANUFACTURING SYSTEMS MANAGEMENT

Southern Methodist University (M)

MANUFACTURING SYSTEMS TECHNOLOGY

Jacksonville State University (M)

MARINE ENGINEERING TECHNOLOGY

Thomas Edison State College (A,B)

MARITIME STUDIES

University of West Florida (B)

MARITIME STUDIES–BACHELOR OF MARITIME STUDIES (BMS)

Memorial University of Newfoundland (B)

MARKETING

American Public University System (B)
Athabasca University (UC)
Brenau University (B)

City University of Seattle (GC,UC)
Columbia Southern University (B)
Columbus State Community College (A)
Dallas Baptist University (M,B)
Darton College (UC)
Excelsior College (B)
Fort Hays State University (B)
Franklin Pierce University (A,B,UC)
Franklin University (B)
Golden Gate University (GC,M)
Indiana Tech (B)
J. Sargeant Reynolds Community College (A)
Lakeland College (B)
LeTourneau University (M)
Lynn University (M)
Metropolitan State University (B)
Myers University (B)
National University (B)
New Mexico State University (B)
Northeastern University (A)
Northwest Technical College (UC)
Piedmont Community College (UC)
Regis University (B)
Saint Mary-of-the-Woods College (B)
Southern New Hampshire University (GC,M,A,B)
Strayer University (A,B)
Thomas Edison State College (B)
University of Houston–Victoria (B)
University of Maryland University College (B)
University of North Texas (M)
University of Northwestern Ohio (A)
University of Wisconsin–Platteville (UC)
University of Wisconsin–Platteville (UC)
Upper Iowa University (B,UC)
Western Wyoming Community College (A)

MARKETING AND MANAGEMENT

Butler Community College (A)

MARKETING AND RETAILING

Blue Ridge Community College (A)

MARKETING AND SALES MANAGEMENT

Sullivan University (A)

MARKETING AND SALES TECHNOLOGY

The University of Toledo (A,UC)

MARKETING CONCENTRATION

Colorado Technical University Colorado Springs (M,B)
Sullivan University (B)

MARKETING CONCENTRATION (10-MONTH PROGRAM)

American InterContinental University Online (M)

MARKETING CONCENTRATION (COMPLETION PROGRAM)

American InterContinental University Online (B)

MARKETING MANAGEMENT

Bellevue University (B)
Concordia University, St. Paul (B)
New England College (M)
University of Dallas (GC,M)
University of Management and Technology (B)

MARKETING SPECIALIZATION

Florida Tech University Online (M)

MARKETING, MANAGEMENT, AND TECHNOLOGY

University of Northwestern Ohio (A)

MARKETING/MANAGEMENT

Lake Region State College (A)
Williston State College (A,UC)

MARRIAGE AND FAMILY THERAPY

Amridge University (M)
Liberty University (M)
Saybrook Graduate School and Research Center (M)

MARRIAGE EDUCATION (FOR CREDIT)

University of Bridgeport (UC)

MARRIAGE EDUCATION (NON-CREDIT)

University of Bridgeport (UC)

MASS COMMUNICATION AND MEDIA MANAGEMENT

Lynn University (M)

MASS MEDIA ARTS AND JOURNALISM

Clarion University of Pennsylvania (M)

MASTER IN MATHEMATICS

The University of Texas at Brownsville (GC)

MASTER OCCUPATIONAL THERAPY

Texas Woman's University

MASTER OF ACADEMIC MEDICINE

University of Southern California (M)

MASTER OF CHURCH MUSIC

Hope International University

MASTER OF DIVINITY

Baptist Bible College of Pennsylvania (M)
Beacon University (M)

Midwestern Baptist Theological Seminary (M)
St. Petersburg Theological Seminary (M)

MASTER OF ENGINEERING

Mississippi State University (M)

MASTER OF ENGINEERING MANAGEMENT

Lawrence Technological University (M)

MASTER OF HEALTH AND HUMAN SERVICES

Youngstown State University (M)

MASTER OF HEALTH CARE ADMINISTRATION

National University (M)

MASTER OF INFORMATION SYSTEMS MANAGEMENT

Walden University (M)

MASTER OF INTERNATIONAL MANAGEMENT IN INTERNATIONAL BUSINESS

Schiller International University (M)

MASTER OF JEWISH EDUCATION

Hebrew College (M)

MASTER OF MINISTRY

Baptist Bible College of Pennsylvania (M)

MASTER OF PROFESSIONAL WRITING

Chatham University (M)

MASTER OF PUBLIC HEALTH

East Tennessee State University (M)

MASTER OF RELIGIOUS STUDIES (MRS)

Southern California Seminary (M)

MASTER OF WORLDVIEW STUDIES IN EDUCATION

Institute for Christian Studies (M)

MASTER READING TEACHER

The University of Texas System (UC)

MASTER TECHNOLOGY TEACHER

The University of Texas System (UC)

MASTERS OF SCIENCE IN HUMAN DEVELOPMENT AND FAMILY STUDIES, FAMILY LIFE AND PARENT EDUCATION CONCENTRATION

North Carolina State University (M)

MASTERS TEACHER CERTIFICATION

The University of Texas at Brownsville (M)

MATERIAL ACQUISITION MANAGEMENT

Florida Institute of Technology (M)

MATERIAL DESIGN, ADVANCED

University of Idaho (UC)

MATERIALS ENGINEERING

Auburn University (M)
State University of New York at Binghamton (M)
University of Illinois at Urbana–Champaign (GC)
University of Southern California (M)

MATERIALS FAILURE ANALYSIS

University of Illinois at Urbana–Champaign (GC)

MATERIALS SCIENCE AND ENGINEERING

Columbia University (M,UC)
University of Florida (M)
University of Washington (M)

MATH

Chadron State College (M,B)

MATH LEARNING AND TEACHING

Drexel University (M)

MATHEMATICAL SCIENCES

University of Illinois at Springfield (B)

MATHEMATICS

Mercy College (B)
Saint Mary-of-the-Woods College (B)
Southwestern Adventist University (B)
Thomas Edison State College (A,B)
University of Arkansas at Little Rock (B)

MATHEMATICS EDUCATION

Florida State University (M)
Western Kentucky University (M)

MATHEMATICS–APPLIED MATHEMATICS

Columbia University (M,UC)

MBA CERTIFICATE IN GLOBAL COMMERCE

Webster University (GC)

MBA FOR AVIATION PROFESSIONALS

Daniel Webster College (M)

MBA–FINANCE CONCENTRATION (10-MONTH PROGRAM)

American InterContinental University Online

MECHANICAL AND AEROSPACE ENGINEERING (DYNAMICS AND CONTROL TRACK)

University of Florida (M)

MECHANICAL AND AEROSPACE ENGINEERING (FUNDAMENTALS OF THERMAL FLUIDS TRANSPORT TRACK)

University of Florida (M)

MECHANICAL AND AEROSPACE ENGINEERING (SOLID MECHANICS AND DESIGN TRACK)

University of Florida (M)

MECHANICAL DESIGN (ME CONCENTRATION)

Kettering University (M)

MECHANICAL ENGINEERING

Auburn University (M)
Columbia University (GC,M)
Georgia Institute of Technology (M)
Kansas State University (M)
Michigan Technological University (D,M)
Missouri University of Science and
 Technology (M)
North Carolina State University (M)
Southern Methodist University (M)
Stanford University (M)
State University of New York at Binghamton
 (M)
The University of Alabama (B)
University of Idaho (M)
University of Illinois at Urbana–Champaign
 (M)
University of Illinois at Urbana–Champaign
 (M)
University of North Dakota (B)
University of Southern California (M)
University of Washington (M)

MECHANICAL ENGINEERING (ENGINEERING MANAGEMENT PROGRAM)

Colorado State University (M)

MECHANICAL ENGINEERING (IND ENGG AND OPERATIONS RES PROGRAM)

Colorado State University (D,M)

MECHANICAL ENGINEERING (MATERIALS ENGINEERING)

Colorado State University (M)

MECHANICAL ENGINEERING (MS OR MENG)

Lehigh University (M)

MECHANICAL ENGINEERING TECHNOLOGY

Indiana State University (B)
Old Dominion University (B)
Thomas Edison State College (A,B)

MECHANICAL ENGINEERING, PHARMACEUTICAL CONCENTRATION

Stevens Institute of Technology

MECHANICAL ENGINEERING/ MATERIALS

University of Illinois at Urbana–Champaign
 (GC)

MECHANICAL ENGINEERING/ MATERIALS FAILURE ANALYSIS

University of Illinois at Urbana–Champaign
 (GC)

MECHANICS AND MAINTENANCE

Thomas Edison State College (A)

MEDIA MANAGEMENT

The New School: A University (GC)

MEDIA PSYCHOLOGY

Fielding Graduate University (D)

MEDIA STUDIES

The New School: A University (M)

MEDIATION

Colorado State University (UC)

MEDIATION AND DISPUTE RESOLUTION CONCENTRATION

Colorado Technical University Colorado
 Springs (M)

MEDICAL ADMINISTRATIVE ASSISTANT

Bryant and Stratton Online (A)
Minnesota State Community and Technical
 College–Fergus Falls (A)

MEDICAL ADMINISTRATIVE SECRETARY TECHNOLOGY

Northwest Technical College (A)

MEDICAL ASSISTANT

Minot State University–Bottineau Campus
 (A,UC)

MEDICAL ASSISTANT TECHNOLOGY

University of Northwestern Ohio (A)

MEDICAL ASSISTING

Kaplan University Online (A)
Keiser University (A)

MEDICAL BILLER/CODER

University of Cincinnati (UC)

MEDICAL BILLING AND CODING

California State University, Dominguez Hills
 (GC)
Colorado Technical University Colorado
 Springs (A)
Drexel University (UC)

MEDICAL CODER/ TRANSCRIPTIONIST

Herkimer County Community College (UC)

MEDICAL CODING

Darton College (UC)
Minot State University–Bottineau Campus
 (UC)
Northwest Technical College (UC)
Sullivan University (UC)

MEDICAL CODING AND BILLING CONCENTRATION

American InterContinental University Online
 (A)

MEDICAL CODING AND INSURANCE

Minnesota State Community and Technical
 College–Fergus Falls (UC)

MEDICAL CODING SPECIALIST

Southwest Wisconsin Technical College (UC)

MEDICAL DEVICE AND DIAGNOSTIC ENGINEERING

University of Southern California (M)

MEDICAL IMAGING

Clarkson College (B)
Thomas Edison State College (A,B)

MEDICAL IMAGING POST-BACCALAUREATE CERTIFICATE

MGH Institute of Health Professions (UC)

MEDICAL INSURANCE

Northwest Technical College (UC)

MEDICAL LAB TECH

Hibbing Community College (A)

MEDICAL LAB TECHNOLOGY

Broome Community College (A)

MEDICAL LABORATORY TECHNOLOGY

Central Virginia Community College (A)
Clark State Community College (A)
Darton College (A)

MEDICAL OFFICE ADMINISTRATION

Presentation College (A)
San Joaquin Valley College–Online (A)

MEDICAL OFFICE ASSISTANT

Edison State Community College (A)
Illinois Eastern Community Colleges, Olney Central College (A)
Minnesota State Community and Technical College–Fergus Falls (UC)

MEDICAL OFFICE CODING SPECIALIST

Sinclair Community College (UC)

MEDICAL OFFICE MANAGEMENT

Kaplan University Online (A)

MEDICAL OFFICE SPECIALIST

Central Texas College (UC)

MEDICAL OFFICE TECHNOLOGY

Northwest Technical College (UC)

MEDICAL PHYSICS

Georgia Institute of Technology (M)

MEDICAL PRACTICES OFFICE MANAGER

Northwest Technical College (A)

MEDICAL SECRETARY

Minot State University–Bottineau Campus (A)

MEDICAL SECRETARY TECHNOLOGY

Northwest Technical College (UC)

MEDICAL TECHNOLOGY

Darton College (A)

MEDICAL TRANSCRIPTION

California State University, Dominguez Hills (GC)
Central Texas College (UC)
Kaplan University Online (A)
Minnesota State Community and Technical College–Fergus Falls (UC)
Minot State University–Bottineau Campus (UC)
North Dakota State College of Science (UC)
Northwest Technical College (UC)
Presentation College (UC)
Southwest Wisconsin Technical College (UC)
Williston State College (A,UC)

MEDICAL TRANSCRIPTIONIST

Northeast Iowa Community College (UC)

MEDICINE

Saint Francis University (M)

MENTAL HEALTH AND HUMAN SERVICES

The University of Maine at Augusta (B)

MENTAL HEALTH AND REHABILITATION SERVICES

Thomas Edison State College (B)

MENTAL HEALTH COUNSELING

Prescott College (M)
Walden University (M)

MENTAL HEALTH NURSE PRACTITIONER

University of Missouri–Columbia (M)

MENTAL HEALTH PRACTICES IN SCHOOLS

University of Missouri–Columbia (M)

MENTAL HEALTH PRACTICES IN SCHOOLS (EDUCATIONAL SPECIALIST)

University of Missouri–Columbia

MENTAL HEALTH REHABILITATION TECHNICIAN–COMMUNITY

University of Southern Maine (UC)

MERCHANDISING

Kansas State University (M)
North Dakota State University (GC,M)
San Joaquin Delta College (UC)
University of North Texas (GC,M)

METEOROLOGY–BROADCAST METEOROLOGY PROGRAM

Mississippi State University

METEOROLOGY–OPERATIONAL METEOROLOGY PROGRAM

Mississippi State University

MICROCOMPUTER OFFICE SPECIALIST

Lake Superior College (UC)

MICROELECTRONICS AND PHOTONICS

Stevens Institute of Technology (M)

MICROELECTRONICS MANUFACTURING ENGINEERING

Rochester Institute of Technology (M)

MICROFINANCE MANAGEMENT

Southern New Hampshire University (GC)

MICROSOFT SYSTEM ADMINISTRATOR

Central Texas College (UC)

MIDDLE EASTERN STUDIES

American Public University System (B)

MIDDLE GRADES

University of Illinois at Urbana–Champaign (UC)

MIDDLE GRADES EDUCATION

Brenau University (M)

MIDDLE/SECONDARY TEACHING

Indiana State University (UC)

MIDWIFERY

Philadelphia University (M)

MILD/MODERATE SPECIAL EDUCATION

Northwestern State University of Louisiana (UC)

MILITARY HISTORY

Austin Peay State University (M)

MILITARY HISTORY, MILITARY MANAGEMENT, INTELLIGENCE STUDIES

American Public University System (B)

MILITARY SPECIALTIES

Fort Hays State University (B)

MILITARY STUDIES

American Public University System (M)

MINING ENGINEERING

Missouri University of Science and
Technology (M)

MINISTERIAL LEADERSHIP

Amridge University (M)

MINISTERIAL STUDIES–BROAD FIELD PLAN

Global University (M)

MINISTERIAL STUDIES–EDUCATION CONCENTRATION

Global University (M)

MINISTERIAL STUDIES–LEADERSHIP CONCENTRATION

Global University (M)

MINISTERIAL STUDIES–MISSIONS CONCENTRATION

Global University (M)

MINISTRY

Amridge University (M)
Crossroads College (B)
Global University (UC)
Hope International University (M)
Liberty University (D)

MINISTRY (MINISTERIAL LEADERSHIP AND YOUTH MINISTRY CONCENTRATIONS)

Indiana Wesleyan University (M)

MINISTRY AND LEADERSHIP DEGREE COMPLETION PROGRAM

Life Pacific College (B)

MINISTRY LEADERSHIP

Crown College (M)

MINISTRY STUDIES

Judson College (B)

MINISTRY–LEADERSHIP AND RENEWAL

Regent University (D)

MINISTRY/BIBLE

Amridge University (B)

MIS CONCENTRATION AND SAP EMPHASIS

Central Michigan University (M)

MISSILE SYSTEMS ENGINEERING

The University of Alabama in Huntsville (M)

MISSIONS

Global University (B)

MISSIONS STUDIES

Taylor University (UC)

MODERN LANGUAGES–CERTIFICATE OF ADVANCED STUDY

University of Denver (UC)

MOLECULAR BIOLOGY

Lehigh University (M)

MOLECULAR LABORATORY DIAGNOSTICS

Michigan State University (UC)

MORTGAGE BANKING

North Lake College (A)

MOTION PICTURES AND TELEVISION

Academy of Art University (M,A,B)

MS–FINANCIAL ENGINEERING

Stevens Institute of Technology

MULTI-CRAFT TECHNOLOGY

West Virginia University at Parkersburg (A)

MULTI-CULTURAL EDUCATION

Park University (M)

MULTICULTURAL AND TRANSNATIONAL LITERATURES EMPHASIS

East Carolina University (M)

MULTICULTURAL LITERATURE

East Carolina University (GC)

MULTIDISCIPLINARY SCIENCE

Texas Tech University (M)

MULTIDISCIPLINARY STUDIES

Liberty University (B)
Siena Heights University (B)
Texas Tech University (B)
Webster University (M)
West Virginia University (B)

MULTIDISCIPLINARY STUDIES–EDUCATION CONCENTRATION

Liberty University (B)

MULTIDISCIPLINARY STUDY

Johnson County Community College (A)

MULTIMEDIA APPLICATIONS

University of Massachusetts Lowell (UC)

MULTIMEDIA COMMUNICATIONS

Bristol Community College (UC)

MULTIMEDIA NETWORKING

Columbia University (UC)

MULTIMEDIA TECHNOLOGY

Stevens Institute of Technology (GC)

MUSEUM STUDIES

Prescott College (M)

MUSIC

Auburn University (M)
Judson College (B)
Prescott College (B)
Thomas Edison State College (B)

MUSIC EDUCATION

East Carolina University (M)
Stephen F. Austin State University (M)
University of South Florida (M)

MUSIC EDUCATION–MASTER OF MUSIC EDUCATION

University of Southern Mississippi (M)

MUSIC EDUCATION–MASTERS IN MUSIC EDUCATION

Duquesne University (M)

MUSIC THERAPY

Georgia College & State University (M)
Saint Mary-of-the-Woods College (M)
Saint Mary-of-the-Woods College (M)

NANOSCALE MATERIALS SCIENCE

Stanford University (GC)

NANOTECHNOLOGY

Columbia University (UC)

NATIONAL SECURITY STUDIES

American Public University System (M)

NATIVE STUDIES

Laurentian University (B)

NATIVE STUDIES (HONOURS)

Laurentian University (B)

NATURAL RESOURCE MANAGEMENT–CERTIFICATE OF ADVANCED STUDY

University of Denver (UC)

NATURAL RESOURCES

Oregon State University (B)
Virginia Polytechnic Institute and State University (GC,M)

NATURAL RESOURCES AND CONSERVATION

Prescott College (M,B)

NATURAL RESOURCES AND ENVIRONMENTAL SCIENCES

University of Illinois at Urbana–Champaign (M)

NATURAL RESOURCES AND THE ENVIRONMENT

Colorado State University (UC)

NATURAL SCIENCES

Santa Rosa Junior College (A)

NATURAL SCIENCES/ MATHEMATICS

Thomas Edison State College (B)

NEGOTIATION, CONFLICT RESOLUTION, AND PEACEBUILDING

California State University, Dominguez Hills (M)

NEONATAL NURSE PRACTITIONER

East Carolina University (M)
Vanderbilt University (M)

NETWORK AND COMMUNICATIONS MANAGEMENT

DeVry University Online (M,B)

NETWORK AND INTERNET ADMINISTRATION

Southwest Virginia Community College (UC)

NETWORK CENTRIC SYSTEMS

University of Southern California (GC)

NETWORK SECURITY AND INFORMATION ASSURANCE

New Jersey Institute of Technology (GC)

NETWORK SECURITY MANAGEMENT

Northeastern University (GC)

NETWORK SYSTEMS ADMINISTRATION

DeVry University Online (A)

NETWORK+ CERTIFICATION AND COMPUTER TECHNOLOGY

Cleveland Institute of Electronics (UC)

NETWORKED INFORMATION SYSTEMS

Stevens Institute of Technology (GC,M)

NETWORKING (ELECTRICAL ENGINEERING)

Stanford University (GC)

NETWORKING AND SYSTEMS

Columbia University (UC)

NETWORKING AND SYSTEMS ADMINISTRATION

Rochester Institute of Technology (M)

NETWORKING TECHNOLOGIES (MSCIT)

Regis University (GC)

NETWORKING/ TELECOMMUNICATIONS

City University of Seattle (UC)

NETWORKS AND DISTRIBUTED SYSTEMS

University of Illinois at Urbana–Champaign (GC)

NEW CHURCH DEVELOPMENT

Calvin Theological Seminary (M)

NEW LEARNING AND NEW LITERACIES EMPHASIS

University of Illinois at Urbana–Champaign (M)

NEW MEDIA ENGINEERING

Columbia University (UC)

NEW TESTAMENT

Johnson Bible College (M)

NEWFOUNDLAND STUDIES

Memorial University of Newfoundland (UC)

NON-PROFIT MANAGEMENT AND LEADERSHIP

Lawrence Technological University (GC)

NON-PROFIT ORGANIZATION MANAGEMENT

Green Mountain College (M)

NONDESTRUCTIVE TESTING TECHNOLOGY

Thomas Edison State College (A,B)

NONPROFIT AND ASSOCIATION FINANCIAL MANAGEMENT

University of Maryland University College (GC)

NONPROFIT AND COMMUNITY SERVICES MANAGEMENT

Park University (M)

NONPROFIT MANAGEMENT

George Mason University (GC)
Hope International University (M)
Northeastern University (GC)
Regis University (M)
University of Central Florida (GC,M)
University of Southern Maine (UC)
Walden University (GC)

NONPROFIT MANAGEMENT (POST-BACCALAUREATE)

The University of North Carolina at Greensboro (UC)

NONPROFIT MANAGEMENT AND LEADERSHIP

Walden University (M)

NONTRADITIONAL PHARMD

The Ohio State University (D)

NOT-FOR-PROFIT

University of Dallas (M)

NOT-FOR-PROFIT MANAGEMENT

North Park University (M)

NUCLEAR CRITICALITY SAFETY

The University of Tennessee (GC)

NUCLEAR ENGINEERING

The University of Tennessee (M)

NUCLEAR ENGINEERING TECHNOLOGY

Excelsior College (B)
Thomas Edison State College (A,B)

NUCLEAR MEDICINE TECHNOLOGY

Thomas Edison State College (A,B)

NUCLEAR TECHNOLOGY

Excelsior College (A)

NURSE CLINICIAN EDUCATOR

The University of Texas at El Paso (UC)

NURSE EDUCATOR

Florida State University (M)
Graceland University (GC,M)
Missouri State University (GC)
The University of North Carolina at Charlotte (M)
The University of Toledo (M)

NURSE MIDWIFERY

East Carolina University (M,)
University of Cincinnati (M)

NURSE PRACTITIONER

University of St. Francis (M)

NURSE PRACTITIONER AND CLINICAL SPECIALIST

University of Colorado at Colorado Springs (M)

NURSE-MIDWIFERY

Philadelphia University (UC)

NURSING

Alcorn State University (M)
Allen College (M)
Angelo State University (M)
Athabasca University (M)
Ball State University (M,B)
California State University, Chico (M,B)
California State University, Dominguez Hills (M)
California State University, San Bernardino (M)
Clarion University of Pennsylvania (B)
Clemson University (M,B)
Concordia University Wisconsin (M)
Duquesne University (D,M)
Excelsior College (M,A,B)
Gonzaga University (M)
Graceland University (B)
IIA College (A)
Illinois State University (D,B)
Independence University (M)
Jacksonville State University (M)
Kaplan University Online (M,A,B)
Liberty University (M)
Memorial University of Newfoundland (M)

Mercy College (B)
Metropolitan State University (M)
Middle Tennessee State University (M,B)
Mississippi University for Women (B)
Missouri State University–West Plains (B)
Motlow State Community College (A)
National University (B)
New Mexico State University (D,B)
Northwestern Michigan College (A)
Northwest Technical College (A)
Old Dominion University (B)
Pennsylvania College of Technology (B)
Rush University (D,M)
Sacred Heart University (B)
Saint Francis Medical Center College of Nursing (M)
Saint Joseph's College of Maine (M,B)
Saint Louis University (GC,D,M)
Samuel Merritt College (M)
Seton Hall University (M)
Southern Illinois University Edwardsville (B)
Southwestern Adventist University (B)
State University of New York at Plattsburgh (B)
Texas Christian University (M)
Texas Woman's University (D)
Thomas Edison State College (M,B)
The University of Alabama (M,B)
University of Arkansas (M)
University of Calgary (B)
University of Central Florida (B)
University of Central Missouri (B)
University of Michigan–Flint (B)
The University of North Carolina at Greensboro (M,B)
University of North Dakota (B)
University of Phoenix (M)
University of South Alabama (M,B)
University of Southern Indiana (M,B)
The University of Texas at Brownsville (B)
The University of Texas at Tyler (M,B)
The University of Texas System (D)
West Virginia University (M)
Wheeling Jesuit University (M)

NURSING ADMINISTRATION

Fort Hays State University (M)
George Mason University (M)
Independence University (M)
Mercy College (M)
University of West Florida (M)

NURSING ADMINISTRATION AND LEADERSHIP

Saint Joseph's College of Maine (GC)

NURSING AND HEALTHCARE EDUCATION

Saint Joseph's College of Maine (GC)

NURSING AND RURAL FAMILY NURSING

University of Central Missouri (M)

NURSING CARE HEALTH CARE LEADERSHIP

Clarkson College

NURSING COMMUNITY HEALTH

Independence University (M)

NURSING COMPLETION PROGRAM

California State University, Dominguez Hills (B)

NURSING EDUCATION

Clarkson College (M,)
East Carolina University (M,)
Fort Hays State University (M)
Indiana State University
Jacksonville State University (GC)
Mansfield University of Pennsylvania (M)
Mercy College (M)
University of Central Florida (GC)
University of Missouri–Columbia (M)
The University of Texas System (GC)
The University of Toledo (UC)

NURSING EDUCATION AND NURSING ADMINISTRATION MAJORS

Indiana Wesleyan University (M)

NURSING FAST TRACK

University of St. Francis (B)

NURSING FOR NURSE PRACTITIONERS

University of Phoenix (M)

NURSING FOR REGISTERED NURSES

Minot State University (B)

NURSING GERONTOLOGY

Independence University (M)

NURSING HEALTH CARE LEADERSHIP

Clarkson College (M)

NURSING HOME ADMINISTRATION

Southeast Community College Area (UC)

NURSING INFORMATICS

Vanderbilt University (M)

NURSING LEADERSHIP

East Carolina University (M)

NURSING LEADERSHIP IN HEALTH SYSTEMS MANAGEMENT

Drexel University (M,UC)

NURSING MANAGEMENT

Penn State University Park (UC)

NURSING PRACTICE

Metropolitan State University (D)
Vanderbilt University (D)

NURSING SCIENCE

Vanderbilt University (D)

NURSING WELLNESS

Independence University (M)

NURSING–ACCELERATED RN TO BSN

Holy Names University (B)
University of Louisville (B)

NURSING–AD-LPN TO BSN NURSING COMPLETION

Presentation College (B)

NURSING–ADMINISTRATION AND EDUCATION OPTIONS

The University of Texas at Tyler (M)

NURSING–BACCALAUREATE PROGRAM FOR REGISTERED NURSES

University of Manitoba (B)

NURSING–BACHELOR OF SCIENCE IN NURSING

Allen College (B)
Angelo State University (B)

NURSING–BACHELORS OF SCIENCE IN NURSING

Independence University (B)

NURSING–BSN COMPLETION FOR RN'S

Concordia University Wisconsin (B)

NURSING–BSN COMPLETION PROGRAM FOR RNS

University of Illinois at Chicago (B)

NURSING–BSN FOR REGISTERED NURSES

Laurentian University (B)

NURSING–BSN TRACK

Walden University (M)

NURSING–CASE MANAGEMENT FOR RURAL POPULATIONS/ CLINICAL NURSE LEADER

The University of Alabama (M)

NURSING–CLINICAL NURSE SPECIALIST

East Carolina University (M,)
University of Missouri–Columbia (M)

NURSING–CONTINENCE CARE NURSE

Metropolitan State University (UC)

NURSING–DOCTOR OF NURSING PRACTICE

Chatham University (D)
Duquesne University (D)

NURSING–EDUCATION SPECIALIZATION

University of North Dakota (M)

NURSING–FAMILY NURSE PRACTITIONER

Clarion University of Pennsylvania (M)
East Carolina University (M,)

NURSING–FAMILY NURSE PRACTITIONER SPECIALIZATION

Indiana State University (M)

NURSING–FORENSIC NURSING

Duquesne University

NURSING–GERONTOLOGICAL/ ADULT AND FAMILY NURSE PRACTITIONER

University of Massachusetts Boston (GC)

NURSING–INNOVATION AND INTRA/ENTREPRENEURSHIP IN ADVANCED NURSING PRACTICE

Drexel University (M,,UC)

NURSING–LEADERSHIP AND MANAGEMENT TRACK

University of Central Florida (M)

NURSING–LPN CERTIFICATE TO BSN NURSING COMPLETION

Presentation College (B)

NURSING–LPN-BS

Indiana State University (B)

NURSING–MASTER OF BUSINESS ADMINISTRATION, HEALTH CARE MANAGEMENT

University of Phoenix (M)

NURSING–MASTER OF SCIENCE IN FORENSIC NURSING

Fitchburg State College (M)

NURSING–NEONATAL NURSE PRACTITIONER

East Carolina University

NURSING–NURSE EDUCATOR OPTION

University of Wyoming (M)

NURSING–NURSE EDUCATOR TRACK

University of Central Florida (M)

NURSING–NURSE LEADER AND NURSE EDUCATOR OPTIONS

Old Dominion University (M)

NURSING–NURSING ADMINISTRATION SPECIALIZATION

Indiana State University (M)

NURSING–NURSING EDUCATION SPECIALIZATION

Indiana State University (M)

NURSING–NURSING PRACTICE, ADVANCED

Athabasca University (GC)

NURSING–NURSING/HEALTH CARE EDUCATION

University of Phoenix (M)

NURSING–ONLINE RN TO BSN

California State University, San Bernardino (B)

NURSING–OSTOMY CARE NURSE

Metropolitan State University (UC)

NURSING–PATIENT CARE SERVICES ADMINISTRATION– FAMILY NURSE PRACTITIONER

Sacred Heart University (M)

NURSING–POST-BSN

Duquesne University (UC)

NURSING–POST-LPN

Athabasca University (B)

NURSING–POST-MASTERS

Duquesne University (GC)

NURSING–POST-RN

Athabasca University (B)
Memorial University of Newfoundland (B)

NURSING–PRACTICAL NURSING

North Dakota State College of Science (A)

NURSING–REGISTERED NURSING

Clark State Community College (A)

NURSING–RN COMPLETION PROGRAM FOR ASSOCIATE DEGREE-HOLDING NURSES

University of South Florida (B)

NURSING–RN OPTION

The University of Texas at Tyler (B)

NURSING–RN TO BA COMPLETION

The College of St. Scholastica (B)

NURSING–RN TO BS

Indiana State University (B)
Southern Illinois University Edwardsville (B)
Texas Woman's University (B)
University of Massachusetts Boston (B)

NURSING–RN TO BS COMPLETION

Indiana Wesleyan University (B)

NURSING–RN TO BSN

Austin Peay State University (B)
Brenau University (B)
California State University, San Marcos (B)
Chatham University (B)
Clarkson College (B)
Drexel University (B)
East Carolina University (B)
Florida State University (B)
Fort Hays State University (B)
Jefferson College of Health Sciences (B)
Keiser University (B)
Liberty University (B)
Loyola University New Orleans (B)
Mansfield University of Pennsylvania (B)
Marymount University (B)
Northwestern State University of Louisiana (B)
Penn State University Park (B)
Regis University (B)
Seton Hall University (B)
Southwestern College (B)
University of Maine at Fort Kent (B)
University of North Alabama (B)
University of Phoenix (B)
University of Southern Maine (B)
University of Southern Mississippi (B)

The University of Texas at El Paso (B)
The University of Texas System (B)
University of Wyoming (B)
Washington State University (B)
West Virginia University (B)

NURSING–RN TO BSN COMPLETION

Bowling Green State University (B)
Cleveland State University (B)
Presentation College (B)
Southeast Missouri State University (B)
The University of North Carolina at Charlotte (B)
West Texas A&M University (B)

NURSING–RN TO BSN ONLINE OPTION (BACHELOR'S COMPLETION PROGRAM)

University of Missouri–Columbia (B)

NURSING–RN TO BSN/MSN

Duquesne University (B)
The University of Alabama (M)

NURSING–RN TO MSN

The University of Texas at Tyler (M)
Wheeling Jesuit University (B)

NURSING–RN TRACK

Walden University (M)

NURSING–SCHOOL NURSE

University of Illinois at Chicago (UC)

NURSING–STEP NURSING PROGRAM

Jacksonville State University (B)

NURSING–WOMEN'S HEALTH COMPLETION PROGRAM FOR NURSE PRACTITIONERS

Drexel University (M)

NURSING–WOMEN'S HEALTH NURSE PRACTITIONER

Drexel University (M)
University of Cincinnati (M)

NURSING–WOUND CARE NURSE

Metropolitan State University (UC)

NURSING–WOUND OSTOMY CONTINENCE NURSE

Metropolitan State University (UC)

NURSING/HEALTH CARE EDUCATION

University of Phoenix (M)

NUTRITION

East Carolina University (M)
Huntington College of Health Sciences (A)

NUTRITION AND DIETETICS

Central Michigan University (M)

NUTRITION SCIENCE

Kaplan University Online (B)

NUTRITION–MASTER OF SCIENCE OF NUTRITION

Huntington College of Health Sciences (M)

OBJECT-ORIENTED ANALYSIS AND DESIGN USING UML

University of Washington (UC)

OBJECT-ORIENTED TECHNOLOGIES (MSCIT)

Regis University (GC)

OCCUPATION AND TECHNICAL STUDIES

Old Dominion University (D)

OCCUPATIONAL AND TECHNICAL STUDIES

Old Dominion University (M,B)

OCCUPATIONAL HEALTH

Medical College of Wisconsin (M)

OCCUPATIONAL HEALTH NURSING

University of South Florida (GC)

OCCUPATIONAL HEALTH PSYCHOLOGY

Kansas State University (UC)

OCCUPATIONAL SAFETY

East Carolina University (M)

OCCUPATIONAL SAFETY AND HEALTH

Columbia Southern University (M,B)

OCCUPATIONAL SAFETY AND HEALTH FOCUS

University of Connecticut (B)

OCCUPATIONAL STUDIES

Thomas Edison State College (A)

OCCUPATIONAL STUDIES IN AVIATION STUDIES

Excelsior College (A)

OCCUPATIONAL THERAPY

Misericordia University (D)
University of Southern Indiana (M)
West Virginia University (M)

OCEAN ENGINEERING

Virginia Polytechnic Institute and State University (M)

OCEANOGRAPHY

University of West Florida (B)

OFFICE ADMINISTRATION

Central New Mexico Community College (A)
Delaware Technical & Community College, Jack F. Owens Campus (A)
Ivy Tech Community College–Bloomington (A)
Ivy Tech Community College–Central Indiana (A)
Ivy Tech Community College–Columbus (A)
Ivy Tech Community College–East Central (A)
Ivy Tech Community College–Kokomo (A)
Ivy Tech Community College–Lafayette (A)
Ivy Tech Community College–North Central (A)
Ivy Tech Community College–Northeast (A)
Ivy Tech Community College–Northwest (A)
Ivy Tech Community College–Southeast (A)
Ivy Tech Community College–Southern Indiana (A)
Ivy Tech Community College–Southwest (A)
Ivy Tech Community College–Wabash Valley (A)
Ivy Tech Community College–Whitewater (A)
Northwestern State University of Louisiana (A)
Southwestern Adventist University (B)

OFFICE ADMINISTRATION (ADMINISTRATIVE SUPPORT)

Darton College (A)

OFFICE ADMINISTRATION (SECRETARIAL SCIENCE)

Darton College (A)

OFFICE AND BUSINESS ADMINISTRATION

AIB College of Business (A)

OFFICE APPLICATIONS SPECIALIST

Northwestern Michigan College (UC)

OFFICE ASSISTANT

Central Texas College (UC)

OFFICE INFORMATION SYSTEMS

Northwest Missouri State University (B)
Western Wyoming Community College (A)

OFFICE MANAGEMENT

Central Texas College (A)

OFFICE MANAGEMENT LEVELS 1&2

Central Texas College (UC)

OFFICE PROFESSIONAL

Union County College (UC)

OFFICE SOFTWARE APPLICATIONS

Seminole Community College (UC)

OFFICE SUPPORT

Seminole Community College (UC)

OFFICE SUPPORT SYSTEMS

Utah State University (A)

OFFICE SYSTEMS ADMINISTRATION

Southwestern Adventist University (B)

OFFICE SYSTEMS TECHNOLOGY

Randolph Community College (A)

OFFICE TECHNOLOGY

Southwestern Adventist University (A)
State University of New York College of Agriculture and Technology at Morrisville (UC)

OHIO READING ENDORSEMENT PROGRAM

Bowling Green State University (GC)

ON-LINE MASTER OF SCIENCE IN PHYSICAL EDUCATION

Canisius College (M)

ONLINE ACCELERATED TEACHER CERTIFICATION PROGRAM (OATCERT)

Saint Joseph's University (UC)

ONLINE ADMINISTRATION OF HEALTH CARE INSTITUTIONS

Benedictine University (M)

ONLINE BACHELOR OF GENERAL STUDIES (DEGREE COMPLETION PROGRAM)

University of Missouri–Columbia (B)

ONLINE BBA

LeTourneau University (B)

ONLINE DISASTER MANAGEMENT

Benedictine University (M)

ONLINE FINANCE

Benedictine University (M)

ONLINE HEALTH EDUCATION

Benedictine University (M)

ONLINE HEALTH POLICY

Benedictine University (M)

ONLINE HEALTHCARE ADMINISTRATION

Benedictine University (M)

ONLINE INTERNATIONAL BUSINESS

Benedictine University (M)

ONLINE MARKETING

Benedictine University (M)

ONLINE MBA

The University of Scranton (M)

ONLINE MBA IN HEALTH CARE MANAGEMENT

The University of Scranton (M)

ONLINE MPH

Benedictine University (M)

ONLINE PRINCIPAL LICENSURE PROGRAM AND MASTERS DEGREE IN CURRICULUM AND INSTRUCTION

University of Colorado at Colorado Springs (M)

ONLINE TEACHING

Boise State University (GC)
Roosevelt University (GC)

ONLINE TEACHING AND LEARNING

New Mexico State University (UC)

OPERATIONS AND SUPPLY CHAIN MANAGEMENT

Golden Gate University (GC,M)

OPERATIONS MANAGEMENT

Excelsior College (B)
Kettering University (M)

New England College (M)
Oregon Institute of Technology (B)
Southern New Hampshire University (GC)
Southwestern College (B)
Thomas Edison State College (B)
The University of Alabama (M)

OPERATIONS MANAGEMENT CONCENTRATION

Colorado Technical University Colorado Springs (M)

OPERATIONS MANAGEMENT CONCENTRATION (10-MONTH PROGRAM)

American InterContinental University Online (M)

OPERATIONS MANAGEMENT CONCENTRATION (COMPLETION PROGRAM)

American InterContinental University Online (B)

OPERATIONS RESEARCH

Columbia University (UC)
Florida Institute of Technology (M)
Georgia Institute of Technology (M)
Southern Methodist University (M)

OPTICAL SCIENCES

The University of Arizona (GC,M)

OPTICS, IMAGING, AND COMMUNICATIONS

Stanford University (GC)

OPTION IN ONLINE TEACHING AND LEARNING

California State University, East Bay (M)

OREGON TRANSFER

Chemeketa Community College (A)

OREGON TRANSFER MODULE

Chemeketa Community College (UC)

ORGANIC AGRICULTURE

Washington State University (UC)

ORGANIZATION AND MANAGEMENT

Capella University (D,M)

ORGANIZATION DYNAMICS

Immaculata University (B)

ORGANIZATION MANAGEMENT AND DEVELOPMENT

Fielding Graduate University (M,UC)

ORGANIZATIONAL ADMINISTRATION

Metropolitan State University (B)
Southeast Missouri State University (B)

ORGANIZATIONAL AND HUMAN RESOURCE DEVELOPMENT (OHRD)

Abilene Christian University (M)

ORGANIZATIONAL BEHAVIOR

National University (B)

ORGANIZATIONAL COMMUNICATION

Penn State University Park (UC)
Seminole Community College (A)

ORGANIZATIONAL COMMUNICATIONS

Northeastern University (B)
Upper Iowa University (UC)

ORGANIZATIONAL CONSULTING

Saybrook Graduate School and Research Center (GC)

ORGANIZATIONAL DEVELOPMENT

University of North Texas (B)
University of the Incarnate Word (M,B)

ORGANIZATIONAL DEVELOPMENT AND LEADERSHIP

Widener University (B)

ORGANIZATIONAL DIVERSITY SPECIALIST

Sullivan University (UC)

ORGANIZATIONAL EFFECTIVENESS SPECIALIST

Sullivan University (UC)

ORGANIZATIONAL LEADERSHIP

Crown College (M)
Daniel Webster College (B)
Eastern University (D,M)
Fort Hays State University (GC,B)
Gonzaga University (M)
Kansas State University (GC)
Mercy College (M)
National University (M)
Nichols College (M)
Penn State University Park (B)
Quinnipiac University (B)
Regent University (D,M)
Roosevelt University (B,UC)
Southern New Hampshire University (M)
Syracuse University (B,UC)
University of St. Francis (B)

Upper Iowa University (UC)

ORGANIZATIONAL LEADERSHIP (BSOL)

Thomas Edison State College (B)

ORGANIZATIONAL LEADERSHIP AND MANAGEMENT

Regent University (B)

ORGANIZATIONAL LEADERSHIP IN ANIMAL ADVOCACY

Duquesne University (GC)

ORGANIZATIONAL LEADERSHIP–MASTER OF PROFESSIONAL STUDIES IN ORGANIZATIONAL LEADERSHIP

University of Denver (M)

ORGANIZATIONAL LEADERSHIP, GENERAL DEGREE

Quinnipiac University (M)

ORGANIZATIONAL LEADERSHIP, INFORMATION SYSTEMS AND TECHNOLOGY SPECIALIZATION

University of Phoenix (D)

ORGANIZATIONAL LEADERSHIP/ INFORMATION SYSTEMS AND TECHNOLOGY

University of Phoenix (D)

ORGANIZATIONAL MANAGEMENT

Concordia University, St. Paul (M)
Mercy College (B)
Misericordia University (M)
St. Joseph's College, Long Island Campus (B)
St. Joseph's College, New York (B)
Spring Arbor University (M)
University of La Verne (B)
University of Phoenix (D)

ORGANIZATIONAL MANAGEMENT AND LEADERSHIP

Concordia University, St. Paul (B)

ORGANIZATIONAL MANAGEMENT–SPORTS MANAGEMENT EMPHASIS

Concordia University, St. Paul (M)

ORGANIZATIONAL MANAGEMENT, HUMAN RESOURCES EMPHASIS

Concordia University, St. Paul (M)

ORGANIZATIONAL MANAGEMENT, HUMAN SERVICES OPTION

Chadron State College (M)

ORGANIZATIONAL PERFORMANCE

Bellevue University (M)

ORGANIZATIONAL PSYCHOLOGY AND DEVELOPMENT CONCENTRATION (10-MONTH PROGRAM)

American InterContinental University Online (M)

ORGANIZATIONAL PSYCHOLOGY AND DEVELOPMENT CONCENTRATION (COMPLETION PROGRAM)

American InterContinental University Online (B)

ORGANIZATIONAL SECURITY AND MANAGEMENT

University of Phoenix (B)

ORGANIZATIONAL SECURITY–CERTIFICATE OF ADVANCED STUDY

University of Denver (UC)

ORGANIZATIONAL SYSTEMS

Saybrook Graduate School and Research Center (D,M)

ORGANIZATIONAL SYSTEMS MANAGEMENT

Bellevue University (B)

ORIENTATION AND MOBILITY

Texas Tech University (UC)
University of Arkansas at Little Rock (M)

ORNAMENTAL HORTICULTURE

Utah State University (A)

PACKAGING

Michigan State University (M)

PACKAGING OF ELECTRONIC AND OPTICAL DEVICES

Southern Methodist University (M)

PACS ADMINISTRATOR

Clarkson College (UC)

PACS MANAGER

Clarkson College (UC)

PAINTING

Savannah College of Art and Design (M)

PARAEDUCATION

Minot State University–Bottineau Campus (A,UC)

PARAEDUCATOR

Lake Region State College (A)
Williston State College (A)

PARALEGAL

Darton College (A)
Franklin Pierce University (UC)
Herkimer County Community College (A)
Ivy Tech Community College–Bloomington (A)
Ivy Tech Community College–Central Indiana (A)
Ivy Tech Community College–Columbus (A)
Ivy Tech Community College–Kokomo (A)
Ivy Tech Community College–Southeast (A)
Ivy Tech Community College–Southern Indiana (A)
Ivy Tech Community College–Southwest (A)
Ivy Tech Community College–Wabash Valley (A)
Ivy Tech Community College–Whitewater (A)
Minnesota School of Business–Richfield (A,B)
Minnesota State Community and Technical College–Fergus Falls (A)
The University of Texas System (UC)
University of Washington (GC)

PARALEGAL CERTIFICATE

California State University, Dominguez Hills (GC)

PARALEGAL ONLINE

Bryant and Stratton Online (A)

PARALEGAL ONLINE CERTIFICATE PROGRAM

The University of Texas at San Antonio (UC)

PARALEGAL STUDIES

California State University, San Marcos (UC)
Colorado Technical University Colorado Springs (A)
Hodges University (A)
IIA College (A)
Ivy Tech Community College–East Central (A)
Ivy Tech Community College–Kokomo (A)
Ivy Tech Community College–Lafayette (A)
Ivy Tech Community College–North Central (A)
Ivy Tech Community College–Northeast (A)
Ivy Tech Community College–Northwest (A)
Kaplan University Online (A,B)
Keiser University (A)

Lake Superior College (A)
Mount Wachusett Community College (A)
Peirce College (A,B,UC)
Saint Mary-of-the-Woods College (A,B,UC)
Tompkins Cortland Community College (A)
University of Massachusetts Lowell (UC)

PARAMEDICINE COMPLETION

Western Kentucky University (A)

PARAPROFESSIONAL EDUCATION

University of Phoenix (A)

PART-TIME/INTERNET-BASED MASTER OF PUBLIC HEALTH

The Johns Hopkins University (M)

PASTORAL COUNSELING

Amridge University (M)
Liberty University (M)

PASTORAL MINISTRY

Summit Pacific College

PASTORAL STUDIES

Southwestern College (B)

PASTORAL THEOLOGY

Saint Mary-of-the-Woods College (M)

PATHWAY TO PARALEGAL (POST-BACCALAUREATE)

Kaplan University Online (UC)

PATIENT AND PRODUCT SAFETY

University of Southern California (GC)

PEACE AND CONFLICT RESOLUTION (INTERNATIONAL FOCUS)

Saybrook Graduate School and Research Center (GC)

PEACE STUDIES

Prescott College (M)

PEDIATRIC NURSE PRACTITIONER

University of Missouri–Columbia (M)
Vanderbilt University (M)

PENSIONS AND EXECUTIVE COMPENSATION

The American College (UC)

PERFORMANCE CONSULTING

Roosevelt University (GC)

PERFORMANCE EXCELLENCE IN TECHNOLOGY MANAGEMENT

University of Colorado at Boulder (GC)

PERFORMANCE IMPROVEMENT

East Carolina University (GC)

PERFUSION TECHNOLOGY

Thomas Edison State College (B)

PERSONAL FINANCIAL PLANNING

Kansas State University (M,UC)
University of Missouri–Columbia (GC,M)

PESTICIDE APPLICATION TRAINING

Colorado State University (UC)

PETROLEUM ENGINEERING

University of Southern California (M)

PETROLEUM ENGINEERING (SMART OILFIELD TECHNOLOGIES)

University of Southern California (GC,M)

PHARMACEUTICAL BUSINESS

University of the Sciences in Philadelphia (M)

PHARMACEUTICAL ENGINEERING

New Jersey Institute of Technology (M)
University of Michigan (M)

PHARMACEUTICAL MANAGEMENT

Drexel University (M)
New Jersey Institute of Technology (GC)

PHARMACEUTICAL MANUFACTURING

New Jersey Institute of Technology (GC)
Stevens Institute of Technology (M)

PHARMACEUTICAL MANUFACTURING PRACTICES

Stevens Institute of Technology (GC)

PHARMACEUTICAL SCIENCES, COSMETIC SCIENCE EMPHASIS

University of Cincinnati (M)

PHARMACEUTICAL TECHNOLOGY

New Jersey Institute of Technology (GC)

PHARMACEUTICALÁ MANAGEMENT

New Jersey Institute of Technology (GC)

PHARMACOGENETICS ESSENTIALS

Northeastern University (GC)

PHARMACY

Auburn University (D)
University of Cincinnati (D)

PHARMACY TECHNICIAN

North Dakota State College of Science (A)
Vincennes University (A)

PHARMACY TECHNOLOGY

Minnesota State Community and Technical College–Fergus Falls (A,UC)

PHILOSOPHY

American Public University System (B)
Holy Apostles College and Seminary (M)
Prescott College (M)
Thomas Edison State College (B)
University of Illinois at Springfield (B)
University of Waterloo (B)

PHILOSOPHY AND RELIGION

Butler Community College (A)

PHILOSOPHY, POLITICS, AND ECONOMICS

Eastern Oregon University (B)

PHOTOGRAPHY

Academy of Art University (M,A,B)
Prescott College (M)
Thomas Edison State College (B)

PHYSICAL ACTIVITY AND HEALTH

Eastern Oregon University (B)

PHYSICAL EDUCATION

Florida State University (M)
Jacksonville State University (M)
University of Arkansas (M)
University of South Florida (M)

PHYSICAL EDUCATION EXERCISE AND SPORT SCIENCE

University of Central Missouri (M)

PHYSICAL EDUCATION PEDAGOGY

Western Kentucky University (M)

PHYSICAL EDUCATION STUDIES

Monroe Community College (A)

PHYSICAL EDUCATION TEACHER EDUCATION

West Virginia University (M)

PHYSICAL EDUCATION– COACHING SPECIALIZATION

Ball State University (M)

PHYSICAL EDUCATION, HEALTH, AND LEISURE STUDIES

Central Washington University (M)

PHYSICAL THERAPIST ASSISTANT

Clark State Community College (A)

PHYSICAL THERAPY (IMPRINTS)

The University of Texas System (UC)

PHYSICAL THERAPY–POST- PROFESSIONAL DOCTOR OF PHYSICAL THERAPY

Rosalind Franklin University of Medicine and Science (D)

PHYSICAL THERAPY– TRANSITIONAL DOCTOR OF PHYSICAL THERAPY

MGH Institute of Health Professions (D)

PHYSICAL THERAPY– TRANSITIONAL DOCTORATE OF PHYSICAL THERAPY

Utica College (D)

PHYSICIAN ASSISTANCE–MASTER OF PHYSICIAN ASSISTANCE (MPA)

Chatham University

PHYSICIAN ASSISTANT

Lock Haven University of Pennsylvania (M)

PHYSICIAN EXECUTIVE

The University of Tennessee (M)

PHYSICIANS ASSISTANT STUDIES

Drexel University (M)

PHYSICIANS EXECUTIVE MBA

Auburn University (M)

PHYSICS

Michigan State University (D,M)

PHYSICS (WINPC)

Indiana University of Pennsylvania (UC)

PLASTICS ENGINEERING FUNDAMENTALS

University of Massachusetts Lowell (GC)

PLAYWRITING AND SCREENWRITING

Prescott College (M)

POLICING ELECTIVE

Athabasca University (M)

POLICY AND MANAGEMENT IN DISTANCE EDUCATION

University of Maryland University College (GC)

POLICY STUDIES

State University of New York Empire State College (M)

POLITICAL ECONOMY (3 YEAR)

Athabasca University (B)

POLITICAL ECONOMY (4 YEAR)

Athabasca University (B)

POLITICAL MANAGEMENT

The George Washington University (M)

POLITICAL SCIENCE

American Public University System (M,B)
Austin Peay State University (B)
Darton College (A)
Northeastern University (B)
Prescott College (B)
Regent University (B)
Thomas Edison State College (B)
University of Maryland University College (B)
University of Windsor (B)
University of Wisconsin–Whitewater (B)
Virginia Polytechnic Institute and State University (M)

POLITICAL SCIENCE (3 YEAR)

Athabasca University (B)

POLITICAL SCIENCE (4 YEAR)

Athabasca University (B)

POLITICAL SCIENCE–CRIMINAL JUSTICE

Buena Vista University (B)

POLITICAL SCIENCE– ENVIRONMENTAL POLITICS AND POLICY

Virginia Polytechnic Institute and State University (GC)

POLITICAL SCIENCE– FOUNDATIONS OF POLITICAL ANALYSIS

Virginia Polytechnic Institute and State University (GC)

POLITICAL SCIENCE– INFORMATION POLICY AND SOCIETY

Virginia Polytechnic Institute and State University (GC)

POLYMER SCIENCE AND ENGINEERING

Lehigh University (M)

POLYSOMNOGRAPHIC TECHNOLOGY

Oregon Institute of Technology (A,UC)

POST-BACCALAUREATE CERTIFICATE IN CLINICAL TRIALS MANAGEMENT

Thomas Edison State College (UC)

POST-BACCALAUREATE CERTIFICATE IN HEALTH INFORMATION ADMINISTRATION

The University of Toledo (UC)

POST-BACCALAUREATE CERTIFICATE IN HOMELAND SECURITY

Thomas Edison State College (UC)

POST-BACCALAUREATE CERTIFICATE IN HUMAN RESOURCE MANAGEMENT

Thomas Edison State College (UC)

POST-BACCALAUREATE CERTIFICATE IN ONLINE LEARNING AND TEACHING

Thomas Edison State College (UC)

POST-BACCALAUREATE CERTIFICATE IN ORGANIZATIONAL MANAGEMENT AND LEADERSHIP

Thomas Edison State College (UC)

POST-BACCALAUREATE CERTIFICATE IN PUBLIC SERVICE LEADERSHIP

Thomas Edison State College (UC)

POST-BACCALAUREATE TEACHER PREPARATION PROGRAMS (WITH MAT OPTION)

Walden University (UC)

POST-DOCTORAL PSYCHOLOGY CERTIFICATES

Walden University (UC)

POST-MASTER'S CERTIFICATE— NURSING EDUCATION

Indiana State University

POST-MASTER'S CERTIFICATE IN NURSE EDUCATOR

Thomas Edison State College (GC)

POST-MASTERS NURSING ADMINISTRATION

Fort Hays State University (UC)

POST-MASTERS NURSING EDUCATION

Fort Hays State University (UC)

POST-MBA MASTER OF GLOBAL MANAGEMENT

Thunderbird School of Global Management (M)

POST-MBA MASTERS–GLOBAL MANAGEMENT ON-DEMAND

Thunderbird School of Global Management

POSTSECONDARY LITERACY INSTRUCTION

University of Cincinnati (UC)

POSTSECONDARY STUDIES

Memorial University of Newfoundland (M)

POSTSECONDARY TEACHING

Colorado State University (UC)

POWER ELECTRONICS

University of Colorado at Boulder (GC)

POWER ELECTRONICS AND MACHINE DRIVES (EE CONCENTRATION)

Kettering University (M)

POWER SYSTEM PROTECTION AND RELAYING

University of Idaho (UC)

POWER SYSTEMS ENGINEERING

New Jersey Institute of Technology (GC)

PRACTICAL NURSING

Northland Community and Technical College–
  Thief River Falls (A)

PRACTICAL THEOLOGY

Amridge University (M)
Regent University (M)

PRACTICE OF TECHNICAL COMMUNICATIONS

New Jersey Institute of Technology (GC)

PRE-ASSOCIATE CERTIFICATE IN ACCOUNTING

Thomas Edison State College (UC)

PRE-ASSOCIATE CERTIFICATE IN COMPUTER AIDED DESIGN

Thomas Edison State College (UC)

PRE-ASSOCIATE CERTIFICATE IN COMPUTER INFORMATION SYSTEMS

Thomas Edison State College (UC)

PRE-ASSOCIATE CERTIFICATE IN COMPUTER SCIENCE

Thomas Edison State College (UC)

PRE-ASSOCIATE CERTIFICATE IN DENTAL ASSISTANT (JOINTLY SPONSORED BY UMDNJ AND TESC)

Thomas Edison State College (UC)

PRE-ASSOCIATE CERTIFICATE IN ELECTRONICS

Thomas Edison State College (UC)

PRE-ASSOCIATE CERTIFICATE IN FINANCE

Thomas Edison State College (UC)

PRE-ASSOCIATE CERTIFICATE IN FITNESS AND WELLNESS SERVICES

Thomas Edison State College (UC)

PRE-ASSOCIATE CERTIFICATE IN HUMAN RESOURCE MANAGEMENT

Thomas Edison State College (UC)

PRE-ASSOCIATE CERTIFICATE IN LABOR STUDIES

Thomas Edison State College (UC)

PRE-ASSOCIATE CERTIFICATE IN MARKETING

Thomas Edison State College (UC)

PRE-ASSOCIATE CERTIFICATE IN OPERATIONS MANAGEMENT

Thomas Edison State College (UC)

PRE-ASSOCIATE CERTIFICATE IN PUBLIC ADMINISTRATION

Thomas Edison State College (UC)

PRE-BACCALAUREATE

North Iowa Area Community College (A)

PRE-BACHELOR OF ARTS

Miami Dade College (A)

PRE-DENTAL

Community College of Denver (A)

PRE-ENGINEERING

Community College of Denver (A)

PRE-KINDERGARTEN HANDICAPPED ENDORSEMENT

University of Central Florida (GC)

PRE-KINDERGARTEN/PRIMARY EDUCATION (AGE 3–GRADE 3)

Nova Southeastern University (B)

PRE-LAW

Darton College (A)

PRE-PHARMACY

Community College of Denver (A)

PRE-PHYSICAL THERAPY

Community College of Denver (A)

PRE-PHYSICIAN

Community College of Denver (A)

PRE-PHYSICS

Community College of Denver (A)

PRECLINICAL DRUG DEVELOPMENT

University of Southern California (GC)

PREPARATION FOR CERTIFIED BOOKKEEPER EXAM

The University of Toledo (UC)

PREPARATION FOR CLINICAL NURSE FACULTY

California State University, San Marcos (UC)

PRINCIPAL ENDORSEMENT PROGRAM

University of Wyoming (UC)

PRINCIPAL'S CERTIFICATION

Drexel University (UC)

PRINT MEDIA

Rochester Institute of Technology (M)

PRIOR LEARNING ASSESSMENT

DePaul University (UC)

PRIVATE SECURITY

Kaplan University Online (UC)

PRIVATE SECURITY AND LOSS PREVENTION

Indiana State University (UC)

PRIVATE SECURITY MANAGEMENT

Kaplan University Online (UC)

PROCESS ENGINEERING

University of South Florida (GC)

PROCUREMENT AND ACQUISITIONS MANAGEMENT

Webster University (M)

PROCUREMENT AND CONTRACT MANAGEMENT

University of Maryland University College
  (GC)

PRODUCT CREATION AND INNOVATIVE MANUFACTURING

Stanford University (GC)

PRODUCT DEVELOPMENT ENGINEERING

University of Southern California (M)

PRODUCTION AND INVENTORY CONTROL

California State University, Dominguez Hills
  (UC)

PROFESSIONAL (WEEKEND) PROGRAM

The University of Tennessee (M)

PROFESSIONAL ACCOUNTING

Strayer University (M,)

PROFESSIONAL AERONAUTICS

Embry-Riddle Aeronautical University (A,B)

PROFESSIONAL AND TECHNICAL COMMUNICATIONS

New Jersey Institute of Technology (M)

PROFESSIONAL ARTS

Saint Joseph's College of Maine (B)

PROFESSIONAL COUNSELING

Amridge University (M)
Liberty University (M)

PROFESSIONAL DEVELOPMENT

Amberton University (M)

PROFESSIONAL DEVELOPMENT FOR TEACHERS (POSTBACCALAUREATE)

Kaplan University Online (UC)

PROFESSIONAL DOCTOR OF OCCUPATIONAL THERAPY

Chatham University (D)

PROFESSIONAL IN HUMAN RESOURCES

DePaul University (UC)

PROFESSIONAL MASTER OF ENGINEERING IN FIRE PROTECTION

University of Maryland, College Park (M)

PROFESSIONAL PROGRAM IN NURSING

University of Wisconsin–Green Bay (B)

PROFESSIONAL STUDIES

Austin Peay State University (B)
Drexel University (B)
Fairfield University (B)
Hodges University (M)
Rochester Institute of Technology (M)
Saint Joseph's College of Maine (UC)
Virginia Polytechnic Institute and State University (UC)
Widener University (B)

PROFESSIONAL STUDIES, INFORMATION TECHNOLOGY CONCENTRATION

Middle Tennessee State University (B)

PROFESSIONAL STUDIES, ORGANIZATIONAL LEADERSHIP CONCENTRATION

Middle Tennessee State University (B)

PROFESSIONAL STUDIES, STRATEGIC LEADERSHIP CONCENTRATION

Middle Tennessee State University (M)

PROFESSIONAL TECHNOLOGY STUDIES

Pace University (B)

PROFESSIONAL WRITING

Saint Mary-of-the-Woods College (B)
Taylor University (UC)
University of Central Florida (GC)
University of Colorado Denver (UC)
Washington State University (UC)

PROFESSIONAL WRITING–MASTER OF PROFESSIONAL WRITING (MPW)

Chatham University

PROGRAM MANAGEMENT (MNM)

Regis University (GC)

PROGRAM OF PROFESSIONAL PREPARATION READING CERTIFICATE

University of Southern California (UC)

PROGRAMMER ANALYST–FAST TRACK---PROGRAMMER ANALYST SHORT-TERM CERTIFICATE

Sinclair Community College (UC)

PROGRAMMING

Union County College (UC)

PROGRAMMING AND ANALYSIS (WWW PROGRAMMING SPECIALIZATION)

Seminole Community College (A)

PROGRAMMING AND SOFTWARE DEVELOPMENT

The University of Toledo (A,UC)

PROJECT ENGINEERING AND MANAGEMENT

Montana Tech of The University of Montana (M)

PROJECT MANAGEMENT

Athabasca University (GC,M)
City University of Seattle (GC,M,UC)
DePaul University (UC)
DeVry University Online (M)
Florida Institute of Technology (M)
The George Washington University (M)
Grantham University (M)
Lawrence Technological University (GC)
Lehigh University (UC)
Mississippi State University (M)
Missouri State University (GC,M)
New Jersey Institute of Technology (GC)
Northeastern University (GC)
Penn State University Park (GC,M)
Rochester Institute of Technology (GC)
Stevens Institute of Technology (GC,M)
University of Colorado at Boulder (GC)
University of Dallas (GC,M)
University of Management and Technology (GC,M,UC)
University of Maryland University College (GC)
University of Washington (UC)
University of Wisconsin–Platteville (GC)
University of Wisconsin–Platteville (GC)
University of Wisconsin–Platteville (M)
University of Wisconsin–Platteville (M)

PROJECT MANAGEMENT CONCENTRATION

Colorado Technical University Colorado Springs (M,B)

PROJECT MANAGEMENT CONCENTRATION (10-MONTH PROGRAM)

American InterContinental University Online (M)

PROJECT MANAGEMENT CONCENTRATION (COMPLETION PROGRAM)

American InterContinental University Online (B)

PROJECT MANAGEMENT FOR THE LIFE SCIENCES INDUSTRIES

Stevens Institute of Technology (GC)

PROJECT MANAGEMENT–CERTIFICATE OF ADVANCED STUDY

University of Denver (UC)

PROJECT MANAGEMENT–EXECUTIVE PROJECT MANAGEMENT (MSM)

Regis University (GC)

PROJECT MANAGEMENT–MASTER OF PROJECT MANAGEMENT

American Graduate University (M)

PSYCHIATRIC MENTAL HEALTH NURSE PRACTITIONER

Vanderbilt University (M)

PSYCHIATRIC REHABILITATION

University of Medicine and Dentistry of New Jersey (M)

PSYCHIATRIC-MENTAL HEALTH

New Mexico State University (M)

PSYCHOLOGIE

Laurentian University (B)

PSYCHOLOGY

American Public University System (B)
Baker College of Flint (B)
Burlington College (B)
Capella University (D,M)
Chadron State College (B)
Columbia College (B)
Columbia Southern University (B)
Community College of Denver (A)
Dallas Baptist University (B)
Darton College (A)
Drexel University (B)
Eastern Oregon University (B)
Foothill College (A)
Judson College (B)
Kaplan University Online (B)
Laurentian University (B)
LeTourneau University (B)
Liberty University (A,B)
Limestone College (B)
Lynn University (B)
Mercy College (M,B)
Middlesex Community College (A)
National University (B)
New York Institute of Technology (B)
Northcentral University (D,M,B)
Northeastern University (B)
Northwestern State University of Louisiana (B)
Penn State University Park (B)
Regent University (A,B)
Roosevelt University (B)
Saint Joseph's College of Maine (A)
Saint Mary-of-the-Woods College (B)
Saybrook Graduate School and Research Center (D)
Seminole Community College (A)
Southern New Hampshire University (B)
Southwestern Adventist University (B)
Thomas Edison State College (B)
University of Houston–Victoria (B)
University of Maryland University College (B)
University of Massachusetts Lowell (B)
University of Phoenix (M,A,B)
University of Wyoming (B)
Upper Iowa University (B)
Utah State University (B)

Walden University (D,M,B)
West Hills Community College (A)

PSYCHOLOGY (3 YEAR)

Athabasca University (B)

PSYCHOLOGY (4 YEAR)

Athabasca University (B)

PSYCHOLOGY (CHILD AND ADOLESCENT DEVELOPMENT CONCENTRATION)

Southern New Hampshire University (B)

PSYCHOLOGY IN CREATIVITY STUDIES SPECIALIZATION

Saybrook Graduate School and Research Center (M)

PSYCHOLOGY OF THE WORKPLACE

Jamestown Community College (GC)

PSYCHOLOGY–APPLIED PSYCHOLOGY

City University of Seattle (B)

PSYCHOLOGY–INDUSTRIAL/ORGANIZATIONAL PSYCHOLOGY

Austin Peay State University (M)

PSYCHOLOGY–MARRIAGE AND FAMILY THERAPY SPECIALIZATION

Northcentral University (D)

PSYCHOLOGY–SCHOOL COUNSELING SPECIALIZATION

Utah State University (M)

PSYCHOLOGY, GENERAL

East Carolina University (M)

PSYCHOLOGY/FAMILY STUDIES

Corban College (B)

PUBLIC ADMINISTRATION

American Public University System (M)
Athabasca University (UC)
Bellevue University (M)
California State University, Dominguez Hills (M)
California State University, San Bernardino (M)
DeVry University Online (M)
East Tennessee State University (M)
Florida Gulf Coast University (M)
Florida Institute of Technology (M)
Golden Gate University (M,B,UC)
Hodges University (M)
Indiana State University (GC,M)

Kansas State University (GC)
Marist College (M)
Memorial University of Newfoundland (UC)
National University (M)
Nova Southeastern University (M)
Regis University (B,UC)
Strayer University (M)
Thomas Edison State College (B)
University of Colorado Denver (M)
University of Illinois at Springfield (M)
University of La Verne (B)
University of Management and Technology (UC)
University of North Dakota (M)
University of Phoenix (M)
The University of Texas System (M)
University of Wyoming (M)
Upper Iowa University (B)
Walden University (M)
Wayland Baptist University (M)

PUBLIC ADMINISTRATION (MSA)

University of West Florida (M)

PUBLIC ADMINISTRATION–FIRE SCIENCE EMPHASIS

Upper Iowa University (B)

PUBLIC ADMINISTRATION–LAW ENFORCEMENT EMPHASIS

Upper Iowa University (B)

PUBLIC ADMINISTRATION: HEALTH CARE ADMINISTRATION

University of Hawaii–West Oahu (B)

PUBLIC AFFAIRS

Northeastern University (B)

PUBLIC AND COMMUNITY HEALTH

Medical College of Wisconsin (M)

PUBLIC AND NON-PROFIT MANAGEMENT–MASTER OF PUBLIC AND NON-PROFIT MANAGEMENT

Metropolitan State University (M)

PUBLIC HEALTH

American Public University System (M,B)
Independence University (M)
Medical College of Wisconsin (GC)
University of Illinois at Springfield (M)
University of West Florida (M)
Walden University (D,M)
West Virginia University (M)
Youngstown State University (M)

PUBLIC HEALTH ADMINISTRATION

University of South Florida (M)

PUBLIC HEALTH GENERALIST

University of South Florida (GC)

PUBLIC HEALTH INFORMATICS

University of Illinois at Chicago (M,UC)

PUBLIC HEALTH OR SCHOOL HEALTH NURSING

University of Missouri–Columbia (M)

PUBLIC HEALTH POLICY AND PROGRAMS

University of South Florida (GC)

PUBLIC HEALTH PRACTICE

University of South Florida (M)

PUBLIC HEALTH–CAREER MASTER OF PUBLIC HEALTH PROGRAM

Emory University (M)

PUBLIC JUSTICE

State University of New York at Oswego (B)

PUBLIC LIBRARY TECHNOLOGY (PLT)

Marshall University (UC)

PUBLIC MANAGEMENT

Park University (M)

PUBLIC PERSONNEL ADMINISTRATION

Indiana State University (GC)

PUBLIC POLICY

New England College (M)

PUBLIC POLICY ADMINISTRATION

Mississippi State University (M)

PUBLIC POLICY AND ADMINISTRATION

Walden University (D)

PUBLIC RELATIONS

Golden Gate University (GC)
University of Maryland University College (GC)
Webster University (M)

PUBLIC RELATIONS AND MARKETING COMMUNICATIONS–CERTIFICATE OF ADVANCED STUDY

University of Denver (UC)

PUBLIC RELATIONS AND ORGANIZATIONAL COMMUNICATION

Seminole Community College (A)

PUBLIC RELATIONS COMMUNICATIONS–PROFESSIONAL WRITING

Rochester Institute of Technology (UC)

PUBLIC SAFETY

Capella University (D,M,B)

PUBLIC SAFETY AND BUSINESS/ORGANIZATION SECURITY

Amridge University (B)

PUBLIC SAFETY AND CRIMINAL JUSTICE

Amridge University (B)

PUBLIC SAFETY AND HOMELAND SECURITY

Amridge University (B)

PUBLIC SAFETY AND SECURITY

Concordia University, St. Paul (B)

PUBLIC SAFETY MANAGEMENT

Cardinal Stritch University (B)
Franklin University (B)

PUBLIC SERVICE MANAGEMENT

DePaul University (M)

PUBLIC WORKS OPTION

The University of Tennessee (M)

PUBLISHING

Pace University (M)

PURCHASING

California State University, Dominguez Hills (UC)
Columbus State Community College (GC)

QUALITY

Eastern Michigan University (M)

QUALITY ASSURANCE

California State University, Dominguez Hills (M,B,UC)
Southern Polytechnic State University (M)

QUALITY ASSURANCE SCIENCE

California National University for Advanced Studies (B)

QUALITY ENGINEERING

Lehigh University (M)

QUALITY IMPLEMENTATION

Rochester Institute of Technology (UC)

QUALITY IMPROVEMENT AND OUTCOMES MANAGEMENT

George Mason University (GC)

QUALITY LEADERSHIP

Saint Joseph's College of Maine (M)

QUALITY MANAGEMENT CERTIFICATE

University of Wisconsin–Stout (UC)

QUALITY MANAGEMENT, BASIC

Rochester Institute of Technology (UC)

QUALITY SCHOOLS

Graceland University (M)

QUALITY SYSTEMS

Bowling Green State University (GC)

QUALITY SYSTEMS FOR PRODUCT AND PROCESS ENGINEERING

University of Colorado at Boulder (GC)

QUANTITATIVE CONSTRUCTION MANAGEMENT

University of Washington (UC)

QUANTITATIVE METHODS IN FINANCE AND RISK MANAGEMENT (STATISTICS)

Stanford University (GC)

QUANTITATIVE SOFTWARE ENGINEERING

Stevens Institute of Technology (GC,M)

RADIATION HEALTH PHYSICS

Oregon State University (M)

RADIATION PROTECTION

Thomas Edison State College (A,B)

RADIATION THERAPY

Thomas Edison State College (A,B)

RADIOLOGIC AND IMAGING SCIENCES

University of Southern Indiana (B)

RADIOLOGIC SCIENCE

Northwestern State University of Louisiana (B)

RADIOLOGIC SCIENCES

Midwestern State University (B)
University of Central Florida (B)

RADIOLOGIC SCIENCES (BACHELOR'S COMPLETION PROGRAM–RADIOGRAPHY)

University of Missouri–Columbia (B)

RADIOLOGIC SCIENCES (EDUCATION OR ADMINISTRATION MAJOR)

Midwestern State University (M)

RADIOLOGIC SCIENCES PREREQUISITE PROGRAM

Clarion University of Pennsylvania (UC)

RADIOLOGIC TECHNOLOGY

Minnesota State Community and Technical College–Fergus Falls (A)

RADIOLOGIC TECHNOLOGY COMPLETION PROGRAM

Presentation College (B)

RADIOLOGIC TECHNOLOGY CONTINUING EDUCATION UNITS (CEUS)

Sinclair Community College (UC)

RADIOLOGIC TECHNOLOGY PROGRAM

Southeast Community College Area (A)

RADIOLOGICAL SCIENCE–RADIOLOGICAL SCIENCE DEGREE COMPLETION

Oregon Institute of Technology (B)

RADIOLOGICAL SCIENCES

Saint Joseph's College of Maine (B)
Weber State University (B,UC)

RADIOLOGIST ASSISTANT

Bloomsburg University of Pennsylvania (M)

RANGELAND ECOSYSTEM SCIENCE

Colorado State University (M)

READING

Concordia University Wisconsin (M)
New Mexico State University (UC)

Saint Leo University (GC)

READING AND LANGUAGE

University of Massachusetts Lowell (M)

READING AND LITERACY

Benedictine University (M)
City University of Seattle (M)

READING CONCENTRATION

Saint Leo University (M)

READING INSTRUCTION FOR SPECIAL EDUCATION (RISE)

Penn State University Park (GC)

READING K-12

University of Nebraska at Kearney (M)

READING SPECIALIST

Fort Hays State University (UC)
The University of Texas System (UC)

READING TEACHER CERTIFICATION

University of Wisconsin–Stout (UC)

READING, ELEMENTARY EDUCATION

Utah State University (UC)

READING, LANGUAGE, AND LITERACY

The University of North Carolina at Charlotte (M)

READING, SECONDARY EDUCATION

Utah State University (UC)

REAL ESTATE

North Lake College (A)
Orange Coast College (A)
Thomas Edison State College (B)
University of Wyoming (UC)

REAL ESTATE MANAGEMENT

New England College (M)

RECEPTION SERVICES

Minot State University–Bottineau Campus (UC)

RECORDS MANAGEMENT

The George Washington University (UC)

RECREATION

California State University, East Bay (B)

RECREATION MANAGEMENT

Minot State University–Bottineau Campus (A,UC)

RECREATION SERVICES

Thomas Edison State College (A,B)

REGENTS BACHELOR OF ARTS

West Virginia University (B)

REGENTS BACHELOR OF ARTS DEGREE

Marshall University (B)

REGENTS ONLINE DEGREE PROGRAM

Austin Peay State University (B)

REGISTERED EMPLOYEE BENEFITS CONSULTANT(R) (REBC(R)) DESIGNATION

The American College (UC)

REGISTERED HEALTH UNDERWRITER(R) (RHU(R)) DESIGNATION

The American College (UC)

REGULATORY AFFAIRS

Lehigh University (GC)
San Diego State University (M)

REGULATORY AFFAIRS FOR DRUGS, BIOLOGICS, AND MEDICAL DEVICES

Northeastern University (M)

REGULATORY AFFAIRS–MEDICAL DEVICES

University of South Florida (GC)

REGULATORY SCIENCE

University of Southern California (M)

REHABILITATION COUNSELING

Auburn University (M)
San Diego State University (M)
University of Arkansas at Little Rock (M)
The University of Tennessee (M)
West Virginia University (M)

REHABILITATION SCIENCE

Concordia University Wisconsin (M)

REHABILITATION SCIENCES

The University of British Columbia (GC)

REHABILITATION TEACHING

University of Arkansas at Little Rock (M)

REHABILITATIVE SCIENCE

Clarion University of Pennsylvania (M)

RELIABILITY AND MAINTAINABILITY ENGINEERING

The University of Tennessee (GC,M)

RELIGION

American Public University System (B)
Liberty University (M,A,B)
Southwestern Adventist University (B)
Thomas Edison State College (B)

RELIGIOUS EDUCATION

Defiance College (A,B)
Global University (B)

RELIGIOUS STUDIES

Global University (A)
Henry Ford Community College (A)
Indiana Wesleyan University (UC)
Judson College (B)
Laurentian University (B)
Prescott College (M)
Regent University (B)
University of Waterloo (B)

RENEWAL STUDIES

Regent University (D)

RESEARCH ADMINISTRATION

Cleveland State University (GC)

RESEARCH AND DEVELOPMENT

University of Colorado at Boulder (GC)

RESIDENTIAL INTERIORS

Colorado State University (UC)

RESOURCE DEVELOPMENT (MNM)

Regis University (GC)

RESOURCE INTERPRETATION

Stephen F. Austin State University (M)

RESPECIALIZATION IN CLINICAL PSYCHOLOGY

Fielding Graduate University (UC)

RESPIRATORY CARE

Independence University (B)
Oregon Institute of Technology (B)
Southeast Community College Area (A)
Thomas Edison State College (A,B)

RESPIRATORY CARE LEADERSHIP

Northeastern University (M)

RESPIRATORY THERAPY

Independence University (A)
J. Sargeant Reynolds Community College (A)

RESPIRATORY THERAPY (BACHELOR'S COMPLETION PROGRAM)

University of Missouri–Columbia (B)

RESTAURANT AND HOSPITALITY MANAGEMENT (EXECUTIVE RESTAURANT AND HOSPITALITY MANAGEMENT)

The University of Alabama (B)

RESTAURANT AND HOSPITALITY MANAGEMENT (RESTAURANT, HOTEL, AND MEETINGS MANAGEMENT)

The University of Alabama (B)

RESTAURANT, HOTEL, AND INSTITUTIONAL MANAGEMENT

Texas Tech University (M)

RETAIL LEADERSHIP

Drexel University (UC)

RETAIL MANAGEMENT

Strayer University (B)

RETAILING–FIVE COURSE SEQUENCE IN RETAILING

University of North Texas (UC)

RISK ANALYSIS (MANAGEMENT SCIENCE AND ENGINEERING)

Stanford University (GC)

RISK MANAGEMENT AND INSURANCE

Excelsior College (B)

RISK MANAGEMENT/INSURANCE

Florida State University (M)

RN-BSN TRANSITION PROGRAM

Stephen F. Austin State University (B)

ROTORCRAFT SYSTEMS ENGINEERING

The University of Alabama in Huntsville (M)

RURAL PUBLIC SAFETY ADMINISTRATION

University of Maine at Fort Kent (B)

SAFETY AND HEALTH TECHNOLOGY

Rochester Institute of Technology (UC)

SAFETY AND SECURITY MANAGEMENT CONCENTRATION

Tiffin University (M)

SAFETY SCIENCE

Indiana University of Pennsylvania (M)

SAFETY SCIENCES

Indiana University of Pennsylvania (GC)

SAFETY TECHNOLOGY

Rochester Institute of Technology (B)

SALES

Northwest Technical College (UC)

SALES AND MARKETING

Northwest Technical College (UC)

SALES, MARKETING, AND MANAGEMENT

Northwest Technical College (A)

SCHOOL ADMINISTRATION

Indiana State University (UC)

SCHOOL ADMINISTRATION/ EDUCATIONAL LEADERSHIP

Wayne State College

SCHOOL AND CHURCH ADMINISTRATION

Shasta Bible College (M)

SCHOOL BUILDING LEADER IN EDUCATIONAL ADMINISTRATION AND SUPERVISION

St. John's University (M)
St. John's University (M)

SCHOOL BUSINESS ADMINISTRATION

University of the Southwest (M)

SCHOOL BUSINESS MANAGEMENT

University of Southern California (UC)
University of Wisconsin–Whitewater (M)

SCHOOL COUNSELING

University of the Southwest (M)

SCHOOL COUNSELING LICENSURE

New Mexico State University (UC)

SCHOOL DISTRICT LEADER PROFESSIONAL DIPLOMA

St. John's University (GC)
St. John's University (GC)

SCHOOL LIBRARY MEDIA

Utah State University (UC)

SCHOOL LIBRARY MEDIA SERVICES

Indiana State University (GC)

SCHOOL LIBRARY MEDIA SPECIALIST

University of Washington (UC)

SCHOOL MEDIA

Syracuse University (GC)

SCHOOL MEDIA SPECIALIST

Northwestern State University of Louisiana (UC)

SCHOOL PRINCIPALSHIP, K-6 OR 7-12

University of Nebraska at Kearney (M)

SCHOOL SOCIAL WORK COMPETENCY SERIES

Michigan State University (UC)

SCHOOL SYSTEMS, SUPERINTENDENCY, AND LEADERSHIP

Webster University

SCHOOL TECHNOLOGY COORDINATION

Boise State University (GC)

SCHOOL/COMMUNITY SAFETY

Colorado State University (UC)

SCIENCE

Excelsior College (A,B)

SCIENCE AND MATH

Coastline Community College (A)

SCIENCE EDUCATION

Florida State University (M)
The University of Texas System (M)

SCIENCE OF INSTRUCTION

Drexel University (M)

SCIENCE TEACHER EDUCATION

East Carolina University (M)

SCIENCE, GENERAL NON-MAJOR

University of Waterloo (B)

SCIENCE, MATH, AND TECHNOLOGY

State University of New York Empire State College (A,B)

SCIENCES RELIGIEUSES

Laurentian University (B)

SECONDARY EDUCATION

Fitchburg State College (M)
Montgomery County Community College (A)
Utah State University (M)

SECONDARY EDUCATION (CURRICULUM, TEACHING, AND LEARNING)

The University of Alabama (M,)

SECONDARY EDUCATION (SECOND LANGUAGE ACQUISITION AND TEACHING)

The University of Alabama (M,)

SECONDARY EDUCATION SCIENCE CONCENTRATION

The University of Alabama

SECONDARY EDUCATION– BIOLOGY

Nova Southeastern University (B)

SECONDARY EDUCATION– COMPOSITE SOCIAL SCIENCE

Dickinson State University (B)

SECONDARY EDUCATION– ENGLISH

Dickinson State University (B)
Saint Mary-of-the-Woods College (B)

SECONDARY EDUCATION– HISTORY

Dickinson State University (B)

SECONDARY EDUCATION–MATH

Dickinson State University (B)

SECONDARY EDUCATION– MATHEMATICS

Nova Southeastern University (B)
Saint Mary-of-the-Woods College (B)

SECONDARY EDUCATION– SCIENCE EMPHASIS

West Virginia University (M)

SECONDARY EDUCATION–SOCIAL STUDIES

Saint Mary-of-the-Woods College (B)

SECONDARY EDUCATION–SOCIAL STUDIES EMPHASIS

West Virginia University (M)

SECRETARIAL (ADMINISTRATIVE, LEGAL, MEDICAL)

University of Northwestern Ohio (A)

SECURE AND DEPENDABLE COMPUTING SYSTEMS

University of Idaho (UC)

SECURE NETWORK SYSTEMS DESIGN

Stevens Institute of Technology (GC)

SECURITY ADMINISTRATION

Southwestern College (M)

SECURITY ENGINEERING

Southern Methodist University (M)

SECURITY MANAGEMENT

American Public University System (M,B)
Bellevue University (M,B)
Southwestern College (B)

SECURITY MANAGEMENT AND HOMELAND SECURITY

University of Massachusetts Lowell (UC)

SECURITY MANAGEMENT GRADUATE SPECIALIZATION

Michigan State University (UC)

SECURITY MANAGEMENT– MASTER OF APPLIED SCIENCE IN SECURITY MANAGEMENT

University of Denver (M)

SECURITY STUDIES

East Carolina University (GC)
University of Massachusetts Lowell (GC)

SEED ANALYSIS TRAINING

Colorado State University (UC)

SELF-DESIGN

Granite State College (B)

SELF-DESIGNED

St. Cloud State University (B)

SELF-DESIGNED CONCENTRATION

Green Mountain College (M)

SENIOR LIVING MANAGEMENT

Rochester Institute of Technology (GC)

SERVICE SOCIAL (EN FRANÇAIS)

Laurentian University (B)

SIGNAL PROCESSING

Stanford University (GC)

SITE PLANNING

University of Washington (UC)

SIX SIGMA EBLACK BELT (20 WEEKS)

Colorado State University (UC)

SIX SIGMA EGREEN BELT (12 WEEKS)

Colorado State University (UC)

SMALL BUSINESS ADMINISTRATION

Middlesex Community College (A)

SMALL BUSINESS ENTREPRENEURSHIP

Myers University (B)

SMALL BUSINESS MANAGEMENT

Herkimer County Community College (UC)
Middlesex Community College (UC)

SMALL BUSINESS MANAGEMENT/ ENTREPRENEURSHIP

Cerro Coso Community College (A)

SOCIAL AND BEHAVIORAL SCIENCES

Coastline Community College (A)
Santa Rosa Junior College (A)

SOCIAL DEVELOPMENT STUDIES

University of Waterloo (B)

SOCIAL PSYCHOLOGY

Park University (B)

SOCIAL SCIENCE

California State University, Chico (B)
Central Texas College (A)
Montgomery County Community College (A)
Southern New Hampshire University (B)
University of Maryland University College (B)
University of North Dakota (B)
West Hills Community College (A)

SOCIAL SCIENCE/HISTORY

Saint Mary-of-the-Woods College (B)

SOCIAL SCIENCES

Buena Vista University (B)
Cerro Coso Community College (A)
Daniel Webster College (B)
Northern Virginia Community College (A)
Rose State College (A)
Southwestern Adventist University (B)
Syracuse University (M)
Thomas Edison State College (B)
University of Waterloo (B)
University of Wyoming (B)
Upper Iowa University (B)
Washington State University (B)

SOCIAL SCIENCES: APPLIED TRACK

University of Hawaii–West Oahu (B)

SOCIAL SCIENCES: EARLY CHILDHOOD EDU, POLITICAL SCI

University of Hawaii–West Oahu (B)

SOCIAL SERVICES

Thomas Edison State College (A,B)
The University of Maine at Augusta (A)

SOCIAL SERVICES ADMINISTRATION

Thomas Edison State College (B)

SOCIAL SERVICES FOR SPECIAL POPULATIONS

Thomas Edison State College (A,B)

SOCIAL STUDIES EDUCATION

University of Missouri–Columbia (M)

SOCIAL THEORY, SOCIAL STRUCTURE, AND CHANGE

State University of New York Empire State College (A,B)

SOCIAL WORK

Central Texas College (A)
Cleveland State University (M)

Colorado State University (M)
Darton College (A)
Florida State University (M)
Memorial University of Newfoundland (M)
Missouri State University (M)
New Mexico State University (M)
Northampton County Area Community College (A)
Seminole Community College (A)
The University of Alabama (M)
University of Manitoba (B)
University of North Dakota (M)
University of Wyoming (M)
Utah State University (M)
Vincennes University (A)

SOCIAL WORK–ADVANCED STANDING

Colorado State University (M)

SOCIAL WORK–NATIVE HUMAN SERVICES

Laurentian University (B)

SOCIAL WORK, ADVANCED STANDING PROGRAM

The University of Tennessee (M)

SOCIAL WORK, EXTENDED STUDY PROGRAM

The University of Tennessee (M)

SOCIALLY ENGAGED SPIRITUALITY

Saybrook Graduate School and Research Center (GC)

SOCIOLOGY

Adams State College (B)
American Public University System (B)
Columbia College (B)
Community College of Denver (A)
Dallas Baptist University (B)
Darton College (A)
Fort Hays State University (B)
Laurentian University (B)
National University (B)
New Mexico State University (M,B)
New York Institute of Technology (B)
North Dakota State University (B)
Northeastern University (B)
Seminole Community College (A)
Thomas Edison State College (B)
University of Colorado Denver (B)
University of North Alabama (B)

SOCIOLOGY (3 YEAR)

Athabasca University (B)

SOCIOLOGY (4 YEAR)

Athabasca University (B)

SOFTWARE APPLICATIONS FOR THE PROFESSIONAL

Sinclair Community College (UC)

SOFTWARE APPLICATIONS SPECIALIST

Central Texas College (UC)

SOFTWARE DEVELOPMENT

Bellevue University (B)
Butler Community College (A)
Virginia Polytechnic Institute and State University (GC)

SOFTWARE DEVELOPMENT AND MANAGEMENT

Rochester Institute of Technology (M)

SOFTWARE ENGINEERING

DePaul University (M)
Drexel University (M)
East Carolina University (M)
Florida State University (B)
Kansas State University (M)
National University (B)
North Dakota State University (GC)
Southern Methodist University (M)
Texas Tech University (M)
University of Colorado at Boulder (GC)
University of Illinois at Urbana–Champaign (GC)
University of Management and Technology (M)
University of Maryland University College (GC)
University of Michigan–Dearborn (M)
Walden University (M)
West Virginia University (M)
Westwood Online (A)

SOFTWARE ENGINEERING ADMINISTRATION

University of West Florida (M)

SOFTWARE PRODUCTIVITY

University of Cincinnati (UC)

SOFTWARE SYSTEMS

Stanford University (GC)

SOFTWARE SYSTEMS, ADVANCED

Stanford University (GC)

SOIL MANAGEMENT

Texas Tech University (GC)

SPACE STUDIES

American Public University System (M,B)
University of Colorado at Colorado Springs (M)
University of North Dakota (M)

SPACE SYSTEMS ENGINEERING

Stevens Institute of Technology (M)

SPACECRAFT DESIGN AND OPERATION PROFICIENCY

Stanford University (GC)

SPANISH

Mercy College (B)
University of Phoenix (M)

SPATIAL ANALYSIS AND MANAGEMENT

Jacksonville State University (UC)

SPATIAL ANALYSIS AND MANAGEMENT CONCENTRATION

Jacksonville State University (M)

SPECIAL EDUCATION

Abilene Christian University (M)
Campbellsville University (M)
Cardinal Stritch University (M)
East Carolina University (M)
Florida State University (M)
Fort Hays State University (M)
Northwest Missouri State University (M)
Old Dominion University (M)
Prescott College (B)
St. Cloud State University (B)
Texas Tech University (M)
University of Arkansas (M)
University of Central Florida (GC)
University of Houston–Victoria (M)
University of North Dakota (M)
University of the Southwest (M)
University of West Florida (M)
Utah State University (M,B)
West Virginia University (M)

SPECIAL EDUCATION (CROSS-CATEGORICAL EMPHASIS)

The University of North Carolina at Greensboro (M)

SPECIAL EDUCATION (GIFTED AND TALENTED)

The University of Alabama (M,)

SPECIAL EDUCATION (GIFTED)

University of South Alabama (M)

SPECIAL EDUCATION ALTERNATIVE LICENSURE

New Mexico State University (UC)

SPECIAL EDUCATION AND LEVEL I SPECIALIST CREDENTIAL MILD/MODERATE

National University (M)

SPECIAL EDUCATION ENDORSEMENT PROGRAMS (WITH MS EDUCATION OPTION)

Walden University (UC)

SPECIAL EDUCATION GENERALIST

University of Colorado Denver (UC)

SPECIAL EDUCATION LEADERSHIP

Regent University

SPECIAL EDUCATION SUPERVISORY CERTIFICATE

Penn State University Park (UC)

SPECIAL EDUCATION–EARLY CHILDHOOD INTERVENTION SPECIALIST

The University of Toledo (M)

SPECIAL EDUCATION–GIFTED EDUCATION

University of Nebraska at Kearney (M)

SPECIAL EDUCATION–INSTRUCTIONAL SPECIALIST I

Buena Vista University (UC)

SPECIAL EDUCATION–ORIENTATION AND MOBILITY

University of Massachusetts Boston (GC,M)

SPECIAL EDUCATION–SIGN LANGUAGE INTERPRETING TRACK (BACHELOR COMPLETION PROGRAM)

University of Cincinnati (B)

SPECIAL EDUCATION–TEACHING OF STUDENTS WITH VISUAL IMPAIRMENTS

University of Massachusetts Boston (M)

SPECIAL EDUCATION, ADAPTED CURRICULUM

The University of North Carolina at Charlotte (GC)

SPECIAL EDUCATION, GENERAL CURRICULUM TEACHER LICENSURE

The University of North Carolina at Charlotte (GC)

SPECIAL EDUCATION, GENERIC

Texas Tech University (UC)

SPECIALIST CERTIFICATE IN AGING

University of North Texas (GC)

SPECIALIST IN BLOOD BANK CERTIFICATE

Rush University (GC)

SPECIALIZED MINISTRIES–YOUTH AND YOUNG ADULT MINISTRY

Southwestern College (M)

SPECIALTY CONSTRUCTION

Southern Polytechnic State University (UC)

SPEECH

Darton College (A)

SPEECH LANGUAGE AND AUDITORY PATHOLOGY

East Carolina University (M)

SPEECH LANGUAGE PATHOLOGY

Florida State University (M)

SPEECH LANGUAGE PATHOLOGY ASSISTANT

Lake Region State College (A)
Williston State College (A)

SPEECH-LANGUAGE PATHOLOGY

Texas Woman's University (M)
University of Wyoming (M)

SPEECH/LANGUAGE PATHOLOGY ASSISTANT

Chemeketa Community College (A,UC)

SPIRITUAL FORMATION AND LEADERSHIP

Spring Arbor University (M)

SPORT BUSINESS CONCENTRATION

Saint Leo University (M)

SPORT COACHING EDUCATION

University of Southern Mississippi (M)

SPORT MANAGEMENT

Drexel University (M)
Nichols College (M)
Southern New Hampshire University (GC,M)
University of Southern Mississippi (M)

SPORTS AND ATHLETICS ADMINISTRATION

Lynn University (M)

SPORTS AND ENTERTAINMENT MANAGEMENT

University of Dallas (GC,M)

SPORTS AND HEALTH SCIENCES

American Public University System (B)

SPORTS COACHING

United States Sports Academy (M,B,UC)

SPORTS COACHING (INTERNATIONAL CERTIFICATION)

United States Sports Academy (UC)

SPORTS FITNESS

United States Sports Academy (M)

SPORTS LEADERSHIP

Duquesne University (M)

SPORTS MANAGEMENT

American Public University System (M)
Missouri State University (GC)
Northampton County Area Community
  College (A)
Tiffin University (M)
United States Sports Academy (D,M,B,UC)
University of Phoenix (A)
West Virginia University (M)

SPORTS MANAGEMENT (INTERNATIONAL CERTIFICATION)

United States Sports Academy (UC)

SPORTS MANAGEMENT–OLYMPISM EMPHASIS

United States Sports Academy (D)

SPORTS MEDICINE

United States Sports Academy (M,UC)

SPORTS NUTRITION

Simmons College (GC)

SPORTS STUDIES

United States Sports Academy (M,B)

STATISTICAL METHODS FOR PRODUCT AND PROCESS IMPROVEMENT

Rochester Institute of Technology (GC)

STATISTICAL QUALITY

Rochester Institute of Technology (GC)

STATISTICAL THEORY AND METHOD

Colorado State University (UC)

STATISTICS

Colorado State University (M)

STRATEGIC BUSINESS MANAGEMENT (MSM)

Regis University (GC)

STRATEGIC COMMUNICATION AND LEADERSHIP

Seton Hall University (M)

STRATEGIC FORESIGHT

Regent University (GC,M)

STRATEGIC INTELLIGENCE

American Public University System (M)

STRATEGIC LEADERSHIP

Black Hills State University (M)
Mountain State University (M)
New England College (M)
Regent University (D)
Southwestern College (B)

STRATEGIC PLANNING FOR CRITICAL INFRASTRUCTURE

University of Washington (M)

STRATEGIC PUBLIC RELATIONS

The George Washington University (M)

STRATEGIC TECHNOLOGY MANAGEMENT

University of Illinois at Urbana–Champaign
  (GC)
University of Illinois at Urbana–Champaign
  (GC)

STRUCTURAL DESIGN

Rochester Institute of Technology (UC)

STRUCTURAL ENGINEERING

University of Idaho (UC)
University of Wisconsin–Platteville (GC)
University of Wisconsin–Platteville (GC)

STRUCTURAL/GEOTECHNICAL ENGINEERING

University of Wisconsin–Platteville (GC)
University of Wisconsin–Platteville (GC)

STRUCTURED LEARNING

Heritage College (A)

STUDENT AFFAIRS

Regent University (M)

STUDENT AFFAIRS AND HIGHER EDUCATION

Indiana State University (M)

SUBSTANCE ABUSE AND ADDICTIONS STUDIES

University of Hawaii–West Oahu (UC)

SUBSTANCE ABUSE/ADDICTION COUNSELING

East Carolina University (GC)

SUPERINTENDENCY

The University of Texas of the Permian Basin

SUPERINTENDENT CERTIFICATE

The University of Texas System

SUPERINTENDENT PROFESSIONAL

Texas Tech University (UC)

SUPERVISION AND MANAGEMENT

San Joaquin Delta College (UC)

SUPERVISORY LEADERSHIP

Northwest Technical College (UC)

SUPERVISORY LEADERSHIP ESSENTIALS

Northwest Technical College (UC)

SUPERVISORY MANAGEMENT

Northwest Technical College (A)

SUPERVISORY MANAGMENT

Gateway Technical College (A)

SUPPLY CHAIN AND INFORMATION SYSTEMS

Penn State University Park (GC)

SUPPLY CHAIN MANAGEMENT

Columbus State Community College (GC)
Lehigh University (UC)
National University (GC)
Northeastern University
Penn State University Park (M)

SUPPLY CHAIN MANAGEMENT/ MARKET LOGISTICS

University of Dallas (GC,M)

SUPPLY MANAGEMENT

American Graduate University (M)

SURGICAL TECHNOLOGY

New England Institute of Technology (A)
Southeast Community College Area (A)

SURGICAL TECHNOLOGY ACCELERATED OPTION, CERTIFICATE OF GRADUATION

Vincennes University (GC)

SURGICAL TECHNOLOGY COMPLETION PROGRAM

Presentation College (A)

SURGICAL TECHNOLOGY–FIRST ASSIST

Vincennes University (UC)

SURVEYING

Thomas Edison State College (A,B)

SUSTAINABILITY EDUCATION

Prescott College (M)

SUSTAINABLE BUSINESS PRACTICES

Green Mountain College (M)

SUSTAINABLE COMMUNITY DEVELOPMENT

Prescott College (M,B)

SUSTAINABLE DESIGN

New Jersey Institute of Technology (GC)

SUSTAINABLE NATURAL RESOURCES

Oregon State University (GC)

SYSTEM SAFETY AND SECURITY

University of Southern California (GC,M)

SYSTEM SOFTWARE

University of Illinois at Urbana–Champaign (GC)

SYSTEMS ANALYSIS

University of Maryland University College (GC)

SYSTEMS AND ENGINEERING MANAGEMENT

Texas Tech University (D,M)

SYSTEMS ARCHITECTURE ENGINEERING

University of Southern California (GC,M)

SYSTEMS ENGINEERING

Missouri University of Science and Technology (M)
New Mexico State University (UC)
Penn State University Park (M)
Southern Methodist University (M)
Southern Polytechnic State University (M)
Stevens Institute of Technology (M)
The University of Alabama in Huntsville (M)
University of Colorado at Colorado Springs (M)
University of Florida (M)
University of Illinois at Urbana–Champaign (GC)
University of Illinois at Urbana–Champaign (GC)
Virginia Polytechnic Institute and State University (M)
Walden University (M)

SYSTEMS ENGINEERING (INDUSTRIAL AND MANUFACTURING ENGINEERING CONCENTRATION)

Kettering University (M)

SYSTEMS ENGINEERING SPECIALIZATION (IN DEVELOPMENT)

Colorado State University (M)

SYSTEMS MANAGEMENT

Florida Institute of Technology (M)

TAXATION

Golden Gate University (GC,M)

TAXATION–MASTER OF TAXATION

Nova Southeastern University (M)

TEACHER ASSISTANT

University of Calgary (UC)

TEACHER CERTIFICATION

Prescott College (UC)

TEACHER EDUCATION (MIDDLE GRADES)

Darton College (A)

TEACHER EDUCATION (SECONDARY EDUCATION)

Darton College (A)

TEACHER EDUCATION (SPECIAL EDUCATION)

Darton College (A)

TEACHER EDUCATION TRANSFER

Genesee Community College (A)

TEACHER INTERN (POSTBACCALAUREATE)

Kaplan University Online (UC)

TEACHER LEADERSHIP

Roosevelt University (M)
University of Illinois at Springfield (M)

TEACHERS COMMUNICATIONS AND CRISIS SKILLS

Darton College (UC)

TEACHING

Kaplan University Online (M)
La Sierra University (M)
Liberty University (M)
National University (M)
Saint Leo University (M)
State University of New York Empire State
  College (M)
Texas Woman's University (M)

TEACHING AND LEARNING

Lock Haven University of Pennsylvania (M)

TEACHING AND LEARNING WITH TECHNOLOGY

University of North Texas (M)

TEACHING AND LEARNING, ADVANCED STUDIES

Middle Tennessee State University (M)

TEACHING AND TRAINING AT A DISTANCE

University of Maryland University College
  (GC)

TEACHING ASSISTANT

Herkimer County Community College (UC)

TEACHING AT-RISK STUDENTS

Park University (M)

TEACHING CHILDREN WITH DISABILITIES IN CHILDHOOD EDUCATION

St. John's University (M)
St. John's University (M)

TEACHING ENGLISH TO SPEAKERS OF OTHER LANGUAGES

The New School: A University (M)

TEACHING ENGLISH AS A SECOND LANGUAGE

St. Cloud State University (M)

TEACHING ENGLISH AS A SECOND LANGUAGE (TESL)

Drexel University (UC)

TEACHING ENGLISH AS A SECOND OR FOREIGN LANGUAGE

Indiana State University (GC)

TEACHING ENGLISH TO SPEAKERS OF OTHER LANGUAGES (TESOL)

University of Missouri–Columbia (M)

TEACHING IN THE VIRTUAL CLASSROOM

Fielding Graduate University (UC)

TEACHING MATHEMATICS

University of Idaho (M)

TEACHING OF LANGUAGES (MATL)

University of Southern Mississippi (M)

TEACHING OF SCIENCE

New Mexico State University (M)

TEACHING WITH TECHNOLOGY AND DISTANCE LEARNING CERTIFICATE

Colorado State University (UC)

TEACHING–INSTRUCTIONAL TECHNOLOGY

Northwest Missouri State University (M)

TEACHING–ONLINE TEACHING

Cerro Coso Community College (UC)

TEACHING, LEARNING, AND CURRICULUM

Drexel University (M)

TEACHING/LEARNING IN NURSING AND HEALTH SCIENCES

University of Illinois at Chicago (UC)

TECHNICAL COMMUNICATION

Southern Polytechnic State University (GC)
Texas Tech University (M)

TECHNICAL COMMUNICATION AND RHETORIC

Texas Tech University (D)

TECHNICAL COMMUNICATION, BASIC

Rochester Institute of Technology (UC)

TECHNICAL COMMUNICATIONS

Gateway Technical College (A)
Northeastern University (B)

TECHNICAL COMMUNICATIONS, ADVANCED

Rochester Institute of Technology (UC)

TECHNICAL EDUCATION AND INDUSTRY TRAINING

University of Central Florida (B)

TECHNICAL INFORMATION DESIGN

Rochester Institute of Technology (GC)

TECHNICAL MANAGEMENT

DeVry University Online (B)
Embry-Riddle Aeronautical University (A,B)
Southern New Hampshire University (B)

TECHNICAL SALES

Bellevue University (B)

TECHNICAL STUDIES

Excelsior College (A)

TECHNICAL WRITING

California State University, Dominguez Hills
  (GC)

TECHNOLOGICAL EDUCATION, ADVANCED

Bowling Green State University (B)

TECHNOLOGY

Darton College (UC)
Excelsior College (A,B)

TECHNOLOGY ADMINISTRATION

Washburn University (B)

TECHNOLOGY AND INFORMATION MANAGEMENT

Upper Iowa University (B)

TECHNOLOGY APPRENTICESHIP

Vincennes University (A)

TECHNOLOGY APPRENTICESHIP–GENERAL STUDIES OPTION

Vincennes University (A)

TECHNOLOGY EDUCATION

Ball State University (M)

TECHNOLOGY FACILITATOR

East Carolina University (GC)

TECHNOLOGY FOR EDUCATION AND TRAINING

The University of South Dakota (M)

TECHNOLOGY IN DISTANCE EDUCATION

University of Maryland University College (GC)

TECHNOLOGY IN EDUCATION (GLOBAL)

University of Michigan–Flint (M)

TECHNOLOGY IN SCHOOLS

University of Missouri–Columbia (M)

TECHNOLOGY IN SCHOOLS (EDUCATIONAL SPECIALIST)

University of Missouri–Columbia

TECHNOLOGY INTEGRATION

Boise State University (GC)
Graceland University (M)

TECHNOLOGY LEADERSHIP

Fort Hays State University (B)

TECHNOLOGY MANAGEMENT

Bowling Green State University (D)
City University of Seattle (GC,M)
Indiana State University (D,B)
Kansas State University (B)
Missouri State University–West Plains (B)
National University (M)
Pennsylvania College of Technology (B)
State University of New York Institute of Technology (M)
Stevens Institute of Technology (GC,M)
University of Bridgeport (M)
University of Maryland University College (M)
University of Phoenix (M)
University of Wisconsin–Stout (M)
Western Kentucky University (M,B)

TECHNOLOGY MANAGEMENT (DEGREE COMPLETION)

Eastern Michigan University (B)

TECHNOLOGY MANAGEMENT (MS-TMGT)

Texas A&M University–Commerce (M)

TECHNOLOGY MANAGEMENT CONCENTRATION

Colorado Technical University Colorado Springs (M)

TECHNOLOGY MANAGEMENT–CERTIFICATE OF ADVANCED STUDY

University of Denver (UC)

TECHNOLOGY MANAGEMENT–MASTER OF APPLIED SCIENCE IN TECHNOLOGY MANAGEMENT

University of Denver (M)

TECHNOLOGY SYSTEMS–COMPUTER NETWORKING MANAGEMENT

East Carolina University (M)

TECHNOLOGY SYSTEMS–DIGITAL COMMUNICATIONS

East Carolina University (M)

TECHNOLOGY SYSTEMS–DISTRIBUTION AND LOGISTICS

East Carolina University (M)

TECHNOLOGY SYSTEMS–INFORMATION SECURITY

East Carolina University (M)

TECHNOLOGY SYSTEMS–MANUFACTURING

East Carolina University (M)

TECHNOLOGY SYSTEMS–PERFORMANCE IMPROVEMENT

East Carolina University (M)

TECHNOLOGY SYSTEMS–QUALITY SYSTEMS

East Carolina University (M)

TECHNOLOGY–BACHELOR TECHNOLOGY (BTECH)

Memorial University of Newfoundland (B)

TECHNOLOGY–HUMAN RESOURCE DEVELOPMENT

The University of Texas at Tyler (M,B)

TECHNOLOGY-BASED DISTRIBUTED LEARNING

The University of British Columbia (GC)

TECHNOLOGY-BASED LEARNING FOR SCHOOLS

The University of British Columbia (GC)

TELECOMMUNICATION MANAGEMENT

Stevens Institute of Technology (M)

TELECOMMUNICATION SYSTEMS

DePaul University (M)

TELECOMMUNICATIONS

Columbia University (UC)
Pace University (GC,B)
Southern Methodist University (M)
Stanford University (GC)
University of Colorado at Boulder (M)

TELECOMMUNICATIONS AND NETWORK MANAGEMENT

Syracuse University (M)

TELECOMMUNICATIONS ENGINEERING TECHNOLOGY

Rochester Institute of Technology (M,B)

TELECOMMUNICATIONS MANAGEMENT

Stevens Institute of Technology (GC)
University of Maryland University College (GC,M)

TELECOMMUNICATIONS MANAGEMENT AND POLICY–CERTIFICATE OF ADVANCED STUDY

University of Denver (UC)

TELECOMMUNICATIONS NETWORKING

New Jersey Institute of Technology (GC)

TELECOMMUNICATIONS NETWORKS–CERTIFICATE OF ADVANCED STUDY

University of Denver (UC)

TELECOMMUNICATIONS SYSTEMS MANAGEMENT

Murray State University (B)

TELECOMMUNICATIONS TECHNOLOGY–CERTIFICATE OF ADVANCED STUDY

University of Denver (UC)

TELECOMMUNICATIONS TECHNOLOGY–VERIZON

Erie Community College (A)
Erie Community College, South Campus (A)

TELECOMMUNICATIONS–DATA COMMUNICATIONS

Rochester Institute of Technology (UC)

TELECOMMUNICATIONS–MASTER OF APPLIED SCIENCE IN TELECOMMUNICATIONS

University of Denver (M)

TELECOMMUNICATIONS– NETWORK MANAGEMENT

Rochester Institute of Technology (UC)

TELECOMMUNICATIONS–VOICE COMMUNICATIONS

Rochester Institute of Technology (UC)

TELECOMUNICATIONS TECHOLOGY–VERIZON

Erie Community College, North Campus (A)

TELEVISION ARTS

Regent University (M)

TESOL

Regent University (M,UC)
University of North Texas (UC)

TEXAS TEACHER CERTIFICATION–SECONDARY EDUCATION

University of North Texas (UC)

TEXTILE AND APPAREL MARKETING

Philadelphia University (M)

TEXTILES OFF-CAMPUS PROGRAMS (TOP)

North Carolina State University (M)

THE ARTS

State University of New York Empire State College (A,B)
Triton College (A)

THEATER

Prescott College (B)
Thomas Edison State College (B)

THEATER ARTS

Regent University (M)

THEATRE

Regent University (B)

THEOLOGICAL STUDIES

Covenant Theological Seminary (M)
Liberty University (M)

THEOLOGY

The Catholic Distance University (M,B)
Franciscan University of Steubenville (M)
Global University (UC)
Holy Apostles College and Seminary (M)
Saint Mary-of-the-Woods College (B)
Southwestern Adventist University (B)

TOTAL QUALITY MANAGEMENT ENGINEERING

University of South Florida (GC)

TOURISM AND TRAVEL MANAGEMENT

Chemeketa Community College (A,UC)

TOXICOLOGY AND INDUSTRIAL HYGIENE

Drexel University (UC)

TRADE & INDUSTRIAL (T&I) EDUCATION

The University of Texas System (UC)

TRADITIONAL MBA

Nichols College (M)

TRAFFIC SAFETY EDUCATION

University of Wisconsin–Stout (UC)

TRAINING AND DEVELOPMENT

North Carolina State University (M)
Roosevelt University (GC,M)
Southern New Hampshire University (GC)
University of St. Francis (M)
University of Wisconsin–Stout (M)

TRAINING AND DEVELOPMENT– CERTIFICATE OF ADVANCED STUDY

University of Denver (UC)

TRANSFER DEGREE

Bellevue Community College (A)
Illinois Eastern Community Colleges, Frontier Community College (A)
Illinois Eastern Community Colleges, Lincoln Trail College (A)
Illinois Eastern Community Colleges, Olney Central College (A)
Illinois Eastern Community Colleges, Wabash Valley College (A)
NorthWest Arkansas Community College (A)

TRANSFER DEGREE FOR BUSINESS STUDENTS

Bellevue Community College (A)

TRANSFER STUDIES

Anne Arundel Community College (A)

TRANSFORMATIVE LEADERSHIP

Bethune-Cookman University (M)
California Institute of Integral Studies (M)

TRANSFORMATIVE STUDIES

California Institute of Integral Studies (D)

TRANSITIONAL DOCTOR OF OCCUPATIONAL THERAPY

University of St. Augustine for Health Sciences (D)

TRANSITIONAL DOCTOR OF PHYSICAL THERAPY

University of St. Augustine for Health Sciences (D)

TRANSPERSONAL PSYCHOLOGY

Burlington College (B)
Naropa University (M)

TRANSPERSONAL PSYCHOLOGY, ECOPSYCHOLOGY CONCENTRATION

Naropa University (M)

TRANSPERSONAL STUDIES

Atlantic University (M)

TRANSPORTATION

New Jersey Institute of Technology (M)

TRANSPORTATION AND LOGISTICS MANAGEMENT

American Public University System (M,B)

TRANSPORTATION BUSINESS

Minnesota School of Business–Richfield (A)

TRANSPORTATION POLICY, OPERATIONS, AND LOGISTICS

George Mason University (M)

TRANSPORTATION SYSTEMS ANALYSIS

University of South Florida (GC)

TRAVEL AND HOSPITALITY MANAGEMENT

AIB College of Business (A)

TRAVEL AND HOSPITALITY MANAGEMENT/BUSINESS ADMIN

AIB College of Business (A)

TRAVEL AND TOURISM– HOSPITALITY AND EVENTS MANAGEMENT

Herkimer County Community College (A)

TRAVEL MANAGEMENT

University of Northwestern Ohio (A)

TURFGRASS MANAGEMENT

Penn State University Park (UC)

TURFGRASS MANAGEMENT, ADVANCED

Penn State University Park (UC)

TURFGRASS SCIENCE

Penn State University Park (B)

TYPEFACE DESIGN

Savannah College of Art and Design (GC)

ULTRASOUND–DEGREE COMPLETION IN ULTRASOUND, ECHOCARDIOGRAPHY OPTION

Oregon Institute of Technology (B)

ULTRASOUND–DEGREE COMPLETION IN ULTRASOUND, VASCULAR TECHNOLOGY OPTION

Oregon Institute of Technology (B)

UNCLASSIFIED STUDENT STATUS

University of Dubuque (M)

UNDERGRADUATE HUMANISTIC TRADITIONS

Virginia Polytechnic Institute and State University (UC)

UNIFIED K-8 GENERAL AND SPECIAL EDUCATION

University of Southern Maine (UC)

UNIVERSITY STUDIES

Dickinson State University (B)
North Dakota State University (B)
University of Maine at Fort-Kent (B)
The University of Tennessee at Martin (B)

UNIVERSITY TRANSFER

Clark State Community College (A)
Piedmont Community College (A)

UNIX

University of Massachusetts Lowell (UC)

URBAN FORESTRY TECHNOLOGY

Minot State University–Bottineau Campus (UC)

UTAH MATHEMATICS ENDORSEMENT PROJECT

Utah State University (UC)

VACCINES–TECHNOLOGIES, TRENDS, AND BIOTERRORISM

Northeastern University (GC)

VALUE DRIVEN ORGANIZATION

Central Michigan University (M)

VARIOUS SUBJECTS–BIOQUALITY, ENTREPRENEUR, HUMAN RESOURCES MANAGEMENT

Central Carolina Community College (UC)

VARIOUS SUBJECTS–INCOME TAX PREPARER, LIBRARY SERVICES, MANAGER TRAINEE

Central Carolina Community College (UC)

VARIOUS SUBJECTS–MEDICAL TRANSCRIPTION, NETWORKING, NEWS WRITING

Central Carolina Community College (UC)

VARIOUS SUBJECTS–PAYROLL ACCOUNTING, PHOTO JOURNALISM, SMALL BUSINESS FINANCIAL ADVISOR I AND II

Central Carolina Community College (UC)

VENTURE AND INNOVATION MANAGEMENT

New Jersey Institute of Technology (GC)

VETERINARY MEDICINE ONLINE

Colorado State University (UC)

VIOLENCE PREVENTION AND RESPONSE

Saybrook Graduate School and Research Center (GC)

VIRTUAL BUSINESS

Minot State University (B)

VIRTUAL REALITY IN EDUCATION AND TRAINING

East Carolina University (GC)

VISION SPECIALIST

Mississippi State University (GC)

VISIONARY ART AND CONSCIOUSNESS

Atlantic University (M)

VISUAL COMMUNICATION

Savannah College of Art and Design (B)

VISUAL COMMUNICATION AND GRAPHICS

Southern Polytechnic State University (GC)

VISUAL COMMUNICATION CONCENTRATION

American InterContinental University Online (A)

VISUAL COMMUNICATION– DIGITAL DESIGN CONCENTRATION (COMPLETION PROGRAM)

American InterContinental University Online (B)

VISUAL COMMUNICATION–WEB DESIGN CONCENTRATION (COMPLETION PROGRAM)

American InterContinental University Online (B)

VISUAL COMMUNICATIONS

Westwood Online (B)

VISUAL IMPAIRMENT

Indiana State University (UC)
Texas Tech University (UC)

VISUAL IMPAIRMENT AND BLINDNESS

Illinois State University (UC)

VOCATIONAL BUSINESS EDUCATION

Indiana State University (UC)

VOCATIONAL DIVERSIFIED OCCUPATIONS ENDORSEMENT

University of Nebraska at Kearney (UC)

VOCATIONAL EDUCATION– INFORMATION TECHNOLOGIES

East Carolina University (M)

VOCATIONAL REHABILITATION COUNSELING

University of Wisconsin–Stout (M)

VOCATIONAL REHABILITATION–REHABILITATION COUNSELING

University of Wisconsin–Stout (M)

VOCATIONAL TEACHER PREPARATION

State University of New York at Oswego (M,B)

VOICE CAPTIONING

AIB College of Business (A)

VOLUNTEER AND COMMUNITY RESOURCE MANAGEMENT

University of North Texas (GC)

WATER RESOURCES ENGINEERING

University of Idaho (UC)

WATER/WASTEWATER SPECIALIZATION

Mountain Empire Community College (A)

WATERSHED MANAGEMENT

Michigan State University (UC)

WEATHER FORECASTING

Penn State University Park (UC)

WEB ADMINISTRATION

University of Washington (UC)

WEB CONSULTANT FOR SMALL BUSINESS

University of Washington (UC)

WEB DESIGN

The University of Toledo (UC)

WEB DESIGN AND DEVELOPMENT TECHNOLOGIES–CERTIFICATE OF ADVANCED STUDY

University of Denver (UC)

WEB DESIGN AND MULTIMEDIA

Westwood Online (B)

WEB DESIGNER

Texas State Technical College Waco (A)

WEB DEVELOPER

College of Southern Maryland (UC)
Texas State Technical College Waco (A)

WEB DEVELOPMENT

Fort Hays State University (UC)
Franklin University (B)

Minnesota State Community and Technical College–Fergus Falls (UC)
Minot State University (GC)

WEB GRAPHIC DESIGN

DeVry University Online (A)

WEB MBA

Georgia College & State University (M)

WEB PAGE DEVELOPMENT, BASIC

Bristol Community College (UC)

WEB PROGRAMMING–VISUAL BASIC OR JAVA TRACK SHORT-TERM CERTIFICATE

Sinclair Community College (UC)

WEB PUBLISHING

Middlesex Community College (UC)

WEB SERVICES

Webster University (GC)

WEB SITE DESIGN

Webster University (UC)

WEB SITE DEVELOPMENT

Webster University (UC)

WEB SITE DEVELOPMENT CERTIFICATE

Western Wyoming Community College (UC)

WEB TECHNOLOGIES

Bellevue University (B)
Wake Technical Community College (A)

WEB TECHNOLOGOES

Piedmont Community College (A)

WEB TECHNOLOGY

Motlow State Community College (A)
Pellissippi State Technical Community College (A)

WEB TECHNOLOGY ESSENTIALS

University of Washington (UC)

WEB TECHNOLOGY FOCUS

University of Connecticut (B)

WEBMASTER

Union County College (UC)

WEBMASTER TECHNOLOGY

Daniel Webster College (UC)

WEBSITE DESIGN AND DEVELOPMENT

University of Massachusetts Lowell (UC)

WEBSITE DEVELOPER

East Carolina University (GC)

WELDING ENGINEERING

The Ohio State University (M)

WELLNESS PROGRAM

Chatham University (M)

WELLNESS–MASTER OF ARTS IN WELLNESS (MAW)

Chatham University

WESTERN AMERICAN STUDIES

Western Wyoming Community College (UC)

WETLANDS MANAGEMENT

Prescott College (M)

WILDLIFE MANAGEMENT

Prescott College (M)

WIRELESS AND ELECTRONIC COMMUNICATIONS

Cleveland Institute of Electronics (UC)

WIRELESS AND MOBILE COMMUNICATIONS

Columbia University (UC)

WIRELESS COMMUNICATION TECHNOLOGY CAMPUS CERTIFICATE

University of Illinois at Chicago (UC)

WIRELESS COMMUNICATIONS

Stevens Institute of Technology (GC)

WIRELESS COMMUNICATIONS (EE CONCENTRATION)

Kettering University (M)

WIRELESS ENGINEERING

University of South Florida (GC)

WIRELESS NETWORK AND TECHNOLOGIES

University of Colorado at Boulder (GC)

WIRELESS PERSONAL COMMUNICATION

Stanford University (GC)

WOMEN'S HEALTH

Rosalind Franklin University of Medicine and Science (GC,M)

WOMEN'S STUDIES

Laurentian University (B,UC)
Washington State University (B)
Western Kentucky University (GC)

WOMEN'S STUDIES (3 YEAR)

Athabasca University (B)

WOMEN'S STUDIES (4 YEAR)

Athabasca University (B)

WOOD AND PAPER SCIENCE

North Carolina State University (M)

WORD PROCESSING–ADMINISTRATIVE SUPPORT

University of Northwestern Ohio (A)

WORKFORCE DEVELOPMENT EDUCATION

University of Arkansas (M)

WORKFORCE EDUCATION LEADERSHIP

Mississippi State University (M)

WORKFORCE LEADERSHIP (FORMERLY OCCUPATIONAL TRAINING AND DEVELOPMENT)

University of Louisville (B)

WORKFORCE TRAINING AND DEVELOPMENT

University of Southern Mississippi (M)

WORLD SECURITY AND STRATEGIC STUDIES

Bellevue University (B)

WORSHIP

Hope International University (GC)

WORSHIP STUDIES

Liberty University (M)

WRITING AND COMMUNICATIONS CONCENTRATION

Green Mountain College (M)

WRITING AND LITERATURE

Burlington College (B)

YOUTH DEVELOPMENT

Clemson University (M)
Kansas State University (GC,M)
Michigan State University (M)

YOUTH DEVELOPMENT (HUMAN DEVELOPMENT AND FAMILY STUDIES)

University of Missouri–Columbia (M)

YOUTH DEVELOPMENT SPECIALIST

Michigan State University (UC)

YOUTH MINISTRY

Southwestern College (B)

YOUTH MINISTRY LEADERSHIP MODULE

Defiance College (UC)

YOUTH PROGRAM MANAGEMENT AND EVALUATION

Michigan State University

NON-DEGREE-RELATED COURSE SUBJECT AREAS

Index of individual courses offered by institutions, arranged by subject. U=Undergraduate; G=Graduate; N=Noncredit

ACCOUNTING AND COMPUTER SCIENCE

Acadia University (U)
Arapahoe Community College (U)
Arkansas State University–Mountain Home (U)
Athens Technical College (N)
Barton County Community College (U)
Bellevue University (U,G)
Belmont Technical College (U)
Black Hills State University (U)
Blue Ridge Community College (N)
Bristol Community College (U)
Cabrillo College (U)
California State University, San Bernardino (U)
California State University, San Marcos (N,U)
Cape Fear Community College (U)
Carlow University (U)
Carroll University (U)
Centennial College (U)
Central Michigan University (U,G)
Central Texas College (U)
Chadron State College (U,G)
Chicago State University (U)
Citrus College (U)
Clackamas Community College (U)
Clark State Community College (U)
Cleveland Community College (U)
Cleveland Institute of Electronics (N)
Cleveland State University (U)
Colorado State University (N,U)
Community College of Beaver County (N,U)
Cuyahoga Community College (U)
Darton College (U)
Daytona State College (U)
DeSales University (U)
Diné College (U)
Drake University (G)
Duquesne University (U,G)
East Arkansas Community College (U)
East Central Community College (U)
Eastern Illinois University (U)
Eastern Iowa Community College District (N)
Eastern Kentucky University (U)
Eastern Michigan University (G)
Eastern West Virginia Community and Technical College (U)
Elizabethtown College (U)
Ellsworth Community College (U)
Excelsior College (U)
Finger Lakes Community College (U)
Fitchburg State College (U)
Flathead Valley Community College (N)
Fort Hays State University (N,U)
Fort Valley State University (U)
Fox Valley Technical College (U)
Gadsden State Community College (U)
Galveston College (N,U)
Golden West College (U)
Greenville Technical College (U)

Hocking College (U)
Holyoke Community College (U)
Illinois Eastern Community Colleges, Lincoln Trail College (U)
Indiana State University (U)
Jacksonville State University (U,G)
John A. Logan College (U)
Kansas State University (U)
Lackawanna College (U)
Lake Region State College (U)
Lewis-Clark State College (U)
Los Angeles Trade-Technical College (U)
Lurleen B. Wallace Community College (U)
Macon State College (U)
Marshalltown Community College (U)
Middlesex Community College (U)
Misericordia University (U)
Mississippi Delta Community College (U)
Mississippi State University (U)
Mitchell Technical Institute (U)
Mt. Hood Community College (U)
Mount Olive College (U)
Murray State College (U)
New Jersey Institute of Technology (U,G)
New Mexico Junior College (U)
North Central State College (U)
Northeast Alabama Community College (U)
Northeast Iowa Community College (U)
North Florida Community College (U)
Northwestern Oklahoma State University (U)
Nova Southeastern University (G)
Okaloosa-Walton College (U)
Oklahoma Panhandle State University (U)
Palomar College (U)
Pamlico Community College (U)
Plymouth State University (N)
Prairie View A&M University (U)
Pulaski Technical College (U)
Quinebaug Valley Community College (N)
Richmond Community College (U)
Rose State College (U)
Sacramento City College (U)
Saddleback College (U)
Saint Charles Community College (U)
Saint Francis University (U)
St. Louis Community College System (U)
St. Mary's University (N)
San Diego Community College District (N,U)
Santa Monica College (U)
Seminole Community College (U)
Sinclair Community College (U)
Southern New Hampshire University (U,G)
South Piedmont Community College (U)
State University of New York at Binghamton (N)
Sullivan County Community College (N,U)
Texas A&M University–Commerce (U)
Texas A&M University–Kingsville (U)
Thomas College (U)
Three Rivers Community College (U)
Treasure Valley Community College (U)
Tri-County Community College (N,U)

Union University (U)
University of Alaska Anchorage, Kodiak College (U)
The University of Arizona (U)
University of Cincinnati (N)
University of Idaho (G)
University of Maine at Machias (U)
University of Management and Technology (U,G)
University of New Orleans (U,G)
The University of North Carolina at Charlotte (N)
University of Southern Indiana (N)
University of South Florida (G)
University of the Virgin Islands (U)
University of Vermont (U)
University of West Florida (G)
University of Wisconsin–Parkside (G)
University of Wisconsin–Superior (U)
University of Wisconsin–Whitewater (U)
Upper Iowa University (N)
West Hills Community College (N)
West Los Angeles College (U)
West Texas A&M University (G)
West Virginia University at Parkersburg (N)
Wharton County Junior College (U)
Williston State College (U)
Yuba College (U)

ACCOUNTING AND RELATED SERVICES

Adams State College (N)
AIB College of Business (U)
Alcorn State University (G)
Amberton University (U)
American Graduate University (G)
American University (G)
Anne Arundel Community College (U)
Arapahoe Community College (U)
Arizona Western College (U)
Arkansas State University–Beebe (U)
Athabasca University (N,U,G)
Athens Technical College (U)
Auburn University (U)
Baltimore City Community College (N,U)
Beaufort County Community College (N,U)
Bellevue Community College (U)
Belmont Technical College (U)
Bergen Community College (U)
Berkeley College (U)
Berkeley College–New York City Campus (U)
Berkeley College–Westchester Campus (U)
Blackhawk Technical College (U)
Blue Mountain Community College (U)
Boise State University (U)
Brazosport College (U)
Brenau University (U,G)
Bridgewater State College (N)
Brigham Young University (U)
Bristol Community College (U)
Broward Community College (U)

Bryant and Stratton Online (U)
Buena Vista University (U)
Burlington County College (U)
Butler Community College (U)
Cabrillo College (U)
Caldwell Community College and Technical
 Institute (N,U)
California National University for Advanced
 Studies (U,G)
California State University, Dominguez Hills
 (N)
California State University, Sacramento (U)
California State University, San Bernardino
 (U)
Campbell University (U)
Carl Sandburg College (U)
Carroll Community College (N,U)
Cayuga County Community College (U)
Central Carolina Community College (U)
Centralia College (U)
Central New Mexico Community College (U)
Central Texas College (U)
Central Virginia Community College (U)
Central Washington University (U,G)
Central Wyoming College (U)
Chadron State College (U,G)
Chaminade University of Honolulu (U)
Charter Oak State College (U)
Chatham University (U,G)
Chemeketa Community College (U)
Chicago State University (U)
Cincinnati State Technical and Community
 College (U)
City Colleges of Chicago, Harold Washington
 College (U)
Clackamas Community College (U)
Clemson University (N)
Cleveland State Community College (U)
Cleveland State University (N,U,G)
Clinton Community College (U)
College of San Mateo (U)
College of Southern Maryland (U)
College of The Albemarle (N,U)
College of the Sequoias (U)
College of the Siskiyous (U)
Colorado Mountain College District System
 (U)
Colorado State University (G)
Columbia College (U)
Columbus State Community College (U)
Community College of Denver (U)
Concordia University Wisconsin (U)
Corning Community College (U)
Dakota State University (U)
Dallas Baptist University (U,G)
Dallas County Community College District
 (U)
Danville Community College (U)
Darton College (U)
De Anza College (U)
Delaware County Community College (U)
Delaware Technical & Community College,
 Jack F. Owens Campus (U)
DeVry University Online (U,G)
Drake University (U)
Drexel University (U,G)
East Carolina University (G)
Eastern Illinois University (G)
Eastern Michigan University (N,G)
Eastern Oregon University (U)
Eastern Washington University (U)
Eastern Wyoming College (U)

East Los Angeles College (U)
East Tennessee State University (U)
Edgecombe Community College (N,U)
Edison State Community College (N,U)
Elgin Community College (U)
Elizabeth City State University (U)
Elizabethtown College (U)
Erie Community College (U)
Erie Community College, North Campus (U)
Erie Community College, South Campus (U)
Eugenio María de Hostos Community College
 of the City University of New York (U)
Everest College (U)
Everett Community College (U)
Flathead Valley Community College (U)
Florida Gulf Coast University (U)
Florida Institute of Technology (G)
Foothill College (U)
Fort Hays State University (N)
Fort Valley State University (U)
Franklin University (U)
Frank Phillips College (U)
Fulton-Montgomery Community College (N)
Galveston College (N,U)
Gateway Technical College (U)
Genesee Community College (U)
George C. Wallace Community College (U)
Georgia State University (G)
Golden Gate University (U,G)
Golden West College (U)
Governors State University (U)
Graceland University (U)
Grantham University (U,G)
Hagerstown Community College (N)
Halifax Community College (U)
Harrisburg Area Community College (U)
Haywood Community College (U)
Herkimer County Community College (U)
Hibbing Community College (N,U)
Hillsborough Community College (N)
Hopkinsville Community College (N,U)
Houston Community College System (U)
Illinois Eastern Community Colleges, Olney
 Central College (U)
Illinois Eastern Community Colleges, Wabash
 Valley College (U)
Indiana State University (U)
Indiana Tech (U)
Indiana University of Pennsylvania (U)
Indiana University–Purdue University Fort
 Wayne (U)
Indiana University System (N)
Indian River Community College (U)
Ivy Tech Community College–Northwest (U)
Jacksonville State University (U,G)
James A. Rhodes State College (U)
James Madison University (U)
Jamestown Community College (N)
Jefferson Community College (U)
John A. Logan College (U)
Johnson County Community College (U)
John Wood Community College (U)
J. Sargeant Reynolds Community College (U)
Kansas State University (U)
Kaskaskia College (U)
Kauai Community College (U,G)
Kean University (N,U,G)
Kentucky State University (U)
Kirtland Community College (U)
Lakeland College (U)
Lakeland Community College (N,U)
Lake Region State College (U)

Lake Superior College (U)
Laredo Community College (U)
Lehigh Carbon Community College (U)
Liberty University (U,G)
Limestone College (U)
Long Beach City College (U)
Los Angeles Harbor College (U)
Louisiana State University and Agricultural
 and Mechanical College (U)
Luzerne County Community College (U)
Macon State College (U)
Manatee Community College (U)
Mansfield University of Pennsylvania (U)
Marist College (U,G)
Marshall University (U,G)
Massasoit Community College (U)
Mayville State University (U)
McDowell Technical Community College (U)
Medical College of Wisconsin (G)
Mercer County Community College (U)
Mercy College (U)
Metropolitan State University (U)
Miami Dade College (U)
Middlesex Community College (U)
Middle Tennessee State University (U)
Midstate College (U)
Midway College (U)
Minnesota School of Business–Richfield (U)
Minot State University (U)
Minot State University–Bottineau Campus (U)
Mississippi State University (U)
Missouri State University (U,G)
Moberly Area Community College (U)
Monroe Community College (U)
Montcalm Community College (N,U)
Montgomery Community College (U)
Montgomery County Community College
 (N,U)
Mountain Empire Community College (U)
Mountain View College (U)
Mt. Hood Community College (U)
Mt. San Antonio College (U)
Myers University (U)
Nassau Community College (U)
National University (U,G)
Naugatuck Valley Community College (N,U)
New Jersey City University (U,G)
New Mexico Highlands University (U,G)
New River Community College (U)
New York Institute of Technology (U,G)
Nipissing University (U)
Northampton County Area Community
 College (U)
North Arkansas College (U)
North Carolina State University (U)
North Dakota State College of Science (U)
Northeastern University (U)
Northeast Iowa Community College (U)
Northeast State Technical Community College
 (U)
North Iowa Area Community College (U)
North Lake College (U)
Northland Community and Technical College–
 Thief River Falls (U)
North Seattle Community College (U)
NorthWest Arkansas Community College (U)
Northwestern Michigan College (U)
Northwestern Oklahoma State University (U)
Northwestern State University of Louisiana
 (U)
Northwest Technical College (U)
Northwood University, Texas Campus (U)

Okaloosa-Walton College (U)
Oklahoma Panhandle State University (U)
Oklahoma State University (U)
Old Dominion University (U,G)
Orange Coast College (U)
Oregon Institute of Technology (U)
Oxnard College (U)
Pace University (U)
Palm Beach Community College (U)
Palomar College (U)
Pamlico Community College (U)
Parkland College (U)
Park University (U)
Patrick Henry Community College (U)
Pellissippi State Technical Community
  College (U)
Peninsula College (U)
Pennsylvania College of Technology (U)
Philadelphia University (U,G)
Pikes Peak Community College (U)
Pine Technical College (U)
Portland Community College (U)
Pratt Community College (U)
Prescott College (U)
Pulaski Technical College (U)
Randolph Community College (N,U)
Rappahannock Community College (U)
Reading Area Community College (U)
Red Rocks Community College (U)
Regent University (N,G)
Regis University (U,G)
Rend Lake College (N)
Richland Community College (U)
Riverside Community College District (U)
Roosevelt University (U)
Rose State College (U)
Sacramento City College (U)
Sacred Heart University (G)
Saddleback College (U)
St. Clair County Community College (U)
St. Edward's University (U,G)
St. John's University (U)
Saint Joseph's College of Maine (U,G)
Saint Leo University (U)
Saint Mary-of-the-Woods College (U)
St. Mary's University (N)
San Diego Community College District (U)
San Joaquin Delta College (U)
Santa Monica College (U)
Santa Rosa Junior College (U)
Schenectady County Community College (U)
Schiller International University (U,G)
Seattle Central Community College (U)
Seminole Community College (U)
Shippensburg University of Pennsylvania
  (U,G)
Simpson College (U)
Southeast Community College Area (U)
Southeastern Community College (U)
Southeastern Oklahoma State University
  (N,U)
Southern Arkansas University Tech (U)
Southern New Hampshire University (U,G)
South Piedmont Community College (U)
Southwestern Adventist University (U)
Southwestern Community College (U)
Southwest Wisconsin Technical College (U)
State University of New York at Binghamton
  (N)
State University of New York at Oswego (G)
State University of New York College at
  Potsdam (N)

State University of New York College of
  Agriculture and Technology at Morrisville
  (U)
State University of New York Empire State
  College (U)
State University of New York Institute of
  Technology (U,G)
Stephen F. Austin State University (U)
Strayer University (U,G)
Syracuse University (G)
Tacoma Community College (U)
Taft College (U)
Taylor University (N)
Temple University (G)
Texas A&M University–Commerce (G)
Texas Tech University (U)
Three Rivers Community College (U)
Thunderbird School of Global Management
  (G)
Tompkins Cortland Community College (U)
Tri-County Community College (N,U)
Trine University (U)
Triton College (U)
Tyler Junior College (N,U)
Union County College (U)
The University of Akron (U,G)
The University of Alabama (U)
University of Alaska Fairbanks (U)
University of Arkansas at Little Rock (U)
University of Arkansas at Pine Bluff (U)
University of Central Missouri (N)
University of Cincinnati (N,U)
University of Colorado Denver (U,G)
University of Dallas (G)
The University of Findlay (U,G)
University of Hawaii–West Oahu (U)
University of Houston–Downtown (U)
University of Houston–Victoria (U,G)
University of Idaho (U)
University of Illinois at Chicago (G)
University of Illinois at Springfield (U)
The University of Maine at Augusta (U)
University of Maryland University College
  (U,G)
University of Michigan–Flint (N,U,G)
University of Minnesota, Crookston (U)
University of Minnesota, Twin Cities Campus
  (U)
University of Missouri–Columbia (U)
University of Nevada, Reno (U)
University of North Alabama (U,G)
The University of North Carolina at Chapel
  Hill (U)
The University of North Carolina at Charlotte
  (N)
University of North Dakota (U)
University of Northern Iowa (U)
University of Northwestern Ohio (U)
University of Phoenix (G)
University of Southern Mississippi (U)
The University of Tennessee at Martin (N)
The University of Texas at Brownsville (N)
The University of Texas at El Paso (U)
The University of Texas at San Antonio (U)
The University of Texas at Tyler (U)
The University of Texas System (U)
University of the Southwest (U)
University of the Virgin Islands (U)
University of Toronto (N)
University of Vermont (N)
University of Virginia (U)
University of Washington (U)

University of Waterloo (U)
University of Wisconsin–La Crosse (G)
University of Wisconsin–Parkside (G)
University of Wisconsin–Whitewater (G)
Upper Iowa University (N,U)
Utah State University (U)
Utah Valley State College (U)
Vincennes University (U)
Virginia Polytechnic Institute and State
  University (G)
Wake Technical Community College (N,U)
Wayland Baptist University (U,G)
Weber State University (U)
Westchester Community College (U)
Western Wyoming Community College (U)
West Hills Community College (N)
West Virginia University at Parkersburg (U)
Westwood Online (U)
Wichita State University (U)
Wilfrid Laurier University (U)
Wisconsin Indianhead Technical College
  (N,U)
Wytheville Community College (U)
York County Community College (U)
York Technical College (U)
York University (U)
Youngstown State University (N)

AEROSPACE, AERONAUTICAL AND ASTRONAUTICAL ENGINEERING

Auburn University (G)
Embry-Riddle Aeronautical University (U)
Georgia Institute of Technology (N,G)
Indiana State University (U)
Middle Tennessee State University (U,G)
Missouri University of Science and
  Technology (N)
New Mexico Institute of Mining and
  Technology (U,G)
North Dakota State University (N)
Old Dominion University (G)
Portland Community College (U)
St. Cloud State University (U)
Stanford University (N,G)
The University of Alabama (U)
University of Colorado at Boulder (N,G)
University of Colorado at Colorado Springs
  (G)
University of Florida (N)
University of Southern California (N)
Utah Valley State College (U,G)
Virginia Polytechnic Institute and State
  University (G)

AGRICULTURAL AND DOMESTIC ANIMAL SERVICES

Central Wyoming College (N)
Kansas State University (U)
Missouri State University (U,G)
North Carolina State University (U)
Treasure Valley Community College (U)

AGRICULTURAL AND FOOD PRODUCTS PROCESSING

Fort Valley State University (U)
Kansas State University (N,U,G)
North Carolina State University (U,G)
NorthWest Arkansas Community College (U)

University of Arkansas (G)
University of Minnesota, Crookston (U)
University of Missouri–Columbia (U,G)
Wisconsin Indianhead Technical College
  (N,U)

AGRICULTURAL BUSINESS AND MANAGEMENT

Allen County Community College (U)
Arkansas State University–Beebe (U)
Arkansas Tech University (U)
Athabasca University (G)
Clark State Community College (U)
Connors State College (U)
Dawson Community College (U)
Delaware Technical & Community College,
  Jack F. Owens Campus (U)
Eastern Oregon University (U)
Fort Valley State University (U)
Hope International University (G)
Kansas State University (U,G)
Middle Tennessee State University (U)
Missouri State University (U)
Mitchell Technical Institute (N)
Murray State University (U)
North Arkansas College (U)
North Central Texas College (U)
Northeast Iowa Community College (U)
Nova Scotia Agricultural College (U)
Oregon State University (U)
Parkland College (U)
Sam Houston State University (U)
State University of New York College of
  Agriculture and Technology at Morrisville
  (U)
Texas Tech University (U)
University of Arkansas at Pine Bluff (U)
The University of British Columbia (U)
University of Idaho (U)
University of Missouri–Columbia (N,U,G)
University of Northwestern Ohio (U)
University of Saskatchewan (N,U)
The University of Tennessee (U)
Wisconsin Indianhead Technical College
  (N,U)
Yuba College (U)

AGRICULTURAL PRODUCTION

Colorado State University (U)
Kansas State University (U)
North Arkansas College (U)
North Carolina State University (U)
Nova Scotia Agricultural College (U)
Texas A&M University–Commerce (U)
Treasure Valley Community College (U)

AGRICULTURAL PUBLIC SERVICES

Kansas State University (G)

AGRICULTURAL/BIOLOGICAL ENGINEERING AND BIOENGINEERING

Fort Valley State University (U)
University of Idaho (U,G)

AGRICULTURE

Allen County Community College (U)
Auburn University (U)

California State University, Chico (U)
Central Carolina Community College (U)
Clemson University (G)
Colorado State University (U,G)
Dawson Community College (U)
Delaware Technical & Community College,
  Jack F. Owens Campus (U)
Henderson Community College (U)
Illinois State University (U)
Kansas State University (N,U,G)
Mississippi State University (G)
Missouri State University–West Plains (U)
Murray State University (U)
North Carolina State University (U,G)
NorthWest Arkansas Community College (U)
Nova Scotia Agricultural College (N,U)
Oregon State University (U)
Rend Lake College (U)
Saybrook Graduate School and Research
  Center (G)
Sierra College (U)
State University of New York College of
  Agriculture and Technology at Morrisville
  (U)
Stephen F. Austin State University (U)
Texas A&M University–Commerce (G)
Texas A&M University–Kingsville (U,G)
Texas Tech University (U,G)
Three Rivers Community College (U)
The University of Arizona (U)
University of Arkansas at Pine Bluff (U)
The University of British Columbia (U)
University of Illinois at Urbana–Champaign
  (G)
University of Minnesota, Twin Cities Campus
  (U)
University of Saskatchewan (U)
University of Vermont (U)
University of Wyoming (U)
Virginia Polytechnic Institute and State
  University (U)
Wisconsin Indianhead Technical College
  (N,U)

AGRICULTURE AND AGRICULTURE OPERATIONS RELATED

Delaware Technical & Community College,
  Jack F. Owens Campus (U)
Kansas State University (U,G)
Louisiana State University and Agricultural
  and Mechanical College (G)
Murray State University (U)
North Carolina State University (G)
Oregon State University (U)
Treasure Valley Community College (U)
The University of Arizona (U)
University of California, Riverside (N)
University of Saskatchewan (N)
Utah State University (G)
Virginia Polytechnic Institute and State
  University (U,G)
Yuba College (U)

AIR FORCE J.R.O.T.C/R.O.T.C

California State University, San Bernardino
  (U)
University of Arkansas at Pine Bluff (N)

AIR TRANSPORTATION

Central Wyoming College (N)
Community College of Beaver County (U)
Elizabeth City State University (U)
Embry-Riddle Aeronautical University (N,G)
San Diego Community College District (U)
Utah Valley State College (U)
Western Michigan University (U)
West Los Angeles College (U)

ALLIED HEALTH AND MEDICAL ASSISTING SERVICES

Allen County Community College (U)
Anne Arundel Community College (U)
Arapahoe Community College (U)
Athens Technical College (N,U)
Blackhawk Technical College (U)
Blackstone Career Institute (N)
Bowling Green State University (U)
Brenau University (U)
Bridgewater State College (N)
Butler Community College (U)
Cabrillo College (U)
California State University, San Bernardino
  (U)
California State University, San Marcos (U)
Carroll Community College (U)
Central Michigan University (U)
Central Oregon Community College (U)
Central Texas College (U)
Central Virginia Community College (U)
Chemeketa Community College (U)
Cincinnati State Technical and Community
  College (U)
Clackamas Community College (U)
Clark State Community College (U)
Clemson University (N)
Cleveland State Community College (U)
Columbus State Community College (U)
Cuyahoga Community College (U)
Danville Community College (U)
Darton College (U)
Daytona State College (U)
De Anza College (U)
East Central Community College (U)
East Tennessee State University (N)
Elgin Community College (U)
Everett Community College (U)
Flathead Valley Community College (U)
Fox Valley Technical College (U)
Frank Phillips College (N)
Galveston College (U)
Gateway Technical College (U)
Georgia Highlands College (U)
Hagerstown Community College (N)
Harrisburg Area Community College (U)
Hocking College (U)
Ilisagvik College (U)
Indian River Community College (U)
James A. Rhodes State College (U)
Kirtland Community College (U)
Lamar State College–Port Arthur (N)
Laredo Community College (U)
Lock Haven University of Pennsylvania (N)
Marshalltown Community College (N,U)
McDowell Technical Community College (U)
Middle Tennessee State University (N)
Midstate College (U)
Minot State University–Bottineau Campus (U)
Montgomery Community College (N,U)

Moorpark College (U)
Mt. Hood Community College (U)
Murray State College (U)
National University (U)
New Mexico Junior College (U)
Northampton County Area Community
College (U)
North Central State College (U)
North Dakota State College of Science (U)
North Dakota State University (N)
Northwestern Connecticut Community College
(U)
Northwest Technical College (U)
Okaloosa-Walton College (U)
Okefenokee Technical College (N,U,G)
Orange Coast College (U)
Pamlico Community College (U)
Pasco-Hernando Community College (U)
Peninsula College (U)
Plymouth State University (N)
Portland Community College (U)
Pulaski Technical College (U)
Quinebaug Valley Community College (N)
Randolph Community College (N)
Rappahannock Community College (U)
The Richard Stockton College of New Jersey
(U,G)
Rose State College (U)
Sacramento City College (U)
Saint Charles Community College (U)
San Diego Community College District (U)
Santa Rosa Junior College (U)
South Piedmont Community College (U)
Southwest Wisconsin Technical College (U)
Tacoma Community College (U)
Texas State University–San Marcos (U)
Three Rivers Community College (N,U)
Tri-County Community College (U)
The University of Akron (N,U)
University of California, Davis (N,U)
University of Illinois at Chicago (N)
University of Northwestern Ohio (U)
The University of Texas System (N,G)
The University of Toledo (U)
Vincennes University (U)
Wake Technical Community College (U)
West Los Angeles College (U)
Wharton County Junior College (U)
Wilmington University (U)
Youngstown State University (N)

ALLIED HEALTH DIAGNOSTIC, INTERVENTION, AND TREATMENT PROFESSIONS

Arapahoe Community College (U)
Beaufort County Community College (U)
Brenau University (G)
California State University, San Bernardino
(G)
Capital Community College (U)
Columbus State Community College (U)
Danville Community College (U)
Darton College (U)
Eastern Washington University (N)
East Tennessee State University (U)
Galveston College (U)
James Madison University (N)
Jefferson College of Health Sciences (N,U)
John A. Logan College (U)
Labette Community College (U)
Lamar State College–Port Arthur (N)

Misericordia University (U)
Moorpark College (U)
NorthWest Arkansas Community College (U)
Okaloosa-Walton College (U)
Oregon Institute of Technology (U)
Randolph Community College (N)
Rose State College (U)
Sacramento City College (U)
Santa Monica College (U)
Saybrook Graduate School and Research
Center (G)
South Piedmont Community College (U)
State University of New York College at
Cortland (U,G)
Tacoma Community College (U)
The University of Akron (U)
University of Michigan–Flint (U)
University of Minnesota, Twin Cities Campus
(U)
University of the Sciences in Philadelphia (G)
University of Vermont (U)
University of West Florida (G)
Washburn University (U)

ALTERNATIVE AND COMPLEMENTARY MEDICAL SUPPORT SERVICES

Arapahoe Community College (U)
Atlantic University (N,G)
DePaul University (N)
Drexel University (G)
East Tennessee State University (N)
Lamar State College–Port Arthur (N)
Mt. San Antonio College (U)
Okaloosa-Walton College (U)
Rose State College (U)
Sacramento City College (U)
Saybrook Graduate School and Research
Center (G)
Treasure Valley Community College (U)
West Hills Community College (N)

ALTERNATIVE AND COMPLEMENTARY MEDICINE AND MEDICAL SYSTEMS

Arapahoe Community College (U)
Atlantic University (N,G)
California State University, Dominguez Hills
(N)
Drexel University (G)
Lamar State College–Port Arthur (N)
Rose State College (U)
Saybrook Graduate School and Research
Center (G)
West Hills Community College (N)

AMERICAN LITERATURE (UNITED STATES AND CANADIAN)

Allen County Community College (U)
Arapahoe Community College (U)
Bellevue Community College (U)
Bellevue University (U)
Bergen Community College (U)
Berkeley College (U)
Berkeley College–New York City Campus (U)
Berkeley College–Westchester Campus (U)
Blue Mountain Community College (U)
Bowling Green State University (U,G)

Brenau University (U)
Brigham Young University (U)
Burlington County College (U)
California State University, San Bernardino
(U)
Campbell University (U)
Central Carolina Community College (U)
Central Texas College (U)
Charter Oak State College (U)
Chemeketa Community College (U)
Cleveland Community College (U)
Columbia College (U)
Columbus State Community College (U)
Community College of Beaver County (U)
Cuyahoga Community College (U)
Dallas Baptist University (U)
Darton College (U)
Dawson Community College (U)
Delaware County Community College (U)
East Central Community College (U)
Elizabethtown College (U)
Everett Community College (U)
Excelsior College (U)
Galveston College (U)
Georgia State University (U)
Greenville Technical College (U)
Harrisburg Area Community College (U)
Hillsborough Community College (U)
Hofstra University (U)
Houston Community College System (U)
Jacksonville State University (U)
James Madison University (N)
Jefferson Community College (U)
J. Sargeant Reynolds Community College (U)
Lamar State College–Port Arthur (N)
Laredo Community College (U)
Lehigh Carbon Community College (U)
Limestone College (U)
Linn-Benton Community College (U)
Louisiana State University and Agricultural
and Mechanical College (U)
Manatee Community College (U)
Maranatha Baptist Bible College (U)
Mercy College (G)
Miami Dade College (U)
Middle Tennessee State University (U)
Minot State University (U)
Mississippi University for Women (U)
Monroe Community College (U)
Montgomery Community College (U)
Mt. Hood Community College (U)
Mount Olive College (U)
Murray State College (U)
Myers University (U)
Naugatuck Valley Community College (U)
New Mexico Junior College (U)
New River Community College (U)
North Carolina State University (U)
North Central Texas College (U)
Northeast Alabama Community College (U)
Oklahoma State University (U)
Oregon State University (U)
Oxnard College (U)
Pace University (U)
Pamlico Community College (U)
Park University (U)
Pellissippi State Technical Community
College (U)
Peninsula College (U)
Piedmont Technical College (U)
Pikes Peak Community College (U)
Pratt Community College (U)

Pulaski Technical College (U)
Rappahannock Community College (U)
Rose State College (U)
St. Cloud State University (U)
Saint Francis University (U)
St. Louis Community College System (U)
San Diego Community College District (U)
San Joaquin Delta College (U)
Spoon River College (U)
Sullivan County Community College (U)
Tacoma Community College (U)
Taylor University (U)
Texas State University–San Marcos (U)
Texas Tech University (U)
Three Rivers Community College (U)
Triton College (U)
Tyler Junior College (U)
The University of Alabama (U)
University of Alaska Fairbanks (U)
University of Arkansas at Pine Bluff (U)
University of Colorado at Colorado Springs (U)
University of Colorado Denver (U)
University of Maine at Machias (U)
University of Missouri–Columbia (U)
University of Nevada, Reno (U)
University of New Orleans (U,G)
The University of Tennessee (U)
The University of Texas of the Permian Basin (U)
University of Vermont (U)
University of Washington (U)
University of Waterloo (U)
University of Wisconsin–Superior (U)
University of Wyoming (U)
Utah Valley State College (U)
Wake Technical Community College (U)
Washburn University (U)
Westchester Community College (U)
Western Washington University (U)
West Los Angeles College (U)
West Shore Community College (U)
Wharton County Junior College (U)
Wilfrid Laurier University (U)
York County Community College (U)
Youngstown State University (N)

AMERICAN SIGN LANGUAGE (ASL)

Arapahoe Community College (U)
Blue Ridge Community College (U)
Bristol Community College (U)
Daemen College (U)
Hillsborough Community College (U)
James A. Rhodes State College (U)
John A. Logan College (U)
Missouri State University–West Plains (U)
New River Community College (U)
Palomar College (U)
Pine Technical College (U)
Presentation College (U)
Riverside Community College District (U)
Saddleback College (U)
San Diego Community College District (U)
Union County College (U)
University of Arkansas at Little Rock (U)
The University of Maine at Augusta (U)
University of Maine at Machias (U)
University of New Orleans (U,G)

ANIMAL SCIENCES

Auburn University (N,U)
Central Wyoming College (N)
Clemson University (G)
Colorado State University (N,U)
Duquesne University (N)
Fort Valley State University (U,G)
Haywood Community College (U)
Kansas State University (U,G)
Linn-Benton Community College (U)
Manor College (U)
Minnesota School of Business–Richfield (U)
Murray State University (U)
North Carolina State University (U)
Nova Scotia Agricultural College (N,U)
Oklahoma State University (U)
Plymouth State University (N)
State University of New York College of Technology at Canton (U)
Texas A&M University–Commerce (U)
Texas Tech University (G)
The University of Arizona (U)
University of Arkansas at Pine Bluff (U)
The University of British Columbia (U)
Virginia Polytechnic Institute and State University (N)
West Hills Community College (N)
Yuba College (U)

ANTHROPOLOGY

American University (U)
Arapahoe Community College (U)
Athabasca University (N,U)
Bellevue Community College (U)
Bergen Community College (U)
Berkeley College (U)
Berkeley College–New York City Campus (U)
Berkeley College–Westchester Campus (U)
Blue Mountain Community College (U)
Boise State University (U)
Brenau University (U)
Bridgewater State College (U)
Brigham Young University (U)
Broome Community College (U)
Broward Community College (U)
Burlington County College (U)
Cabrillo College (U)
California State University, Chico (U)
California State University, Sacramento (U)
Cayuga County Community College (U)
Central Arizona College (U)
Central Carolina Community College (U)
Centralia College (U)
Central Texas College (U)
Central Washington University (U)
Central Wyoming College (U)
Cerritos College (U)
Cerro Coso Community College (U)
Chaminade University of Honolulu (U)
Chemeketa Community College (U)
Citrus College (U)
Coastline Community College (U)
College of San Mateo (U)
Colorado Mountain College District System (U)
Colorado State University (U)
Columbia College (U)
Columbia International University (N,G)
Columbus State Community College (U)
Community College of Denver (U)
Crafton Hills College (U)

Cumberland County College (U)
Cuyahoga Community College (U)
Dallas County Community College District (U)
Dawson Community College (U)
De Anza College (U)
Delaware County Community College (U)
Diné College (U)
Eastern Kentucky University (U)
Eastern Oregon University (U)
Edison State Community College (U)
Elgin Community College (U)
Erie Community College (U)
Erie Community College, North Campus (U)
Erie Community College, South Campus (U)
Everett Community College (U)
Evergreen Valley College (U)
Flathead Valley Community College (U)
Foothill College (U)
Framingham State College (U)
Galveston College (U)
Genesee Community College (U)
Golden West College (U)
Governors State University (U,G)
Grand Rapids Community College (U)
Greenfield Community College (U)
Harrisburg Area Community College (U)
Haywood Community College (U)
Henry Ford Community College (U)
Hibbing Community College (U)
Hofstra University (U)
Honolulu Community College (U)
Hope International University (U)
Houston Community College System (U)
Indiana University of Pennsylvania (U)
Indian River Community College (U)
Jacksonville State University (U)
Johnson County Community College (U)
John Wood Community College (U)
Lake Superior College (U)
Linn-Benton Community College (U)
Long Beach City College (U)
Los Angeles Trade-Technical College (U)
Louisiana State University and Agricultural and Mechanical College (U)
Manatee Community College (U)
Massasoit Community College (U)
Memorial University of Newfoundland (U)
Mercer County Community College (U)
Metropolitan State University (U)
Middlesex Community College (U)
Minot State University (U)
Missouri State University (U)
Monmouth University (U)
Montgomery County Community College (U)
Moorpark College (U)
Mt. Hood Community College (U)
Mt. San Antonio College (U)
Murray State University (U)
Nassau Community College (U)
New York Institute of Technology (U)
Northampton County Area Community College (U)
North Arkansas College (U)
North Carolina State University (U)
North Seattle Community College (U)
Northwestern Michigan College (U)
Okaloosa-Walton College (U)
Oklahoma State University (U)
Orange Coast College (U)
Oregon Institute of Technology (U)
Oregon State University (U)

Oxnard College (U)
Pace University (U)
Palm Beach Community College (U)
Palomar College (U)
Parkland College (U)
Pellissippi State Technical Community College (U)
Peninsula College (U)
Pennsylvania Highlands Community College (U)
Pikes Peak Community College (U)
Portland Community College (U)
Pulaski Technical College (U)
Quinebaug Valley Community College (U)
Reading Area Community College (U)
Red Rocks Community College (U)
Regis University (G)
Rend Lake College (U)
The Richard Stockton College of New Jersey (U)
Riverside Community College District (U)
Rochester Institute of Technology (U)
Rockland Community College (U)
Sacramento City College (U)
Saddleback College (U)
Saint Charles Community College (U)
St. Cloud State University (U)
St. Edward's University (U)
Sam Houston State University (U)
San Diego Community College District (U)
San Joaquin Delta College (U)
Santa Rosa Junior College (U)
Seattle Central Community College (U)
Seminole Community College (U)
Sierra College (U)
Southeast Arkansas College (U)
State University of New York at Binghamton (U)
State University of New York at Oswego (U,G)
State University of New York at Plattsburgh (U)
State University of New York College at Cortland (U)
State University of New York College at Potsdam (U)
Syracuse University (G)
Tacoma Community College (U)
Temple University (U)
Texas Tech University (U)
Tri-County Community College (U)
Triton College (U)
Tunxis Community College (U)
The University of Akron (U)
University of Alaska Fairbanks (U)
The University of Arizona (U)
University of Arkansas at Little Rock (U)
University of Cincinnati (U)
University of Colorado Denver (U)
University of Hawaii–West Oahu (U)
University of Idaho (U)
University of Illinois at Urbana–Champaign (U)
The University of Kansas (U)
University of Louisville (U)
The University of Maine at Augusta (U)
University of Maine at Fort Kent (U)
University of Maryland University College (U)
University of Massachusetts Boston (U)
University of Missouri–Columbia (U)
University of Nevada, Reno (U)

University of New Orleans (U,G)
The University of North Carolina at Chapel Hill (U)
The University of North Carolina at Greensboro (U)
University of North Dakota (U)
University of North Texas (U,G)
University of Oklahoma (U)
University of Pennsylvania (U,G)
University of Saskatchewan (U)
University of Southern Maine (U)
University of Southern Mississippi (U)
University of South Florida (U)
The University of Tennessee (U)
The University of Texas at El Paso (U)
The University of Texas at San Antonio (U)
The University of Texas at Tyler (U)
University of Utah (U)
University of Vermont (U)
University of Washington (U)
University of Waterloo (U)
University of West Florida (U)
University of Wisconsin Colleges (U)
University of Wisconsin–Whitewater (U)
Utah State University (U)
Utah Valley State College (U)
Wake Technical Community College (U)
Washington State University (U)
Weber State University (U)
Westchester Community College (U)
Western Michigan University (U)
Western Washington University (U)
Western Wyoming Community College (U)
West Los Angeles College (U)
Wichita State University (U)
Wilfrid Laurier University (U)
Yuba College (U)

APPAREL AND TEXTILES

Academy of Art University (U,G)
Arapahoe Community College (U)
Blackhawk Technical College (N)
Drexel University (U)
Kansas State University (G)
Missouri State University (U)
Nassau Community College (U)
North Carolina State University (U)
NorthWest Arkansas Community College (U)
Philadelphia University (G)
Rose State College (U)
San Diego Community College District (N,U)
University of Arkansas at Pine Bluff (U)
University of North Texas (U,G)
Virginia Polytechnic Institute and State University (U)
Western Michigan University (U)

APPLIED HORTICULTURE/ HORTICULTURAL BUSINESS SERVICES

Central Wyoming College (N)
Cincinnati State Technical and Community College (U)
Clark State Community College (U)
Haywood Community College (U)
Kansas State University (U)
Lakeland Community College (N)
Minot State University–Bottineau Campus (U)
Naugatuck Valley Community College (U)
Oklahoma State University (U)

Texas Tech University (U)
University of California, Riverside (N)
University of Minnesota, Twin Cities Campus (U)
University of Saskatchewan (N)
Virginia Polytechnic Institute and State University (N,U,G)
West Hills Community College (N)

APPLIED MATHEMATICS

Anne Arundel Community College (U)
Arapahoe Community College (U)
Beulah Heights University (U)
Blue Mountain Community College (U)
Bowling Green State University (U)
Butler Community College (U)
California Polytechnic State University, San Luis Obispo (U)
California State University, San Marcos (U)
Central Texas College (U)
Central Virginia Community College (U)
Chadron State College (U)
Chemeketa Community College (U)
Clinton Community College (U)
Columbia University (N,G)
Corning Community College (U)
Darton College (U)
Delaware Technical & Community College, Jack F. Owens Campus (U)
Eastern Michigan University (U)
Embry-Riddle Aeronautical University (U)
Eugene Bible College (U)
Everett Community College (U)
Fox Valley Technical College (U)
Georgia Institute of Technology (G)
Grand Rapids Community College (N,U)
Harrisburg Area Community College (U)
Henry Ford Community College (U)
Hillsborough Community College (U)
Holyoke Community College (U)
Jacksonville State University (U)
James Madison University (N)
Lakeland Community College (U)
Laredo Community College (U)
Linn-Benton Community College (U)
Lock Haven University of Pennsylvania (U)
Macon State College (U)
Manatee Community College (U)
Midstate College (U)
Misericordia University (U)
Mt. Hood Community College (U)
Murray State College (U)
Myers University (U)
Naugatuck Valley Community College (U)
Northampton County Area Community College (U)
North Dakota State College of Science (U)
North Dakota State University (U)
Northeast Iowa Community College (U)
North Iowa Area Community College (U)
NorthWest Arkansas Community College (U)
Northwest Technical College (U)
Okaloosa-Walton College (U)
Oxnard College (U)
Pamlico Community College (U)
Pulaski Technical College (U)
Red Rocks Community College (U)
The Richard Stockton College of New Jersey (U)
Sacramento City College (U)
San Diego Community College District (U)

Seminole Community College (U)
Sierra College (U)
Southeast Arkansas College (U)
South Piedmont Community College (U)
Southwest Wisconsin Technical College (U)
Tacoma Community College (U)
Taft College (U)
Taylor University (N)
The University of Akron (G)
University of Alaska Fairbanks (U)
University of Idaho (G)
The University of Maine at Augusta (U)
University of Management and Technology (U)
University of New Orleans (U,G)
The University of Tennessee (U)
University of Washington (U)
Utah State University (U)
Vincennes University (U)
Western Wyoming Community College (U)
West Los Angeles College (U)
Wisconsin Indianhead Technical College (N,U)
York County Community College (U)
Yuba College (U)

ARCHEOLOGY

Bellevue Community College (U)
Blue Mountain Community College (U)
Chemeketa Community College (U)
Cuyahoga Community College (U)
Erie Community College (U)
Erie Community College, North Campus (U)
Erie Community College, South Campus (U)
Foothill College (U)
Golden West College (U)
James Madison University (N)
Palomar College (U)
Pellissippi State Technical Community College (U)
State University of New York at Oswego (U)
The University of Akron (U)
University of Arkansas at Little Rock (U)
University of California, Los Angeles (G)
University of Louisville (U)
University of Massachusetts Boston (U)
University of Saskatchewan (U)
University of South Florida (U)
The University of Texas at Tyler (U)
University of Washington (U)
University of West Florida (U)

ARCHITECTURAL ENGINEERING

Georgia Institute of Technology (G)
Sinclair Community College (U)
University of Arkansas at Pine Bluff (U)
University of New Orleans (U,G)

ARCHITECTURAL ENGINEERING TECHNOLOGY

Honolulu Community College (U)
University of New Orleans (U,G)

ARCHITECTURAL HISTORY AND CRITICISM

Massachusetts College of Art and Design (U)
Riverside Community College District (U)
Vermont Technical College (U)

ARCHITECTURAL TECHNOLOGY

Wake Technical Community College (U)

ARCHITECTURE

Bowling Green State University (U)
Grand Rapids Community College (U)
James Madison University (N)
Massachusetts College of Art and Design (U)
Pennsylvania College of Technology (U)
Prairie View A&M University (U)
Riverside Community College District (U)
Santa Monica College (U)
Temple University (U)
Texas Tech University (G)
Triton College (U)
University of Colorado Denver (G)
University of Illinois at Urbana–Champaign (N)
The University of North Carolina at Charlotte (N)
Virginia Polytechnic Institute and State University (N)

ARCHITECTURE RELATED

Arapahoe Community College (U)
Central Michigan University (U)
Georgia Institute of Technology (G)
Lawrence Technological University (G)
University of Illinois at Urbana–Champaign (N)

AREA STUDIES

Acadia University (N)
American Public University System (U)
California Institute of Integral Studies (N,G)
De Anza College (U)
Delaware County Community College (U)
Naropa University (N)
Oxnard College (U)
Southwestern Community College (U)
Taylor University (U)
Triton College (U)
The University of British Columbia (U)
University of Maryland University College (U)
University of Missouri–Columbia (U)
University of Nevada, Reno (U)
University of North Alabama (U,G)
The University of North Carolina at Chapel Hill (U)
University of Northern Iowa (U)
University of South Florida (U)
University of Waterloo (U)
Western Michigan University (U)
Western Washington University (U)

AREA, ETHNIC, CULTURAL, AND GENDER STUDIES RELATED

Arapahoe Community College (U)
Berkeley College (U)
Berkeley College–New York City Campus (U)
Berkeley College–Westchester Campus (U)
California State University, Chico (U)
California State University, San Bernardino (U)
Centennial College (U)
Central Texas College (U)
Central Wyoming College (N,U)

Chemeketa Community College (U)
Cleveland State University (U,G)
Columbia College (U)
Cuyahoga Community College (U)
Delaware County Community College (U)
DeVry University Online (U)
Diné College (U)
Edgecombe Community College (N)
Elizabethtown College (U)
Everett Community College (U)
Foothill College (U)
Georgia State University (U)
Hibbing Community College (U)
Kansas State University (U)
Louisiana State University and Agricultural and Mechanical College (U)
Massachusetts College of Art and Design (U)
Mercy College (U)
Middlesex Community College (U)
Middle Tennessee State University (N,U)
Moorpark College (U)
Naropa University (N,U,G)
Oregon State University (U)
Oxnard College (U)
Palomar College (U)
Park University (U)
Prescott College (G)
Providence College and Theological Seminary (N,G)
Sacramento City College (U)
San Diego Community College District (U)
Sierra College (U)
State University of New York at Binghamton (U)
State University of New York at Plattsburgh (U)
Strayer University (U)
Taylor University (U)
Temple University (U)
Tunxis Community College (U)
The University of Akron (N,U)
University of Arkansas at Little Rock (U)
University of Bridgeport (U)
University of Colorado at Colorado Springs (U)
University of Connecticut (U)
University of Illinois at Urbana–Champaign (U)
The University of Kansas (U)
University of Minnesota, Duluth (U)
University of Missouri–Columbia (U)
University of Nevada, Reno (U)
University of New Orleans (U,G)
The University of North Carolina at Chapel Hill (N)
University of South Florida (U)
The University of Toledo (U)
University of Utah (U)
University of Waterloo (U)
University of Wisconsin–Whitewater (U,G)
Westchester Community College (U)
West Los Angeles College (U)

ARMY J.R.O.T.C/R.O.T.C

Eastern Michigan University (U)
John Wood Community College (U)
The University of Akron (U)

ASTRONOMY AND ASTROPHYSICS

Arapahoe Community College (U)
Athabasca University (N,U)

Austin Peay State University (U)
Bellevue Community College (U)
Brenau University (U)
Brigham Young University (U)
Butler Community College (U)
California State University, San Bernardino (U)
Central Virginia Community College (U)
Chemeketa Community College (U)
Citrus College (U)
Clackamas Community College (U)
Clemson University (U)
Coastline Community College (U)
College of San Mateo (U)
College of Southern Maryland (U)
Colorado Mountain College District System (U)
Columbia College (U)
Community College of Denver (U)
Crafton Hills College (U)
Culver-Stockton College (U)
Dallas County Community College District (U)
Delaware County Community College (U)
Eastern Illinois University (U)
Evergreen Valley College (U)
Grand Rapids Community College (U)
Greenville Technical College (U)
Harrisburg Area Community College (U)
Henry Ford Community College (U)
Hillsborough Community College (U)
Honolulu Community College (U)
Hopkinsville Community College (U)
Houston Community College System (U)
Illinois Eastern Community Colleges, Lincoln Trail College (U)
James Madison University (N)
John Wood Community College (U)
Judson University (U)
Lake Superior College (U)
Lamar State College–Port Arthur (U)
Lehigh Carbon Community College (U)
Limestone College (U)
Linn-Benton Community College (U)
Long Beach City College (U)
Los Angeles Trade-Technical College (U)
Maranatha Baptist Bible College (U)
Michigan Technological University (N,U)
Middlesex Community College (U)
Middle Tennessee State University (U)
Missouri State University (U)
Montgomery County Community College (U)
Mountain Empire Community College (U)
Nassau Community College (U)
Naugatuck Valley Community College (U)
Northampton County Area Community College (U)
Northeast State Technical Community College (U)
North Seattle Community College (U)
Oxnard College (U)
Palm Beach Community College (U)
Parkland College (U)
Peninsula College (U)
Pennsylvania Highlands Community College (U)
Pikes Peak Community College (U)
Red Rocks Community College (U)
Riverside Community College District (U)
Sacramento City College (U)
St. Clair County Community College (U)
St. Cloud State University (U)

San Diego Community College District (U)
San Joaquin Delta College (U)
Santa Rosa Junior College (U)
Schenectady County Community College (U)
Seattle Pacific University (G)
Seminole Community College (U)
Sierra College (U)
Southeastern Oklahoma State University (U)
Stephen F. Austin State University (U)
Triton College (U)
Tyler Junior College (U)
Union County College (U)
The University of Akron (U)
The University of Alabama (U)
University of Arkansas at Little Rock (U)
University of La Verne (N)
University of Maine at Fort Kent (U)
University of Minnesota, Duluth (U)
University of Missouri–Columbia (U)
The University of North Carolina at Chapel Hill (U)
University of Oklahoma (U)
University of Oregon (U)
The University of Tennessee (U)
University of the Virgin Islands (U)
University of Washington (U)
University of Waterloo (U)
University of Wisconsin–Superior (U)
University of Wyoming (U)
Upper Iowa University (U)
Utah Valley State College (U)
Wake Technical Community College (U)
Wichita State University (U)
Wilfrid Laurier University (U)
Yuba College (U)

ATMOSPHERIC SCIENCES AND METEOROLOGY

Bellevue Community College (U)
Carroll Community College (U)
Central Wyoming College (U)
Clarion University of Pennsylvania (U)
Dallas Baptist University (U)
Delaware County Community College (U)
Jacksonville State University (U)
Miami Dade College (U)
Millersville University of Pennsylvania (U)
Mountain Empire Community College (U)
Nassau Community College (U)
Oregon State University (U)
Santa Rosa Junior College (U)
Seminole Community College (U)
The University of Arizona (U)
University of Arkansas at Little Rock (U)
University of California, Riverside (N)
The University of Kansas (U)
University of Missouri–Columbia (U)
University of the Virgin Islands (U)
University of Washington (U)
Utah Valley State College (U)

AUDIOVISUAL COMMUNICATIONS TECHNOLOGIES

Arapahoe Community College (U)
Hofstra University (U)
Lackawanna College (U)
Rose State College (U)
Sacramento City College (U)
San Diego Community College District (U)
The University of Akron (U)

University of Southern Indiana (N)
University of the Virgin Islands (U)

BEHAVIORAL SCIENCES

Allen County Community College (U)
Anne Arundel Community College (U)
Arapahoe Community College (U)
Barclay College (U)
Berkeley College–New York City Campus (U)
Boise State University (U)
Butler Community College (U)
California State University, Chico (U)
Canisius College (G)
Capital Community College (U)
Central Michigan University (U,G)
Charter Oak State College (U)
Chatham University (U)
Citrus College (U)
Clark State Community College (U)
College of the Sequoias (U)
Columbia College (U)
Community College of Beaver County (U)
Dallas Christian College (U)
Danville Community College (U)
Daytona State College (U)
East Tennessee State University (N)
Excelsior College (U)
Fitchburg State College (U,G)
Florida Institute of Technology (N)
Fort Valley State University (U)
Galveston College (U)
Golden West College (U)
Graceland University (U)
Grand Rapids Community College (U)
Granite State College (U)
Haywood Community College (U)
Hope International University (U)
Jacksonville State University (U,G)
Jefferson Community College (U)
Johnson State College (U)
Judson College (U)
Kansas State University (U)
Lackawanna College (U)
Medical College of Wisconsin (G)
Middlesex Community College (U)
Mississippi Delta Community College (U)
Moorpark College (U)
Murray State College (U)
Nassau Community College (U)
Naugatuck Valley Community College (U)
Northampton County Area Community College (U)
North Central State College (U)
Northeast Alabama Community College (U)
NorthWest Arkansas Community College (U)
Northwest Technical College (U)
Okaloosa-Walton College (U)
Oklahoma Panhandle State University (U)
Ouachita Technical College (U)
Palomar College (U)
Pamlico Community College (U)
Pellissippi State Technical Community College (U)
St. Cloud State University (G)
Saint Francis University (U)
Santa Monica College (U)
Santa Rosa Junior College (U)
Seminole Community College (U)
Sinclair Community College (U)
South Piedmont Community College (U)
State University of New York College at Potsdam (U)

Sullivan County Community College (U)
Tacoma Community College (U)
Taylor University (U)
Texas State University–San Marcos (U)
Union University (U)
The University of Akron (U)
University of Alaska, Prince William Sound
  Community College (U)
University of Connecticut (U)
The University of Kansas (G)
University of Louisville (U)
The University of Maine at Augusta (U)
University of Maine at Fort Kent (U)
University of Management and Technology
  (U)
University of Missouri–Columbia (U)
University of New Orleans (U,G)
University of North Dakota (U)
University of North Texas (N,U,G)
The University of South Dakota (U)
The University of Texas at Brownsville (U)
The University of Texas of the Permian Basin
  (U)
University of the Pacific (N,U)
University of West Florida (G)
Utah Valley State College (U)
Vincennes University (U)
Westchester Community College (U)
West Los Angeles College (U)
Wharton County Junior College (U)
Yuba College (U)

BIBLICAL AND OTHER THEOLOGICAL LANGUAGES AND LITERATURES

Abilene Christian University (U)
Assemblies of God Theological Seminary (G)
Beacon University (N,G)
Beulah Heights University (U,G)
Black Hills State University (U)
Calvin Theological Seminary (G)
The Catholic Distance University (N,U,G)
Central Bible College (N)
Cincinnati Christian University (U,G)
Cleveland State Community College (U)
College of Emmanuel and St. Chad (G)
Columbia International University (G)
Dallas Christian College (U)
Denver Seminary (G)
Earlham School of Religion (G)
Eugene Bible College (U)
Global University (N)
Gordon-Conwell Theological Seminary (N,G)
Grand Rapids Theological Seminary of
  Cornerstone University (N,G)
Hebrew College (N,U,G)
Heritage Christian University (N,U,G)
Horizon College & Seminary (U)
Immaculata University (U)
Indiana Wesleyan University (U)
Lamar State College–Port Arthur (U)
Liberty University (U)
Life Pacific College (N)
Lincoln Christian College (N,U,G)
Master's College and Seminary (U)
New Mexico Junior College (U)
Peninsula College (U)
Providence College and Theological Seminary
  (N,U,G)
Saint Francis University (U)
San Joaquin Delta College (U)

Santa Monica College (U)
Southwestern Adventist University (U)
Taylor University (N,U)
Trinity Episcopal School for Ministry (G)
University of Missouri–Columbia (U)
University of Waterloo (U)
Western Seminary (N,G)
Western Washington University (U)

BIBLICAL STUDIES

Abilene Christian University (U,G)
Andover Newton Theological School (N,G)
Arlington Baptist College (N,U)
Assemblies of God Theological Seminary (G)
Atlantic University (N,G)
Bakke Graduate University (G)
Baltimore Hebrew University (G)
The Baptist College of Florida (U)
Barclay College (U)
Beacon University (N,U,G)
Beulah Heights University (U)
Bowling Green State University (U)
Calvin Theological Seminary (G)
Campbell University (U)
Central Bible College (N,U)
Central Carolina Community College (U)
Central Texas College (U)
Cincinnati Christian University (U,G)
Clear Creek Baptist Bible College (N,U)
College of Emmanuel and St. Chad (G)
Columbia International University (N,U,G)
Conception Seminary College (U,G)
Concordia College–New York (U)
Corban College (U)
Covenant Theological Seminary (N,G)
Crown College (G)
Dallas Baptist University (U)
Dallas Christian College (U)
Defiance College (U)
Denver Seminary (G)
Earlham School of Religion (G)
East Central Community College (U)
Eastern Mennonite University (G)
Eastern University (N,U)
Eugene Bible College (U)
Global University (N)
Gordon-Conwell Theological Seminary (N,G)
Grand Rapids Theological Seminary of
  Cornerstone University (N,G)
Hebrew College (N,U,G)
Heritage Christian University (N,U,G)
Hobe Sound Bible College (N,U)
Hope International University (N,U,G)
Horizon College & Seminary (U,G)
Indiana Wesleyan University (U)
Johnson Bible College (U,G)
Judson College (U)
Judson University (U)
Liberty University (U,G)
Life Pacific College (N,U)
Limestone College (U)
Lincoln Christian College (N,U,G)
Lipscomb University (U,G)
Malone College (U,G)
Maranatha Baptist Bible College (U,G)
Master's College and Seminary (U)
McMurry University (U)
Miami Dade College (U)
Montgomery Community College (N)
Mount Olive College (U)
Park University (U)

Patrick Henry College (U)
Providence College and Theological Seminary
  (N,U,G)
Regent College (N,U,G)
Regent University (G)
Saint Francis University (U)
Saint Joseph's College of Maine (N,U)
Shasta Bible College (N,U)
Summit Pacific College (N,U)
Taylor University (N,U)
Trinity Episcopal School for Ministry (N,G)
Unification Theological Seminary (N,G)
The University of Findlay (U)
University of Southern Mississippi (U)
University of the Southwest (U)
University of Waterloo (U)
Western Seminary (N,G)
Williamson Christian College (U)

BILINGUAL, MULTILINGUAL, AND MULTICULTURAL EDUCATION

Baltimore City Community College (U)
California State University, San Bernardino
  (U)
East Carolina University (U)
Golden West College (U)
Hamline University (G)
Indiana State University (G)
Middle Tennessee State University (N)
Murray State University (G)
New Mexico Highlands University (U,G)
North Lake College (U)
Northwestern Oklahoma State University (G)
Okaloosa-Walton College (U)
Oxnard College (U)
Pace University (U,G)
Palomar College (U)
Plymouth State University (U)
Prescott College (U)
Sacramento City College (U)
Seattle Pacific University (G)
Tacoma Community College (U)
Texas A&M University–Kingsville (U,G)
Texas Woman's University (G)
Triton College (U)
The University of Akron (U,G)
University of Alaska Fairbanks (U)
University of Arkansas at Pine Bluff (N,U)
University of North Dakota (U)
The University of Texas at Brownsville (U)
University of the Southwest (U)

BIOCHEMISTRY, BIOPHYSICS AND MOLECULAR BIOLOGY

Arapahoe Community College (U)
Athens Technical College (U)
Barton County Community College (U)
Chatham University (U)
Drake University (U)
Graceland University (U)
Huntington College of Health Sciences (U)
Kansas State University (U)
McMurry University (U)
Palomar College (U)
Peninsula College (U)
Santa Monica College (U)
State University of New York at Plattsburgh
  (U)
The University of Akron (U)
University of Colorado Denver (U)

University of Minnesota, Twin Cities Campus (U,G)
University of Southern Mississippi (G)
University of Waterloo (U)

BIOETHICS/MEDICAL ETHICS

Arapahoe Community College (U)
Cleveland State University (U,G)
Judson College (U)
Lock Haven University of Pennsylvania (U)
Medical College of Wisconsin (G)
Saint Francis University (U,G)
Triton College (U)
University of Louisville (G)
University of New Orleans (U)

BIOLOGICAL AND BIOMEDICAL SCIENCES RELATED

Athabasca University (U)
Brigham Young University (U)
Cabrillo College (U)
Caldwell Community College and Technical Institute (U)
Chemeketa Community College (U)
Clark State Community College (U)
Cleveland State University (U)
Coastline Community College (U)
Columbia College (U)
Columbus State Community College (U)
Danville Community College (U)
Darton College (U)
DeVry University Online (U)
Eastern Illinois University (U)
Erie Community College (U)
Erie Community College, North Campus (U)
Erie Community College, South Campus (U)
George Mason University (G)
Immaculata University (U)
Jacksonville State University (U)
James Madison University (N)
Lake Region State College (U)
Laredo Community College (U)
Miami Dade College (U)
Michigan Technological University (U)
Middlesex Community College (U)
Minot State University–Bottineau Campus (U)
Northampton County Area Community College (U)
Oxnard College (U)
Pennsylvania College of Technology (U)
Reading Area Community College (U)
Roosevelt University (U)
Sacramento City College (U)
Saint Leo University (U)
Southeast Community College Area (U)
South Piedmont Community College (U)
University of Colorado at Colorado Springs (U)
University of New Orleans (U,G)
University of Pennsylvania (N)
University of South Alabama (U)
University of Waterloo (U)
University of West Florida (U)
University of Wyoming (U)
Western Michigan University (U)

BIOLOGICAL AND PHYSICAL SCIENCES

Allen County Community College (U)
Anne Arundel Community College (U)

Athabasca University (U)
Avila University (U)
Baltimore City Community College (U)
Beacon University (N,U)
Bellevue University (U)
Berkeley College (U)
Berkeley College–New York City Campus (U)
Berkeley College–Westchester Campus (U)
Boise State University (U)
Cabrillo College (U)
Caldwell Community College and Technical Institute (U)
Cayuga County Community College (U)
Central Carolina Community College (U)
Chadron State College (U)
Chemeketa Community College (U)
Citrus College (U)
Clark State Community College (U)
Cleveland State Community College (U)
Clinton Community College (U)
Dallas Baptist University (U)
Daytona State College (U)
Delaware County Community College (U)
Diné College (U)
East Central Community College (U)
Eastern Illinois University (U)
Eastern Michigan University (U)
Eugene Bible College (U)
Eugenio María de Hostos Community College of the City University of New York (U)
Ferris State University (U)
Fitchburg State College (U)
Flathead Valley Community College (U)
Fort Hays State University (U)
George C. Wallace Community College (U)
Golden West College (U)
Greenfield Community College (U)
Gulf Coast Community College (U)
Harrisburg Area Community College (U)
Hibbing Community College (U)
Hopkinsville Community College (U)
Huntington College of Health Sciences (U)
Immaculata University (U)
Indiana State University (U)
Jacksonville State University (U)
James Madison University (N)
Jefferson College (U)
Judson College (U)
Kansas State University (U)
Kaskaskia College (U)
Kentucky State University (U,G)
Lake Superior College (U)
Laredo Community College (U)
Lehigh University (G)
Louisiana State University and Agricultural and Mechanical College (U)
Massasoit Community College (U)
Mercy College (U)
Miami Dade College (U)
Middlesex Community College (U)
Midway College (U)
Mississippi Delta Community College (U)
Mississippi State University (U)
Murray State College (U)
National University (U)
New River Community College (U)
Northampton County Area Community College (U)
North Arkansas College (U)
North Carolina State University (U,G)
North Central State College (U)
Northeast Iowa Community College (U)

Northeast State Technical Community College (U)
Northern State University (U)
North Lake College (U)
North Seattle Community College (U)
Northwestern Connecticut Community College (U)
Northwestern State University of Louisiana (U)
Northwest Technical College (U)
Okaloosa-Walton College (U)
Oklahoma Panhandle State University (U)
Ouachita Technical College (U)
Pace University (U)
Palm Beach Community College (U)
Palomar College (U)
Pamlico Community College (U)
Patrick Henry Community College (U)
Peninsula College (U)
Pikes Peak Community College (U)
Quinebaug Valley Community College (U)
Sacramento City College (U)
Sacred Heart University (U)
Saint Francis University (U)
St. Louis Community College System (U)
San Diego Community College District (U)
Santa Monica College (U)
Seminole Community College (U)
Southern Arkansas University Tech (U)
Sullivan County Community College (U)
Syracuse University (U)
Tacoma Community College (U)
Taft College (U)
Taylor University (U)
Texas State University–San Marcos (U)
Union County College (U)
Union University (U)
The University of Akron (U)
The University of Alabama (U)
University of Alaska Anchorage, Kodiak College (U)
University of Alaska Fairbanks (U)
University of Arkansas at Pine Bluff (U)
University of Massachusetts Boston (G)
University of New Orleans (U,G)
University of Pennsylvania (U)
The University of Texas at San Antonio (U)
University of Waterloo (U)
Upper Iowa University (N)
Utah Valley State College (U)
Westchester Community College (U)
Western Michigan University (U)
Western Wyoming Community College (U)
West Virginia University at Parkersburg (U)
York Technical College (U)

BIOLOGY

Acadia University (U)
Adams State College (G)
Allen County Community College (U)
Arapahoe Community College (U)
Arkansas State University–Mountain Home (U)
Arkansas Tech University (U)
Athabasca University (N,U)
Baltimore City Community College (U)
Bellevue Community College (U)
Blue Mountain Community College (U)
Bowling Green State University (U,G)
Brigham Young University (U)
Bristol Community College (U)

Broome Community College (U)
Broward Community College (U)
Burlington County College (U)
Caldwell Community College and Technical Institute (U)
California State University, Dominguez Hills (U)
Capital Community College (U)
Carlow University (U)
Carroll Community College (U)
Cayuga County Community College (U)
Centennial College (U)
Central New Mexico Community College (U)
Central Virginia Community College (U)
Central Washington University (U)
Central Wyoming College (U)
Chatham University (U,G)
Chemeketa Community College (U)
Citrus College (U)
City Colleges of Chicago, Harold Washington College (U)
Clackamas Community College (U)
Clarion University of Pennsylvania (U)
Clark State Community College (U)
Cleveland Community College (U)
Cleveland State University (U)
Coastline Community College (U)
The College of St. Scholastica (U,G)
College of Southern Maryland (U)
College of The Albemarle (U)
Colorado Mountain College District System (U)
Colorado State University (U)
Community College of Denver (U)
Crafton Hills College (U)
Culver-Stockton College (U)
Cuyahoga Community College (U)
Dallas Baptist University (U)
Dallas Christian College (U)
Dallas County Community College District (U)
Danville Community College (U)
Dawson Community College (U)
De Anza College (U)
Delaware County Community College (U)
DeSales University (U)
Diné College (U)
East Carolina University (U)
Eastern Illinois University (U)
Eastern Kentucky University (U)
Eastern Michigan University (U)
Eastern Oregon University (U)
Eastern Wyoming College (U)
Edison State Community College (U)
Elizabeth City State University (U)
Eugene Bible College (U)
Everett Community College (U)
Excelsior College (U)
Finger Lakes Community College (U)
Fort Valley State University (U)
Framingham State College (U)
Frank Phillips College (U)
Gadsden State Community College (U)
Galveston College (U)
George C. Wallace Community College (U)
Georgia Highlands College (U)
Georgia State University (U)
Golden West College (U)
Graceland University (U)
Harford Community College (U)
Henderson Community College (U)
Herkimer County Community College (U)

Hillsborough Community College (U)
Hofstra University (U)
Houston Community College System (U)
Huntington College of Health Sciences (U)
Immaculata University (U)
Indiana State University (U)
Indiana University–Purdue University Fort Wayne (U)
Indian River Community College (U)
Ivy Tech Community College–North Central (U)
Ivy Tech Community College–Wabash Valley (U)
Jackson State University (U)
Jacksonville State University (U,G)
James Madison University (U)
Jefferson College (U)
Jefferson Community College (U)
John A. Logan College (U)
Johnson County Community College (U)
Johnson State College (U)
J. Sargeant Reynolds Community College (U)
Kean University (U)
Kirtland Community College (U)
Lakeland Community College (U)
Lake Region State College (U)
Laredo Community College (U)
Lehigh Carbon Community College (U)
Liberty University (U)
Limestone College (U)
Long Beach City College (U)
Louisiana State University and Agricultural and Mechanical College (N,U)
Lurleen B. Wallace Community College (U)
Malone College (U)
Manatee Community College (U)
Marian College of Fond du Lac (U)
Mayville State University (U)
McMurry University (U)
Memorial University of Newfoundland (U)
Mercy College (U)
Mesa Community College (U)
Mesa State College (U)
Miami Dade College (U)
Middlesex Community College (U)
Minnesota School of Business–Richfield (U)
Mississippi State University (U)
Moberly Area Community College (U)
Monroe Community College (U)
Montcalm Community College (U)
Montgomery County Community College (U)
Mountain Empire Community College (U)
Mt. Hood Community College (U)
Mount Olive College (U)
Mt. San Antonio College (U)
Mount Wachusett Community College (U)
Murray State College (U)
Nassau Community College (U)
Naugatuck Valley Community College (U)
New Mexico Junior College (U)
New River Community College (U)
New York Institute of Technology (U)
Northampton County Area Community College (U)
North Central Texas College (U)
North Dakota State College of Science (U)
Northeast Alabama Community College (U)
Northeast Iowa Community College (U)
Northern Virginia Community College (U)
North Iowa Area Community College (U)
North Lake College (U)

Northland Community and Technical College–Thief River Falls (U)
NorthWest Arkansas Community College (U)
Northwestern Michigan College (U)
Okaloosa-Walton College (U)
Oklahoma Panhandle State University (U)
Orange Coast College (U)
Ouachita Technical College (U)
Oxnard College (U)
Pace University (U)
Palomar College (U)
Pamlico Community College (U)
Parkland College (U)
Park University (U)
Pasco-Hernando Community College (U)
Patrick Henry College (U)
Pellissippi State Technical Community College (U)
Pennsylvania College of Technology (U)
Piedmont Community College (U)
Piedmont Technical College (U)
Portland Community College (U)
Pratt Community College (U)
Pulaski Technical College (U)
Queen's University at Kingston (U)
Randolph Community College (N)
Rend Lake College (U)
Rockland Community College (U)
Rose State College (U)
Sacramento City College (U)
Saint Charles Community College (U)
St. Cloud State University (U)
Saint Francis University (U)
St. Joseph's College, Long Island Campus (U)
St. Joseph's College, New York (U)
San Diego Community College District (U)
Santa Monica College (U)
Schenectady County Community College (U)
Shippensburg University of Pennsylvania (U,G)
Sierra College (U)
Southeastern Community College (U)
Southeastern Oklahoma State University (U)
South Piedmont Community College (U)
Southwestern Community College (U)
Spoon River College (U)
State University of New York at Oswego (U)
State University of New York at Plattsburgh (U)
State University of New York College at Potsdam (U)
State University of New York Empire State College (U)
Tacoma Community College (U)
Taylor University (U)
Texas A&M University–Commerce (U)
Texas Christian University (U)
Texas State University–San Marcos (U)
Three Rivers Community College (U)
Treasure Valley Community College (U)
Tri-County Community College (U)
Triton College (U)
Tyler Junior College (U)
The University of Akron (U)
The University of Alabama (U)
University of Alaska Fairbanks (U)
University of Arkansas at Little Rock (U,G)
University of Arkansas at Pine Bluff (U)
University of Cincinnati Raymond Walters College (U)
University of Colorado Denver (U)
University of Dubuque (U)

University of Houston–Victoria (U)
University of Idaho (U)
The University of Kansas (U)
University of Maryland University College (U)
University of Massachusetts Boston (U)
University of Minnesota, Crookston (U)
University of Minnesota, Twin Cities Campus (U)
University of Missouri–Columbia (U)
University of New Orleans (U,G)
The University of North Carolina at Chapel Hill (U)
The University of North Carolina at Charlotte (G)
University of North Texas (U)
University of Pittsburgh at Bradford (U)
University of South Alabama (G)
The University of South Dakota (U)
University of Southern Indiana (U)
University of Southern Mississippi (U,G)
University of South Florida (U)
The University of Texas at San Antonio (U,G)
The University of Texas at Tyler (U)
The University of Texas System (U)
University of the Southwest (U)
University of Utah (U)
University of Waterloo (U)
University of West Florida (U)
University of Wisconsin Colleges (U)
University of Wisconsin–Superior (U)
Upper Iowa University (N,U)
Utah State University (U)
Utah Valley State College (U)
Utica College (U)
Wake Technical Community College (U)
Washburn University (U)
Westchester Community College (U)
Westfield State College (U)
West Shore Community College (U)
West Virginia University at Parkersburg (U)
Wharton County Junior College (U)
Wilfrid Laurier University (U)
Williston State College (U)
Worcester State College (U)
Wytheville Community College (U)
Yuba College (U)

BIOLOGY/BIOTECHNOLOGY LABORATORY TECHNICIAN

Athens Technical College (U)
Charter Oak State College (U)
Clark State Community College (U)
Cleveland Community College (U)
University of Minnesota, Twin Cities Campus (U)

BIOMATHEMATICS AND BIOINFORMATICS

Eastern Michigan University (G)
Wake Technical Community College (U)

BIOMEDICAL/MEDICAL ENGINEERING

Central Carolina Community College (U)
Columbia University (G)
Georgia Institute of Technology (G)
Stanford University (G)
University of Colorado at Boulder (N,G)

University of South Florida (G)

BIOPSYCHOLOGY

Golden West College (U)
Jacksonville State University (U)
Johnson State College (U)
State University of New York at Plattsburgh (U)
University of Minnesota, Twin Cities Campus (U)
Wilfrid Laurier University (U)

BIOTECHNOLOGY

Central Carolina Community College (U)
Cleveland Community College (U)
Eastern Michigan University (U)
Stanford University (G)
Tompkins Cortland Community College (U)

BOTANY/PLANT BIOLOGY

Bellevue Community College (U)
Brigham Young University (U)
Central Wyoming College (N)
Eastern Oregon University (U)
Henderson Community College (U)
Indiana State University (U)
Oregon State University (U)
Oxnard College (U)
Palomar College (U)
St. Cloud State University (U)
Santa Monica College (U)
Tacoma Community College (U)
Temple University (N)
Texas A&M University–Commerce (U)
The University of Akron (U)
University of Arkansas at Little Rock (U)
University of Saskatchewan (N)
University of Wyoming (U)
West Shore Community College (U)
Wilfrid Laurier University (U)

BUILDING/CONSTRUCTION FINISHING, MANAGEMENT, AND INSPECTION

Athabasca University (N)
Bowling Green State University (G)
Central Michigan University (U)
Central New Mexico Community College (U)
Clackamas Community College (U)
Clemson University (N)
East Carolina University (G)
Eastern Illinois University (G)
Florida State University (N)
Fox Valley Technical College (U)
Georgia Institute of Technology (G)
James Madison University (N)
National University (U)
New Mexico Junior College (N)
Pennsylvania College of Technology (U)
Quinebaug Valley Community College (N)
Red Rocks Community College (U)
San Diego State University (U)
Southern Polytechnic State University (U)
University of Arkansas at Little Rock (U)
The University of North Carolina at Charlotte (N)
University of North Florida (U,G)
University of Washington (U,G)

Weber State University (U)

BUSINESS ADMINISTRATION, MANAGEMENT AND OPERATIONS

Acadia University (U)
AIB College of Business (U)
Allen County Community College (U)
Amberton University (U,G)
The American College (U,G)
American Graduate University (G)
American InterContinental University Online (G)
American Public University System (U)
Anne Arundel Community College (U)
Antioch University McGregor (G)
Arapahoe Community College (U)
Arkansas State University–Beebe (U)
Arkansas State University–Mountain Home (U)
Arkansas Tech University (U)
Athabasca University (N,U,G)
Auburn University (G)
Avila University (U)
Baker College of Flint (U)
Baltimore City Community College (N,U)
Beacon University (N,U,G)
Beaufort County Community College (U)
Belhaven College (U)
Bellevue Community College (U)
Bellevue University (U,G)
Bergen Community College (U)
Berkeley College (U)
Berkeley College–New York City Campus (U)
Berkeley College–Westchester Campus (U)
Blackhawk Technical College (U)
Black Hills State University (U)
Bloomfield College (U)
Blue Ridge Community College (U)
Brazosport College (U)
Brenau University (U,G)
Bridgewater State College (N)
Brigham Young University (U)
Bryant and Stratton Online (U)
Buena Vista University (U)
Caldwell Community College and Technical Institute (N,U)
California National University for Advanced Studies (U,G)
California Polytechnic State University, San Luis Obispo (N)
California State University, San Bernardino (U)
California State University, San Marcos (U)
Campbell University (U)
Cape Cod Community College (U)
Capella University (G)
Capital Community College (U)
Cardinal Stritch University (N)
Carroll Community College (N,U)
Cayuga County Community College (U)
Centennial College (U)
Centralia College (U)
Central Michigan University (U,G)
Central New Mexico Community College (U)
Central Oregon Community College (U)
Central Texas College (U)
Central Washington University (U,G)
Chadron State College (U,G)
Chaminade University of Honolulu (U)
Charter Oak State College (U)
Chatham University (G)

Chemeketa Community College (U)
Cincinnati State Technical and Community College (U)
City Colleges of Chicago, Harold Washington College (U)
Clackamas Community College (U)
Clarion University of Pennsylvania (G)
Clark State Community College (U)
Clatsop Community College (U)
Clemson University (G)
Cleveland Community College (U)
Cleveland State University (N)
Clinton Community College (U)
Coastline Community College (U)
College of Mount St. Joseph (U,G)
College of The Albemarle (N,U)
Colorado State University (G)
Columbia College (U,G)
Columbia-Greene Community College (U)
Columbus State Community College (U)
Community College of Beaver County (N,U)
Community College of Denver (N,U)
Concordia University Wisconsin (G)
Connors State College (U)
Corban College (U)
Corning Community College (U)
Crafton Hills College (U)
Crown College (G)
Culver-Stockton College (U)
Cumberland County College (U)
Cuyahoga Community College (U)
Dallas Baptist University (U,G)
Danville Community College (U)
Darton College (N,U)
Dawson Community College (U)
De Anza College (U)
Delaware County Community College (U)
Delaware Technical & Community College, Jack F. Owens Campus (U)
DeSales University (U)
Diné College (U)
Drake University (U,G)
Drexel University (U,G)
Duquesne University (U,G)
East Carolina University (U,G)
East Central Community College (U)
Eastern Illinois University (G)
Eastern Kentucky University (G)
Eastern Michigan University (U,G)
Eastern Washington University (N)
Eastern Wyoming College (U)
East Tennessee State University (N,G)
Edgecombe Community College (N,U)
Edison State Community College (N,U)
Elizabeth City State University (U)
Elizabethtown College (U)
Embry-Riddle Aeronautical University (U,G)
Endicott College (U)
Erie Community College (U)
Erie Community College, North Campus (U)
Erie Community College, South Campus (U)
Everest College (U)
Everett Community College (U)
Excelsior College (U,G)
Fielding Graduate University (N)
Fitchburg State College (U,G)
Flathead Valley Community College (U)
Florida Institute of Technology (G)
Fontbonne University (U,G)
Foothill College (U)
Fort Hays State University (N,U)
Fox Valley Technical College (U)

Framingham State College (U,G)
Franklin University (U,G)
Fulton-Montgomery Community College (N)
Gadsden State Community College (U)
Galveston College (U)
George C. Wallace Community College (U)
George Fox University (G)
Global University (N)
Golden West College (U)
Graceland University (U)
Grand Rapids Community College (U)
Granite State College (U)
Grantham University (U)
Halifax Community College (N)
Harrisburg Area Community College (U)
Haywood Community College (U)
Henderson Community College (U)
Herkimer County Community College (U)
Hibbing Community College (U)
Hillsborough Community College (U)
Holyoke Community College (U)
Hope International University (G)
Hopkinsville Community College (U)
Houston Community College System (U)
Ilisagvik College (U)
Immaculata University (U)
Indiana State University (U)
Indiana Tech (U)
Indiana University–Purdue University Fort Wayne (G)
Iona College (U,G)
Ivy Tech Community College–Bloomington (U)
Ivy Tech Community College–Columbus (U)
Ivy Tech Community College–East Central (U)
Ivy Tech Community College–Northwest (U)
Ivy Tech Community College–Southeast (U)
Ivy Tech Community College–Southern Indiana (U)
Ivy Tech Community College–Southwest (U)
Ivy Tech Community College–Wabash Valley (U)
Ivy Tech Community College–Whitewater (U)
Jacksonville State University (U,G)
James Madison University (G)
Jamestown Community College (N)
Jefferson College of Health Sciences (U)
Jefferson Community College (U)
John A. Logan College (U)
Johnson State College (U)
John Wood Community College (U)
Jones International University (U)
J. Sargeant Reynolds Community College (U)
Judson College (U)
Kansas State University (U)
Kaplan University Online (N)
Kaskaskia College (U)
Kauai Community College (U)
Kean University (N)
Kentucky State University (U)
Kettering University (N)
Kirtland Community College (U)
Lackawanna College (U)
Lakeland College (G)
Lake Region State College (U)
Lake-Sumter Community College (U)
Lamar State College–Port Arthur (N,U)
Laredo Community College (U)
Lawrence Technological University (U,G)
Lehigh Carbon Community College (U)
Lehigh University (N,G)

Lewis-Clark State College (U)
Liberty University (G)
Limestone College (U)
Linn-Benton Community College (U)
Lipscomb University (G)
Long Beach City College (U)
Louisiana State University and Agricultural and Mechanical College (U)
Luzerne County Community College (U)
Malone College (U)
Manatee Community College (U)
Manor College (U)
Mansfield University of Pennsylvania (U)
Marian College of Fond du Lac (U)
Marist College (G)
Marshall University (U)
Marymount University (G)
Massachusetts College of Liberal Arts (U)
Massasoit Community College (U)
Mayville State University (U)
McDowell Technical Community College (U)
McMurry University (U)
Memorial University of Newfoundland (U)
Mercy College (U,G)
Mesa Community College (U)
Metropolitan State University (U,G)
Miami Dade College (U)
Middlesex Community College (U,N,U)
Middle Tennessee State University (N,U)
Millersville University of Pennsylvania (U,G)
Milwaukee School of Engineering (G)
Minnesota School of Business–Richfield (U,G)
Minot State University (G)
Minot State University–Bottineau Campus (U)
Misericordia University (U)
Mississippi State University (G)
Missouri University of Science and Technology (G)
Moberly Area Community College (U)
Montcalm Community College (N,U)
Montgomery Community College (N,U)
Montgomery County Community College (U)
Mt. Hood Community College (U)
Mount Olive College (U)
Mt. San Antonio College (U)
Mount Wachusett Community College (U)
Murray State College (U)
Murray State University (U)
Myers University (U,G)
Nassau Community College (U)
National University (U,G)
Naugatuck Valley Community College (U)
New Jersey City University (G)
New Jersey Institute of Technology (G)
New Mexico Highlands University (U,G)
New Mexico Junior College (U)
New Mexico State University (U)
New York Institute of Technology (U,G)
Nipissing University (U)
Northampton County Area Community College (U)
North Central State College (U)
North Central Texas College (U)
Northcentral University (U,G)
North Dakota State College of Science (U)
Northeast Alabama Community College (U)
Northeastern Illinois University (U)
Northeastern University (U)
Northeast State Technical Community College (U)
Northern Virginia Community College (U)

Northland Community and Technical College–
  Thief River Falls (U)
NorthWest Arkansas Community College (U)
Northwestern Michigan College (U)
Northwestern Oklahoma State University
  (U,G)
Northwestern State University of Louisiana
  (U)
Northwest Technical College (U)
Northwood University, Texas Campus (U)
The Ohio State University (G)
Okaloosa-Walton College (U)
Oklahoma Panhandle State University (U)
Oklahoma State University (U)
Oregon Institute of Technology (U)
Ouachita Technical College (U)
Oxnard College (U)
Pace University (U,G)
Palomar College (U)
Pamlico Community College (U)
Park University (U,G)
Pasco-Hernando Community College (U)
Patrick Henry Community College (U)
Pellissippi State Technical Community
  College (U)
Peninsula College (U)
Philadelphia University (U)
Piedmont Technical College (U)
Pikes Peak Community College (U)
Pittsburgh Technical Institute (U)
Plymouth State University (N,U)
Portland Community College (U)
Pratt Community College (U)
Prescott College (U)
Pulaski Technical College (U)
Rappahannock Community College (U)
Reading Area Community College (U)
Regent University (N,U,G)
Regis University (U)
Rend Lake College (N)
The Richard Stockton College of New Jersey
  (U)
Richmond Community College (U)
Riverside Community College District (N,U)
Rochester Institute of Technology (U,G)
Roosevelt University (U)
Rose State College (U)
Sacramento City College (U)
Sacred Heart University (U,G)
St. Ambrose University (U,G)
St. Clair County Community College (U)
St. Edward's University (N,U,G)
Saint Francis University (U,G)
St. John's University (U)
St. Joseph's College, Long Island Campus (G)
St. Joseph's College, New York (G)
Saint Joseph's College of Maine (U,G)
Saint Leo University (U)
St. Louis Community College System (N)
Saint Mary-of-the-Woods College (U,G)
San Diego Community College District (U)
Santa Monica College (U)
Santa Rosa Junior College (U)
Saybrook Graduate School and Research
  Center (N,G)
Schenectady County Community College (U)
Schiller International University (U,G)
Seminole Community College (U)
Shippensburg University of Pennsylvania (G)
Sinclair Community College (U)
Sonoma State University (N)
Southeast Arkansas College (U)

Southeast Community College Area (U)
Southeastern Community College (U)
Southeastern Oklahoma State University
  (U,G)
Southern Arkansas University Tech (U)
Southern New Hampshire University (U,G)
South Piedmont Community College (U)
Southwestern College (G)
Spring Arbor University (U)
State University of New York at Binghamton
  (N)
State University of New York at Oswego
  (U,G)
State University of New York at Plattsburgh
  (U,G)
State University of New York College at
  Potsdam (N,U)
State University of New York College of
  Technology at Canton (U)
State University of New York Institute of
  Technology (U,G)
Stephen F. Austin State University (U)
Sullivan County Community College (U)
Syracuse University (G)
Tacoma Community College (N)
Taft College (U)
Taylor University (N,U)
Temple University (G)
Texas A&M University–Commerce (U)
Texas A&M University–Kingsville (G)
Texas Tech University (N,U)
Texas Woman's University (U,G)
Thomas College (U)
Three Rivers Community College (U)
Thunderbird School of Global Management
  (N,G)
Treasure Valley Community College (U)
Tri-County Community College (N,U)
Trine University (U)
Tunxis Community College (U)
Tyler Junior College (N,U)
United States Sports Academy (G)
The University of Akron (U,G)
University of Alaska Fairbanks (U)
University of Arkansas at Little Rock (U,G)
University of Arkansas at Pine Bluff (U)
University of California, Los Angeles (G)
University of Cincinnati Raymond Walters
  College (U)
University of Colorado Denver (G)
University of Dallas (G)
University of Denver (G)
The University of Findlay (U,G)
University of Hawaii–West Oahu (U)
University of Houston–Downtown (U)
University of Idaho (G)
University of Illinois at Chicago (N,G)
University of Illinois at Springfield (U,G)
University of Illinois at Urbana–Champaign
  (U,G)
The University of Maine at Augusta (U)
University of Management and Technology
  (U,G)
University of Maryland University College
  (U,G)
University of Massachusetts Boston (U)
University of Michigan–Flint (N,G)
University of Minnesota, Crookston (U)
University of Minnesota, Twin Cities Campus
  (U)
University of Missouri–Columbia (U)
University of New Orleans (U,G)

University of North Alabama (G)
The University of North Carolina at Chapel
  Hill (U)
The University of North Carolina at Charlotte
  (N)
The University of North Carolina at
  Greensboro (N)
The University of North Carolina Wilmington
  (U)
University of North Dakota (U,G)
University of North Texas (N,U,G)
University of Northwestern Ohio (U)
University of Oklahoma (U)
University of St. Francis (U,G)
University of South Florida (N,G)
The University of Tennessee (U)
The University of Tennessee at Martin (N)
The University of Texas at Brownsville (N)
The University of Texas at San Antonio (U,G)
The University of Texas at Tyler (G)
University of the Southwest (U)
University of the Virgin Islands (G)
University of Toronto (N)
University of Vermont (N)
University of Virginia (N)
The University of Virginia's College at Wise
  (U)
University of Washington (N)
University of West Florida (G)
University of Wisconsin–La Crosse (G)
University of Wisconsin–Parkside (G)
University of Wisconsin–Platteville (N)
University of Wisconsin–Stout (G)
University of Wisconsin–Superior (U)
University of Wisconsin–Whitewater (U,G)
University of Wyoming (G)
Upper Iowa University (U)
Utah State University (U,G)
Utah Valley State College (U)
Vincennes University (U)
Virginia Polytechnic Institute and State
  University (N)
Wake Technical Community College (N)
Wayland Baptist University (U,G)
Wayne State College (U,G)
Weber State University (U)
Western Wyoming Community College (U)
West Los Angeles College (U)
West Shore Community College (U)
West Virginia State University (U)
West Virginia University at Parkersburg (U)
Westwood Online (U)
Wharton County Junior College (U)
Wilmington University (U,G)
Wisconsin Indianhead Technical College
  (N,U)
Worcester Polytechnic Institute (G)
Worcester State College (N,U)
York County Community College (U)
York Technical College (U)
York University (U)
Youngstown State University (N)

BUSINESS OPERATIONS SUPPORT AND ASSISTANT SERVICES

AIB College of Business (U)
Athabasca University (N)
Bellevue Community College (U)
Blackhawk Technical College (N,U)
Blue Mountain Community College (U)
Blue Ridge Community College (U)

Bridgewater State College (N)
Caldwell Community College and Technical Institute (N,U)
California State University, San Marcos (U)
Carroll Community College (N)
Central Carolina Community College (U)
Central Michigan University (U)
Central New Mexico Community College (U)
Central Texas College (U)
Central Virginia Community College (U)
Central Wyoming College (N)
Cerritos College (U)
Chatham University (G)
Chemeketa Community College (U)
Cincinnati State Technical and Community College (U)
Clemson University (N)
Coastline Community College (U)
College of The Albemarle (N)
Community College of Beaver County (N)
Community College of Denver (N)
Corning Community College (U)
Crown College (G)
Dallas County Community College District (U)
Danville Community College (U)
Delaware County Community College (U)
East Carolina University (U)
Eastern West Virginia Community and Technical College (U)
East Los Angeles College (U)
Edgecombe Community College (N)
Edison State Community College (N,U)
Everest College (U)
Galveston College (U)
Hopkinsville Community College (N,U)
Indiana State University (U)
Indiana University–Purdue University Fort Wayne (N)
Iona College (U)
Ivy Tech Community College–Bloomington (U)
Ivy Tech Community College–Central Indiana (U)
Ivy Tech Community Course–Columbus (U)
Ivy Tech Community College–East Central (U)
Ivy Tech Community College–Northwest (U)
Ivy Tech Community College–Southeast (U)
Ivy Tech Community College–Southern Indiana (U)
Ivy Tech Community College–Southwest (U)
Ivy Tech Community College–Wabash Valley (U)
Ivy Tech Community College–Whitewater (U)
James A. Rhodes State College (U)
Jamestown Community College (N)
J. Sargeant Reynolds Community College (U)
Kaskaskia College (U)
Kirtland Community College (U)
Lakeland Community College (N)
Lake Superior College (U)
Lamar State College–Port Arthur (N)
Lehigh Carbon Community College (U)
Lewis-Clark State College (U)
Marion Technical College (U)
Minot State University–Bottineau Campus (U)
Mitchell Technical Institute (N)
Montgomery Community College (U)
Montgomery County Community College (N)
Mt. Hood Community College (U)
Mount Wachusett Community College (N)

Nashville State Technical Community College (N)
Naugatuck Valley Community College (U)
North Central Texas College (U)
North Dakota State University (N)
Northland Community and Technical College–Thief River Falls (U)
NorthWest Arkansas Community College (U)
Orange Coast College (U)
Oxnard College (U)
Palomar College (U)
Piedmont Community College (U)
Pikes Peak Community College (U)
Plymouth State University (N)
Portland Community College (U)
Providence College and Theological Seminary (G)
Pulaski Technical College (U)
Randolph Community College (N)
Rend Lake College (N)
Richmond Community College (N)
Sacramento City College (U)
Saint Francis University (U)
San Diego Community College District (U)
Santa Rosa Junior College (U)
Seminole Community College (U)
Sinclair Community College (U)
State University of New York at Binghamton (N)
Taylor University (N)
Tompkins Cortland Community College (N)
Tyler Junior College (U)
The University of Akron (U)
University of Arkansas at Pine Bluff (N)
University of Cincinnati (N)
The University of Maine at Augusta (U)
University of Minnesota, Twin Cities Campus (U)
University of Missouri–Columbia (U,G)
The University of North Carolina at Charlotte (N)
University of Northwestern Ohio (U)
University of Phoenix (U)
Utah State University (U)
Vincennes University (U)
Wake Technical Community College (U)
Western Wyoming Community College (U)
West Los Angeles College (U)
West Virginia University at Parkersburg (N,U)
Wisconsin Indianhead Technical College (N,U)
Wytheville Community College (U)
York County Community College (U)
Youngstown State University (N)

BUSINESS, MANAGEMENT, AND MARKETING RELATED

Acadia University (U)
Adams State College (U)
AIB College of Business (U)
Albany State University (G)
Allen County Community College (U)
American InterContinental University Online (U)
Anne Arundel Community College (N,U)
Arapahoe Community College (U)
Arkansas State University–Beebe (U)
Athabasca University (N,U,G)
Athens Technical College (N)
Avila University (U)
Beacon University (N,U,G)

Bellevue Community College (U)
Bellevue University (U,G)
Berkeley College (U)
Berkeley College–New York City Campus (U)
Berkeley College–Westchester Campus (U)
Blackhawk Technical College (U)
Black Hills State University (U,G)
Bloomsburg University of Pennsylvania (U,G)
Blue Mountain Community College (U)
Blue Ridge Community College (N,U)
Boise State University (U)
Bowling Green State University (U)
Bradley University (U)
Brazosport College (U)
Brenau University (U,G)
Bridgewater State College (N)
Brigham Young University (U)
Buena Vista University (U)
Buffalo State College, State University of New York (U)
Butler Community College (U)
California Polytechnic State University, San Luis Obispo (N)
California State University, Dominguez Hills (N)
California State University, Sacramento (U,G)
California State University, San Bernardino (U)
Cape Fear Community College (U)
Capella University (G)
Capital Community College (U)
Carlow University (U,G)
Carroll Community College (N,U)
Carroll University (U)
Centennial College (U)
Central Carolina Community College (U)
Centralia College (U)
Central Michigan University (U,G)
Central New Mexico Community College (U)
Central Texas College (U)
Chadron State College (U,G)
Charter Oak State College (U)
Chatham University (U)
Chemeketa Community College (U)
City Colleges of Chicago, Harold Washington College (U)
Clackamas Community College (U)
Clark State Community College (U)
Clemson University (N)
Cleveland Community College (U)
College of The Albemarle (N)
Colorado State University (N,G)
Columbia College (U,G)
Community College of Beaver County (N,U)
Community College of Denver (N,U)
Concordia University Wisconsin (U)
Connors State College (U)
Dallas Baptist University (U,G)
Danville Community College (U)
Darton College (N)
Daytona State College (U)
Delaware County Community College (U)
DeSales University (U)
Diné College (U)
Drexel University (U,G)
Duquesne University (U)
East Carolina University (U,G)
Eastern Michigan University (U,G)
Eastern Washington University (N)
Eastern West Virginia Community and Technical College (U)
East Tennessee State University (N)

Edgecombe Community College (N,U)
Elgin Community College (U)
Elizabeth City State University (U)
Endicott College (U)
Excelsior College (U)
Fort Valley State University (U)
Framingham State College (G)
Fulton-Montgomery Community College (N)
Galveston College (N)
Gateway Technical College (U)
Genesee Community College (U)
George Mason University (G)
Glenville State College (U)
Golden Gate University (U,G)
Golden West College (U)
Grand Rapids Community College (U)
Grand View College (U)
Granite State College (U)
Grantham University (U)
Greenville Technical College (U)
Hagerstown Community College (N)
Harrisburg Area Community College (U)
Henderson Community College (U)
Hibbing Community College (U)
Holyoke Community College (U)
Hope International University (U)
Hopkinsville Community College (N)
Independence University (U)
Indiana State University (U)
Indiana University of Pennsylvania (U,G)
Indiana University–Purdue University Fort
  Wayne (N)
Indian River Community College (U)
Iona College (U,G)
Jacksonville State University (U,G)
James Madison University (N)
Jamestown Community College (N)
Jefferson Community College (U)
John A. Logan College (U)
Jones International University (G)
J. Sargeant Reynolds Community College (U)
Kansas State University (U)
Kean University (N)
Kettering University (N)
Kirtland Community College (U)
Lakeland Community College (N)
Lake-Sumter Community College (U)
Lamar State College–Port Arthur (N)
Laredo Community College (U)
Lehigh Carbon Community College (U)
Liberty University (U,G)
Los Angeles Trade-Technical College (U)
Louisiana State University and Agricultural
  and Mechanical College (U)
Lurleen B. Wallace Community College (U)
Manatee Community College (U)
Marist College (U,G)
Marymount University (G)
Mercy College (G)
Middlesex Community College (U)
Middle Tennessee State University (N)
Midstate College (U)
Milwaukee School of Engineering (U)
Minot State University–Bottineau Campus (U)
Misericordia University (U)
Missouri University of Science and
  Technology (G)
Mitchell Technical Institute (N,U)
Moorpark College (U)
Myers University (U)
Naugatuck Valley Community College (U)
New Jersey Institute of Technology (G)

New Mexico Highlands University (U,G)
New Mexico Junior College (N)
New River Community College (U)
New York Institute of Technology (U)
Nipissing University (U)
Northampton County Area Community
  College (U)
North Carolina State University (U)
North Central Texas College (U)
North Dakota State College of Science (U)
Northern Virginia Community College (U)
North Florida Community College (U)
North Iowa Area Community College (U)
North Lake College (U)
NorthWest Arkansas Community College (U)
Northwestern Connecticut Community College
  (U)
Northwestern Michigan College (U)
Northwestern State University of Louisiana
  (U)
Northwest Technical College (U)
Northwood University (U)
Northwood University, Texas Campus (U)
Okaloosa-Walton College (U)
Okefenokee Technical College (N,U,G)
Oklahoma Panhandle State University (U)
Orange Coast College (U)
Oregon State University (N)
Oxnard College (U)
Palomar College (U)
Pamlico Community College (U)
Park University (U,G)
Pasco-Hernando Community College (U)
Pellissippi State Technical Community
  College (U)
Peninsula College (U)
Pine Technical College (U)
Plymouth State University (N,G)
Portland Community College (U)
Prairie View A&M University (U)
Quinebaug Valley Community College (U)
Regent University (N,U,G)
Regis University (G)
The Richard Stockton College of New Jersey
  (G)
Rose State College (U)
Sacramento City College (U)
Saddleback College (U)
St. Edward's University (U)
Saint Francis University (U,G)
St. John's University (G)
Saint Joseph's College of Maine (G)
St. Louis Community College System (N)
Saint Mary-of-the-Woods College (G)
Sam Houston State University (U)
San Diego Community College District (U)
San Diego State University (U)
Seminole Community College (U)
Sinclair Community College (U)
Sonoma State University (N)
Southeast Arkansas College (U)
Southeastern Oklahoma State University (U)
Southern New Hampshire University (U,G)
South Piedmont Community College (U)
Southwestern Adventist University (U,G)
Southwestern College (N)
State University of New York at Binghamton
  (N)
State University of New York College at
  Potsdam (U)
Syracuse University (U)
Taylor University (N,U)

Texas A&M University–Commerce (U,G)
Thunderbird School of Global Management
  (N,G)
Tompkins Cortland Community College (N)
Tri-County Community College (U)
Triton College (U)
Union University (U)
United States Sports Academy (N,U)
The University of Akron (U)
The University of Alabama (U)
University of Alaska Fairbanks (U)
University of Arkansas at Little Rock (U,G)
University of Bridgeport (U)
University of Colorado Denver (G)
University of Dubuque (U)
The University of Findlay (N)
University of Hawaii–West Oahu (U)
University of Houston–Downtown (U)
University of Idaho (G)
University of Illinois at Chicago (N,G)
University of Illinois at Springfield (U)
University of Louisville (N)
The University of Maine at Augusta (U)
University of Maine at Fort Kent (U)
University of Maine at Machias (U)
University of Management and Technology
  (U)
University of Maryland University College
  (G)
University of Massachusetts Boston (N)
University of Michigan–Flint (N)
University of Minnesota, Twin Cities Campus
  (U)
University of Missouri–Columbia (N,U)
The University of Montana–Western (U)
University of New Orleans (N,U,G)
University of North Alabama (U)
The University of North Carolina at Chapel
  Hill (N)
The University of North Carolina at Charlotte
  (N,U)
University of North Texas (U,G)
University of Pittsburgh at Bradford (U)
University of South Florida (G)
The University of Texas at San Antonio (U,G)
University of the Southwest (U)
University of West Florida (N)
University of Wisconsin–Parkside (G)
University of Wisconsin–Stout (U)
University of Wisconsin–Whitewater (U,G)
Upper Iowa University (U)
Utah Valley State College (U)
Vincennes University (U)
Washburn University (U)
Webster University (G)
West Los Angeles College (U)
West Shore Community College (U)
West Virginia University at Parkersburg (U)
Wharton County Junior College (U)
Williston State College (U)
York County Community College (U)
Youngstown State University (N)

BUSINESS/COMMERCE

Acadia University (U)
Adams State College (N,U)
AIB College of Business (U)
Allen County Community College (U)
The American College (U,G)
American Public University System (G)
Arizona Western College (U)

Athabasca University (N,U)
Athens Technical College (U)
Baltimore City Community College (U)
Bellevue Community College (U)
Bellevue University (U,G)
Berkeley College (U)
Berkeley College–New York City Campus (U)
Berkeley College–Westchester Campus (U)
Black Hills State University (U)
Blue Mountain Community College (U)
Blue Ridge Community College (N)
Bowling Green State University (N,U)
Brenau University (U,G)
Bridgewater State College (N)
Bristol Community College (U)
Broome Community College (U)
Broward Community College (U)
Bryant and Stratton Online (U)
Buena Vista University (U)
Cabrillo College (U)
Caldwell Community College and Technical
  Institute (U)
California State University, San Marcos (N)
Cape Fear Community College (N)
Capital Community College (U)
Carroll Community College (N)
Cayuga County Community College (U)
Central Carolina Community College (U)
Central Michigan University (U,G)
Central New Mexico Community College (U)
Central Washington University (U)
Cerritos College (U)
Chadron State College (U,G)
Chemeketa Community College (U)
Cincinnati State Technical and Community
  College (U)
Citrus College (U)
Clark State Community College (U)
Clemson University (N,U)
Cleveland State Community College (U)
Cleveland State University (N)
Coastline Community College (U)
College of San Mateo (U)
College of Southern Maryland (U)
College of The Albemarle (N,U)
College of the Sequoias (U)
College of the Siskiyous (U)
Colorado Mountain College District System
  (U)
Colorado State University (N,U,G)
Columbia College (U)
Community College of Beaver County (N)
Community College of Denver (N)
Concordia University, St. Paul (N,U,G)
Daemen College (U)
Dallas Baptist University (G)
Danville Community College (U)
Darton College (U)
Delaware County Community College (U)
DeVry University Online (U,G)
Drake University (U,G)
Drexel University (U,G)
East Carolina University (U,G)
Eastern Michigan University (U,G)
Eastern Oregon University (U)
Eastern Washington University (N,U)
Eastern Wyoming College (U)
Edgecombe Community College (N,U)
Edison State Community College (N,U)
Elaine P. Nunez Community College (U)
Elizabeth City State University (U)
Elizabethtown College (U)

Elizabethtown Community and Technical
  College (U)
Ellsworth Community College (U)
Embry-Riddle Aeronautical University (U,G)
Endicott College (N,U,G)
Erie Community College (U)
Erie Community College, North Campus (U)
Erie Community College, South Campus (U)
Eugenio María de Hostos Community College
  of the City University of New York (U)
Everett Community College (U)
Evergreen Valley College (U)
Finger Lakes Community College (U)
Flathead Valley Community College (N)
Florida Institute of Technology (G)
Fulton-Montgomery Community College (N)
Gateway Community College (U)
Genesee Community College (U)
George C. Wallace Community College (U)
Georgia State University (G)
Golden West College (U)
Grand Rapids Community College (U)
Grantham University (U)
Halifax Community College (U)
Harrisburg Area Community College (U)
Haywood Community College (U)
Herkimer County Community College (U)
Hillsborough Community College (U)
Illinois Eastern Community Colleges, Frontier
  Community College (U)
Illinois Eastern Community Colleges, Lincoln
  Trail College (U)
Illinois Eastern Community Colleges, Olney
  Central College (U)
Illinois Eastern Community Colleges, Wabash
  Valley College (U)
Indiana State University (U)
Indiana Tech (U)
Indiana University–Purdue University Fort
  Wayne (U)
Indian River Community College (U)
Iona College (G)
Jacksonville State University (U,G)
James A. Rhodes State College (U)
James Madison University (N,U)
Jamestown Community College (N)
Jefferson College (U)
Jefferson Community College (U)
John A. Logan College (U)
John Wood Community College (U)
Kansas State University (U)
Kirtland Community College (U)
Lakeland College (U)
Lake-Sumter Community College (U)
Lake Superior College (U)
Lamar State College–Port Arthur (N)
Liberty University (U)
Limestone College (U)
Linn-Benton Community College (U)
Lock Haven University of Pennsylvania (N)
Los Angeles Harbor College (U)
Macon State College (U)
Malone College (U)
Manatee Community College (U)
Manor College (U)
Marshalltown Community College (U)
Marymount University (G)
Massasoit Community College (N,U)
McDowell Technical Community College (U)
Mercer County Community College (U)
Mercy College (U,G)
Middlesex Community College (N,U)

Middle Tennessee State University (N)
Midwestern State University (U)
Mississippi Delta Community College (U)
Mississippi State University (G)
Monroe Community College (U)
Monroe County Community College (U)
Montana Tech of The University of Montana
  (U)
Montcalm Community College (U)
Montgomery Community College (U)
Montgomery County Community College (U)
Moorpark College (U)
Mountain Empire Community College (U)
Murray State University (U)
Myers University (U,G)
Nassau Community College (U)
National University (U,G)
New Jersey City University (U)
New Jersey Institute of Technology (U)
New Mexico Highlands University (U,G)
New Mexico State University (U)
Nipissing University (U)
Northampton County Area Community
  College (U)
North Carolina State University (U)
North Dakota State University (N)
Northern State University (U)
North Iowa Area Community College (U)
North Lake College (U)
Northland Community and Technical College–
  Thief River Falls (U)
North Seattle Community College (U)
Northwestern Oklahoma State University (U)
The Ohio State University (U)
Okaloosa-Walton College (U)
Oregon Institute of Technology (U)
Oregon State University (U)
Oxnard College (U)
Pace University (N,U,G)
Palm Beach Community College (U)
Palomar College (U)
Pamlico Community College (U)
Park University (U)
Pasco-Hernando Community College (U)
Passaic County Community College (U)
Pellissippi State Technical Community
  College (U)
Peninsula College (U)
Pennsylvania College of Technology (U)
Piedmont Technical College (U)
Pikes Peak Community College (U)
Plymouth State University (N,G)
Pulaski Technical College (U)
Queen's University at Kingston (U)
Reading Area Community College (U)
Regent University (N,U,G)
Rend Lake College (N,U)
Riverside Community College District (U)
Rockland Community College (U)
Rose State College (U)
Sacramento City College (U)
Saint Charles Community College (U)
Saint Francis University (U,G)
St. Louis Community College System (N)
Saint Mary-of-the-Woods College (U)
San Diego Community College District (U)
San Diego State University (N,U)
San Joaquin Delta College (U)
Santa Monica College (U)
Santa Rosa Junior College (U)
Schiller International University (U)
Seminole Community College (U)

Sierra College (U)
Southeast Arkansas College (U)
Southeast Community College Area (U)
Southeastern Illinois College (U)
Southeastern Oklahoma State University (U)
Southern Illinois University Edwardsville (G)
Southern New Hampshire University (U,G)
South Piedmont Community College (U)
Southwestern College (U)
State University of New York at Binghamton (N)
State University of New York College at Potsdam (N)
State University of New York College of Agriculture and Technology at Morrisville (U)
State University of New York Empire State College (G)
State University of New York Institute of Technology (U,G)
Strayer University (U,G)
Sullivan County Community College (N)
Syracuse University (G)
Tacoma Community College (U)
Taft College (U)
Taylor University (N,U)
Temple University (G)
Texas A&M University–Commerce (U)
Texas State Technical College Waco (N)
Texas State University–San Marcos (U)
Texas Woman's University (G)
Thomas College (U,G)
Thunderbird School of Global Management (N)
Tompkins Cortland Community College (U)
Treasure Valley Community College (U)
Trine University (U)
Tunxis Community College (N)
Tyler Junior College (N,U)
The University of Akron (U)
The University of Alabama (U)
University of Alaska Fairbanks (U)
University of Bridgeport (U)
University of California, Los Angeles (G)
University of Cincinnati (N,U)
University of Colorado at Colorado Springs (G)
University of Colorado Denver (G)
The University of Findlay (U)
University of Idaho (U)
University of Illinois at Chicago (N,G)
University of Illinois at Urbana–Champaign (N)
The University of Maine at Augusta (U)
University of Maine at Fort Kent (U)
University of Maine at Machias (U)
University of Management and Technology (G)
University of Michigan–Flint (N,U)
University of Missouri–Columbia (U)
University of Nevada, Reno (U)
University of North Alabama (G)
The University of North Carolina at Charlotte (N)
University of North Texas (U)
The University of Texas at San Antonio (U)
The University of Texas at Tyler (U)
University of Wisconsin Colleges (U)
University of Wyoming (U)
Vincennes University (U)
Virginia Polytechnic Institute and State University (N)

Wake Technical Community College (U)
Westchester Community College (U)
Western Wyoming Community College (U)
West Los Angeles College (U)
West Virginia University at Parkersburg (U)
Wharton County Junior College (U)
Wilfrid Laurier University (U)
Wisconsin Indianhead Technical College (N,U)
York County Community College (U)
York Technical College (U)

BUSINESS/CORPORATE COMMUNICATIONS

Abilene Christian University (U)
Acadia University (U)
Adams State College (U)
American Graduate University (G)
Arapahoe Community College (U)
Arkansas State University–Beebe (U)
Athabasca University (N,U,G)
Beaufort County Community College (N)
Bellevue Community College (U)
Bellevue University (G)
Brenau University (U,G)
Bridgewater State College (U)
Brigham Young University (U)
Bryant and Stratton Online (U)
Buena Vista University (U)
Caldwell Community College and Technical Institute (N,U)
California National University for Advanced Studies (U)
California Polytechnic State University, San Luis Obispo (N)
California State University, Dominguez Hills (N)
California State University, Sacramento (U)
Campbell University (U)
Capella University (G)
Carroll Community College (U)
Central Michigan University (U,G)
Central Texas College (U)
Chadron State College (U)
Chemeketa Community College (U)
Cleveland State University (N)
Clinton Community College (U)
Coastline Community College (U)
College of San Mateo (U)
College of Southern Maryland (U)
College of The Albemarle (N,U)
College of the Siskiyous (U)
Colorado Mountain College District System (U)
Colorado State University (G)
Columbus State Community College (U)
Community College of Beaver County (N)
Community College of Denver (U)
Dallas Baptist University (U,G)
Darton College (N)
Delaware County Community College (U)
Drexel University (U,G)
East Carolina University (U)
Eastern Michigan University (U,G)
Eastern Washington University (N)
Edgecombe Community College (N,U)
Edison State Community College (U)
Elizabeth City State University (U)
Elizabethtown College (U)
Erie Community College (U)
Erie Community College, North Campus (U)

Erie Community College, South Campus (U)
Finger Lakes Community College (U)
Galveston College (U)
Grand Rapids Community College (N,U)
Herkimer County Community College (U)
Indiana University–Purdue University Fort Wayne (N)
Iona College (U,G)
Jacksonville State University (U,G)
James Madison University (N)
Jamestown Community College (N)
Jefferson Community College (U)
Jones International University (U,G)
Lakeland Community College (N)
Lake-Sumter Community College (U)
Lake Superior College (U)
Laredo Community College (U)
Lehigh University (N)
Liberty University (U)
Limestone College (U)
Macon State College (U)
Massasoit Community College (U)
Mercy College (G)
Middlesex Community College (U)
Middle Tennessee State University (N,U)
Midwestern State University (U)
Montgomery Community College (N)
Murray State College (U)
Myers University (U)
New Mexico Junior College (N)
Northampton County Area Community College (U)
North Arkansas College (U)
North Central State College (U)
NorthWest Arkansas Community College (U)
Northwestern Michigan College (U)
Northwestern Oklahoma State University (U)
Okaloosa-Walton College (U)
Oklahoma State University (U)
Old Dominion University (U)
Oregon State University (U)
Oxnard College (U)
Park University (U)
Pasco-Hernando Community College (N)
Pennsylvania College of Technology (U)
Pikes Peak Community College (U)
Plymouth State University (N,U,G)
Quinebaug Valley Community College (N)
Rappahannock Community College (U)
Regis University (G)
Rend Lake College (U)
Richland Community College (U)
Roosevelt University (U,G)
Rose State College (U)
Sacramento City College (U)
St. Clair County Community College (U)
St. Edward's University (U,G)
Saint Francis University (U,G)
Saint Joseph's College of Maine (G)
Saint Leo University (U)
San Diego Community College District (U)
San Joaquin Delta College (U)
Santa Rosa Junior College (U)
Schiller International University (U,G)
Seminole Community College (U)
Sonoma State University (N)
Southeast Arkansas College (U)
Southeast Community College Area (U)
Southern New Hampshire University (U,G)
Southwest Wisconsin Technical College (U)
State University of New York at Binghamton (N)

Stephen F. Austin State University (U)
Taylor University (N)
Temple University (N)
Texas A&M University–Kingsville (U)
Thunderbird School of Global Management (N,G)
Tompkins Cortland Community College (U)
Tyler Junior College (U)
The University of Akron (U)
University of Arkansas at Pine Bluff (U)
University of Colorado Denver (G)
University of Denver (U)
The University of Findlay (G)
University of Illinois at Chicago (N)
The University of Maine at Augusta (U)
University of Michigan–Flint (N)
University of Minnesota, Twin Cities Campus (U)
University of New Orleans (U,G)
The University of North Carolina at Chapel Hill (N,U)
The University of North Carolina at Charlotte (N)
University of Oklahoma (U)
University of Pennsylvania (N)
The University of Texas at Tyler (U)
University of Toronto (N)
University of Washington (U)
University of West Florida (U)
Upper Iowa University (U)
Utah Valley State College (U)
West Hills Community College (N)
West Virginia University at Parkersburg (N,U)
York County Community College (U)
York University (U)

BUSINESS/MANAGERIAL ECONOMICS

Adams State College (U)
Allen County Community College (U)
American Graduate University (G)
Anne Arundel Community College (U)
Athabasca University (N,U,G)
Bellevue University (U,G)
Berkeley College (U)
Berkeley College–New York City Campus (U)
Berkeley College–Westchester Campus (U)
Brenau University (U,G)
Bridgewater State College (N,U)
Buena Vista University (U)
Caldwell Community College and Technical Institute (N)
California National University for Advanced Studies (U)
Central Michigan University (U,G)
Central New Mexico Community College (U)
Central Texas College (U)
Chadron State College (U,G)
Chatham University (U)
Cleveland Community College (U)
Colorado State University (G)
Columbia College (G)
Community College of Beaver County (N,U)
Connors State College (U)
Corning Community College (U)
Crown College (G)
Dallas Baptist University (U,G)
Delaware County Community College (U)
Drake University (U)
Drexel University (U,G)
East Arkansas Community College (U)

Edgecombe Community College (N)
Elizabeth City State University (U)
Embry-Riddle Aeronautical University (U)
Florida Institute of Technology (G)
Fort Valley State University (U)
Gadsden State Community College (U)
Grand View College (U)
Grantham University (U,G)
Harrisburg Area Community College (U)
Henderson Community College (U)
Immaculata University (U)
Indian River Community College (U)
Jacksonville State University (U,G)
Kaplan University Online (N)
Labette Community College (U)
Lakeland Community College (N)
Lamar State College–Port Arthur (N)
Liberty University (U)
Linn-Benton Community College (U)
Manatee Community College (U)
Marist College (G)
Marshall University (U)
McMurry University (U)
Mercy College (G)
Middlesex Community College (U)
Middle Tennessee State University (N)
Mississippi State University (G)
Montgomery Community College (U)
Myers University (U)
Naugatuck Valley Community College (U)
New Mexico Highlands University (U,G)
Northampton County Area Community College (U)
Northwood University, Texas Campus (U)
Okaloosa-Walton College (U)
Old Dominion University (U)
Palomar College (U)
Pamlico Community College (U)
Pikes Peak Community College (U)
Regis University (U,G)
Richmond Community College (U)
Rose State College (U)
Sacramento City College (U)
Saddleback College (U)
St. Edward's University (U,G)
Saint Francis University (U,G)
Saint Joseph's College of Maine (G)
San Diego Community College District (U)
Schiller International University (U,G)
Southeast Arkansas College (U)
South Piedmont Community College (U)
State University of New York at Binghamton (N)
State University of New York at Oswego (U)
State University of New York College at Cortland (U)
State University of New York College at Potsdam (U)
Syracuse University (G)
Taylor University (U)
Texas A&M University–Commerce (U,G)
Thomas College (G)
Thunderbird School of Global Management (N)
The University of Akron (U)
University of Colorado Denver (G)
The University of Findlay (N,U,G)
University of Illinois at Chicago (G)
The University of Maine at Augusta (U)
University of Minnesota, Twin Cities Campus (U)
University of Missouri–Columbia (U)

University of Nevada, Reno (U)
University of New Orleans (U,G)
University of North Dakota (U)
University of South Florida (G)
University of Toronto (N)
University of Vermont (N,U)
University of Waterloo (U)
University of Wisconsin–Parkside (G)
West Los Angeles College (U)
West Virginia University at Parkersburg (U)
Williston State College (U)
York University (U)
Youngstown State University (N)

CARPENTRY

South Piedmont Community College (U)
University of Arkansas at Pine Bluff (N)

CELL BIOLOGY AND ANATOMICAL SCIENCES

Allen County Community College (U)
Cabrillo College (U)
Carl Sandburg College (U)
Central Arizona College (U)
Clark State Community College (U)
Coastline Community College (U)
Darton College (U)
Eastern Michigan University (U)
Edison State Community College (U)
Fox Valley Technical College (U)
Henry Ford Community College (U)
Hocking College (U)
Huntington College of Health Sciences (U)
John Wood Community College (U)
Lehigh University (G)
Louisiana State University and Agricultural and Mechanical College (U)
Okaloosa-Walton College (U)
Palomar College (U)
Parkland College (U)
Piedmont Technical College (U)
Santa Monica College (U)
South Piedmont Community College (U)
Southwestern Community College (U)
Texas State University–San Marcos (U)
Tyler Junior College (U)
The University of Akron (U)
The University of Arizona (U)
University of Colorado Denver (U)
University of Minnesota, Twin Cities Campus (U)
University of Pennsylvania (U)
The University of Texas at San Antonio (U)
University of Waterloo (U)

CHEMICAL ENGINEERING

Brigham Young University (U)
Cleveland State University (G)
Columbia University (N,G)
Kansas State University (G)
Lehigh University (N,G)
Michigan State University (N,U,G)
Michigan Technological University (U)
Mississippi State University (G)
North Carolina State University (G)
Stanford University (G)
Texas Tech University (G)
University of Idaho (U,G)
University of Illinois at Chicago (G)

University of North Dakota (U)
University of South Florida (G)

CHEMISTRY

Acadia University (U)
American University (U)
Anne Arundel Community College (U)
Arapahoe Community College (U)
Athabasca University (N,U)
Athens Technical College (U)
Barton County Community College (U)
Bellevue Community College (U)
Boise State University (U)
Brazosport College (U)
Brigham Young University (U)
Butler Community College (U)
Carlow University (U)
Central Carolina Community College (U)
Centralia College (U)
Central Virginia Community College (U)
Central Washington University (U)
Central Wyoming College (U)
Chatham University (U)
Chemeketa Community College (U)
Clackamas Community College (U)
Clarion University of Pennsylvania (U)
Clark State Community College (U)
Cleveland State University (U)
Coastline Community College (U)
College of San Mateo (U)
Colorado Mountain College District System (U)
Columbia College (U)
Columbus State Community College (U)
Community College of Denver (U)
Corning Community College (U)
Cuyahoga Community College (U)
East Carolina University (U)
East Central Community College (U)
Eastern Michigan University (U)
Eastern Oregon University (U)
Edison State Community College (U)
Elizabeth City State University (U)
Erie Community College (U)
Erie Community College, North Campus (U)
Erie Community College, South Campus (U)
Fort Valley State University (U)
Fox Valley Technical College (U)
Gadsden State Community College (U)
Galveston College (U)
George C. Wallace Community College (U)
Georgia State University (U)
Graceland University (U)
Grantham University (U)
Gulf Coast Community College (U)
Hibbing Community College (U)
Honolulu Community College (U)
Hopkinsville Community College (U)
Houston Community College System (U)
Huntington College of Health Sciences (U,G)
Illinois Eastern Community Colleges, Wabash Valley College (U)
Illinois State University (U)
Indiana State University (U)
Jackson State University (U)
Jacksonville State University (U,G)
Jefferson College (U)
Johnson County Community College (U)
J. Sargeant Reynolds Community College (U)
Kansas State University (U)
Lake Region State College (U)

Lehigh University (N,G)
Marshall University (U)
Massasoit Community College (U)
Mayville State University (U)
McMurry University (U)
Millersville University of Pennsylvania (U)
Mississippi Delta Community College (U)
Missouri State University (U)
Missouri University of Science and Technology (N)
Mt. Hood Community College (U)
Mt. San Antonio College (U)
New River Community College (U)
Northampton County Area Community College (U)
North Carolina State University (U)
North Dakota State College of Science (U)
Northeast Alabama Community College (U)
Northeast Iowa Community College (U)
Northeast State Technical Community College (U)
Northern Virginia Community College (U)
North Iowa Area Community College (U)
North Lake College (U)
NorthWest Arkansas Community College (U)
Northwestern Michigan College (U)
Northwestern State University of Louisiana (U)
Northwest Technical College (U)
Okaloosa-Walton College (U)
Oklahoma Panhandle State University (U)
Oregon State University (U)
Oxnard College (U)
Pace University (U)
Palm Beach Community College (U)
Palomar College (U)
Pamlico Community College (U)
Parkland College (U)
Peninsula College (U)
Pennsylvania College of Technology (U)
Piedmont Technical College (U)
Pratt Community College (U)
Rochester Institute of Technology (U)
Rockland Community College (U)
Sacramento City College (U)
Sacred Heart University (U)
St. Clair County Community College (U)
St. Cloud State University (U)
Sam Houston State University (U)
San Diego Community College District (U)
San Joaquin Delta College (U)
Sierra College (U)
Sinclair Community College (U)
Southeastern Community College (U)
South Piedmont Community College (U)
State University of New York at Oswego (U)
Tacoma Community College (U)
Treasure Valley Community College (U)
Triton College (U)
Union County College (U)
The University of Akron (U)
University of Arkansas at Pine Bluff (U)
University of Central Florida (G)
University of Colorado at Colorado Springs (U)
The University of Findlay (U)
University of Illinois at Springfield (U)
University of Maryland University College (U)
University of New Orleans (U,G)
The University of North Carolina at Chapel Hill (U)

The University of North Carolina Wilmington (G)
University of North Dakota (U)
University of North Texas (U,G)
University of Oklahoma (U)
University of Pittsburgh at Bradford (U)
The University of South Dakota (U)
University of Southern Mississippi (U)
University of South Florida (U,G)
The University of Tennessee (U)
University of Utah (U)
University of Washington (U)
University of Waterloo (N,U)
University of Wisconsin Colleges (U)
University of Wisconsin–Stout (U)
University of Wyoming (U)
Utah State University (U)
Vincennes University (U)
Wake Technical Community College (U)
Washburn University (U)
Weber State University (U)
Westchester Community College (U)
Williston State College (U)
Yuba College (U)

CITY/URBAN, COMMUNITY AND REGIONAL PLANNING

Athabasca University (N)
Cleveland State University (U,G)
East Tennessee State University (G)
Middle Tennessee State University (N)
Prescott College (G)
University of Missouri–Columbia (N)
University of New Orleans (U,G)
University of Southern Mississippi (G)
University of Washington (N,G)

CIVIL ENGINEERING

Auburn University (G)
Brigham Young University (U)
Cleveland State University (U,G)
Colorado State University (G)
Columbia University (N,G)
Georgia Institute of Technology (N,G)
Kansas State University (G)
Louisiana State University and Agricultural and Mechanical College (G)
Mississippi State University (G)
Missouri University of Science and Technology (N,G)
North Carolina State University (G)
Southern Methodist University (G)
Stanford University (N,G)
Texas Tech University (G)
The University of British Columbia (U)
University of Colorado at Boulder (N,G)
University of Colorado Denver (U)
University of Florida (N,G)
University of Idaho (U,G)
University of Illinois at Urbana–Champaign (G)
University of New Orleans (U,G)
The University of North Carolina at Charlotte (N)
University of North Dakota (U)
The University of Texas at San Antonio (U)
University of Washington (G)
Virginia Polytechnic Institute and State University (U)

CIVIL ENGINEERING TECHNOLOGY

Auburn University (G)
Cincinnati State Technical and Community College (U)
James A. Rhodes State College (U)
Missouri University of Science and Technology (G)
North Dakota State College of Science (U)
Rochester Institute of Technology (U)
Sinclair Community College (U)
Southern Methodist University (G)
Southern Polytechnic State University (U)
The University of Arizona (U)
University of South Florida (G)
The University of Texas at San Antonio (U)
Wake Technical Community College (U)

CLASSICAL AND ANCIENT STUDIES

DeSales University (U)
Florida State University (U)
Moorpark College (U)
Okaloosa-Walton College (U)
Queen's University at Kingston (U)
University of Illinois at Urbana–Champaign (U)
The University of Kansas (U)
University of Massachusetts Boston (U)
University of Missouri–Columbia (U)
University of New Orleans (U,G)
The University of North Carolina at Charlotte (U)
The University of North Carolina at Greensboro (U,G)

CLINICAL CHILD PSYCHOLOGY

Arapahoe Community College (U)
California State University, San Bernardino (U)
Central Texas College (U)
Cumberland County College (U)
Liberty University (U)
Long Beach City College (U)
Middlesex Community College (U)
Northampton County Area Community College (U)
Rend Lake College (U)
Santa Monica College (U)
Saybrook Graduate School and Research Center (G)

CLINICAL PSYCHOLOGY

Arapahoe Community College (U)
Athabasca University (N)
Capella University (G)
Delaware County Community College (U)
Jacksonville State University (U,G)
Naropa University (U)
Northampton County Area Community College (U)
North Dakota State University (N,U,G)
Oxnard College (U)
Prescott College (G)
Sacramento City College (U)
Saint Mary-of-the-Woods College (U)
Saybrook Graduate School and Research Center (G)

University of Hawaii–West Oahu (U)

CLINICAL/MEDICAL LABORATORY SCIENCE AND ALLIED PROFESSIONS

Arapahoe Community College (U)
California State University, Sacramento (U)
Central Carolina Community College (N)
Central New Mexico Community College (U)
Darton College (U)
Drexel University (G)
Erie Community College (U)
Erie Community College, North Campus (U)
Erie Community College, South Campus (U)
Hibbing Community College (U)
Loma Linda University (U)
Marion Technical College (U)
Michigan State University (G)
Randolph Community College (N)
Sacramento City College (U)
University of Illinois at Urbana–Champaign (G)
The University of Texas System (N,U)
Weber State University (G)

COGNITIVE PSYCHOLOGY AND PSYCHOLINGUISTICS

Arapahoe Community College (U)
California State University, San Bernardino (U)
Charter Oak State College (U)
Community College of Beaver County (U)
Iona College (U)
Northeast Iowa Community College (U)
Sacramento City College (U)
San Diego Community College District (U)
Treasure Valley Community College (U)
The University of Kansas (U)
University of Southern Mississippi (G)
The University of Texas of the Permian Basin (U)
University of Washington (U)
Wilfrid Laurier University (U)

COGNITIVE SCIENCE

Arapahoe Community College (U)
Queen's University at Kingston (U)
San Diego Community College District (U)
Saybrook Graduate School and Research Center (G)

COMMUNICATION AND JOURNALISM RELATED

American University (U,G)
Arapahoe Community College (U)
Athabasca University (U)
Austin Peay State University (G)
Barton County Community College (U)
Bowling Green State University (U)
Buena Vista University (U)
Cabrillo College (U)
California State University, Dominguez Hills (N)
California State University, San Bernardino (U)
California State University, San Marcos (N)
Central Carolina Community College (U)
Central Michigan University (G)

Central Washington University (U)
Chatham University (U)
City Colleges of Chicago, Harold Washington College (U)
Clarion University of Pennsylvania (G)
Cleveland State University (U)
Coastline Community College (U)
Columbus State Community College (U)
Dallas Baptist University (U)
Drake University (U)
East Carolina University (U)
Eastern Michigan University (U)
East Tennessee State University (N)
Elizabethtown College (U)
Everett Community College (U)
Finger Lakes Community College (U)
Fort Hays State University (N,U)
Fox Valley Technical College (U)
Galveston College (U)
Georgia State University (U)
Grand Rapids Community College (N,U)
Henderson Community College (U)
Indian River Community College (U)
Iona College (U,G)
James Madison University (N)
Jefferson Community College (U)
Jones International University (G)
Kean University (N)
Lackawanna College (U)
Lakeland Community College (N)
Louisiana State University and Agricultural and Mechanical College (U)
Malone College (U)
Mansfield University of Pennsylvania (U)
Marshall University (U)
Metropolitan State University (U)
Middlesex Community College (U)
Mississippi State University (U)
Missouri State University (U)
Moorpark College (U)
Mount Wachusett Community College (U)
Naugatuck Valley Community College (U)
New Jersey Institute of Technology (G)
New Mexico Junior College (U)
The New School: A University (N,U)
Northampton County Area Community College (U)
Northern Virginia Community College (U)
Northwestern State University of Louisiana (U)
Pace University (U)
Palomar College (U)
Park University (U)
Peninsula College (U)
Prairie View A&M University (U)
Regent University (N,U,G)
Rose State College (U)
Sacramento City College (U)
Saddleback College (U)
St. Clair County Community College (U)
St. John's University (U)
St. Louis Community College System (U)
San Diego Community College District (U)
Santa Monica College (U)
Santa Rosa Junior College (U)
Seminole Community College (U)
Southeastern Illinois College (U)
Southern New Hampshire University (U)
Southern Polytechnic State University (U,G)
Southwest Wisconsin Technical College (U)
State University of New York at Binghamton (N)

State University of New York at Oswego (U)
State University of New York College at
  Potsdam (U)
Sullivan County Community College (N)
Tacoma Community College (U)
Taylor University (N,U)
Triton College (N)
The University of Akron (U)
University of Alaska Fairbanks (U)
University of Arkansas at Little Rock (U)
The University of Findlay (U)
University of Houston–Victoria (U)
University of Illinois at Springfield (U)
University of Minnesota, Twin Cities Campus
  (U)
University of New Haven (U)
University of New Orleans (N)
The University of North Carolina at Chapel
  Hill (G)
University of North Dakota (U)
University of South Alabama (U)
University of Southern Indiana (N)
University of South Florida (N)
University of the Virgin Islands (U)
University of Wisconsin Colleges (U)
University of Wisconsin–Superior (U)
University of Wisconsin–Whitewater (U,G)
Utah Valley State College (U)
Valley City State University (U)
Webster University (G)
Western Washington University (U)
Western Wyoming Community College (U)
West Virginia State University (U)
West Virginia University at Parkersburg (U)

COMMUNICATION AND MEDIA

Abilene Christian University (U)
Anne Arundel Community College (U)
Arapahoe Community College (U)
Arkansas State University–Beebe (U)
Athabasca University (N,U)
Auburn University (U)
Bellevue Community College (U)
Bellevue University (U)
Berkeley College (U)
Berkeley College–New York City Campus (U)
Berkeley College–Westchester Campus (U)
Beulah Heights University (U)
Blue Ridge Community College (N)
Bowling Green State University (U)
Bradley University (U)
Brenau University (U)
Bridgewater State College (N,U,G)
Brigham Young University (U)
Buena Vista University (U)
Buffalo State College, State University of
  New York (U)
Burlington County College (U)
Caldwell Community College and Technical
  Institute (U)
California State University, Chico (U)
California State University, San Bernardino
  (U,G)
Carroll University (U)
Central New Mexico Community College (U)
Central Texas College (U)
Central Wyoming College (U)
Charter Oak State College (U)
Cincinnati State Technical and Community
  College (U)
Citrus College (U)

Clarion University of Pennsylvania (U,G)
Clark State Community College (U)
Clemson University (N,U,G)
Cleveland Institute of Electronics (U)
Cleveland State University (U)
Coastline Community College (U)
College of Southern Maryland (U)
College of The Albemarle (N)
Concordia University, St. Paul (N)
Dallas Baptist University (U)
Danville Community College (U)
Darton College (U)
Dawson Community College (U)
DeVry University Online (U,G)
Drake University (U)
Duquesne University (U,G)
East Carolina University (U)
Eastern Michigan University (U)
Eastern Washington University (U)
Edgecombe Community College (N)
Elizabethtown College (U)
Elizabethtown Community and Technical
  College (U)
Fitchburg State College (U,G)
Fontbonne University (U)
Fort Valley State University (U)
Franklin University (U)
Golden Gate University (U)
Gonzaga University (G)
Governors State University (N,U)
Granite State College (U)
Halifax Community College (U)
Hillsborough Community College (U)
Hocking College (U)
Holyoke Community College (U)
Hopkinsville Community College (N,U)
Illinois Eastern Community Colleges, Olney
  Central College (U)
Indiana University–Purdue University Fort
  Wayne (U)
Indiana Wesleyan University (U)
Iona College (U)
James A. Rhodes State College (U)
James Madison University (U)
Jamestown Community College (N)
Jefferson Community College (U)
Judson University (U)
Labette Community College (U)
Lackawanna College (U)
Lakeland Community College (N)
Lake Superior College (U)
Lewis-Clark State College (U)
Liberty University (U)
Louisiana State University and Agricultural
  and Mechanical College (U)
Malone College (U)
Marist College (U,G)
Marshall University (U)
Massasoit Community College (N)
Mesa Community College (U)
Middlesex Community College (U)
Middle Tennessee State University (U)
Midwestern State University (U)
Millersville University of Pennsylvania (U)
Minnesota School of Business–Richfield (U)
Mississippi State University (U)
Missouri State University (G)
Monmouth University (U,G)
Monroe Community College (U)
Moorpark College (U)
Mountain Empire Community College (U)
Myers University (U)

Naugatuck Valley Community College (U)
New Mexico Junior College (U)
The New School: A University (N,U)
New York Institute of Technology (U)
Northampton County Area Community
  College (U)
North Dakota State University (U,G)
Northeast Iowa Community College (U)
Northland Community and Technical College–
  Thief River Falls (U)
North Seattle Community College (U)
NorthWest Arkansas Community College (U)
Northwestern Oklahoma State University (U)
Northwest Missouri State University (U)
Nyack College (U)
Old Dominion University (U)
Oregon State University (N,U)
Oxnard College (U)
Pace University (U)
Palm Beach Community College (U)
Palomar College (U)
Parkland College (U)
Park University (U)
Passaic County Community College (U)
Patrick Henry Community College (U)
Pellissippi State Technical Community
  College (U)
Piedmont Community College (U)
Piedmont Technical College (U)
Plymouth State University (U)
Pratt Community College (U)
Prescott College (U,G)
Providence College and Theological Seminary
  (U)
Regent University (U,G)
Regis University (U)
Riverside Community College District (U)
Rochester Institute of Technology (U)
Sacramento City College (U)
Sacred Heart University (U)
St. Cloud State University (U)
St. Edward's University (U)
Saint Joseph's College of Maine (U)
San Diego Community College District (U)
Santa Monica College (U)
Santa Rosa Junior College (U)
Seminole Community College (U)
Shippensburg University of Pennsylvania
  (U,G)
Sierra College (U)
Simpson College (U)
Sinclair Community College (U)
Southeastern Oklahoma State University (U)
Southern New Hampshire University (U)
South Piedmont Community College (U)
Southwest Wisconsin Technical College (U)
State University of New York at Binghamton
  (N)
State University of New York at Oswego (U)
State University of New York College at
  Cortland (U)
State University of New York College at
  Potsdam (N)
State University of New York Empire State
  College (U)
State University of New York Institute of
  Technology (U,G)
Syracuse University (G)
Taylor University (N)
Temple University (U,G)
Texas A&M University–Commerce (U)
Tompkins Cortland Community College (U)

Tunxis Community College (U)
Union County College (U)
The University of Akron (U)
The University of Alabama (U)
University of Arkansas at Little Rock (U)
University of Arkansas at Pine Bluff (U)
University of Colorado at Colorado Springs (U)
University of Colorado Denver (U)
University of Denver (G)
University of Dubuque (U)
University of Houston–Downtown (U)
University of Illinois at Springfield (U,G)
University of Louisville (G)
The University of Maine at Augusta (U)
University of Maine at Fort Kent (U)
University of Maryland University College (U)
University of Massachusetts Boston (U)
University of Minnesota, Twin Cities Campus (U,G)
University of Nevada, Reno (U)
University of North Alabama (U)
The University of North Carolina at Chapel Hill (U,G)
University of North Dakota (U)
University of Northern Iowa (U)
University of Oklahoma (U)
University of St. Francis (U)
University of Southern Indiana (U)
University of Southern Maine (U)
University of Southern Mississippi (G)
The University of Texas at San Antonio (U)
The University of Texas of the Permian Basin (U)
University of the Pacific (U)
University of the Virgin Islands (U)
The University of Toledo (U)
University of Toronto (N)
University of Washington (U)
University of West Florida (U)
University of Wisconsin–Superior (U)
University of Wisconsin–Whitewater (U)
University of Wyoming (U)
Upper Iowa University (N,U)
Utah Valley State College (U)
Virginia Polytechnic Institute and State University (U)
Weber State University (U)
Westchester Community College (U)
West Virginia State University (U,G)
West Virginia University at Parkersburg (N)
Wichita State University (U)
Wilfrid Laurier University (U)
Wisconsin Indianhead Technical College (N,U)
Worcester State College (N,U)
York University (U)
Yuba College (U)

COMMUNICATION DISORDERS SCIENCES AND SERVICES

Athabasca University (N,U)
Auburn University (U)
Bridgewater State College (U)
Brigham Young University (U)
California State University, Northridge (N)
East Carolina University (G)
Fontbonne University (G)
Fort Hays State University (U)
Illinois State University (U)

Jackson State University (G)
James Madison University (N)
Lakeland Community College (N)
MGH Institute of Health Professions (G)
Murray State University (U,G)
Oklahoma State University (U)
Red Rocks Community College (U)
Texas A&M University–Kingsville (U,G)
Texas Woman's University (G)
The University of Akron (G)
University of Cincinnati (U,G)
The University of North Carolina at Greensboro (U)
University of Vermont (N,G)
Utah State University (U)

COMMUNICATIONS TECHNOLOGIES AND SUPPORT SERVICES RELATED

Bloomsburg University of Pennsylvania (N)
Dallas Baptist University (U)
Drexel University (U)
Galveston College (U)
Iona College (G)
Northampton County Area Community College (U)
Palomar College (U)
Sacramento City College (U)
Wayne State College (G)
West Virginia University at Parkersburg (N)

COMMUNICATIONS TECHNOLOGY

Arapahoe Community College (U)
Athabasca University (N,U)
Bowling Green State University (U)
California State University, San Bernardino (U,G)
Central Michigan University (G)
Dakota State University (U)
Dallas Baptist University (U)
DeVry University Online (G)
Eastern Iowa Community College District (N)
East Tennessee State University (U)
Foothill College (U)
Grantham University (G)
James Madison University (U)
Jones International University (U)
Lakeland Community College (N)
Mercy College (U)
Middlesex Community College (U)
National University (U)
North Lake College (U)
Okaloosa-Walton College (U)
Pamlico Community College (U)
Regent University (U,G)
Roosevelt University (G)
Sacramento City College (U)
San Diego Community College District (U)
Santa Rosa Junior College (U)
South Piedmont Community College (U)
Temple University (U,G)
The University of Akron (N)
University of Illinois at Urbana–Champaign (G)
University of New Haven (G)
University of North Texas (G)
University of West Florida (N,U)

COMMUNITY HEALTH SERVICES

Athabasca University (N,U,G)
Blue Ridge Community College (N)
Brenau University (U)
California State University, Chico (U)
California State University, San Bernardino (U)
California State University, San Marcos (N)
Canisius College (G)
Central Michigan University (U)
Colorado State University (N)
Dallas Baptist University (U)
Danville Community College (U)
Duquesne University (G)
Edgecombe Community College (N)
Galveston College (U)
Houston Community College System (U)
Independence University (G)
Indiana State University (U)
Jacksonville State University (U)
Jefferson College of Health Sciences (U)
Kansas State University (G)
Lakeland Community College (N)
Louisiana State University and Agricultural and Mechanical College (U)
Medical College of Wisconsin (G)
Mercy College (G)
Middlesex Community College (U)
New Mexico State University (U)
Old Dominion University (U)
Pace University (G)
Rappahannock Community College (U)
Saybrook Graduate School and Research Center (G)
Seminole Community College (U)
State University of New York College at Cortland (U,G)
State University of New York College at Potsdam (U)
Temple University (G)
The University of Akron (U)
University of Arkansas at Little Rock (U)
The University of Maine at Augusta (U)
University of Southern Maine (U)
University of Southern Mississippi (U,G)
The University of Texas at Tyler (U)
Vincennes University (U)
Western Washington University (U)
West Virginia University at Parkersburg (U)

COMMUNITY ORGANIZATION AND ADVOCACY

Athabasca University (N,U,G)
California Institute of Integral Studies (N,G)
Central Michigan University (U)
Colorado State University (N)
Duquesne University (G)
Kansas State University (G)
Lakeland Community College (N)
Medical College of Wisconsin (G)
Mercy College (U)
Michigan State University (N,G)
Pace University (U,G)
Prescott College (G)
Saybrook Graduate School and Research Center (G)
The University of Akron (U)
University of Massachusetts Boston (U)
University of New Orleans (U)
University of North Texas (G)

University of Southern Mississippi (U)
University of Vermont (U)
University of Waterloo (U)

COMMUNITY PSYCHOLOGY

Athabasca University (N,U,G)
Central Texas College (U)
Colorado State University (N)
Dallas Christian College (U)
Delaware County Community College (U)
Kansas State University (G)
Middlesex Community College (U)
Naropa University (U)
St. Cloud State University (G)
Saybrook Graduate School and Research
  Center (G)
Texas State University–San Marcos (U)
Treasure Valley Community College (U)
University of Maine at Machias (U)
University of Massachusetts Boston (U)

COMPARATIVE LITERATURE

Arapahoe Community College (U)
Arkansas State University–Mountain Home
  (U)
Athabasca University (U)
Bellevue Community College (U)
Bellevue University (U)
Burlington College (U)
California State University, San Marcos (N)
Columbus State Community College (U)
Community College of Denver (U)
Delaware County Community College (U)
DeSales University (U)
East Tennessee State University (U)
Foothill College (U)
Graceland University (U)
Indiana University–Purdue University Fort
  Wayne (U)
Jefferson Community College (U)
Limestone College (U)
Lock Haven University of Pennsylvania (U)
Louisiana State University and Agricultural
  and Mechanical College (U)
Macon State College (U)
Mercy College (U,G)
Middlesex Community College (U)
Naropa University (U)
Pace University (U)
San Diego Community College District (U)
State University of New York at Binghamton
  (U)
Texas State University–San Marcos (U)
The University of Maine at Augusta (U)
University of Minnesota, Twin Cities Campus
  (U)
University of New Orleans (U,G)
University of Southern Mississippi (U)

COMPARATIVE PSYCHOLOGY

San Diego Community College District (U)

COMPUTER AND INFORMATION SCIENCES

Allen County Community College (U)
Anne Arundel Community College (N,U)
Arapahoe Community College (U)
Arizona Western College (U)
Arkansas State University–Beebe (U)

Arkansas Tech University (U)
Athabasca University (N,U,G)
Athens Technical College (U)
Barton County Community College (U)
Beaufort County Community College (N,U)
Bellevue Community College (U)
Bellevue University (U)
Belmont Technical College (U)
Blue Ridge Community College (N,U)
Bowling Green State University (U)
Bradley University (U)
Brazosport College (U)
Brenau University (U,G)
Brigham Young University (N)
Bristol Community College (U)
Burlington County College (U)
Cabrillo College (U)
Caldwell Community College and Technical
  Institute (U)
California National University for Advanced
  Studies (U,G)
California Polytechnic State University, San
  Luis Obispo (N)
California State University, Dominguez Hills
  (N)
California State University, Sacramento (U)
California State University, San Marcos (N)
Carroll Community College (U)
Centennial College (U)
Central Carolina Community College (N)
Centralia College (N)
Central Michigan University (G)
Central New Mexico Community College (U)
Central Oregon Community College (U)
Central Texas College (U)
Central Virginia Community College (U)
Central Wyoming College (U)
Chadron State College (U)
Charter Oak State College (U)
Chemeketa Community College (U)
Cincinnati State Technical and Community
  College (U)
Citrus College (U)
Clemson University (N)
Cleveland State Community College (U)
Cleveland State University (U)
Clinton Community College (U)
Coastline Community College (U)
The College of St. Scholastica (U)
College of The Albemarle (N,U)
College of the Sequoias (U)
Columbia College (U)
Columbus State Community College (U)
Community College of Beaver County (N,U)
Community College of Denver (N)
Connors State College (U)
Culver-Stockton College (U)
Cuyahoga Community College (U)
Dakota State University (U,G)
Dallas Baptist University (U,G)
Dallas County Community College District
  (U)
De Anza College (U)
Delaware County Community College (N,U)
DeVry University Online (U,G)
Diné College (U)
Drake University (U)
Drexel University (U,G)
Duquesne University (N,U)
East Carolina University (U,G)
East Central Community College (U)
Eastern Illinois University (G)

Eastern Iowa Community College District (N)
Eastern West Virginia Community and
  Technical College (U)
Eastern Wyoming College (U)
East Los Angeles College (U)
East Tennessee State University (N)
Edgecombe Community College (N,U)
Edison State Community College (N,U)
Elgin Community College (U)
Everett Community College (U)
Evergreen Valley College (U)
Excelsior College (U)
Finger Lakes Community College (U)
Florida State University (G)
Foothill College (U)
Fort Hays State University (U)
Fort Valley State University (U)
Fox Valley Technical College (U)
Galveston College (U)
Genesee Community College (U)
George C. Wallace Community College (U)
Georgia Institute of Technology (G)
Georgia State University (U)
Golden West College (U)
Graceland University (U)
Grantham University (U)
Harford Community College (N)
Haywood Community College (U)
Henderson Community College (U)
Henry Ford Community College (U)
Herkimer County Community College (U)
Hibbing Community College (N,U)
Hillsborough Community College (U)
Hofstra University (U,G)
Hopkinsville Community College (N,U)
Illinois Eastern Community Colleges, Olney
  Central College (U)
Immaculata University (U)
Indiana Tech (U)
Indiana Wesleyan University (U)
Indian River Community College (U)
Jacksonville State University (U,G)
Jamestown Community College (N)
Jefferson Community College (U)
John A. Logan College (U)
John Wood Community College (U)
Kansas State University (U)
Kaplan University Online (N)
Kaskaskia College (U)
Kean University (N)
Kentucky State University (U)
Knowledge Systems Institute (G)
Lakeland Community College (N,U)
Lake Superior College (U)
Lamar State College–Port Arthur (N,U)
Laredo Community College (U)
Lehigh Carbon Community College (U)
Lewis-Clark State College (U)
Limestone College (U)
Long Beach City College (U)
Los Angeles Harbor College (U)
Louisiana State University and Agricultural
  and Mechanical College (U)
Luzerne County Community College (U)
Macon State College (U)
Manatee Community College (U)
Manor College (U)
Mansfield University of Pennsylvania (U)
Marshall University (U,G)
Massasoit Community College (N,U)
Mercer County Community College (U)
Mercy College (U,G)

Miami Dade College (U)
Michigan State University (N,U)
Michigan Technological University (U)
Middlesex Community College (U)
Middle Tennessee State University (N)
Midstate College (U)
Midwestern State University (U)
Milwaukee School of Engineering (U)
Mississippi State University (U)
Missouri State University (U,G)
Missouri University of Science and
    Technology (N,G)
Mitchell Technical Institute (N,U)
Monroe County Community College (U)
Montcalm Community College (N)
Montgomery Community College (N,U)
Montgomery County Community College (U)
Moorpark College (U)
Motlow State Community College (U)
Mountain Empire Community College (U)
Mt. Hood Community College (U)
Mt. San Antonio College (U)
Murray State University (U)
Myers University (U)
Nassau Community College (U)
National University (G)
Naugatuck Valley Community College (U)
New Jersey Institute of Technology (U)
New York Institute of Technology (N)
Northampton County Area Community
    College (U)
North Central Texas College (U)
North Dakota State College of Science (U)
North Dakota State University (N,U)
Northeast State Technical Community College
    (U)
Northern State University (U)
Northern Virginia Community College (U)
North Lake College (U)
Northland Community and Technical College–
    Thief River Falls (U)
NorthWest Arkansas Community College (U)
Northwestern Connecticut Community College
    (N,U)
Northwestern Michigan College (U)
Northwestern State University of Louisiana
    (U)
Northwest Missouri State University (U,G)
Nova Southeastern University (G)
Okaloosa-Walton College (U)
Okefenokee Technical College (N,U,G)
Oklahoma Panhandle State University (U)
Orange Coast College (U)
Oregon Institute of Technology (U)
Ouachita Technical College (U)
Oxnard College (U)
Pace University (N,G)
Palm Beach Community College (U)
Palomar College (U)
Pamlico Community College (U)
Parkland College (U)
Park University (U,G)
Pasco-Hernando Community College (N,U)
Passaic County Community College (U)
Pellissippi State Technical Community
    College (U)
Peninsula College (U)
Pennsylvania College of Technology (U)
Plymouth State University (G)
Portland Community College (U)
Pulaski Technical College (U)
Randolph Community College (N,U)

Reading Area Community College (U)
Red Rocks Community College (U)
Regis University (G)
Riverside Community College District (N,U)
Sacramento City College (U)
Sacred Heart University (U)
St. Clair County Community College (U)
Saint Francis University (U)
Saint Leo University (U)
St. Louis Community College System (U)
Saint Mary-of-the-Woods College (U)
San Diego Community College District (N,U)
Santa Rosa Junior College (U)
Seminole Community College (U)
Sierra College (U)
Sinclair Community College (U)
Southeastern Community College (U)
Southeastern Oklahoma State University (U)
Southern Methodist University (G)
Southern New Hampshire University (U)
Southern Polytechnic State University (G)
South Piedmont Community College (U)
Southwest Wisconsin Technical College (U)
State University of New York at Binghamton
    (N,G)
State University of New York at Oswego (U)
State University of New York at Plattsburgh
    (U)
State University of New York College at
    Potsdam (N)
State University of New York College of
    Technology at Canton (U)
Syracuse University (U,G)
Tacoma Community College (N,U)
Taylor University (N,U)
Texas A&M University–Commerce (U,G)
Texas A&M University–Kingsville (U)
Texas Woman's University (U)
Three Rivers Community College (U)
Tompkins Cortland Community College (U)
Tri-County Community College (N,U)
Triton College (N)
Tunxis Community College (N,U)
Tyler Junior College (N,U)
The University of Akron (N,U,G)
The University of Alabama (U)
University of Alaska Fairbanks (U,G)
University of Arkansas at Pine Bluff (U)
The University of British Columbia (U)
University of California, Davis (U)
University of Cincinnati (N,U)
University of Dallas (G)
University of Denver (G)
University of Dubuque (U)
University of Houston–Victoria (U,G)
University of Illinois at Urbana–Champaign
    (N,U,G)
The University of Maine at Augusta (U)
University of Management and Technology
    (U)
University of Maryland University College
    (U)
University of Massachusetts Boston (U)
University of Michigan–Dearborn (U,G)
University of Missouri–Columbia (U)
University of Nevada, Reno (U)
University of New Orleans (U,G)
University of North Alabama (U)
The University of North Carolina at Chapel
    Hill (U)
The University of North Carolina at Charlotte
    (U)

University of North Florida (U)
University of North Texas (U,G)
University of Northwestern Ohio (U)
University of Pittsburgh at Bradford (U)
University of St. Francis (U)
University of South Alabama (U)
University of Southern Indiana (N)
University of South Florida (G)
The University of Tennessee at Martin (N)
The University of Texas of the Permian Basin
    (U)
The University of Texas System (U,G)
University of the Southwest (U)
University of the Virgin Islands (U)
The University of Toledo (U)
University of Washington (N)
University of Waterloo (U)
Utah Valley State College (U)
Vermont Technical College (U)
Vincennes University (U)
Virginia Polytechnic Institute and State
    University (N)
Weber State University (U)
Webster University (U)
Westchester Community College (U)
Westfield State College (U)
West Hills Community College (N)
West Los Angeles College (U)
West Shore Community College (U)
West Virginia State University (U)
West Virginia University at Parkersburg (N,U)
Wharton County Junior College (U)
Wilmington University (G)
Wisconsin Indianhead Technical College
    (N,U)
Worcester State College (N,U)
Wytheville Community College (U)
York County Community College (U)
Youngstown State University (N)

COMPUTER AND INFORMATION SCIENCES AND SUPPORT SERVICES RELATED

Arapahoe Community College (U)
Athabasca University (U,G)
Bellevue Community College (U)
Bellevue University (U)
Belmont Technical College (U)
Blackhawk Technical College (U)
Boise State University (U)
Bowling Green State University (N)
Bristol Community College (U)
Caldwell Community College and Technical
    Institute (N)
California State University, San Marcos (U)
Central Michigan University (G)
Central Texas College (U)
Chatham University (U)
Chemeketa Community College (U)
Clark State Community College (U)
Dakota State University (U,G)
Dallas County Community College District
    (U)
Delaware County Community College (N,U)
Drexel University (G)
Duquesne University (G)
East Carolina University (U)
Eastern Iowa Community College District (N)
East Tennessee State University (N)
Edgecombe Community College (N,U)
Elaine P. Nunez Community College (U)

Galveston College (U)
Halifax Community College (U)
Immaculata University (U)
Indian River Community College (U)
Iona College (U)
Jacksonville State University (U,G)
Jamestown Community College (N)
Lakeland Community College (N)
Limestone College (U)
Lock Haven University of Pennsylvania (N)
Marshall University (U)
Mercy College (G)
Middlesex Community College (U)
Mountain View College (N,U)
Myers University (U)
New York Institute of Technology (N)
Northampton County Area Community
    College (U)
North Arkansas College (N)
Northcentral University (G)
North Dakota State College of Science (U)
NorthWest Arkansas Community College (U)
Northwestern Michigan College (U)
Nova Southeastern University (G)
Pace University (U,G)
Palomar College (U)
Pikes Peak Community College (U)
Portland Community College (U)
Regis University (G)
Sacramento City College (U)
Saint Francis University (U)
Saint Leo University (U)
St. Louis Community College System (U)
San Diego Community College District (U)
Santa Rosa Junior College (U)
Seminole Community College (U)
Southern Methodist University (G)
South Piedmont Community College (U)
Southwest Virginia Community College (N)
State University of New York at Binghamton
    (N,U,G)
Taylor University (N)
Texas Tech University (G)
Treasure Valley Community College (U)
Tri-County Community College (N)
Tyler Junior College (U)
The University of Akron (N)
The University of Alabama (G)
University of Central Florida (U)
University of Connecticut (U)
University of Dallas (G)
University of Denver (G)
The University of Maine at Augusta (U)
The University of Texas System (U)
University of Washington (N)
Wake Technical Community College (N,U)
Weber State University (U)
Webster University (G)
Westchester Community College (U)
York Technical College (N)
Yuba College (U)

COMPUTER ENGINEERING

California National University for Advanced
    Studies (G)
Cleveland Institute of Electronics (U)
Cleveland State University (U,G)
College of The Albemarle (N)
Dallas County Community College District
    (U)
Delaware County Community College (N,U)

Drexel University (G)
Edison State Community College (U)
Georgia Institute of Technology (N,G)
Grantham University (U)
Jacksonville State University (G)
Kansas State University (G)
Knowledge Systems Institute (G)
Lakeland Community College (N)
Marshall University (U)
Mississippi State University (G)
Myers University (U)
North Carolina State University (G)
North Dakota State University (G)
Oxnard College (U)
Southern Methodist University (G)
Southern Polytechnic State University (G)
State University of New York at Binghamton
    (G)
University of Colorado at Boulder (N,G)
University of Florida (N,G)
University of Idaho (U,G)
University of Michigan–Dearborn (G)
University of New Haven (U)
University of South Florida (G)
University of Washington (U)
University of West Florida (N)
Virginia Polytechnic Institute and State
    University (U,G)
Western Michigan University (G)

COMPUTER ENGINEERING TECHNOLOGIES

Drexel University (G)
Georgia Institute of Technology (G)
Grantham University (U)
Haywood Community College (U)
Knowledge Systems Institute (G)
Prairie View A&M University (U)
Southern Methodist University (G)
UC San Diego Extension (N)
University of California, Davis (N)
University of Illinois at Urbana–Champaign
    (N)

COMPUTER PROGRAMMING

Acadia University (U)
Arapahoe Community College (U)
Arkansas State University–Beebe (U)
Athabasca University (N,U)
Athens Technical College (N)
Bellevue Community College (U)
Bellevue University (U)
Belmont Technical College (U)
Bergen Community College (U)
Blackhawk Technical College (U)
Blue Ridge Community College (N,U)
Bowling Green State University (U)
Bristol Community College (U)
Bryant and Stratton Online (U)
Butler Community College (U)
California State University, San Marcos (U)
Carroll Community College (N,U)
Centennial College (N)
Central Carolina Community College (U)
Centralia College (N)
Central New Mexico Community College (U)
Central Texas College (U)
Cerro Coso Community College (U)
Chemeketa Community College (U)
Citrus College (U)

Clemson University (N)
Cleveland Community College (U)
Cleveland Institute of Electronics (N)
Cleveland State University (U)
Clinton Community College (U)
Coastline Community College (U)
College of San Mateo (U)
College of The Albemarle (N)
Columbia-Greene Community College (U)
Columbus State Community College (U)
Columbus State University (G)
Community College of Beaver County (U)
Community College of Denver (N)
Corning Community College (U)
Dakota State University (U)
Dallas County Community College District
    (U)
Danville Community College (U)
Daytona State College (U)
De Anza College (U)
Delaware County Community College (N,U)
DePaul University (U)
Eastern Iowa Community College District (N)
East Tennessee State University (N)
Edgecombe Community College (N,U)
Edison State Community College (U)
Eugenio María de Hostos Community College
    of the City University of New York (U)
Finger Lakes Community College (U)
Flathead Valley Community College (N)
Galveston College (N,U)
Golden West College (U)
Granite State College (U)
Grantham University (U)
Greenville Technical College (U)
Hagerstown Community College (N)
Harford Community College (N)
Harrisburg Area Community College (U)
Haywood Community College (U)
Hibbing Community College (U)
Hillsborough Community College (U)
Hofstra University (U)
Indiana State University (U)
Indian River Community College (U)
Iona College (U)
Jackson State University (U)
Jacksonville State University (U,G)
James A. Rhodes State College (U)
James Madison University (N)
Kean University (N)
Kentucky State University (U)
Knowledge Systems Institute (G)
Labette Community College (U)
Lakeland Community College (N)
Lamar State College–Port Arthur (N,U)
Limestone College (U)
Lock Haven University of Pennsylvania (U)
Long Beach City College (U)
Los Angeles Harbor College (U)
Macon State College (U)
Mesa Community College (U)
Middlesex Community College (U)
Middle Tennessee State University (N)
Minot State University (U)
Montcalm Community College (U)
Montgomery County Community College (U)
Mount Wachusett Community College (U)
Murray State University (U)
Myers University (U)
National University (G)
North Carolina State University (U)
North Dakota State College of Science (U)

North Dakota State University (N)
Northeastern University (U)
North Lake College (U)
North Seattle Community College (U)
NorthWest Arkansas Community College (U)
Northwestern Michigan College (U)
Nova Southeastern University (G)
'Okaloosa-Walton College (U)
Orange Coast College (U)
Oxnard College (U)
Pace University (U,G)
Palomar College (U)
Pamlico Community College (U)
Parkland College (U)
Park University (U)
Pasco-Hernando Community College (N,U)
Piedmont Community College (U)
Pikes Peak Community College (U)
Portland Community College (N)
Red Rocks Community College (U)
Regis University (U,G)
Riverside Community College District (N)
Rose State College (U)
Sacramento City College (U)
Saint Leo University (U)
San Diego Community College District (U)
San Diego State University (N)
Santa Monica College (U)
Santa Rosa Junior College (U)
Seminole Community College (U)
Sinclair Community College (U)
Southeast Arkansas College (U)
Southern Polytechnic State University (N,G)
South Piedmont Community College (U)
Southwest Wisconsin Technical College (U)
State University of New York at Binghamton
  (N)
State University of New York College at
  Cortland (U)
State University of New York College at
  Potsdam (N)
Tacoma Community College (U)
Taylor University (N)
Texas A&M University–Kingsville (N)
Texas State Technical College Waco (N,U)
Tompkins Cortland Community College (U)
Treasure Valley Community College (U)
Tri-County Community College (N)
Tyler Junior College (N,U)
The University of Akron (N)
University of California, Davis (N,U)
University of Central Missouri (N)
University of Cincinnati (N)
University of Colorado Denver (U)
University of Connecticut (U)
University of Idaho (U)
University of Illinois at Urbana–Champaign
  (N)
University of Management and Technology
  (U)
University of New Orleans (U,G)
University of North Dakota (N)
University of North Florida (U)
University of South Florida (N,G)
The University of Texas at San Antonio (U)
University of the Virgin Islands (U)
University of Vermont (N)
University of Washington (N,U)
University of West Florida (U)
Utah State University (G)
Wake Technical Community College (N)
Westchester Community College (U)

Westwood Online (U)
Wisconsin Indianhead Technical College
  (N,U)
Wytheville Community College (U)
York County Community College (U)
Yuba College (U)

COMPUTER SCIENCE

Acadia University (U)
Anne Arundel Community College (U)
Arapahoe Community College (U)
Arkansas State University–Mountain Home
  (U)
Athabasca University (N,U,G)
Auburn University (U,G)
Azusa Pacific University (U,G)
Bellevue Community College (U)
Belmont Technical College (U)
Bergen Community College (U)
Beulah Heights University (U)
Bowling Green State University (U)
Bristol Community College (U)
Broome Community College (U)
Broward Community College (U)
Buffalo State College, State University of
  New York (U)
Cabrillo College (U)
California State University, Chico (G)
Carlow University (U)
Carroll University (U,G)
Cayuga County Community College (U)
Central Carolina Community College (U)
Central Texas College (U)
Central Wyoming College (U)
Chemeketa Community College (U)
Clackamas Community College (U)
Clarion University of Pennsylvania (U)
Cleveland Institute of Electronics (N)
Cleveland State University (U)
College of The Albemarle (N,U)
College of the Siskiyous (U)
Colorado Mountain College District System
  (U)
Colorado State University (U,G)
Columbia University (N,G)
Columbus State University (U)
Community College of Beaver County (N,U)
Concordia University Wisconsin (U)
Corning Community College (U)
Dakota State University (U)
Dallas Baptist University (U)
Dallas County Community College District
  (U)
Danville Community College (U)
Delaware County Community College (N,U)
Delaware Technical & Community College,
  Jack F. Owens Campus (U)
DePaul University (U,G)
DeSales University (U)
Drexel University (U,G)
East Carolina University (G)
Eastern Iowa Community College District (N)
Eastern Oregon University (U)
Edgecombe Community College (N)
Edison State Community College (U)
Embry-Riddle Aeronautical University (U)
Erie Community College (U)
Erie Community College, North Campus (U)
Erie Community College, South Campus (U)
Fitchburg State College (U)
Florida Gulf Coast University (U)

Fort Valley State University (U)
Framingham State College (U)
Franklin University (U)
Gadsden State Community College (U)
Galveston College (U)
Gateway Technical College (U)
George Mason University (U,G)
Georgia Institute of Technology (G)
Georgia State University (U)
Golden West College (U)
Grantham University (U)
Halifax Community College (U)
Harrisburg Area Community College (U)
Haywood Community College (U)
Hibbing Community College (U)
Hillsborough Community College (U)
Holyoke Community College (U)
Houston Community College System (U)
Immaculata University (U)
Indiana State University (U)
Indiana University–Purdue University Fort
  Wayne (U)
Indian River Community College (U)
Jacksonville State University (U,G)
James Madison University (N,G)
J. Sargeant Reynolds Community College (U)
Kansas State University (G)
Kentucky State University (U)
Knowledge Systems Institute (G)
Labette Community College (U)
Lakeland College (U)
Lamar State College–Port Arthur (N,U)
Laredo Community College (U)
Lehigh Carbon Community College (U)
Limestone College (U)
Long Beach City College (U)
Marymount University (G)
Massachusetts College of Liberal Arts (U)
Memorial University of Newfoundland (U)
Mercy College (U,G)
Mesa Community College (U)
Middlesex Community College (U)
Middle Tennessee State University (N)
Midway College (U)
Minnesota School of Business–Richfield (U)
Minot State University (U)
Mississippi State University (U,G)
Missouri State University–West Plains (U)
Missouri University of Science and
  Technology (N,G)
Moberly Area Community College (U)
Montgomery County Community College (U)
Murray State University (U)
Myers University (U)
National University (G)
Naugatuck Valley Community College (U)
New Jersey Institute of Technology (U,G)
New Mexico Highlands University (U)
New Mexico Institute of Mining and
  Technology (G)
New River Community College (U)
Northampton County Area Community
  College (U)
North Dakota State University (N)
Northeast Alabama Community College (U)
Nova Southeastern University (G)
Okaloosa-Walton College (U)
Old Dominion University (U)
Oxnard College (U)
Pace University (U)
Palomar College (U)
Piedmont Technical College (U)

ikes Peak Community College (U)
ortland Community College (U)
.ed Rocks Community College (U)
.egis University (U,G)
.end Lake College (U)
.ichmond Community College (U)
.iverside Community College District (U)
.ockland Community College (U)
.oosevelt University (U)
.ose State College (U)
acramento City College (U)
acred Heart University (U,G)
addleback College (U)
t. John's University (U)
an Diego Community College District (N,U)
an Joaquin Delta College (U)
anta Monica College (U)
anta Rosa Junior College (U)
eminole Community College (U)
hippensburg University of Pennsylvania (U)
ierra College (U)
impson College (U)
outheast Arkansas College (U)
outheastern Oklahoma State University (U)
outhern Arkansas University Tech (U)
outhern Methodist University (G)
outhern Polytechnic State University (U,G)
tanford University (N,G)
tate University of New York at Binghamton (N)
tate University of New York at Oswego (U)
tevens Institute of Technology (U)
acoma Community College (U)
aft College (U)
aylor University (U)
exas A&M University–Commerce (U)
exas A&M University–Kingsville (U)
exas State Technical College Waco (U)
exas Tech University (G)
hree Rivers Community College (U)
ri-County Community College (N,U)
yler Junior College (U)
Jnion University (U)
he University of Akron (N,U)
he University of Alabama (U)
Jniversity of Alaska Fairbanks (U)
Jniversity of Arkansas at Pine Bluff (U)
Jniversity of California, Davis (N)
Jniversity of Central Missouri (U)
Jniversity of Colorado at Boulder (N,G)
he University of Findlay (U)
University of Idaho (U,G)
University of Illinois at Springfield (U,G)
University of Illinois at Urbana–Champaign (N,G)
University of Management and Technology (U)
University of Massachusetts Boston (U)
University of Michigan–Dearborn (U,G)
University of Michigan–Flint (U)
University of New Orleans (U,G)
University of Phoenix (U)
University of Pittsburgh at Bradford (U)
University of Saskatchewan (U)
The University of Texas at Brownsville (U)
The University of Texas at San Antonio (U,G)
The University of Texas at Tyler (U,G)
The University of Texas of the Permian Basin (U)
University of the Southwest (U)
University of the Virgin Islands (U)
University of Vermont (N,U)

The University of Virginia's College at Wise (U)
University of Washington (U,G)
University of Waterloo (U)
University of West Florida (U,G)
Utah State University (G)
Virginia Polytechnic Institute and State University (U,G)
Weber State University (U)
Westchester Community College (U)
Western Michigan University (G)
Western Wyoming Community College (U)
Westfield State College (U)
West Los Angeles College (U)
West Virginia State University (U)
Wharton County Junior College (U)
Williston State College (U)
Worcester State College (N)
York Technical College (U)

COMPUTER SOFTWARE AND MEDIA APPLICATIONS

Adams State College (N)
AIB College of Business (U)
Allen County Community College (U)
Arapahoe Community College (U)
Athabasca University (N,U)
Athens Technical College (N)
Baltimore City Community College (N,U)
Beaufort County Community College (N)
Bellevue Community College (U)
Bellevue University (U)
Belmont Technical College (U)
Berkeley College (U)
Berkeley College–New York City Campus (U)
Berkeley College–Westchester Campus (U)
Blackhawk Technical College (N)
Blue Ridge Community College (N,U)
Bowling Green State University (N,U,G)
Brigham Young University (N)
Bristol Community College (U)
Bryant and Stratton Online (U)
Burlington County College (U)
Caldwell Community College and Technical Institute (N)
California State University, Sacramento (U)
Cape Cod Community College (U)
Capital Community College (U)
Cardinal Stritch University (N)
Carl Sandburg College (U)
Carroll Community College (N)
Carroll University (G)
Centralia College (N,U)
Central Texas College (U)
Central Wyoming College (N)
Chatham University (N)
Chemeketa Community College (U)
Cincinnati State Technical and Community College (U)
Clark State Community College (U)
Clemson University (N)
Cleveland Community College (U)
Cleveland Institute of Electronics (N)
Cleveland State University (N,U)
Coastline Community College (U)
College of The Albemarle (N)
College of the Sequoias (U)
Colorado Mountain College District System (U)
Columbus State Community College (U)
Community College of Beaver County (N,U)

Community College of Denver (N,U)
Corning Community College (U)
Daemen College (U)
Dallas Baptist University (U,G)
Dallas County Community College District (U)
Danville Community College (U)
Darton College (N,U)
Dawson Community College (U)
Delaware County Community College (N,U)
Duquesne University (G)
East Arkansas Community College (U)
East Carolina University (G)
Eastern Iowa Community College District (N)
Eastern Michigan University (G)
Eastern Wyoming College (U)
East Tennessee State University (N)
Edgecombe Community College (N,U)
Edison State Community College (N,U)
Erie Community College (U)
Erie Community College, North Campus (U)
Erie Community College, South Campus (U)
Excelsior College (U)
Finger Lakes Community College (N)
Flathead Valley Community College (N,U)
Florida State University (N)
Fontbonne University (U,G)
Frank Phillips College (N)
Fulton-Montgomery Community College (N)
Galveston College (U)
Glenville State College (U)
Golden West College (U)
Grand Rapids Community College (N)
Granite State College (N)
Grantham University (U)
Hagerstown Community College (N)
Halifax Community College (N)
Harrisburg Area Community College (U)
Haywood Community College (U)
Henry Ford Community College (U)
Herkimer County Community College (U)
Hibbing Community College (N,U)
Hillsborough Community College (U)
Hofstra University (U)
Ilisagvik College (U)
Illinois Eastern Community Colleges, Lincoln Trail College (U)
Immaculata University (U)
Indiana University–Purdue University Fort Wayne (N)
Indiana Wesleyan University (U)
Indian River Community College (U)
Iona College (U)
Jacksonville State University (U,G)
James A. Rhodes State College (U)
Jamestown Community College (N)
Jefferson College (U)
Jefferson College of Health Sciences (U)
Johnson County Community College (N,U)
John Wood Community College (U)
Jones International University (U,G)
J. Sargeant Reynolds Community College (U)
Judson University (U)
Kansas State University (G)
Kaskaskia College (U)
Kean University (N)
Knowledge Systems Institute (G)
Labette Community College (U)
Lake-Sumter Community College (U)
Lake Superior College (U)
Lamar State College–Port Arthur (N,U)
Laredo Community College (U)

Limestone College (U)
Linn-Benton Community College (U)
Long Beach City College (U)
Los Angeles Trade-Technical College (U)
Lurleen B. Wallace Community College (U)
Luzerne County Community College (N)
Macon State College (U)
Marion Technical College (U)
Massasoit Community College (N,U)
Mercer County Community College (U)
Mercy College (G)
Mesa Community College (U)
Middlesex Community College (N,U)
Middle Tennessee State University (N)
Midstate College (U)
Mitchell Technical Institute (N,U)
Monroe County Community College (U)
Montana Tech of The University of Montana (U)
Montgomery Community College (N,U)
Montgomery County Community College (U)
Mt. Hood Community College (U)
Mt. San Antonio College (N)
Mount Wachusett Community College (N,U)
Murray State College (U)
Myers University (U)
National University (U,G)
New Mexico Junior College (U)
New York Institute of Technology (N)
Northampton County Area Community College (U)
North Arkansas College (N)
North Central Texas College (U)
North Dakota State University (N)
North Florida Community College (U)
North Iowa Area Community College (N)
North Seattle Community College (U)
NorthWest Arkansas Community College (U)
Northwestern Connecticut Community College (N)
Northwestern Michigan College (U)
Northwestern State University of Louisiana (U)
Nova Southeastern University (G)
Okaloosa-Walton College (U)
Orange Coast College (U)
Oregon State University (N)
Ouachita Technical College (U)
Oxnard College (U)
Pace University (U,G)
Palomar College (U)
Pamlico Community College (U)
Parkland College (U)
Pasco-Hernando Community College (N,U)
Pellissippi State Technical Community College (U)
Peninsula College (U)
Pikes Peak Community College (U)
Plymouth State University (N,U)
Portland Community College (N,U)
Quinebaug Valley Community College (N)
Randolph Community College (N,U)
Red Rocks Community College (U)
Rend Lake College (N)
Richland Community College (U)
Riverside Community College District (N)
Rose State College (U)
Sacramento City College (U)
Saint Charles Community College (N)
Saint Leo University (U)
St. Louis Community College System (U)
San Diego Community College District (N,U)

San Diego State University (N)
San Francisco State University (N)
San Joaquin Delta College (U)
Santa Rosa Junior College (U)
Schenectady County Community College (U)
Seattle Pacific University (G)
Seminole Community College (U)
Sinclair Community College (U)
Sonoma State University (N)
Southeast Arkansas College (U)
Southeastern Illinois College (U)
Southeastern Oklahoma State University (N)
Southern Methodist University (G)
South Piedmont Community College (U)
Southwest Wisconsin Technical College (U)
Spring Arbor University (U)
State University of New York at Binghamton (N)
State University of New York College at Cortland (U)
State University of New York College at Potsdam (N)
State University of New York College of Agriculture and Technology at Morrisville (U)
Taylor University (N)
Texas A&M University–Kingsville (N)
Texas State Technical College Waco (N,U)
Texas Woman's University (N)
Three Rivers Community College (N)
Tompkins Cortland Community College (N,U)
Tyler Junior College (N,U)
The University of Akron (N,U,G)
University of Alaska Fairbanks (U)
University of California, Riverside (N)
University of Central Missouri (N)
University of Cincinnati (U)
University of Cincinnati Raymond Walters College (U)
University of Connecticut (U)
University of Illinois at Urbana–Champaign (N,G)
University of Lethbridge (U)
The University of Maine at Augusta (U)
University of Management and Technology (U)
University of Michigan–Flint (N)
University of Minnesota, Twin Cities Campus (U)
The University of Montana–Western (N,U)
The University of North Carolina at Charlotte (N)
University of North Dakota (N)
University of North Texas (U,G)
University of Southern Indiana (N)
University of South Florida (N,G)
The University of Texas at Brownsville (N)
University of Vermont (N)
University of Washington (N)
University of West Florida (U)
Utah State University (G)
Virginia Polytechnic Institute and State University (N)
Wake Technical Community College (N,U)
Washburn University (N)
Western Michigan University (U)
Western Wyoming Community College (U)
West Hills Community College (N)
West Virginia University (N)
Westwood Online (U)
Wharton County Junior College (U)
Wytheville Community College (U)

York County Community College (U)
Youngstown State University (N)

COMPUTER SYSTEMS ANALYSIS

Arapahoe Community College (U)
Athabasca University (N,U,G)
Bellevue University (U)
Bridgewater State College (N)
Bristol Community College (U)
Centralia College (N)
Central Michigan University (G)
Central Texas College (U)
College of Southern Maryland (U)
Dakota State University (U)
Dallas Baptist University (U,G)
Dallas County Community College District (U)
Delaware County Community College (N)
East Tennessee State University (N)
Edgecombe Community College (U)
Edison State Community College (U)
Erie Community College (U)
Erie Community College, North Campus (U)
Erie Community College, South Campus (U)
Georgia Institute of Technology (G)
Grantham University (U)
Haywood Community College (U)
Hofstra University (U)
Immaculata University (U)
Iona College (G)
Jacksonville State University (U,G)
Lamar State College–Port Arthur (N)
Limestone College (U)
Macon State College (U)
Mercy College (G)
Middlesex Community College (N)
Myers University (U)
National University (G)
Nova Southeastern University (G)
Oxnard College (U)
Pace University (G)
Palomar College (U)
Plymouth State University (N)
Red Rocks Community College (U)
Rose State College (U)
Sacramento City College (U)
St. Edward's University (N,U,G)
Saint Leo University (U)
Seminole Community College (U)
Southeast Arkansas College (U)
Southern Polytechnic State University (G)
Texas State Technical College Waco (U)
Tri-County Community College (U)
Tyler Junior College (U)
The University of Akron (N)
University of California, Davis (U)
University of Dallas (G)
University of Illinois at Urbana–Champaign (G)
University of Management and Technology (U)
University of New Orleans (U,G)
University of Washington (N)
Utah State University (G)
Westchester Community College (U)
Wytheville Community College (U)

COMPUTER SYSTEMS NETWORKING AND TELECOMMUNICATIONS

Alpena Community College (U)
Arapahoe Community College (U)
Athabasca University (U)
Bellevue University (U)
Blackhawk Technical College (U)
Blue Ridge Community College (N,U)
Bowling Green State University (U)
Bristol Community College (U)
Bryant and Stratton Online (U)
Capella University (G)
Carroll Community College (N,U)
Cayuga County Community College (U)
Centennial College (N)
Central Texas College (U)
Charter Oak State College (U)
Chemeketa Community College (U)
Cincinnati State Technical and Community
  College (U)
Clemson University (N)
Cleveland Community College (U)
Cleveland State University (N)
College of Southern Maryland (U)
College of The Albemarle (N)
Colorado State University (G)
Corning Community College (U)
Dallas Baptist University (U,G)
Dallas County Community College District
  (U)
Darton College (U)
De Anza College (U)
Delaware County Community College (N,U)
DePaul University (G)
DeVry University Online (G)
East Carolina University (G)
Eastern Iowa Community College District (N)
Eastern Michigan University (U)
East Tennessee State University (N)
Edgecombe Community College (U)
Edison State Community College (U)
Fulton-Montgomery Community College (N)
Galveston College (U)
George Mason University (G)
Grand Rapids Community College (U)
Grantham University (U)
Hagerstown Community College (N)
Halifax Community College (N)
Harford Community College (N)
Haywood Community College (U)
Herkimer County Community College (U)
Hofstra University (U)
Illinois Eastern Community Colleges, Lincoln
  Trail College (U)
Indiana University–Purdue University Fort
  Wayne (N)
Iona College (G)
Jacksonville State University (U,G)
James Madison University (N)
Jamestown Community College (N)
Johnson County Community College (U)
Jones International University (U,G)
Kaplan University Online (N)
Labette Community College (U)
Lamar State College–Port Arthur (N,U)
Limestone College (U)
Long Beach City College (U)
Macon State College (U)
McDowell Technical Community College (U)
Mercer County Community College (N)

Michigan State University (U,G)
Middle Tennessee State University (N)
Murray State University (U,G)
Myers University (U)
Naugatuck Valley Community College (U)
New Jersey Institute of Technology (U,G)
North Central Texas College (U)
North Lake College (U)
North Seattle Community College (U)
NorthWest Arkansas Community College (U)
Northwestern Michigan College (U)
Nova Southeastern University (G)
Okaloosa-Walton College (U)
Ouachita Technical College (U)
Oxnard College (U)
Pace University (U,G)
Palomar College (U)
Pamlico Community College (U)
Pasco-Hernando Community College (U)
Patrick Henry Community College (U)
Pikes Peak Community College (U)
Plymouth State University (N)
Portland Community College (N)
Pulaski Technical College (U)
Red Rocks Community College (U)
Regis University (U,G)
Riverside Community College District (U)
Rose State College (U)
Sacramento City College (U)
Saint Leo University (U)
San Diego Community College District (U)
San Joaquin Delta College (U)
Santa Rosa Junior College (U)
Seminole Community College (U)
Sinclair Community College (U)
Sonoma State University (N)
Southeast Arkansas College (U)
Southeastern Oklahoma State University (N)
Southern Arkansas University Tech (U)
Southern Methodist University (G)
Southern Polytechnic State University (G)
South Piedmont Community College (U)
Southwest Wisconsin Technical College (U)
State University of New York at Binghamton
  (N)
State University of New York at Oswego (U)
Syracuse University (G)
Taylor University (N)
Texas State Technical College Waco (U)
Tompkins Cortland Community College (N)
Tunxis Community College (U)
Tyler Junior College (U)
The University of Akron (N,U)
The University of Alabama (U)
University of Central Missouri (N)
University of Colorado at Boulder (N,G)
University of Dallas (G)
University of Denver (G)
University of Illinois at Urbana–Champaign
  (G)
University of Management and Technology
  (U)
University of Maryland University College
  (G)
University of Minnesota, Twin Cities Campus
  (U)
The University of Texas at Brownsville (N)
The University of Texas System (N)
University of West Florida (U)
University of Wisconsin–Stout (N)
Utah State University (G)
Wake Technical Community College (U)

Westchester Community College (U)
Westwood Online (U)
Wharton County Junior College (U)
Wytheville Community College (U)
Youngstown State University (N)
Yuba College (U)

COMPUTER/INFORMATION TECHNOLOGY ADMINISTRATION AND MANAGEMENT

Alpena Community College (U)
American InterContinental University Online
  (U,G)
American Public University System (U)
Arapahoe Community College (U)
Athabasca University (N,U,G)
Auburn University (N)
Baker College of Flint (U)
Bellevue University (U)
Bloomfield College (U)
Blue Ridge Community College (N,U)
Bridgewater State College (U)
Bristol Community College (U)
Bryant and Stratton Online (U)
Caldwell Community College and Technical
  Institute (N)
California State University, Dominguez Hills
  (N)
Cape Fear Community College (U)
Capella University (G)
Capital Community College (U)
Carroll Community College (U)
Centennial College (N)
Central Washington University (U)
Cincinnati State Technical and Community
  College (U)
Cleveland Community College (U)
Cleveland Institute of Electronics (N)
College of Southern Maryland (N)
College of The Albemarle (N)
Community College of Denver (U)
Dakota State University (U)
Dallas Baptist University (G)
Dallas County Community College District
  (U)
Delaware County Community College (U)
Drexel University (G)
Duquesne University (G)
East Carolina University (U,G)
Eastern Iowa Community College District (N)
Edgecombe Community College (N,U)
Edison State Community College (N,U)
Elgin Community College (U)
Erie Community College (U)
Erie Community College, North Campus (U)
Erie Community College, South Campus (U)
Finger Lakes Community College (U)
Flathead Valley Community College (N)
Florida State University (N)
Galveston College (N,U)
Grand Rapids Community College (U)
Granite State College (U)
Grantham University (U)
Greenfield Community College (U)
Haywood Community College (U)
Hillsborough Community College (U)
Houston Community College System (U)
Immaculata University (U)
Jacksonville State University (U,G)
Jones International University (U)
Kaplan University Online (N)

Kettering University (N)
Knowledge Systems Institute (G)
Lakeland Community College (N)
Lamar State College–Port Arthur (N)
Lawrence Technological University (U,G)
Liberty University (U)
Limestone College (U)
Macon State College (U)
McMurry University (U)
Mercer County Community College (N)
Mercy College (G)
Mesa Community College (U)
Middle Tennessee State University (N)
Missouri State University–West Plains (U)
Myers University (U)
New Jersey Institute of Technology (G)
New Mexico State University (U)
New York Institute of Technology (N)
North Arkansas College (N,U)
North Central Texas College (U)
Northcentral University (U)
North Dakota State College of Science (U)
NorthWest Arkansas Community College (U)
Nova Southeastern University (G)
Orange Coast College (U)
Oregon Institute of Technology (U)
Oxnard College (U)
Pace University (G)
Palomar College (U)
Pamlico Community College (U)
Pasco-Hernando Community College (U)
Patrick Henry Community College (U)
Pittsburgh Technical Institute (U)
Portland Community College (N)
Prairie View A&M University (G)
Regis University (U,G)
Rose State College (U)
Sacramento City College (U)
St. Edward's University (N,G)
Saint Joseph's College of Maine (U)
San Diego Community College District (U)
Schiller International University (G)
Seminole Community College (U)
Sonoma State University (N)
Southeast Arkansas College (U)
Southern Methodist University (G)
South Piedmont Community College (U)
Southwestern College (U)
State University of New York at Binghamton
 (N)
State University of New York College of
 Agriculture and Technology at Morrisville
 (U)
State University of New York Empire State
 College (U)
Syracuse University (G)
Taylor University (N,U)
Tyler Junior College (U)
The University of Akron (N)
University of Arkansas at Pine Bluff (N)
University of California, Davis (N)
University of Cincinnati Raymond Walters
 College (U)
University of Connecticut (U)
University of Denver (G)
University of Houston–Downtown (U)
University of Illinois at Urbana–Champaign
 (G)
University of Management and Technology
 (U)
University of Maryland University College
 (G)

University of Massachusetts Boston (U)
University of North Texas (U)
University of Southern Indiana (U)
The University of Tennessee (N)
The University of Toledo (U)
University of Toronto (N)
University of Vermont (N)
University of Virginia (N,U)
University of Washington (N)
Vincennes University (U)
West Los Angeles College (U)
West Virginia University at Parkersburg (N,U)
York County Community College (U)

CONSTRUCTION ENGINEERING

Haywood Community College (U)
Seminole Community College (U)
Southern Methodist University (G)
University of South Florida (G)

CONSTRUCTION ENGINEERING TECHNOLOGY

Bowling Green State University (G)
Clemson University (N)
Coastline Community College (U)
Delaware County Community College (U)
Indiana State University (U)
Ivy Tech Community College–Northeast (U)
James Madison University (N)
National University (U)
Pennsylvania College of Technology (U)
University of Southern Mississippi (G)
University of Washington (U,G)

CONSTRUCTION MANAGEMENT

Auburn University (N)
Central Michigan University (U)
Clemson University (U,G)
Colorado State University (N,U)
Columbus State Community College (U)
East Carolina University (G)
Haywood Community College (U)
Indiana State University (U)
State University of New York at Binghamton
 (N)
Texas A&M University–Commerce (G)
University of Arkansas at Little Rock (U)
Wake Technical Community College (U)

CONSTRUCTION TRADES

Athens Technical College (U)
Central Michigan University (U)
Fox Valley Technical College (U)
Haywood Community College (U)
Lock Haven University of Pennsylvania (N)
Los Angeles Trade-Technical College (U)

CONSTRUCTION TRADES RELATED

Alpena Community College (N,U)
Bowling Green State University (N)
Delaware County Community College (U)
Haywood Community College (U)
James A. Rhodes State College (U)
James Madison University (N)
Sullivan County Community College (N)
University of Arkansas at Little Rock (U)

University of Illinois at Urbana–Champaign
 (N)
West Virginia University at Parkersburg (N)

COSMETOLOGY AND RELATED PERSONAL GROOMING SERVICES

Athens Technical College (U)
Gadsden State Community College (U)
Haywood Community College (U)
James Madison University (N)
Northeast Iowa Community College (U)
Pamlico Community College (U)
Southwest Wisconsin Technical College (U)
Wake Technical Community College (U)
Wytheville Community College (U)

COUNSELING PSYCHOLOGY

Amberton University (G)
Athabasca University (N,U,G)
Atlantic University (N,G)
The Baptist College of Florida (U)
Burlington College (U)
Capella University (G)
Carlow University (G)
Central Texas College (U)
Chadron State College (G)
Chatham University (G)
Cincinnati Christian University (G)
Columbus State Community College (U)
Corban College (U)
Delaware County Community College (U)
Eastern Kentucky University (G)
Grand Rapids Theological Seminary of
 Cornerstone University (G)
Immaculata University (G)
Indiana State University (G)
Jackson State University (G)
James Madison University (N)
Liberty University (G)
Malone College (G)
Master's College and Seminary (U)
Mercy College (G)
Mississippi State University (U,G)
Missouri State University (G)
Missouri State University–West Plains (U,G)
Naropa University (U)
National University (U,G)
Northampton County Area Community
 College (U)
Oklahoma State University (U)
Oregon State University (G)
Palomar College (U)
Prescott College (U)
Providence College and Theological Seminary
 (N,G)
Regent University (G)
St. Cloud State University (U)
St. Edward's University (G)
Santa Rosa Junior College (U)
Saybrook Graduate School and Research
 Center (G)
Shasta Bible College (U,G)
Southeastern Oklahoma State University (G)
State University of New York at Oswego
 (U,G)
Taylor University (U)
The University of Akron (G)
University of Alaska Fairbanks (G)
University of Bridgeport (U)
University of Hawaii–West Oahu (U)

The University of Maine at Augusta (U)
University of Massachusetts Boston (N,G)
University of Missouri–Columbia (G)
University of Nevada, Reno (U,G)
The University of North Carolina at Charlotte (N)
The University of South Dakota (G)
University of the Pacific (N,U)
The University of Toledo (G)
University of Wisconsin–Stout (G)
University of Wisconsin–Superior (U)
Upper Iowa University (U)
Wayland Baptist University (G)
Wayne State College (U,G)
Western Michigan University (U,G)

CRAFTS, FOLK ART AND ARTISANRY

Blackhawk Technical College (N)
Cleveland State University (G)
Community College of Denver (N)
Hillsborough Community College (N)
James Madison University (N)
Middle Tennessee State University (N)
Naugatuck Valley Community College (N)
Temple University (U)
The University of Tennessee at Martin (N)
West Virginia University at Parkersburg (N)

CREATIVE WRITING

Acadia University (N)
Adams State College (N)
Arkansas State University–Beebe (U)
Athabasca University (U)
Athens Technical College (N)
Atlantic University (N,G)
Bellevue Community College (U)
Blackhawk Technical College (N)
Blue Ridge Community College (N)
Bowling Green State University (U,G)
Bridgewater State College (N)
Brigham Young University (N)
Burlington College (U)
Caldwell Community College and Technical Institute (N)
Cardinal Stritch University (N)
Carroll Community College (N)
Central New Mexico Community College (U)
Chatham University (U,G)
Chemeketa Community College (U)
City Colleges of Chicago, Harold Washington College (U)
Clark State Community College (U)
Clemson University (N)
College of Southern Maryland (U)
Columbus State Community College (U)
Community College of Denver (U)
Dallas Baptist University (U)
Dallas County Community College District (U)
Darton College (N)
Dawson Community College (U)
Delaware County Community College (U)
DeVry University Online (U)
Drake University (U)
Earlham School of Religion (G)
Eastern Washington University (U)
East Tennessee State University (N)
Erie Community College (U)
Erie Community College, North Campus (U)

Erie Community College, South Campus (U)
Genesee Community College (U)
Hillsborough Community College (U)
Hocking College (U)
Holyoke Community College (U)
James Madison University (N)
Jamestown Community College (N)
Jefferson Community College (U)
John A. Logan College (U)
Judson College (U)
Kean University (N)
Kirtland Community College (U)
Lamar State College–Port Arthur (N)
Limestone College (U)
Linn-Benton Community College (U)
Long Beach City College (U)
Massasoit Community College (N)
Mercy College (U)
Mesa Community College (U)
Middlesex Community College (N,U)
Minot State University (U)
Missouri State University (U)
Mt. Hood Community College (U)
Mt. San Antonio College (U)
Naropa University (N,U)
National University (G)
Naugatuck Valley Community College (U)
The New School: A University (N,U)
New York Institute of Technology (U)
Northampton County Area Community College (U)
NorthWest Arkansas Community College (U)
Northwestern Michigan College (U)
Northwestern State University of Louisiana (U)
Oklahoma State University (U)
Oregon State University (U)
Oxnard College (U)
Park University (U)
Piedmont Community College (U)
Portland Community College (N)
Prescott College (U,G)
Queen's University at Kingston (U)
Randolph Community College (N)
Richland Community College (U)
Riverside Community College District (N)
Rose State College (U)
Sacramento City College (U)
St. Clair County Community College (U)
St. Cloud State University (U)
Saint Mary-of-the-Woods College (U)
Sam Houston State University (U)
San Diego Community College District (U)
San Joaquin Delta College (U)
Santa Rosa Junior College (U)
Sinclair Community College (U)
Southeastern Oklahoma State University (N)
Southwest Virginia Community College (U)
Spring Arbor University (U)
State University of New York at Binghamton (N,U)
State University of New York College at Cortland (U)
State University of New York College at Potsdam (N)
State University of New York College of Agriculture and Technology at Morrisville (U)
Tacoma Community College (U)
Taft College (U)
Taylor University (N,U)
Texas A&M University–Commerce (U)

Texas State University–San Marcos (U)
Three Rivers Community College (U)
Tompkins Cortland Community College (U)
Treasure Valley Community College (U)
Tyler Junior College (U)
The University of Akron (U)
The University of Alabama (U)
University of Arkansas at Little Rock (U)
University of Colorado Denver (U)
University of Denver (G)
University of Illinois at Urbana–Champaign (N)
The University of Kansas (U)
The University of Maine at Augusta (U)
University of Maine at Fort Kent (U)
University of Maine at Machias (U)
University of Minnesota, Morris (U)
University of Missouri–Columbia (U)
University of Nevada, Reno (U)
University of New Orleans (N,U,G)
The University of North Carolina at Chapel Hill (N,U)
University of North Florida (U)
The University of South Dakota (U)
University of Southern Mississippi (U)
University of South Florida (N)
The University of Tennessee (N,U)
The University of Texas at El Paso (G)
The University of Texas System (U)
University of the Pacific (U)
University of the Southwest (U)
University of Utah (U)
University of Washington (N,U)
University of Wisconsin Colleges (U)
University of Wisconsin–Whitewater (U,G)
Utah Valley State College (U)
Vincennes University (U)
Western Washington University (U)
West Hills Community College (N)
West Los Angeles College (U)
Wharton County Junior College (U)
Youngstown State University (N)

CRIMINAL JUSTICE AND CORRECTIONS

Adams State College (U)
Albany State University (U)
Allen County Community College (U)
Alpena Community College (U)
American InterContinental University Online (U)
American Public University System (U,G)
Anne Arundel Community College (U)
Arapahoe Community College (U)
Arizona Western College (U)
Arkansas State University–Beebe (U)
Athabasca University (N,U)
Athens Technical College (U)
Baltimore City Community College (U)
Bergen Community College (U)
Berkeley College (U)
Blackhawk Technical College (N,U)
Blue Ridge Community College (N,U)
Boise State University (U,G)
Brenau University (U)
Bristol Community College (U)
Buena Vista University (U)
Burlington County College (U)
Butler Community College (U)
Cabrillo College (U)

Caldwell Community College and Technical Institute (N)
California State University, Sacramento (U)
California State University, San Bernardino (U,G)
Capella University (G)
Carroll Community College (U)
Central Carolina Community College (N,U)
Centralia College (U)
Central New Mexico Community College (U)
Central Texas College (U)
Central Washington University (U)
Cerro Coso Community College (U)
Chaminade University of Honolulu (U,G)
Chemeketa Community College (U)
Citrus College (U)
Clackamas Community College (U)
Clatsop Community College (U)
Clinton Community College (U)
College of Southern Maryland (U)
College of the Sequoias (U)
Columbia College (U,G)
Community College of Beaver County (U)
Dallas Baptist University (U,G)
Danville Community College (U)
Darton College (U)
Dawson Community College (U)
Daytona State College (U)
Delaware County Community College (U)
Delaware Technical & Community College, Jack F. Owens Campus (U)
DeSales University (U)
East Arkansas Community College (U)
East Carolina University (G)
Eastern Wyoming College (U)
East Tennessee State University (U)
Edison State Community College (U)
Elizabeth City State University (U)
Erie Community College (U)
Erie Community College, North Campus (U)
Erie Community College, South Campus (U)
Everett Community College (U)
Excelsior College (U)
Finger Lakes Community College (U)
Florida Gulf Coast University (U)
Fort Hays State University (U)
Fort Valley State University (U)
Fox Valley Technical College (U)
Galveston College (U)
Genesee Community College (U)
Georgia State University (U)
Glenville State College (U)
Golden West College (U)
Governors State University (N)
Grand Rapids Community College (U)
Grand View College (U)
Granite State College (U)
Grantham University (U)
Harrisburg Area Community College (U)
Haywood Community College (U)
Henry Ford Community College (U)
Herkimer County Community College (U)
Hibbing Community College (U)
Hillsborough Community College (U)
Holyoke Community College (U)
Hopkinsville Community College (N)
Indiana State University (U,G)
Indiana University of Pennsylvania (G)
Indiana Wesleyan University (U)
Indian River Community College (U)
Ivy Tech Community College–Bloomington (U)

Ivy Tech Community College–Central Indiana (U)
Ivy Tech Community College–East Central (U)
Ivy Tech Community College–Kokomo (U)
Ivy Tech Community College–Southeast (U)
Ivy Tech Community College–Southern Indiana (U)
Ivy Tech Community College–Southwest (U)
Ivy Tech Community College–Whitewater (U)
Jacksonville State University (U,G)
James A. Rhodes State College (U)
James Madison University (N)
Jefferson College (U)
Jefferson Community College (U)
John Wood Community College (U)
J. Sargeant Reynolds Community College (U)
Judson College (U)
Judson University (U)
Kean University (U)
Laredo Community College (U)
Lehigh Carbon Community College (U)
Liberty University (U)
Limestone College (U)
Linn-Benton Community College (U)
Los Angeles Harbor College (U)
Los Angeles Trade-Technical College (U)
Mansfield University of Pennsylvania (U)
Marian College of Fond du Lac (U)
Mercy College (U)
Mesa Community College (U)
Metropolitan State University (U,G)
Michigan State University (G)
Middlesex Community College (U)
Middle Tennessee State University (U)
Midwestern State University (U)
Minot State University (U)
Mississippi Delta Community College (U)
Missouri State University (G)
Monmouth University (G)
Monroe Community College (U)
Montcalm Community College (U)
Montgomery Community College (U)
Mountain Empire Community College (U)
Mount Olive College (U)
Mount Wachusett Community College (U)
Murray State College (U)
Myers University (U)
National University (U)
Naugatuck Valley Community College (U)
New Jersey City University (U)
New Mexico Junior College (U)
New Mexico State University (U,G)
New River Community College (U)
New York Institute of Technology (U)
Northampton County Area Community College (U)
North Central Texas College (U)
Northcentral University (G)
Northeast Alabama Community College (U)
Northern Virginia Community College (U)
NorthWest Arkansas Community College (U)
Northwestern Michigan College (U)
Northwestern Oklahoma State University (U)
Northwestern State University of Louisiana (U)
Okaloosa-Walton College (U)
Old Dominion University (U)
Ouachita Technical College (U)
Oxnard College (U)
Pace University (U)
Palomar College (U)

Pamlico Community College (U)
Park University (U)
Passaic County Community College (U)
Peninsula College (U)
Pikes Peak Community College (U)
Plymouth State University (U)
Prairie View A&M University (G)
Randolph Community College (U)
Rappahannock Community College (U)
Red Rocks Community College (U)
Rend Lake College (U)
Richmond Community College (U)
Roger Williams University (U)
Roosevelt University (U)
Rose State College (U)
Saint Charles Community College (U)
St. Cloud State University (U,G)
St. Edward's University (U)
St. John's University (U,G)
Saint Leo University (U)
San Diego Community College District (U)
San Joaquin Delta College (U)
Santa Rosa Junior College (U)
Saybrook Graduate School and Research Center (G)
Schenectady County Community College (U)
Seminole Community College (U)
Shippensburg University of Pennsylvania (U,G)
Simpson College (U,G)
Southeast Arkansas College (U)
Southeastern Oklahoma State University (U)
Southern New Hampshire University (G)
South Piedmont Community College (U)
Spring Arbor University (U)
State University of New York at Oswego (U)
State University of New York College of Technology at Canton (U)
State University of New York Empire State College (U)
Tacoma Community College (U)
Taft College (U)
Taylor University (U)
Texas A&M University–Commerce (U)
Texas A&M University–Kingsville (U)
Three Rivers Community College (U)
Tompkins Cortland Community College (U)
Tri-County Community College (U)
Tunxis Community College (N,U)
Tyler Junior College (U)
Union County College (U)
The University of Akron (U)
The University of Alabama (U)
University of Alaska Fairbanks (U)
University of Arkansas at Little Rock (U,G)
University of Central Missouri (U,G)
University of Cincinnati (U)
University of Colorado at Colorado Springs (G)
University of Connecticut (U)
The University of Findlay (U)
University of Hawaii–West Oahu (U)
University of Houston–Downtown (U)
University of Idaho (U)
University of Illinois at Springfield (U)
The University of Maine at Augusta (U)
University of Maine at Fort Kent (N,U)
University of Management and Technology (U,G)
University of Maryland University College (U)
University of Massachusetts Boston (U,G)

University of Missouri–Columbia (N)
University of Nevada, Reno (U)
University of North Alabama (U)
The University of North Carolina at Chapel Hill (U)
The University of North Carolina Wilmington (U)
University of North Dakota (U)
University of Pittsburgh at Bradford (U)
The University of South Dakota (U,G)
University of Southern Mississippi (U,G)
University of South Florida (U,G)
The University of Tennessee at Martin (N)
The University of Texas at Brownsville (N)
The University of Texas at El Paso (U)
The University of Texas at Tyler (U)
The University of Texas of the Permian Basin (G)
University of the Southwest (U)
University of Wisconsin–Platteville (N)
University of Wyoming (U)
Upper Iowa University (U)
Vincennes University (U)
Wake Technical Community College (U)
Washburn University (G)
Wayland Baptist University (U)
Wayne State College (U,G)
Westchester Community College (U)
Western Nebraska Community College (U)
Westfield State College (U)
West Los Angeles College (U)
West Shore Community College (U)
West Virginia University at Parkersburg (U)
Westwood Online (U)
Wharton County Junior College (U)
Wilmington University (U,G)
Youngstown State University (U)

CRIMINOLOGY

Adams State College (U)
American University (U,G)
Athabasca University (N,U)
Bellevue Community College (U)
Berkeley College (U)
Berkeley College–New York City Campus (U)
Berkeley College–Westchester Campus (U)
Blue Mountain Community College (U)
Brenau University (U)
Bridgewater State College (U)
Bristol Community College (U)
Buena Vista University (U)
Butler Community College (U)
Central Texas College (U)
Chadron State College (U)
Charter Oak State College (U)
Chemeketa Community College (U)
Dallas Baptist University (U,G)
Danville Community College (U)
DeSales University (U)
East Carolina University (G)
Eastern Oregon University (U)
Elizabethtown Community and Technical College (U)
Everest College (U)
Everett Community College (U)
Golden West College (U)
Grand Rapids Community College (U)
Grand View College (U)
Haywood Community College (U)
Holyoke Community College (U)
Houston Community College System (U)

Indiana State University (U,G)
Indiana University of Pennsylvania (G)
Jacksonville State University (U,G)
Jefferson Community College (U)
Labette Community College (U)
Lock Haven University of Pennsylvania (U)
Los Angeles Harbor College (U)
Louisiana State University and Agricultural and Mechanical College (U)
Memorial University of Newfoundland (G)
Middlesex Community College (U)
Montgomery County Community College (U)
Mountain Empire Community College (U)
Mount Olive College (U)
Mount Wachusett Community College (U)
Myers University (U)
National University (G)
Neumann College (U)
New Jersey City University (G)
New Mexico Highlands University (U)
North Central Texas College (U)
Northern State University (U)
Okaloosa-Walton College (U)
Pace University (U)
Pamlico Community College (U)
Park University (U)
Pikes Peak Community College (U)
Plymouth State University (U)
Pratt Community College (U)
Riverside Community College District (U)
Roger Williams University (U)
Saint Joseph's College of Maine (U)
Saint Leo University (U)
Santa Rosa Junior College (U)
Seminole Community College (U)
Southeast Arkansas College (U)
Southeastern Oklahoma State University (U)
Southern Maine Community College (U)
Texas State University–San Marcos (U)
Tunxis Community College (U)
The University of Akron (U)
University of Arkansas at Little Rock (U)
University of Connecticut (G)
The University of Findlay (U)
University of Hawaii–West Oahu (U)
The University of Maine at Augusta (U)
University of Management and Technology (U,G)
University of Missouri–Columbia (N)
University of Northern Iowa (U,G)
The University of South Dakota (U)
University of Southern Mississippi (U)
University of South Florida (U)
The University of Texas at Tyler (U)
The University of Texas of the Permian Basin (U,G)
The University of Toledo (U)
University of Washington (U)
University of Waterloo (U)
University of Wisconsin–Platteville (N)
Upper Iowa University (U)

CULINARY ARTS AND RELATED SERVICES

Blackhawk Technical College (U)
Burlington County College (U)
Cabrillo College (U)
Central New Mexico Community College (U)
Central Texas College (U)
Central Wyoming College (N)
Columbus State Community College (U)

East Tennessee State University (N)
Erie Community College (U)
Erie Community College, North Campus (U)
Erie Community College, South Campus (U)
Galveston College (U)
Hagerstown Community College (N)
Hibbing Community College (U)
Hopkinsville Community College (N)
James Madison University (N)
Middle Tennessee State University (N)
Naugatuck Valley Community College (U)
New York Institute of Technology (N)
Oxnard College (U)
Santa Rosa Junior College (U)
Schenectady County Community College (U)
Southern Maine Community College (U)
Southwest Wisconsin Technical College (U)
State University of New York College at Potsdam (N)
The University of Texas at Brownsville (N)
Wake Technical Community College (U)
York County Community College (U)

CURRICULUM AND INSTRUCTION

Alcorn State University (U)
Athabasca University (G)
Baltimore City Community College (U)
Bloomsburg University of Pennsylvania (G)
Boise State University (U)
Brenau University (U)
Bridgewater State College (U)
Brigham Young University (U)
Buena Vista University (U,G)
California State University, Chico (U)
Canisius College (G)
Central Michigan University (G)
Cerritos College (U)
Chadron State College (G)
Chemeketa Community College (U)
Cleveland State University (G)
The College of St. Scholastica (G)
Columbia College (U)
Columbia International University (G)
Concordia University Wisconsin (G)
Dallas Baptist University (G)
Drexel University (G)
Duquesne University (G)
East Carolina University (U)
Eastern Kentucky University (U,G)
East Tennessee State University (U,G)
Flathead Valley Community College (U)
Fort Valley State University (U)
Hofstra University (U)
Illinois State University (G)
Indiana State University (U,G)
Jacksonville State University (U,G)
Lehigh Carbon Community College (U)
Liberty University (G)
Louisiana State University and Agricultural and Mechanical College (U)
Marian College of Fond du Lac (G)
McMurry University (U)
Mercy College (U)
Mississippi State University (U,G)
Missouri State University (G)
Mitchell Technical Institute (U)
New Mexico Highlands University (U,G)
North Carolina State University (G)
North Dakota State University (G)
Northwestern Oklahoma State University (U)
Pace University (G)

Regis University (G)
Roosevelt University (U)
Saint Joseph's College of Maine (G)
Seattle Pacific University (G)
Southern Arkansas University Tech (U)
Southwest Wisconsin Technical College (U)
State University of New York at Binghamton (N)
State University of New York at Oswego (G)
Stephen F. Austin State University (U)
Texas A&M University–Commerce (G)
Texas Tech University (G)
The University of Akron (N,U,G)
University of Alaska Fairbanks (G)
University of Arkansas (U)
University of Central Missouri (U,G)
University of Illinois at Urbana–Champaign (G)
The University of Kansas (U,G)
University of Missouri–Columbia (U,G)
University of Nevada, Reno (U,G)
University of New Orleans (U)
The University of North Carolina at Greensboro (G)
University of North Florida (U)
University of North Texas (U,G)
University of Saskatchewan (U)
University of Southern Mississippi (G)
University of South Florida (U,G)
The University of Tennessee (U)
The University of Texas at Brownsville (U)
The University of Texas at San Antonio (G)
The University of Texas at Tyler (U)
The University of Texas of the Permian Basin (U,G)
The University of Texas System (U,G)
University of the Pacific (G)
The University of Toledo (U,G)
University of Washington (U)
University of Wisconsin–Superior (U)
University of Wisconsin–Whitewater (U)
Utah State University (G)
Vanguard University of Southern California (U)
Virginia Polytechnic Institute and State University (G)
Western Washington University (U)

DANCE

Brigham Young University (U)
California State University, Chico (U)
Central Wyoming College (N)
Chatham University (U)
Laredo Community College (U)
Long Beach City College (U)
Mesa State College (U)
Naugatuck Valley Community College (N)
New Mexico Junior College (N)
North Central Texas College (U)
Texas State University–San Marcos (U)
The University of North Carolina at Greensboro (U,G)
The University of Texas at Brownsville (N)
University of the Pacific (U)
West Virginia University at Parkersburg (N)

DATA ENTRY/MICROCOMPUTER APPLICATIONS

AIB College of Business (U)
Allen County Community College (U)

Arkansas State University–Beebe (U)
Athabasca University (N)
Athens Technical College (N)
Berkeley College (U)
Berkeley College–New York City Campus (U)
Berkeley College–Westchester Campus (U)
Bristol Community College (U)
Butler Community College (U)
Centralia College (N)
Central Wyoming College (N,U)
Cerritos College (U)
Chemeketa Community College (U)
Clemson University (N)
Cleveland Institute of Electronics (N)
Cleveland State Community College (U)
Cleveland State University (N)
College of The Albemarle (N)
Dallas County Community College District (U)
Delaware County Community College (U)
East Carolina University (U)
Eastern Iowa Community College District (N)
Edgecombe Community College (N,U)
Elgin Community College (U)
Erie Community College (U)
Erie Community College, North Campus (U)
Erie Community College, South Campus (U)
Foothill College (U)
George C. Wallace Community College (U)
Grantham University (U)
Halifax Community College (N)
Haywood Community College (U)
Hibbing Community College (U)
Holyoke Community College (U)
Jackson State University (U)
James Madison University (N)
John Wood Community College (U)
Lakeland Community College (N)
Lamar State College–Port Arthur (N,U)
Limestone College (U)
Middlesex Community College (U)
Mitchell Technical Institute (N)
Montcalm Community College (U)
Myers University (U)
Naugatuck Valley Community College (N)
Northampton County Area Community College (U)
North Central Texas College (U)
North Dakota State University (N,U)
Oxnard College (U)
Palomar College (U)
Pulaski Technical College (U)
Sacramento City College (U)
St. Louis Community College System (U)
San Diego Community College District (U)
Seminole Community College (U)
Southeast Arkansas College (U)
State University of New York College at Potsdam (N)
Tacoma Community College (U)
Taylor University (N)
Texas State Technical College Waco (U)
Tri-County Community College (U)
The University of Akron (N)
University of Arkansas at Little Rock (U)
University of Minnesota, Crookston (U)
University of North Texas (U)
University of West Florida (U)
Utah State University (U)
Wake Technical Community College (N)
West Los Angeles College (U)

DATA PROCESSING

Adams State College (N)
Athabasca University (N,U)
Auburn University (N)
Bristol Community College (U)
Central New Mexico Community College (U)
Cincinnati State Technical and Community College (U)
Clemson University (N)
College of The Albemarle (N)
Dallas County Community College District (U)
Delaware County Community College (U)
East Carolina University (U,G)
Jacksonville State University (U)
John A. Logan College (U)
Lakeland Community College (N)
Lamar State College–Port Arthur (N)
Limestone College (U)
Naugatuck Valley Community College (N)
Northeast Alabama Community College (U)
Pulaski Technical College (U)
Red Rocks Community College (U)
Seminole Community College (U)
State University of New York College at Potsdam (U)
Taylor University (N)
Tompkins Cortland Community College (N)
The University of Akron (N)
University of Illinois at Urbana–Champaign (G)
University of Minnesota, Crookston (U)
Utah State University (U)
Wake Technical Community College (N)
Westchester Community College (U)

DEMOGRAPHY AND POPULATION

Athabasca University (U)
Delaware County Community College (U)
University of Southern Mississippi (G)

DENTAL SUPPORT SERVICES AND ALLIED PROFESSIONS

Blackhawk Technical College (U)
Cape Cod Community College (N)
Central Carolina Community College (U)
Danville Community College (U)
Eugenio María de Hostos Community College of the City University of New York (U)
Gulf Coast Community College (U)
James A. Rhodes State College (U)
John A. Logan College (U)
Linn-Benton Community College (U)
Middlesex Community College (U)
Monroe Community College (U)
Montgomery County Community College (U)
Okaloosa-Walton College (U)
Oregon Institute of Technology (U)
Oxnard College (U)
Peninsula College (U)
Pennsylvania College of Technology (U)
Portland Community College (U)
Sacramento City College (U)
Tunxis Community College (U)
University of Bridgeport (U)
The University of British Columbia (U)
University of Idaho (U)
University of Southern Indiana (U)
Vermont Technical College (U)

Wake Technical Community College (U)
West Los Angeles College (U)

DENTISTRY AND ORAL SCIENCES (ADVANCED/GRADUATE)

Danville Community College (U)
West Los Angeles College (U)

DESIGN AND APPLIED ARTS

Academy of Art University (U,G)
American InterContinental University Online (U)
Brenau University (U)
Buffalo State College, State University of New York (U)
California State University, Dominguez Hills (N)
Central Wyoming College (N)
Colorado State University (U)
Corning Community College (U)
Danville Community College (U)
Edison State Community College (U)
John A. Logan College (U)
Long Beach City College (U)
Massachusetts College of Art and Design (U)
Minneapolis College of Art and Design (N,U,G)
New Mexico Junior College (U)
New York Institute of Technology (U)
Piedmont Technical College (U)
Pikes Peak Community College (U)
Red Rocks Community College (U)
Sacramento City College (U)
San Francisco State University (N)
San Joaquin Delta College (U)
Sierra College (U)
Tacoma Community College (U)
The University of Akron (U)
University of Alaska Fairbanks (U)
University of California, Los Angeles (G)
University of Illinois at Urbana–Champaign (U)
West Los Angeles College (U)
Westwood Online (U)

DEVELOPMENTAL AND CHILD PSYCHOLOGY

Anne Arundel Community College (U)
Arkansas State University–Beebe (U)
Athabasca University (N,U,G)
Bellevue Community College (U)
Bergen Community College (U)
Black Hills State University (U,G)
Blue Mountain Community College (U)
Brenau University (U)
Brigham Young University (U)
Broward Community College (U)
Burlington College (U)
Burlington County College (U)
Butler Community College (U)
Canisius College (G)
Cape Cod Community College (U)
Capital Community College (U)
Centralia College (U)
Central Texas College (U)
Chadron State College (U)
Chemeketa Community College (U)
City Colleges of Chicago, Harold Washington College (U)

Coastline Community College (U)
Colorado Mountain College District System (U)
Colorado State University (U)
Columbia-Greene Community College (U)
Columbus State Community College (U)
Community College of Beaver County (U)
Concordia University, St. Paul (U,G)
Crafton Hills College (U)
Dallas County Community College District (U)
Danville Community College (U)
Dawson Community College (U)
Daytona State College (U)
De Anza College (U)
Delaware County Community College (U)
East Central Community College (U)
East Tennessee State University (U)
Erie Community College (U)
Erie Community College, North Campus (U)
Erie Community College, South Campus (U)
Frank Phillips College (U)
Galveston College (U)
Genesee Community College (U)
Georgia Highlands College (U)
Golden West College (U)
Gordon-Conwell Theological Seminary (N,G)
Governors State University (U,G)
Graceland University (U)
Grand Rapids Community College (U)
Gulf Coast Community College (U)
Halifax Community College (U)
Harrisburg Area Community College (U)
Haywood Community College (U)
Herkimer County Community College (U)
Hillsborough Community College (U)
Houston Community College System (U)
Huntington College of Health Sciences (U)
Indiana State University (G)
Jacksonville State University (U,G)
Jefferson Community College (U)
John Wood Community College (U)
J. Sargeant Reynolds Community College (U)
Judson College (U)
Kansas State University (U)
Kaskaskia College (U)
Labette Community College (U)
Lehigh Carbon Community College (U)
Liberty University (U)
Long Beach City College (U)
Los Angeles Trade-Technical College (U)
Louisiana State University and Agricultural and Mechanical College (U)
Malone College (U)
Manatee Community College (U)
Marshall University (U)
Mercy College (U)
Middlesex Community College (U)
Misericordia University (U)
Mississippi State University (U)
Missouri State University (U)
Montgomery County Community College (U)
Mountain Empire Community College (U)
Mount Olive College (U)
Naropa University (U)
Nassau Community College (U)
National University (U)
Naugatuck Valley Community College (U)
New River Community College (U)
Northampton County Area Community College (U)
North Central Texas College (U)

North Dakota State College of Science (U)
North Dakota State University (U)
Northeast Iowa Community College (U)
NorthWest Arkansas Community College (U)
Oxnard College (U)
Palm Beach Community College (U)
Palomar College (U)
Parkland College (U)
Patrick Henry Community College (U)
Peninsula College (U)
Portland Community College (U)
Reading Area Community College (U)
Red Rocks Community College (U)
Richland Community College (U)
Rose State College (U)
Saddleback College (U)
Saint Joseph's College of Maine (U)
Santa Monica College (U)
Saybrook Graduate School and Research Center (G)
Seattle Central Community College (U)
Seminole Community College (U)
Sierra College (U)
Simmons College (N)
Sinclair Community College (U)
Southern New Hampshire University (U)
Southwest Virginia Community College (U)
State University of New York at Oswego (U)
State University of New York College at Cortland (U,G)
Tacoma Community College (U)
Taylor University (U)
Texas A&M University–Commerce (U)
Texas State University–San Marcos (U)
Texas Tech University (U)
Three Rivers Community College (U)
Tompkins Cortland Community College (U)
Triton College (U)
Tunxis Community College (U)
University of Arkansas (U)
University of Arkansas at Little Rock (U)
University of Bridgeport (U)
University of Hawaii–West Oahu (U)
The University of Kansas (U)
The University of Maine at Augusta (U)
University of Maine at Fort Kent (U)
University of Minnesota, Twin Cities Campus (U)
University of Missouri–Columbia (U)
University of Nevada, Reno (U)
University of New Orleans (U,G)
University of North Texas (U,G)
The University of Texas at Brownsville (G)
The University of Texas at El Paso (U)
The University of Texas System (U)
University of the Southwest (U)
The University of Toledo (U)
University of Utah (U)
University of Washington (U)
University of Waterloo (U)
University of Wisconsin–Stout (U,G)
Vincennes University (U)
Western Michigan University (G)
Western Nebraska Community College (U)
Western Washington University (U)
West Hills Community College (N)
Wilfrid Laurier University (U)
Wytheville Community College (U)
York Technical College (U)

DIETETICS AND CLINICAL NUTRITION SERVICES

Auburn University (N)
Buffalo State College, State University of
  New York (U)
California State University, Dominguez Hills
  (N)
Central Michigan University (G)
Cuyahoga Community College (U)
Eastern Michigan University (U,G)
Erie Community College (U)
Erie Community College, North Campus (U)
Erie Community College, South Campus (U)
Kansas State University (U)
Northampton County Area Community
  College (U)
Southern Maine Community College (U)
South Piedmont Community College (U)
Sullivan County Community College (N)
University of North Dakota (U)
University of North Florida (U,G)
Westchester Community College (U)

DRAFTING/DESIGN ENGINEERING TECHNOLOGIES

Blackhawk Technical College (N)
Butler Community College (U)
Chemeketa Community College (U)
Colorado State University (G)
Columbus State Community College (U)
Dallas County Community College District
  (U)
Danville Community College (U)
Indiana State University (U)
Kentucky State University (U)
Long Beach City College (U)
North Dakota State College of Science (U)
Orange Coast College (U)
Pittsburgh Technical Institute (U)
Sinclair Community College (U)
University of Alaska Fairbanks (U)
Wake Technical Community College (U)
Wytheville Community College (U)

DRAMATIC/THEATER ARTS AND STAGECRAFT

Arkansas State University–Mountain Home
  (U)
Bergen Community College (U)
Brigham Young University (U)
California State University, San Marcos (N)
Central Carolina Community College (U)
Central Wyoming College (N)
Chaminade University of Honolulu (U)
Columbus State Community College (U)
Eastern Michigan University (U)
Eastern Oregon University (U)
Edison State Community College (U)
Erie Community College (U)
Erie Community College, North Campus (U)
Erie Community College, South Campus (U)
Foothill College (U)
Fort Valley State University (U)
Graceland University (U)
Jefferson Community College (U)
John A. Logan College (U)
Kaskaskia College (U)
Limestone College (U)
Louisiana State University and Agricultural
  and Mechanical College (U)

McMurry University (U)
Metropolitan State University (U)
Northern State University (U)
Northwest Missouri State University (U)
Oxnard College (U)
Parkland College (U)
Pikes Peak Community College (U)
Queen's University at Kingston (U)
Sacramento City College (U)
Siêrra College (U)
Southeastern Oklahoma State University (N)
State University of New York at Oswego (U)
Texas Christian University (U)
Triton College (U)
The University of Akron (U,G)
University of Alaska Fairbanks (U)
University of Arkansas (U)
University of Colorado Denver (U)
University of Louisville (U)
University of New Orleans (G)
The University of North Carolina at Chapel
  Hill (U)
University of Oklahoma (U)
The University of South Dakota (U)
Utah Valley State College (U)
West Los Angeles College (U)
West Virginia University at Parkersburg (U)

ECOLOGY, EVOLUTION, AND POPULATION BIOLOGY

Arkansas State University–Beebe (U)
Bellevue Community College (U)
Burlington County College (U)
California Institute of Integral Studies (N,G)
Coastline Community College (U)
Edison State Community College (U)
John Wood Community College (U)
Judson College (U)
Louisiana State University and Agricultural
  and Mechanical College (U)
Oregon State University (U)
Palomar College (U)
Santa Monica College (U)
University of Minnesota, Twin Cities Campus
  (U)
University of Waterloo (U)
Yuba College (U)

ECONOMICS

Abilene Christian University (U)
Acadia University (U)
AIB College of Business (U)
Allen County Community College (U)
Anne Arundel Community College (U)
Arapahoe Community College (U)
Arkansas State University–Beebe (U)
Arkansas State University–Mountain Home
  (U)
Athabasca University (N,U,G)
Athens Technical College (U)
Avila University (U)
Baltimore City Community College (U)
Bellevue Community College (U)
Berkeley College (U)
Berkeley College–New York City Campus (U)
Berkeley College–Westchester Campus (U)
Black Hills State University (U)
Boise State University (U)
Brazosport College (U)
Brenau University (U,G)

Bridgewater State College (G)
Brigham Young University (U)
Bristol Community College (U)
Broward Community College (U)
Butler Community College (U)
California National University for Advanced
  Studies (U)
California State University, Sacramento (U)
California State University, San Bernardino
  (U)
Cape Cod Community College (U)
Carroll Community College (U)
Carroll University (U)
Cayuga County Community College (U)
Central Carolina Community College (U)
Central Michigan University (U,G)
Central New Mexico Community College (U)
Central Texas College (U)
Central Virginia Community College (U)
Central Washington University (U)
Central Wyoming College (U)
Chadron State College (U,G)
Chaminade University of Honolulu (U)
Chatham University (U)
Chemeketa Community College (U)
Citrus College (U)
Clarion University of Pennsylvania (U)
Clemson University (U)
Cleveland Community College (U)
Clinton Community College (U)
Coastline Community College (U)
The College of St. Scholastica (U)
College of Southern Maryland (U)
College of The Albemarle (U)
Colorado Mountain College District System
  (U)
Colorado State University (U)
Columbia College (U)
Columbus State Community College (U)
Community College of Beaver County (U)
Community College of Denver (U)
Concordia University Wisconsin (U)
Corning Community College (U)
Crafton Hills College (U)
Cumberland County College (U)
Cuyahoga Community College (U)
Dallas Baptist University (U,G)
Dallas County Community College District
  (U)
Darton College (U)
Daytona State College (U)
De Anza College (U)
Delaware County Community College (U)
Delaware Technical & Community College,
  Jack F. Owens Campus (U)
DeSales University (U)
DeVry University Online (U,G)
Drake University (U,G)
East Central Community College (U)
Eastern Oregon University (U)
Eastern West Virginia Community and
  Technical College (U)
Eastern Wyoming College (U)
Edison State Community College (U)
Embry-Riddle Aeronautical University (U)
Erie Community College (U)
Erie Community College, North Campus (U)
Erie Community College, South Campus (U)
Everett Community College (U)
Finger Lakes Community College (U)
Florida State University (U)
Fontbonne University (U)

Foothill College (U)
Fort Hays State University (N,U)
Fox Valley Technical College (U)
Framingham State College (U)
Franklin University (U)
Frank Phillips College (U)
Gadsden State Community College (U)
Galveston College (U)
Genesee Community College (U)
George C. Wallace Community College (U)
Georgia Highlands College (U)
Georgia State University (U,G)
Glenville State College (U)
Golden Gate University (U,G)
Grand Rapids Community College (U)
Grantham University (U)
Greenville Technical College (U)
Gulf Coast Community College (U)
Halifax Community College (U)
Harrisburg Area Community College (U)
Haywood Community College (U)
Hibbing Community College (U)
Hillsborough Community College (U)
Hocking College (U)
Holyoke Community College (U)
Hope International University (U)
Hopkinsville Community College (U)
Houston Community College System (U)
Illinois Eastern Community Colleges, Olney
  Central College (U)
Indiana State University (U)
Indiana University–Purdue University Fort
  Wayne (U)
Iona College (U)
Ivy Tech Community College–North Central
  (U)
Ivy Tech Community College–Northwest (U)
Jacksonville State University (U,G)
Jefferson College (U)
Jefferson Community College (U)
Johnson County Community College (U)
John Wood Community College (U)
J. Sargeant Reynolds Community College (U)
Judson College (U)
Kean University (U)
Kentucky State University (U)
Lackawanna College (U)
Lakeland Community College (U)
Lake-Sumter Community College (U)
Lake Superior College (U)
Lamar State College–Port Arthur (U)
Laredo Community College (U)
Lehigh Carbon Community College (U)
Lewis-Clark State College (U)
Liberty University (U)
Limestone College (U)
Linn-Benton Community College (U)
Long Beach City College (U)
Los Angeles Harbor College (U)
Louisiana State University and Agricultural
  and Mechanical College (U)
Lurleen B. Wallace Community College (U)
Mansfield University of Pennsylvania (U)
Marist College (U)
Marshall University (U)
Memorial University of Newfoundland (U)
Mercer County Community College (U)
Mercy College (U)
Mesa Community College (U)
Metropolitan State University (U,G)
Miami Dade College (U)
Michigan State University (U)

Middlesex Community College (U)
Middle Tennessee State University (U,G)
Midway College (U)
Millersville University of Pennsylvania (U)
Minot State University (U)
Mississippi Delta Community College (U)
Missouri State University (U,G)
Monroe County Community College (U)
Montcalm Community College (U)
Montgomery County Community College (U)
Motlow State Community College (U)
Mountain Empire Community College (U)
Mt. Hood Community College (U)
Mount Olive College (U)
Mt. San Antonio College (U)
Mount Wachusett Community College (U)
Murray State College (U)
Myers University (U)
Nassau Community College (U)
Naugatuck Valley Community College (U)
New Jersey City University (U)
New Mexico Highlands University (U)
New Mexico Junior College (U)
New River Community College (U)
New York Institute of Technology (U)
Nipissing University (U)
Northampton County Area Community
  College (U)
North Arkansas College (U)
North Central Texas College (U)
North Dakota State College of Science (U)
Northeast Alabama Community College (U)
Northeast State Technical Community College
  (U)
Northern State University (U)
Northern Virginia Community College (U)
North Iowa Area Community College (U)
North Lake College (U)
North Seattle Community College (U)
NorthWest Arkansas Community College (U)
Northwestern Michigan College (U)
Northwestern State University of Louisiana
  (U)
Northwood University, Texas Campus (U)
Okaloosa-Walton College (U)
Oklahoma Panhandle State University (U)
Oklahoma State University (U)
Orange Coast College (U)
Oregon Institute of Technology (U)
Oregon State University (U)
Oxnard College (U)
Pace University (U)
Palm Beach Community College (U)
Palomar College (U)
Parkland College (U)
Park University (U)
Patrick Henry College (U)
Patrick Henry Community College (U)
Peirce College (U)
Peninsula College (U)
Philadelphia University (U)
Pikes Peak Community College (U)
Portland Community College (U)
Prairie View A&M University (U,G)
Pratt Community College (U)
Pulaski Technical College (U)
Queen's University at Kingston (U)
Randolph Community College (U)
Reading Area Community College (U)
Richmond Community College (U)
Riverside Community College District (N,U)
Rockland Community College (U)

Rose State College (U)
Sacred Heart University (G)
St. Ambrose University (U)
Saint Charles Community College (U)
St. Clair County Community College (U)
St. Cloud State University (U)
St. Edward's University (U)
St. John's University (U,G)
Sam Houston State University (U)
San Diego Community College District (U)
Santa Monica College (U)
Santa Rosa Junior College (U)
Seminole Community College (U)
Shippensburg University of Pennsylvania (U)
Sierra College (U)
Sinclair Community College (U)
Southeast Arkansas College (U)
Southeast Community College Area (U)
Southeastern Community College (U)
Southeastern Oklahoma State University (U)
Southern New Hampshire University (U)
South Piedmont Community College (U)
Southwestern College (U)
Southwest Wisconsin Technical College (U)
State University of New York at Binghamton
  (U)
State University of New York at Oswego
  (U,G)
State University of New York College at
  Cortland (U)
State University of New York College at
  Potsdam (U)
Stephen F. Austin State University (U)
Strayer University (U,G)
Taft College (U)
Taylor University (U)
Temple University (U,G)
Texas A&M University–Commerce (N,U,G)
Texas A&M University–Kingsville (U,G)
Texas Tech University (U)
Tri-County Community College (U)
Trine University (U)
Triton College (U)
Tyler Junior College (U)
UC San Diego Extension (U,G)
Union County College (U)
The University of Akron (U,G)
The University of Alabama (U)
University of Alaska Fairbanks (U)
University of Arkansas at Little Rock (U,G)
University of Arkansas at Pine Bluff (U)
University of Bridgeport (U)
University of California, Los Angeles (G)
University of Cincinnati (U)
University of Colorado at Colorado Springs
  (U)
University of Colorado Denver (U)
The University of Findlay (U)
University of Hawaii–West Oahu (U)
University of Idaho (U)
University of Illinois at Chicago (G)
University of Illinois at Springfield (U)
The University of Kansas (U)
The University of Maine at Augusta (U)
University of Maine at Fort Kent (U)
University of Maine at Machias (U)
University of Management and Technology
  (U,G)
University of Maryland University College
  (U)
University of Massachusetts Boston (U)
University of Minnesota, Crookston (U)

University of Minnesota, Twin Cities Campus (U)
University of Missouri–Columbia (U,G)
University of Nevada, Reno (U)
University of New Orleans (U,G)
University of North Alabama (U)
The University of North Carolina at Chapel Hill (U)
University of North Dakota (U)
University of North Texas (U)
University of Oklahoma (U)
University of Oregon (U)
University of Pittsburgh at Bradford (U)
University of Saskatchewan (U)
University of Southern Indiana (U,G)
University of Southern Mississippi (G)
The University of Tennessee (U)
The University of Texas at San Antonio (U,G)
The University of Texas System (U)
University of the Southwest (U)
The University of Toledo (U)
University of Toronto (N)
University of Utah (U)
The University of Virginia's College at Wise (U)
University of Washington (U)
University of Waterloo (U)
University of West Florida (U)
University of Wisconsin Colleges (U)
University of Wisconsin–La Crosse (G)
University of Wisconsin–Parkside (G)
University of Wisconsin–Stout (U)
University of Wisconsin–Whitewater (U,G)
Utah State University (U)
Utica College (U)
Vincennes University (U)
Wake Technical Community College (U)
Washington State University (U)
Wayland Baptist University (U,G)
Wayne State College (U,G)
Westchester Community College (U)
Western Michigan University (U,G)
Western Washington University (U)
Western Wyoming Community College (U)
West Los Angeles College (U)
Wilfrid Laurier University (U)
Worcester State College (U)
Wytheville Community College (U)
York Technical College (U)
York University (U)
Youngstown State University (U)
Yuba College (U)

EDUCATION

Abilene Christian University (U,G)
Acadia University (U)
Adams State College (G)
Albany State University (U)
American University (U,G)
Antioch University McGregor (G)
Arapahoe Community College (U)
Auburn University (G)
Beaufort County Community College (U)
Bellevue Community College (U)
Bergen Community College (U)
Bethel College (U,G)
Black Hills State University (G)
Bloomfield College (U)
Blue Ridge Community College (U)
Boise State University (U)
Bowling Green State University (G)

Bradley University (U,G)
Brenau University (U,G)
Bridgewater State College (U)
Brigham Young University (U,G)
Bristol Community College (U)
Brock University (U)
Bryn Athyn College of the New Church (U)
Buena Vista University (U,G)
Buffalo State College, State University of New York (U)
California Polytechnic State University, San Luis Obispo (G)
California State University, Chico (U,G)
California State University, Dominguez Hills (N,U)
California State University, San Bernardino (U,G)
Canisius College (G)
Capella University (G)
Cardinal Stritch University (G)
Carlow University (U,G)
Centennial College (G)
Central Arizona College (U)
Central Bible College (U)
Central Carolina Community College (U)
Centralia College (U)
Central Texas College (U)
Central Washington University (U,G)
Chadron State College (U,G)
Chaminade University of Honolulu (U,G)
Chatham University (U,G)
Chemeketa Community College (U)
Cincinnati Christian University (U,G)
Clackamas Community College (U)
Clarion University of Pennsylvania (G)
Cleveland Community College (U)
Cleveland State Community College (U)
Cleveland State University (U,G)
College of Mount St. Joseph (U,G)
College of Southern Maryland (N)
College of the Sequoias (U)
Colorado State University (N,U,G)
Columbia College (U,G)
Columbia International University (N,G)
Columbus State University (U)
Community College of Beaver County (U)
Community College of Denver (N)
Concordia College–New York (U)
Concordia University, St. Paul (U,G)
Corning Community College (U)
Crown College (G)
Cuyahoga Community College (U)
Daemen College (U)
Dallas Baptist University (U,G)
Dallas County Community College District (U)
Danville Community College (U)
Darton College (U)
Daytona State College (U)
Drake University (U,G)
Drexel University (G)
Duquesne University (G)
East Carolina University (U,G)
East Central Community College (U)
Eastern Illinois University (U)
Eastern Michigan University (N,U,G)
Eastern Washington University (N,U)
East Tennessee State University (U,G)
Elizabeth City State University (U,G)
Endicott College (U,G)
Erie Community College (U)
Erie Community College, North Campus (U)

Erie Community College, South Campus (U)
Eugene Bible College (U)
Finger Lakes Community College (U)
Fitchburg State College (U,G)
Fontbonne University (G)
Framingham State College (G)
Galveston College (U)
Genesee Community College (U)
Georgia College & State University (G)
Goucher College (G)
Governors State University (N)
Graceland University (G)
Greenfield Community College (U)
Halifax Community College (U)
Hamline University (N,G)
Harrisburg Area Community College (U)
Haywood Community College (U)
Hobe Sound Bible College (N)
Hofstra University (U)
Hope International University (G)
Hopkinsville Community College (N)
Indiana State University (U,G)
Indiana University–Purdue University Fort Wayne (U)
Iona College (G)
Jackson State University (U,G)
Jacksonville State University (U,G)
James Madison University (N)
Jefferson College (U)
Jefferson Community College (U)
John A. Logan College (U)
J. Sargeant Reynolds Community College (U)
Judson College (U)
Kansas State University (N)
Kean University (N)
Lackawanna College (U)
Lake-Sumter Community College (U)
Laredo Community College (U)
Lehigh Carbon Community College (U)
Lewis-Clark State College (U)
Liberty University (U)
Linn-Benton Community College (U)
Lock Haven University of Pennsylvania (N,U,G)
Louisiana State University and Agricultural and Mechanical College (U)
Macon State College (U)
Mansfield University of Pennsylvania (U,G)
Marian College of Fond du Lac (U,G)
Marquette University (N,U,G)
Marymount University (G)
Massachusetts College of Liberal Arts (G)
Mayville State University (U)
McDowell Technical Community College (U)
Memorial University of Newfoundland (U)
Mercy College (U)
Mesa State College (U,G)
Miami Dade College (U)
Michigan State University (G)
Middlesex Community College (U)
Middle Tennessee State University (U)
Midwestern State University (U)
Midwives College of Utah (N,U,G)
Millersville University of Pennsylvania (U,G)
Minot State University (U)
Missouri State University (G)
Monmouth University (U,G)
Montgomery County Community College (U)
Mount Olive College (U)
Murray State University (U)
Naropa University (N,G)
National University (U,G)

New Mexico Highlands University (U,G)
Northampton County Area Community College (U)
North Central Texas College (U)
Northcentral University (G)
North Dakota State University (U,G)
Northeast State Technical Community College (U)
Northern State University (G)
Northern Virginia Community College (U)
North Lake College (U)
Northwestern Oklahoma State University (U)
Northwest Missouri State University (G)
Oregon State University (U,G)
Oxnard College (U)
Pace University (N,U,G)
Palm Beach Community College (U)
Pamlico Community College (U)
Park University (G)
Pasco-Hernando Community College (N)
Peninsula College (U)
Plymouth State University (G)
Portland Community College (U)
Prairie View A&M University (G)
Pratt Community College (U)
Prescott College (U,G)
Pulaski Technical College (U)
Quinebaug Valley Community College (U)
Regent University (N,U,G)
Roosevelt University (U,G)
Sacred Heart University (G)
St. Edward's University (U)
St. John's University (U,G)
Saint Mary-of-the-Woods College (U,G)
San Diego Community College District (U)
San Diego State University (N)
Santa Monica College (U)
Seattle Pacific University (G)
Seminole Community College (U)
Shippensburg University of Pennsylvania (U,G)
Southeastern Illinois College (U)
Southern Arkansas University Tech (U)
Southern Illinois University Edwardsville (G)
South Piedmont Community College (U)
Southwestern Adventist University (U,G)
Southwestern College (G)
Spoon River College (U)
State University of New York at Binghamton (G)
State University of New York at Oswego (G)
State University of New York at Plattsburgh (U,G)
State University of New York College at Cortland (G)
State University of New York Empire State College (U,G)
Sullivan County Community College (N)
Taylor University (U)
Temple University (U)
Texas A&M University–Commerce (G)
Texas A&M University–Kingsville (U,G)
Texas Tech University (G)
Texas Woman's University (G)
Treasure Valley Community College (U)
Tri-County Community College (U)
Tyler Junior College (U)
Union University (U,G)
The University of Akron (U,G)
University of Alaska Anchorage, Kodiak College (U)
University of Alaska Fairbanks (U)

University of Arkansas at Little Rock (U,G)
University of Arkansas at Pine Bluff (U,G)
The University of British Columbia (U,G)
University of Calgary (G)
University of California, Davis (U)
University of Cincinnati (U)
University of Colorado Denver (G)
University of Dubuque (U)
University of Houston–Downtown (U)
University of Houston–Victoria (U,G)
University of Illinois at Urbana–Champaign (G)
University of La Verne (N)
University of Lethbridge (G)
University of Louisville (G)
University of Maine at Machias (U)
University of Massachusetts Boston (G)
University of Minnesota, Morris (U)
University of Missouri–Columbia (N,U,G)
The University of Montana–Western (U)
University of Nevada, Reno (G)
University of New Haven (G)
University of New Orleans (U,G)
University of North Alabama (U,G)
The University of North Carolina at Charlotte (U,G)
University of North Dakota (U)
University of Northern Iowa (U,G)
University of North Florida (U,G)
University of North Texas (N,U,G)
University of Oklahoma (U)
University of Phoenix (G)
University of St. Thomas (N)
University of Sioux Falls (G)
University of South Alabama (U)
The University of South Dakota (U,G)
University of Southern Indiana (U,G)
University of Southern Maine (U)
University of Southern Mississippi (G)
University of South Florida (U,G)
The University of Tennessee (U)
The University of Tennessee at Martin (N)
The University of Texas at El Paso (U,G)
The University of Texas of the Permian Basin (U)
The University of Texas System (U,G)
University of the Southwest (U)
The University of Toledo (U,G)
University of Vermont (U)
University of Virginia (G)
University of Washington (U)
University of Wisconsin–Stout (U,G)
University of Wisconsin–Superior (U,G)
University of Wisconsin–Whitewater (U)
University of Wyoming (G)
Utah State University (G)
Valley City State University (G)
Vanguard University of Southern California (U)
Vincennes University (U)
Virginia Polytechnic Institute and State University (N)
Washburn University (N,U,G)
Wayne State College (U,G)
Webster University (G)
Western Michigan University (U)
Westfield State College (U,G)
West Los Angeles College (U)
West Texas A&M University (U)
West Virginia State University (U)
West Virginia University (N)
Wheeling Jesuit University (U)

EDUCATION (SPECIFIC LEVELS AND METHODS)

Arapahoe Community College (U)
Arkansas Tech University (U)
Auburn University (G)
Blackhawk Technical College (U)
Blue Ridge Community College (U)
Brenau University (U)
Buena Vista University (U)
Canisius College (G)
Central Michigan University (G)
Chadron State College (U,G)
Cleveland State University (G)
Community College of Denver (U)
Danville Community College (U)
Darton College (U)
Drexel University (G)
East Arkansas Community College (U)
Eastern Michigan University (G)
Granite State College (U)
Halifax Community College (N)
Hamline University (G)
Honolulu Community College (U)
Indiana State University (G)
Indiana University System (N)
Iona College (G)
Jacksonville State University (U,G)
James A. Rhodes State College (U)
James Madison University (N,U)
Judson College (U)
Kansas State University (N)
Kean University (U,G)
La Sierra University (U,G)
Lehigh Carbon Community College (U)
Liberty University (G)
Limestone College (U)
Lincoln Christian College (N,U)
Louisiana State University and Agricultural and Mechanical College (U)
McDowell Technical Community College (U)
McMurry University (U)
Minot State University (U)
Mississippi State University (U)
Missouri State University (G)
Northampton County Area Community College (U)
North Dakota State University (G)
Northwestern State University of Louisiana (U)
Oregon State University (G)
Pacific Oaks College (U,G)
Pamlico Community College (U)
Pasco-Hernando Community College (U)
Pine Technical College (U)
Regis University (G)
Roosevelt University (U)
St. Clair County Community College (U)
St. John's University (G)
Saint Mary-of-the-Woods College (U)
San Diego State University (U,G)
San Francisco State University (N)
Seattle Pacific University (G)
Seminole Community College (N)
South Piedmont Community College (U)
State University of New York College at Cortland (U,G)
State University of New York College at Potsdam (G)
Stephen F. Austin State University (G)
Tompkins Cortland Community College (U)
The University of Akron (N,U,G)

The University of Alabama (U)
University of Alaska Fairbanks (G)
The University of Arizona (G)
University of Arkansas at Little Rock (U,G)
University of Calgary (N)
University of Maine at Fort Kent (U)
University of Maine at Machias (U)
University of Maryland University College
  (G)
University of Missouri–Columbia (N)
The University of Montana–Western (U)
University of New Orleans (U,G)
University of North Dakota (U)
University of St. Thomas (U)
University of Saskatchewan (U)
University of South Alabama (G)
University of Southern Indiana (U)
University of South Florida (G)
The University of Tennessee at Martin (N)
The University of Texas at Tyler (U)
The University of Texas of the Permian Basin
  (U,G)
University of Vermont (G)
University of Wisconsin–Stout (N)
Utah State University (G)
Virginia Polytechnic Institute and State
  University (U)
Western Washington University (U)
Western Wyoming Community College (U)

EDUCATION (SPECIFIC SUBJECT AREAS)

Adams State College (G)
Alcorn State University (U)
Arapahoe Community College (U)
Arkansas Tech University (U,G)
Auburn University (G)
Azusa Pacific University (G)
Baltimore Hebrew University (G)
Blue Ridge Community College (U)
Brenau University (U)
Buena Vista University (U)
California State University, San Bernardino
  (U,G)
California State University, San Marcos (U,G)
Canisius College (G)
Carroll University (G)
Central Michigan University (G)
Central Wyoming College (U)
Chadron State College (U,G)
Cleveland State University (G)
Columbus State University (G)
Community College of Denver (U)
Darton College (U)
Drexel University (G)
East Carolina University (U)
Eastern Illinois University (U)
Eastern Michigan University (U,G)
Edgecombe Community College (U)
Elizabeth City State University (U)
Flathead Valley Community College (U)
Fort Hays State University (G)
Glenville State College (U)
Granite State College (G)
Hamline University (N,G)
Indiana State University (G)
Iona College (G)
Jacksonville State University (U,G)
Judson College (U)
Kansas State University (N)

Kauai Community College (G)
Kean University (U)
La Sierra University (U,G)
Lehigh Carbon Community College (U)
Liberty University (G)
Millersville University of Pennsylvania (U,G)
Mississippi State University (U,G)
Missouri State University (G)
Nashville State Technical Community College
  (U)
National University (G)
New Mexico Highlands University (G)
New Mexico Institute of Mining and
  Technology (G)
Northampton County Area Community
  College (U)
North Carolina State University (U,G)
Northeastern Illinois University (G)
Oregon State University (G)
Pace University (U)
Pasco-Hernando Community College (N)
Randolph Community College (U)
Roosevelt University (U)
St. Ambrose University (U,G)
St. John's University (G)
Saint Joseph's College of Maine (U,G)
Saint Mary-of-the-Woods College (U)
San Diego State University (U)
Seattle Pacific University (G)
Seminole Community College (U)
Simpson College (G)
Sioux Falls Seminary (G)
South Piedmont Community College (U)
State University of New York at Oswego
  (U,G)
State University of New York College at
  Cortland (U,G)
State University of New York College at
  Potsdam (U,G)
Three Rivers Community College (U)
The University of Akron (U,G)
University of Arkansas (G)
University of Central Missouri (U)
University of Illinois at Chicago (G)
University of Illinois at Urbana–Champaign
  (G)
University of Maryland University College
  (G)
University of Massachusetts Boston (G)
University of Michigan–Flint (N)
University of Minnesota, Duluth (U,G)
University of Minnesota, Morris (U)
University of Missouri–Columbia (G)
University of New Haven (G)
University of New Orleans (U,G)
The University of North Carolina Wilmington
  (U,G)
University of North Dakota (U,G)
University of Saskatchewan (N,U)
University of Sioux Falls (U)
University of Southern Indiana (G)
University of South Florida (G)
The University of Texas of the Permian Basin
  (U,G)
The University of Texas System (U,G)
University of the Pacific (G)
University of Utah (U)
University of West Florida (N)
Utah State University (G)
Virginia Polytechnic Institute and State
  University (U,G)
Wayne State College (U,G)

Western Washington University (U)
West Texas A&M University (G)
Yuba College (U)

EDUCATION RELATED

Acadia University (U,G)
Arapahoe Community College (U)
Arkansas Tech University (U,G)
Arlington Baptist College (U)
Athabasca University (N,G)
Athens Technical College (U)
Atlantic University (N,G)
Auburn University (G)
Barclay College (U)
Black Hills State University (U,G)
Blue Ridge Community College (N,U)
Boise State University (G)
Brenau University (U,G)
Brigham Young University (U)
Brock University (U)
Broward Community College (U)
Buena Vista University (U,G)
Buffalo State College, State University of
  New York (U,G)
California State University, Dominguez Hills
  (U)
California State University, San Bernardino
  (N,U)
California State University, San Marcos (G)
Canisius College (G)
Carroll Community College (U)
Central Virginia Community College (U)
Chadron State College (N,U,G)
Chemeketa Community College (U)
Clarion University of Pennsylvania (U)
Cleveland State University (N,G)
College of Southern Maryland (U)
College of The Albemarle (U)
Colorado Mountain College District System
  (U)
Colorado State University (G)
Columbia International University (G)
Concordia University Wisconsin (G)
Crown College (G)
Dakota State University (U,G)
Dallas Baptist University (U,G)
Dallas County Community College District
  (U)
Darton College (U)
Drake University (U)
Drexel University (G)
Eastern Michigan University (N,G)
East Tennessee State University (U,G)
Elaine P. Nunez Community College (U)
Elgin Community College (U)
Fitchburg State College (U,G)
Florida Gulf Coast University (U,G)
Fort Hays State University (U,G)
Fulton-Montgomery Community College (N)
Gadsden State Community College (U)
Gateway Technical College (U)
Genesee Community College (U)
Governors State University (N)
Hamline University (N,G)
Haywood Community College (U)
Hebrew College (N,U,G)
Illinois State University (U)
Immaculata University (G)
Indiana State University (U,G)
Indiana University System (G)
Institute for Christian Studies (G)

Jacksonville State University (U,G)
Jones International University (G)
Kansas State University (N)
La Sierra University (G)
Lehigh Carbon Community College (U)
Liberty University (G)
Manhattan School of Music (U,G)
Memorial University of Newfoundland (U,G)
Michigan State University (G)
Midway College (U)
Midwestern State University (G)
Minot State University–Bottineau Campus (U)
Mississippi State University (G)
Moorpark College (U)
Naropa University (N)
New Mexico Highlands University (U,G)
New Mexico Junior College (U)
New Mexico State University (G)
Northampton County Area Community
  College (N,U)
North Arkansas College (U)
Northcentral University (U)
North Florida Community College (U)
Northwestern Oklahoma State University (G)
Northwestern State University of Louisiana
  (U,G)
Nova Southeastern University (G)
The Ohio State University (G)
Oklahoma State University (U)
Old Dominion University (U,G)
Oregon State University (U,G)
Pace University (G)
Park University (U)
Pasco-Hernando Community College (N,U)
Portland Community College (N)
Providence College and Theological Seminary
  (N,G)
Pulaski Technical College (U)
Red Rocks Community College (U)
Regent University (N)
Regis University (G)
Roosevelt University (U,G)
St. John's University (G)
Saint Mary-of-the-Woods College (U,G)
San Diego Community College District (U)
San Diego State University (U)
San Joaquin Delta College (U)
Sarasota County Technical Institute (N)
Seminole Community College (U)
Shasta Bible College (U,G)
Silver Lake College (U)
Southeastern Oklahoma State University
  (N,U,G)
South Piedmont Community College (U)
State University of New York at Plattsburgh
  (U,G)
State University of New York College at
  Cortland (G)
Stephen F. Austin State University (G)
Taylor University (U)
Texas Tech University (G)
Texas Woman's University (G)
Tunxis Community College (N)
The University of Akron (N,U,G)
University of Alaska Fairbanks (G)
University of Arkansas at Little Rock (U,G)
University of California, Riverside (N)
University of Central Florida (U,G)
University of Cincinnati (G)
University of Colorado Denver (G)
University of Idaho (U)
University of Illinois at Springfield (U,G)

University of La Verne (N)
University of Lethbridge (U,G)
University of Maine at Fort Kent (U)
University of Massachusetts Lowell (N)
University of Missouri–Columbia (N,U,G)
University of Nevada, Reno (U,G)
The University of North Carolina at
  Greensboro (G)
University of North Texas (G)
University of Saskatchewan (N,G)
University of Southern Mississippi (U)
The University of Texas at Brownsville (G)
The University of Texas at El Paso (U)
The University of Texas at San Antonio (U)
The University of Texas of the Permian Basin
  (U)
The University of Texas System (U,G)
University of the Pacific (U)
The University of Toledo (U,G)
University of West Florida (N,G)
University of Wisconsin–Whitewater (U)
Vanguard University of Southern California
  (U)
Virginia Polytechnic Institute and State
  University (G)
Wayland Baptist University (U,G)
Western Michigan University (U)
Western Nebraska Community College (U)
Yuba College (U)

EDUCATIONAL ADMINISTRATION AND SUPERVISION

American InterContinental University Online
  (G)
Arapahoe Community College (U)
Arkansas Tech University (G)
Athabasca University (N,G)
Azusa Pacific University (G)
Brenau University (U,G)
Bridgewater State College (U,G)
Brigham Young University (U)
California State University, Dominguez Hills
  (N,U)
Calvin College (G)
Campbellsville University (G)
Canisius College (G)
Capella University (G)
Cardinal Stritch University (G)
Chadron State College (U,G)
Charter Oak State College (U)
College of The Albemarle (N)
Columbia International University (G)
Concordia University Wisconsin (G)
Crown College (G)
Dallas Baptist University (G)
Drexel University (G)
Eastern Illinois University (G)
Eastern Kentucky University (G)
Eastern Michigan University (U,G)
Elizabeth City State University (G)
Fitchburg State College (G)
Florida Gulf Coast University (U)
Fort Hays State University (U)
George Fox University (G)
Hamline University (N)
Illinois State University (G)
Indiana State University (G)
Indiana University–Purdue University Fort
  Wayne (G)
Iona College (G)
Jackson State University (G)

Jacksonville State University (U,G)
Kansas State University (N)
Kean University (G)
Lehigh Carbon Community College (U)
Liberty University (G)
Mercy College (U)
Michigan State University (G)
Mississippi State University (G)
Missouri State University (G)
Murray State University (G)
National University (G)
New Jersey City University (G)
New Mexico Highlands University (U,G)
Northampton County Area Community
  College (U)
North Carolina State University (G)
North Dakota State University (G)
Northeastern Illinois University (G)
Northwestern Oklahoma State University (G)
Northwestern State University of Louisiana
  (G)
The Ohio State University (G)
Oregon State University (G)
Pace University (G)
Park University (G)
Pasco-Hernando Community College (U)
Regent University (N)
Regis University (G)
Roosevelt University (G)
Saddleback College (U)
St. Cloud State University (U)
St. John's University (G)
Saint Joseph's College of Maine (G)
San Diego State University (G)
Saybrook Graduate School and Research
  Center (N,G)
Shasta Bible College (G)
Silver Lake College (G)
Southeastern Oklahoma State University (G)
South Piedmont Community College (U)
State University of New York at Plattsburgh
  (G)
State University of New York College at
  Cortland (G)
Stephen F. Austin State University (G)
Temple University (G)
Texas A&M University–Commerce (G)
Texas A&M University–Kingsville (G)
Texas Tech University (G)
Union University (G)
The University of Akron (U,G)
University of Alaska Fairbanks (U,G)
University of Arkansas at Little Rock (G)
University of Calgary (G)
University of Colorado at Colorado Springs
  (G)
The University of Kansas (G)
University of Michigan–Flint (N)
University of Missouri–Columbia (G)
University of New Orleans (U,G)
University of North Florida (G)
University of North Texas (N,U,G)
University of St. Thomas (G)
University of Sioux Falls (G)
University of South Alabama (G)
University of Southern Mississippi (U,G)
University of South Florida (G)
The University of Texas at El Paso (U)
The University of Texas of the Permian Basin
  (G)
University of Wisconsin–Superior (G)
Utah State University (G)

Vanguard University of Southern California (U)
Virginia Polytechnic Institute and State University (G)
Wayne State College (G)
Webster University (G)
Western Michigan University (U)
Western Washington University (U)
Youngstown State University (G)

EDUCATIONAL ASSESSMENT, EVALUATION, AND RESEARCH

Acadia University (G)
Arapahoe Community College (U)
Athabasca University (N,U,G)
Azusa Pacific University (G)
Black Hills State University (G)
Bowling Green State University (G)
Brenau University (U,G)
Bridgewater State College (U)
California State University, Sacramento (G)
Canisius College (G)
Carroll Community College (U)
Chadron State College (U,G)
Cleveland State University (G)
Columbia College (G)
Corning Community College (U)
Dallas Baptist University (G)
Drexel University (G)
East Carolina University (U,G)
Eastern Michigan University (U,G)
East Tennessee State University (G)
George Fox University (G)
Governors State University (N)
Indiana State University (G)
Iona College (G)
Jacksonville State University (U,G)
Kansas State University (N)
Liberty University (G)
Louisiana State University and Agricultural and Mechanical College (U)
Medical College of Wisconsin (G)
Middle Tennessee State University (G)
Mississippi State University (G)
Northwestern State University of Louisiana (G)
Pace University (G)
Plymouth State University (G)
St. John's University (G)
Saint Joseph's College of Maine (U,G)
Silver Lake College (G)
Southeastern Oklahoma State University (G)
State University of New York College at Cortland (U)
Texas Tech University (G)
Union University (G)
The University of Akron (U,G)
University of Arkansas at Little Rock (G)
University of Calgary (G)
University of Central Missouri (U,G)
The University of Findlay (G)
University of Lethbridge (G)
University of Michigan–Flint (N)
University of Missouri–Columbia (N,G)
University of New Orleans (U,G)
The University of North Carolina at Greensboro (G)
University of North Texas (U,G)
University of St. Francis (G)
University of St. Thomas (G)
University of Sioux Falls (G)

University of Southern Maine (G)
University of Southern Mississippi (U,G)
University of South Florida (G)
The University of Texas at El Paso (U)
The University of Toledo (G)
Utah State University (G)
Western Michigan University (G)
West Texas A&M University (G)

EDUCATIONAL PSYCHOLOGY

Arapahoe Community College (U)
Athabasca University (N,G)
Bergen Community College (U)
Black Hills State University (U)
Brenau University (U,G)
Brigham Young University (U)
Burlington College (U)
Burlington County College (U)
Caldwell Community College and Technical Institute (U)
Canisius College (G)
Capella University (G)
Chadron State College (U,G)
College of Southern Maryland (U)
Columbia International University (N)
Concordia University Wisconsin (G)
Delaware County Community College (U)
East Carolina University (U,G)
Eastern Michigan University (G)
East Tennessee State University (U)
Elizabeth City State University (U)
Eugene Bible College (U)
Harford Community College (U)
Indiana State University (G)
Indiana Wesleyan University (G)
Jackson State University (U)
Jacksonville State University (U,G)
Jefferson Community College (U)
Johnson State College (U)
Kansas State University (N)
Lehigh Carbon Community College (U)
Liberty University (U,G)
Louisiana State University and Agricultural and Mechanical College (U)
McMurry University (U)
Mercy College (U)
Michigan State University (G)
Middlesex Community College (U)
Middle Tennessee State University (U)
Mississippi State University (U,G)
Naropa University (N)
New River Community College (U)
Northampton County Area Community College (U)
North Carolina State University (U)
Northern State University (U,G)
Northwestern State University of Louisiana (G)
Okaloosa-Walton College (U)
State University of New York at Oswego (U)
State University of New York College at Cortland (U,G)
Stephen F. Austin State University (U,G)
Taylor University (U)
Texas Tech University (U)
Triton College (U)
The University of Akron (G)
The University of Arizona (G)
University of Arkansas at Little Rock (G)
University of Calgary (G)
University of Central Missouri (U,G)

University of Illinois at Urbana–Champaign (U)
University of La Verne (N)
University of Louisville (G)
University of Massachusetts Boston (G)
University of Missouri–Columbia (U,G)
University of Nevada, Reno (U)
University of North Texas (N,U,G)
University of Saskatchewan (U)
University of South Alabama (U)
University of Southern Indiana (U)
University of South Florida (G)
The University of Texas at El Paso (U)
The University of Texas of the Permian Basin (U,G)
The University of Texas System (G)
University of Washington (U)
University of Waterloo (U)
University of Wisconsin–La Crosse (G)
Utah State University (G)

EDUCATIONAL/INSTRUCTIONAL MEDIA DESIGN

Acadia University (U,G)
Adams State College (G)
Arapahoe Community College (U)
Arkansas Tech University (U,G)
Athabasca University (N)
Azusa Pacific University (G)
Black Hills State University (G)
Bloomsburg University of Pennsylvania (G)
Boise State University (U,G)
Bowling Green State University (U)
Brenau University (U)
California State University, Sacramento (G)
California State University, San Bernardino (U,G)
Capella University (G)
Chadron State College (U,G)
Charter Oak State College (U)
Dakota State University (G)
Dallas Baptist University (G)
Danville Community College (U)
Delaware Technical & Community College, Jack F. Owens Campus (U)
Drexel University (G)
Duquesne University (G)
East Carolina University (G)
Eastern Michigan University (G)
East Tennessee State University (G)
Elizabeth City State University (U)
Florida State University (G)
Georgia State University (G)
Hamline University (N,G)
Henry Ford Community College (U)
Indiana State University (G)
Iona College (G)
Jacksonville State University (U,G)
Jones International University (G)
La Sierra University (G)
Lawrence Technological University (G)
Liberty University (G)
Malone College (U)
Maranatha Baptist Bible College (U)
Massachusetts College of Liberal Arts (G)
Michigan State University (G)
Mississippi State University (U,G)
National University (G)
New Jersey City University (G)
New York Institute of Technology (G)
North Dakota State University (G)

Northeastern Illinois University (U)
North Florida Community College (U)
Northwestern State University of Louisiana
  (U,G)
Northwest Missouri State University (N,G)
Nova Southeastern University (G)
Pace University (G)
Palomar College (U)
Pasco-Hernando Community College (U)
Roosevelt University (U,G)
St. John's University (G)
San Diego State University (U,G)
Sonoma State University (U)
Southern Polytechnic State University (U)
Southwest Wisconsin Technical College (U)
State University of New York at Plattsburgh
  (G)
Taylor University (U)
Temple University (U)
Texas A&M University–Commerce (G)
Texas Tech University (G)
Tyler Junior College (N,U)
The University of Akron (N,U,G)
University of Arkansas at Little Rock (G)
The University of British Columbia (U,G)
University of Calgary (G)
University of Central Florida (G)
The University of Findlay (G)
University of Illinois at Urbana–Champaign
  (G)
University of Maryland University College
  (G)
University of Massachusetts Boston (G)
University of Massachusetts Lowell (N)
University of Michigan–Flint (N)
University of Missouri–Columbia (G)
University of New Orleans (G)
University of North Texas (U,G)
University of St. Thomas (G)
University of Saskatchewan (N)
University of South Alabama (G)
University of South Florida (G)
The University of Texas System (U,G)
University of West Florida (G)
University of Wyoming (G)
Utah State University (G)
Western Michigan University (U,G)
Youngstown State University (G)

ELECTRICAL AND ELECTRONIC ENGINEERING TECHNOLOGIES

Alpena Community College (U)
Arapahoe Community College (U)
Boise State University (U)
Bradley University (G)
California National University for Advanced
  Studies (U,G)
Central Carolina Community College (U)
Clemson University (U,G)
Cleveland Institute of Electronics (U)
Cleveland State University (U)
Coastline Community College (U)
College of The Albemarle (U)
Drexel University (U)
Fort Valley State University (U)
Grantham University (U)
Indiana State University (U,G)
Missouri University of Science and
  Technology (N,G)
Moberly Area Community College (U)
Palm Beach Community College (U)

Pamlico Community College (U)
St. Clair County Community College (U)
Southern Methodist University (G)
Southern Polytechnic State University (U)
Texas Tech University (G)
University of Colorado at Boulder (N,G)
University of Idaho (G)
University of Illinois at Chicago (G)
University of New Orleans (U,G)
The University of North Carolina at Charlotte
  (N)
University of North Texas (U,G)
University of South Florida (G)
University of Vermont (G)
University of Washington (G)
Virginia Polytechnic Institute and State
  University (U)
Wake Technical Community College (U)

ELECTRICAL AND POWER TRANSMISSION INSTALLATION

Central Wyoming College (N)
Cleveland Institute of Electronics (N)
University of Northwestern Ohio (U)

ELECTRICAL, ELECTRONICS AND COMMUNICATIONS ENGINEERING

Arkansas Tech University (U)
California State University, Sacramento (G)
Cleveland State University (G)
Columbia University (G)
Drexel University (G)
Grantham University (U)
Indiana State University (G)
Kansas State University (G)
Kettering University (N)
Michigan Technological University (U,G)
Mississippi State University (G)
Missouri University of Science and
  Technology (G)
Oklahoma State University (U)
Pittsburgh Technical Institute (U)
Southern Methodist University (G)
Stanford University (N,G)
State University of New York at Binghamton
  (G)
University of Colorado Denver (U,G)
University of Illinois at Chicago (G)
University of South Florida (G)

ELECTRICAL/ELECTRONICS MAINTENANCE AND REPAIR TECHNOLOGY

Athens Technical College (U)
Central Wyoming College (N)
Cleveland Institute of Electronics (N)
James A. Rhodes State College (U)
Long Beach City College (U)
Northampton County Area Community
  College (U)
Sacramento City College (U)
South Piedmont Community College (U)
Utah Valley State College (U)

ELECTROMECHANICAL AND INSTRUMENTATION AND MAINTENANCE TECHNOLOGIES

Blackhawk Technical College (U)
Indiana State University (G)
Northampton County Area Community
  College (U)
Sacramento City College (U)

ENGINEERING

Auburn University (N)
California National University for Advanced
  Studies (U,G)
Chatham University (U)
Cleveland Institute of Electronics (U)
Cleveland State University (U,G)
Colorado State University (U)
Columbia University (N)
Drexel University (G)
Eastern Michigan University (G)
Grantham University (U)
Harrisburg Area Community College (U)
Haywood Community College (U)
Jacksonville State University (U)
Kansas State University (G)
Kettering University (N)
Lawrence Technological University (G)
Memorial University of Newfoundland (U)
Mississippi State University (G)
Missouri University of Science and
  Technology (N,G)
North Carolina State University (G)
Northern Virginia Community College (U)
Quinebaug Valley Community College (U)
Southern Illinois University Edwardsville (G)
Stanford University (N,G)
State University of New York at Binghamton
  (G)
Sullivan County Community College (N)
Tacoma Community College (U)
Temple University (G)
Texas Tech University (G)
UC San Diego Extension (N)
Union County College (U)
The University of Akron (G)
The University of Alabama (U)
The University of Arizona (G)
University of Colorado Denver (U,G)
University of Florida (N,G)
University of Idaho (G)
University of Illinois at Chicago (G)
University of Illinois at Urbana–Champaign
  (N,G)
University of Mary Washington (G)
University of Michigan–Dearborn (G)
University of New Orleans (U,G)
The University of North Carolina at Charlotte
  (N,U)
University of Oklahoma (U)
University of South Alabama (U)
University of South Florida (U,G)
The University of Texas at San Antonio (U,G)
The University of Toledo (G)
University of Vermont (N)
Virginia Polytechnic Institute and State
  University (N,U)
Western Michigan University (U)

ENGINEERING DESIGN

Edison State Community College (U)
Georgia Institute of Technology (G)
Kettering University (N)
Southern Methodist University (G)
Southern Polytechnic State University (U)
Stanford University (G)
University of Colorado Denver (G)
University of South Florida (G)

ENGINEERING MECHANICS

Columbus State Community College (U)
Missouri University of Science and
  Technology (G)
New Mexico Institute of Mining and
  Technology (G)
Rochester Institute of Technology (U)
Southern Methodist University (G)
Stanford University (G)
The University of Alabama (G)
The University of Arizona (G)

ENGINEERING PHYSICS

Northampton County Area Community
  College (U)
Tacoma Community College (U)

ENGINEERING RELATED

Cleveland State University (G)
Drexel University (G)
Eastern Michigan University (G)
Kansas State University (G)
Kettering University (N)
Lakeland Community College (N)
Michigan State University (G)
Missouri University of Science and
  Technology (N)
The Ohio State University (U,G)
San Diego Community College District (U)
Southern Methodist University (G)
Stevens Institute of Technology (N)
Tacoma Community College (U)
Texas Tech University (G)
The University of Akron (U)
University of Cincinnati (U,G)
University of Colorado Denver (G)
University of Illinois at Chicago (G)
University of Southern California (N)
The University of Toledo (G)
University of Washington (G)
West Virginia University (N)

ENGINEERING SCIENCE

Auburn University (G)
Drexel University (G)
Eastern Michigan University (G)
Kansas State University (G)
Missouri University of Science and
  Technology (G)
Southern Methodist University (G)
State University of New York at Binghamton
  (G)
UC San Diego Extension (U)
University of Colorado Denver (U)
University of Michigan–Dearborn (N,G)

ENGINEERING TECHNOLOGIES RELATED

Arapahoe Community College (U)

Cincinnati State Technical and Community
  College (U)
Colorado State University (U)
Columbus State Community College (U)
Drexel University (G)
East Carolina University (G)
Eastern Michigan University (G)
Haywood Community College (U)
James A. Rhodes State College (U)
Mississippi State University (G)
New Jersey Institute of Technology (G)
Old Dominion University (U)
Southern Methodist University (G)
University of Colorado Denver (G)
University of North Texas (U)
University of Southern Mississippi (U)
The University of Texas at San Antonio (G)
The University of Toledo (U)
University of West Florida (U)
Virginia Polytechnic Institute and State
  University (N)
Western Washington University (U)
West Virginia University (G)

ENGINEERING TECHNOLOGY

Cleveland State University (U)
Drexel University (G)
East Carolina University (U)
Southern Methodist University (G)
The University of Akron (U)
University of Idaho (G)
University of Illinois at Chicago (G)
Wake Technical Community College (U)

ENGINEERING-RELATED FIELDS

Auburn University (G)
Cleveland State University (U,G)
Drexel University (G)
Indiana University of Pennsylvania (G)
Kettering University (N)
Missouri University of Science and
  Technology (N)
Quinebaug Valley Community College (N)
Southern Methodist University (G)
University of New Orleans (U,G)

ENGINEERING-RELATED TECHNOLOGIES

Cleveland State University (G)
Drexel University (G)
Hopkinsville Community College (U)
Indiana State University (U)
Mitchell Technical Institute (U)
Northampton County Area Community
  College (U)
Southern Methodist University (G)
University of North Texas (U)

ENGINEERING/INDUSTRIAL MANAGEMENT

California National University for Advanced
  Studies (G)
Cleveland State University (G)
Columbia University (N,G)
Drexel University (G)
Eastern Michigan University (G)
Edison State Community College (U)
Florida Institute of Technology (G)

Georgia Institute of Technology (G)
Haywood Community College (U)
Indiana University–Purdue University Fort
  Wayne (U)
Kansas State University (G)
Lehigh University (N)
Middle Tennessee State University (N)
Missouri University of Science and
  Technology (N,G)
Montana Tech of The University of Montana
  (G)
Northampton County Area Community
  College (U)
Northcentral University (G)
Oregon Institute of Technology (U)
Southern Methodist University (G)
Stanford University (G)
The University of Alabama in Huntsville (G)
University of Colorado at Boulder (N,G)
University of Colorado Denver (G)
University of Michigan–Dearborn (G)
University of South Florida (G)
The University of Texas at San Antonio (G)
University of Washington (G)
Western Michigan University (G)

ENGLISH

Abilene Christian University (U)
Acadia University (U)
AIB College of Business (U)
Allen County Community College (U)
American Public University System (U)
Arapahoe Community College (U)
Arizona Western College (U)
Arkansas State University–Beebe (U)
Athabasca University (N,U)
Barclay College (U)
Barton County Community College (U)
Beaufort County Community College (U)
Bellevue Community College (U)
Bellevue University (U)
Belmont Technical College (U)
Beulah Heights University (U)
Black Hills State University (U)
Bloomfield College (U)
Blue Ridge Community College (U)
Bowling Green State University (U,G)
Bradley University (U)
Brenau University (U)
Bristol Community College (U)
Buena Vista University (U)
Buffalo State College, State University of
  New York (U)
Burlington County College (U)
Cabrillo College (U)
Caldwell Community College and Technical
  Institute (U)
California State University, Chico (U)
California State University, San Bernardino
  (U)
Capital Community College (U)
Carlow University (U)
Carl Sandburg College (U)
Carroll University (U)
Cayuga County Community College (U)
Central Carolina Community College (U)
Centralia College (U)
Central New Mexico Community College (U)
Central Texas College (U)
Central Virginia Community College (U)
Central Washington University (U)

Cerro Coso Community College (U)
Chadron State College (G)
Chaminade University of Honolulu (U)
Chatham University (U)
Citrus College (U)
Clark State Community College (U)
Clemson University (G)
Cleveland State University (U)
Clinton Community College (U)
Coastline Community College (U)
College of The Albemarle (N)
Colorado State University (U)
Columbus State Community College (U)
Community College of Beaver County (U)
Community College of Denver (U)
Corning Community College (U)
Cuyahoga Community College (U)
Dakota State University (U)
Dallas Baptist University (U)
Danville Community College (U)
Darton College (U)
Daytona State College (U)
De Anza College (U)
Delaware County Community College (U)
DeSales University (U)
Drake University (U)
East Carolina University (G)
East Central Community College (U)
Eastern Michigan University (U)
Eastern Oregon University (U)
Eastern Washington University (U)
Eastern West Virginia Community and
    Technical College (U)
Eastern Wyoming College (U)
East Tennessee State University (U)
Edgecombe Community College (N)
Elgin Community College (U)
Elizabethtown College (U)
Embry-Riddle Aeronautical University (U)
Endicott College (U)
Erie Community College (U)
Erie Community College, North Campus (U)
Erie Community College, South Campus (U)
Eugenio María de Hostos Community College
    of the City University of New York (U)
Excelsior College (U)
Fitchburg State College (U)
Flathead Valley Community College (U)
Fort Hays State University (U)
Framingham State College (U)
Gadsden State Community College (U)
Galveston College (U)
Georgia Highlands College (U)
Georgia State University (U)
Glenville State College (U)
Golden West College (U)
Grand Rapids Community College (U)
Grand View College (U)
Harford Community College (U)
Harrisburg Area Community College (U)
Haywood Community College (U)
Henderson Community College (U)
Henry Ford Community College (U)
Herkimer County Community College (U)
Hillsborough Community College (U)
Hocking College (U)
Hofstra University (U)
Honolulu Community College (U)
Hopkinsville Community College (N,U)
Huntington College of Health Sciences (U)
Illinois State University (U)
Indiana State University (U)

Jacksonville State University (U)
James Madison University (N,U)
Jefferson Community College (U)
John A. Logan College (U)
Johnson State College (U)
Judson College (U)
Judson University (U)
Kansas State University (U)
Kaskaskia College (U)
Kentucky State University (U)
Lackawanna College (U)
Laredo Community College (U)
Lehigh Carbon Community College (U)
Liberty University (G)
Limestone College (U)
Linn-Benton Community College (U)
Lipscomb University (U)
Long Beach City College (U)
Los Angeles Harbor College (U)
Los Angeles Trade-Technical College (U)
Louisiana State University and Agricultural
    and Mechanical College (U)
Lurleen B. Wallace Community College (U)
Macon State College (U)
Mansfield University of Pennsylvania (U)
McMurry University (U)
Memorial University of Newfoundland (U)
Mercy College (U,G)
Mesa Community College (U)
Mesa State College (U)
Miami Dade College (U)
Middlesex Community College (U)
Middle Tennessee State University (U)
Minot State University (U)
Mississippi Delta Community College (U)
Moberly Area Community College (U)
Montcalm Community College (U)
Montgomery Community College (N,U)
Moorpark College (U)
Naropa University (G)
Nassau Community College (N)
National University (U)
Naugatuck Valley Community College (U)
Neumann College (U)
New River Community College (U)
New York Institute of Technology (U)
Northampton County Area Community
    College (U)
North Carolina State University (U)
North Central Texas College (U)
North Dakota State College of Science (U)
Northeast State Technical Community College
    (U)
Northern State University (U)
Northern Virginia Community College (U)
North Lake College (U)
NorthWest Arkansas Community College (U)
Northwestern Oklahoma State University (U)
Northwestern State University of Louisiana
    (U)
Oklahoma Panhandle State University (U)
Oregon State University (N,U)
Oxnard College (U)
Pace University (U)
Palomar College (U)
Pamlico Community College (U)
Park University (U)
Pasco-Hernando Community College (N)
Passaic County Community College (U)
Peirce College (U)
Piedmont Community College (U)
Pikes Peak Community College (U)

Plymouth State University (U)
Prescott College (U)
Pulaski Technical College (U)
Regent University (U)
Rend Lake College (U)
Richmond Community College (U)
Riverside Community College District (U)
Rockland Community College (U)
Rose State College (U)
Sacramento City College (U)
Saddleback College (U)
Saint Charles Community College (U)
St. Cloud State University (U)
St. Edward's University (U)
St. John's University (U)
St. Joseph's College, Long Island Campus (U)
St. Joseph's College, New York (U)
Saint Leo University (U)
Saint Mary-of-the-Woods College (U)
Sam Houston State University (U)
San Diego Community College District (U)
Santa Monica College (U)
Santa Rosa Junior College (U)
Seminole Community College (U)
Shawnee State University (N)
Shippensburg University of Pennsylvania
    (U,G)
Sierra College (U)
Simpson College (U)
Southeast Arkansas College (U)
Southeast Community College Area (U)
Southeastern Community College (U)
Southeastern Illinois College (U)
Southern Arkansas University Tech (U)
Southern Maine Community College (U)
South Piedmont Community College (U)
Southwestern Adventist University (U)
Southwestern College (U)
Spoon River College (U)
State University of New York at Binghamton
    (U)
State University of New York at Plattsburgh
    (U)
Strayer University (U)
Sullivan County Community College (N,U)
Taft College (U)
Taylor University (U)
Texas A&M University–Commerce (U)
Texas A&M University–Kingsville (U,G)
Texas State University–San Marcos (U)
Texas Tech University (G)
Texas Woman's University (N,U)
Tompkins Cortland Community College (U)
Tri-County Community College (U)
Tunxis Community College (U)
Union County College (U)
The University of Akron (U,G)
The University of Alabama (U)
University of Alaska Fairbanks (U)
University of Arkansas at Little Rock (U,G)
University of Arkansas at Pine Bluff (U)
The University of British Columbia (U)
University of Cincinnati (U)
University of Colorado Denver (U)
University of Houston–Downtown (U)
University of Idaho (U)
University of Illinois at Springfield (U)
University of Illinois at Urbana–Champaign
    (N,U)
The University of Kansas (U)
University of La Verne (N)
University of Louisville (U)

The University of Maine at Augusta (U)
University of Maine at Fort Kent (U)
University of Maine at Machias (U)
University of Management and Technology (U)
University of Massachusetts Boston (U,G)
University of Minnesota, Twin Cities Campus (U)
University of Missouri–Columbia (U)
University of Nevada, Reno (U)
University of New Orleans (U,G)
University of North Alabama (U,G)
The University of North Carolina Wilmington (U)
University of Northern Iowa (U)
University of St. Francis (U)
University of Saskatchewan (U)
University of Sioux Falls (U)
The University of South Dakota (U)
University of Southern Indiana (U)
University of Southern Mississippi (U)
University of South Florida (U,G)
The University of Tennessee (U)
The University of Texas at El Paso (U)
The University of Texas System (U)
University of the Pacific (U)
University of the Virgin Islands (U)
The University of Toledo (U)
University of Vermont (N,U)
University of Washington (N,U)
University of West Florida (U)
University of Wisconsin Colleges (N,U)
University of Wisconsin–Superior (U)
University of Wisconsin–Whitewater (U,G)
Upper Iowa University (U)
Utah State University (U,G)
Utah Valley State College (U)
Utica College (U)
Virginia Polytechnic Institute and State University (G)
Washington State University (U)
Wayne State College (U)
Weber State University (U)
Westchester Community College (U)
Western Michigan University (U)
Western Washington University (U)
West Los Angeles College (U)
West Virginia State University (U)
Wharton County Junior College (U)
Wilfrid Laurier University (U)
Worcester State College (U,G)
York Technical College (U)

ENGLISH AS A SECOND LANGUAGE

Acadia University (N)
Arapahoe Community College (U)
Athabasca University (N,U)
Blackhawk Technical College (N)
California State University, San Marcos (N)
Centennial College (G)
Central Carolina Community College (N)
Coastline Community College (N)
Dallas County Community College District (U)
Delaware Technical & Community College, Jack F. Owens Campus (U)
Drexel University (G)
Edgecombe Community College (N)
Ferris State University (U)
Foothill College (U)

Grand Rapids Community College (N)
Hamline University (N,G)
Hopkinsville Community College (N)
Illinois State University (U)
Indiana State University (G)
James Madison University (N)
Kean University (N)
Linn-Benton Community College (N)
Long Beach City College (U)
Middle Tennessee State University (N)
Montgomery County Community College (N)
Mt. San Antonio College (U)
Murray State University (G)
Naugatuck Valley Community College (N)
Northampton County Area Community College (U)
Northern Virginia Community College (U)
North Lake College (U)
Oregon State University (N,G)
Oxnard College (U)
Pamlico Community College (U)
Red Rocks Community College (U)
Regent University (N,G)
Sacramento City College (U)
Saint Charles Community College (N)
St. Cloud State University (U,G)
San Diego Community College District (U)
San Diego State University (N)
Santa Monica College (U)
South Piedmont Community College (U)
Tacoma Community College (U)
Texas A&M University–Kingsville (G)
Tompkins Cortland Community College (U)
University of Illinois at Chicago (N)
University of La Verne (N)
University of New Orleans (U,G)
The University of North Carolina at Chapel Hill (U)
The University of North Carolina at Charlotte (U)
University of Pennsylvania (N)
University of Saskatchewan (N,U)
University of South Florida (N)
The University of Texas at Brownsville (N)
The University of Texas of the Permian Basin (U)
The University of Texas System (U)
University of the Southwest (U)
University of Washington (N,U)
University of Wisconsin–Whitewater (U,G)
Valley City State University (U)
Wake Technical Community College (N)
Westchester Community College (U)
Western Washington University (U)
West Hills Community College (N)
West Los Angeles College (U)
Wharton County Junior College (N)

ENGLISH AS A SECOND/FOREIGN LANGUAGE (TEACHING)

Athabasca University (N)
Ball State University (G)
Buena Vista University (G)
Centennial College (G)
Dallas Baptist University (G)
Drexel University (G)
Hamline University (N,G)
Hopkinsville Community College (N)
Indiana State University (G)
Lehigh Carbon Community College (U)
Lincoln Christian College (U,G)

Murray State University (G)
New Mexico Highlands University (G)
Northampton County Area Community College (U)
North Carolina State University (U)
Northwestern Connecticut Community College (U)
Oregon State University (G)
Plymouth State University (U)
Seattle Pacific University (G)
The University of Akron (U)
University of Massachusetts Boston (G)
University of Nevada, Reno (U)
University of North Dakota (G)
University of Saskatchewan (N,U)
University of South Florida (U)
The University of Texas System (G)
Western Washington University (U)

ENGLISH COMPOSITION

Acadia University (U)
Adams State College (U)
AIB College of Business (U)
Allen County Community College (U)
Alpena Community College (U)
American Public University System (U)
Anne Arundel Community College (U)
Arapahoe Community College (U)
Arkansas State University–Beebe (U)
Arkansas State University–Mountain Home (U)
Athabasca University (N,U)
Athens Technical College (U)
Baltimore City Community College (U)
Barclay College (U)
Beacon University (N,U)
Bellevue Community College (U)
Belmont Technical College (U)
Bergen Community College (U)
Berkeley College (U)
Berkeley College–New York City Campus (U)
Berkeley College–Westchester Campus (U)
Black Hills State University (U)
Blue Ridge Community College (U)
Boise State University (U)
Bowling Green State University (U)
Brazosport College (U)
Brenau University (U)
Bridgewater State College (U)
Brigham Young University (U)
Bristol Community College (U)
Broome Community College (U)
Broward Community College (U)
Buena Vista University (U)
Buffalo State College, State University of New York (U)
Burlington County College (U)
Butler Community College (U)
Cabrillo College (U)
Caldwell Community College and Technical Institute (U)
Campbell University (U)
Cape Cod Community College (U)
Carl Sandburg College (U)
Carroll Community College (U)
Central Arizona College (U)
Centralia College (U)
Central New Mexico Community College (U)
Central Oregon Community College (U)
Central Texas College (U)
Central Virginia Community College (U)

Central Wyoming College (N,U)
Cerritos College (U)
Chadron State College (U)
Chaminade University of Honolulu (U)
Chemeketa Community College (U)
Citrus College (U)
City Colleges of Chicago, Harold Washington
  College (U)
Clackamas Community College (U)
Clarion University of Pennsylvania (U)
Clark State Community College (U)
Clemson University (N,U)
Cleveland Community College (U)
Cleveland State Community College (U)
Coastline Community College (U)
College of San Mateo (U)
College of Southern Maryland (U)
College of The Albemarle (N,U)
College of the Sequoias (U)
College of the Siskiyous (U)
Colorado Mountain College District System
  (U)
Colorado State University (U)
Columbia-Greene Community College (U)
Columbus State Community College (U)
Community College of Beaver County (U)
Community College of Denver (U)
Corning Community College (U)
Cumberland County College (U)
Cuyahoga Community College (U)
Daemen College (U)
Dakota State University (U)
Dallas Baptist University (U)
Dallas Christian College (U)
Dallas County Community College District
  (U)
Danville Community College (U)
Darton College (U)
Dawson Community College (U)
De Anza College (U)
Delaware County Community College (U)
Delaware Technical & Community College,
  Jack F. Owens Campus (U)
DeSales University (U)
DeVry University Online (U)
East Arkansas Community College (U)
East Central Community College (U)
Eastern Kentucky University (U)
Eastern Michigan University (U)
Eastern Wyoming College (U)
East Tennessee State University (U)
Edgecombe Community College (U)
Edison State Community College (U)
Elaine P. Nunez Community College (U)
Elgin Community College (U)
Elizabeth City State University (U)
Elizabethtown Community and Technical
  College (U)
Embry-Riddle Aeronautical University (U)
Erie Community College (U)
Erie Community College, North Campus (U)
Erie Community College, South Campus (U)
Everett Community College (U)
Evergreen Valley College (U)
Excelsior College (U)
Flathead Valley Community College (U)
Fontbonne University (U)
Foothill College (U)
Frank Phillips College (U)
Galveston College (U)
Garrett College (U)
Genesee Community College (U)

George C. Wallace Community College (U)
George Mason University (U)
Georgia Highlands College (U)
Golden Gate University (U,G)
Golden West College (U)
Governors State University (U)
Graceland University (U)
Grand Rapids Community College (U)
Grand View College (U)
Grantham University (U)
Greenfield Community College (U)
Greenville Technical College (U)
Gulf Coast Community College (U)
Halifax Community College (U)
Harford Community College (U)
Harrisburg Area Community College (U)
Haywood Community College (U)
Henry Ford Community College (U)
Hibbing Community College (U)
Hillsborough Community College (U)
Hocking College (U)
Honolulu Community College (U)
Hopkinsville Community College (N)
Houston Community College System (U)
Ilisagvik College (U)
Illinois Eastern Community Colleges, Lincoln
  Trail College (U)
Illinois Eastern Community Colleges, Olney
  Central College (U)
Immaculata University (U)
Indiana State University (U)
Indiana Tech (U)
Indiana University–Purdue University Fort
  Wayne (U)
Indiana Wesleyan University (U)
Ivy Tech Community College–Kokomo (U)
Ivy Tech Community College–North Central
  (U)
Ivy Tech Community College–Northwest (U)
Jacksonville State University (U)
James Madison University (N,U)
Jamestown Community College (N)
Jefferson College (U)
Jefferson College of Health Sciences (U)
Jefferson Community College (U)
John A. Logan College (U)
Johnson County Community College (U)
John Wood Community College (U)
J. Sargeant Reynolds Community College (U)
Judson College (U)
Judson University (U)
Kaskaskia College (U)
Kentucky State University (U)
Kirtland Community College (U)
Labette Community College (U)
Lackawanna College (U)
Lake-Sumter Community College (U)
Lake Superior College (U)
Lamar State College–Port Arthur (U)
Laredo Community College (U)
Lehigh Carbon Community College (U)
Lewis-Clark State College (U)
Liberty University (U)
Limestone College (U)
Lock Haven University of Pennsylvania (U)
Long Beach City College (U)
Los Angeles Harbor College (U)
Los Angeles Trade-Technical College (U)
Louisiana State University and Agricultural
  and Mechanical College (N,U)
Macon State College (U)
Malone College (U)

Manatee Community College (U)
Marion Technical College (U)
Marshall University (U)
Massachusetts College of Liberal Arts (U)
Mayville State University (U)
McMurry University (U)
Mercer County Community College (U)
Mercy College (U)
Mesa Community College (U)
Metropolitan State University (U)
Miami Dade College (U)
Middlesex Community College (U)
Middle Tennessee State University (U)
Midstate College (U)
Millersville University of Pennsylvania (U,G)
Minot State University (U)
Mississippi Delta Community College (U)
Monroe Community College (U)
Monroe County Community College (U)
Montana Tech of The University of Montana
  (U)
Montgomery Community College (N,U)
Montgomery County Community College (U)
Moorpark College (U)
Mountain Empire Community College (U)
Mt. Hood Community College (U)
Mount Olive College (U)
Mt. San Antonio College (U)
Mount Wachusett Community College (U)
Murray State University (U)
Myers University (U)
Nassau Community College (U)
Naugatuck Valley Community College (U)
New England Institute of Technology (U)
New Mexico Junior College (U)
New River Community College (U)
New York Institute of Technology (U)
Northampton County Area Community
  College (U)
North Arkansas College (U)
North Carolina State University (U)
North Central Missouri College (U)
North Central Texas College (U)
North Dakota State College of Science (U)
Northeast Alabama Community College (U)
Northeast Iowa Community College (U)
Northeast State Technical Community College
  (U)
Northern State University (U)
North Florida Community College (U)
North Iowa Area Community College (U)
North Lake College (U)
North Seattle Community College (U)
NorthWest Arkansas Community College
  (N,U)
Northwestern Connecticut Community College
  (U)
Northwestern Michigan College (U)
Northwestern State University of Louisiana
  (U)
Northwest Technical College (U)
Northwood University, Texas Campus (U)
Okaloosa-Walton College (U)
Oklahoma State University (U)
Orange Coast College (U)
Oregon State University (U)
Ouachita Technical College (U)
Oxnard College (U)
Pace University (U)
Palomar College (U)
Pamlico Community College (U)
Parkland College (U)

Park University (U)
Pasco-Hernando Community College (U)
Patrick Henry College (U)
Patrick Henry Community College (U)
Peirce College (U)
Pellissippi State Technical Community
  College (U)
Peninsula College (U)
Pennsylvania Highlands Community College
  (U)
Piedmont Community College (U)
Piedmont Technical College (U)
Pikes Peak Community College (U)
Plymouth State University (U)
Portland Community College (U)
Presentation College (U)
Pulaski Technical College (U)
Queen's University at Kingston (U)
Randolph Community College (U)
Rappahannock Community College (U)
Reading Area Community College (U)
Red Rocks Community College (U)
Rend Lake College (U)
The Richard Stockton College of New Jersey
  (U)
Richland Community College (U)
Rochester Institute of Technology (U)
Rockland Community College (U)
Roosevelt University (U)
Rose State College (U)
Sacramento City College (U)
Sacred Heart University (U)
St. Clair County Community College (U)
St. Cloud State University (U)
Saint Joseph's College of Maine (U)
Saint Leo University (U)
San Diego Community College District (U)
San Diego State University (N)
San Joaquin Delta College (U)
Santa Monica College (U)
Santa Rosa Junior College (U)
Savannah College of Art and Design (U)
Schenectady County Community College (U)
Schiller International University (U)
Seattle Central Community College (U)
Seminole Community College (U)
Sierra College (U)
Sinclair Community College (U)
Southeast Arkansas College (U)
Southeast Community College Area (U)
Southeastern Community College (U)
Southeastern Oklahoma State University (U)
Southern Union State Community College (U)
South Piedmont Community College (U)
Southwestern College (U)
Southwestern Community College (U)
Southwest Virginia Community College (U)
Spoon River College (U)
Spring Arbor University (U)
State University of New York College at
  Cortland (U)
State University of New York College of
  Agriculture and Technology at Morrisville
  (U)
State University of New York Empire State
  College (U)
Strayer University (U)
Tacoma Community College (U)
Taft College (U)
Taylor University (N,U)
Texas A&M University–Commerce (U,G)
Texas State Technical College Waco (U)

Texas State University–San Marcos (U)
Texas Tech University (U,G)
Texas Woman's University (N)
Tompkins Cortland Community College (U)
Triton College (U)
Tunxis Community College (U)
Tyler Junior College (U)
The University of Akron (U)
The University of Alabama (U)
University of Alaska Fairbanks (U)
University of Alaska, Prince William Sound
  Community College (U)
University of Arkansas (U)
University of Arkansas at Little Rock (U)
The University of British Columbia (N)
University of Cincinnati Raymond Walters
  College (U)
University of Colorado at Colorado Springs
  (U)
University of Colorado Denver (U)
University of Houston–Victoria (U)
University of Idaho (U)
University of Illinois at Urbana–Champaign
  (N,U)
The University of Kansas (U)
University of La Verne (N)
The University of Maine at Augusta (U)
University of Maine at Machias (U)
University of Massachusetts Boston (U)
University of Minnesota, Crookston (U)
University of Minnesota, Duluth (U)
University of Minnesota, Morris (U)
University of Missouri–Columbia (U)
The University of Montana–Western (U)
University of Nevada, Reno (U)
University of New Orleans (N,U,G)
University of North Alabama (U)
The University of North Carolina at Chapel
  Hill (U)
University of North Dakota (U)
University of North Florida (U)
University of North Texas (U)
University of Oklahoma (U)
University of Pennsylvania (N,U,G)
The University of South Dakota (U)
University of Southern Indiana (U)
University of Southern Maine (U)
University of Southern Mississippi (U)
University of South Florida (U)
The University of Tennessee (N,U)
The University of Texas at Brownsville (U)
The University of Texas at San Antonio (U)
The University of Texas of the Permian Basin
  (U)
The University of Texas System (U)
University of the Southwest (U)
University of the Virgin Islands (U)
The University of Toledo (U)
University of Washington (U)
University of Waterloo (U)
University of West Florida (U)
University of Wisconsin Colleges (U)
University of Wyoming (U)
Upper Iowa University (N,U)
Utah Valley State College (U)
Valley City State University (U)
Vincennes University (U)
Virginia Polytechnic Institute and State
  University (U)
Wake Technical Community College (U)
Washburn University (U)
Weber State University (U)

Westchester Community College (U)
Western Michigan University (U)
Western Nebraska Community College (U)
Western Wyoming Community College (U)
West Los Angeles College (U)
West Shore Community College (U)
West Virginia State University (U)
West Virginia University at Parkersburg (U)
Wharton County Junior College (U)
Wilfrid Laurier University (N)
Williston State College (U)
Wytheville Community College (U)
York County Community College (U)
York Technical College (U)
Yuba College (U)

ENGLISH LANGUAGE AND LITERATURE RELATED

Acadia University (U)
Adams State College (U)
Arapahoe Community College (U)
Arkansas Tech University (U)
Athens Technical College (N)
Avila University (U)
Beacon University (N,U)
Bellevue Community College (U)
Belmont Technical College (U)
Berkeley College (U)
Berkeley College–New York City Campus (U)
Berkeley College–Westchester Campus (U)
Brenau University (U)
Brigham Young University (N)
Capital Community College (U)
Central Texas College (U)
Charter Oak State College (U)
Clatsop Community College (U)
College of the Siskiyous (U)
Columbus State Community College (U)
Corning Community College (U)
Cuyahoga Community College (U)
Dakota State University (U)
Dallas Baptist University (U)
Danville Community College (U)
Daytona State College (U)
DeSales University (U)
Eastern Oregon University (U)
Erie Community College (U)
Erie Community College, North Campus (U)
Erie Community College, South Campus (U)
Genesee Community College (U)
Georgia Highlands College (U)
Golden Gate University (U)
Greenville Technical College (U)
Haywood Community College (U)
Holyoke Community College (U)
Jacksonville State University (U)
Jefferson Community College (U)
John A. Logan College (U)
Lake-Sumter Community College (U)
Lehigh Carbon Community College (U)
Limestone College (U)
Los Angeles Harbor College (U)
Los Angeles Trade-Technical College (U)
Louisiana State University and Agricultural
  and Mechanical College (U)
Mansfield University of Pennsylvania (U)
McDowell Technical Community College (U)
Mercy College (G)
Metropolitan State University (U)
Middlesex Community College (U)
Missouri State University (U)

Mount Olive College (U)
Nassau Community College (U)
Naugatuck Valley Community College (U)
New York Institute of Technology (U)
Northampton County Area Community
  College (U)
North Central Texas College (U)
North Florida Community College (U)
NorthWest Arkansas Community College (U)
Northwestern Michigan College (U)
Oklahoma Panhandle State University (U)
Pamlico Community College (U)
Pennsylvania College of Technology (U)
Prairie View A&M University (U)
Quinebaug Valley Community College (U)
Rose State College (U)
Sacred Heart University (U)
Saint Francis University (U)
San Diego Community College District (U)
Southern New Hampshire University (U)
South Piedmont Community College (U)
Syracuse University (U)
Taft College (U)
Texas State University–San Marcos (U)
Three Rivers Community College (U)
The University of Akron (U,G)
The University of Alabama (U)
University of Alaska Fairbanks (U)
University of Arkansas at Little Rock (U)
University of Dubuque (U)
University of La Verne (N)
University of Maine at Machias (U)
University of Minnesota, Crookston (U)
University of Minnesota, Twin Cities Campus
  (U)
University of Missouri–Columbia (U)
University of New Orleans (U,G)
The University of Tennessee (U)
The University of Texas of the Permian Basin
  (U,G)
The University of Texas System (U)
University of the Virgin Islands (U)
Utah Valley State College (U)
Westchester Community College (U)
West Los Angeles College (U)
West Virginia University at Parkersburg (U)
Wharton County Junior College (U)
York County Community College (U)
York University (U)
Youngstown State University (N)

ENGLISH LITERATURE (BRITISH AND COMMONWEALTH)

Arapahoe Community College (U)
Beacon University (U)
Bellevue Community College (U)
Bellevue University (U)
Bowling Green State University (U,G)
Bristol Community College (U)
Capital Community College (U)
Central Oregon Community College (U)
Central Texas College (U)
Chadron State College (U)
Clackamas Community College (U)
College of The Albemarle (U)
College of the Siskiyous (U)
Columbia College (U)
Columbus State Community College (U)
Community College of Beaver County (U)
Danville Community College (U)
Darton College (U)

DeSales University (U)
Eugene Bible College (U)
Galveston College (U)
George C. Wallace Community College (U)
Halifax Community College (U)
Harford Community College (U)
Harrisburg Area Community College (U)
Houston Community College System (U)
Jacksonville State University (U)
Jefferson Community College (U)
Johnson County Community College (U)
Judson College (U)
Laredo Community College (U)
Lehigh Carbon Community College (U)
Louisiana State University and Agricultural
  and Mechanical College (U)
Malone College (U)
Mercy College (U,G)
Middlesex Community College (U)
Minot State University (U)
Montgomery County Community College (U)
Mount Olive College (U)
Murray State College (U)
Neumann College (U)
Northampton County Area Community
  College (U)
North Central State College (U)
North Central Texas College (U)
Northeast Alabama Community College (U)
Northeast Iowa Community College (U)
Northwestern Oklahoma State University (U)
Oklahoma State University (U)
Pasco-Hernando Community College (U)
Patrick Henry Community College (U)
Peninsula College (U)
Piedmont Technical College (U)
Queen's University at Kingston (U)
Rose State College (U)
Saint Francis University (U)
Taylor University (U)
Texas State University–San Marcos (U)
Texas Tech University (U)
Three Rivers Community College (U)
The University of Akron (U)
The University of Alabama (U)
The University of Kansas (U,G)
University of La Verne (N)
University of Minnesota, Twin Cities Campus
  (U)
University of Missouri–Columbia (U)
University of New Orleans (U,G)
University of Saskatchewan (U)
University of Southern Indiana (U)
University of Southern Mississippi (U)
The University of Tennessee (U)
The University of Texas of the Permian Basin
  (U)
University of Utah (U)
University of Waterloo (U)
University of Wyoming (U)
Utah State University (U)
Wake Technical Community College (U)
Wharton County Junior College (U)
Wilfrid Laurier University (U)

ENTREPRENEURIAL AND SMALL BUSINESS OPERATIONS

Acadia University (N)
Adams State College (N)
AIB College of Business (U)
Arapahoe Community College (U)

Bellevue Community College (U)
Berkeley College (U)
Berkeley College–New York City Campus (U)
Berkeley College–Westchester Campus (U)
Blue Ridge Community College (U)
Bridgewater State College (U)
Broward Community College (U)
Buena Vista University (U)
Central Michigan University (G)
Central New Mexico Community College (U)
Central Texas College (U)
Cleveland State University (N)
Columbia College (U)
Community College of Beaver County (N)
Community College of Denver (U)
Daemen College (U)
Dallas Baptist University (G)
DeSales University (U)
DeVry University Online (G)
Drexel University (G)
Eastern Michigan University (U)
East Tennessee State University (N)
Erie Community College (U)
Erie Community College, North Campus (U)
Erie Community College, South Campus (U)
Flathead Valley Community College (N)
Fulton-Montgomery Community College (N)
Haywood Community College (U)
Herkimer County Community College (U)
Iona College (U)
James Madison University (N)
Jamestown Community College (N)
Jones International University (U,G)
Lakeland Community College (N,U)
Lamar State College–Port Arthur (N)
Michigan State University (G)
Minnesota School of Business–Richfield (U)
Minot State University (U)
Mitchell Technical Institute (N)
Myers University (U)
Nashville State Technical Community College
  (U)
Nassau Community College (U)
New Mexico Junior College (N)
New River Community College (U)
Northampton County Area Community
  College (U)
NorthWest Arkansas Community College (U)
Palomar College (U)
Peninsula College (U)
Piedmont Community College (U)
Rend Lake College (N)
Saint Charles Community College (N)
St. Edward's University (G)
Saint Joseph's College of Maine (G)
Santa Monica College (U)
Schenectady County Community College (U)
Shippensburg University of Pennsylvania (G)
Sinclair Community College (U)
Southeast Arkansas College (U)
Southern New Hampshire University (U)
South Piedmont Community College (U)
State University of New York at Binghamton
  (N)
State University of New York at Plattsburgh
  (U,G)
State University of New York College at
  Potsdam (N,U)
Sullivan County Community College (N)
Syracuse University (G)
Taylor University (N)
United States Sports Academy (G)

The University of Akron (N)
University of Bridgeport (U)
University of Central Missouri (N)
University of Houston–Victoria (G)
University of Illinois at Urbana–Champaign
  (G)
University of Maine at Machias (U)
University of Maryland University College
  (G)
University of Minnesota, Crookston (U)
University of Minnesota, Twin Cities Campus
  (U)
University of New Orleans (U,G)
University of South Florida (N)
Upper Iowa University (U)
Vincennes University (U)
Wake Technical Community College (N)
Worcester State College (N)
Youngstown State University (N)

ENVIRONMENTAL CONTROL TECHNOLOGIES

Athabasca University (N,U)
Bowling Green State University (U)
California State University, Dominguez Hills
  (N)
Columbus State Community College (U)
Jacksonville State University (U,G)
Judson University (U)
Lakeland Community College (N)
New York Institute of Technology (U)
Oxnard College (U)
Sullivan County Community College (N)
University of Alaska, Prince William Sound
  Community College (U)
The University of British Columbia (U)
The University of Findlay (G)

ENVIRONMENTAL DESIGN

Chatham University (U)
Colorado State University (N)
Saint Mary-of-the-Woods College (G)
Sonoma State University (U)
Southern Methodist University (G)
University of Illinois at Urbana–Champaign
  (N)

ENVIRONMENTAL PSYCHOLOGY

Saybrook Graduate School and Research
  Center (G)
University of Dubuque (U)
University of Missouri–Columbia (U)

ENVIRONMENTAL/ ENVIRONMENTAL HEALTH ENGINEERING

Alcorn State University (G)
Bowling Green State University (U)
California National University for Advanced
  Studies (U,G)
Clackamas Community College (U)
Cleveland State University (G)
Colorado State University (N)
Columbia University (N,G)
Florida Gulf Coast University (U)
Fort Valley State University (G)
Georgia Institute of Technology (N,G)
Harrisburg Area Community College (U)

Lakeland Community College (N)
Louisiana State University and Agricultural
  and Mechanical College (G)
Medical College of Wisconsin (G)
Mercy College (U)
Missouri University of Science and
  Technology (N)
New Mexico Institute of Mining and
  Technology (G)
Old Dominion University (G)
Oregon State University (G)
Pennsylvania College of Technology (U)
Rochester Institute of Technology (G)
St. Cloud State University (U)
Southern Methodist University (G)
Stanford University (G)
Texas A&M University–Kingsville (G)
Texas Tech University (G)
Three Rivers Community College (U)
University of Colorado at Boulder (N,G)
University of Florida (N,G)
University of Idaho (U,G)
University of Illinois at Springfield (G)
University of Massachusetts Boston (U)
University of South Florida (G)
Worcester Polytechnic Institute (G)
York Technical College (U)

ETHNIC, CULTURAL MINORITY, AND GENDER STUDIES

American Public University System (G)
Arapahoe Community College (U)
Athabasca University (N)
Berkeley College (U)
Berkeley College–New York City Campus (U)
Berkeley College–Westchester Campus (U)
Beulah Heights University (U)
Bowling Green State University (U)
Bridgewater State College (U)
Burlington College (U)
California Institute of Integral Studies (N,G)
California State University, Chico (U)
California State University, San Bernardino
  (U)
Central Texas College (U)
Chemeketa Community College (U)
Colorado State University (U)
Columbus State Community College (U)
De Anza College (U)
Delaware County Community College (U)
Eastern Michigan University (U,G)
Eastern Washington University (U)
Edgecombe Community College (U)
Georgia State University (U)
Hebrew College (N,U,G)
Hope International University (N)
Kansas State University (U)
Louisiana State University and Agricultural
  and Mechanical College (U)
Middlesex Community College (U)
Moorpark College (U)
Naropa University (N,U)
Oregon State University (U)
Pace University (U)
Palomar College (U)
Prairie View A&M University (G)
Prescott College (U,G)
Queen's University at Kingston (U)
Randolph Community College (U)
The Richard Stockton College of New Jersey
  (U)

Sacramento City College (U)
San Diego State University (U)
Santa Rosa Junior College (U)
Saybrook Graduate School and Research
  Center (G)
State University of New York at Plattsburgh
  (U)
State University of New York College at
  Cortland (U)
Syracuse University (U,G)
Tompkins Cortland Community College (U)
Treasure Valley Community College (U)
The University of Akron (U)
University of Alaska Fairbanks (U)
University of Arkansas at Little Rock (U)
The University of British Columbia (U)
University of Colorado Denver (U)
University of Connecticut (U)
The University of Findlay (U)
University of Illinois at Urbana–Champaign
  (U)
The University of Kansas (U)
University of La Verne (N)
University of Louisville (U)
University of Minnesota, Twin Cities Campus
  (U)
University of Missouri–Columbia (U)
The University of North Carolina at Chapel
  Hill (N,U)
University of South Florida (U)
The University of Toledo (U)
University of Washington (U)
University of Waterloo (U)
University of Wisconsin Colleges (U)
University of Wisconsin–Whitewater (U)
University of Wyoming (U)
Virginia Polytechnic Institute and State
  University (U,G)
Western Michigan University (U)
Western Washington University (U)
Western Wyoming Community College (U)

EXPERIMENTAL PSYCHOLOGY

Acadia University (U)
Burlington College (U)
Naropa University (U)
Northampton County Area Community
  College (U)
State University of New York College at
  Cortland (U)

FAMILY AND CONSUMER ECONOMICS

Athens Technical College (N)
California State University, San Marcos (N)
Carroll Community College (N)
Cleveland State University (N)
College of the Siskiyous (U)
Eastern Illinois University (U,G)
East Los Angeles College (U)
Immaculata University (U)
Jacksonville State University (U)
Kansas State University (N)
Lakeland Community College (N)
Louisiana State University and Agricultural
  and Mechanical College (U)
North Dakota State University (G)
The Ohio State University (U)
Oregon State University (N)
Palomar College (U)

Pasco-Hernando Community College (N)
Pulaski Technical College (U)
Sacramento City College (U)
Sam Houston State University (U)
Southeastern Oklahoma State University (N)
Stephen F. Austin State University (U)
Taylor University (N)
Texas Tech University (G)
Texas Woman's University (U,G)
The University of Alabama (U,G)
The University of Arizona (G)
University of Idaho (U)
University of Minnesota, Twin Cities Campus (U)
University of Northern Iowa (U)
University of North Texas (U,G)
University of Wyoming (U)
Utah State University (U)
Wake Technical Community College (N)
Western Michigan University (U,G)
Wichita State University (U)

FAMILY AND CONSUMER SCIENCES/HUMAN SCIENCES

Bowling Green State University (G)
Bradley University (U)
Central Michigan University (U)
Central Texas College (U)
Chadron State College (U)
Delaware County Community College (U)
Immaculata University (U)
Jacksonville State University (U)
James Madison University (N)
Kansas State University (N,U,G)
Kean University (N)
Liberty University (G)
Mississippi Delta Community College (U)
Mt. San Antonio College (U)
Northwestern State University of Louisiana (U)
Palomar College (U)
Sacramento City College (U)
Santa Rosa Junior College (U)
Saybrook Graduate School and Research Center (G)
Texas A&M University–Kingsville (U,G)
Treasure Valley Community College (U)
The University of Akron (U)
The University of Alabama (U)
The University of Maine at Augusta (U)
University of Minnesota, Twin Cities Campus (U)
Utah State University (U,G)
Western Michigan University (U)

FAMILY AND CONSUMER SCIENCES/HUMAN SCIENCES BUSINESS SERVICES

Cardinal Stritch University (N)
Jacksonville State University (U)
Palomar College (U)
Sacramento City College (U)
The University of Alabama (U)
The University of Arizona (U)

FAMILY AND CONSUMER SCIENCES/HUMAN SCIENCES RELATED

Central Michigan University (U)
Central Washington University (U)

Chadron State College (U)
Galveston College (N)
Jacksonville State University (U,G)
Kansas State University (N,U,G)
Mesa Community College (U)
Palomar College (U)
Southeastern Illinois College (U)
The University of Alabama (U)
Western Michigan University (U)

FAMILY PSYCHOLOGY

Arapahoe Community College (U)
Canisius College (G)
Capital Community College (U)
Central Texas College (U)
College of the Siskiyous (U)
Community College of Denver (N)
Dallas Baptist University (U)
Fort Hays State University (N)
Iona College (U)
Kansas State University (N,G)
Los Angeles Trade-Technical College (U)
Middlesex Community College (U)
Northcentral University (G)
Palomar College (U)
Peninsula College (U)
Saybrook Graduate School and Research Center (G)
Seminole Community College (U)
Texas State University–San Marcos (U)
University of Alaska Fairbanks (G)

FILM/VIDEO AND PHOTOGRAPHIC ARTS

Academy of Art University (U,G)
Arapahoe Community College (U)
Auburn University (U)
Blackhawk Technical College (N)
Blue Ridge Community College (N)
Bowling Green State University (U)
Brigham Young University (U)
Burlington County College (U)
Cabrillo College (U)
California State University, Dominguez Hills (N)
Central Wyoming College (N)
Chatham University (U,G)
Cleveland State University (N)
College of San Mateo (U)
Community College of Denver (N)
Everett Community College (U)
Flathead Valley Community College (N,U)
Foothill College (U)
Grand Rapids Community College (U)
Houston Community College System (U)
James Madison University (N)
John A. Logan College (U)
Kean University (N)
Lakeland Community College (N,U)
Long Beach City College (U)
Los Angeles Trade-Technical College (U)
Massasoit Community College (U)
Minneapolis College of Art and Design (N,U,G)
Missouri State University (U)
Mount Wachusett Community College (U)
North Seattle Community College (U)
Oregon State University (N)
Oxnard College (U)
Plymouth State University (N)

Regent University (N,U)
The Richard Stockton College of New Jersey (U)
Riverside Community College District (U)
Sam Houston State University (U)
San Diego State University (N)
Seattle Central Community College (U)
Sinclair Community College (U)
State University of New York College at Cortland (U)
Temple University (U)
University of Alaska Fairbanks (U)
The University of British Columbia (U)
University of California, Los Angeles (G)
University of Cincinnati Raymond Walters College (U)
University of Missouri–Columbia (U)
The University of North Carolina at Charlotte (N)
University of Southern Indiana (N)
The University of Toledo (U)
Wake Technical Community College (N)
Western Michigan University (U,G)
West Virginia State University (U,G)
Worcester State College (N)
York University (U)

FINANCE AND FINANCIAL MANAGEMENT SERVICES

Adams State College (U)
AIB College of Business (U)
The American College (U,G)
Anne Arundel Community College (N,U)
Arapahoe Community College (U)
Athabasca University (N,U)
Bellevue University (U)
Bergen Community College (U)
Berkeley College (U)
Berkeley College–New York City Campus (U)
Berkeley College–Westchester Campus (U)
Black Hills State University (U)
Brenau University (G)
Bridgewater State College (N)
Buena Vista University (U)
Caldwell Community College and Technical Institute (N)
California National University for Advanced Studies (U)
California State University, Dominguez Hills (N)
California State University, San Bernardino (U)
Carroll Community College (N)
Carroll University (U)
Centennial College (N)
Central Michigan University (G)
Central Wyoming College (N)
Chaminade University of Honolulu (U)
Charter Oak State College (U)
Colorado State University (U,G)
Columbus State Community College (U)
Community College of Denver (N)
Concordia University Wisconsin (U)
Dallas Baptist University (U,G)
Darton College (N,U)
Delaware County Community College (U)
DePaul University (N)
DeSales University (U)
DeVry University Online (G)
Drake University (G)
Drexel University (U,G)

Eastern Michigan University (U)
Embry-Riddle Aeronautical University (U)
Erie Community College (U)
Erie Community College, North Campus (U)
Erie Community College, South Campus (U)
Florida Gulf Coast University (U)
Florida State University (N)
Foothill College (U)
Framingham State College (G)
Franklin University (U)
Golden Gate University (U,G)
Granite State College (U)
Grantham University (U,G)
Haywood Community College (U)
Hillsborough Community College (U)
Indiana State University (U,G)
Indiana University of Pennsylvania (U)
Iona College (U,G)
Jacksonville State University (U,G)
James A. Rhodes State College (U)
Jamestown Community College (N)
Kansas State University (N,U,G)
Kaplan University Online (N)
Kean University (N,U)
Labette Community College (U)
Lakeland Community College (N)
Lamar State College–Port Arthur (N)
Lawrence Technological University (G)
Lehigh Carbon Community College (U)
Limestone College (U)
Louisiana State University and Agricultural
    and Mechanical College (U)
Marist College (U,G)
Mercer County Community College (N)
Metropolitan State University (U)
Middlesex Community College (N)
Midway College (U)
Missouri State University (U,G)
Murray State College (U)
Myers University (U)
New River Community College (U)
New York Institute of Technology (U)
Nipissing University (U)
Northcentral University (G)
Northeastern University (U)
Northwestern State University of Louisiana
    (U)
Oklahoma State University (U)
Old Dominion University (U,G)
Pace University (U)
Palomar College (U)
Park University (U)
Pennsylvania College of Technology (U)
Philadelphia University (U,G)
Plymouth State University (N)
Prairie View A&M University (U,G)
Randolph Community College (U)
Regis University (U,G)
Rockland Community College (U)
Roger Williams University (U)
Sacramento City College (U)
Sacred Heart University (G)
St. Ambrose University (U)
Saint Charles Community College (N)
Sam Houston State University (U)
San Joaquin Delta College (U)
Schiller International University (G)
Shippensburg University of Pennsylvania (U)
Simpson College (U)
Southern New Hampshire University (U)
Southern Union State Community College (U)
South Piedmont Community College (U)

Spring Arbor University (U)
State University of New York at Binghamton
    (N)
State University of New York College at
    Cortland (U)
State University of New York College at
    Potsdam (N)
State University of New York Empire State
    College (U)
Stephen F. Austin State University (U)
Strayer University (U)
Syracuse University (G)
Texas A&M University–Commerce (N,G)
Texas A&M University–Kingsville (U)
The University of Akron (U)
The University of Alabama (U,G)
University of Arkansas at Little Rock (U,G)
University of Dallas (G)
University of Houston–Downtown (U)
University of Idaho (U)
University of Illinois at Chicago (G)
The University of Maine at Augusta (U)
University of Management and Technology
    (U)
University of Minnesota, Twin Cities Campus
    (U)
University of Missouri–Columbia (U)
University of New Orleans (N,U,G)
University of North Alabama (U)
The University of North Carolina at Charlotte
    (N)
University of Oklahoma (U)
University of South Florida (N)
The University of Texas at Tyler (U)
The University of Texas of the Permian Basin
    (G)
University of Toronto (N)
University of Utah (U)
University of Waterloo (U)
University of Wisconsin–La Crosse (G)
University of Wisconsin–Parkside (G)
University of Wisconsin–Whitewater (G)
Upper Iowa University (U)
Wayland Baptist University (U)
Webster University (G)
West Virginia University (N)
Wilfrid Laurier University (U)

FINE AND STUDIO ART

Academy of Art University (U,G)
Acadia University (U)
Alpena Community College (U)
Athabasca University (N,U)
Atlantic University (N,G)
Bellevue University (U)
Brazosport College (U)
Brigham Young University (U)
Burlington College (U)
Burlington County College (U)
Butler Community College (U)
Caldwell Community College and Technical
    Institute (U)
California State University, Dominguez Hills
    (N)
California State University, San Marcos (N)
Campbell University (U)
Cape Cod Community College (U)
Carl Sandburg College (U)
Central Arizona College (U)
Central Texas College (U)
Central Wyoming College (N,U)

Chemeketa Community College (U)
College of Southern Maryland (U)
College of The Albemarle (U)
Colorado Mountain College District System
    (U)
Colorado State University (U)
Community College of Beaver County (U)
Community College of Denver (N,U)
Concordia University, St. Paul (N)
Connors State College (U)
Corning Community College (U)
Dakota State University (U)
Dallas Baptist University (U)
Dawson Community College (U)
Drake University (U)
Duquesne University (U)
East Carolina University (G)
Eastern Kentucky University (U)
Eastern Michigan University (U)
Eastern Washington University (U)
East Los Angeles College (U)
Edison State Community College (U)
Erie Community College (U)
Erie Community College, North Campus (U)
Erie Community College, South Campus (U)
Foothill College (U)
George C. Wallace Community College (U)
Governors State University (U,G)
Greenville Technical College (U)
Halifax Community College (U)
Haywood Community College (U)
Hibbing Community College (U)
Hopkinsville Community College (N,U)
Houston Community College System (U)
Indiana Wesleyan University (U)
James Madison University (N)
John A. Logan College (U)
John Wood Community College (U)
Judson University (U)
Kaskaskia College (U)
Kean University (N,U)
Labette Community College (U)
Lakeland Community College (N,U)
Lake Superior College (U)
Laredo Community College (U)
Lock Haven University of Pennsylvania (U)
Louisiana State University and Agricultural
    and Mechanical College (U)
Lurleen B. Wallace Community College (U)
Malone College (U)
Mercy College (U)
Mesa State College (U)
Middlesex Community College (N,U)
Middle Tennessee State University (N)
Minneapolis College of Art and Design
    (N,U,G)
Mississippi State University (U)
Moberly Area Community College (U)
Mountain Empire Community College (U)
Naugatuck Valley Community College (U)
North Arkansas College (U)
North Central Texas College (U)
Northeastern Illinois University (U)
NorthWest Arkansas Community College (U)
Northwestern State University of Louisiana
    (U)
Oregon State University (N)
Oxnard College (U)
Pace University (U)
Palomar College (U)
Parkland College (U)
Patrick Henry Community College (U)

Pennsylvania College of Technology (U)
Piedmont Community College (U)
Piedmont Technical College (U)
Rappahannock Community College (U)
Red Rocks Community College (U)
Richland Community College (U)
Rockland Community College (U)
Sacred Heart University (U)
Saint Leo University (U)
San Diego Community College District (U)
Savannah College of Art and Design (U,G)
Shippensburg University of Pennsylvania (U)
Sinclair Community College (U)
Southwestern Community College (U)
Spoon River College (U)
State University of New York College at
   Cortland (U)
Tacoma Community College (U)
Taylor University (U)
Texas Christian University (U)
Texas State University–San Marcos (U)
Tompkins Cortland Community College (U)
Trine University (U)
Triton College (U)
Tyler Junior College (U)
Union County College (U)
University of Alaska Fairbanks (U)
University of Colorado Denver (U)
The University of Findlay (U)
University of Illinois at Springfield (U)
University of Illinois at Urbana–Champaign
   (N,U)
University of Minnesota, Twin Cities Campus
   (U)
University of Nevada, Reno (U)
The University of North Carolina at Chapel
   Hill (N,U)
University of North Texas (U)
University of St. Francis (U)
University of Sioux Falls (U)
University of Southern Indiana (U)
University of South Florida (U)
The University of Texas of the Permian Basin
   (U)
The University of Texas System (U)
University of Utah (U)
University of West Florida (U)
University of Wisconsin–Superior (U)
Utah Valley State College (U)
Wilfrid Laurier University (U)

FIRE PROTECTION

Arizona Western College (U)
Bellevue Community College (U)
Blackhawk Technical College (N,U)
Cabrillo College (U)
Caldwell Community College and Technical
   Institute (U)
Central New Mexico Community College (U)
Central Texas College (U)
Chemeketa Community College (U)
Cleveland Community College (N,U)
Cogswell Polytechnical College (U)
Fox Valley Technical College (U)
Gulf Coast Community College (U)
Hillsborough Community College (U)
Honolulu Community College (U)
Houston Community College System (U)
Ivy Tech Community College–Northeast (U)
Ivy Tech Community College–Northwest (U)
Jacksonville State University (G)

James Madison University (N)
Middlesex Community College (U)
NorthWest Arkansas Community College (U)
Oklahoma State University (N,U)
Oxnard College (U)
Palomar College (U)
Pamlico Community College (U)
Passaic County Community College (U)
Pikes Peak Community College (U)
Portland Community College (U)
Red Rocks Community College (U)
San Diego Community College District (U)
Santa Rosa Junior College (U)
Schenectady County Community College (U)
Seminole Community College (U)
Sierra College (U)
Southeast Arkansas College (U)
State University of New York Empire State
   College (U)
Tyler Junior College (U)
The University of Akron (U)
University of Illinois at Urbana–Champaign
   (N)
University of Maryland University College
   (U)
University of Missouri–Columbia (N)
The University of North Carolina at Charlotte
   (N)
The University of Texas at Tyler (U)
Utah Valley State College (U)
Vincennes University (U)
West Los Angeles College (U)
Wharton County Junior College (N)
Worcester Polytechnic Institute (G)

FISHING AND FISHERIES SCIENCES AND MANAGEMENT

Colorado State University (U,G)
Oregon State University (U)
University of Arkansas at Pine Bluff (U,G)
Virginia Polytechnic Institute and State
   University (U)
West Virginia University at Parkersburg (N)

FOOD SCIENCE AND TECHNOLOGY

Brigham Young University (U)
Burlington County College (U)
Central Michigan University (G)
Central Wyoming College (N)
Community College of Denver (N)
Delaware County Community College (U)
Eastern Michigan University (U,G)
Galveston College (U)
Honolulu Community College (U)
Jamestown Community College (N)
J. Sargeant Reynolds Community College (U)
Kansas State University (N,U)
Michigan State University (U)
Middle Tennessee State University (U)
NorthWest Arkansas Community College (U)
Orange Coast College (U)
Sam Houston State University (U)
Santa Rosa Junior College (U)
Texas Tech University (U)
University of California, Davis (U)
University of Minnesota, Twin Cities Campus
   (U)
University of Missouri–Columbia (U,G)
University of North Texas (U,G)

University of Vermont (N)

FOODS, NUTRITION, AND RELATED SERVICES

Acadia University (U)
Athabasca University (N,U)
Auburn University (N,G)
Bergen Community College (U)
Blackhawk Technical College (N)
Bowling Green State University (U,G)
Cabrillo College (U)
California State University, Sacramento (U)
Central Michigan University (G)
Central New Mexico Community College (U)
Central Texas College (U)
Central Wyoming College (N)
Charter Oak State College (U)
Chemeketa Community College (U)
Cleveland State University (N)
College of the Sequoias (U)
Colorado State University (U)
Columbus State Community College (U)
Community College of Denver (N)
Danville Community College (U)
De Anza College (U)
East Carolina University (G)
Eastern Michigan University (U,G)
Eastern Washington University (U)
East Los Angeles College (U)
Elizabethtown Community and Technical
   College (U)
Framingham State College (U,G)
Galveston College (N,U)
Harrisburg Area Community College (U)
Hibbing Community College (U)
Hillsborough Community College (U)
Honolulu Community College (U)
Houston Community College System (U)
Huntington College of Health Sciences
   (N,U,G)
Illinois Eastern Community Colleges, Frontier
   Community College (U)
Immaculata University (U)
Indiana University of Pennsylvania (U,G)
Jacksonville State University (U)
James Madison University (N)
Jefferson College of Health Sciences (U)
Jefferson Community College (U)
Kansas State University (N,U)
Lake-Sumter Community College (U)
Lamar State College–Port Arthur (U)
Lock Haven University of Pennsylvania (U)
Long Beach City College (U)
Mesa Community College (U)
Middlesex Community College (U)
Nassau Community College (U)
New Mexico State University (U)
Northampton County Area Community
   College (U)
North Dakota State College of Science (U)
North Dakota State University (U)
NorthWest Arkansas Community College (U)
Oklahoma State University (U)
Orange Coast College (U)
Oregon State University (G)
Palomar College (U)
Portland Community College (U)
Rose State College (U)
Sacramento City College (U)
Sam Houston State University (U)
Santa Monica College (U)

Southeast Arkansas College (U)
Southeast Community College Area (U)
South Piedmont Community College (U)
Southwest Wisconsin Technical College (U)
Stephen F. Austin State University (U)
Texas Tech University (U)
Treasure Valley Community College (U)
The University of Akron (U)
The University of Alabama (U)
University of Arkansas at Little Rock (U)
University of Bridgeport (U,G)
The University of British Columbia (U)
University of Central Missouri (U)
University of Cincinnati Raymond Walters College (U)
University of Maine at Machias (U)
University of Minnesota, Crookston (U)
University of Minnesota, Twin Cities Campus (U)
University of Missouri–Columbia (U,G)
University of Nevada, Reno (U)
University of North Alabama (U)
The University of North Carolina at Chapel Hill (U)
University of Southern Mississippi (U)
The University of Texas at Brownsville (N)
University of Utah (U)
University of Wyoming (U)
Western Nebraska Community College (U)
West Los Angeles College (U)
West Virginia University at Parkersburg (N)
Wisconsin Indianhead Technical College (N,U)
Youngstown State University (U)
Yuba College (U)

FORENSIC PSYCHOLOGY

Charter Oak State College (U)
West Virginia University (N)

FORESTRY

Haywood Community College (U)
James Madison University (N)
Minot State University–Bottineau Campus (U)
Mississippi State University (U)
Mount Wachusett Community College (N)
North Carolina State University (U)
The Ohio State University (U)
Oregon State University (U)
Sierra College (U)
Stephen F. Austin State University (G)
The University of British Columbia (U)
University of Missouri–Columbia (N)
Virginia Polytechnic Institute and State University (N,G)

FUNERAL SERVICE AND MORTUARY SCIENCE

Arapahoe Community College (U)
St. Louis Community College System (U)
Vincennes University (U)

GENETICS

Capital Community College (U)
Charter Oak State College (U)
Eastern Michigan University (U)
Jacksonville State University (U)
Labette Community College (U)
North Carolina State University (U)

San Diego Community College District (U)
University of Arkansas at Little Rock (U)
University of Illinois at Urbana–Champaign (N,G)
University of Minnesota, Twin Cities Campus (U)

GEOGRAPHY AND CARTOGRAPHY

Allen County Community College (U)
Anne Arundel Community College (U)
Arapahoe Community College (U)
Arkansas State University–Beebe (U)
Athabasca University (U)
Auburn University (U)
Ball State University (U)
Bellevue Community College (U)
Black Hills State University (U)
Bowling Green State University (U)
Brazosport College (U)
Brenau University (U)
Bridgewater State College (U)
Brigham Young University (U)
Bristol Community College (U)
Broward Community College (U)
Cabrillo College (U)
California State University, Chico (U)
Campbell University (U)
Carl Sandburg College (U)
Central Connecticut State University (U)
Centralia College (U)
Central Texas College (U)
Central Washington University (U)
Central Wyoming College (U)
Chadron State College (U)
Chemeketa Community College (U)
Cleveland State University (U)
College of Southern Maryland (U)
Colorado Mountain College District System (U)
Colorado State University (U)
Columbus State Community College (U)
Community College of Denver (U)
Connors State College (U)
Crafton Hills College (U)
Danville Community College (U)
Delaware County Community College (U)
East Arkansas Community College (U)
Eastern Kentucky University (U)
Eastern Michigan University (U,G)
Eastern Oregon University (U)
Eastern Washington University (U)
East Tennessee State University (U)
Edison State Community College (U)
Erie Community College (U)
Erie Community College, North Campus (U)
Erie Community College, South Campus (U)
Everett Community College (U)
Florida State University (U)
Galveston College (U)
George Mason University (U)
Governors State University (U)
Grand Rapids Community College (U)
Harrisburg Area Community College (U)
Hopkinsville Community College (U)
Houston Community College System (U)
Illinois Eastern Community Colleges, Lincoln Trail College (U)
Indiana State University (U)
Jacksonville State University (U,G)
James A. Rhodes State College (U)

James Madison University (N)
Jefferson College (U)
Jefferson Community College (U)
Kansas State University (U)
Kaskaskia College (U)
Labette Community College (U)
Lakeland Community College (U)
Lake Superior College (U)
Laredo Community College (U)
Lehigh Carbon Community College (U)
Limestone College (U)
Lock Haven University of Pennsylvania (U)
Long Beach City College (U)
Los Angeles Trade-Technical College (U)
Louisiana State University and Agricultural and Mechanical College (U)
Marshall University (U)
Massasoit Community College (U)
Michigan State University (U)
Middlesex Community College (U)
Midway College (U)
Midwestern State University (U)
Moberly Area Community College (U)
Montgomery County Community College (U)
Murray State University (U)
Myers University (U)
Northampton County Area Community College (U)
North Iowa Area Community College (U)
NorthWest Arkansas Community College (U)
Northwestern Connecticut Community College (U)
Northwest Missouri State University (N,U,G)
Oklahoma State University (U)
Oregon State University (G)
Palomar College (U)
Park University (U)
Pikes Peak Community College (U)
Plymouth State University (U)
Portland Community College (U)
Pratt Community College (U)
Queen's University at Kingston (U)
Red Rocks Community College (U)
Riverside Community College District (U)
Rockland Community College (U)
Rose State College (U)
Sacramento City College (U)
Saddleback College (U)
Saint Charles Community College (U)
St. Clair County Community College (U)
Seattle Central Community College (U)
Seattle Pacific University (G)
Seminole Community College (U)
Shippensburg University of Pennsylvania (U,G)
Sierra College (U)
Southeast Arkansas College (U)
Southern Arkansas University Tech (U)
South Piedmont Community College (U)
Southwestern Community College (U)
State University of New York College at Cortland (U,G)
State University of New York College at Potsdam (U)
Tacoma Community College (U)
Taylor University (U)
The University of Akron (U)
The University of Alabama (U)
University of Alaska Fairbanks (U)
The University of Arizona (U)
University of Arkansas (U)
University of Arkansas at Little Rock (U)

The University of British Columbia (U)
University of California, Riverside (N)
University of Central Missouri (G)
University of Cincinnati (U)
University of Colorado at Colorado Springs (U)
University of Colorado Denver (U)
University of Idaho (U)
The University of Kansas (U)
University of Louisville (U)
University of Maine at Fort Kent (U)
University of Massachusetts Boston (U)
University of Minnesota, Morris (U)
University of Missouri–Columbia (U)
University of Nevada, Reno (U)
University of New Orleans (U,G)
University of North Alabama (U,G)
The University of North Carolina at Chapel Hill (U)
The University of North Carolina at Charlotte (N)
University of North Dakota (U)
University of Northern Iowa (U,G)
University of Oklahoma (U)
University of Oregon (U)
University of Saskatchewan (U)
University of Sioux Falls (U)
University of Southern Mississippi (U,G)
University of South Florida (U)
The University of Tennessee (U)
The University of Texas at San Antonio (U)
The University of Texas at Tyler (U)
University of the Virgin Islands (U)
The University of Toledo (U)
University of Washington (U)
University of Wisconsin Colleges (U)
University of Wyoming (U)
Virginia Polytechnic Institute and State University (U,G)
Weber State University (U)
Westchester Community College (U)
Western Michigan University (U)
Wichita State University (U)
Wilfrid Laurier University (U)
York University (U)

GEOLOGICAL AND EARTH SCIENCES/GEOSCIENCES

Acadia University (U)
Arapahoe Community College (U)
Arkansas State University–Beebe (U)
Athabasca University (N,U)
Bellevue Community College (U)
Bergen Community College (U)
Boise State University (U)
Bowling Green State University (U)
Bridgewater State College (U)
Brigham Young University (U)
Broward Community College (U)
Cabrillo College (U)
California State University, Sacramento (U)
Centralia College (U)
Central Oregon Community College (U)
Charter Oak State College (U)
Chemeketa Community College (U)
Clark State Community College (U)
Cleveland State University (U)
Community College of Denver (U)
Crafton Hills College (U)
Cuyahoga Community College (U)
Dallas Baptist University (U)

Eastern Michigan University (G)
Eastern Wyoming College (U)
Elgin Community College (U)
Flathead Valley Community College (U)
Fort Hays State University (U)
Framingham State College (U)
Georgia State University (U)
Harrisburg Area Community College (U)
Hillsborough Community College (U)
Honolulu Community College (U)
Jacksonville State University (U,G)
James Madison University (N)
Lake Superior College (U)
Louisiana State University and Agricultural and Mechanical College (U)
Middle Tennessee State University (U)
Mississippi State University (U)
Missouri University of Science and Technology (N)
Montgomery County Community College (U)
Mountain Empire Community College (U)
Murray State University (U)
Nassau Community College (U)
New Mexico Junior College (U)
Northampton County Area Community College (U)
Northeastern Illinois University (U)
North Seattle Community College (U)
NorthWest Arkansas Community College (U)
Oklahoma State University (U)
Oregon State University (U,G)
Oxnard College (U)
Palomar College (U)
Park University (U)
Peninsula College (U)
Pennsylvania College of Technology (U)
Rend Lake College (U)
Rose State College (U)
Sacramento City College (U)
Sam Houston State University (U)
San Diego State University (N,U)
Santa Monica College (U)
Santa Rosa Junior College (U)
Seminole Community College (U)
State University of New York at Oswego (U)
State University of New York at Plattsburgh (U)
State University of New York College at Potsdam (U)
Tacoma Community College (U)
Taft College (U)
Texas A&M University–Kingsville (U)
Treasure Valley Community College (U)
Trine University (U)
The University of Akron (U)
The University of Arizona (U,G)
University of Arkansas at Little Rock (U)
University of Cincinnati (U)
University of Colorado Denver (U)
The University of Kansas (U)
University of La Verne (N)
University of Maine at Fort Kent (U)
University of Minnesota, Twin Cities Campus (U)
University of Missouri–Columbia (U)
The University of Montana–Western (U)
University of New Orleans (U,G)
The University of North Carolina at Chapel Hill (U)
The University of North Carolina at Greensboro (U)
University of North Texas (U)

University of Oklahoma (U)
University of Oregon (U)
University of Pennsylvania (U)
University of Saskatchewan (U)
University of South Florida (U)
The University of Texas at San Antonio (U)
The University of Texas System (U)
University of Washington (U)
University of Waterloo (U)
University of Wisconsin Colleges (U)
Wake Technical Community College (U)
Weber State University (U)
West Shore Community College (U)
Wharton County Junior College (U)
Wilfrid Laurier University (U)
Youngstown State University (U)

GEOLOGICAL/GEOPHYSICAL ENGINEERING

Arapahoe Community College (U)
Hillsborough Community College (U)
Palomar College (U)
Rose State College (U)
University of Idaho (G)
University of New Orleans (U,G)

GERONTOLOGY

Acadia University (U)
Adams State College (N)
The American College (U)
Athabasca University (N)
Athens Technical College (N)
Bowling Green State University (G)
Butler Community College (U)
California State University, Dominguez Hills (N)
California State University, Sacramento (U)
Carroll Community College (N)
Coastline Community College (U)
The College of St. Scholastica (U)
College of The Albemarle (N)
Flathead Valley Community College (U)
Florida Gulf Coast University (U)
Genesee Community College (U)
Georgia State University (U)
Independence University (G)
Jacksonville State University (U)
Jefferson College of Health Sciences (U)
Kansas State University (G)
Lakeland Community College (N)
Liberty University (U)
Limestone College (U)
Massasoit Community College (N)
Middlesex Community College (N)
Minot State University–Bottineau Campus (U)
Northeastern Illinois University (G)
The Ohio State University (N)
Randolph Community College (N)
The Richard Stockton College of New Jersey (U)
Sacramento City College (U)
Sacred Heart University (G)
Saddleback College (U)
Sam Houston State University (U)
San Diego State University (U)
Saybrook Graduate School and Research Center (G)
Southeastern Oklahoma State University (U)
State University of New York at Oswego (G)
Texas Tech University (G)

University of Alaska Fairbanks (U)
The University of Arizona (G)
University of Arkansas at Little Rock (U,G)
University of Colorado at Colorado Springs (U)
University of Maryland University College (U)
University of Massachusetts Boston (G)
University of Missouri–Columbia (U,G)
University of New Orleans (U,G)
University of North Alabama (U)
University of North Texas (N,G)
University of Phoenix (G)
University of South Alabama (U,G)
University of Southern Indiana (U)
University of Vermont (U)
University of Washington (U,G)
University of Waterloo (U)
University of Wisconsin–Stout (N)
University of Wisconsin–Superior (N)
Utica College (U)
Weber State University (U)
West Hills Community College (N)
Wichita State University (U)

GEROPSYCHOLOGY

Jacksonville State University (U)

GRAPHIC COMMUNICATIONS

Academy of Art University (U,G)
Arapahoe Community College (U)
California State University, Dominguez Hills (N)
Carroll Community College (N)
Central Wyoming College (N)
Columbus State Community College (U)
Community College of Beaver County (N)
Corning Community College (U)
Cuyahoga Community College (U)
Dallas Baptist University (U)
Danville Community College (U)
De Anza College (U)
Everett Community College (U)
Macon State College (U)
Murray State University (U)
Palomar College (U)
Plymouth State University (N)
Riverside Community College District (N,U)
Rose State College (U)
Sacramento City College (U)
Santa Rosa Junior College (U)
Spoon River College (U)
Texas State Technical College Waco (N)
University of North Dakota (N)

GROUND TRANSPORTATION

Arapahoe Community College (U)
The University of Texas at Brownsville (N)

HEALTH AIDES/ATTENDANTS/ ORDERLIES

Arapahoe Community College (U)
Community College of Denver (N)
Cuyahoga Community College (U)
James Madison University (N)
Lamar State College–Port Arthur (N)
Pamlico Community College (U)
South Piedmont Community College (N)

HEALTH AND MEDICAL ADMINISTRATIVE SERVICES

Alpena Community College (U)
American Public University System (U)
Arapahoe Community College (U)
Arkansas Tech University (U)
Athabasca University (U)
Avila University (U)
Bellevue University (U,G)
Berkeley College (U)
Berkeley College–New York City Campus (U)
Berkeley College–Westchester Campus (U)
Blackhawk Technical College (U)
Blue Ridge Community College (N)
Boise State University (U,G)
Bowling Green State University (U)
Brenau University (G)
Bridgewater State College (N)
Bristol Community College (N)
Buena Vista University (U)
California State University, Chico (U)
California State University, Dominguez Hills (N)
Carroll Community College (N)
Central Michigan University (U,G)
Cincinnati State Technical and Community College (U)
Cleveland State University (G)
Coastline Community College (U)
The College of St. Scholastica (U,G)
Columbus State Community College (U)
Daemen College (U)
Dakota State University (U)
Dallas County Community College District (U)
Darton College (U)
East Georgia College (N)
Edgecombe Community College (N,U)
Elaine P. Nunez Community College (U)
Erie Community College (U)
Erie Community College, North Campus (U)
Erie Community College, South Campus (U)
Florida Gulf Coast University (U)
Franklin University (U)
Granite State College (U)
Harris-Stowe State University (U)
Iona College (U,G)
Jamestown Community College (N)
Jefferson College of Health Sciences (U)
Johnson County Community College (N)
Lake-Sumter Community College (U)
Lehigh Carbon Community College (U)
Linn-Benton Community College (U)
Loma Linda University (G)
Macon State College (U)
Medical College of Wisconsin (G)
Miami Dade College (U)
Minnesota School of Business–Richfield (U)
Minot State University–Bottineau Campus (U)
Misericordia University (U)
Montgomery County Community College (N)
Mt. Hood Community College (U)
North Dakota State College of Science (U)
Northwest Technical College (U)
Orange Coast College (U)
Oregon State University (N,U,G)
Ottawa University (U)
Pace University (G)
Pamlico Community College (U)
Park University (U)
Pasco-Hernando Community College (N)

Pulaski Technical College (U)
Quinebaug Valley Community College (N,U)
Roger Williams University (U)
Saint Joseph's College of Maine (U,G)
Seminole Community College (N)
Southeast Community College Area (U)
State University of New York at Binghamton (N)
State University of New York Institute of Technology (U,G)
Tacoma Community College (U)
Texas State University–San Marcos (U)
Three Rivers Community College (U)
The University of Akron (U)
University of Central Florida (U,G)
University of Dallas (G)
University of Idaho (U)
University of Maryland University College (G)
University of Minnesota, Crookston (U)
University of Minnesota, Twin Cities Campus (U)
University of Missouri–Columbia (G)
The University of North Carolina at Charlotte (N)
The University of North Carolina at Greensboro (N)
University of North Dakota (N)
University of North Florida (U)
University of North Texas (G)
University of St. Francis (U)
University of Southern Indiana (U)
Wayland Baptist University (U,G)
Weber State University (U,G)
West Hills Community College (N)
Youngstown State University (N)

HEALTH AND PHYSICAL EDUCATION/FITNESS

Allen County Community College (U)
American University (U)
Anne Arundel Community College (U)
Arapahoe Community College (U)
Auburn University (U)
Austin Peay State University (U,G)
Blue Ridge Community College (U)
Brigham Young University (U)
Broward Community College (U)
Butler Community College (U)
California State University, Sacramento (U)
Canisius College (G)
Carroll Community College (U)
Cayuga County Community College (U)
Central Carolina Community College (U)
Centralia College (U)
Central Michigan University (U)
Central Oregon Community College (U)
Central Texas College (U)
Central Washington University (G)
Central Wyoming College (N,U)
Chemeketa Community College (U)
Clarion University of Pennsylvania (U)
Cleveland State University (N)
College of San Mateo (U)
College of Southern Maryland (U)
College of The Albemarle (U)
College of the Siskiyous (U)
Colorado State University (N,U)
Columbus State Community College (U)
Corning Community College (U)
Crafton Hills College (U)

Dakota State University (U)
Dallas Baptist University (U)
Danville Community College (U)
Darton College (U)
East Arkansas Community College (U)
Eastern Oregon University (U)
Eastern Washington University (N,U)
Eastern Wyoming College (U)
East Los Angeles College (U)
Elizabeth City State University (U)
Erie Community College (U)
Erie Community College, North Campus (U)
Erie Community College, South Campus (U)
Finger Lakes Community College (U)
Fort Hays State University (U,G)
Fort Valley State University (U)
Gadsden State Community College (U)
Galveston College (U)
Georgia Highlands College (U)
Haywood Community College (U)
Hopkinsville Community College (U)
Illinois Eastern Community Colleges, Frontier
  Community College (U)
Indiana State University (U)
Jackson State University (U)
Jacksonville State University (U,G)
James Madison University (N,U)
Jefferson College (U)
Jefferson College of Health Sciences (U)
John Wood Community College (U)
J. Sargeant Reynolds Community College (U)
Kean University (N)
Labette Community College (U)
Lakeland Community College (N,U)
Lake Region State College (U)
Laredo Community College (U)
Lehigh Carbon Community College (U)
Linn-Benton Community College (U)
Lock Haven University of Pennsylvania (U)
Los Angeles Trade-Technical College (U)
Louisiana State University and Agricultural
  and Mechanical College (U)
Malone College (U)
Mercer County Community College (U)
Mesa State College (U)
Middle Tennessee State University (U)
Millersville University of Pennsylvania (U,G)
Minot State University–Bottineau Campus (U)
Mississippi Delta Community College (U)
Missouri State University (U,G)
Mountain Empire Community College (U)
Mount Olive College (U)
Nassau Community College (U)
Naugatuck Valley Community College (N)
New Mexico Highlands University (U,G)
Northampton County Area Community
  College (U)
North Carolina State University (U)
North Dakota State College of Science (U)
Northern State University (U)
NorthWest Arkansas Community College (U)
Northwestern State University of Louisiana
  (U)
Oklahoma State University (U)
Pacific Union College (U)
Palomar College (U)
Parkland College (U)
Pasco-Hernando Community College (U)
Patrick Henry Community College (U)
Peninsula College (U)
Pennsylvania Highlands Community College
  (U)

Piedmont Community College (U)
Portland Community College (U)
Rappahannock Community College (U)
Rend Lake College (U)
Rose State College (N,U)
Saint Charles Community College (U)
San Diego Community College District (U)
San Joaquin Delta College (U)
Sierra College (U)
Southeast Arkansas College (U)
Southeastern Oklahoma State University
  (N,U,G)
Southern Arkansas University Tech (U)
State University of New York at Binghamton
  (U)
State University of New York at Plattsburgh
  (U)
State University of New York College at
  Cortland (U,G)
Texas Woman's University (U,G)
Treasure Valley Community College (U)
Triton College (U)
United States Sports Academy (N,U,G)
University of Arkansas at Little Rock (U)
University of California, Los Angeles (G)
University of Central Missouri (U)
University of Idaho (U)
University of Louisville (U)
University of Minnesota, Duluth (U)
University of Missouri–Columbia (U)
University of Northern Iowa (U)
University of North Texas (U)
University of Oklahoma (U)
University of Sioux Falls (U)
University of Southern Mississippi (U,G)
The University of Texas at San Antonio (U)
The University of Texas at Tyler (U)
The University of Texas of the Permian Basin
  (U,G)
Utah Valley State College (U)
Valley City State University (U)
Washburn University (U)
Westchester Community College (U)
West Los Angeles College (U)
West Virginia University at Parkersburg (U)
Wytheville Community College (U)
Youngstown State University (U)

HEALTH PROFESSIONS RELATED

Arapahoe Community College (U)
Arkansas State University–Mountain Home
  (U)
Athabasca University (N,U,G)
Bellevue Community College (U)
Bowling Green State University (N)
Brenau University (U,G)
Broome Community College (U)
Butler Community College (U)
Cabrillo College (U)
Central Michigan University (U,G)
Central Texas College (U)
Central Virginia Community College (U)
Central Wyoming College (N)
Charter Oak State College (N)
Chemeketa Community College (U)
Cincinnati State Technical and Community
  College (U)
Clark State Community College (U)
Cleveland State University (N,G)
College of Southern Maryland (N)
Colorado Mountain College District System
  (U)

Columbus State Community College (U)
Daemen College (U)
Dallas Baptist University (U)
Dallas County Community College District
  (U)
Danville Community College (U)
Darton College (U)
DeVry University Online (G)
Drake University (U,G)
Drexel University (U,G)
Eastern Kentucky University (U)
Elgin Community College (U)
Ellsworth Community College (U)
Eugenio María de Hostos Community College
  of the City University of New York (U)
Everett Community College (U)
Frank Phillips College (N)
Fulton-Montgomery Community College (N)
Galveston College (U)
George Mason University (G)
Georgia College & State University (U,G)
Governors State University (N)
Hillsborough Community College (U)
Hofstra University (U)
Huntington College of Health Sciences (N,G)
Illinois Eastern Community Colleges, Lincoln
  Trail College (U)
Illinois State University (U)
Iona College (U,G)
Jacksonville State University (U,G)
James Madison University (U)
Jefferson College of Health Sciences (U)
Kaplan University Online (N)
Kean University (N)
Lakeland Community College (N)
Lake Superior College (U)
Lamar State College–Port Arthur (U)
Lehigh Carbon Community College (U)
Lock Haven University of Pennsylvania (G)
Loma Linda University (U,G)
Massasoit Community College (N)
Medical College of Wisconsin (G)
Mercy College (U)
Mesa Community College (U)
MGH Institute of Health Professions (G)
Miami Dade College (N)
Midwestern State University (U,G)
Minot State University–Bottineau Campus (U)
Mississippi State University (G)
Mitchell Technical Institute (N)
Montana Tech of The University of Montana
  (U,G)
Montcalm Community College (N)
Montgomery County Community College
  (N,U)
Naugatuck Valley Community College (U)
North Dakota State College of Science (U)
NorthWest Arkansas Community College (U)
Okaloosa-Walton College (U)
Oregon State University (G)
Pasco-Hernando Community College (N)
Passaic County Community College (U)
Peninsula College (U)
Pennsylvania College of Technology (U)
Pine Technical College (N,U)
Pittsburgh Technical Institute (U)
Plymouth State University (N)
Portland Community College (N,U)
The Richard Stockton College of New Jersey
  (U)
Riverside Community College District (N)
Rockland Community College (U)

Rose State College (U)
Sacramento City College (U)
Sacred Heart University (U,G)
Sam Houston State University (U)
San Diego Community College District (U)
Santa Rosa Junior College (U)
Sarasota County Technical Institute (N)
Seminole Community College (U)
Shawnee State University (U)
Sinclair Community College (N)
Southeast Arkansas College (U)
Southeast Community College Area (U)
Southeastern Illinois College (U)
South Piedmont Community College (U)
Spoon River College (U)
State University of New York at Binghamton (N)
State University of New York at Plattsburgh (U)
State University of New York Institute of Technology (U,G)
Sullivan County Community College (N)
Tacoma Community College (U)
Temple University (G)
Texas State University–San Marcos (U)
Union University (G)
The University of Akron (U,G)
The University of Alabama (U,G)
University of Alaska Fairbanks (U)
University of Arkansas at Little Rock (U)
University of California, Davis (U)
University of Cincinnati Raymond Walters College (U)
University of Colorado at Colorado Springs (U,G)
University of Connecticut (N,U,G)
University of Illinois at Chicago (N,G)
University of Illinois at Urbana–Champaign (G)
The University of Maine at Augusta (U)
University of Maine at Fort Kent (U)
University of Medicine and Dentistry of New Jersey (U,G)
University of Minnesota, Twin Cities Campus (U)
University of Missouri–Columbia (N,U)
University of New Orleans (U,G)
The University of North Carolina at Greensboro (U)
University of North Dakota (N)
University of St. Augustine for Health Sciences (N)
University of St. Francis (U)
University of St. Thomas (G)
University of Sioux Falls (U)
University of Southern Indiana (N,G)
University of Southern Maine (U)
University of Southern Mississippi (U)
The University of Texas at Tyler (U,G)
The University of Texas System (U,G)
University of the Sciences in Philadelphia (G)
The University of Toledo (U)
University of Wisconsin–La Crosse (U)
University of Wisconsin–Stout (G)
University of Wyoming (U)
Upper Iowa University (U)
West Hills Community College (N)
West Virginia State University (U)
West Virginia University (N)
West Virginia University at Parkersburg (U)
Wheeling Jesuit University (U)
Worcester State College (U,G)

Wytheville Community College (U)
York University (U)
Youngstown State University (U,G)

HEALTH PSYCHOLOGY

Acadia University (U)
Arapahoe Community College (U)
Barton County Community College (U)
Independence University (G)
Jacksonville State University (G)
Saybrook Graduate School and Research Center (G)
State University of New York College at Cortland (U)
University of Alaska Fairbanks (U,G)
University of Arkansas at Little Rock (U)
University of Maine at Machias (U)
University of Wisconsin–Superior (G)

HEALTH SERVICES/ALLIED HEALTH/HEALTH SCIENCES

Anne Arundel Community College (N)
Arapahoe Community College (U)
Ball State University (U)
Belmont Technical College (U)
California State University, San Marcos (N)
Cape Fear Community College (U)
Capital Community College (U)
Carl Sandburg College (U)
Central Michigan University (U)
Central Oregon Community College (U)
Central Wyoming College (N)
Charter Oak State College (U)
Cleveland State University (G)
Cuyahoga Community College (U)
Darton College (U)
Diné College (U)
Drake University (G)
Drexel University (U)
East Arkansas Community College (U)
Florida Gulf Coast University (U)
Gadsden State Community College (U)
Galveston College (U)
Heritage College (N,U)
Iona College (U,G)
Jefferson Community College (U)
Kaplan University Online (N)
Macon State College (U)
Mercy College (U,G)
Minot State University (U)
Minot State University–Bottineau Campus (U)
Mitchell Technical Institute (U)
Monmouth University (U)
Northeastern University (U)
Northern Virginia Community College (U)
NorthWest Arkansas Community College (U)
Okaloosa-Walton College (U)
Oregon State University (U)
Pamlico Community College (U)
Pasco-Hernando Community College (N)
Rend Lake College (U)
Roger Williams University (U)
Roger State College (U)
Sacramento City College (U)
Santa Monica College (U)
Shawnee State University (U)
South Piedmont Community College (U)
State University of New York at Binghamton (U,G)
State University of New York at Oswego (U)

State University of New York College at Cortland (U)
Strayer University (G)
Tacoma Community College (U)
Texas Woman's University (U,G)
Tyler Junior College (U)
The University of Akron (U)
University of Arkansas at Little Rock (U)
University of Connecticut (U)
University of Illinois at Chicago (G)
University of Minnesota, Twin Cities Campus (U)
University of Missouri–Columbia (N)
University of North Florida (U,G)
University of South Florida (G)
The University of Texas at San Antonio (U)
University of the Sciences in Philadelphia (G)
University of West Florida (G)
Upper Iowa University (U)
West Hills Community College (N)
West Los Angeles College (U)
West Virginia University (N)

HEALTH/MEDICAL PREPARATORY PROGRAMS

Arapahoe Community College (U)
Athabasca University (U,G)
Athens Technical College (U)
Beaufort County Community College (U)
Brenau University (U)
Caldwell Community College and Technical Institute (N)
California State University, San Marcos (N)
Cleveland State University (G)
Community College of Denver (U)
Daemen College (U)
Darton College (U)
Edgecombe Community College (U)
Excelsior College (U,G)
Gateway Community College (U)
Gulf Coast Community College (U)
Hibbing Community College (U)
Hocking College (U)
James A. Rhodes State College (U)
James Madison University (N)
Jefferson College of Health Sciences (U)
Johnson County Community College (N)
Labette Community College (U)
Lake-Sumter Community College (U)
Lake Superior College (U)
Lock Haven University of Pennsylvania (U)
Long Beach City College (U)
Medical College of Wisconsin (G)
Mesa Community College (U)
Naugatuck Valley Community College (N)
Okaloosa-Walton College (U)
Pace University (G)
Rockland Community College (U)
Rose State College (U)
Saddleback College (U)
Southwest Wisconsin Technical College (U)
The University of Akron (U)
University of Minnesota, Twin Cities Campus (U)
University of Missouri–Columbia (N)
West Los Angeles College (U)

HEATING, AIR CONDITIONING, VENTILATION AND REFRIGERATION MAINTENANCE TECHNOLOGY

Blackhawk Technical College (U)
Flathead Valley Community College (U)
Lakeland Community College (N)
Los Angeles Trade-Technical College (U)
Mitchell Technical Institute (N)
Oxnard College (U)
Sacramento City College (U)
South Piedmont Community College (U)
University of North Dakota (N)
Wake Technical Community College (U)

HEAVY/INDUSTRIAL EQUIPMENT MAINTENANCE TECHNOLOGIES

Wake Technical Community College (U)

HISTORIC PRESERVATION AND CONSERVATION

Lakeland Community College (N)

HISTORY

Acadia University (U)
Adams State College (U)
Allen County Community College (U)
American Public University System (U,G)
Andover Newton Theological School (G)
Anne Arundel Community College (N,U)
Arapahoe Community College (U)
Arkansas State University–Beebe (U)
Arkansas State University–Mountain Home (U)
Arkansas Tech University (U)
Assemblies of God Theological Seminary (G)
Athabasca University (N,U,G)
Azusa Pacific University (U)
Baltimore Hebrew University (G)
Barton County Community College (U)
Bellevue Community College (U)
Bergen Community College (U)
Berkeley College (U)
Berkeley College–New York City Campus (U)
Berkeley College–Westchester Campus (U)
Bloomfield College (U)
Blue Ridge Community College (U)
Boise State University (U)
Bowling Green State University (U)
Brazosport College (U)
Brenau University (U)
Bridgewater State College (U)
Brigham Young University (N,U)
Bristol Community College (U)
Broome Community College (U)
Broward Community College (U)
Buena Vista University (U)
Buffalo State College, State University of New York (U)
Burlington College (U)
Burlington County College (U)
Butler Community College (U)
Cabrillo College (U)
Caldwell Community College and Technical Institute (U)
California State University, Chico (U)
California State University, Dominguez Hills (N)

California State University, Sacramento (U)
Campbell University (U)
Cape Cod Community College (U)
Capital Community College (U)
Carroll Community College (U)
Carroll University (U)
Cayuga County Community College (U)
Central Arizona College (U)
Central Carolina Community College (U)
Centralia College (U)
Central Oregon Community College (U)
Central Texas College (U)
Central Virginia Community College (U)
Central Washington University (U)
Central Wyoming College (N)
Cerritos College (U)
Chadron State College (U,G)
Chaminade University of Honolulu (U)
Chatham University (U)
Chemeketa Community College (U)
Cincinnati Christian University (U,G)
Cincinnati State Technical and Community College (U)
Citrus College (U)
Clark State Community College (U)
Clatsop Community College (U)
Clemson University (G)
Cleveland Community College (U)
Cleveland State Community College (U)
Cleveland State University (U)
Clinton Community College (U)
Coastline Community College (U)
College of Southern Maryland (U)
College of The Albemarle (U)
College of the Sequoias (U)
College of the Siskiyous (U)
Colorado Mountain College District System (U)
Columbia College (U)
Columbia International University (G)
Columbus State Community College (U)
Community College of Beaver County (U)
Community College of Denver (U)
Concordia University Wisconsin (U)
Corban College (U)
Corning Community College (U)
Crafton Hills College (U)
Cumberland County College (U)
Cuyahoga Community College (U)
Dallas Baptist University (U)
Dallas Christian College (U)
Dallas County Community College District (U)
Danville Community College (U)
Darton College (U)
Daytona State College (U)
De Anza College (U)
Delaware County Community College (U)
Denver Seminary (G)
DeSales University (U)
Drake University (U,G)
East Arkansas Community College (U)
East Central Community College (U)
Eastern Kentucky University (U)
Eastern Michigan University (U)
Eastern Washington University (U)
Eastern West Virginia Community and Technical College (U)
East Los Angeles College (U)
East Tennessee State University (U)
Edgecombe Community College (U)
Edison State Community College (U)

Elaine P. Nunez Community College (U)
Elizabeth City State University (U)
Elizabethtown College (U)
Elizabethtown Community and Technical College (U)
Erie Community College (U)
Erie Community College, North Campus (U)
Erie Community College, South Campus (U)
Eugene Bible College (U)
Everett Community College (U)
Evergreen Valley College (U)
Excelsior College (U)
Finger Lakes Community College (U)
Florida Gulf Coast University (U)
Foothill College (U)
Fort Hays State University (U)
Fort Valley State University (U)
Framingham State College (U)
Frank Phillips College (U)
Gadsden State Community College (U)
Galveston College (U)
Genesee Community College (U)
George C. Wallace Community College (U)
Georgia Highlands College (U)
Georgia State University (U)
Glenville State College (U)
Golden West College (U)
Graceland University (U)
Grand Rapids Community College (U)
Grand View College (U)
Granite State College (U)
Grantham University (U)
Greenfield Community College (U)
Greenville Technical College (U)
Gulf Coast Community College (U)
Hamline University (U)
Harrisburg Area Community College (U)
Haywood Community College (U)
Henderson Community College (U)
Henry Ford Community College (U)
Hibbing Community College (U)
Hofstra University (U)
Holyoke Community College (U)
Honolulu Community College (U)
Hope International University (N,U)
Hopkinsville Community College (U)
Houston Community College System (U)
Illinois Eastern Community Colleges, Wabash Valley College (U)
Illinois State University (U)
Immaculata University (U)
Indiana State University (U)
Indiana University–Purdue University Fort Wayne (U)
Indiana Wesleyan University (U)
Ivy Tech Community College–Kokomo (U)
Ivy Tech Community College–Northwest (U)
Jackson State University (U)
Jacksonville State University (U)
James Madison University (N,U)
Jefferson College (U)
Jefferson Community College (U)
John A. Logan College (U)
Johnson County Community College (U)
Johnson State College (U)
John Wood Community College (U)
J. Sargeant Reynolds Community College (U)
Judson College (U)
Judson University (U)
Kansas State University (U)
Kaskaskia College (U)
Kean University (U)

Labette Community College (U)
Lackawanna College (U)
Lakeland Community College (N,U)
Lake Region State College (U)
Lake Superior College (U)
Laredo Community College (U)
Lehigh Carbon Community College (U)
Lewis-Clark State College (U)
Liberty University (U)
Limestone College (U)
Linn-Benton Community College (U)
Lock Haven University of Pennsylvania (U)
Long Beach City College (U)
Los Angeles Trade-Technical College (U)
Louisiana State University and Agricultural
  and Mechanical College (U)
Lurleen B. Wallace Community College (U)
Macon State College (U)
Malone College (U)
Manatee Community College (U)
Mansfield University of Pennsylvania (U)
Marian College of Fond du Lac (U)
Marshall University (U)
Massasoit Community College (U)
McMurry University (U)
Mercer County Community College (U)
Mercy College (U)
Mesa Community College (U)
Mesa State College (U)
Metropolitan State University (U)
Middlesex Community College (U)
Minot State University (U)
Misericordia University (U)
Mississippi Delta Community College (U)
Missouri State University (U,G)
Moberly Area Community College (U)
Montgomery County Community College (U)
Mountain Empire Community College (U)
Mount Olive College (U)
Mount Wachusett Community College (U)
Murray State College (U)
Murray State University (U)
Myers University (U)
Nassau Community College (U)
National University (U)
New Mexico Junior College (U)
New River Community College (U)
Northampton County Area Community
  College (U)
North Arkansas College (U)
North Carolina State University (U)
North Central Texas College (U)
North Dakota State College of Science (U)
Northeast Iowa Community College (U)
Northeast State Technical Community College
  (U)
Northern Virginia Community College (U)
North Iowa Area Community College (U)
North Lake College (U)
NorthWest Arkansas Community College (U)
Northwestern Connecticut Community College
  (U)
Northwestern Michigan College (U)
Northwestern Oklahoma State University (U)
Northwestern State University of Louisiana
  (U)
Northwest Missouri State University (U)
Okaloosa-Walton College (U)
Oklahoma Panhandle State University (U)
Oklahoma State University (U)
Oregon State University (U)
Ouachita Technical College (U)

Oxnard College (U)
Pace University (U)
Palomar College (U)
Pamlico Community College (U)
Parkland College (U)
Park University (U)
Pasco-Hernando Community College (U)
Passaic County Community College (U)
Patrick Henry College (U)
Patrick Henry Community College (U)
Peirce College (U)
Pellissippi State Technical Community
  College (U)
Peninsula College (U)
Pennsylvania College of Technology (U)
Piedmont Community College (U)
Piedmont Technical College (U)
Pikes Peak Community College (U)
Portland Community College (U)
Prairie View A&M University (U)
Pratt Community College (U)
Prescott College (U,G)
Pulaski Technical College (U)
Queen's University at Kingston (U)
Quinebaug Valley Community College (U)
Randolph Community College (U)
Rappahannock Community College (U)
Red Rocks Community College (U)
Regent University (U)
Regis University (U)
Rend Lake College (U)
Richland Community College (U)
Riverside Community College District (U)
Rockland Community College (U)
Roger Williams University (U)
Rose State College (U)
Sacramento City College (U)
Sacred Heart University (U)
Saddleback College (U)
Saint Charles Community College (U)
St. Clair County Community College (U)
St. Cloud State University (U)
St. Edward's University (U)
Saint Francis University (U)
St. John's University (U)
St. Joseph's College, Long Island Campus (U)
St. Joseph's College, New York (U)
St. Louis Community College System (U)
Saint Mary-of-the-Woods College (U)
Sam Houston State University (U)
San Diego Community College District (U)
San Diego State University (N,U)
San Joaquin Delta College (U)
Santa Monica College (U)
Schenectady County Community College (U)
Schiller International University (U)
Seattle Pacific University (G)
Seminole Community College (U)
Shippensburg University of Pennsylvania
  (U,G)
Sierra College (U)
Sinclair Community College (U)
Southeast Arkansas College (U)
Southeast Community College Area (U)
Southeastern Community College (U)
Southeastern Illinois College (U)
Southeastern Oklahoma State University (U)
Southern Arkansas University Tech (U)
Southern Union State Community College (U)
South Piedmont Community College (U)
Southwestern Adventist University (U)
Southwest Virginia Community College (U)

Spring Arbor University (U)
State University of New York at Oswego (U)
State University of New York at Plattsburgh
  (U)
State University of New York Empire State
  College (U)
Strayer University (U)
Syracuse University (G)
Tacoma Community College (U)
Taft College (U)
Taylor University (U)
Texas A&M University–Commerce (U)
Texas A&M University–Kingsville (U)
Texas Christian University (U)
Texas State University–San Marcos (U)
Texas Tech University (U)
Texas Woman's University (U)
Three Rivers Community College (U)
Tri-County Community College (U)
Trine University (U)
Triton College (U)
Tunxis Community College (U)
Tyler Junior College (U)
Unification Theological Seminary (N,G)
Union County College (U)
The University of Akron (U,G)
The University of Alabama (U)
University of Alaska Fairbanks (U)
The University of Arizona (U)
University of Arkansas (U)
University of Arkansas at Little Rock (U,G)
University of Bridgeport (U)
The University of British Columbia (U)
University of Cincinnati (U)
University of Colorado at Colorado Springs
  (U)
University of Colorado Denver (U,G)
The University of Findlay (U)
University of Hawaii–West Oahu (U)
University of Houston–Victoria (U)
University of Idaho (U)
University of Illinois at Springfield (U)
University of Illinois at Urbana–Champaign
  (U)
The University of Kansas (U,G)
University of La Verne (N)
The University of Maine at Augusta (U)
University of Maine at Fort Kent (U)
University of Management and Technology
  (U)
University of Massachusetts Boston (U,G)
University of Minnesota, Duluth (U)
University of Minnesota, Morris (U)
University of Missouri–Columbia (U)
The University of Montana–Western (U)
University of Nevada, Reno (U)
University of New Orleans (U,G)
University of North Alabama (U)
The University of North Carolina at Chapel
  Hill (N,U)
The University of North Carolina at Charlotte
  (U)
The University of North Carolina at
  Greensboro (U)
The University of North Carolina Wilmington
  (U)
University of North Dakota (U)
University of North Texas (U)
University of Oklahoma (U)
University of Oregon (G)
University of St. Francis (U)
University of Saskatchewan (U)

University of Sioux Falls (U)
The University of South Dakota (U)
University of Southern Indiana (U)
University of South Florida (U)
The University of Tennessee (U)
The University of Texas at Tyler (U)
The University of Texas of the Permian Basin (U)
The University of Texas System (U)
University of the Southwest (U)
The University of Toledo (U)
University of Utah (U)
University of Washington (U)
University of Waterloo (U)
University of West Florida (U)
University of Wisconsin Colleges (U)
University of Wisconsin–Superior (U)
University of Wisconsin–Whitewater (U,G)
University of Wyoming (U)
Upper Iowa University (N,U)
Utah State University (U)
Utah Valley State College (U)
Vermont Technical College (U)
Vincennes University (U)
Virginia Polytechnic Institute and State University (N,U)
Wake Technical Community College (U)
Washburn University (U)
Washington State University (U)
Wayland Baptist University (U)
Weber State University (U)
Westchester Community College (U)
Western Michigan University (U,G)
Western Washington University (U)
Western Wyoming Community College (U)
Westfield State College (U,G)
West Los Angeles College (U)
West Shore Community College (U)
West Virginia University at Parkersburg (U)
Wharton County Junior College (U)
Wichita State University (U)
Wilfrid Laurier University (U)
Williston State College (U)
Worcester State College (U,G)
Wytheville Community College (U)
York Technical College (U)
York University (U)
Youngstown State University (U)

HOLOCAUST AND RELATED STUDIES

Cleveland Community College (U)

HOSPITALITY ADMINISTRATION

Anne Arundel Community College (U)
Arapahoe Community College (U)
Arkansas Tech University (U)
Athens Technical College (U)
Baltimore City Community College (U)
Black Hills State University (G)
Bowling Green State University (U)
Burlington County College (U)
Centennial College (G)
Central Michigan University (G)
Central Texas College (U)
Chemeketa Community College (U)
Colorado Mountain College District System (U)
Columbus State Community College (U)
Corning Community College (U)

Cuyahoga Community College (U)
East Carolina University (U)
Eastern Michigan University (U)
Erie Community College (U)
Erie Community College, North Campus (U)
Erie Community College, South Campus (U)
Galveston College (N,U)
Genesee Community College (U)
Hocking College (U)
Holyoke Community College (U)
Indiana University of Pennsylvania (U)
Ivy Tech Community College–Northwest (U)
John A. Logan College (U)
Lakeland Community College (N)
Metropolitan State University (U)
Middlesex Community College (U)
Mt. San Antonio College (U)
Naugatuck Valley Community College (U)
North Dakota State University (U)
NorthWest Arkansas Community College (U)
Orange Coast College (U)
Riverside Community College District (U)
Rochester Institute of Technology (G)
Roosevelt University (U,G)
Schenectady County Community College (U)
Schiller International University (U,G)
Southwest Wisconsin Technical College (U)
Spring Arbor University (U)
State University of New York College of Agriculture and Technology at Morrisville (U)
Stephen F. Austin State University (U)
Tompkins Cortland Community College (U)
The University of Akron (U)
The University of Alabama (U)
University of Nevada, Reno (U)
University of New Orleans (U,G)
The University of North Carolina at Chapel Hill (U)
The University of North Carolina at Charlotte (N)
University of North Texas (U,G)
Utah Valley State College (U)
Virginia Polytechnic Institute and State University (U)
York County Community College (U)

HOUSING AND HUMAN ENVIRONMENTS

Chadron State College (U)
Fontbonne University (U)
Henry Ford Community College (U)
Saybrook Graduate School and Research Center (G)

HUMAN DEVELOPMENT, FAMILY STUDIES, AND RELATED SERVICES

Abilene Christian University (G)
American Public University System (U)
Arapahoe Community College (U)
Athabasca University (N,U,G)
Beulah Heights University (U)
Blackhawk Technical College (N)
Blue Ridge Community College (U)
Bowling Green State University (U)
Brenau University (U)
Brigham Young University (N)
Burlington College (U)
Butler Community College (U)

Caldwell Community College and Technical Institute (U)
California State University, Chico (U)
California State University, Sacramento (U)
Capital Community College (U)
Central Arizona College (U)
Centralia College (U)
Central Michigan University (U)
Cerro Coso Community College (U)
Chadron State College (U)
Chemeketa Community College (U)
Clackamas Community College (U)
Cleveland Community College (U)
Cleveland State University (N)
Clinton Community College (U)
College of Southern Maryland (U)
College of The Albemarle (U)
College of the Sequoias (U)
Community College of Denver (U)
Concordia University, St. Paul (U,G)
Corban College (U)
Crafton Hills College (U)
Dallas County Community College District (U)
Danville Community College (U)
De Anza College (U)
Delaware County Community College (U)
East Carolina University (U)
Eastern Illinois University (U,G)
Edgecombe Community College (U)
Edison State Community College (U)
Elizabeth City State University (U)
Endicott College (U)
Erikson Institute (N)
Everett Community College (U)
Granite State College (U)
Haywood Community College (U)
Hillsborough Community College (U)
Hope International University (U)
Houston Community College System (U)
Immaculata University (G)
Jacksonville State University (U,G)
J. Sargeant Reynolds Community College (U)
Kansas State University (U)
Lakeland Community College (N)
Lehigh Carbon Community College (U)
Lewis-Clark State College (U)
Linn-Benton Community College (U)
Long Beach City College (U)
Los Angeles Trade-Technical College (U)
Malone College (U)
Massasoit Community College (U)
Mayville State University (U)
Miami Dade College (U)
Mississippi State University (U)
Missouri State University (U)
Moberly Area Community College (U)
Mountain Empire Community College (U)
Mount Wachusett Community College (U)
Murray State University (U)
Naropa University (N)
Naugatuck Valley Community College (U)
Northampton County Area Community College (U)
North Dakota State University (N,U,G)
North Florida Community College (U)
North Iowa Area Community College (N)
North Lake College (U)
North Seattle Community College (U)
Orange Coast College (U)
Oregon Institute of Technology (U)
Oxnard College (U)

Pacific Oaks College (U,G)
Palomar College (U)
Peninsula College (U)
Piedmont Community College (U)
Portland Community College (U)
Prescott College (U,G)
Randolph Community College (U)
Reading Area Community College (U)
Saddleback College (U)
San Joaquin Delta College (U)
Santa Rosa Junior College (U)
Saybrook Graduate School and Research
  Center (G)
Schenectady County Community College (U)
Seminole Community College (U)
South Piedmont Community College (U)
Spoon River College (U)
State University of New York Empire State
  College (U)
Tacoma Community College (U)
Taft College (U)
Taylor University (N)
The University of Alabama (U)
University of Alaska Fairbanks (U,G)
University of Bridgeport (N,U)
University of Idaho (U)
University of Illinois at Urbana–Champaign
  (U)
The University of Kansas (U)
The University of Maine at Augusta (U)
University of Missouri–Columbia (U)
The University of North Carolina at
  Greensboro (U)
University of North Texas (U,G)
University of Southern Mississippi (U,G)
The University of Tennessee at Martin (N)
The University of Texas of the Permian Basin
  (U)
University of Waterloo (U)
University of Wisconsin–Stout (N)
Utah State University (G)
Vanguard University of Southern California
  (U)
Weber State University (U)
Westchester Community College (U)
Western Washington University (U)
Wisconsin Indianhead Technical College
  (N,U)
York County Community College (U)
York University (U)

HUMAN RESOURCES MANAGEMENT

Adams State College (U)
AIB College of Business (U)
The American College (U,G)
American Public University System (U)
Athabasca University (N,U,G)
Bellevue University (U)
Berkeley College (U)
Berkeley College–New York City Campus (U)
Berkeley College–Westchester Campus (U)
Black Hills State University (U)
Boise State University (U,G)
Bowling Green State University (U)
Brenau University (U)
Butler Community College (U)
California National University for Advanced
  Studies (U,G)
California State University, Dominguez Hills
  (N)

Capella University (G)
Capital Community College (U)
Centennial College (U)
Central Michigan University (U,G)
Central Texas College (U)
Central Washington University (U)
Chadron State College (U,G)
Clemson University (G)
College of Southern Maryland (U)
Colorado State University (N,G)
Columbus State Community College (U)
Dakota State University (U)
Dallas Baptist University (U,G)
Dallas County Community College District
  (U)
Delaware County Community College (U)
DePaul University (N)
DeSales University (U)
DeVry University Online (G)
Drake University (U,G)
Eastern Michigan University (N,U,G)
Eastern Washington University (N,U)
Edison State Community College (N,U)
Elizabeth City State University (U)
Elizabethtown College (U)
Erie Community College (U)
Erie Community College, North Campus (U)
Erie Community College, South Campus (U)
Florida Institute of Technology (G)
Florida State University (U)
Franklin University (U)
Granite State College (U)
Grantham University (U)
Herkimer County Community College (U)
Holyoke Community College (U)
Hopkinsville Community College (N)
Houston Community College System (U)
Illinois Eastern Community Colleges, Wabash
  Valley College (U)
Immaculata University (U)
Indiana State University (U,G)
Iona College (G)
Jacksonville State University (G)
James Madison University (N,U)
Jamestown Community College (N)
Jefferson College of Health Sciences (U)
Jefferson Community College (U)
Jones International University (U)
Kansas State University (G)
Labette Community College (U)
Lamar State College–Port Arthur (N)
Lawrence Technological University (U,G)
Lehigh Carbon Community College (U)
Limestone College (U)
Louisiana State University and Agricultural
  and Mechanical College (G)
Massasoit Community College (N)
Metropolitan State University (U)
Middlesex Community College (U)
Middle Tennessee State University (N,U)
Minot State University (U)
Misericordia University (U)
Montgomery Community College (U)
Mount Wachusett Community College (U)
Myers University (U)
National University (G)
Neumann College (U)
Nipissing University (U)
North Arkansas College (U)
Northcentral University (G)
Northeastern University (U)
Northeast Iowa Community College (U)

North Iowa Area Community College (U)
Northwood University, Texas Campus (U)
Nova Southeastern University (G)
Oregon State University (N)
Ouachita Technical College (U)
Park University (U)
Pellissippi State Technical Community
  College (U)
Pennsylvania Highlands Community College
  (U)
Plymouth State University (U)
Providence College and Theological Seminary
  (N)
Regent University (N)
Rend Lake College (N)
Riverside Community College District (U)
Saint Charles Community College (N)
St. Edward's University (U,G)
St. Joseph's College, Long Island Campus (G)
St. Joseph's College, New York (G)
Saint Leo University (U)
Saint Mary-of-the-Woods College (U)
Schiller International University (U,G)
Simpson College (U)
Southern New Hampshire University (U,G)
Southwest Wisconsin Technical College (U)
Spring Arbor University (U)
State University of New York Institute of
  Technology (U,G)
Taylor University (N)
The University of Akron (N,U,G)
University of Alaska Fairbanks (U)
University of Arkansas at Little Rock (U,G)
University of Connecticut (G)
The University of Findlay (U,G)
University of Hawaii–West Oahu (U)
University of Illinois at Urbana–Champaign
  (G)
University of Louisville (N)
The University of Maine at Augusta (U)
University of Management and Technology
  (U)
University of Maryland University College
  (U,G)
University of Michigan–Flint (G)
University of Minnesota, Twin Cities Campus
  (U)
University of Missouri–Columbia (N,U)
University of New Orleans (U,G)
The University of North Carolina at Charlotte
  (N)
University of North Dakota (N)
University of North Texas (G)
University of Phoenix (U,G)
University of Southern Indiana (N)
The University of Texas at Tyler (U,G)
The University of Toledo (U)
University of Toronto (N)
University of Virginia (N)
University of West Florida (N)
University of Wisconsin–Stout (N,U,G)
Upper Iowa University (U)
Utah State University (U,G)
Virginia Polytechnic Institute and State
  University (U)
Washburn University (N)
Wayland Baptist University (G)
Western Michigan University (G)
West Virginia University at Parkersburg (U)
Wilmington University (U)
Worcester State College (N)
York University (U)

HUMAN SERVICES

Amridge University (N,U,G)
Athabasca University (N,U,G)
Beaufort County Community College (U)
Bellevue University (U)
Buena Vista University (U)
Burlington College (U)
Cape Fear Community College (U)
Capella University (G)
Capital Community College (U)
Central Michigan University (U)
Chadron State College (U)
Chatham University (U)
Clinton Community College (U)
Coastline Community College (U)
College of The Albemarle (N)
Colorado State University (G)
Corning Community College (U)
Cuyahoga Community College (U)
Dawson Community College (U)
Delaware Technical & Community College,
  Jack F. Owens Campus (U)
Elgin Community College (U)
Flathead Valley Community College (U)
Florida Gulf Coast University (U)
Greenville Technical College (U)
Herkimer County Community College (U)
Holyoke Community College (U)
Houston Community College System (U)
Indiana State University (U)
James A. Rhodes State College (U)
James Madison University (N)
Jamestown Community College (N)
Lackawanna College (U)
Limestone College (U)
Mercy College (U,G)
Metropolitan State University (U)
Middlesex Community College (U)
Misericordia University (U)
Mount Wachusett Community College (U)
Murray State University (G)
New Mexico State University (U)
Oxnard College (U)
Piedmont Community College (U)
Prescott College (U,G)
Quinebaug Valley Community College (U)
Randolph Community College (N,U)
St. Edward's University (G)
Saint Joseph's College of Maine (U)
Saint Mary-of-the-Woods College (U)
Sinclair Community College (U)
Southeast Community College Area (U)
South Piedmont Community College (U)
Tacoma Community College (U)
Tompkins Cortland Community College (U)
The University of Akron (G)
University of Bridgeport (U)
University of Connecticut (G)
University of Illinois at Springfield (G)
The University of Maine at Augusta (U)
University of Massachusetts Boston (N)
University of Wisconsin–Superior (U)
Upper Iowa University (U)
Wake Technical Community College (U)
Washburn University (U)
Western Washington University (U)
Worcester State College (N)

INDUSTRIAL AND ORGANIZATIONAL PSYCHOLOGY

AIB College of Business (U)
Athabasca University (N,U,G)
Berkeley College (U)
Berkeley College–New York City Campus (U)
Berkeley College–Westchester Campus (U)
Capella University (G)
Central Michigan University (U)
Chadron State College (U,G)
DeSales University (U)
Graceland University (U)
Indiana State University (G)
Kansas State University (G)
Lehigh Carbon Community College (U)
Middle Tennessee State University (N)
Northcentral University (G)
Old Dominion University (U)
Saint Joseph's College of Maine (U)
Saybrook Graduate School and Research
  Center (N,G)
Schiller International University (G)
Temple University (U)
Texas State University–San Marcos (U)
Tunxis Community College (U)
University of Arkansas (U)
University of Colorado Denver (U)
University of North Dakota (U)
University of North Texas (G)
University of the Southwest (U)
Upper Iowa University (N,U)

INDUSTRIAL ENGINEERING

Cleveland State University (G)
Kettering University (N)
New Mexico State University (G)
Southern Methodist University (G)
State University of New York at Binghamton
  (G)
Texas A&M University–Commerce (U,G)
The University of Alabama in Huntsville (G)
The University of Arizona (G)
University of Florida (N,G)
University of South Florida (G)
Western Michigan University (U)

INDUSTRIAL PRODUCTION TECHNOLOGIES

East Carolina University (U,G)
Eastern Illinois University (U)
Edison State Community College (U)
Elaine P. Nunez Community College (U)
Endicott College (U)
Missouri State University (U,G)
Roger Williams University (U)
Southwestern College (U)
University of Minnesota, Crookston (U)
The University of Texas at Tyler (U)
Wayne State College (U,G)

INFORMATION SCIENCE/STUDIES

Arapahoe Community College (U)
Athabasca University (G)
Belmont Technical College (U)
Bowling Green State University (U)
Brenau University (U)
Bridgewater State College (N)
Brigham Young University (U)

Bristol Community College (U)
Carlow University (U)
Central New Mexico Community College (U)
Central Virginia Community College (U)
Chadron State College (U)
Chemeketa Community College (U)
Cincinnati State Technical and Community
  College (U)
Coastline Community College (U)
College of Southern Maryland (U)
College of The Albemarle (N)
Colorado State University (N)
Cuyahoga Community College (U)
Dakota State University (U,G)
Dallas Baptist University (G)
Delaware County Community College (U)
DePaul University (U,G)
Drake University (U,G)
Drexel University (G)
East Carolina University (U)
Eugenio María de Hostos Community College
  of the City University of New York (U)
Florida Gulf Coast University (U)
Florida Institute of Technology (G)
Florida State University (G)
Fort Hays State University (U)
Franklin University (U)
Galveston College (U)
Georgia State University (G)
Golden Gate University (U,G)
Graceland University (U)
Grantham University (U)
Harrisburg Area Community College (U)
Haywood Community College (U)
Hibbing Community College (U)
Indiana University of Pennsylvania (U)
Iona College (U)
Jacksonville State University (U,G)
James Madison University (N)
J. Sargeant Reynolds Community College (U)
Kansas State University (U)
Lamar State College–Port Arthur (N)
Lawrence Technological University (G)
Limestone College (U)
Louisiana State University and Agricultural
  and Mechanical College (U)
Marist College (G)
Marymount University (G)
McDowell Technical Community College (U)
Metropolitan State University (U)
Minot State University (U)
Missouri State University (N)
Myers University (U)
National University (U)
New Jersey Institute of Technology (U,G)
North Carolina State University (G)
Pace University (U,G)
Palomar College (U)
Peninsula College (U)
Prairie View A&M University (U)
Regis University (U)
The Richard Stockton College of New Jersey
  (G)
Rose State College (U)
Saint Francis University (U)
San Diego Community College District (U)
San Francisco State University (N)
Santa Rosa Junior College (U)
Schiller International University (U)
Shippensburg University of Pennsylvania
  (U,G)
Southern Methodist University (G)

Southern New Hampshire University (U)
Southern Polytechnic State University (U)
State University of New York at Oswego
  (U,G)
State University of New York Institute of
  Technology (U,G)
Strayer University (U,G)
Syracuse University (G)
Tacoma Community College (U)
Taylor University (N,U)
Tunxis Community College (N)
Tyler Junior College (N)
The University of Akron (N,G)
University of Illinois at Chicago (G)
University of Illinois at Urbana–Champaign
  (N)
The University of Maine at Augusta (U)
University of Maryland University College
  (U)
University of Minnesota, Crookston (U)
University of Missouri–Columbia (G)
The University of North Carolina at Charlotte
  (G)
University of North Texas (G)
University of Oregon (G)
University of Southern Maine (N)
University of South Florida (G)
The University of Texas at San Antonio (U)
The University of Texas System (U)
University of the Sciences in Philadelphia (U)
University of Washington (N)
University of West Florida (G)
Vincennes University (U)
West Los Angeles College (U)

INSURANCE

The American College (U,G)
Drake University (G)
Indiana State University (U)
Indian River Community College (N)
Mississippi State University (U)
Naugatuck Valley Community College (U)
Palomar College (U)
Pasco-Hernando Community College (N)
Saint Charles Community College (N)
Southeast Arkansas College (U)
Sullivan County Community College (N)
University of Toronto (N)
University of Waterloo (U)

INTERCULTURAL/ MULTICULTURAL AND DIVERSITY STUDIES

Anne Arundel Community College (U)
Berkeley College (U)
Berkeley College–New York City Campus (U)
Berkeley College–Westchester Campus (U)
De Anza College (U)
Eugene Bible College (U)
Grand Rapids Theological Seminary of
  Cornerstone University (G)
Hibbing Community College (U)
Hope International University (U)
Illinois State University (U)
Roosevelt University (U)
San Diego Community College District (U)
Santa Monica College (U)
Santa Rosa Junior College (U)
Saybrook Graduate School and Research
  Center (G)

South Piedmont Community College (U)
University of Alaska Fairbanks (G)
University of Missouri–Columbia (U)
West Virginia University at Parkersburg (U)

INTERIOR ARCHITECTURE

Academy of Art University (U,G)
Chatham University (U,G)

INTERNATIONAL AGRICULTURE

Dallas Baptist University (U)

INTERNATIONAL AND COMPARATIVE EDUCATION

Drexel University (G)
University of Minnesota, Morris (U)

INTERNATIONAL BUSINESS

AIB College of Business (U)
American Public University System (U)
Athabasca University (N,G)
Avila University (U)
Berkeley College (U)
Berkeley College–New York City Campus (U)
Berkeley College–Westchester Campus (U)
Black Hills State University (U)
Bradley University (U)
Brenau University (U,G)
California National University for Advanced
  Studies (U)
Capella University (G)
Central New Mexico Community College (U)
Chatham University (U)
Coastline Community College (U)
College of Southern Maryland (U)
Colorado State University (G)
Dallas Baptist University (G)
Drexel University (G)
Eastern Washington University (N)
Georgia State University (U)
Iona College (U,G)
Jacksonville State University (U)
James Madison University (N)
Jones International University (U,G)
Kean University (U)
Lawrence Technological University (G)
Limestone College (U)
Long Beach City College (U)
Marist College (G)
Massasoit Community College (U)
Mercy College (U)
Metropolitan State University (U)
Minnesota School of Business–Richfield (U)
Misericordia University (U)
Montcalm Community College (U)
Myers University (U)
Nipissing University (U)
North Central State College (U)
Northcentral University (G)
NorthWest Arkansas Community College (U)
Nova Southeastern University (G)
Oxnard College (U)
Pace University (U)
Palomar College (U)
Park University (G)
Pennsylvania College of Technology (U)
Philadelphia University (G)
Regent University (N,U,G)
Regis University (G)

Sacred Heart University (U)
Saddleback College (U)
Schiller International University (U,G)
Shippensburg University of Pennsylvania
  (U,G)
Southeast Arkansas College (U)
Southern New Hampshire University (G)
State University of New York Empire State
  College (U)
Strayer University (U,G)
Thunderbird School of Global Management
  (N,G)
Tompkins Cortland Community College (U)
Tufts University (G)
University of Dallas (G)
The University of Findlay (U)
University of Illinois at Urbana–Champaign
  (G)
University of Management and Technology
  (U)
University of Maryland University College
  (U,G)
University of Washington (U)
Upper Iowa University (N,U)
Washington State University (U)

INTERNATIONAL RELATIONS AND AFFAIRS

American Public University System (U,G)
American University (U,G)
Athabasca University (N,U,G)
Drake University (U)
Fort Valley State University (U)
Miami Dade College (U)
New Jersey City University (U)
Regent University (N)
Schiller International University (U)
Southern New Hampshire University (U)
Tufts University (U)
University of Massachusetts Boston (U,G)
University of Missouri–Columbia (U)
University of Vermont (U)
University of Waterloo (U)
West Los Angeles College (U)

INTERNATIONAL/GLOBAL STUDIES

Bowling Green State University (U)
Drexel University (G)
Excelsior College (U)
National University (U)
Regent University (N)
Santa Rosa Junior College (U)
Southern New Hampshire University (G)
State University of New York at Binghamton
  (U)
Thunderbird School of Global Management
  (N)
University of Management and Technology
  (U)

JOURNALISM

Arapahoe Community College (U)
Arkansas Tech University (U,G)
Athabasca University (N,U)
Bergen Community College (U)
Brenau University (U)
Cabrillo College (U)
California State University, Sacramento (U)

Central Carolina Community College (U)
Cerritos College (U)
Citrus College (U)
Cleveland State University (N)
Coastline Community College (U)
Cuyahoga Community College (U)
Dallas County Community College District (U)
De Anza College (U)
Delaware County Community College (U)
Drake University (U,G)
East Carolina University (U)
Eastern Kentucky University (U)
Erie Community College (U)
Erie Community College, North Campus (U)
Erie Community College, South Campus (U)
Everett Community College (U)
Galveston College (U)
Georgia State University (U)
Henry Ford Community College (U)
Indiana University–Purdue University Fort Wayne (U)
Iona College (G)
James Madison University (N)
Jamestown Community College (N)
Jefferson Community College (U)
Linn-Benton Community College (U)
Louisiana State University and Agricultural and Mechanical College (U)
Marist College (U)
Marshall University (U)
Massasoit Community College (N)
Middlesex Community College (U)
Middle Tennessee State University (U)
Mt. San Antonio College (U)
Mount Wachusett Community College (U)
Murray State University (U)
New York Institute of Technology (U)
Northampton County Area Community College (U)
North Seattle Community College (U)
Northwestern State University of Louisiana (U)
Oklahoma State University (U)
Palomar College (U)
Parkland College (U)
Peninsula College (U)
Pikes Peak Community College (U)
The Richard Stockton College of New Jersey (U)
Sacramento City College (U)
Saddleback College (U)
Saint Mary-of-the-Woods College (U)
San Diego Community College District (U)
Santa Monica College (U)
Santa Rosa Junior College (U)
Seattle Central Community College (U)
Simpson College (U)
Southwestern Community College (U)
State University of New York at Oswego (U)
Taylor University (U)
Temple University (U,G)
Texas A&M University–Commerce (U)
Texas State University–San Marcos (U)
Texas Tech University (U)
The University of Akron (U)
The University of Alabama (U)
University of Alaska Fairbanks (U)
University of Arkansas (U)
University of Arkansas at Little Rock (U)
University of Idaho (U)

University of Maryland University College (U)
University of Minnesota, Twin Cities Campus (U)
University of Missouri–Columbia (N,G)
University of New Orleans (U,G)
The University of North Carolina at Chapel Hill (U,G)
University of North Texas (U)
University of Oklahoma (U)
University of Southern Indiana (U)
University of South Florida (N)
University of the Virgin Islands (U)
The University of Toledo (U)
University of Washington (U)
University of Wisconsin Colleges (U)
University of Wisconsin–Whitewater (U,G)

LANDSCAPE ARCHITECTURE

California State University, Dominguez Hills (U)
Central Wyoming College (N)
Chatham University (G)
Colorado State University (U)
James Madison University (N)
Mississippi State University (U)
The University of British Columbia (U)
University of Illinois at Urbana–Champaign (N)
University of Saskatchewan (N)
Wake Technical Community College (U)

LANGUAGES (AMERICAN INDIAN/NATIVE AMERICAN)

Central Wyoming College (U)
Palomar College (U)

LANGUAGES (CLASSICS AND CLASSICAL)

Arkansas State University–Mountain Home (U)
Columbia International University (N,G)
Louisiana State University and Agricultural and Mechanical College (U)
Moorpark College (U)
Patrick Henry College (U)
Southern Union State Community College (U)
University of Alaska Fairbanks (U)
University of Colorado Denver (U)
University of Louisville (U)
University of Massachusetts Boston (U)
University of Minnesota, Twin Cities Campus (U)
University of Missouri–Columbia (U)
The University of North Carolina at Chapel Hill (U)
University of Waterloo (U)

LANGUAGES (EAST ASIAN)

Bowling Green State University (U)
Darton College (U)
Naropa University (G)
Northern Virginia Community College (U)
Southside Virginia Community College (U)
Unification Theological Seminary (N,G)
The University of Akron (U)
University of Toronto (N)
Western Washington University (U)

LANGUAGES (FOREIGN LANGUAGES RELATED)

Acadia University (U)
Anne Arundel Community College (N)
Blackhawk Technical College (N)
Black Hills State University (U)
Blue Ridge Community College (N)
Boise State University (U)
California State University, San Bernardino (U)
California State University, San Marcos (N)
Centennial College (U)
Central Carolina Community College (U)
Central Wyoming College (N)
City Colleges of Chicago, Harold Washington College (U)
Clarion University of Pennsylvania (U)
Cleveland State University (N)
Coastline Community College (U)
Colorado Mountain College District System (U)
Community College of Denver (N)
Cumberland County College (U)
Cuyahoga Community College (U)
Darton College (U)
Daytona State College (U)
Eastern Washington University (N)
Flathead Valley Community College (U)
Fort Hays State University (U)
Fort Valley State University (U)
Fulton-Montgomery Community College (N)
Global University (N)
Grand Rapids Theological Seminary of Cornerstone University (G)
Greenville Technical College (U)
Illinois State University (U)
Jacksonville State University (U)
Laredo Community College (U)
Louisiana State University and Agricultural and Mechanical College (U)
McMurry University (U)
Mercy College (U)
Middlesex Community College (U)
Moorpark College (U)
New Mexico Junior College (N)
Okaloosa-Walton College (U)
Oxnard College (U)
Pace University (U)
Palomar College (U)
Portland Community College (N)
Prairie View A&M University (U)
Pulaski Technical College (U)
Randolph Community College (N,U)
Rend Lake College (N)
Riverside Community College District (U)
Sacred Heart University (U)
Santa Monica College (U)
Santa Rosa Junior College (U)
Seattle Central Community College (U)
State University of New York College at Potsdam (U)
Triton College (N)
University of Arkansas at Little Rock (U,G)
University of California, Los Angeles (G)
University of Illinois at Springfield (U)
University of Illinois at Urbana–Champaign (U)
University of Missouri–Columbia (N,U)
University of New Orleans (U,G)
The University of North Carolina at Chapel Hill (U)

University of Southern Indiana (U)
The University of Tennessee (N)
University of Toronto (N)
University of Waterloo (U)
University of Wisconsin–Whitewater (U)
Utah Valley State College (U)
Wake Technical Community College (N)
Webster University (U)
West Los Angeles College (U)

LANGUAGES (GERMANIC)

Bowling Green State University (U)
Brigham Young University (U)
Darton College (U)
Eastern Michigan University (G)
Eastern Washington University (U)
Georgia State University (U)
James Madison University (N)
Louisiana State University and Agricultural
   and Mechanical College (U)
Northern State University (U)
Oklahoma State University (U)
Queen's University at Kingston (U)
The University of Akron (U)
University of Arkansas (U)
University of Illinois at Urbana–Champaign
   (U)
University of Minnesota, Twin Cities Campus
   (U)
University of Missouri–Columbia (U)
University of Nevada, Reno (U)
University of New Orleans (U,G)
The University of North Carolina at
   Greensboro (U)
University of St. Thomas (U)
University of South Florida (G)
The University of Tennessee (U)
University of Toronto (N)
University of Waterloo (U)
Wilfrid Laurier University (U)

LANGUAGES (IRANIAN/PERSIAN)

Palomar College (U)

LANGUAGES (MIDDLE/NEAR EASTERN AND SEMITIC)

Brigham Young University (U)
Hebrew College (N,U,G)
Henry Ford Community College (U)
Lincoln Christian College (N,U,G)
Northern Virginia Community College (U)
University of Colorado at Colorado Springs
   (U)

LANGUAGES (MODERN GREEK)

Bowling Green State University (U)
Eugene Bible College (U)
North Carolina State University (U)
University of Washington (U)
University of Waterloo (U)
Western Washington University (U)

LANGUAGES (ROMANCE LANGUAGES)

Arapahoe Community College (U)
Boise State University (U)
Bowling Green State University (U,G)
Brigham Young University (U)

Broward Community College (U)
Burlington County College (U)
Cabrillo College (U)
California State University, Sacramento (U)
Capital Community College (U)
Carroll Community College (N)
Central Arizona College (U)
Chatham University (U)
Clemson University (N)
Coastline Community College (U)
College of San Mateo (U)
College of Southern Maryland (U)
Columbus State Community College (U)
Community College of Denver (N)
Connors State College (U)
Darton College (U)
East Arkansas Community College (U)
Erie Community College (U)
Erie Community College, North Campus (U)
Erie Community College, South Campus (U)
Evergreen Valley College (U)
Georgia State University (U)
Golden West College (U)
Hillsborough Community College (N)
Houston Community College System (U)
Iona College (G)
James Madison University (N)
John Wood Community College (U)
Kean University (N)
Louisiana State University and Agricultural
   and Mechanical College (U)
Marian College of Fond du Lac (U)
Moorpark College (U)
Mountain Empire Community College (U)
Nassau Community College (U)
North Carolina State University (U)
Northern Virginia Community College (U)
North Lake College (U)
Oklahoma State University (U)
Oregon State University (N)
Palomar College (U)
Piedmont Technical College (U)
Pulaski Technical College (N)
Reading Area Community College (U)
St. John's University (U)
St. Louis Community College System (U)
Southeastern Oklahoma State University
   (N,U)
Southwest Virginia Community College (U)
State University of New York at Binghamton
   (N,U)
State University of New York at Plattsburgh
   (U)
State University of New York College at
   Potsdam (N)
Texas State University–San Marcos (U)
Texas Tech University (N,U)
Triton College (U)
Tyler Junior College (U)
The University of Akron (U)
The University of Alabama (U)
University of Alaska Fairbanks (U)
University of Arkansas (U)
The University of British Columbia (U)
University of California, Davis (U)
University of Illinois at Urbana–Champaign
   (U)
The University of Maine at Augusta (U)
University of Massachusetts Boston (U)
University of Minnesota, Twin Cities Campus
   (U)
University of Missouri–Columbia (N,U)

University of Nevada, Reno (U)
University of New Orleans (U,G)
The University of North Carolina at Chapel
   Hill (U)
University of South Florida (U)
The University of Tennessee (N,U)
The University of Texas at San Antonio (U,G)
University of Toronto (N)
University of Vermont (N,U)
University of Waterloo (U)
Virginia Polytechnic Institute and State
   University (U)
Westchester Community College (U)
Western Michigan University (U)
Western Washington University (U)
West Hills Community College (N)
Wilfrid Laurier University (U)

LANGUAGES (SLAVIC, BALTIC AND ALBANIAN)

University of Minnesota, Twin Cities Campus
   (U)
The University of North Carolina at Chapel
   Hill (U)
University of Washington (U)
University of Waterloo (U)

LANGUAGES (SOUTH ASIAN)

Arapahoe Community College (U)
Lakeland Community College (N)
North Carolina State University (U)
University of Toronto (N)
West Los Angeles College (U)

LEATHERWORKING AND UPHOLSTERY

Blackhawk Technical College (N)

LEGAL PROFESSIONS AND STUDIES RELATED

Arapahoe Community College (U)
Chadron State College (U)
Chatham University (U)
Clackamas Community College (U)
Clarion University of Pennsylvania (U)
Clemson University (N)
Cuyahoga Community College (U)
De Anza College (U)
East Arkansas Community College (U)
Eastern Michigan University (U)
Erie Community College (U)
Erie Community College, North Campus (U)
Erie Community College, South Campus (U)
Florida Gulf Coast University (G)
Iona College (G)
Kean University (N)
Lock Haven University of Pennsylvania (N)
Los Angeles Trade-Technical College (U)
Middlesex Community College (U)
Minnesota School of Business–Richfield (U)
Mount Wachusett Community College (U)
Northern Virginia Community College (U)
Palomar College (U)
Portland Community College (N)
Pulaski Technical College (U)
Quinebaug Valley Community College (N)
Roosevelt University (N,G)
Rose State College (U)

Southern Union State Community College (U)
South Piedmont Community College (U)
State University of New York at Binghamton (N)
Sullivan County Community College (N)
Texas State University–San Marcos (U)
University of Alaska Fairbanks (G)
University of Central Florida (U)
University of Illinois at Springfield (G)
The University of Montana–Western (N)
University of Southern Indiana (N)
The University of Texas at San Antonio (N)
West Los Angeles College (U)

LEGAL RESEARCH AND ADVANCED PROFESSIONAL STUDIES

Arapahoe Community College (U)
Drake University (U)
Eastern Michigan University (U,G)
Missouri State University (G)
Naugatuck Valley Community College (U)
Palomar College (U)
Rose State College (U)
Schiller International University (G)
Seminole Community College (U)
Strayer University (G)
The University of Akron (G)

LEGAL STUDIES (NON-PROFESSIONAL GENERAL, UNDERGRADUATE)

Adams State College (U)
Anne Arundel Community College (U)
Arapahoe Community College (U)
Athabasca University (U)
Athens Technical College (U)
Berkeley College (U)
Berkeley College–New York City Campus (U)
Berkeley College–Westchester Campus (U)
Brenau University (U)
Broward Community College (U)
Cabrillo College (U)
Cape Fear Community College (U)
Carroll Community College (N,U)
Central Arizona College (U)
Central New Mexico Community College (U)
Central Texas College (U)
Cerritos College (U)
Chadron State College (U)
College of San Mateo (U)
College of Southern Maryland (U)
College of The Albemarle (U)
Columbus State Community College (U)
De Anza College (U)
Delaware County Community College (U)
DeVry University Online (U)
Eastern Michigan University (U)
Elgin Community College (U)
Embry-Riddle Aeronautical University (U)
Finger Lakes Community College (U)
Flathead Valley Community College (N)
Galveston College (N)
Grantham University (U)
Hillsborough Community College (U)
Iona College (U)
James A. Rhodes State College (U)
Limestone College (U)
Louisiana State University and Agricultural and Mechanical College (U)

Manor College (U)
Marion Technical College (U)
Marist College (U)
Mercy College (U)
Metropolitan State University (U)
Middlesex Community College (U)
Minnesota School of Business–Richfield (U)
Mountain Empire Community College (U)
Mt. San Antonio College (U)
Murray State University (U)
Myers University (U)
Nassau Community College (U)
Naugatuck Valley Community College (U)
New York Institute of Technology (U)
Northeastern University (U)
NorthWest Arkansas Community College (U)
Northwestern Michigan College (U)
Oklahoma State University (U)
Oxnard College (U)
Pace University (U)
Palomar College (U)
Parkland College (U)
Pasco-Hernando Community College (N)
Patrick Henry College (U)
Philadelphia University (U)
Piedmont Technical College (U)
Pulaski Technical College (U)
Randolph Community College (U)
Roger Williams University (U)
Roosevelt University (U)
Rose State College (U)
St. John's University (U)
Sam Houston State University (U)
San Diego Community College District (U)
San Joaquin Delta College (U)
Schenectady County Community College (U)
Sinclair Community College (U)
State University of New York at Binghamton (N,U)
State University of New York Empire State College (U)
Strayer University (U)
Tacoma Community College (U)
Texas Tech University (U)
Tompkins Cortland Community College (U)
Trine University (U)
Triton College (U)
Tyler Junior College (U)
University of Alaska Fairbanks (U)
University of Arkansas (U)
University of Minnesota, Morris (U)
The University of Toledo (U)
University of Waterloo (U)
Upper Iowa University (U)
Utah Valley State College (U)
West Los Angeles College (U)

LEGAL SUPPORT SERVICES

Adams State College (U)
Anne Arundel Community College (U)
Arapahoe Community College (U)
Blackhawk Technical College (U)
Blackstone Career Institute (N)
Blue Ridge Community College (N)
Bryant and Stratton Online (U)
Carroll Community College (N,U)
Cleveland State University (N)
Coastline Community College (U)
College of Mount St. Joseph (U)
College of the Sequoias (U)
Colorado State University (N)

Columbus State Community College (U)
Cuyahoga Community College (U)
Duquesne University (N)
Eastern Illinois University (N)
Eastern Michigan University (U)
East Tennessee State University (N)
Johnson County Community College (U)
Manatee Community College (U)
Northeastern University (U)
Palomar College (U)
Pasco-Hernando Community College (U)
Randolph Community College (N)
Riverside Community College District (U)
Seminole Community College (U)
Tyler Junior College (U)
University of Central Missouri (N)
The University of North Carolina at Charlotte (N)
University of North Dakota (N)
The University of Texas System (N)
Wake Technical Community College (N)
West Los Angeles College (U)
West Virginia University (N)

LIBERAL ARTS AND SCIENCES, GENERAL STUDIES AND HUMANITIES

Acadia University (U)
American Public University System (U)
Amridge University (N,U)
Arapahoe Community College (U)
Arizona Western College (U)
Arkansas State University–Mountain Home (U)
Athabasca University (N)
Beaufort County Community College (U)
Bellevue Community College (U)
Berkeley College (U)
Berkeley College–New York City Campus (U)
Berkeley College–Westchester Campus (U)
Beulah Heights University (U)
Bowling Green State University (U)
Brenau University (U)
Brigham Young University (U)
Burlington College (U)
Caldwell Community College and Technical Institute (U)
California State University, Chico (U)
California State University, San Bernardino (U)
Centralia College (U)
Central Oregon Community College (U)
Chadron State College (U)
Chemeketa Community College (U)
Citrus College (U)
Clinton Community College (U)
Coastline Community College (U)
College of the Siskiyous (U)
Community College of Beaver County (U)
Community College of Denver (U)
Corban College (U)
Crossroads College (N,U)
Dallas Baptist University (U,G)
Dallas County Community College District (U)
Darton College (U)
Delaware County Community College (U)
DePaul University (U)
DeVry University Online (U)
Drake University (U)
Eastern Michigan University (U)

Eastern West Virginia Community and
  Technical College (U)
East Los Angeles College (U)
East Tennessee State University (N,U,G)
Elgin Community College (U)
Erie Community College (U)
Erie Community College, North Campus (U)
Erie Community College, South Campus (U)
Everett Community College (U)
Excelsior College (U,G)
Finger Lakes Community College (U)
Five Towns College (U)
Fort Hays State University (U,G)
Fort Valley State University (U)
Galveston College (U)
Granite State College (U)
Haywood Community College (U)
Henry Ford Community College (U)
Herkimer County Community College (U)
Hibbing Community College (U)
Hocking College (U)
Hofstra University (U)
Honolulu Community College (U)
Hope International University (U)
Illinois Eastern Community Colleges, Olney
  Central College (U)
Illinois Eastern Community Colleges, Wabash
  Valley College (U)
Indiana University of Pennsylvania (G)
Indiana University System (U)
Indiana Wesleyan University (U)
Iona College (U)
Jackson State University (U)
Jacksonville State University (U,G)
James A. Rhodes State College (U)
James Madison University (N)
Jamestown Community College (N)
John A. Logan College (U)
John Wood Community College (U)
Judson University (U)
Kean University (U)
Labette Community College (U)
Lake Superior College (U)
Lehigh Carbon Community College (U)
Lewis-Clark State College (U)
Linn-Benton Community College (U)
Lock Haven University of Pennsylvania (G)
Long Beach City College (U)
Los Angeles Trade-Technical College (U)
Luzerne County Community College (U)
Malone College (U)
Marist College (U)
McDowell Technical Community College (U)
Mercy College (U)
Miami Dade College (U)
Middlesex Community College (U)
Middle Tennessee State University (U)
Midwestern State University (U)
Minnesota School of Business–Richfield (U)
Minot State University–Bottineau Campus (U)
Monroe Community College (U)
Montgomery Community College (U)
Montgomery County Community College (U)
Mount Olive College (U)
Naropa University (U,G)
Naugatuck Valley Community College (U)
The New School: A University (N,U)
NorthWest Arkansas Community College (U)
Okaloosa-Walton College (U)
Oregon State University (U)
Ouachita Technical College (U)
Pace University (N)

Palomar College (U)
Patrick Henry College (U)
Peirce College (U)
Peninsula College (U)
Pratt Community College (U)
Prescott College (U)
Pulaski Technical College (U)
Quinebaug Valley Community College (U)
Rend Lake College (U)
The Richard Stockton College of New Jersey
  (U)
Rockland Community College (U)
Roosevelt University (U)
Rose State College (U)
Sacred Heart University (U)
St. Edward's University (G)
St. John's University (G)
Saint Leo University (U)
Saint Mary-of-the-Woods College (U)
San Diego Community College District (U)
Santa Rosa Junior College (U)
Seminole Community College (U)
Siena Heights University (U)
Simpson College (U)
Sinclair Community College (U)
Southeast Community College Area (U)
Southern New Hampshire University (U)
Southwestern College (U)
State University of New York at Binghamton
  (N)
Sullivan County Community College (N)
Syracuse University (U)
Taylor University (U)
Texas State University–San Marcos (U)
Texas Tech University (U)
Trine University (U)
Triton College (U)
Tyler Junior College (U)
The University of Akron (U)
The University of Alabama (U)
University of Alaska Fairbanks (U)
University of Arkansas at Little Rock (U)
University of Bridgeport (U)
University of California, Los Angeles (G)
University of Cincinnati (U)
University of Colorado Denver (U)
University of Connecticut (U)
University of Denver (G)
University of Illinois at Springfield (U)
University of Illinois at Urbana–Champaign
  (U)
The University of Kansas (U)
The University of Maine at Augusta (U)
University of Maine at Fort Kent (U)
University of Massachusetts Boston (U)
University of Minnesota, Twin Cities Campus
  (U,G)
University of Missouri–Columbia (U)
The University of Montana–Western (U)
University of New Orleans (N,U,G)
The University of North Carolina at
  Greensboro (U,G)
The University of North Carolina Wilmington
  (G)
University of Pennsylvania (U)
The University of South Dakota (U)
University of Southern Maine (U)
University of Southern Mississippi (U)
University of South Florida (U)
The University of Tennessee (U)
The University of Texas at El Paso (U)

The University of Texas of the Permian Basin
  (U)
The University of Texas System (U)
The University of Toledo (U,G)
University of Waterloo (U)
University of West Florida (U)
University of Wyoming (U)
Upper Iowa University (U)
Utah State University (U)
Utica College (U)
Vincennes University (U)
Virginia Polytechnic Institute and State
  University (G)
Washburn University (G)
Westfield State College (U)
West Los Angeles College (U)
West Shore Community College (U)
Wharton County Junior College (U)
York University (U)
Yuba College (U)

LIBRARY ASSISTANT

Belmont Technical College (U)
Capital Community College (U)
James Madison University (N)
Northampton County Area Community
  College (U)
Palomar College (U)
Rose State College (U)
Sacramento City College (U)

LIBRARY SCIENCE

Central Oregon Community College (U)
Central Wyoming College (U)
Chadron State College (U)
Clarion University of Pennsylvania (U,G)
Drexel University (G)
East Carolina University (G)
Eastern Kentucky University (G)
Foothill College (U)
Golden West College (U)
Henderson Community College (U)
Kauai Community College (G)
Lake-Sumter Community College (U)
Long Beach City College (U)
Louisiana State University and Agricultural
  and Mechanical College (U)
Mansfield University of Pennsylvania (G)
Marshall University (U)
Mayville State University (U)
Memorial University of Newfoundland (U,G)
Missouri State University (G)
Northern State University (U)
Palomar College (U)
Riverside Community College District (U)
Rose State College (U)
Sacramento City College (U)
St. John's University (G)
San Diego Community College District (U)
Santa Monica College (U)
Santa Rosa Junior College (U)
Seattle Pacific University (G)
Seminole Community College (U)
Sierra College (U)
Syracuse University (G)
Tacoma Community College (U)
Texas Woman's University (G)
Union University (U)
The University of Alabama (G)
University of Alaska Fairbanks (U)

The University of Arizona (G)
University of Central Missouri (U,G)
University of Cincinnati Raymond Walters
   College (U)
University of Idaho (U,G)
University of Illinois at Urbana–Champaign
   (N,G)
The University of Maine at Augusta (U)
University of Missouri–Columbia (G)
University of Nevada, Reno (U,G)
The University of North Carolina at
   Greensboro (G)
University of North Texas (N,U,G)
University of South Florida (U,G)
University of Vermont (U,G)
The University of Virginia's College at Wise
   (U)
University of Washington (U,G)
University of Wisconsin–Stout (G)
University of Wisconsin–Whitewater (U)
Valley City State University (U)
West Los Angeles College (U)

LIBRARY SCIENCE RELATED

Belmont Technical College (U)
Black Hills State University (U)
Bowling Green State University (U)
Cabrillo College (U)
Central Carolina Community College (U)
Centralia College (U)
Central Virginia Community College (U)
Chadron State College (U)
Coastline Community College (U)
The College of St. Scholastica (G)
Colorado Mountain College District System
   (U)
Drexel University (G)
Everett Community College (U)
Evergreen Valley College (U)
Florida State University (G)
Harrisburg Area Community College (U)
Illinois State University (U)
Indiana State University (U,G)
Jones International University (G)
Louisiana State University and Agricultural
   and Mechanical College (U)
Miami Dade College (U)
North Seattle Community College (U)
Northwestern State University of Louisiana
   (U)
Oxnard College (U)
Palomar College (U)
Rose State College (U)
Sacramento City College (U)
Saddleback College (U)
San Diego Community College District (U)
Santa Rosa Junior College (U)
Seminole Community College (U)
State University of New York at Plattsburgh
   (U)
Syracuse University (G)
Tacoma Community College (U)
Texas A&M University–Commerce (G)
The University of British Columbia (U)
University of Idaho (U,G)
The University of Maine at Augusta (U)
University of Missouri–Columbia (G)
The University of Montana–Western (U)
The University of North Carolina at
   Greensboro (G)
University of North Texas (N,U,G)

University of Oklahoma (U)
University of Southern Mississippi (U)
University of Washington (G)
Utah State University (G)
Western Washington University (U)

LINGUISTIC, COMPARATIVE, AND RELATED LANGUAGE STUDIES

Acadia University (U)
Adams State College (N)
Athabasca University (N,U)
Brenau University (U)
Bridgewater State College (G)
Caldwell Community College and Technical
   Institute (N)
Capital Community College (U)
Cleveland State University (U,G)
Coastline Community College (U)
Columbia International University (G)
Daemen College (U)
Darton College (U)
Foothill College (U)
Golden West College (U)
Hebrew College (N,U,G)
Illinois State University (U,G)
James Madison University (N,U)
Jamestown Community College (N)
J. Sargeant Reynolds Community College (U)
Kentucky State University (U)
Louisiana State University and Agricultural
   and Mechanical College (U)
Mesa Community College (U)
Middlesex Community College (U)
Middle Tennessee State University (N)
Millersville University of Pennsylvania (U,G)
Mountain Empire Community College (U)
Northern State University (U)
Northwest Missouri State University (U)
The Ohio State University (U)
Oregon State University (N)
Pace University (U)
Plymouth State University (U)
Riverside Community College District (N,U)
Sacred Heart University (U)
Seattle Pacific University (U)
State University of New York at Binghamton
   (U)
State University of New York College at
   Potsdam (N)
Strayer University (U)
Tacoma Community College (U)
Triton College (U)
Tunxis Community College (U)
The University of Akron (U)
The University of Alabama (U)
University of Alaska Fairbanks (U)
University of Colorado Denver (U)
University of Denver (G)
University of Idaho (U)
University of Management and Technology
   (G)
University of Massachusetts Boston (U,G)
University of Minnesota, Twin Cities Campus
   (U)
University of Missouri–Columbia (U)
University of Nevada, Reno (U)
University of New Orleans (U,G)
University of North Dakota (U)
University of North Texas (U,G)
University of Oregon (U)
University of Southern Indiana (U)

University of Southern Mississippi (U,G)
The University of Texas at El Paso (U)
The University of Texas at San Antonio (U)
The University of Texas System (U)
University of Waterloo (U)
University of Wisconsin–La Crosse (U)
Virginia Polytechnic Institute and State
   University (U)
Weber State University (U)

MANAGEMENT INFORMATION SYSTEMS

American Public University System (U)
Arapahoe Community College (U)
Athabasca University (N,U,G)
Beaufort County Community College (U)
Bellevue Community College (U)
Bellevue University (U,G)
Brenau University (U,G)
Bristol Community College (U)
Buena Vista University (U)
California National University for Advanced
   Studies (U,G)
California Polytechnic State University, San
   Luis Obispo (N)
California State University, Sacramento (U)
Carlow University (U)
Carroll Community College (U)
Central Carolina Community College (N)
Centralia College (N,U)
Central Michigan University (G)
Central Texas College (U)
Central Washington University (U)
Cerritos College (U)
Chadron State College (U,G)
Charter Oak State College (U)
Chemeketa Community College (U)
Cincinnati State Technical and Community
   College (U)
Cleveland State University (N)
Coastline Community College (U)
College of The Albemarle (N)
Colorado State University (G)
Culver-Stockton College (U)
Dallas Baptist University (U,G)
Delaware County Community College (U)
Drake University (U)
Drexel University (G)
Duquesne University (G)
East Carolina University (U)
East Los Angeles College (U)
Edgecombe Community College (N,U)
Edison State Community College (U)
Embry-Riddle Aeronautical University (G)
Endicott College (U)
Excelsior College (U)
Fort Hays State University (N)
Galveston College (U)
Georgia College & State University (G)
Granite State College (U)
Grantham University (U,G)
Haywood Community College (U)
Houston Community College System (U)
Indiana State University (U)
Indiana University of Pennsylvania (U)
Iona College (U,G)
Jacksonville State University (U,G)
Kansas State University (U)
Kentucky State University (U)
Kettering University (N)
Labette Community College (U)

Lakeland Community College (N)
Lamar State College–Port Arthur (N)
Lawrence Technological University (G)
Lewis-Clark State College (U)
Limestone College (U)
Louisiana State University and Agricultural
  and Mechanical College (U)
Manatee Community College (U)
Marion Technical College (U)
Marshall University (U)
McMurry University (U)
Mercy College (U,G)
Metropolitan State University (U,G)
Middle Tennessee State University (N)
Milwaukee School of Engineering (U)
Minot State University (U,G)
Missouri State University (N)
Motlow State Community College (U)
Mount Olive College (U)
Mount Wachusett Community College (U)
Myers University (U)
Neumann College (G)
New Jersey Institute of Technology (U,G)
New Mexico Highlands University (U,G)
New Mexico Institute of Mining and
  Technology (U)
New York Institute of Technology (G)
North Arkansas College (U)
Northeast Iowa Community College (U)
Nova Southeastern University (G)
Oklahoma State University (U)
Old Dominion University (U,G)
Oregon Institute of Technology (U)
Pace University (G)
Park University (U)
Patrick Henry Community College (U)
Philadelphia University (U,G)
Piedmont Technical College (U)
Prairie View A&M University (G)
Regis University (U)
Saddleback College (U)
St. Cloud State University (U)
Saint Francis University (U)
St. Louis Community College System (N)
Schiller International University (U)
Seminole Community College (U)
Shippensburg University of Pennsylvania
  (U,G)
Southwest Wisconsin Technical College (U)
State University of New York at Binghamton
  (N)
State University of New York College at
  Potsdam (U)
State University of New York Empire State
  College (U)
Syracuse University (G)
Tacoma Community College (N)
Taylor University (N,U)
Texas A&M University–Commerce (U)
Thunderbird School of Global Management
  (G)
Tunxis Community College (U)
Tyler Junior College (N)
Union University (U)
University of Arkansas at Little Rock (U)
University of Colorado Denver (G)
University of Dallas (G)
The University of Findlay (N)
University of Illinois at Springfield (G)
University of Management and Technology
  (U,G)
University of Massachusetts Boston (U)

University of Michigan–Flint (N)
University of Minnesota, Crookston (U)
University of New Orleans (U,G)
University of Oregon (U)
University of Pittsburgh at Bradford (U)
University of Southern Mississippi (U)
The University of Texas at San Antonio (G)
University of Toronto (N)
University of Waterloo (G)
University of Wisconsin–Parkside (G)
University of Wisconsin–Whitewater (U,G)
Upper Iowa University (N,U)
Utah Valley State College (U)
Virginia Polytechnic Institute and State
  University (G)
Wayland Baptist University (U,G)
Webster University (G)
Westchester Community College (U)
West Virginia University (N)
West Virginia University at Parkersburg (U)
York County Community College (U)

MANAGEMENT SCIENCES AND QUANTITATIVE METHODS

Athabasca University (N,G)
Bellevue University (U,G)
Berkeley College (U)
Berkeley College–New York City Campus (U)
Berkeley College–Westchester Campus (U)
Boise State University (G)
Brenau University (U,G)
Burlington County College (U)
Central Michigan University (G)
Chadron State College (U,G)
Colorado State University (N,G)
Concordia University Wisconsin (U)
Dallas Baptist University (U)
Delaware County Community College (U)
DePaul University (N)
Drake University (U)
Drexel University (U,G)
Elizabeth City State University (U)
Elizabethtown Community and Technical
  College (U)
Embry-Riddle Aeronautical University (U,G)
Endicott College (U)
Florida Gulf Coast University (U)
Florida Institute of Technology (G)
Granite State College (U)
Jacksonville State University (U,G)
James Madison University (N)
Kettering University (N)
Lakeland Community College (N)
Limestone College (U)
Louisiana State University and Agricultural
  and Mechanical College (U)
Marist College (G)
Mercy College (U,G)
Mesa State College (U)
Miami Dade College (U)
Myers University (U)
National University (U)
Neumann College (G)
New Jersey Institute of Technology (G)
New Mexico Highlands University (U)
New Mexico Institute of Mining and
  Technology (G)
Nipissing University (U)
Old Dominion University (U)
Philadelphia University (U,G)
Regis University (G)

Saint Joseph's College of Maine (G)
Saint Leo University (U)
Shippensburg University of Pennsylvania (U)
Southeast Community College Area (N)
Stanford University (G)
State University of New York College of
  Agriculture and Technology at Morrisville
  (U)
Syracuse University (G)
Texas A&M University–Kingsville (U)
Tompkins Cortland Community College (U)
University of Colorado Denver (G)
The University of Findlay (N)
University of Illinois at Urbana–Champaign
  (N,U,G)
The University of Maine at Augusta (U)
University of Management and Technology
  (U)
University of Michigan–Flint (U,G)
University of New Orleans (U,G)
The University of Texas at San Antonio (G)
The University of Texas at Tyler (G)
University of Toronto (N)
University of Wisconsin–Parkside (G)
University of Wisconsin–Stout (G)
Upper Iowa University (U)
Western Washington University (U)
York University (U)

MANUFACTURING ENGINEERING

Cleveland State University (G)
Cuyahoga Community College (U)
East Arkansas Community College (U)
East Carolina University (U)
Hopkinsville Community College (N)
Kettering University (N)
Missouri University of Science and
  Technology (G)
New Mexico State University (G)
State University of New York at Binghamton
  (G)
University of Minnesota, Crookston (U)

MARKETING

Acadia University (U)
AIB College of Business (U)
Anne Arundel Community College (U)
Arapahoe Community College (U)
Arkansas Tech University (U)
Athabasca University (N,U,G)
Athens Technical College (U)
Bellevue Community College (U)
Bellevue University (U)
Berkeley College (U)
Berkeley College–New York City Campus (U)
Berkeley College–Westchester Campus (U)
Blackhawk Technical College (U)
Black Hills State University (U)
Blue Ridge Community College (N,U)
Brenau University (U,G)
Brigham Young University (U)
Broward Community College (U)
Buena Vista University (U)
Burlington County College (U)
Butler Community College (U)
Caldwell Community College and Technical
  Institute (U)
California National University for Advanced
  Studies (U,G)
Cape Cod Community College (U)

Cape Fear Community College (U)
Capella University (G)
Capital Community College (U)
Carroll Community College (U)
Centennial College (U)
Central Carolina Community College (U)
Central Michigan University (U,G)
Central Texas College (U)
Central Virginia Community College (U)
Central Washington University (U)
Chadron State College (U,G)
Charter Oak State College (U)
Chatham University (U)
Clemson University (U)
College of San Mateo (U)
College of Southern Maryland (U)
College of The Albemarle (U)
Colorado State University (U,G)
Columbia College (U)
Columbus State Community College (U)
Concordia University Wisconsin (U)
Corban College (U)
Dallas Baptist University (U,G)
Dallas County Community College District (U)
Danville Community College (U)
Delaware County Community College (U)
DeSales University (U)
DeVry University Online (U,G)
Drake University (U)
Drexel University (U,G)
Eastern Illinois University (G)
Eastern Kentucky University (U)
Eastern Michigan University (U,G)
Eastern West Virginia Community and Technical College (U)
East Tennessee State University (N)
Edison State Community College (U)
Elgin Community College (U)
Embry-Riddle Aeronautical University (U)
Erie Community College (U)
Erie Community College, North Campus (U)
Erie Community College, South Campus (U)
Finger Lakes Community College (U)
Florida Gulf Coast University (U)
Florida Institute of Technology (G)
Fort Hays State University (U)
Fort Valley State University (U)
Fox Valley Technical College (U)
Franklin University (U)
Frank Phillips College (U)
Galveston College (U)
Genesee Community College (U)
Georgia State University (U)
Golden Gate University (U,G)
Golden West College (U)
Governors State University (U)
Graceland University (U)
Grantham University (U,G)
Greenville Technical College (U)
Harrisburg Area Community College (U)
Hillsborough Community College (U)
Houston Community College System (U)
Huntington College of Health Sciences (U)
Illinois Eastern Community Colleges, Frontier Community College (U)
Illinois State University (U)
Indiana State University (U)
Indiana University of Pennsylvania (U)
Iona College (U,G)
Ivy Tech Community College–Northwest (U)
Jacksonville State University (U,G)

James Madison University (N)
Jamestown Community College (N)
Jefferson Community College (U)
John A. Logan College (U)
Johnson County Community College (U)
Johnson State College (U)
J. Sargeant Reynolds Community College (U)
Kansas State University (U)
Kean University (U)
Lakeland Community College (U)
Lamar State College–Port Arthur (N)
Lawrence Technological University (G)
Lehigh Carbon Community College (U)
Liberty University (U)
Limestone College (U)
Long Beach City College (U)
Los Angeles Trade-Technical College (U)
Louisiana State University and Agricultural and Mechanical College (U)
Manatee Community College (U)
Manor College (U)
Marist College (G)
Marshall University (U,G)
Mercy College (U,G)
Metropolitan State University (U,G)
Miami Dade College (U)
Middlesex Community College (U)
Middle Tennessee State University (G)
Minot State University (U)
Minot State University–Bottineau Campus (U)
Missouri State University (U,G)
Montgomery County Community College (U)
Mountain Empire Community College (U)
Mount Wachusett Community College (U)
Murray State College (U)
Murray State University (G)
Myers University (U)
Nassau Community College (U)
New River Community College (U)
New York Institute of Technology (U,G)
Nipissing University (U)
Northampton County Area Community College (U)
North Dakota State College of Science (U)
Northeast Iowa Community College (U)
Northwestern State University of Louisiana (U)
Northwest Technical College (U)
Northwood University, Texas Campus (U)
Nova Southeastern University (G)
Oklahoma State University (U)
Old Dominion University (U,G)
Oxnard College (U)
Pace University (U,G)
Palomar College (U)
Parkland College (U)
Park University (U)
Pellissippi State Technical Community College (U)
Pennsylvania College of Technology (U)
Philadelphia University (U,G)
Pikes Peak Community College (U)
Portland Community College (U)
Prairie View A&M University (G)
Randolph Community College (U)
Regis University (U,G)
The Richard Stockton College of New Jersey (U)
Riverside Community College District (U)
Rockland Community College (U)
Rose State College (U)
Sacred Heart University (U,G)

Saddleback College (U)
Saint Charles Community College (N)
St. Edward's University (G)
St. John's University (U)
Saint Joseph's College of Maine (U,G)
Saint Leo University (U)
St. Louis Community College System (U)
Saint Mary-of-the-Woods College (U)
Sam Houston State University (U)
San Diego Community College District (U)
San Diego State University (U)
Santa Monica College (U)
Santa Rosa Junior College (U)
Schiller International University (U,G)
Seminole Community College (U)
Shippensburg University of Pennsylvania (U)
Simpson College (U)
Sinclair Community College (U)
Southeast Arkansas College (U)
Southeastern Oklahoma State University (U)
Southern New Hampshire University (U,G)
South Piedmont Community College (U)
Spring Arbor University (U)
State University of New York at Plattsburgh (U)
Syracuse University (G)
Taylor University (N,U)
Texas A&M University–Commerce (U,G)
Texas A&M University–Kingsville (U)
Texas Tech University (U)
Thunderbird School of Global Management (N)
Tompkins Cortland Community College (U)
Tri-County Community College (U)
Trine University (U)
Triton College (U)
Union University (U)
United States Sports Academy (G)
University of Alaska Fairbanks (U)
University of Arkansas at Little Rock (U,G)
University of Colorado Denver (G)
University of Dallas (G)
The University of Findlay (U,G)
University of Houston–Downtown (U)
University of Illinois at Chicago (N,G)
University of Illinois at Urbana–Champaign (N)
The University of Maine at Augusta (U)
University of Maryland University College (G)
University of Massachusetts Boston (U)
University of Michigan–Flint (U,G)
University of Minnesota, Crookston (U)
University of Minnesota, Twin Cities Campus (U)
University of Missouri–Columbia (U)
University of Nevada, Reno (U)
University of New Orleans (U,G)
University of North Alabama (U)
The University of North Carolina at Charlotte (N)
University of Northern Iowa (U)
University of North Texas (N,U,G)
University of Oklahoma (U)
University of Phoenix (G)
University of Pittsburgh at Bradford (U)
University of Southern Indiana (G)
University of Southern Mississippi (U,G)
University of South Florida (U)
The University of Texas at San Antonio (U)
The University of Texas at Tyler (U)
University of the Southwest (U)

University of Toronto (N)
University of Washington (U)
University of Wisconsin–Whitewater (U,G)
Upper Iowa University (N,U)
Virginia Polytechnic Institute and State
　University (N,U,G)
Wake Technical Community College (U)
Washington State University (U)
Wayland Baptist University (U)
Webster University (G)
West Los Angeles College (U)
West Shore Community College (U)
West Virginia University (G)
West Virginia University at Parkersburg (U)
Wharton County Junior College (U)
Wilmington University (U)
Worcester Polytechnic Institute (G)
Wytheville Community College (U)
York University (U)

MASONRY

Pamlico Community College (U)

MATERIALS ENGINEERING

Cuyahoga Community College (U)
Missouri University of Science and
　Technology (N)
New Mexico Institute of Mining and
　Technology (G)
Prairie View A&M University (U)
Stanford University (N,G)
University of Florida (N)
University of Idaho (G)
University of Illinois at Urbana–Champaign
　(G)
University of South Florida (G)
University of Washington (U,G)

MATERIALS SCIENCE

Columbia University (N,G)
Quinebaug Valley Community College (U)
University of Florida (N,G)
University of Illinois at Urbana–Champaign
　(G)
University of Minnesota, Twin Cities Campus
　(U)

MATHEMATICS

Acadia University (N)
AIB College of Business (U)
Allen County Community College (U)
Arapahoe Community College (U)
Arkansas State University–Beebe (U)
Arkansas State University–Mountain Home
　(U)
Arkansas Tech University (U)
Athabasca University (N,U)
Athens Technical College (U)
Barclay College (U)
Beacon University (N,U)
Bellevue Community College (U)
Beulah Heights University (U)
Black Hills State University (U)
Boise State University (U)
Bowling Green State University (U,G)
Brazosport College (U)
Brenau University (U)
Bristol Community College (U)
Burlington County College (U)

Butler Community College (U)
Cabrillo College (U)
Caldwell Community College and Technical
　Institute (U)
California Polytechnic State University, San
　Luis Obispo (N)
California State University, Dominguez Hills
　(N)
California State University, Sacramento (U)
California State University, San Bernardino
　(U)
California State University, San Marcos (N,U)
Cape Cod Community College (U)
Carlow University (U)
Carroll Community College (U)
Cayuga County Community College (U)
Centennial College (U)
Central Carolina Community College (U)
Centralia College (U)
Central New Mexico Community College (U)
Central Oregon Community College (U)
Central Texas College (U)
Central Wyoming College (U)
Cerro Coso Community College (U)
Chadron State College (U,G)
Chaminade University of Honolulu (U)
Charter Oak State College (U)
Chatham University (U)
Chemeketa Community College (U)
Citrus College (U)
City Colleges of Chicago, Harold Washington
　College (U)
Clackamas Community College (U)
Clatsop Community College (U)
Clemson University (N,U)
Cleveland State Community College (U)
Coastline Community College (U)
College of San Mateo (U)
College of Southern Maryland (U)
College of the Sequoias (U)
College of the Siskiyous (U)
Colorado State University (U,G)
Columbia College (U)
Columbus State Community College (U)
Community College of Beaver County (U)
Community College of Denver (U)
Connors State College (U)
Corban College (U)
Corning Community College (U)
Cuyahoga Community College (U)
Dakota State University (U)
Dallas Baptist University (U)
Dallas County Community College District
　(U)
Danville Community College (U)
Darton College (U)
Daytona State College (U)
De Anza College (U)
Delaware County Community College (U)
Delaware Technical & Community College,
　Jack F. Owens Campus (U)
DeSales University (U)
DeVry University Online (U,G)
Diné College (U)
East Arkansas Community College (U)
East Central Community College (U)
Eastern Iowa Community College District (N)
Eastern Michigan University (U,G)
East Los Angeles College (U)
Edison State Community College (U)
Elgin Community College (U)
Erie Community College (U)

Erie Community College, North Campus (U)
Erie Community College, South Campus (U)
Eugene Bible College (U)
Everett Community College (U)
Evergreen Valley College (U)
Excelsior College (U)
Fitchburg State College (U)
Florida Gulf Coast University (U)
Fontbonne University (U)
Fort Valley State University (U)
Framingham State College (U)
Gadsden State Community College (U)
Galveston College (U)
Gateway Technical College (U)
Genesee Community College (U)
George C. Wallace Community College (U)
Georgia Highlands College (U)
Georgia Institute of Technology (N,G)
Georgia State University (U)
Golden Gate University (U,G)
Golden West College (U)
Granite State College (U)
Grantham University (U)
Greenfield Community College (U)
Greenville Technical College (U)
Gulf Coast Community College (U)
Halifax Community College (U)
Hamline University (G)
Harford Community College (U)
Harrisburg Area Community College (U)
Haywood Community College (U)
Henderson Community College (U)
Henry Ford Community College (U)
Hibbing Community College (U)
Hocking College (U)
Holyoke Community College (U)
Hopkinsville Community College (N,U)
Houston Community College System (U)
Huntington College of Health Sciences (U)
Illinois Eastern Community Colleges, Lincoln
　Trail College (U)
Illinois Eastern Community Colleges, Olney
　Central College (U)
Illinois Eastern Community Colleges, Wabash
　Valley College (U)
Illinois State University (U)
Indiana State University (U)
Indiana Tech (U)
Indiana University of Pennsylvania (U)
Indiana University–Purdue University Fort
　Wayne (U)
Indiana Wesleyan University (U)
Ivy Tech Community College–Bloomington
　(U)
Ivy Tech Community College–Central Indiana
　(U)
Ivy Tech Community College–Columbus (U)
Ivy Tech Community College–East Central
　(U)
Ivy Tech Community College–Northwest (U)
Ivy Tech Community College–Southern
　Indiana (U)
Ivy Tech Community College–Southwest (U)
Ivy Tech Community College–Wabash Valley
　(U)
Ivy Tech Community College–Whitewater (U)
Jackson State University (U)
Jacksonville State University (U)
Jefferson College (U)
Jefferson Community College (U)
John A. Logan College (U)
Johnson County Community College (U)

John Wood Community College (U)
J. Sargeant Reynolds Community College (U)
Judson University (U)
Kaskaskia College (U)
Kean University (N)
Labette Community College (U)
Lackawanna College (U)
Lake Region State College (U)
Lake Superior College (U)
Lamar State College–Port Arthur (U)
Laredo Community College (U)
Lehigh Carbon Community College (U)
Limestone College (U)
Linn-Benton Community College (N,U)
Long Beach City College (U)
Los Angeles Trade-Technical College (U)
Louisiana State University and Agricultural
   and Mechanical College (N,U)
Lurleen B. Wallace Community College (U)
Macon State College (U)
Mansfield University of Pennsylvania (U)
Marion Technical College (U)
Marshall University (U)
Massasoit Community College (U)
McMurry University (U)
Memorial University of Newfoundland (U)
Mercer County Community College (U)
Mesa Community College (U)
Metropolitan State University (U)
Miami Dade College (U)
Michigan State University (U)
Michigan Technological University (U)
Middlesex Community College (U)
Middle Tennessee State University (U,G)
Midway College (U)
Minnesota School of Business–Richfield (U)
Minot State University (U)
Mississippi Delta Community College (U)
Mississippi State University (U)
Moberly Area Community College (U)
Monroe Community College (U)
Monroe County Community College (U)
Montana Tech of The University of Montana
   (U)
Montgomery County Community College (U)
Moorpark College (U)
Motlow State Community College (U)
Mountain Empire Community College (U)
Mount Olive College (U)
Mount Wachusett Community College (U)
Murray State College (U)
Myers University (U)
Nassau Community College (N,U)
Naugatuck Valley Community College (U)
New England Institute of Technology (U)
New Jersey City University (U)
New Mexico Institute of Mining and
   Technology (G)
New Mexico Junior College (U)
New Mexico State University (U)
New River Community College (U)
Northampton County Area Community
   College (U)
North Arkansas College (U)
North Carolina State University (U)
North Central Missouri College (U)
North Central Texas College (U)
North Dakota State College of Science (U)
North Dakota State University (U)
Northeast Alabama Community College (U)
Northeastern Illinois University (U)

Northeast State Technical Community College
   (U)
Northern State University (U)
Northern Virginia Community College (U)
North Iowa Area Community College (U)
North Lake College (U)
Northland Community and Technical College–
   Thief River Falls (U)
North Seattle Community College (U)
NorthWest Arkansas Community College
   (N,U)
Northwestern Connecticut Community College
   (U)
Northwestern State University of Louisiana
   (U)
Northwest Missouri State University (U)
Okaloosa-Walton College (U)
Oklahoma Panhandle State University (U)
Oregon Institute of Technology (U)
Ouachita Technical College (U)
Oxnard College (U)
Pace University (U)
Pacific Union College (U)
Palomar College (U)
Pamlico Community College (U)
Park University (U)
Pasco-Hernando Community College (U)
Patrick Henry Community College (U)
Peninsula College (U)
Pennsylvania College of Technology (U)
Pennsylvania Highlands Community College
   (U)
Pine Technical College (U)
Portland Community College (U)
Pratt Community College (U)
Presentation College (U)
Pulaski Technical College (U)
Randolph Community College (U)
Rappahannock Community College (U)
Reading Area Community College (U)
Red Rocks Community College (U)
Regent University (U)
Rend Lake College (U)
Riverside Community College District (U)
Rockland Community College (U)
Rose State College (U)
Sacramento City College (U)
Sacred Heart University (G)
Saddleback College (U)
St. Ambrose University (U)
Saint Charles Community College (U)
St. Clair County Community College (U)
St. Cloud State University (U)
St. John's University (U)
Saint Leo University (U)
St. Louis Community College System (U)
Saint Mary-of-the-Woods College (U)
San Diego Community College District (U)
Santa Rosa Junior College (U)
Schenectady County Community College (U)
Schiller International University (U)
Seattle Pacific University (G)
Seminole Community College (U)
Shippensburg University of Pennsylvania (U)
Sierra College (U)
Sinclair Community College (U)
Southeast Arkansas College (U)
Southeast Community College Area (N,U)
Southeastern Community College (U)
Southeastern Illinois College (U)
Southeastern Oklahoma State University
   (N,U)

Southern Arkansas University Tech (U)
Southern Maine Community College (U)
Southern Union State Community College (U)
South Piedmont Community College (U)
Southwest Wisconsin Technical College (U)
State University of New York at Binghamton
   (N)
State University of New York at Plattsburgh
   (U)
State University of New York College at
   Cortland (U)
State University of New York College of
   Agriculture and Technology at Morrisville
   (U)
Stevens Institute of Technology (U)
Strayer University (U,G)
Tacoma Community College (U)
Taft College (U)
Taylor University (N,U)
Temple University (U)
Texas A&M University–Commerce (U)
Texas State Technical College Waco (U)
Texas State University–San Marcos (U,G)
Texas Tech University (G)
Three Rivers Community College (U)
Tompkins Cortland Community College (U)
Triton College (U)
Union County College (U)
The University of Akron (U,G)
The University of Alabama (U)
University of Alaska Fairbanks (U)
The University of Arizona (U)
University of Arkansas at Little Rock (U,G)
University of California, Los Angeles (G)
University of Cincinnati (U)
University of Colorado at Colorado Springs
   (U)
The University of Findlay (U)
University of Idaho (U,G)
University of Illinois at Springfield (U)
University of Illinois at Urbana–Champaign
   (U,G)
The University of Kansas (U)
The University of Maine at Augusta (U)
University of Management and Technology
   (U)
University of Maryland University College
   (U)
University of Massachusetts Boston (U)
University of Michigan–Flint (U)
University of Minnesota, Crookston (U)
University of Minnesota, Twin Cities Campus
   (U)
University of Missouri–Columbia (U)
The University of Montana–Western (U)
University of Nevada, Reno (U)
University of New Orleans (N,U,G)
The University of North Carolina at Charlotte
   (U)
The University of North Carolina at
   Greensboro (U)
University of North Dakota (N,U)
University of Northern Iowa (U)
University of North Texas (U)
University of Oklahoma (U)
University of Pennsylvania (U)
University of Saskatchewan (U)
The University of South Dakota (U)
University of South Florida (U)
The University of Tennessee (N,U)
The University of Texas at Brownsville (U)
The University of Texas at San Antonio (U,G)

The University of Texas at Tyler (U)
The University of Texas of the Permian Basin (U)
The University of Texas System (U)
The University of Toledo (U)
University of Utah (U)
University of Vermont (N)
University of Washington (U)
University of Waterloo (U)
University of West Florida (U)
University of Wisconsin Colleges (N,U)
University of Wyoming (U)
Upper Iowa University (U)
Utah State University (U)
Utah Valley State College (U)
Utica College (U)
Vincennes University (U)
Virginia Polytechnic Institute and State University (U,G)
Wake Technical Community College (U)
Washington State University (U)
Wayne State College (G)
Weber State University (U)
Webster University (U)
Westchester Community College (U)
Western Washington University (U)
West Los Angeles College (U)
West Shore Community College (U)
West Virginia University at Parkersburg (U)
Williston State College (U)
Worcester State College (U)
York Technical College (U)
York University (U)
Youngstown State University (U)

MATHEMATICS AND COMPUTER SCIENCE

Arapahoe Community College (U)
Athabasca University (N,U,G)
Austin Peay State University (U)
Campbell University (U)
Central Texas College (U)
Chadron State College (U,G)
Chemeketa Community College (U)
City Colleges of Chicago, Harold Washington College (U)
Columbia College (U)
Concordia University, St. Paul (N)
Dallas County Community College District (U)
Danville Community College (U)
Darton College (U)
Delaware County Community College (U)
Drake University (U)
Eastern Iowa Community College District (N)
Edison State Community College (U)
Fort Hays State University (U)
Franklin University (U)
Frank Phillips College (U)
Golden West College (U)
Grantham University (U)
Harrisburg Area Community College (U)
Haywood Community College (U)
Herkimer County Community College (U)
Indiana State University (U)
Jacksonville State University (U,G)
James Madison University (N)
John A. Logan College (U)
Laredo Community College (U)
Macon State College (U)
Marion Technical College (U)

Marshall University (U)
Middlesex Community College (U)
Pamlico Community College (U)
Peninsula College (U)
Pulaski Technical College (U)
Sacramento City College (U)
San Diego Community College District (U)
Seminole Community College (U)
Shippensburg University of Pennsylvania (U)
Southeast Arkansas College (U)
State University of New York College at Cortland (U)
Taylor University (N)
Texas State University–San Marcos (U)
Union University (U)
The University of Akron (U,G)
University of Alaska Fairbanks (U)
University of Idaho (G)
University of New Orleans (U,G)
University of South Florida (U)
University of Wisconsin Colleges (U)
University of Wisconsin–Superior (U)
Westchester Community College (U)
West Hills Community College (N)
Yuba College (U)

MATHEMATICS AND STATISTICS RELATED

AIB College of Business (U)
Anne Arundel Community College (U)
Arapahoe Community College (U)
Bellevue Community College (U)
Berkeley College (U)
Berkeley College–New York City Campus (U)
Berkeley College–Westchester Campus (U)
Blue Ridge Community College (U)
Brenau University (U)
Brigham Young University (U)
Bristol Community College (U)
Broward Community College (U)
Burlington County College (U)
Butler Community College (U)
Central Arizona College (U)
Central Texas College (U)
Chadron State College (U,G)
Charter Oak State College (U)
Chemeketa Community College (U)
City Colleges of Chicago, Harold Washington College (U)
Coastline Community College (U)
College of Southern Maryland (U)
College of The Albemarle (U)
Colorado Mountain College District System (U)
Dallas Baptist University (U)
Dallas County Community College District (U)
Darton College (U)
De Anza College (U)
DeSales University (U)
East Arkansas Community College (U)
Eastern Illinois University (U)
Eastern Kentucky University (U)
Eastern Michigan University (G)
Embry-Riddle Aeronautical University (U)
Ferris State University (U)
Finger Lakes Community College (U)
Frank Phillips College (U)
Genesee Community College (U)
Glenville State College (U)
Grand Rapids Community College (U)

Grantham University (U)
Henry Ford Community College (U)
Houston Community College System (U)
Illinois Eastern Community Colleges, Wabash Valley College (U)
Indiana State University (U)
Jacksonville State University (U)
James A. Rhodes State College (U)
Jefferson Community College (U)
Kettering University (N)
Labette Community College (U)
Lawrence Technological University (U)
Lehigh Carbon Community College (U)
Lewis-Clark State College (U)
Long Beach City College (U)
Los Angeles Trade-Technical College (U)
Louisiana State University and Agricultural and Mechanical College (U)
Macon State College (U)
Manatee Community College (U)
Marshall University (U)
McDowell Technical Community College (U)
Mercy College (U)
Middlesex Community College (U)
Missouri State University (U)
Mount Wachusett Community College (U)
Murray State University (U)
Nassau Community College (U)
Neumann College (U)
New Mexico Junior College (U)
Northampton County Area Community College (U)
Northern State University (U)
Northwestern Michigan College (U)
Okaloosa-Walton College (U)
Oklahoma State University (U)
Oregon State University (U)
Pace University (U)
Palomar College (U)
Pamlico Community College (U)
Parkland College (U)
Pasco-Hernando Community College (U)
Passaic County Community College (U)
Peirce College (U)
Pellissippi State Technical Community College (U)
Peninsula College (U)
Piedmont Community College (U)
Piedmont Technical College (U)
Portland Community College (U)
Sacramento City College (U)
Sam Houston State University (U)
San Diego Community College District (U)
San Joaquin Delta College (U)
Seattle Central Community College (U)
Seminole Community College (U)
Sierra College (U)
Southeast Arkansas College (U)
Southwestern Community College (U)
Southwest Virginia Community College (U)
State University of New York Empire State College (U)
Taft College (U)
Texas Tech University (U)
Treasure Valley Community College (U)
Tyler Junior College (U)
The University of Akron (U,G)
University of Alaska Fairbanks (U)
University of Arkansas (U)
University of Arkansas at Little Rock (U)
University of Bridgeport (U)
University of Colorado Denver (U)

University of Idaho (U,G)
University of Illinois at Urbana–Champaign (U)
The University of Maine at Augusta (U)
University of Missouri–Columbia (U)
University of New Orleans (U,G)
The University of North Carolina at Chapel Hill (U)
The University of North Carolina at Greensboro (U)
University of Southern Maine (U)
University of Southern Mississippi (U)
The University of Texas at Brownsville (U)
The University of Texas System (U)
University of Utah (U)
University of Vermont (N)
University of Washington (U)
University of Waterloo (N,U)
University of West Florida (U)
University of Wisconsin Colleges (U)
Upper Iowa University (U)
Utah State University (U)
West Shore Community College (U)

MECHANIC AND REPAIR TECHNOLOGIES RELATED

Arkansas Tech University (U)
Athens Technical College (U)
Cleveland Institute of Electronics (N)
Oxnard College (U)

MECHANICAL ENGINEERING

California National University for Advanced Studies (U,G)
Cleveland State University (G)
Colorado State University (G)
Columbia University (N,G)
Georgia Institute of Technology (N,G)
Kansas State University (G)
Kettering University (N)
Louisiana State University and Agricultural and Mechanical College (U)
Michigan Technological University (U,G)
Missouri University of Science and Technology (G)
New Mexico Institute of Mining and Technology (G)
New Mexico State University (G)
New York Institute of Technology (U)
The Ohio State University (G)
Old Dominion University (G)
Rochester Institute of Technology (U)
Southern Methodist University (G)
Stanford University (N)
State University of New York at Binghamton (G)
Texas Tech University (G)
The University of Alabama in Huntsville (G)
The University of Arizona (G)
University of Colorado at Boulder (N,G)
University of Colorado at Colorado Springs (U,G)
University of Colorado Denver (U)
University of Florida (N,G)
University of Idaho (U,G)
University of Illinois at Urbana–Champaign (N,G)
University of Michigan–Dearborn (G)
University of New Orleans (U,G)
The University of North Carolina at Charlotte (N)

University of North Dakota (U)
University of South Florida (G)
The University of Texas at San Antonio (U)
University of Washington (U,G)
Virginia Polytechnic Institute and State University (G)

MECHANICAL ENGINEERING RELATED TECHNOLOGIES

Blackhawk Technical College (U)
Blue Ridge Community College (U)
Cincinnati State Technical and Community College (U)
Cleveland Institute of Electronics (N)
Cleveland State University (G)
Columbus State Community College (U)
Indiana State University (U)
Kansas State University (G)
Southern Methodist University (G)
State University of New York at Binghamton (G)
University of Idaho (G)

MECHANICS AND REPAIR

Central Wyoming College (N,U)
Cleveland Institute of Electronics (N)

MEDICAL BASIC SCIENCES

Arapahoe Community College (U)
Athabasca University (N)
Central Wyoming College (N)
Jacksonville State University (U,G)
Laredo Community College (U)
Minot State University–Bottineau Campus (U)
Montgomery Community College (U)
NorthWest Arkansas Community College (U)
Okaloosa-Walton College (U)
Randolph Community College (N)
Rockland Community College (U)
Sarasota County Technical Institute (N)
Triton College (N)
The University of Akron (U)
The University of Montana–Western (N)
The University of Texas at Brownsville (N)

MEDICAL CLINICAL SCIENCES/ GRADUATE MEDICAL STUDIES

Arapahoe Community College (U)
Daemen College (G)
Loma Linda University (G)
Union University (U)
University of Illinois at Chicago (N)

MEDICAL ILLUSTRATION AND INFORMATICS

Arapahoe Community College (U)
Nova Southeastern University (G)
University of Illinois at Chicago (G)
University of Missouri–Columbia (N)

MEDIEVAL AND RENAISSANCE STUDIES

Adams State College (U)
Bellevue Community College (U)
California State University, Sacramento (U)
Elizabethtown College (U)

Seattle Central Community College (U)
Taylor University (U)
Triton College (U)
The University of British Columbia (U)
University of New Orleans (U,G)
University of Waterloo (U)
Western Michigan University (U)
Western Washington University (U)

MENTAL AND SOCIAL HEALTH SERVICES AND ALLIED PROFESSIONS

Arapahoe Community College (U)
Athabasca University (N,U,G)
Central Texas College (U)
Central Wyoming College (N)
College of The Albemarle (N)
Columbus State Community College (U)
Fort Valley State University (G)
Missouri State University (N)
Mount Wachusett Community College (U)
The Ohio State University (N)
State University of New York College at Cortland (U)
Tompkins Cortland Community College (U)
The University of Maine at Augusta (U)
University of Missouri–Columbia (U,G)

METALLURGICAL ENGINEERING

The University of British Columbia (U)

MICROBIOLOGICAL SCIENCES AND IMMUNOLOGY

Acadia University (U)
Baltimore City Community College (U)
Brigham Young University (U)
Central New Mexico Community College (U)
Community College of Denver (U)
Gateway Community College (U)
Graceland University (U)
Harrisburg Area Community College (U)
Honolulu Community College (U)
North Dakota State College of Science (U)
Oxnard College (U)
Rend Lake College (U)
The University of Akron (U)
University of Arkansas (U)
University of Idaho (U)
University of Minnesota, Crookston (U)
The University of South Dakota (U)
University of Southern Mississippi (U)
University of Waterloo (U)
University of Wisconsin–La Crosse (G)
Weber State University (U)

MILITARY STUDIES

American Public University System (U,G)
Central Texas College (U)
City Colleges of Chicago, Harold Washington College (U)
Eastern Michigan University (U)
John Wood Community College (U)
Louisiana State University and Agricultural and Mechanical College (U)
Myers University (U)
University of Colorado at Colorado Springs (U)
Washburn University (U)

MILITARY TECHNOLOGIES

American Public University System (U,G)
Fort Valley State University (U)

MISSIONARY STUDIES AND MISSIOLOGY

Amridge University (N,U,G)
Assemblies of God Theological Seminary (G)
Barclay College (U)
Calvin Theological Seminary (G)
Columbia International University (N,U,G)
Covenant Theological Seminary (N,G)
Crown College (U,G)
Dallas Baptist University (U,G)
Eugene Bible College (U)
Global University (N)
Grand Rapids Theological Seminary of Cornerstone University (G)
Hobe Sound Bible College (N,U)
Nebraska Christian College (U)
Providence College and Theological Seminary (N,G)
Taylor University (U)
Trinity Episcopal School for Ministry (N,G)

MOVEMENT AND MIND-BODY THERAPIES

Atlantic University (N,G)
Central Wyoming College (N)
Prescott College (G)
University of the Pacific (U)

MULTI-/INTERDISCIPLINARY STUDIES RELATED

Acadia University (U)
Avila University (U)
Berkeley College (U)
Berkeley College–New York City Campus (U)
Berkeley College–Westchester Campus (U)
Burlington College (U)
California State University, San Bernardino (U)
Central Michigan University (U,G)
Central Texas College (U)
City Colleges of Chicago, Harold Washington College (U)
Columbia College (U)
Fort Hays State University (U,G)
Grand Rapids Theological Seminary of Cornerstone University (G)
Granite State College (U)
Hibbing Community College (U)
Jones International University (U,G)
Lehigh Carbon Community College (U)
Metropolitan State University (U)
Mississippi State University (U)
Naropa University (U,G)
North Carolina State University (U)
Pace University (U)
Roosevelt University (U)
Saint Joseph's College of Maine (U)
Santa Rosa Junior College (U)
Taylor University (U)
Temple University (U)
University of Arkansas at Little Rock (U)
University of Connecticut (U)
University of Illinois at Springfield (U)
University of Minnesota, Morris (U)

The University of North Carolina at Greensboro (U)
University of Oregon (U)
University of Waterloo (U)
Wayne State College (U)

MUSEUM STUDIES

Brenau University (U)
California State University, Dominguez Hills (N)
Chatham University (U)
East Tennessee State University (G)
James Madison University (N)
Middlesex Community College (U)
University of Idaho (U)

MUSIC

Acadia University (N)
Allen County Community College (U)
Arapahoe Community College (U)
Arkansas State University–Beebe (U)
Arkansas Tech University (U)
Athabasca University (N,U)
Bellevue Community College (U)
Boise State University (U)
Bowling Green State University (U)
Brenau University (U)
Bridgewater State College (U)
Brigham Young University (U)
Butler Community College (U)
Cabrillo College (U)
Caldwell Community College and Technical Institute (U)
California State University, Dominguez Hills (N,U)
California State University, Sacramento (U)
Carl Sandburg College (U)
Carroll Community College (U)
Central Texas College (U)
Central Virginia Community College (U)
Central Wyoming College (N,U)
Cerro Coso Community College (U)
Chaminade University of Honolulu (U)
Chatham University (U)
Chemeketa Community College (U)
Citrus College (U)
City Colleges of Chicago, Harold Washington College (U)
Clackamas Community College (U)
Clarion University of Pennsylvania (U)
Clemson University (U)
Cleveland Community College (U)
Cleveland State Community College (U)
Clinton Community College (U)
College of Mount St. Joseph (U)
The College of St. Scholastica (U,G)
College of the Sequoias (U)
Colorado State University (U)
Community College of Denver (N)
Cuyahoga Community College (U)
Dakota State University (U)
Dallas County Community College District (U)
Danville Community College (U)
Darton College (U)
Daytona State College (U)
De Anza College (U)
DeSales University (U)
Drake University (G)
Duquesne University (G)

East Central Community College (U)
Eastern Oregon University (U)
Eastern West Virginia Community and Technical College (U)
Elgin Community College (U)
Elizabeth City State University (U)
Erie Community College (U)
Erie Community College, North Campus (U)
Erie Community College, South Campus (U)
Eugene Bible College (U)
Everett Community College (U)
Evergreen Valley College (U)
Florida State University (U)
Foothill College (U)
Fort Hays State University (U)
Framingham State College (U)
Gadsden State Community College (U)
Galveston College (U)
Genesee Community College (U)
Global University (N)
Greenville Technical College (U)
Gulf Coast Community College (U)
Haywood Community College (U)
Henderson Community College (U)
Hibbing Community College (U)
Holyoke Community College (U)
Hope International University (G)
Hopkinsville Community College (N,U)
Indiana State University (U)
Indiana Wesleyan University (U)
Jackson State University (U)
Jacksonville State University (U)
James Madison University (N)
Jefferson College (U)
John Wood Community College (U)
Judson College (U)
Kansas State University (U)
Kaskaskia College (U)
Kean University (N)
Kentucky State University (U)
Labette Community College (U)
Laredo Community College (U)
Lehigh Carbon Community College (U)
Limestone College (U)
Lock Haven University of Pennsylvania (U)
Long Beach City College (U)
Louisiana State University and Agricultural and Mechanical College (U)
Lurleen B. Wallace Community College (U)
Manhattan School of Music (N,U,G)
Mansfield University of Pennsylvania (U)
Massasoit Community College (U)
Metropolitan State University (U)
Midway College (U)
Millersville University of Pennsylvania (U)
Mississippi Delta Community College (U)
Missouri State University (U)
Mountain Empire Community College (U)
Mount Olive College (U)
Murray State College (U)
Murray State University (U)
Nassau Community College (U)
Naugatuck Valley Community College (U)
New River Community College (U)
Northampton County Area Community College (U)
North Carolina State University (U)
North Central Texas College (U)
Northeast Alabama Community College (U)
Northeastern Illinois University (U)
Northeast State Technical Community College (U)

Northern State University (U)
North Lake College (U)
North Seattle Community College (U)
NorthWest Arkansas Community College (U)
Northwestern Michigan College (U)
Northwest Missouri State University (U)
Oklahoma Panhandle State University (U)
Orange Coast College (U)
Oxnard College (U)
Palomar College (U)
Parkland College (U)
Patrick Henry College (U)
Peninsula College (U)
Piedmont Technical College (U)
Plymouth State University (U)
Portland Community College (U)
Pratt Community College (U)
Randolph Community College (U)
Red Rocks Community College (U)
Rend Lake College (U)
Riverside Community College District (U)
Sacred Heart University (U)
Saddleback College (U)
Saint Charles Community College (U)
Saint Mary-of-the-Woods College (G)
San Diego Community College District (U)
Santa Monica College (U)
Schenectady County Community College (U)
Sierra College (U)
Southeastern Community College (U)
Southeastern Illinois College (U)
Southeastern Oklahoma State University (U)
Southwestern Community College (U)
Spring Arbor University (U)
State University of New York at Plattsburgh (U)
State University of New York College at Potsdam (U)
Stephen F. Austin State University (U,G)
Tacoma Community College (U)
Taylor University (U)
Temple University (U,G)
Texas State University–San Marcos (U)
Texas Tech University (U,G)
Treasure Valley Community College (U)
Triton College (U)
Tunxis Community College (U)
Tyler Junior College (U)
The University of Akron (U)
University of Alaska Fairbanks (U)
University of Arkansas at Little Rock (U)
University of Bridgeport (U)
The University of British Columbia (U)
University of Colorado Denver (U)
University of Idaho (U)
The University of Maine at Augusta (U)
University of Maine at Fort Kent (U)
University of Massachusetts Boston (U)
University of Minnesota, Twin Cities Campus (U)
University of Nevada, Reno (U)
University of New Orleans (U,G)
The University of North Carolina at Chapel Hill (N,U)
University of Northern Iowa (U)
University of North Florida (U)
University of North Texas (U)
University of St. Thomas (U)
University of Saskatchewan (U)
The University of South Dakota (U)
University of Southern Maine (U)
University of Southern Mississippi (U,G)

University of South Florida (U,G)
The University of Texas of the Permian Basin (U)
The University of Texas System (U)
The University of Toledo (U)
University of Utah (U)
University of Vermont (N)
University of Wisconsin Colleges (U)
University of Wyoming (U)
Virginia Polytechnic Institute and State University (N,U)
Washburn University (U)
Wayland Baptist University (U)
Weber State University (U)
Western Michigan University (U)
Western Washington University (U)
Westfield State College (U)
West Los Angeles College (U)
West Shore Community College (U)
Wichita State University (U)
Williston State College (U)
Yuba College (U)

NATURAL RESOURCES AND CONSERVATION RELATED

Haywood Community College (U)
James Madison University (N)
Kansas State University (U)
Oregon State University (U)
Pikes Peak Community College (U)
Prescott College (G)
Saint Mary-of-the-Woods College (G)
University of California, Davis (U)
University of Maine at Machias (U)
University of Massachusetts Boston (U)
University of New Orleans (U,G)

NATURAL RESOURCES CONSERVATION AND RESEARCH

Athabasca University (U)
Colorado State University (U)
Erie Community College (U)
Erie Community College, North Campus (U)
Erie Community College, South Campus (U)
Haywood Community College (U)
Kansas State University (U)
Oregon State University (U,G)
Pikes Peak Community College (U)
Prescott College (U)
Virginia Polytechnic Institute and State University (N)

NATURAL RESOURCES MANAGEMENT AND POLICY

Athabasca University (U)
Colorado State University (G)
Haywood Community College (U)
Kansas State University (U)
Oregon State University (U,G)
Prescott College (G)
University of Denver (G)
Virginia Polytechnic Institute and State University (G)

NATURAL SCIENCES

Bellevue Community College (U)
Cape Cod Community College (U)
Columbus State Community College (U)

Dallas Baptist University (U)
Danville Community College (U)
Diné College (U)
Endicott College (U)
Haywood Community College (U)
Henry Ford Community College (U)
Kansas State University (U)
Lewis-Clark State College (U)
Middlesex Community College (U)
Oklahoma Panhandle State University (U)
Palomar College (U)
Peninsula College (U)
Pulaski Technical College (U)
Regent University (U)
San Diego Community College District (U)
University of South Florida (U)
University of Wisconsin Colleges (U)
Upper Iowa University (U)
Wayne State College (U)
Westchester Community College (U)
Western Michigan University (U)

NAVAL ARCHITECTURE AND MARINE ENGINEERING

University of New Orleans (U,G)

NEUROSCIENCE

California State University, Chico (U)
Central Wyoming College (N)
Jacksonville State University (U,G)
The University of Texas at San Antonio (G)

NUCLEAR AND INDUSTRIAL RADIOLOGIC TECHNOLOGIES

Galveston College (U)
New Mexico Junior College (U)
Oregon State University (G)

NUCLEAR ENGINEERING

The Ohio State University (G)
University of Missouri–Columbia (U,G)

NUCLEAR ENGINEERING TECHNOLOGY

Excelsior College (U)

NURSING

Alcorn State University (U)
Arapahoe Community College (U)
Arkansas Tech University (U)
Athabasca University (N,U,G)
Azusa Pacific University (G)
Beaufort County Community College (U)
Blackhawk Technical College (U)
Blessing-Rieman College of Nursing (U)
Bloomsburg University of Pennsylvania (U)
Boise State University (U)
Bowling Green State University (U)
Bradley University (U,G)
Brenau University (U,G)
Brigham Young University (U)
Broome Community College (U)
Broward Community College (U)
Butler Community College (N,U)
California State University, Chico (U,G)
California State University, Sacramento (U,G)

California State University, San Bernardino (U)
California State University, San Marcos (N)
Cape Cod Community College (U)
Carlow University (U,G)
Carroll Community College (U)
Central New Mexico Community College (U)
Central Oregon Community College (U)
Central Texas College (U)
Central Wyoming College (U)
Charter Oak State College (N)
Chatham University (N,U,G)
Clarion University of Pennsylvania (U,G)
Clark State Community College (U)
Clatsop Community College (U)
Cleveland State University (U,G)
The College of St. Scholastica (U,G)
College of Southern Maryland (N)
College of the Sequoias (U)
College of the Siskiyous (U)
Columbus State Community College (U)
Community College of Beaver County (U)
Community College of Denver (U)
Concordia University Wisconsin (U,G)
Culver-Stockton College (U)
Cuyahoga Community College (U)
Daemen College (U,G)
Danville Community College (U)
Delaware County Community College (U)
DePaul University (G)
Drexel University (U,G)
Duquesne University (G)
East Carolina University (U,G)
East Central Community College (U)
Eastern Kentucky University (U,G)
Eastern Michigan University (U,G)
Edison State Community College (U)
Elizabethtown Community and Technical College (U)
Everest College (U)
Excelsior College (G)
Finger Lakes Community College (U)
Fitchburg State College (U,G)
Flathead Valley Community College (U)
Florida Gulf Coast University (U)
Florida State University (G)
Fort Hays State University (U,G)
Fox Valley Technical College (U)
Gadsden State Community College (U)
Galveston College (U)
Gateway Technical College (U)
George Mason University (G)
Georgia College & State University (G)
Georgia Highlands College (U)
Georgia State University (U,G)
Gonzaga University (G)
Graceland University (U)
Gulf Coast Community College (U)
Harrisburg Area Community College (U)
Hopkinsville Community College (N,U)
Illinois State University (U,G)
Indiana State University (U,G)
Indiana University–Purdue University Fort Wayne (U,G)
Ivy Tech Community College–Northwest (U)
Jacksonville State University (U,G)
James A. Rhodes State College (U)
James Madison University (N)
Jefferson College of Health Sciences (N,U,G)
J. Sargeant Reynolds Community College (U)
Kaplan University Online (N)
Kauai Community College (U)

Lake-Sumter Community College (U)
Lewis-Clark State College (U)
Long Beach City College (U)
Los Angeles Harbor College (U)
Macon State College (U)
Mansfield University of Pennsylvania (U,G)
Marquette University (U,G)
Marshall University (U)
Marymount University (U)
Memorial University of Newfoundland (U,G)
Mercy College (U)
Mesa Community College (U)
Mesa State College (U)
Metropolitan State University (U,G)
MGH Institute of Health Professions (G)
Miami Dade College (U)
Michigan State University (G)
Middle Tennessee State University (N,U,G)
Midwestern State University (G)
Millersville University of Pennsylvania (U,G)
Minot State University (U)
Misericordia University (U)
Mississippi University for Women (U)
Missouri State University (U,G)
Monmouth University (G)
Monroe County Community College (U)
Montana Tech of The University of Montana (U)
Montgomery County Community College (U)
Moorpark College (U)
Mount Wachusett Community College (U)
Murray State University (U,G)
Nashville State Technical Community College (U)
National University (U)
Naugatuck Valley Community College (U)
Neumann College (G)
New Mexico State University (G)
Northampton County Area Community College (N,U)
North Arkansas College (U)
Northern Virginia Community College (U)
North Iowa Area Community College (N)
Northland Community and Technical College– Thief River Falls (U)
Northwestern Michigan College (U)
Northwestern State University of Louisiana (U)
Northwest Technical College (U)
The Ohio State University (G)
Okaloosa-Walton College (U)
Oklahoma Panhandle State University (U)
Pace University (N,U,G)
Pacific Union College (U)
Peninsula College (U)
Pennsylvania College of Technology (U)
Portland Community College (U)
Prairie View A&M University (U,G)
Rend Lake College (U)
The Richard Stockton College of New Jersey (U,G)
Riverside Community College District (U)
Rockland Community College (N,U)
Rose State College (U)
Sacramento City College (U)
Sacred Heart University (G)
Saddleback College (U)
Saint Charles Community College (U)
St. Clair County Community College (U)
Saint Francis Medical Center College of Nursing (U,G)
Saint Joseph's College of Maine (U,G)

Samuel Merritt College (G)
San Joaquin Delta College (U)
Santa Monica College (U)
Shawnee State University (U)
Southeast Arkansas College (U)
Southeastern Oklahoma State University (U)
Southern Illinois University Edwardsville (U,G)
South Piedmont Community College (U)
Southwestern College (U)
Southwest Wisconsin Technical College (U)
State University of New York at Binghamton (U,G)
State University of New York at Plattsburgh (U)
State University of New York Institute of Technology (U,G)
Sullivan County Community College (U)
Tacoma Community College (U)
Temple University (U)
Texas Woman's University (U,G)
Three Rivers Community College (U)
Tompkins Cortland Community College (U)
Triton College (U)
Union University (U)
The University of Akron (N,U,G)
The University of Alabama (G)
University of Arkansas at Little Rock (U)
The University of British Columbia (U)
University of Calgary (U)
University of California, Riverside (N)
University of Central Florida (U,G)
University of Central Missouri (U,G)
University of Colorado at Colorado Springs (U,G)
University of Houston–Victoria (U)
University of Illinois at Chicago (N,G)
University of Illinois at Urbana–Champaign (G)
University of Louisville (G)
The University of Maine at Augusta (U)
University of Maine at Fort Kent (U)
University of Massachusetts Boston (U,G)
University of Michigan–Flint (U)
University of Minnesota, Twin Cities Campus (U)
University of Missouri–Columbia (U,G)
University of North Alabama (U)
The University of North Carolina at Chapel Hill (N)
The University of North Carolina at Charlotte (N,U,G)
The University of North Carolina at Greensboro (G)
The University of North Carolina Wilmington (U)
University of North Dakota (U)
University of North Florida (U)
University of Phoenix (U,G)
University of Pittsburgh (N,U,G)
University of Pittsburgh at Bradford (U)
University of Pittsburgh at Johnstown (U)
University of St. Francis (U)
University of Saskatchewan (U)
University of South Alabama (U,G)
The University of South Dakota (U)
University of Southern Indiana (N,U,G)
University of Southern Maine (U)
University of Southern Mississippi (U,G)
University of South Florida (U)
The University of Texas at El Paso (U,G)
The University of Texas at Tyler (U,G)

The University of Texas System (G)
University of Vermont (N,U,G)
University of Windsor (U)
University of Wisconsin–La Crosse (U)
University of Wyoming (U,G)
Washburn University (U)
Westchester Community College (U)
Western Nebraska Community College (U)
West Virginia University (N)
West Virginia University at Parkersburg (U)
Wheeling Jesuit University (U,G)
Wisconsin Indianhead Technical College
  (N,U)
York Technical College (U)
York University (U)
Youngstown State University (U)

NUTRITION SCIENCES

Acadia University (U)
Allen County Community College (U)
Bellevue Community College (U)
Brazosport College (U)
Butler Community College (U)
Carroll Community College (U)
Central Michigan University (G)
Central Washington University (U)
Central Wyoming College (N)
City Colleges of Chicago, Harold Washington
  College (U)
Clemson University (U,G)
College of the Siskiyous (U)
Columbus State Community College (U)
Community College of Beaver County (U)
Corning Community College (U)
Danville Community College (U)
East Carolina University (G)
Eastern Michigan University (U)
Endicott College (U)
Erie Community College (U)
Erie Community College, North Campus (U)
Erie Community College, South Campus (U)
Everett Community College (U)
Gadsden State Community College (U)
Georgia State University (U)
Henry Ford Community College (U)
Hillsborough Community College (U)
Holyoke Community College (U)
Huntington College of Health Sciences (U,G)
Illinois Eastern Community Colleges, Frontier
  Community College (U)
Jacksonville State University (U)
James Madison University (U)
Kansas State University (U)
Long Beach City College (U)
Los Angeles Trade-Technical College (U)
Mansfield University of Pennsylvania (U)
Montgomery County Community College (U)
Nassau Community College (U)
Naugatuck Valley Community College (U)
New Mexico State University (G)
North Carolina State University (U)
North Central Texas College (U)
Northeast Iowa Community College (U)
North Florida Community College (U)
NorthWest Arkansas Community College (U)
Palomar College (U)
Pasco-Hernando Community College (U)
Peninsula College (U)
Queen's University at Kingston (U)
Quinebaug Valley Community College (U)
Rend Lake College (U)

Riverside Community College District (U)
Sacramento City College (U)
Sam Houston State University (U)
San Diego Community College District (U)
Santa Monica College (U)
Schenectady County Community College (U)
Seminole Community College (U)
Southeastern Oklahoma State University (N)
State University of New York College at
  Cortland (G)
Texas Woman's University (G)
Three Rivers Community College (U)
Treasure Valley Community College (U)
University of Alaska Fairbanks (U)
University of Dubuque (U)
The University of Maine at Augusta (U)
University of Massachusetts Boston (U)
University of Medicine and Dentistry of New
  Jersey (U,G)
University of North Florida (U)
University of North Texas (U)
University of South Florida (U)
The University of Toledo (U)
University of Vermont (N,U)
Westchester Community College (U)

OCEAN ENGINEERING

Utah Valley State College (U)

OPERATIONS RESEARCH

Drexel University (G)
Philadelphia University (U)
Saybrook Graduate School and Research
  Center (U)
Southern New Hampshire University (G)
The University of Alabama in Huntsville (G)
University of Minnesota, Twin Cities Campus
  (U)

OPHTHALMIC AND OPTOMETRIC SUPPORT SERVICES AND ALLIED PROFESSIONS

Ferris State University (U,G)
Hillsborough Community College (U)
University of Wisconsin–La Crosse (U)
Wytheville Community College (U)

PARKS, RECREATION AND LEISURE

Clemson University (U)
Community College of Denver (N)
Haywood Community College (U)
Kean University (N)
Minot State University–Bottineau Campus (U)
Prescott College (U)
Seattle Pacific University (G)
State University of New York College at
  Cortland (G)
United States Sports Academy (N)
University of Missouri–Columbia (U)
The University of North Carolina at Chapel
  Hill (U)

PARKS, RECREATION AND LEISURE FACILITIES MANAGEMENT

Haywood Community College (U)
Kean University (U)

Minot State University–Bottineau Campus (U)
North Carolina State University (U)
Prescott College (G)
United States Sports Academy (N)
University of Wisconsin–La Crosse (G)
Wayne State College (G)

PARKS, RECREATION, AND LEISURE RELATED

Acadia University (N)
Haywood Community College (U)
James Madison University (N)
Minot State University–Bottineau Campus (U)
Mount Olive College (U)
San Diego State University (U)
United States Sports Academy (N)
University of Southern Mississippi (G)
Western Washington University (U)

PASTORAL COUNSELING AND SPECIALIZED MINISTRIES

Amridge University (N,U,G)
Andover Newton Theological School (G)
Arlington Baptist College (U)
Assemblies of God Theological Seminary (G)
Beulah Heights University (U)
Calvin Theological Seminary (G)
Crown College (U)
Duquesne University (G)
Earlham School of Religion (G)
Eastern Mennonite University (G)
Eugene Bible College (U)
George Fox University (G)
Global University (N)
Gordon-Conwell Theological Seminary (N,G)
Grand Rapids Theological Seminary of
  Cornerstone University (G)
Hobe Sound Bible College (N,U)
Maranatha Baptist Bible College (G)
Master's College and Seminary (U)
Providence College and Theological Seminary
  (N,G)
Regent University (N,G)
St. Ambrose University (G)
Saint Joseph's College of Maine (N,U)
Summit Pacific College (U)
Taylor University (U)

PEACE STUDIES AND CONFLICT RESOLUTION

Atlantic University (N,G)
Brenau University (U)
Caldwell Community College and Technical
  Institute (N)
Drake University (U,G)
Earlham School of Religion (G)
Eastern Mennonite University (G)
Jones International University (G)
Massasoit Community College (N)
Mercy College (G)
Prescott College (G)
St. Edward's University (G)
Saybrook Graduate School and Research
  Center (G)
Taylor University (U)
The University of Akron (U)
University of Massachusetts Boston (G)
The University of North Carolina at
  Greensboro (G)

University of Waterloo (U)

PERSONAL AND CULINARY SERVICES RELATED

Baltimore City Community College (N)
California State University, Dominguez Hills (N)
Central Wyoming College (N)
Community College of Denver (N)
Kean University (N)
Linn-Benton Community College (N)
NorthWest Arkansas Community College (U)
Pace University (N)
Pasco-Hernando Community College (N)
University of Missouri–Columbia (N)

PERSONALITY PSYCHOLOGY

Arapahoe Community College (U)
Community College of Denver (N)
Dallas Baptist University (U)
Erie Community College (U)
Erie Community College, North Campus (U)
Erie Community College, South Campus (U)
Indiana State University (U)
Jefferson Community College (U)
Palomar College (U)
Roosevelt University (U)
San Diego Community College District (U)
University of Alaska Fairbanks (U)
University of Minnesota, Twin Cities Campus (U)
University of New Orleans (U,G)
University of North Dakota (U)
Yuba College (U)

PETROLEUM ENGINEERING

New Mexico Institute of Mining and Technology (G)
Texas Tech University (G)

PHARMACOLOGY AND TOXICOLOGY

Arapahoe Community College (U)
Brenau University (U)
Cleveland State Community College (U)
Drexel University (G)
Jacksonville State University (G)
Northwestern Michigan College (U)
Oregon State University (N)
Peninsula College (U)
Queen's University at Kingston (U)
Santa Monica College (U)

PHARMACY, PHARMACEUTICAL SCIENCES, AND ADMINISTRATION

Arapahoe Community College (U)
Auburn University (G)
Charter Oak State College (N)
Cleveland State University (U)
Delaware County Community College (U)
Drake University (U,G)
Long Beach City College (U)
New Jersey Institute of Technology (G)
Oregon State University (N)
Portland Community College (N)
Randolph Community College (N)
St. John's University (U)

Shawnee State University (N)
The University of Akron (U)
University of Illinois at Chicago (N,G)
University of Illinois at Urbana–Champaign (G)
The University of North Carolina at Greensboro (N)
University of Washington (U)
Vincennes University (U)
Wake Technical Community College (U)
West Virginia University (N)

PHILOSOPHY

Acadia University (U)
Allen County Community College (U)
Alpena Community College (U)
American Public University System (U)
Anne Arundel Community College (U)
Arapahoe Community College (U)
Arkansas State University–Beebe (U)
Athabasca University (N,U,G)
Beacon University (G)
Bellevue Community College (U)
Belmont Technical College (U)
Bergen Community College (U)
Berkeley College (U)
Berkeley College–New York City Campus (U)
Berkeley College–Westchester Campus (U)
Beulah Heights University (U)
Boise State University (U)
Bowling Green State University (U)
Brenau University (U)
Brigham Young University (U)
Bristol Community College (U)
Broward Community College (U)
Burlington College (U)
Butler Community College (U)
Cabrillo College (U)
California State University, San Marcos (N)
Carlow University (U)
Carroll Community College (U)
Carroll University (U)
Centralia College (U)
Central New Mexico Community College (U)
Central Texas College (U)
Central Virginia Community College (U)
Chadron State College (U)
Chaminade University of Honolulu (U)
Chemeketa Community College (U)
Citrus College (U)
Clarion University of Pennsylvania (U)
Cleveland State University (U,G)
Coastline Community College (U)
College of San Mateo (U)
College of Southern Maryland (U)
Colorado Mountain College District System (U)
Columbus State Community College (U)
Community College of Beaver County (U)
Community College of Denver (U)
Corning Community College (U)
Cuyahoga Community College (U)
Dallas Baptist University (U)
Dallas County Community College District (U)
Darton College (U)
Daytona State College (U)
Delaware County Community College (U)
DeSales University (U)
Duquesne University (U)
East Carolina University (U)

Eastern Mennonite University (G)
Eastern Michigan University (U)
Eastern Oregon University (U)
Eastern Washington University (U)
East Los Angeles College (U)
Edison State Community College (U)
Erie Community College (U)
Erie Community College, North Campus (U)
Erie Community College, South Campus (U)
Everett Community College (U)
Finger Lakes Community College (U)
Fontbonne University (U)
Fort Hays State University (U)
Franciscan University of Steubenville (N,U)
Gadsden State Community College (U)
Gateway Community College (U)
Georgia State University (U)
Golden Gate University (U)
Golden West College (U)
Grand Rapids Community College (U)
Harrisburg Area Community College (U)
Harris-Stowe State University (U)
Hibbing Community College (U)
Honolulu Community College (U)
Hope International University (U)
Hopkinsville Community College (U)
Houston Community College System (U)
Indiana University–Purdue University Fort Wayne (U)
Indian River Community College (U)
Institute for Christian Studies (G)
Iona College (U)
Ivy Tech Community College–North Central (U)
James Madison University (U)
Jefferson College (U)
Jefferson College of Health Sciences (U,G)
Jefferson Community College (U)
John Wood Community College (U)
J. Sargeant Reynolds Community College (U)
Lamar State College–Port Arthur (U)
Lehigh Carbon Community College (U)
Lewis-Clark State College (U)
Liberty University (U)
Limestone College (U)
Long Beach City College (U)
Los Angeles Trade-Technical College (U)
Louisiana State University and Agricultural and Mechanical College (U)
Malone College (U)
Marian College of Fond du Lac (U)
Marshall University (U)
Massachusetts College of Liberal Arts (U)
Massasoit Community College (U)
Memorial University of Newfoundland (U)
Mercer County Community College (U)
Metropolitan State University (U)
Middlesex Community College (U)
Minot State University (U)
Misericordia University (U)
Monmouth University (U)
Montana Tech of The University of Montana (U)
Montgomery County Community College (U)
Moorpark College (U)
Mt. San Antonio College (U)
Murray State University (U)
Naropa University (N)
Naugatuck Valley Community College (U)
New York Institute of Technology (U)
Northampton County Area Community College (U)

North Carolina State University (U)
Northern Virginia Community College (U)
North Iowa Area Community College (U)
North Lake College (U)
North Seattle Community College (U)
NorthWest Arkansas Community College (U)
Northwestern Connecticut Community College (U)
Northwestern Michigan College (U)
Northwest Missouri State University (U)
Okaloosa-Walton College (U)
Old Dominion University (U)
Oregon State University (U)
Ouachita Technical College (U)
Oxnard College (U)
Palomar College (U)
Parkland College (U)
Patrick Henry College (U)
Peninsula College (U)
Pulaski Technical College (U)
Queen's University at Kingston (U)
Riverside Community College District (U)
Rockland Community College (U)
Rose State College (U)
Sacramento City College (U)
Sacred Heart University (U)
St. Ambrose University (U)
St. Cloud State University (U)
St. Edward's University (U)
Saint Francis University (U)
St. John's University (U)
Saint Leo University (U)
Sam Houston State University (U)
San Diego Community College District (U)
Santa Rosa Junior College (U)
Shippensburg University of Pennsylvania (U)
Sierra College (U)
Southeast Community College Area (U)
Southeastern Illinois College (U)
Southern Arkansas University Tech (U)
Southwestern College (U)
Spring Arbor University (U)
State University of New York at Binghamton (U)
Tacoma Community College (U)
Taylor University (U)
Texas State University–San Marcos (U)
Triton College (U)
Tunxis Community College (U)
Unification Theological Seminary (N,G)
The University of Akron (U)
The University of Alabama (U)
University of Arkansas at Little Rock (U)
University of Bridgeport (U)
The University of British Columbia (U)
University of Cincinnati (U)
University of Hawaii–West Oahu (U)
University of Houston–Downtown (U)
University of Idaho (U)
University of Illinois at Springfield (U)
University of Illinois at Urbana–Champaign (U)
The University of Kansas (U)
University of Louisville (U)
The University of Maine at Augusta (U)
University of Maine at Fort Kent (U)
University of Maine at Machias (U)
University of Minnesota, Crookston (U)
University of Minnesota, Twin Cities Campus (U)
University of Missouri–Columbia (U)
The University of Montana–Western (U)

University of New Orleans (U,G)
University of North Alabama (U)
The University of North Carolina at Chapel Hill (N,U)
The University of North Carolina at Greensboro (U)
University of North Florida (U)
University of Oklahoma (U)
University of St. Thomas (U)
University of Saskatchewan (U)
University of South Florida (U)
The University of Toledo (U,G)
University of Washington (U)
University of Waterloo (U)
University of West Florida (U)
University of Wisconsin Colleges (U)
Utah State University (U)
Utah Valley State College (U)
Virginia Polytechnic Institute and State University (U)
Wake Technical Community College (U)
Weber State University (U)
Webster University (U)
Westchester Community College (U)
Western Wyoming Community College (U)
Westfield State College (U)
West Los Angeles College (U)
West Virginia University at Parkersburg (U)
Wilfrid Laurier University (U)
Worcester State College (U)
York Technical College (U)
York University (U)
Youngstown State University (U)

PHILOSOPHY AND RELIGIOUS STUDIES RELATED

American Public University System (U)
Amridge University (N,U,G)
Arlington Baptist College (U)
Assemblies of God Theological Seminary (G)
Athabasca University (N,U)
Atlantic University (N,G)
The Baptist College of Florida (U)
Beacon University (N,U)
Bergen Community College (U)
Berkeley College (U)
Berkeley College–New York City Campus (U)
Berkeley College–Westchester Campus (U)
Bowling Green State University (U)
Brigham Young University (U)
Broward Community College (U)
Butler Community College (U)
Cabrillo College (U)
California Institute of Integral Studies (N,G)
The Catholic Distance University (N,U,G)
Central Arizona College (U)
Central Texas College (U)
Central Washington University (U)
Chadron State College (U)
Chaminade University of Honolulu (U)
Charter Oak State College (U)
Chemeketa Community College (U)
City Colleges of Chicago, Harold Washington College (U)
Cleveland State University (G)
Coastline Community College (U)
College of Southern Maryland (U)
Columbia College (U)
Columbus State Community College (U)
Community College of Denver (U)
Crafton Hills College (U)

Crown College (U,G)
Dallas Baptist University (U,G)
Dallas Christian College (U)
Dallas County Community College District (U)
Darton College (U)
De Anza College (U)
Delaware County Community College (U)
Denver Seminary (G)
DeSales University (U)
Duquesne University (U,G)
East Carolina University (U)
Eastern Kentucky University (U)
Eastern Mennonite University (G)
Eastern Michigan University (U)
Edison State Community College (U)
Galveston College (U)
Global University (N)
Gordon-Conwell Theological Seminary (N,G)
Greenville Technical College (U)
Hebrew College (N,U,G)
Hobe Sound Bible College (N,U)
Holy Apostles College and Seminary (G)
Honolulu Community College (U)
Indiana Wesleyan University (U)
Indian River Community College (U)
Institute for Christian Studies (G)
Iona College (U)
John Wood Community College (U)
Judson College (U)
Lake Superior College (U)
Lamar State College–Port Arthur (U)
Life Pacific College (U)
Loma Linda University (G)
Louisiana State University and Agricultural and Mechanical College (U)
Manatee Community College (U)
Master's College and Seminary (U)
Miami Dade College (U)
Middlesex Community College (U)
Murray State University (U)
Naropa University (N,U)
New York Institute of Technology (U)
Oregon State University (U)
Palomar College (U)
Park University (U)
Patrick Henry College (U)
Pellissippi State Technical Community College (U)
Pennsylvania College of Technology (U)
Piedmont Technical College (U)
Prescott College (U,G)
Randolph Community College (U)
Regis University (U,G)
Rend Lake College (U)
Rose State College (U)
Sacramento City College (U)
Sacred Heart University (U)
Saint Francis University (U)
Saint Joseph's College of Maine (U)
Saint Leo University (U)
San Joaquin Delta College (U)
Seattle Central Community College (U)
Southwestern Community College (U)
Spoon River College (U)
State University of New York at Oswego (U)
Taylor University (U)
Triton College (U)
Unification Theological Seminary (N,G)
The University of Akron (U)
The University of Alabama (U)
University of Arkansas (U)

University of Arkansas at Little Rock (U)
University of Bridgeport (U)
University of California, Los Angeles (G)
University of Central Florida (U)
University of Cincinnati (U)
University of Colorado Denver (U)
The University of Findlay (U)
University of Illinois at Urbana–Champaign
 (U)
University of Missouri–Columbia (U)
University of New Orleans (U,G)
University of St. Francis (U)
University of Southern Mississippi (U)
University of South Florida (U)
The University of Texas of the Permian Basin
 (U)
The University of Toledo (U)
University of Waterloo (U)
Upper Iowa University (U)
Westchester Community College (U)

PHYSICAL SCIENCE TECHNOLOGIES

Barton County Community College (U)
Union University (U)

PHYSICAL SCIENCES

Allen County Community College (U)
Arkansas State University–Beebe (U)
Arkansas Tech University (U)
Athabasca University (N,U)
Barclay College (U)
Bellevue Community College (U)
Belmont Technical College (U)
Brigham Young University (U)
Broome Community College (U)
Butler Community College (U)
Cabrillo College (U)
Caldwell Community College and Technical
 Institute (U)
Chadron State College (U)
Chatham University (G)
Chemeketa Community College (U)
Connors State College (U)
Corban College (U)
Cuyahoga Community College (U)
Dallas County Community College District
 (U)
Darton College (U)
East Central Community College (U)
Eugene Bible College (U)
Everett Community College (U)
George C. Wallace Community College (U)
Gulf Coast Community College (U)
Harrisburg Area Community College (U)
Honolulu Community College (U)
Houston Community College System (U)
Indian River Community College (U)
Ivy Tech Community College–Northwest (U)
Jacksonville State University (U,G)
James Madison University (N)
John Wood Community College (U)
Kansas State University (U)
Labette Community College (U)
Lake-Sumter Community College (U)
Lake Superior College (U)
Louisiana State University and Agricultural
 and Mechanical College (U)
Lurleen B. Wallace Community College (U)
Massasoit Community College (U)

Middlesex Community College (U)
Mississippi Delta Community College (U)
Murray State College (U)
Northwestern State University of Louisiana
 (U)
Okaloosa-Walton College (U)
Oklahoma Panhandle State University (U)
Oxnard College (U)
Pace University (U)
Pasco-Hernando Community College (U)
Passaic County Community College (U)
Peninsula College (U)
Pulaski Technical College (U)
Regent University (U)
Rockland Community College (U)
Roosevelt University (U)
Rose State College (U)
Sacramento City College (U)
Sacred Heart University (U)
Saint Francis University (U)
Saint Leo University (U)
San Diego Community College District (U)
Schiller International University (U)
Seminole Community College (U)
Southeastern Oklahoma State University (U)
State University of New York College at
 Potsdam (U)
Taylor University (U)
Temple University (G)
Treasure Valley Community College (U)
The University of Akron (U)
University of Arkansas at Little Rock (U)
The University of Maine at Augusta (U)
University of New Orleans (U,G)
University of North Dakota (U)
The University of South Dakota (U)
The University of Texas at San Antonio (U)
The University of Texas System (U)
University of Waterloo (U)
University of West Florida (U)
University of Wisconsin–Superior (U)
Upper Iowa University (U)
Utah State University (U)
Utah Valley State College (U)
Wayland Baptist University (U)
Wayne State College (U)

PHYSICAL SCIENCES RELATED

Bellevue Community College (U)
Berkeley College (U)
Berkeley College–New York City Campus (U)
Berkeley College–Westchester Campus (U)
Butler Community College (U)
Chadron State College (U)
Chemeketa Community College (U)
City Colleges of Chicago, Harold Washington
 College (U)
Dallas County Community College District
 (U)
James Madison University (N)
Kansas State University (U)
Miami Dade College (U)
Mississippi State University (U)
Nassau Community College (U)
Okaloosa-Walton College (U)
Portland Community College (U)
Roger Williams University (U)
Rose State College (U)
Saint Francis University (U)
Seminole Community College (U)
State University of New York College of
 Technology at Canton (U)

Taylor University (U)
The University of Akron (U)
University of Arkansas at Little Rock (U)
The University of Texas System (U)
University of West Florida (U)

PHYSICS

Acadia University (U)
Arapahoe Community College (U)
Boise State University (U)
Brigham Young University (U)
Butler Community College (U)
California State University, Dominguez Hills
 (U)
Chaminade University of Honolulu (U)
Chatham University (U)
Clackamas Community College (U)
Clemson University (U)
Cleveland State Community College (U)
College of Southern Maryland (U)
Colorado Mountain College District System
 (U)
Community College of Denver (U)
Cuyahoga Community College (U)
Delaware County Community College (U)
Diné College (U)
Eastern Oregon University (U)
Edison State Community College (U)
Fort Hays State University (U)
Georgia State University (U)
Grantham University (U)
Greenville Technical College (U)
Henderson Community College (U)
Hopkinsville Community College (U)
Indiana University of Pennsylvania (U)
Indian River Community College (U)
Jacksonville State University (U)
James Madison University (N)
Jefferson College (U)
John A. Logan College (U)
John Wood Community College (U)
Lehigh Carbon Community College (U)
Louisiana State University and Agricultural
 and Mechanical College (U)
Metropolitan State University (U)
Michigan Technological University (N,U)
Mississippi State University (U)
Missouri State University (U)
New England Institute of Technology (U)
New Jersey City University (U)
North Carolina State University (U)
Northern Virginia Community College (U)
North Lake College (U)
Northwestern Michigan College (U)
Oxnard College (U)
Parkland College (U)
Pellissippi State Technical Community
 College (U)
Saddleback College (U)
St. Cloud State University (U)
St. John's University (U)
Shippensburg University of Pennsylvania (U)
Stevens Institute of Technology (U)
Tacoma Community College (U)
Temple University (U)
Texas A&M University–Kingsville (U)
Union County College (U)
Union University (U)
The University of Arizona (U)
University of Colorado Denver (U)
University of Idaho (U)

University of Massachusetts Boston (U)
University of Minnesota, Crookston (U)
University of Minnesota, Twin Cities Campus (U)
University of Missouri–Columbia (U)
University of New Orleans (U,G)
The University of North Carolina at Chapel Hill (U)
University of North Dakota (U)
University of Oregon (U)
The University of Tennessee (U)
University of Waterloo (N,U)
University of Wyoming (U)
Utah State University (U)
Virginia Polytechnic Institute and State University (U)
Wake Technical Community College (U)
Wayne State College (U)
Weber State University (U)
Wytheville Community College (U)

PHYSIOLOGICAL PSYCHOLOGY/ PSYCHOBIOLOGY

Athabasca University (U)
Chadron State College (U)
Eastern Wyoming College (U)
Mesa Community College (U)

PHYSIOLOGY, PATHOLOGY AND RELATED SCIENCES

Darton College (U)
Erie Community College (U)
Erie Community College, North Campus (U)
Erie Community College, South Campus (U)
Huntington College of Health Sciences (U)
James A. Rhodes State College (U)
Louisiana State University and Agricultural and Mechanical College (U)
New England Institute of Technology (U)
Sacramento City College (U)
San Diego State University (U)
Saybrook Graduate School and Research Center (G)
University of Minnesota, Twin Cities Campus (U)
The University of South Dakota (U)
University of Waterloo (U)

PLANT SCIENCES

Athabasca University (U)
Bellevue Community College (U)
Colorado State University (U)
Cuyahoga Community College (U)
Gateway Technical College (U)
Haywood Community College (U)
James Madison University (N)
John Wood Community College (U)
Kansas State University (G)
Minot State University–Bottineau Campus (U)
Nova Scotia Agricultural College (N,U)
The Ohio State University (U,G)
Oregon State University (U)
Palomar College (U)
Piedmont Technical College (U)
Rend Lake College (U)
Texas Tech University (G)
University of California, Riverside (N)
University of Missouri–Columbia (U)

Virginia Polytechnic Institute and State University (N)
Yuba College (U)

PLUMBING AND RELATED WATER SUPPLY SERVICES

Athens Technical College (U)
Wake Technical Community College (U)

POLITICAL SCIENCE AND GOVERNMENT

Acadia University (U)
Allen County Community College (U)
Alpena Community College (U)
American Public University System (U)
American University (U,G)
Anne Arundel Community College (U)
Arapahoe Community College (U)
Arkansas State University–Beebe (U)
Arkansas Tech University (U)
Athabasca University (N,U,G)
Auburn University (U)
Ball State University (U)
Bellevue Community College (U)
Bergen Community College (U)
Berkeley College (U)
Berkeley College–New York City Campus (U)
Berkeley College–Westchester Campus (U)
Beulah Heights University (U)
Bowling Green State University (U)
Bradley University (G)
Brazosport College (U)
Brenau University (U)
Bridgewater State College (U)
Brigham Young University (U)
Buena Vista University (U)
Buffalo State College, State University of New York (U)
Butler Community College (U)
California State University, Chico (U)
California State University, San Bernardino (U)
Campbell University (U)
Capital Community College (U)
Carlow University (U)
Cayuga County Community College (U)
Centralia College (U)
Central Michigan University (U,G)
Central Texas College (U)
Central Virginia Community College (U)
Central Wyoming College (U)
Chaminade University of Honolulu (U)
Chatham University (U)
Chemeketa Community College (U)
Citrus College (U)
Clinton Community College (U)
Coastline Community College (U)
College of Mount St. Joseph (U)
College of San Mateo (U)
College of Southern Maryland (U)
College of the Siskiyous (U)
Columbia College (U)
Columbus State Community College (U)
Community College of Denver (U)
Connors State College (U)
Crafton Hills College (U)
Cuyahoga Community College (U)
Dallas Baptist University (U)
Danville Community College (U)
Darton College (U)

De Anza College (U)
Drake University (U,G)
Eastern Kentucky University (U)
Eastern Michigan University (U)
Eastern Oregon University (U)
Eastern West Virginia Community and Technical College (U)
Eastern Wyoming College (U)
Erie Community College (U)
Erie Community College, North Campus (U)
Erie Community College, South Campus (U)
Evergreen Valley College (U)
Flathead Valley Community College (U)
Florida State University (U)
Fort Hays State University (U)
Fort Valley State University (U)
Framingham State College (U)
Frank Phillips College (U)
Gadsden State Community College (U)
Galveston College (U)
Gateway Community College (U)
Genesee Community College (U)
Glenville State College (U)
Golden West College (U)
Grand Rapids Community College (U)
Greenville Technical College (U)
Hamline University (N)
Haywood Community College (U)
Henry Ford Community College (U)
Hibbing Community College (U)
Hillsborough Community College (U)
Holyoke Community College (U)
Honolulu Community College (U)
Houston Community College System (U)
Indiana University of Pennsylvania (U,G)
Indiana University–Purdue University Fort Wayne (U)
Institute for Christian Studies (G)
Ivy Tech Community College–North Central (U)
Jacksonville State University (U,G)
James Madison University (N)
Jefferson Community College (U)
John A. Logan College (U)
John Wood Community College (U)
J. Sargeant Reynolds Community College (U)
Judson College (U)
Judson University (U)
Kansas State University (U)
Kean University (U)
Labette Community College (U)
Lake Superior College (U)
Lehigh Carbon Community College (U)
Lewis-Clark State College (U)
Limestone College (U)
Lock Haven University of Pennsylvania (U)
Long Beach City College (U)
Los Angeles Harbor College (U)
Los Angeles Trade-Technical College (U)
Louisiana State University and Agricultural and Mechanical College (U)
Malone College (U)
Memorial University of Newfoundland (U)
Mesa Community College (U)
Mesa State College (U)
Metropolitan State University (U)
Miami Dade College (U)
Middlesex Community College (U)
Middle Tennessee State University (U)
Midwestern State University (U)
Misericordia University (U)
Mississippi Delta Community College (U)

Missouri State University (U,G)
Monroe County Community College (U)
Mount Wachusett Community College (U)
Murray State College (U)
Myers University (U)
New Jersey City University (U)
New York Institute of Technology (U)
North Carolina State University (U)
North Central Texas College (U)
Northeast State Technical Community College (U)
North Lake College (U)
NorthWest Arkansas Community College (U)
Northwest Missouri State University (U)
Nyack College (U)
The Ohio State University (U)
Okaloosa-Walton College (U)
Oklahoma Panhandle State University (U)
Oklahoma State University (U)
Oregon State University (U)
Ouachita Technical College (U)
Oxnard College (U)
Pace University (U)
Palomar College (U)
Parkland College (U)
Park University (U)
Pasco-Hernando Community College (U)
Patrick Henry College (U)
Peninsula College (U)
Piedmont Technical College (U)
Pikes Peak Community College (U)
Pratt Community College (U)
Pulaski Technical College (U)
Quinebaug Valley Community College (U)
Regent University (U,G)
Rend Lake College (U)
Riverside Community College District (U)
Rochester Institute of Technology (U)
Rockland Community College (U)
Rose State College (U)
Sacramento City College (U)
Sacred Heart University (U)
Saddleback College (U)
Saint Charles Community College (U)
St. Clair County Community College (U)
St. John's University (U)
Saint Mary-of-the-Woods College (U)
Sam Houston State University (U)
San Diego Community College District (U)
San Joaquin Delta College (U)
Schiller International University (U)
Seminole Community College (U)
Shippensburg University of Pennsylvania (U,G)
Southeastern Illinois College (U)
Southeastern Oklahoma State University (U)
Southern Arkansas University Tech (U)
State University of New York at Binghamton (U)
State University of New York at Plattsburgh (U)
State University of New York College at Cortland (U)
State University of New York College of Technology at Canton (U)
State University of New York Empire State College (U,G)
Strayer University (U)
Tacoma Community College (U)
Taylor University (U)
Texas State University–San Marcos (U)
Tyler Junior College (U)

Union County College (U)
The University of Akron (U,G)
The University of Alabama (U)
University of Alaska Fairbanks (U)
The University of Arizona (U)
University of Arkansas at Little Rock (U,G)
University of Bridgeport (U)
The University of British Columbia (U)
University of Colorado Denver (U,G)
University of Hawaii–West Oahu (U)
University of Houston–Downtown (U)
University of Idaho (U)
University of Illinois at Springfield (U,G)
University of Illinois at Urbana–Champaign (U)
The University of Kansas (U)
University of Louisville (U)
The University of Maine at Augusta (U)
University of Maine at Fort Kent (U)
University of Maine at Machias (U)
University of Massachusetts Boston (U)
University of Minnesota, Morris (U)
University of Missouri–Columbia (U)
University of New Orleans (U,G)
University of North Alabama (U)
The University of North Carolina at Chapel Hill (N,U)
The University of North Carolina at Charlotte (U)
University of Oklahoma (U)
University of Oregon (U)
University of Saskatchewan (U)
University of Southern Indiana (U)
The University of Tennessee (U)
The University of Texas at El Paso (U)
The University of Texas at San Antonio (U,G)
The University of Texas at Tyler (U)
The University of Texas System (N,U,G)
The University of Toledo (U,G)
University of Utah (U)
University of Washington (U,G)
University of West Florida (U,G)
University of Wisconsin Colleges (U)
University of Wisconsin–Whitewater (U,G)
Upper Iowa University (N,U)
Utah Valley State College (U)
Virginia Polytechnic Institute and State University (U,G)
Wake Technical Community College (U)
Washburn University (U)
Washington State University (U)
Wayland Baptist University (U)
Weber State University (U)
Westchester Community College (U)
West Los Angeles College (U)
York University (U)

POLYMER/PLASTICS ENGINEERING

Lehigh University (N,G)
Quinebaug Valley Community College (U)
The University of Akron (U)
Wake Technical Community College (U)

PRECISION METAL WORKING

Central Wyoming College (N)
Henry Ford Community College (U)

PRECISION SYSTEMS MAINTENANCE AND REPAIR TECHNOLOGIES

James Madison University (N)
Massasoit Community College (N)

PSYCHOLOGY

Acadia University (U)
AIB College of Business (U)
Allen County Community College (U)
Alpena Community College (U)
American Public University System (U)
American University (U,G)
Arapahoe Community College (U)
Arkansas State University–Beebe (U)
Arkansas Tech University (U)
Athabasca University (N,U,G)
Athens Technical College (U)
Austin Peay State University (U)
Avila University (U)
Baltimore City Community College (U)
Barclay College (U)
Beacon University (N,U,G)
Beaufort County Community College (U)
Bellevue Community College (U)
Belmont Technical College (U)
Bergen Community College (U)
Berkeley College (U)
Berkeley College–New York City Campus (U)
Berkeley College–Westchester Campus (U)
Black Hills State University (U)
Bloomfield College (U)
Blue Ridge Community College (U)
Boise State University (U)
Bowling Green State University (U,G)
Bradley University (U)
Brazosport College (U)
Brenau University (U)
Bridgewater State College (U,G)
Brigham Young University (U)
Bristol Community College (U)
Broome Community College (U)
Broward Community College (U)
Buena Vista University (U)
Burlington College (U)
Burlington County College (U)
Butler Community College (U)
Caldwell Community College and Technical Institute (U)
California State University, Chico (U)
California State University, Sacramento (U)
California State University, San Bernardino (U)
Campbell University (U)
Cape Cod Community College (U)
Capella University (G)
Capital Community College (U)
Carlow University (U)
Carl Sandburg College (U)
Carroll Community College (U)
Cayuga County Community College (U)
Centralia College (U)
Central Michigan University (U)
Central New Mexico Community College (U)
Central Texas College (U)
Central Virginia Community College (U)
Central Washington University (U)
Central Wyoming College (N,U)
Chadron State College (U,G)
Chaminade University of Honolulu (U)

Charter Oak State College (U)
Chatham University (U)
Chemeketa Community College (U)
Citrus College (U)
Clarion University of Pennsylvania (U)
Clark State Community College (U)
Clatsop Community College (U)
Cleveland Community College (U)
Cleveland State Community College (U)
Clinton Community College (U)
Coastline Community College (U)
The College of St. Scholastica (U)
College of San Mateo (U)
College of Southern Maryland (U)
College of The Albemarle (U)
College of the Sequoias (U)
College of the Siskiyous (U)
Colorado Mountain College District System (U)
Colorado State University (U)
Columbia College (U)
Columbia-Greene Community College (U)
Columbus State Community College (U)
Columbus State University (U)
Community College of Beaver County (U)
Community College of Denver (U)
Corning Community College (U)
Cumberland County College (U)
Cuyahoga Community College (U)
Daemen College (U)
Dakota State University (U)
Dallas Baptist University (U)
Dallas County Community College District (U)
Danville Community College (U)
Darton College (U)
Dawson Community College (U)
De Anza College (U)
Delaware County Community College (U)
Delaware Technical & Community College, Jack F. Owens Campus (U)
DeSales University (U)
Drake University (U,G)
Drexel University (U)
East Carolina University (G)
East Central Community College (U)
Eastern Illinois University (U)
Eastern Michigan University (U)
Eastern Oregon University (U)
Eastern West Virginia Community and Technical College (U)
East Los Angeles College (U)
East Tennessee State University (U)
Edgecombe Community College (U)
Edison State Community College (U)
Elaine P. Nunez Community College (U)
Elgin Community College (U)
Elizabeth City State University (U)
Embry-Riddle Aeronautical University (G)
Endicott College (U)
Erie Community College (U)
Erie Community College, North Campus (U)
Erie Community College, South Campus (U)
Everett Community College (U)
Evergreen Valley College (U)
Excelsior College (U)
Finger Lakes Community College (U)
Flathead Valley Community College (U)
Florida Gulf Coast University (U)
Fontbonne University (U)
Foothill College (U)
Fort Hays State University (U)

Fort Valley State University (U)
Fox Valley Technical College (U)
Framingham State College (U)
Gadsden State Community College (U)
Galveston College (U)
Gateway Technical College (U)
Genesee Community College (U)
George C. Wallace Community College (U)
Georgia Highlands College (U)
Georgia State University (U)
Golden West College (U)
Governors State University (U)
Graceland University (U)
Grand Rapids Community College (U)
Grand View College (U)
Grantham University (U)
Greenfield Community College (U)
Greenville Technical College (U)
Gulf Coast Community College (U)
Harford Community College (U)
Harrisburg Area Community College (U)
Haywood Community College (U)
Henderson Community College (U)
Henry Ford Community College (U)
Herkimer County Community College (U)
Hibbing Community College (U)
Hillsborough Community College (U)
Hocking College (U)
Holyoke Community College (U)
Honolulu Community College (U)
Hope International University (N,U,G)
Hopkinsville Community College (N,U)
Horizon College & Seminary (U)
Houston Community College System (U)
Huntington College of Health Sciences (U)
Illinois Eastern Community Colleges, Lincoln Trail College (U)
Illinois Eastern Community Colleges, Olney Central College (U)
Illinois Eastern Community Colleges, Wabash Valley College (U)
Immaculata University (U)
Indiana State University (U)
Indiana Tech (U)
Indiana University of Pennsylvania (U)
Indiana University–Purdue University Fort Wayne (U)
Indiana Wesleyan University (U)
Iona College (U,G)
Ivy Tech Community College–East Central (U)
Ivy Tech Community College–North Central (U)
Ivy Tech Community College–Northwest (U)
Ivy Tech Community College–Wabash Valley (U)
Ivy Tech Community College–Whitewater (U)
Jacksonville State University (U,G)
James Madison University (U)
Jefferson College (U)
Jefferson College of Health Sciences (U)
Jefferson Community College (U)
John A. Logan College (U)
Johnson County Community College (U)
Johnson State College (U)
John Wood Community College (U)
J. Sargeant Reynolds Community College (U)
Judson College (U)
Judson University (U)
Kansas State University (U,G)
Kaskaskia College (U)
Kauai Community College (U)

Kean University (U)
Kentucky State University (U)
Kirtland Community College (U)
Labette Community College (U)
Lackawanna College (U)
Lake Region State College (U)
Lake-Sumter Community College (U)
Lake Superior College (U)
Lamar State College–Port Arthur (U)
Laredo Community College (U)
Lehigh Carbon Community College (U)
Lewis-Clark State College (U)
Liberty University (U,G)
Limestone College (U)
Lock Haven University of Pennsylvania (U)
Loma Linda University (G)
Long Beach City College (U)
Los Angeles Harbor College (U)
Los Angeles Trade-Technical College (U)
Louisiana State University and Agricultural and Mechanical College (U)
Lurleen B. Wallace Community College (U)
Macon State College (U)
Malone College (U)
Manor College (U)
Mansfield University of Pennsylvania (U)
Marion Technical College (U)
Marshall University (U)
Massasoit Community College (U)
McMurry University (U)
Memorial University of Newfoundland (U)
Mercy College (G)
Mesa State College (U)
Metropolitan State University (U)
Miami Dade College (U)
Middlesex Community College (U)
Midstate College (U)
Midway College (U)
Millersville University of Pennsylvania (U)
Minot State University (U)
Mississippi Delta Community College (U)
Missouri State University (G)
Moberly Area Community College (U)
Monroe Community College (U)
Monroe County Community College (U)
Montana Tech of The University of Montana (U)
Montcalm Community College (U)
Montgomery Community College (U)
Montgomery County Community College (U)
Moorpark College (U)
Mountain Empire Community College (U)
Mt. Hood Community College (U)
Mount Olive College (U)
Mt. San Antonio College (U)
Mount Wachusett Community College (U)
Myers University (U)
Naropa University (N,U)
Nassau Community College (U)
National University (U)
Naugatuck Valley Community College (U)
Neumann College (U)
New England Institute of Technology (U)
New Mexico Junior College (U)
New River Community College (U)
Northampton County Area Community College (U)
North Arkansas College (U)
North Carolina State University (U)
North Central Texas College (U)
Northcentral University (U)
North Dakota State College of Science (U)

North Dakota State University (G)
Northeast Alabama Community College (U)
Northeastern Illinois University (U)
Northeast State Technical Community College (U)
Northern Virginia Community College (U)
North Florida Community College (U)
North Iowa Area Community College (U)
North Lake College (U)
North Seattle Community College (U)
NorthWest Arkansas Community College (U)
Northwestern Connecticut Community College (U)
Northwestern Michigan College (U)
Northwestern State University of Louisiana (U,G)
Northwest Missouri State University (U)
Nyack College (U)
Okaloosa-Walton College (U)
Oklahoma Panhandle State University (U)
Oklahoma State University (U)
Oregon Institute of Technology (U)
Oregon State University (N,U)
Ouachita Technical College (U)
Oxnard College (U)
Pace University (U)
Palomar College (U)
Pamlico Community College (U)
Parkland College (U)
Park University (U)
Pasco-Hernando Community College (U)
Passaic County Community College (U)
Patrick Henry Community College (U)
Peirce College (U)
Pellissippi State Technical Community College (U)
Peninsula College (U)
Pennsylvania Highlands Community College (U)
Piedmont Community College (U)
Piedmont Technical College (U)
Pikes Peak Community College (U)
Portland Community College (U)
Prairie View A&M University (G)
Pratt Community College (U)
Prescott College (U,G)
Presentation College (U)
Pulaski Technical College (U)
Queen's University at Kingston (U)
Randolph Community College (U)
Rappahannock Community College (U)
Reading Area Community College (U)
Regent University (U,G)
Rend Lake College (U)
The Richard Stockton College of New Jersey (U)
Richland Community College (U)
Richmond Community College (U)
Riverside Community College District (U)
Rochester Institute of Technology (U)
Rockland Community College (U)
Roosevelt University (U)
Rose State College (U)
Sacramento City College (U)
St. Ambrose University (U)
Saint Charles Community College (U)
St. Clair County Community College (U)
St. Cloud State University (U)
Saint Francis University (U)
St. Joseph's College, Long Island Campus (U)
St. Joseph's College, New York (U)
Saint Leo University (U)

Saint Mary-of-the-Woods College (U)
Sam Houston State University (U)
San Diego Community College District (U)
San Diego State University (U)
San Joaquin Delta College (U)
Santa Rosa Junior College (U)
Saybrook Graduate School and Research Center (N,G)
Schenectady County Community College (U)
Schiller International University (U)
Seminole Community College (U)
Shippensburg University of Pennsylvania (U,G)
Sinclair Community College (U)
Southeast Arkansas College (U)
Southeast Community College Area (U)
Southeastern Community College (U)
Southeastern Illinois College (U)
Southeastern Oklahoma State University (U)
Southern Arkansas University Tech (U)
Southern New Hampshire University (U)
South Piedmont Community College (U)
Southwestern Adventist University (U)
Southwest Wisconsin Technical College (U)
Spring Arbor University (U)
State University of New York at Binghamton (U)
State University of New York at Oswego (U,G)
State University of New York College at Cortland (U)
State University of New York College at Potsdam (U)
Stephen F. Austin State University (U,G)
Strayer University (U)
Tacoma Community College (U)
Taft College (U)
Taylor University (U)
Temple University (U)
Texas A&M University–Commerce (U,G)
Texas A&M University–Kingsville (U)
Texas State University–San Marcos (U)
Texas Tech University (U)
Three Rivers Community College (U)
Tompkins Cortland Community College (U)
Treasure Valley Community College (U)
Triton College (U)
Tunxis Community College (U)
Tyler Junior College (U)
Union County College (U)
Union University (U)
The University of Akron (U,G)
The University of Alabama (U)
University of Alaska Fairbanks (U,G)
The University of Arizona (U)
University of Arkansas at Little Rock (U)
University of Bridgeport (U)
The University of British Columbia (U)
University of California, Los Angeles (G)
University of Central Missouri (U)
University of Cincinnati (U)
University of Cincinnati Raymond Walters College (U)
University of Colorado at Colorado Springs (U)
University of Colorado Denver (U)
University of Hawaii–West Oahu (U)
University of Houston–Downtown (U)
University of Houston–Victoria (U,G)
University of Idaho (U,G)
University of Illinois at Springfield (U)

University of Illinois at Urbana–Champaign (U)
The University of Kansas (U,G)
University of Louisville (U)
The University of Maine at Augusta (U)
University of Maine at Fort Kent (U)
University of Maine at Machias (U)
University of Management and Technology (U,G)
University of Maryland University College (U)
University of Massachusetts Boston (U)
University of Minnesota, Crookston (U)
University of Minnesota, Duluth (U)
University of Minnesota, Morris (U)
University of Minnesota, Twin Cities Campus (U)
University of Missouri–Columbia (U)
The University of Montana–Western (U)
University of Nevada, Reno (U)
University of New Orleans (U,G)
University of North Alabama (U)
The University of North Carolina at Chapel Hill (U)
The University of North Carolina at Greensboro (U)
The University of North Carolina Wilmington (U)
University of North Dakota (U)
University of Northern Iowa (U)
University of Pennsylvania (U,G)
University of Saskatchewan (U)
University of South Alabama (U)
The University of South Dakota (U)
University of Southern Indiana (U)
University of Southern Maine (U)
University of South Florida (G)
The University of Tennessee (U)
The University of Texas at San Antonio (U,G)
The University of Texas at Tyler (U)
The University of Texas of the Permian Basin (U,G)
The University of Texas System (U)
University of the Southwest (U)
The University of Toledo (U)
University of Utah (U)
University of Vermont (N,U)
University of Washington (U)
University of Waterloo (U)
University of Wisconsin Colleges (U)
Upper Iowa University (N,U)
Utah State University (U,G)
Utah Valley State College (U)
Utica College (U)
Valley City State University (U)
Vincennes University (U)
Wake Technical Community College (U)
Washburn University (U)
Washington State University (U)
Wayland Baptist University (U)
Wayne State College (G)
Weber State University (U)
Westchester Community College (U)
Western Washington University (U)
Western Wyoming Community College (U)
Westfield State College (U)
West Los Angeles College (U)
West Virginia University at Parkersburg (U)
Wharton County Junior College (U)
Wichita State University (U)
Wilfrid Laurier University (U)
Williston State College (U)

Wisconsin Indianhead Technical College
(N,U)
Worcester State College (U)
Wytheville Community College (U)
York County Community College (U)
York Technical College (U)
Yuba College (U)

PSYCHOLOGY RELATED

Allen County Community College (U)
Athabasca University (U)
Athens Technical College (U)
Atlantic University (N,G)
Beacon University (N,U,G)
Beaufort County Community College (U)
Bellevue Community College (U)
Black Hills State University (U)
Brenau University (U)
Bristol Community College (U)
Buena Vista University (U)
Burlington County College (U)
California State University, Dominguez Hills
(N)
California State University, San Marcos (N)
Cape Cod Community College (U)
Central Michigan University (U)
Central Texas College (U)
Chadron State College (U,G)
Charter Oak State College (U)
Chemeketa Community College (U)
Citrus College (U)
City Colleges of Chicago, Harold Washington
College (U)
Clark State Community College (U)
Columbia College (U)
Community College of Beaver County (U)
Corban College (U)
Dallas Baptist University (U)
Delaware County Community College (U)
Drake University (U)
East Carolina University (G)
Eastern Michigan University (G)
Eastern Washington University (U)
Edison State Community College (U)
Everett Community College (U)
Florida Institute of Technology (N)
Genesee Community College (U)
Granite State College (U)
Grantham University (U)
Illinois Eastern Community Colleges, Lincoln
Trail College (U)
Jacksonville State University (U,G)
James A. Rhodes State College (U)
Jamestown Community College (N)
John A. Logan College (U)
Lake-Sumter Community College (U)
Lehigh Carbon Community College (U)
Limestone College (U)
Louisiana State University and Agricultural
and Mechanical College (U)
Massasoit Community College (U)
McDowell Technical Community College (U)
Mercer County Community College (U)
Mercy College (G)
Middlesex Community College (U)
Midwestern State University (U)
Minot State University (U)
Misericordia University (U)
Naropa University (N,G)
Nassau Community College (U)
Northcentral University (G)

North Dakota State College of Science (U)
NorthWest Arkansas Community College (U)
Northwestern Michigan College (U)
Northwood University, Texas Campus (U)
Okaloosa-Walton College (U)
Palomar College (U)
Portland Community College (N)
Rose State College (U)
Sacramento City College (U)
St. Cloud State University (G)
Saint Mary-of-the-Woods College (G)
San Diego Community College District (U)
Santa Rosa Junior College (U)
Saybrook Graduate School and Research
Center (N,G)
Seminole Community College (U)
South Piedmont Community College (U)
State University of New York at Binghamton
(U)
State University of New York at Plattsburgh
(U)
Taft College (U)
Taylor University (U)
Texas State University–San Marcos (U)
Tompkins Cortland Community College (U)
Treasure Valley Community College (U)
The University of Akron (G)
University of Alaska Fairbanks (G)
The University of Arizona (U)
University of Arkansas at Little Rock (U)
University of Hawaii–West Oahu (U)
University of Idaho (G)
University of Maine at Machias (U)
University of Missouri–Columbia (U)
University of Nevada, Reno (G)
The University of North Carolina at Charlotte
(U)
University of North Texas (U)
University of Vermont (U)
University of Waterloo (U)
University of Wisconsin–Whitewater (G)
Upper Iowa University (U)
Western Nebraska Community College (U)
Wilfrid Laurier University (U)
York University (U)
Yuba College (U)

PSYCHOMETRICS AND
QUANTITATIVE PSYCHOLOGY

University of Alaska Fairbanks (U)
University of New Orleans (U,G)

PSYCHOPHARMACOLOGY

Jacksonville State University (U,G)
Minot State University (U)
University of Arkansas at Little Rock (G)

PUBLIC ADMINISTRATION

American Public University System (U)
Athabasca University (N,U,G)
Austin Peay State University (U)
Brenau University (U)
California State University, San Bernardino
(G)
Central Michigan University (U,G)
Central Texas College (U)
Charter Oak State College (U)
Cleveland State University (U,G)
Cogswell Polytechnical College (U)

College of The Albemarle (N)
Cuyahoga Community College (U)
DeVry University Online (G)
Drake University (G)
Duquesne University (G)
Elizabeth City State University (U)
Eugenio María de Hostos Community College
of the City University of New York (U)
Florida Gulf Coast University (U,G)
Florida State University (U)
Georgia State University (U)
Hamline University (N)
Indiana State University (G)
Jacksonville State University (U,G)
James Madison University (N)
Lackawanna College (U)
Marist College (G)
Mesa State College (U)
Metropolitan State University (U,G)
Midwestern State University (U)
Mississippi State University (G)
Myers University (U)
National University (U,G)
Northcentral University (G)
Pace University (G)
Palomar College (U)
Park University (G)
Regent University (G)
Regis University (U,G)
Roger Williams University (U)
St. Edward's University (U)
Saint Joseph's College of Maine (G)
Saint Leo University (U)
State University of New York at Binghamton
(G)
Stephen F. Austin State University (G)
The University of Akron (U,G)
University of Central Florida (G)
University of Colorado at Colorado Springs
(G)
University of Colorado Denver (G)
The University of Findlay (G)
University of Hawaii–West Oahu (U)
University of Illinois at Springfield (G)
University of Illinois at Urbana–Champaign
(N,G)
University of Maine at Fort Kent (U)
University of Management and Technology
(U)
University of Maryland University College
(G)
University of New Orleans (U,G)
University of North Dakota (G)
University of North Texas (U)
University of South Florida (G)
The University of Texas at Tyler (G)
University of Vermont (U,G)
University of Wyoming (G)
Upper Iowa University (N,U)
Virginia Polytechnic Institute and State
University (U)
Washburn University (U)
Wayland Baptist University (G)
Westfield State College (U,G)
York University (U)
Youngstown State University (G)

PUBLIC ADMINISTRATION AND SOCIAL SERVICE PROFESSIONS RELATED

American Public University System (G)
Athabasca University (N,G)
Brenau University (U)
Central Michigan University (U,G)
Charter Oak State College (U)
Cleveland State University (U,G)
College of The Albemarle (N)
Drake University (G)
George Mason University (G)
Hamline University (N,G)
Indiana State University (G)
Jacksonville State University (U,G)
Kentucky State University (U,G)
Mercy College (U)
Park University (G)
Pine Technical College (U)
Regis University (G)
Roger Williams University (U)
Saybrook Graduate School and Research Center (N,G)
The University of Akron (U)
University of Central Florida (G)
University of Colorado Denver (G)
University of Hawaii–West Oahu (U)
University of Illinois at Chicago (N)
The University of Kansas (U)
University of New Orleans (U,G)
The University of North Carolina at Charlotte (N)
University of the Virgin Islands (G)
The University of Toledo (U)
University of West Florida (G)
Upper Iowa University (U)
Western Michigan University (U)
York University (U)

PUBLIC HEALTH

Arapahoe Community College (U)
Athabasca University (N,U,G)
Bowling Green State University (U)
Cleveland State University (N)
Dallas Baptist University (U)
Diné College (U)
Drake University (G)
Drexel University (G)
East Tennessee State University (G)
Emory University (G)
Georgia State University (U)
Harrisburg Area Community College (U)
James Madison University (N)
Jefferson College of Health Sciences (U)
Medical College of Wisconsin (G)
Mercy College (U)
Middlesex Community College (U)
Montana Tech of The University of Montana (G)
New Jersey City University (U,G)
North Iowa Area Community College (N)
Oregon State University (G)
Oxnard College (U)
Seminole Community College (U)
State University of New York College at Cortland (U,G)
The University of Akron (G)
University of California, Davis (U)
University of Illinois at Chicago (N,G)
University of Illinois at Springfield (G)

University of Illinois at Urbana–Champaign (N)
University of Minnesota, Twin Cities Campus (U,G)
University of North Florida (U,G)
University of Southern Mississippi (G)
University of South Florida (G)
Virginia Polytechnic Institute and State University (N)
Youngstown State University (G)

PUBLIC POLICY ANALYSIS

American Public University System (U)
Athabasca University (N,U,G)
California State University, Sacramento (G)
Central Michigan University (U,G)
Duquesne University (G)
Elizabeth City State University (U)
Patrick Henry College (U)
Regent University (N,G)
Sacramento City College (U)
University of Colorado Denver (G)
University of Denver (U)
University of Maine at Fort Kent (U)
University of Southern Maine (G)
University of South Florida (G)

PUBLIC RELATIONS, ADVERTISING, AND APPLIED COMMUNICATION RELATED

AIB College of Business (U)
Arapahoe Community College (U)
Athabasca University (N,U,G)
Berkeley College (U)
Berkeley College–New York City Campus (U)
Berkeley College–Westchester Campus (U)
Bowling Green State University (U)
Brenau University (U)
Central Michigan University (G)
City Colleges of Chicago, Harold Washington College (U)
Columbus State Community College (U)
Delaware County Community College (U)
Drake University (U,G)
Edison State Community College (U)
Iona College (G)
James Madison University (N)
Jones International University (G)
Judson University (U)
Lakeland Community College (N)
Lamar State College–Port Arthur (N)
Linn-Benton Community College (U)
Los Angeles Trade-Technical College (U)
Middlesex Community College (U)
Monroe Community College (U)
Murray State University (U)
Myers University (U)
Northwestern Oklahoma State University (U)
Okaloosa-Walton College (U)
Oxnard College (U)
Pellissippi State Technical Community College (U)
St. Edward's University (G)
State University of New York at Oswego (U)
Taylor University (N)
The University of Alabama (U)
University of Alaska Fairbanks (U)
University of Minnesota, Twin Cities Campus (U)
University of Missouri–Columbia (G)

The University of South Dakota (U)
University of Southern Indiana (U)
Upper Iowa University (U)
Utah Valley State College (U)
Webster University (U)
West Shore Community College (U)
Wisconsin Indianhead Technical College (N,U)
Worcester State College (N)
Youngstown State University (N)

PUBLISHING

Arapahoe Community College (U)
Clemson University (N)
Community College of Denver (N)
Hagerstown Community College (N)
Middlesex Community College (U)
Pace University (G)
University of Cincinnati (N)
University of Minnesota, Twin Cities Campus (U)
University of South Florida (N)

QUALITY CONTROL AND SAFETY TECHNOLOGIES

Bowling Green State University (G)
California National University for Advanced Studies (U)
California State University, Dominguez Hills (N)
Columbus State Community College (U)
East Carolina University (G)
Eastern Michigan University (G)
Grand Rapids Community College (N)
Ivy Tech Community College–Kokomo (U)
Jacksonville State University (U,G)
James A. Rhodes State College (U)
James Madison University (N)
Kansas State University (G)
Kettering University (N)
Lakeland Community College (N)
Mitchell Technical Institute (N)
Murray State University (G)
Okaloosa-Walton College (U)
Southeastern Oklahoma State University (U)
The University of Alabama in Huntsville (G)
University of South Florida (U)
The University of Texas at Tyler (G)
University of Wisconsin–Platteville (N)
West Virginia University at Parkersburg (N)

RADIO, TELEVISION, AND DIGITAL COMMUNICATION

Athabasca University (N)
Cerritos College (U)
Daytona State College (U)
Eastern Kentucky University (U)
Foothill College (U)
James Madison University (N)
Long Beach City College (U)
Middlesex Community College (U)
Middle Tennessee State University (U)
Murray State University (U)
Oxnard College (U)
Palomar College (U)
Pikes Peak Community College (U)
Riverside Community College District (U)
Saddleback College (U)
Texas A&M University–Commerce (G)

University of Alaska Fairbanks (U)
University of Missouri–Columbia (G)
The University of North Carolina at Chapel Hill (G)
University of Southern Indiana (U)

REAL ESTATE

Arapahoe Community College (U)
Athens Technical College (N)
Ball State University (U)
Blackhawk Technical College (N)
Cabrillo College (U)
California State University, Sacramento (U)
Centralia College (U)
Central New Mexico Community College (U)
Central Texas College (U)
Chadron State College (U)
Citrus College (U)
Clarion University of Pennsylvania (N,U)
College of the Sequoias (U)
Community College of Denver (N)
Crafton Hills College (U)
Cuyahoga Community College (U)
Dallas County Community College District (U)
Darton College (N)
De Anza College (U)
Flathead Valley Community College (U)
Galveston College (N)
Georgia State University (U)
Golden West College (U)
Harford Community College (N)
Hibbing Community College (N)
Hopkinsville Community College (N)
Houston Community College System (U)
Indian River Community College (N)
James Madison University (N)
Jamestown Community College (N)
Johnson County Community College (N)
Lakeland Community College (N)
Laredo Community College (U)
Long Beach City College (U)
Los Angeles Trade-Technical College (U)
Middle Tennessee State University (N)
Mt. San Antonio College (U)
Naugatuck Valley Community College (N,U)
North Lake College (U)
Orange Coast College (U)
Palomar College (U)
Pasco-Hernando Community College (N)
Portland Community College (U)
Quinebaug Valley Community College (N)
Rappahannock Community College (N)
Rend Lake College (U)
Riverside Community College District (U)
Sacramento City College (U)
Saddleback College (U)
San Diego Community College District (U)
Santa Rosa Junior College (U)
Sierra College (U)
Southeast Arkansas College (U)
Sullivan County Community College (N)
Treasure Valley Community College (N,U)
Triton College (N,U)
The University of Akron (U)
University of Alaska Fairbanks (U)
University of Arkansas at Little Rock (U,G)
University of Idaho (U)
University of Maine at Fort Kent (U)
University of New Orleans (U,G)
University of North Dakota (N)

The University of Texas at Brownsville (N)
University of Utah (N)
University of Wyoming (U)
Virginia Polytechnic Institute and State University (N)
Wake Technical Community College (U)
West Hills Community College (N)
West Los Angeles College (U)

REHABILITATION AND THERAPEUTIC PROFESSIONS

Arkansas Tech University (U)
Brenau University (U)
Clarion University of Pennsylvania (G)
Drake University (G)
East Carolina University (G)
Jefferson College of Health Sciences (U)
Saint Mary-of-the-Woods College (G)
Saybrook Graduate School and Research Center (G)
Texas Woman's University (G)
University of Arkansas at Little Rock (G)
The University of British Columbia (U,G)
University of Minnesota, Twin Cities Campus (U)
University of North Texas (N,U,G)
University of St. Augustine for Health Sciences (G)
University of Wisconsin–Stout (G)
Vincennes University (U)
Western Michigan University (U)

RELIGIOUS EDUCATION

Andover Newton Theological School (N,G)
Beulah Heights University (U)
Brigham Young University (U)
Calvin Theological Seminary (G)
Carroll University (U)
The Catholic Distance University (N,G)
Covenant Theological Seminary (N,G)
Crown College (U)
Dallas Baptist University (U,G)
Defiance College (U)
Denver Seminary (G)
DeSales University (U)
Earlham School of Religion (G)
Eugene Bible College (U)
Global University (N)
Gordon-Conwell Theological Seminary (N,G)
Grand Rapids Theological Seminary of Cornerstone University (G)
Master's College and Seminary (U)
Montgomery Community College (U)
Naropa University (N,G)
Regent University (N)
Sacred Heart University (U)
Saint Joseph's College of Maine (U)
St. Petersburg Theological Seminary (N,U,G)
Summit Pacific College (N,U)
Taylor University (U)
University of Sioux Falls (U)
Wayland Baptist University (U,G)
Webster University (U)
Western Seminary (N,G)

RELIGIOUS STUDIES

Amridge University (N,U,G)
Andover Newton Theological School (N,G)
Assemblies of God Theological Seminary (G)

Atlantic University (N,G)
Azusa Pacific University (U)
Bakke Graduate University (G)
Beacon University (N,U)
Bergen Community College (U)
Brigham Young University (N,U)
Bryn Athyn College of the New Church (U,G)
California Institute of Integral Studies (N,G)
California State University, Chico (U)
Calvin Theological Seminary (G)
Campbellsville University (U,G)
The Catholic Distance University (N,G)
Central Virginia Community College (U)
Central Wyoming College (U)
Chaminade University of Honolulu (U,G)
Chatham University (U)
Chemeketa Community College (U)
Cincinnati Christian University (G)
Columbia International University (N,U,G)
Community College of Denver (U)
Concordia College–New York (U)
Corban College (U)
Covenant Theological Seminary (N,G)
Crafton Hills College (U)
Crown College (U)
Dallas Baptist University (U,G)
De Anza College (U)
Delaware County Community College (U)
Denver Seminary (G)
Earlham School of Religion (G)
Eastern Mennonite University (G)
East Tennessee State University (G)
Edison State Community College (U)
Erie Community College (U)
Erie Community College, North Campus (U)
Erie Community College, South Campus (U)
Eugene Bible College (U)
Fontbonne University (U)
Global University (N)
Gordon-Conwell Theological Seminary (N,G)
Grand Rapids Theological Seminary of Cornerstone University (N,G)
Halifax Community College (U)
Haywood Community College (U)
Hebrew College (N,U,G)
Henry Ford Community College (U)
Hope International University (N,U,G)
Hopkinsville Community College (U)
Immaculata University (U)
John A. Logan College (U)
Johnson State College (U)
John Wood Community College (U)
Liberty University (U,G)
Life Pacific College (N)
Limestone College (U)
Lincoln Christian College (N,U,G)
Linn-Benton Community College (U)
Manor College (U)
Maranatha Baptist Bible College (G)
Master's College and Seminary (U)
McMurry University (U)
Memorial University of Newfoundland (U)
Mesa Community College (U)
Miami Dade College (U)
Midway College (U)
Misericordia University (U)
Missouri State University (U,G)
Mountain Empire Community College (U)
Mount Olive College (U)
Mt. San Antonio College (U)
Naropa University (N,U)
Neumann College (U)

Northeast Iowa Community College (U)
Northern Virginia Community College (U)
Nyack College (U)
Okaloosa-Walton College (U)
Pacific Union College (U)
Palomar College (U)
Pasco-Hernando Community College (U)
Patrick Henry Community College (U)
Providence College and Theological Seminary
 (G)
Pulaski Technical College (U)
Queen's University at Kingston (U)
Rappahannock Community College (U)
Regent University (N)
Regis University (U)
Rend Lake College (U)
Riverside Community College District (U)
Sacred Heart University (U)
Saint Francis University (U)
Saint Joseph's College of Maine (N)
St. Petersburg Theological Seminary (N,U,G)
Shasta Bible College (U)
Southeastern Illinois College (U)
Summit Pacific College (N,U)
Taylor University (N,U)
Trinity Episcopal School for Ministry (N,G)
Triton College (U)
Union University (N,U,G)
The University of Alabama (U)
University of Arkansas at Little Rock (U)
University of Bridgeport (U)
University of Central Missouri (U)
University of Dubuque (U)
The University of Findlay (U)
The University of Kansas (U)
University of Missouri–Columbia (U)
The University of North Carolina at Chapel
 Hill (U)
University of North Dakota (U)
University of Northern Iowa (U,G)
University of Saskatchewan (U)
The University of Tennessee (U)
University of the Southwest (U)
The University of Toledo (U)
University of Vermont (U,G)
University of Washington (U)
University of Waterloo (U)
University of West Florida (U)
Virginia Polytechnic Institute and State
 University (U)
Wake Technical Community College (U)
Wayland Baptist University (U,G)
Westchester Community College (U)
Western Michigan University (U)
Western Seminary (N,G)
Wilfrid Laurier University (U)
Williamson Christian College (U)
Wytheville Community College (U)
York County Community College (U)
York University (U)

RELIGIOUS/SACRED MUSIC

Barclay College (U)
Calvin Theological Seminary (G)
Eugene Bible College (U)
Global University (N)
Naropa University (N)
Providence College and Theological Seminary
 (N)
Sioux Falls Seminary (G)
Taylor University (U)

SALES, MERCHANDISING, AND RELATED MARKETING OPERATIONS (GENERAL)

Adams State College (N)
Arapahoe Community College (U)
Athabasca University (N,U,G)
Berkeley College (U)
Berkeley College–New York City Campus (U)
Berkeley College–Westchester Campus (U)
Blue Ridge Community College (U)
Brenau University (G)
California State University, Dominguez Hills
 (N)
California State University, Sacramento (U)
Capella University (G)
Central Michigan University (G)
Central New Mexico Community College (U)
Cerro Coso Community College (U)
Chadron State College (U,G)
Chemeketa Community College (U)
Coastline Community College (U)
Columbia College (U)
Columbus State Community College (U)
Community College of Denver (U)
Dallas Baptist University (U,G)
Delaware County Community College (U)
DeSales University (U)
Drexel University (U,G)
Eastern Michigan University (U,G)
East Tennessee State University (N,U)
Elizabeth City State University (U)
Erie Community College (U)
Erie Community College, North Campus (U)
Erie Community College, South Campus (U)
Fort Hays State University (N)
Genesee Community College (U)
Grantham University (U)
Hofstra University (U)
Ivy Tech Community College–North Central
 (U)
Jacksonville State University (U,G)
James A. Rhodes State College (U)
James Madison University (N)
Kentucky State University (U)
Lakeland College (U)
Lakeland Community College (N)
Lamar State College–Port Arthur (N)
Limestone College (U)
Los Angeles Trade-Technical College (U)
Massasoit Community College (N)
Middle Tennessee State University (U)
Northampton County Area Community
 College (U)
Okaloosa-Walton College (U)
Oklahoma State University (U)
Oregon State University (U)
Palomar College (U)
Park University (U)
Pasco-Hernando Community College (N)
Quinebaug Valley Community College (N)
Regis University (U)
Rend Lake College (N)
Saddleback College (U)
St. Edward's University (U,G)
San Joaquin Delta College (U)
Syracuse University (G)
Taylor University (N)
The University of Akron (U)
University of Bridgeport (U)
University of Colorado Denver (G)
University of Dallas (G)

The University of Findlay (G)
University of Maryland University College
 (U,G)
University of Southern Indiana (N)
University of Wisconsin–La Crosse (G)
University of Wisconsin–Parkside (G)
Wake Technical Community College (N)

SALES, MERCHANDISING, AND RELATED MARKETING OPERATIONS (SPECIALIZED)

Adams State College (N)
The American College (U)
Arapahoe Community College (U)
Athabasca University (N,G)
Bellevue University (U,G)
Berkeley College (U)
Berkeley College–New York City Campus (U)
Berkeley College–Westchester Campus (U)
Blackhawk Technical College (U)
Blue Ridge Community College (N,U)
Brenau University (U,G)
Bridgewater State College (N)
Caldwell Community College and Technical
 Institute (N)
California State University, Dominguez Hills
 (N)
Centralia College (N)
Central Texas College (U)
Chadron State College (U,G)
Chemeketa Community College (U)
Cleveland State University (N)
Coastline Community College (U)
College of The Albemarle (N)
Darton College (N)
Delaware County Community College (U)
Drexel University (G)
East Carolina University (U)
Eastern Michigan University (U)
Edgecombe Community College (N)
Finger Lakes Community College (U)
Herkimer County Community College (U)
Jacksonville State University (U,G)
James A. Rhodes State College (U)
James Madison University (N)
Kirtland Community College (U)
Lakeland Community College (N)
Lake Region State College (U)
Lamar State College–Port Arthur (N)
Manatee Community College (U)
Massasoit Community College (N,U)
Mercy College (G)
Middle Tennessee State University (N)
Missouri State University (G)
Mt. San Antonio College (U)
Myers University (U)
Naugatuck Valley Community College (U)
Orange Coast College (U)
Oregon State University (N)
Oxnard College (U)
Pasco-Hernando Community College (N)
Saddleback College (U)
St. Edward's University (G)
Saint Joseph's College of Maine (G)
Schiller International University (G)
Southeast Community College Area (U)
State University of New York at Plattsburgh
 (U)
State University of New York College at
 Potsdam (N)

State University of New York College of
Technology at Canton (U)
Stephen F. Austin State University (U)
Strayer University (U)
Taylor University (N)
Temple University (U)
Texas Tech University (U)
Thunderbird School of Global Management
(G)
The University of Akron (U)
The University of Alabama (U)
University of Colorado Denver (G)
University of Dallas (G)
University of Michigan–Flint (N)
The University of North Carolina at Charlotte
(N)
University of North Texas (U,G)
The University of Texas at San Antonio (U)
The University of Texas at Tyler (U)
Vincennes University (U)
Westchester Community College (U)
Western Michigan University (U)
West Los Angeles College (U)
Wisconsin Indianhead Technical College
(N,U)
Youngstown State University (N)

SCHOOL PSYCHOLOGY

Athabasca University (N)
Capella University (G)
Chadron State College (G)
City Colleges of Chicago, Harold Washington
College (U)
Eastern Michigan University (G)
Eugene Bible College (U)
Fitchburg State College (U)
Indiana State University (G)
Jacksonville State University (U,G)
Lehigh Carbon Community College (U)
Liberty University (G)
Louisiana State University and Agricultural
and Mechanical College (U)
Mesa Community College (U)
Texas Woman's University (G)
The University of Akron (U)
University of Massachusetts Boston (G)
University of Missouri–Columbia (G)
University of North Texas (N)
Utah State University (G)

SCIENCE TECHNOLOGIES RELATED

Athabasca University (N)
Columbus State Community College (U)
Delaware County Community College (U)
Drexel University (G)
Everett Community College (U)
St. John's University (U)
University of Management and Technology
(U)
University of Wisconsin–Stout (G)
Virginia Polytechnic Institute and State
University (U,G)

SCIENCE, TECHNOLOGY AND SOCIETY

Athabasca University (N)
Delaware County Community College (U)
DePaul University (U)

Erie Community College (U)
Erie Community College, North Campus (U)
Erie Community College, South Campus (U)
Everett Community College (U)
Henry Ford Community College (U)
Ilisagvik College (U)
Iona College (U)
Jacksonville State University (U,G)
Northwestern Connecticut Community College
(U)
Oregon State University (U)
Pace University (U)
Stanford University (G)
Syracuse University (U)
University of Denver (U)
University of Illinois at Urbana–Champaign
(N,G)
University of Management and Technology
(U)
University of Oregon (U)
Western Michigan University (U)

SECURITY AND PROTECTIVE SERVICES RELATED

Arapahoe Community College (U)
Arkansas Tech University (U)
Berkeley College (U)
Berkeley College–New York City Campus (U)
Berkeley College–Westchester Campus (U)
City Colleges of Chicago, Harold Washington
College (U)
Cogswell Polytechnical College (U)
Jacksonville State University (U,G)
John Wood Community College (U)
Seminole Community College (N)
The University of Akron (U)
University of Connecticut (G)
Webster University (G)

SOCIAL AND PHILOSOPHICAL FOUNDATIONS OF EDUCATION

Arapahoe Community College (U)
Athabasca University (N)
Brenau University (U)
Jacksonville State University (U,G)
Northampton County Area Community
College (U)
The University of Akron (U,G)
University of Arkansas at Little Rock (G)
University of North Texas (G)
University of Southern Mississippi (G)
University of South Florida (G)
The University of Texas System (U,G)

SOCIAL PSYCHOLOGY

The American College (U)
Anne Arundel Community College (U)
Athabasca University (N)
Beaufort County Community College (U)
Bellevue Community College (U)
Bergen Community College (U)
Carlow University (U)
Carroll Community College (U)
Cayuga County Community College (U)
College of Mount St. Joseph (U)
Colorado Mountain College District System
(U)
Community College of Beaver County (U)
Corning Community College (U)

Crafton Hills College (U)
Dallas Baptist University (U)
Danville Community College (U)
De Anza College (U)
Delaware County Community College (U)
Eastern Washington University (U)
Elizabethtown Community and Technical
College (U)
Erie Community College (U)
Erie Community College, North Campus (U)
Erie Community College, South Campus (U)
Frank Phillips College (U)
Grand Rapids Community College (U)
Grand View College (U)
Houston Community College System (U)
Jacksonville State University (U)
Jefferson Community College (U)
John Wood Community College (U)
Kansas State University (U)
Liberty University (U)
Limestone College (U)
Long Beach City College (U)
Mercy College (U)
Middlesex Community College (U)
Montgomery County Community College (U)
New York Institute of Technology (U)
Northwestern Oklahoma State University (U)
Old Dominion University (U)
Oxnard College (U)
Palomar College (U)
Parkland College (U)
Park University (U)
Pikes Peak Community College (U)
Plymouth State University (U)
Queen's University at Kingston (U)
Red Rocks Community College (U)
Regis University (U)
Richland Community College (U)
Rose State College (U)
Saint Joseph's College of Maine (U)
San Diego Community College District (U)
Saybrook Graduate School and Research
Center (G)
Sierra College (U)
Sinclair Community College (U)
Southeast Community College Area (U)
State University of New York College at
Cortland (U)
State University of New York College of
Technology at Canton (U)
State University of New York Empire State
College (U)
Taylor University (U)
Texas State University–San Marcos (U)
Texas Tech University (U)
Tompkins Cortland Community College (U)
Triton College (U)
Union University (U)
The University of Akron (G)
University of Alaska Fairbanks (U)
University of Bridgeport (U)
University of Colorado Denver (U)
The University of Kansas (U)
The University of Maine at Augusta (U)
University of Missouri–Columbia (U)
University of North Dakota (U)
University of the Southwest (U)
University of Utah (U)
University of Washington (U)
University of Waterloo (U)
University of Wyoming (U)
Upper Iowa University (U)

Utah State University (U)
Westchester Community College (U)

SOCIAL SCIENCES

Acadia University (U)
Athabasca University (N,U,G)
Bellevue Community College (U)
Bergen Community College (U)
Black Hills State University (U)
Bowling Green State University (U)
Brenau University (U)
Bristol Community College (U)
Broome Community College (U)
Buena Vista University (U)
Burlington County College (U)
Butler Community College (U)
Caldwell Community College and Technical
    Institute (U)
California State University, Chico (U)
Cape Cod Community College (U)
Capital Community College (U)
Cayuga County Community College (U)
Centralia College (U)
Central Texas College (U)
Central Wyoming College (U)
Chadron State College (U)
Chemeketa Community College (U)
Citrus College (U)
College of the Siskiyous (U)
Colorado State University (N,U)
Community College of Beaver County (U)
Concordia University, St. Paul (N)
Connors State College (U)
Cuyahoga Community College (U)
Dallas Baptist University (U)
Dallas County Community College District
    (U)
Danville Community College (U)
De Anza College (U)
Delaware County Community College (U)
DeSales University (U)
Eastern Michigan University (U)
Embry-Riddle Aeronautical University (U)
Endicott College (U)
Eugenio María de Hostos Community College
    of the City University of New York (U)
Everett Community College (U)
Fitchburg State College (U,G)
Foothill College (U)
Fox Valley Technical College (U)
Frank Phillips College (U)
Galveston College (U)
Gateway Community College (U)
Genesee Community College (U)
Georgia State University (U)
Golden West College (U)
Gonzaga University (U,G)
Granite State College (U)
Gulf Coast Community College (U)
Haywood Community College (U)
Henry Ford Community College (U)
Hibbing Community College (U)
Hocking College (U)
Illinois Eastern Community Colleges, Olney
    Central College (U)
Indiana Tech (U)
Jackson State University (U)
Jacksonville State University (U,G)
James Madison University (N)
Jefferson College (U)
Jefferson Community College (U)

John Wood Community College (U)
Judson College (U)
Kansas State University (U)
Kauai Community College (U)
Lackawanna College (U)
Laredo Community College (U)
Lehigh Carbon Community College (U)
Lewis-Clark State College (U)
Liberty University (U)
Loma Linda University (G)
Long Beach City College (U)
Louisiana State University and Agricultural
    and Mechanical College (U)
Massasoit Community College (N)
McDowell Technical Community College (U)
Miami Dade College (U)
Michigan State University (U)
Middlesex Community College (U)
Middle Tennessee State University (U)
Misericordia University (U)
Mississippi Delta Community College (U)
Monroe Community College (U)
Mount Wachusett Community College (U)
Murray State University (U)
New Mexico Junior College (U)
Northampton County Area Community
    College (U)
North Dakota State College of Science (U)
Northeast State Technical Community College
    (U)
North Florida Community College (U)
NorthWest Arkansas Community College (U)
Okaloosa-Walton College (U)
Oklahoma Panhandle State University (U)
Oregon Institute of Technology (U)
Ouachita Technical College (U)
Pace University (U)
Palomar College (U)
Peninsula College (U)
Portland Community College (U)
Pulaski Technical College (U)
Regent University (U)
Rend Lake College (U)
Roosevelt University (U)
Rose State College (U)
Sacramento City College (U)
St. Clair County Community College (U)
St. Joseph's College, Long Island Campus (U)
St. Joseph's College, New York (U)
Saint Mary-of-the-Woods College (U)
San Diego Community College District (U)
Southeastern Community College (U)
Southern Maine Community College (U)
Southern New Hampshire University (U)
South Piedmont Community College (U)
Southwestern College (U)
Southwest Wisconsin Technical College (U)
Spoon River College (U)
State University of New York at Binghamton
    (U,G)
State University of New York at Plattsburgh
    (U)
State University of New York Empire State
    College (G)
Syracuse University (U)
Tacoma Community College (U)
Taft College (U)
Taylor University (U)
Texas State University–San Marcos (U)
Treasure Valley Community College (U)
Tri-County Community College (U)
Trine University (U)

Triton College (U)
The University of Akron (U)
The University of Alabama (U)
University of Alaska Fairbanks (U)
University of Bridgeport (U)
University of California, Los Angeles (G)
The University of Findlay (U)
University of Hawaii–West Oahu (U)
University of Houston–Downtown (U)
University of Idaho (U)
The University of Maine at Augusta (U)
University of Maine at Machias (U)
University of Maryland University College
    (U)
University of Massachusetts Boston (U)
University of New Orleans (U,G)
The University of North Carolina at
    Greensboro (U)
University of North Dakota (U)
University of North Texas (U,G)
University of Pennsylvania (U)
University of St. Francis (U)
University of South Florida (U)
The University of Texas System (U)
The University of Toledo (U)
University of Utah (U)
University of Waterloo (U)
University of Wisconsin Colleges (U)
University of Wisconsin–Stout (G)
University of Wisconsin–Superior (U)
Upper Iowa University (U)
Utah State University (U)
Utah Valley State College (U)
Vincennes University (U)
Westchester Community College (U)
Westfield State College (U)
West Los Angeles College (U)
West Virginia University at Parkersburg (U)
York University (U)

SOCIAL SCIENCES RELATED

Anne Arundel Community College (U)
Athabasca University (N,G)
Bellevue Community College (U)
Berkeley College (U)
Berkeley College–New York City Campus (U)
Berkeley College–Westchester Campus (U)
Blue Ridge Community College (U)
Bristol Community College (U)
Buena Vista University (U)
Burlington County College (U)
Butler Community College (U)
Cayuga County Community College (U)
Central Texas College (U)
Chadron State College (U)
Charter Oak State College (U)
Chemeketa Community College (U)
Cleveland Institute of Electronics (U)
Coastline Community College (U)
Columbia College (U)
Columbus State Community College (U)
Community College of Beaver County (U)
Dallas Baptist University (U)
Dallas County Community College District
    (U)
Delaware County Community College (U)
DePaul University (U)
Drake University (U)
Eastern Illinois University (U)
Erie Community College (U)
Erie Community College, North Campus (U)

Erie Community College, South Campus (U)
Harford Community College (U)
Haywood Community College (U)
Honolulu Community College (U)
James A. Rhodes State College (U)
J. Sargeant Reynolds Community College (U)
Kansas State University (N,U)
Laredo Community College (U)
Lehigh Carbon Community College (U)
Louisiana State University and Agricultural
  and Mechanical College (U)
Malone College (U)
Mercy College (G)
Middlesex Community College (U)
Moberly Area Community College (U)
Murray State University (U)
Northampton County Area Community
  College (U)
North Arkansas College (U)
NorthWest Arkansas Community College (U)
Oregon State University (U)
Palomar College (U)
Parkland College (U)
Pasco-Hernando Community College (U)
Pratt Community College (U)
Rockland Community College (U)
Rose State College (U)
Sacred Heart University (U)
Saddleback College (U)
St. Cloud State University (U)
St. Edward's University (U)
Saint Leo University (U)
Saint Mary-of-the-Woods College (U)
San Diego Community College District (U)
Saybrook Graduate School and Research
  Center (G)
Seminole Community College (U)
State University of New York at Binghamton
  (U,G)
Taft College (U)
Taylor University (U)
Texas State University–San Marcos (U)
The University of Alabama (U)
University of Alaska Fairbanks (U)
University of Denver (U)
University of Hawaii–West Oahu (U)
University of Idaho (U)
The University of Maine at Augusta (U)
University of North Dakota (U)
The University of South Dakota (U)
The University of Texas at Brownsville (U)
The University of Texas System (U)
University of the Virgin Islands (U)
University of Waterloo (U)
Upper Iowa University (U)
Utah State University (G)
Utah Valley State College (U)
Vermont Technical College (U)
Washburn University (N)
West Los Angeles College (U)

SOCIAL WORK

Albany State University (U)
Athabasca University (N,G)
Boise State University (U,G)
Bowling Green State University (U)
Bradley University (U)
Brigham Young University (U)
California State University, Chico (U)
California State University, San Bernardino
  (U)

California State University, San Marcos (U)
Campbellsville University (U,G)
Canisius College (G)
Carlow University (U)
Central Texas College (U)
Chadron State College (U)
Chatham University (U)
City Colleges of Chicago, Harold Washington
  College (U)
Cleveland State University (U,G)
Colorado State University (G)
Columbia College (U)
Concordia College–New York (U)
Darton College (U)
Diné College (U)
Eastern Kentucky University (U)
Eastern Washington University (N,U,G)
Florida State University (G)
Fort Valley State University (U)
Garrett College (N)
Georgia State University (U)
Governors State University (U,G)
Iona College (U)
Jackson State University (U)
Jacksonville State University (U,G)
Kauai Community College (G)
Kentucky State University (U)
Lake Region State College (U)
Limestone College (U)
Louisiana State University and Agricultural
  and Mechanical College (U)
Marshall University (U,G)
Memorial University of Newfoundland (U,G)
Michigan State University (N,G)
Middle Tennessee State University (U)
Missouri State University (U,G)
Murray State University (U)
Naugatuck Valley Community College (U)
New Mexico Highlands University (U)
New York Institute of Technology (U)
Northampton County Area Community
  College (U)
Northeastern Illinois University (U)
Northwestern State University of Louisiana
  (U)
The Ohio State University (U,G)
Piedmont Community College (U)
Saint Francis University (U)
Shippensburg University of Pennsylvania
  (U,G)
State University of New York at Binghamton
  (G)
Stephen F. Austin State University (U)
Tacoma Community College (U)
Taylor University (U)
Temple University (G)
Texas A&M University–Commerce (U,G)
Three Rivers Community College (U)
The University of Akron (U,G)
University of Alaska Fairbanks (U)
University of Arkansas (U)
University of Arkansas at Little Rock (U,G)
The University of British Columbia (U)
University of Calgary (U,G)
University of Illinois at Chicago (N,G)
University of Illinois at Springfield (U)
University of Louisville (G)
University of Michigan–Flint (U)
University of Minnesota, Twin Cities Campus
  (U,G)
University of Missouri–Columbia (U)
University of Nevada, Reno (U)

University of North Alabama (U)
The University of North Carolina Wilmington
  (U)
University of North Dakota (U,G)
University of Northern Iowa (U,G)
University of North Texas (U)
University of Southern Indiana (G)
University of Southern Maine (G)
University of Southern Mississippi (U,G)
The University of Toledo (U)
University of Vermont (N,U,G)
University of Waterloo (U)
University of Wyoming (G)
Utah State University (U)
Vincennes University (U)
Wake Technical Community College (U)
Washburn University (U)
Western Michigan University (U)
Western Washington University (U)
Western Wyoming Community College (U)
West Virginia State University (U)
Wilfrid Laurier University (U)
York University (U)

SOCIOLOGY

Acadia University (U)
Adams State College (U)
AIB College of Business (U)
Allen County Community College (U)
Alpena Community College (U)
Anne Arundel Community College (U)
Arapahoe Community College (U)
Arkansas State University–Beebe (U)
Athabasca University (N,U,G)
Austin Peay State University (U)
Baltimore City Community College (U)
Barclay College (U)
Barton County Community College (U)
Beaufort County Community College (U)
Bellevue Community College (U)
Belmont Technical College (U)
Bergen Community College (U)
Berkeley College (U)
Berkeley College–New York City Campus (U)
Berkeley College–Westchester Campus (U)
Black Hills State University (U)
Boise State University (U)
Bowling Green State University (U)
Bradley University (U)
Brenau University (U)
Bridgewater State College (U)
Brigham Young University (U)
Bristol Community College (U)
Broome Community College (U)
Broward Community College (U)
Buena Vista University (U)
Burlington College (U)
Burlington County College (U)
Butler Community College (U)
Cabrillo College (U)
Caldwell Community College and Technical
  Institute (U)
California Institute of Integral Studies (N,G)
California State University, Chico (U)
California State University, Sacramento (U)
Campbell University (U)
Cape Cod Community College (U)
Capital Community College (U)
Carlow University (U)
Carl Sandburg College (U)
Carroll University (U)

Central Arizona College (U)
Central Carolina Community College (U)
Centralia College (U)
Central New Mexico Community College (U)
Central Texas College (U)
Central Virginia Community College (U)
Central Washington University (U)
Central Wyoming College (U)
Cerritos College (U)
Chadron State College (U)
Chaminade University of Honolulu (U)
Charter Oak State College (U)
Chemeketa Community College (U)
Cincinnati State Technical and Community
   College (U)
Citrus College (U)
City Colleges of Chicago, Harold Washington
   College (U)
Clark State Community College (U)
Clatsop Community College (U)
Clemson University (U)
Cleveland Community College (U)
Cleveland State Community College (U)
Clinton Community College (U)
Coastline Community College (U)
College of San Mateo (U)
College of Southern Maryland (U)
College of The Albemarle (U)
College of the Sequoias (U)
Colorado Mountain College District System
   (U)
Colorado State University (U)
Columbia College (U)
Columbia-Greene Community College (U)
Columbus State Community College (U)
Community College of Beaver County (U)
Community College of Denver (U)
Concordia University, St. Paul (U,G)
Connors State College (U)
Corning Community College (U)
Crafton Hills College (U)
Cumberland County College (U)
Cuyahoga Community College (U)
Daemen College (U)
Dakota State University (U)
Dallas Baptist University (U)
Dallas County Community College District
   (U)
Danville Community College (U)
Darton College (U)
Dawson Community College (U)
De Anza College (U)
Delaware County Community College (U)
Delaware Technical & Community College,
   Jack F. Owens Campus (U)
DeSales University (U)
East Central Community College (U)
Eastern Michigan University (U)
Eastern Washington University (U)
Eastern West Virginia Community and
   Technical College (U)
Eastern Wyoming College (U)
Edgecombe Community College (U)
Edison State Community College (U)
Elaine P. Nunez Community College (U)
Elizabeth City State University (U)
Erie Community College (U)
Erie Community College, North Campus (U)
Erie Community College, South Campus (U)
Eugene Bible College (U)
Everett Community College (U)
Evergreen Valley College (U)

Finger Lakes Community College (U)
Fitchburg State College (U)
Flathead Valley Community College (U)
Florida State University (U)
Foothill College (U)
Fort Hays State University (U)
Fort Valley State University (U)
Framingham State College (U)
Gadsden State Community College (U)
Galveston College (U)
Gateway Technical College (U)
Genesee Community College (U)
Georgia State University (U)
Golden West College (U)
Governors State University (U,G)
Graceland University (U)
Grand Rapids Community College (U)
Grand View College (U)
Grantham University (U)
Greenfield Community College (U)
Greenville Technical College (U)
Gulf Coast Community College (U)
Harrisburg Area Community College (U)
Haywood Community College (U)
Henry Ford Community College (U)
Hibbing Community College (U)
Hillsborough Community College (U)
Holyoke Community College (U)
Hope International University (U)
Hopkinsville Community College (U)
Houston Community College System (U)
Immaculata University (U)
Indiana State University (U)
Indiana University–Purdue University Fort
   Wayne (U)
Indian River Community College (U)
Ivy Tech Community College–North Central
   (U)
Ivy Tech Community College–Northwest (U)
Ivy Tech Community College–Southern
   Indiana (U)
Jackson State University (U)
Jacksonville State University (U,G)
James Madison University (U)
Jamestown Community College (N)
Jefferson College (U)
Jefferson College of Health Sciences (U)
Jefferson Community College (U)
Johnson County Community College (U)
John Wood Community College (U)
J. Sargeant Reynolds Community College (U)
Judson College (U)
Judson University (U)
Kansas State University (U)
Kean University (U)
Kentucky State University (U)
Labette Community College (U)
Lackawanna College (U)
Lakeland Community College (U)
Lake Superior College (U)
Laredo Community College (U)
Lehigh Carbon Community College (U)
Limestone College (U)
Lock Haven University of Pennsylvania (U)
Long Beach City College (U)
Los Angeles Harbor College (U)
Los Angeles Trade-Technical College (U)
Louisiana State University and Agricultural
   and Mechanical College (U)
Lurleen B. Wallace Community College (U)
Malone College (U)
Manatee Community College (U)

Manor College (U)
Mansfield University of Pennsylvania (U)
Marian College of Fond du Lac (U)
Marshall University (U,G)
Massasoit Community College (U)
Memorial University of Newfoundland (U)
Mercer County Community College (U)
Mercy College (U)
Mesa State College (U)
Middlesex Community College (U)
Middle Tennessee State University (U)
Midwestern State University (U)
Millersville University of Pennsylvania (U)
Minot State University (U)
Misericordia University (U)
Mississippi Delta Community College (U)
Missouri State University (U)
Moberly Area Community College (U)
Montana Tech of The University of Montana
   (U)
Montgomery Community College (U)
Montgomery County Community College (U)
Moorpark College (U)
Mountain Empire Community College (U)
Mount Olive College (U)
Mt. San Antonio College (U)
Mount Wachusett Community College (U)
Murray State University (U)
Myers University (U)
Nassau Community College (U)
Naugatuck Valley Community College (U)
New England Institute of Technology (U)
New Mexico Junior College (U)
New Mexico State University (U,G)
New River Community College (U)
New York Institute of Technology (U)
Northampton County Area Community
   College (U)
North Central Texas College (U)
North Dakota State College of Science (U)
Northeast Alabama Community College (U)
Northern State University (U)
Northern Virginia Community College (U)
North Florida Community College (U)
North Lake College (U)
NorthWest Arkansas Community College (U)
Northwestern Connecticut Community College
   (U)
Northwestern Michigan College (U)
Northwestern Oklahoma State University (U)
Okaloosa-Walton College (U)
Oklahoma Panhandle State University (U)
Oklahoma State University (U)
Old Dominion University (U)
Oregon State University (U)
Ouachita Technical College (U)
Oxnard College (U)
Pace University (U)
Palomar College (U)
Parkland College (U)
Pasco-Hernando Community College (U)
Passaic County Community College (U)
Patrick Henry Community College (U)
Peirce College (U)
Pellissippi State Technical Community
   College (U)
Peninsula College (U)
Pennsylvania Highlands Community College
   (U)
Piedmont Community College (U)
Piedmont Technical College (U)
Pikes Peak Community College (U)

Portland Community College (U)
Pratt Community College (U)
Pulaski Technical College (U)
Queen's University at Kingston (U)
Quinebaug Valley Community College (U)
Randolph Community College (U)
Rappahannock Community College (U)
Reading Area Community College (U)
Red Rocks Community College (U)
Regis University (U)
Rend Lake College (U)
The Richard Stockton College of New Jersey (U)
Richland Community College (U)
Richmond Community College (U)
Riverside Community College District (U)
Rochester Institute of Technology (U)
Roger Williams University (U)
Roosevelt University (U)
Rose State College (U)
Sacramento City College (U)
Saddleback College (U)
Saint Charles Community College (U)
St. Clair County Community College (U)
St. Cloud State University (U)
Saint Francis University (U)
St. John's University (U)
Saint Joseph's College of Maine (U)
St. Louis Community College System (U)
Sam Houston State University (U)
San Diego Community College District (U)
San Joaquin Delta College (U)
Santa Monica College (U)
Santa Rosa Junior College (U)
Schenectady County Community College (U)
Seattle Central Community College (U)
Seminole Community College (U)
Shippensburg University of Pennsylvania (U,G)
Sierra College (U)
Sinclair Community College (U)
Southeast Arkansas College (U)
Southeastern Community College (U)
Southeastern Oklahoma State University (U)
Southern Union State Community College (U)
South Piedmont Community College (U)
Southwestern Community College (U)
Southwest Virginia Community College (U)
Southwest Wisconsin Technical College (U)
Spring Arbor University (U)
State University of New York at Binghamton (U)
State University of New York at Oswego (U)
State University of New York at Plattsburgh (U)
State University of New York College at Potsdam (U)
State University of New York Empire State College (U)
Strayer University (U)
Syracuse University (G)
Tacoma Community College (U)
Taft College (U)
Taylor University (U)
Texas A&M University–Commerce (U)
Texas A&M University–Kingsville (U,G)
Texas State University–San Marcos (U)
Texas Tech University (U)
Texas Woman's University (U,G)
Three Rivers Community College (U)
Tompkins Cortland Community College (U)
Treasure Valley Community College (U)

Tri-County Community College (U)
Triton College (U)
Tunxis Community College (U)
Tyler Junior College (U)
Union County College (U)
The University of Akron (U)
University of Alaska Fairbanks (U)
The University of Arizona (U)
University of Arkansas (U)
University of Arkansas at Little Rock (U)
University of Bridgeport (U)
University of Central Florida (U)
University of Cincinnati Raymond Walters College (U)
University of Colorado at Colorado Springs (U)
University of Colorado Denver (U)
University of Connecticut (U)
University of Dubuque (U)
The University of Findlay (U)
University of Hawaii–West Oahu (U)
University of Idaho (U)
University of Illinois at Springfield (U)
University of Illinois at Urbana–Champaign (U)
The University of Kansas (U)
University of Louisville (U)
The University of Maine at Augusta (U)
University of Maine at Fort Kent (U)
University of Maine at Machias (U)
University of Maryland University College (U)
University of Massachusetts Boston (U,G)
University of Minnesota, Crookston (U)
University of Minnesota, Duluth (U)
University of Minnesota, Morris (U)
University of Missouri–Columbia (U,G)
University of Nevada, Reno (U)
University of New Orleans (U,G)
University of North Alabama (U)
The University of North Carolina at Chapel Hill (U)
The University of North Carolina at Charlotte (U)
The University of North Carolina at Greensboro (U)
University of North Dakota (U)
University of Northern Iowa (U,G)
University of North Texas (U)
University of Oklahoma (U)
University of Saskatchewan (U)
University of Sioux Falls (U)
University of South Alabama (U,G)
The University of South Dakota (U)
University of Southern Maine (U)
University of Southern Mississippi (U)
University of South Florida (U)
The University of Tennessee (U)
The University of Texas at Tyler (U)
The University of Texas of the Permian Basin (U)
The University of Texas System (U)
University of the Southwest (U)
The University of Toledo (U)
University of Vermont (U)
University of Washington (U)
University of Waterloo (U)
University of Wisconsin Colleges (U)
Upper Iowa University (N,U)
Utah State University (U)
Utah Valley State College (U)
Vincennes University (U)

Virginia Polytechnic Institute and State University (U)
Wake Technical Community College (U)
Washburn University (U)
Washington State University (U)
Wayland Baptist University (U)
Westchester Community College (U)
Western Michigan University (U)
Western Nebraska Community College (U)
Western Washington University (U)
Western Wyoming Community College (U)
West Shore Community College (U)
West Virginia University at Parkersburg (U)
Wharton County Junior College (U)
Wichita State University (U)
Wilfrid Laurier University (U)
Williston State College (U)
Wisconsin Indianhead Technical College (N,U)
York County Community College (U)
York Technical College (U)
York University (U)
Yuba College (U)

SOIL SCIENCES

Haywood Community College (U)
Lakeland Community College (N)
North Carolina State University (U)
Oregon State University (U)
The University of British Columbia (U)
University of Missouri–Columbia (N)
University of Saskatchewan (N)

SOMATIC BODYWORK AND RELATED THERAPEUTIC SERVICES

Saybrook Graduate School and Research Center (G)

SPECIAL EDUCATION

Acadia University (U)
Arapahoe Community College (U)
Athabasca University (G)
Auburn University (G)
Ball State University (G)
Baltimore City Community College (U)
Blue Ridge Community College (U)
Bowling Green State University (G)
Brenau University (U)
Bridgewater State College (U,G)
Brigham Young University (U)
Buena Vista University (U)
California State University, Sacramento (U)
Carlow University (U,G)
Chadron State College (U,G)
Cleveland State University (U,G)
Coastline Community College (U)
Dakota State University (U)
Drake University (U)
East Carolina University (G)
Eastern Kentucky University (G)
Eastern Michigan University (U)
East Tennessee State University (U)
Elizabeth City State University (U)
Florida State University (G)
Fort Hays State University (U,G)
Framingham State College (G)
Granite State College (G)
Hamline University (G)

Hofstra University (U,G)
Holyoke Community College (U)
Illinois State University (G)
Indiana State University (G)
Indian River Community College (U)
Jackson State University (U,G)
Jacksonville State University (U,G)
James Madison University (N,G)
Johnson State College (U)
John Wood Community College (U)
Kean University (G)
Kentucky State University (G)
Lakeland Community College (N)
La Sierra University (N)
Lehigh Carbon Community College (U)
Liberty University (G)
Millersville University of Pennsylvania (U,G)
Minot State University (U,G)
Mississippi State University (U)
Missouri State University (U)
Murray State University (G)
Nashville State Technical Community College (U)
National University (G)
New Jersey City University (G)
New Mexico Highlands University (U,G)
New Mexico State University (G)
Northampton County Area Community College (U)
North Dakota State University (G)
Northwestern State University of Louisiana (G)
Northwest Missouri State University (G)
The Ohio State University (N)
Oxnard College (U)
Plymouth State University (G)
St. Ambrose University (G)
St. Cloud State University (U)
Saint Mary-of-the-Woods College (U)
Seattle Pacific University (G)
Shippensburg University of Pennsylvania (U,G)
South Piedmont Community College (U)
State University of New York at Plattsburgh (G)
State University of New York College at Cortland (U)
Stephen F. Austin State University (U,G)
Texas A&M University–Commerce (G)
Texas Tech University (G)
The University of Akron (U,G)
The University of Arizona (G)
University of Arkansas at Little Rock (G)
University of Central Missouri (G)
University of Idaho (U)
The University of Kansas (G)
University of La Verne (N)
University of Louisville (G)
University of Maine at Fort Kent (U)
University of Massachusetts Boston (G)
University of Minnesota, Duluth (U,G)
University of New Orleans (U,G)
The University of North Carolina at Greensboro (G)
University of North Florida (U)
University of North Texas (N,U,G)
University of South Alabama (G)
University of Southern Mississippi (U,G)
University of South Florida (G)
The University of Texas at Tyler (U,G)
The University of Texas of the Permian Basin (U,G)

The University of Toledo (G)
University of Utah (U)
University of West Florida (G)
Utah State University (U,G)
Wayne State College (U,G)
Western Washington University (U)

SPEECH AND RHETORIC

Allen County Community College (U)
Arapahoe Community College (U)
Auburn University (U)
Austin Peay State University (U)
Beacon University (N,U)
Bellevue Community College (U)
Bergen Community College (U)
Bowling Green State University (G)
Brigham Young University (U)
Butler Community College (U)
Central New Mexico Community College (U)
Central Virginia Community College (U)
Cerro Coso Community College (U)
Charter Oak State College (U)
Chemeketa Community College (U)
City Colleges of Chicago, Harold Washington College (U)
Clackamas Community College (U)
Cleveland State Community College (U)
College of the Sequoias (U)
Colorado State University (U)
Columbus State Community College (U)
Community College of Denver (U)
Cumberland County College (U)
Cuyahoga Community College (U)
Dakota State University (U)
Dallas Baptist University (U)
Dallas County Community College District (U)
Darton College (U)
East Los Angeles College (U)
Edison State Community College (U)
Flathead Valley Community College (U)
Frank Phillips College (U)
Gadsden State Community College (U)
Galveston College (U)
Graceland University (U)
Grand View College (U)
Hocking College (U)
Honolulu Community College (U)
James Madison University (N)
Jefferson College (U)
John A. Logan College (U)
Johnson County Community College (U)
J. Sargeant Reynolds Community College (U)
Kaskaskia College (U)
Kentucky State University (U)
Labette Community College (U)
Laredo Community College (U)
Lehigh Carbon Community College (U)
Louisiana State University and Agricultural and Mechanical College (U)
Massasoit Community College (U)
Mesa State College (U)
Miami Dade College (U)
Mississippi Delta Community College (U)
Moberly Area Community College (U)
Mountain Empire Community College (U)
New York Institute of Technology (U)
North Central Texas College (U)
Northeast State Technical Community College (U)
Northern Virginia Community College (U)

North Iowa Area Community College (U)
NorthWest Arkansas Community College (U)
Oklahoma Panhandle State University (U)
Oxnard College (U)
Parkland College (U)
Pasco-Hernando Community College (U)
Pellissippi State Technical Community College (U)
Piedmont Technical College (U)
Pulaski Technical College (U)
Rend Lake College (U)
St. Clair County Community College (U)
St. Cloud State University (U)
San Diego Community College District (U)
Santa Monica College (U)
Shippensburg University of Pennsylvania (U)
Sinclair Community College (U)
Southeast Community College Area (U)
Southern Polytechnic State University (U)
Southern Union State Community College (U)
Syracuse University (U)
Tacoma Community College (U)
Taylor University (U)
Three Rivers Community College (U)
Triton College (U)
The University of Akron (U,G)
University of Alaska, Prince William Sound Community College (U)
University of Arkansas at Little Rock (U)
University of Minnesota, Crookston (U)
University of Minnesota, Twin Cities Campus (U,G)
University of New Orleans (U,G)
The University of South Dakota (U,G)
University of Southern Indiana (U)
University of Vermont (U,G)
University of Washington (U)
Valley City State University (U)
Vincennes University (U)
Wayne State College (U)
West Los Angeles College (U)
Wharton County Junior College (U)
Wichita State University (U)

STATISTICS

Allen County Community College (U)
Anne Arundel Community College (U)
Arkansas State University–Beebe (U)
Athabasca University (N,U)
Barton County Community College (U)
Belmont Technical College (U)
Berkeley College (U)
Berkeley College–New York City Campus (U)
Berkeley College–Westchester Campus (U)
Bloomsburg University of Pennsylvania (U)
Brenau University (U)
Brigham Young University (U)
Bristol Community College (U)
Broward Community College (U)
Burlington County College (U)
California State University, Sacramento (U)
Campbell University (U)
Carroll Community College (U)
Cayuga County Community College (U)
Centralia College (U)
Central Texas College (U)
Chadron State College (U,G)
Charter Oak State College (U)
Chemeketa Community College (U)
City Colleges of Chicago, Harold Washington College (U)

Clemson University (G)
Cleveland State Community College (U)
Clinton Community College (U)
Coastline Community College (U)
College of Southern Maryland (U)
Colorado Mountain College District System (U)
Colorado State University (U,G)
Community College of Beaver County (U)
Dallas Baptist University (U,G)
Darton College (U)
De Anza College (U)
Delaware Technical & Community College, Jack F. Owens Campus (U)
DeSales University (U)
Drexel University (G)
Eastern Michigan University (G)
Eastern West Virginia Community and Technical College (U)
East Tennessee State University (U)
Edison State Community College (U)
Elizabeth City State University (U)
Embry-Riddle Aeronautical University (U)
Erie Community College (U)
Erie Community College, North Campus (U)
Erie Community College, South Campus (U)
Franklin University (U)
Galveston College (U)
Genesee Community College (U)
Georgia State University (U)
Graceland University (U)
Grand Rapids Community College (U)
Gulf Coast Community College (U)
Harrisburg Area Community College (U)
Henry Ford Community College (U)
Holyoke Community College (U)
Hopkinsville Community College (U)
Illinois Eastern Community Colleges, Wabash Valley College (U)
Immaculata University (G)
Jacksonville State University (U,G)
James Madison University (U)
Jefferson College of Health Sciences (U)
Jefferson Community College (U)
John Wood Community College (U)
Kansas State University (U)
Kaskaskia College (U)
Lackawanna College (U)
Lakeland Community College (U)
Lehigh Carbon Community College (U)
Limestone College (U)
Long Beach City College (U)
Los Angeles Trade-Technical College (U)
Louisiana State University and Agricultural and Mechanical College (U)
Macon State College (U)
Marist College (U)
Marshall University (U)
Massasoit Community College (U)
Memorial University of Newfoundland (U)
Mercy College (U)
Metropolitan State University (U)
Miami Dade College (U)
Middlesex Community College (U)
Minot State University (U)
Misericordia University (U)
Mississippi State University (U)
Montgomery County Community College (U)
Motlow State Community College (U)
Mount Wachusett Community College (U)
Nassau Community College (U)
Naugatuck Valley Community College (U)

New Jersey Institute of Technology (G)
New River Community College (U)
New York Institute of Technology (U)
Northampton County Area Community College (U)
Northeast Iowa Community College (U)
North Iowa Area Community College (U)
North Lake College (U)
Northwestern Michigan College (U)
Okaloosa-Walton College (U)
Oklahoma State University (U)
Oregon State University (U)
Pace University (U)
Palomar College (U)
Parkland College (U)
Park University (U)
Passaic County Community College (U)
Pellissippi State Technical Community College (U)
Pennsylvania College of Technology (U)
Philadelphia University (U,G)
Piedmont Technical College (U)
Portland Community College (U)
Presentation College (U)
Queen's University at Kingston (U)
Regis University (U)
Rochester Institute of Technology (G)
Rockland Community College (G)
Roosevelt University (U)
Sacramento City College (U)
St. Ambrose University (G)
St. Clair County Community College (U)
St. Cloud State University (U,G)
St. Edward's University (U)
Sam Houston State University (U)
San Diego Community College District (U)
San Joaquin Delta College (U)
Schiller International University (U,G)
Seattle Central Community College (U)
Seminole Community College (U)
Sierra College (U)
Simmons College (N)
Southeast Arkansas College (U)
Southeastern Oklahoma State University (U)
Southern Polytechnic State University (U)
Southwest Virginia Community College (U)
Southwest Wisconsin Technical College (U)
Spoon River College (U)
Stanford University (N,G)
State University of New York at Plattsburgh (U)
State University of New York Empire State College (U)
Syracuse University (U)
Taft College (U)
Texas Tech University (G)
Triton College (U)
The University of Akron (U,G)
The University of Alabama in Huntsville (G)
University of Alaska Fairbanks (U)
University of Arkansas at Little Rock (U)
University of Central Florida (U)
University of Colorado Denver (U)
The University of Findlay (U)
University of Hawaii–West Oahu (U)
University of Houston–Downtown (U)
University of Idaho (U,G)
University of Illinois at Chicago (G)
The University of Kansas (U)
University of Louisville (U)
The University of Maine at Augusta (U)
University of Maine at Machias (U)

University of Management and Technology (U)
University of Massachusetts Boston (U,G)
University of Minnesota, Crookston (U)
University of Minnesota, Morris (U)
University of Missouri–Columbia (U)
University of Nevada, Reno (U)
University of New Orleans (U,G)
The University of North Carolina at Chapel Hill (U)
The University of North Carolina at Charlotte (G)
The University of North Carolina at Greensboro (U)
University of North Dakota (U)
The University of South Dakota (U)
University of Southern Mississippi (G)
The University of Texas at Tyler (U)
The University of Texas of the Permian Basin (G)
The University of Texas System (U)
The University of Toledo (U)
University of Utah (U)
University of Vermont (N,U)
University of Washington (U)
University of Waterloo (U)
University of West Florida (U)
University of Wisconsin Colleges (U)
University of Wisconsin–Parkside (G)
University of Wyoming (U)
Upper Iowa University (N,U)
Utah State University (U)
Wisconsin Indianhead Technical College (N,U)
Worcester State College (U)
York University (U)

STUDENT COUNSELING AND PERSONNEL SERVICES

Canisius College (G)
Cleveland State University (G)
College of the Siskiyous (U)
Indiana State University (G)
Jacksonville State University (U)
James Madison University (N)
Pace University (G)
University of Massachusetts Boston (G)
The University of North Carolina at Greensboro (G)

SURVEYING ENGINEERING

Missouri University of Science and Technology (N)

SYSTEMS ENGINEERING

Florida Institute of Technology (G)
Grantham University (G)
James Madison University (N)
Missouri University of Science and Technology (N,G)
Southern Methodist University (G)
The University of Alabama in Huntsville (G)
University of Florida (N,G)
University of Illinois at Urbana–Champaign (G)
University of New Orleans (U,G)
University of South Florida (G)

SYSTEMS SCIENCE AND THEORY

Florida Institute of Technology (G)
Nova Southeastern University (G)

State University of New York at Binghamton
(G)

TAXATION

Athabasca University (N,G)
Brenau University (U,G)
Carroll Community College (U)
DeVry University Online (U,G)
Drexel University (U)
Elizabeth City State University (U)
Golden Gate University (G)
Indiana University System (N)
James Madison University (N)
Lakeland Community College (N)
Liberty University (U)
Massasoit Community College (N)
Miami Dade College (U)
Middlesex Community College (U)
Minnesota School of Business–Richfield (U)
Missouri State University (G)
Oxnard College (U)
Saint Leo University (U)
State University of New York Institute of
Technology (G)
The University of Akron (U,G)
The University of Maine at Augusta (U)
The University of North Carolina at Charlotte
(N)
University of Toronto (N)

TEACHING ASSISTANTS/AIDES

Arapahoe Community College (U)
Athens Technical College (N)
Blue Mountain Community College (U)
Blue Ridge Community College (U)
Centennial College (U)
Chatham University (G)
Clemson University (N)
Cleveland Community College (U)
College of the Sequoias (U)
College of the Siskiyous (U)
Community College of Denver (U)
Drexel University (G)
Gateway Technical College (U)
Halifax Community College (U)
Haywood Community College (U)
Indian River Community College (U)
Minot State University–Bottineau Campus (U)
Northampton County Area Community
College (U)
South Piedmont Community College (U)
University of Michigan–Flint (N)
The University of Texas System (G)
University of Vermont (U)

TECHNICAL AND BUSINESS
WRITING

AIB College of Business (U)
Arapahoe Community College (U)
Athens Technical College (N,U)
Baltimore City Community College (U)
Belmont Technical College (U)
Black Hills State University (U)
Blue Ridge Community College (N)
Boise State University (U)
Bowling Green State University (U,G)
Brenau University (U)
Bridgewater State College (U)
Bristol Community College (U)

Caldwell Community College and Technical
Institute (N,U)
Carroll Community College (N,U)
Central Texas College (U)
Central Virginia Community College (U)
Chadron State College (U)
Chemeketa Community College (U)
Clackamas Community College (U)
Clark State Community College (U)
Clemson University (N)
Cleveland State Community College (U)
College of Southern Maryland (U)
College of The Albemarle (N)
Columbus State Community College (U)
Community College of Beaver County (U)
Community College of Denver (U)
Darton College (N)
Delaware Technical & Community College,
Jack F. Owens Campus (U)
DeVry University Online (U)
East Carolina University (G)
Eastern Washington University (N)
East Tennessee State University (U)
Edgecombe Community College (U)
Embry-Riddle Aeronautical University (U)
Erie Community College (U)
Erie Community College, North Campus (U)
Erie Community College, South Campus (U)
Grantham University (U)
Harrisburg Area Community College (U)
Haywood Community College (U)
Henry Ford Community College (U)
Hocking College (U)
Indiana State University (U)
Indian River Community College (U)
James Madison University (U)
Jefferson College of Health Sciences (U)
Jefferson Community College (U)
Johnson County Community College (U)
Jones International University (U)
Judson University (U)
Kean University (N)
Lake Superior College (U)
Lamar State College–Port Arthur (N)
Laredo Community College (U)
Lehigh Carbon Community College (U)
Limestone College (U)
Linn-Benton Community College (U)
Louisiana State University and Agricultural
and Mechanical College (U)
Mercer County Community College (N)
Mesa Community College (U)
Middlesex Community College (N,U)
Minnesota School of Business–Richfield (U)
Minot State University (U)
Monroe County Community College (U)
Montana Tech of The University of Montana
(U)
Montgomery Community College (U)
Montgomery County Community College (U)
Mt. Hood Community College (U)
Neumann College (U)
New Jersey Institute of Technology (G)
North Arkansas College (U)
North Carolina State University (U)
North Dakota State College of Science (U)
Northeastern University (U)
Northwestern Connecticut Community College
(N)
Northwestern Michigan College (U)
Northwestern State University of Louisiana
(U)

Oklahoma State University (U)
Oregon Institute of Technology (U)
Oregon State University (U)
Oxnard College (U)
Pace University (U)
Pasco-Hernando Community College (N)
Piedmont Community College (U)
Pikes Peak Community College (U)
Portland Community College (U)
Saint Mary-of-the-Woods College (U)
San Diego Community College District (U)
Sarasota County Technical Institute (N)
Schenectady County Community College (U)
Seminole Community College (U)
Sierra College (U)
Sinclair Community College (U)
Southeast Community College Area (U)
State University of New York at Binghamton
(N)
State University of New York College at
Cortland (U)
State University of New York College of
Agriculture and Technology at Morrisville
(U)
State University of New York Institute of
Technology (G)
Stephen F. Austin State University (U)
Syracuse University (U)
Taylor University (N)
Texas Tech University (U,G)
The University of Akron (U)
University of Alaska Fairbanks (U)
University of Arkansas at Little Rock (U,G)
University of California, Los Angeles (G)
University of Central Florida (G)
University of Cincinnati (U)
University of Colorado Denver (U)
University of Illinois at Chicago (N)
University of Illinois at Urbana–Champaign
(N)
The University of Maine at Augusta (U)
University of Management and Technology
(U)
University of Minnesota, Twin Cities Campus
(U)
University of Missouri–Columbia (U)
University of New Orleans (U,G)
University of North Texas (U)
University of Southern Mississippi (U)
The University of Tennessee (U)
The University of Texas at San Antonio (U)
The University of Toledo (U)
University of Washington (U)
University of West Florida (U)
Wake Technical Community College (N)
Weber State University (U)
Westchester Community College (U)
West Hills Community College (N)
West Los Angeles College (U)
West Virginia State University (U)
West Virginia University at Parkersburg (N)
York County Community College (U)
Youngstown State University (N)

TECHNOLOGY EDUCATION/
INDUSTRIAL ARTS

Adams State College (G)
Bowling Green State University (U,G)
Brigham Young University (U)
Chadron State College (G)
Cleveland State Community College (U)

Cleveland State University (N,G)
Duquesne University (G)
East Carolina University (U,G)
Eastern Michigan University (U,G)
Fort Hays State University (U)
Grand Rapids Community College (U)
Illinois State University (U,G)
Indiana State University (U)
Jacksonville State University (U)
John A. Logan College (U)
Marshall University (G)
Michigan State University (U)
Millersville University of Pennsylvania (G)
Mississippi State University (U)
Montgomery County Community College (N)
National University (G)
Nova Southeastern University (G)
Okaloosa-Walton College (U)
Quinebaug Valley Community College (N)
The University of Akron (U,G)
University of Alaska Fairbanks (U)
University of Central Missouri (U,G)
University of Massachusetts Boston (U,G)
University of Missouri–Columbia (G)
The University of Tennessee (N)
The University of Texas at San Antonio (G)
The University of Texas at Tyler (U)
University of West Florida (N)
University of Wisconsin–Stout (G)
Valley City State University (U,G)
Washburn University (U)
West Virginia University (N)
West Virginia University at Parkersburg (U)

TEXTILE SCIENCES AND ENGINEERING

North Carolina State University (U,G)
Southern Polytechnic State University (U)
Texas Tech University (G)

THEOLOGICAL AND MINISTERIAL STUDIES

Amridge University (N,U,G)
Andover Newton Theological School (G)
Arlington Baptist College (N,U)
Assemblies of God Theological Seminary (G)
Azusa Pacific University (G)
Bakke Graduate University (G)
Barclay College (U)
Bradley University (U)
Calvin Theological Seminary (G)
The Catholic Distance University (N,U,G)
Clear Creek Baptist Bible College (N,U)
College of Emmanuel and St. Chad (G)
Columbia International University (N,U,G)
Conception Seminary College (U,G)
Corban College (U)
Covenant Theological Seminary (N,G)
Crossroads College (N,U)
Crown College (G)
Dallas Baptist University (U,G)
Dallas Christian College (U)
Danville Community College (U)
Denver Seminary (G)
Drew University (N,G)
Duquesne University (U)
Earlham School of Religion (G)
Eastern Mennonite University (G)
Eugene Bible College (U)
Franciscan University of Steubenville (N,U,G)

Global University (N)
Gordon-Conwell Theological Seminary (N,G)
Grand Rapids Theological Seminary of
  Cornerstone University (N,G)
Hope International University (G)
Horizon College & Seminary (U,G)
Institute for Christian Studies (G)
Liberty University (G)
Life Pacific College (U)
Lincoln Christian College (N,U,G)
Master's College and Seminary (U)
Naropa University (N)
Nebraska Christian College (U)
North Park University (N,G)
Providence College and Theological Seminary
  (N,U,G)
Regent College (G)
Regent University (U,G)
Saint Mary-of-the-Woods College (G)
Saybrook Graduate School and Research
  Center (G)
Sioux Falls Seminary (G)
Southwestern Adventist University (U)
Summit Pacific College (N,U)
Taylor University (N,U)
Trinity Episcopal School for Ministry (N,G)
Unification Theological Seminary (N,G)
University of Dubuque (G)
Western Seminary (N,G)
Williamson Christian College (U)

THEOLOGY AND RELIGIOUS VOCATIONS RELATED

Andover Newton Theological School (G)
Assemblies of God Theological Seminary (G)
Bakke Graduate University (G)
Calvin Theological Seminary (G)
The Catholic Distance University (N,U,G)
Clear Creek Baptist Bible College (N,U)
College of Emmanuel and St. Chad (G)
Columbia International University (N,U,G)
Covenant Theological Seminary (N,G)
Dallas Christian College (U)
Defiance College (U)
DeSales University (U)
Duquesne University (U)
Earlham School of Religion (G)
Global University (N)
Gordon-Conwell Theological Seminary (N,G)
Grand Rapids Theological Seminary of
  Cornerstone University (N,G)
Liberty University (U,G)
Lincoln Christian College (U)
Master's College and Seminary (U)
Naropa University (N)
Nebraska Christian College (U)
Providence College and Theological Seminary
  (N,U,G)
Regent College (G)
Regent University (N,U,G)
St. John's University (U)
Saint Mary-of-the-Woods College (U,G)
Saybrook Graduate School and Research
  Center (N)
Sioux Falls Seminary (G)
Taylor University (U)
Trinity Episcopal School for Ministry (N,G)
University of St. Michael's College (N,U,G)
Western Seminary (N,G)

TRANSPORTATION AND MATERIALS MOVING RELATED

American Public University System (G)
Clark State Community College (N)
James Madison University (N)
Missouri University of Science and
  Technology (N)
North Lake College (U)
Riverside Community College District (U)
Sacramento City College (U)

URBAN STUDIES/AFFAIRS

Bakke Graduate University (G)
Cleveland State University (U,G)
Cuyahoga Community College (U)
Florida State University (G)
Grand Rapids Theological Seminary of
  Cornerstone University (G)
Hope International University (G)
James Madison University (N)
Saybrook Graduate School and Research
  Center (G)
The University of Akron (U,G)
University of Missouri–Columbia (G)
University of New Orleans (U,G)
University of Washington (U)
Virginia Polytechnic Institute and State
  University (G)

VEHICLE MAINTENANCE AND REPAIR TECHNOLOGIES

Arapahoe Community College (U)
Central Wyoming College (N,U)
Columbus State Community College (U)
Naugatuck Valley Community College (U)

VETERINARY BIOMEDICAL AND CLINICAL SCIENCES

Athens Technical College (U)
Auburn University (N)
Carroll Community College (N)
Central Wyoming College (N)
Colorado State University (N)
Community College of Denver (U)
Cuyahoga Community College (U)
Lakeland Community College (N)
Minnesota School of Business–Richfield (U)
Plymouth State University (N)
The University of North Carolina at
  Greensboro (N)
Virginia Polytechnic Institute and State
  University (G)
West Hills Community College (N)
West Virginia University (N)
Yuba College (U)

VISUAL AND PERFORMING ARTS

Academy of Art University (U,G)
Arapahoe Community College (U)
Arkansas State University–Beebe (U)
Atlantic University (N,G)
Bergen Community College (U)
Brigham Young University (U)
California State University, San Bernardino
  (U)
Central Wyoming College (N)
Chatham University (U)

City Colleges of Chicago, Harold Washington College (U)
Coastline Community College (U)
College of the Sequoias (U)
Daytona State College (U)
De Anza College (U)
East Los Angeles College (U)
Eugenio María de Hostos Community College of the City University of New York (U)
Everett Community College (U)
Grand Rapids Community College (U)
James Madison University (N)
Jefferson College (U)
John A. Logan College (U)
Kean University (N)
Manhattan School of Music (N,U,G)
Marshall University (U,G)
Massachusetts College of Art and Design (U,G)
Mesa State College (U)
Mt. Hood Community College (U)
North Iowa Area Community College (U)
Pace University (U)
Palomar College (U)
Prescott College (U,G)
Pulaski Technical College (U)
Regent University (N,U,G)
Riverside Community College District (U)
Roosevelt University (U)
Santa Rosa Junior College (U)
Texas Tech University (G)
Texas Woman's University (U,G)
Tompkins Cortland Community College (U)
The University of Akron (U)
University of California, Los Angeles (G)
The University of Findlay (U)
University of Illinois at Springfield (U)
University of Southern Indiana (U)
University of South Florida (U,G)

The University of Texas of the Permian Basin (U)
West Los Angeles College (U)
Wilfrid Laurier University (U)

VISUAL AND PERFORMING ARTS RELATED

Boise State University (U)
Brenau University (U)
Cabrillo College (U)
Central Wyoming College (N)
Clarion University of Pennsylvania (U)
Columbus State Community College (U)
De Anza College (U)
Drake University (U)
Hocking College (U)
Ivy Tech Community College–North Central (U)
Minneapolis College of Art and Design (N,U,G)
Naugatuck Valley Community College (U)
The Ohio State University (U)
Pellissippi State Technical Community College (U)
Red Rocks Community College (U)
Syracuse University (U,G)
University of Oregon (U)
The University of Texas of the Permian Basin (U)
The University of Toledo (U)
University of Wisconsin Colleges (U)
York University (U)

WILDLIFE AND WILDLANDS SCIENCE AND MANAGEMENT

Central Wyoming College (N)
Colorado State University (U,G)
Haywood Community College (U)

Lakeland Community College (N)
Oregon State University (U)
Prescott College (U,G)
University of Missouri–Columbia (N)

WOODWORKING

Blackhawk Technical College (N)
Central Wyoming College (N)
Cerritos College (U)

WORK AND FAMILY STUDIES

Alpena Community College (N)
California State University, San Marcos (N)
Central Michigan University (U)
Kansas State University (N)
Kean University (N)
Monroe County Community College (U)
Palomar College (U)
Rend Lake College (U)
Riverside Community College District (U)
University of Minnesota, Twin Cities Campus (U)
University of Missouri–Columbia (N)
Virginia Polytechnic Institute and State University (N)
West Los Angeles College (U)

ZOOLOGY/ANIMAL BIOLOGY

Brigham Young University (U)
Central Wyoming College (U)
Cerritos College (U)
Eastern Wyoming College (U)
Mississippi State University (U)
North Carolina State University (U)
Northwestern State University of Louisiana (U)
The University of Akron (U)
Utah Valley State College (U)
Weber State University

GEOGRAPHICAL LISTING OF DISTANCE LEARNING PROGRAMS

In this index, the page locations of the profiles are printed in regular type and **In-Depth Descriptions** in **bold type**.

U.S. AND U.S. TERRITORIES

ALABAMA

Amridge University, 81, **336**
Auburn University, 86, **340**
Columbia Southern University, 121
Gadsden State Community College, 149
George C. Wallace Community College, 151
Heritage Christian University, 159
Jacksonville State University, 171
Judson College, 176
Lurleen B. Wallace Community College, 187
Northeast Alabama Community College, 214
Southern Union State Community College, 256
United States Sports Academy, 272
The University of Alabama, 273, **476**
The University of Alabama in Huntsville, 274
University of North Alabama, 294
University of South Alabama, 301

ALASKA

Ilisagvik College, 164
University of Alaska Anchorage, Kodiak College, 274
University of Alaska Fairbanks, 274, **478**
University of Alaska, Prince William Sound Community College, 275

ARIZONA

Arizona Western College, 83
Central Arizona College, 106
Diné College, 132
Everest College, 143
IIA College, 163
Mesa Community College, 193
Northcentral University, 213
Prescott College, 232, **434**
Thunderbird School of Global Management, 269
The University of Arizona, 275
The University of Arizona, 275
University of Phoenix, 299

ARKANSAS

Arkansas State University–Beebe, 83
Arkansas State University–Mountain Home, 83
Arkansas Tech University, 83
East Arkansas Community College, 134
North Arkansas College, 212
NorthWest Arkansas Community College, 217
Ouachita Technical College, 224
Pulaski Technical College, 233
Southeast Arkansas College, 252
Southern Arkansas University Tech, 254
University of Arkansas, 275

University of Arkansas at Little Rock, 275
University of Arkansas at Pine Bluff, 276

CALIFORNIA

Academy of Art University, 77
American Graduate University, 79
Azusa Pacific University, 87
Cabrillo College, 99
California Institute of Integral Studies, 100, **348**
California National University for Advanced Studies, 100
California Polytechnic State University, San Luis Obispo, 100
California State University, Chico, 101
California State University, Dominguez Hills, 101, **350**
California State University, East Bay, 101
California State University, Northridge, 101
California State University, Sacramento, 102
California State University, San Bernardino, 102
California State University, San Marcos, 102
Cerritos College, 110
Cerro Coso Community College, 110
Citrus College, 113
Coastline Community College, 117
Cogswell Polytechnical College, 117
College of San Mateo, 118
College of the Sequoias, 119
College of the Siskiyous, 119
Crafton Hills College, 125
De Anza College, 129
East Los Angeles College, 138
Evergreen Valley College, 144
Fielding Graduate University, 144
Foothill College, 147
Golden Gate University, 153
Golden West College, 153
Holy Names University, 162
Hope International University, 162
La Sierra University, 182
Life Pacific College, 184
Loma Linda University, 185
Long Beach City College, 185
Los Angeles Harbor College, 186
Los Angeles Trade-Technical College, 186
Moorpark College, 203
Mt. San Antonio College, 205
National University, 207
Orange Coast College, 222
Oxnard College, 224
Pacific Oaks College, 225
Pacific Union College, 225
Palomar College, 225
Riverside Community College District, 236
Sacramento City College, 239
Saddleback College, 239
Samuel Merritt College, 245
San Diego Community College District, 245
San Diego State University, 246

San Francisco State University, 246
San Joaquin Delta College, 246
San Joaquin Valley College–Online, 246
Santa Monica College, 246
Santa Rosa Junior College, 247
Saybrook Graduate School and Research Center, 247, **444**
Shasta Bible College, 250
Sierra College, 251
Sonoma State University, 252
Southern California Seminary, 254
Stanford University, 258
Taft College, 264
TUI University, 271, **474**
UC San Diego Extension, 271
University of California, Davis, 277
University of California, Los Angeles, 277
University of California, Riverside, 277
University of La Verne, 286
University of Southern California, 302
University of the Pacific, 307
Vanguard University of Southern California, 316
West Hills Community College, 322
West Los Angeles College, 322
Yuba College, 327

COLORADO

Adams State College, 77, **330**
Arapahoe Community College, 82
Colorado Mountain College District System, 119
Colorado State University, 119, **364**
Colorado State University, 120, **366**
Colorado Technical University Colorado Springs, 120, **368**
Community College of Denver, 123
Denver Seminary, 130
Heritage College, 160
Jones International University, 175
Mesa State College, 193
Naropa University, 206, **412**
Pikes Peak Community College, 230
Red Rocks Community College, 234
Regis University, 235
University of Colorado at Boulder, 280
University of Colorado at Colorado Springs, 280
University of Colorado Denver, 280, **488**
University of Denver, 281, **494**
Westwood Online, 323, **532**

CONNECTICUT

Capital Community College, 104
Central Connecticut State University, 107
Charter Oak State College, 111, **358**
Fairfield University, 144
Gateway Community College, 150
Holy Apostles College and Seminary, 161
Middlesex Community College, 195

Naugatuck Valley Community College, 208
Northwestern Connecticut Community
  College, 218
Quinebaug Valley Community College, 233
Quinnipiac University, 233
Sacred Heart University, 239
Three Rivers Community College, 268
Tunxis Community College, 271
University of Bridgeport, 276
University of Connecticut, 281, **490**
University of New Haven, 293

DELAWARE

Delaware Technical & Community College,
  Jack F. Owens Campus, 130
Wilmington University, 325

DISTRICT OF COLUMBIA

American University, 80
The George Washington University, 151
The George Washington University, 151
Strayer University, 262, **468**

FLORIDA

The Baptist College of Florida, 88
Bethune-Cookman University, 92
Broward Community College, 97
Daytona State College, 129
Embry-Riddle Aeronautical University, 141
Embry-Riddle Aeronautical University, 141
Florida Gulf Coast University, 146
Florida Institute of Technology, 146
Florida Institute of Technology, 146, **388**
Florida State University, 146
Florida Tech University Online, 147
Gulf Coast Community College, 157
Hillsborough Community College, 160
Hobe Sound Bible College, 161
Hodges University, 161
Indian River Community College, 167
Kaplan University Online, 177
Keiser University, 178, **404**
Lake-Sumter Community College, 180
Lynn University, 187, **410**
Manatee Community College, 188
Miami Dade College, 194
North Florida Community College, 216
Nova Southeastern University, 220
Nova Southeastern University, 220, **422**
Nova Southeastern University, 220
Okaloosa-Walton College, 221
Palm Beach Community College, 225
Pasco-Hernando Community College, 227
Saint Leo University, 243
St. Petersburg Theological Seminary, 244
Sarasota County Technical Institute, 247
Schiller International University, 248, **446**
Seminole Community College, 249
University of Central Florida, 277
University of Florida, 282, **496**
University of North Florida, 297
University of St. Augustine for Health
  Sciences, 300
University of South Florida, 303
University of West Florida, 310

GEORGIA

Albany State University, 78
Athens Technical College, 85

Beacon University, 89
Beulah Heights University, 92
Brenau University, 95, **346**
Columbus State University, 122
Darton College, 128, **372**
East Georgia College, 138
Emory University, 141
Fort Valley State University, 148
Georgia College & State University, 152
Georgia Highlands College, 152
Georgia Institute of Technology, 152, **394**
Georgia State University, 152
Macon State College, 187
Middle Georgia College, 195
Okefenokee Technical College, 221
Savannah College of Art and Design, 247,
  442
Southern Polytechnic State University, 255

HAWAII

Chaminade University of Honolulu, 111
Honolulu Community College, 162
Kauai Community College, 178
University of Hawaii–West Oahu, 283

IDAHO

Boise State University, 94
Lewis-Clark State College, 183
University of Idaho, 283
University of Idaho, 284

ILLINOIS

American InterContinental University Online,
  80, **332**
Benedictine University, 90
Blessing-Rieman College of Nursing, 93
Bradley University, 95
Carl Sandburg College, 105
Chicago State University, 112
City Colleges of Chicago, Harold Washington
  College, 113
DePaul University, 131, **374**
DePaul University, 131
DeVry University Online, 131, **376**
Eastern Illinois University, 135
Elgin Community College, 139
Erikson Institute, 142
Governors State University, 154
Illinois Eastern Community Colleges, Frontier
  Community College, 164
Illinois Eastern Community Colleges, Lincoln
  Trail College, 164
Illinois Eastern Community Colleges, Olney
  Central College, 164
Illinois Eastern Community Colleges, Wabash
  Valley College, 164
Illinois State University, 165
John A. Logan College, 174
John Wood Community College, 175
Judson University, 176
Kaskaskia College, 177
Knowledge Systems Institute, 179
Lincoln Christian College, 184
Midstate College, 196
Northeastern Illinois University, 215
North Park University, 217
Parkland College, 226
Rend Lake College, 236
Richland Community College, 236
Roosevelt University, 238, **436**

Rosalind Franklin University of Medicine and
  Science, 238
Rush University, 238
Saint Francis Medical Center College of
  Nursing, 241
Southeastern Illinois College, 253
Southern Illinois University Edwardsville, 254
Spertus Institute of Jewish Studies, 258
Spoon River College, 258
Triton College, 270
University of Illinois at Chicago, 284
University of Illinois at Springfield, 284
University of Illinois at Urbana–Champaign,
  285
University of Illinois at Urbana–Champaign,
  285
University of Illinois at Urbana–Champaign,
  286
University of Illinois at Urbana–Champaign,
  286
University of St. Francis, 300

INDIANA

Anderson University, 81
Ball State University, 87
Earlham School of Religion, 134
Grace College, 154
Indiana State University, 165, **398**
Indiana Tech, 166
Indiana University–Purdue University Fort
  Wayne, 166
Indiana University System, 167, **400**
Indiana Wesleyan University, 167
Ivy Tech Community College–Bloomington,
  168
Ivy Tech Community College–Central Indiana,
  168
Ivy Tech Community College–Columbus, 168
Ivy Tech Community College–East Central,
  169
Ivy Tech Community College–Kokomo, 169
Ivy Tech Community College–Lafayette, 169
Ivy Tech Community College–North Central,
  169
Ivy Tech Community College–Northeast, 169
Ivy Tech Community College–Northwest, 170
Ivy Tech Community College–Southeast, 170
Ivy Tech Community College–Southern
  Indiana, 170
Ivy Tech Community College–Southwest, 170
Ivy Tech Community College–Wabash Valley,
  170
Ivy Tech Community College–Whitewater,
  171
Saint Mary-of-the-Woods College, 244
Saint Mary-of-the-Woods College, 244
Taylor University, 264
Trine University, 270
University of Southern Indiana, 302
Vincennes University, 316

IOWA

AIB College of Business, 78
Allen College, 78
Buena Vista University, 98
Buena Vista University, 98
Drake University, 132
Eastern Iowa Community College District,
  136
Ellsworth Community College, 140

Graceland University, 154
Grand View College, 155
Hawkeye Community College, 158
Marshalltown Community College, 190
Northeast Iowa Community College, 215
North Iowa Area Community College, 216
St. Ambrose University, 240
Simpson College, 251
Southwestern Community College, 257
University of Dubuque, 282
University of Dubuque, 282
University of Northern Iowa, 297
Upper Iowa University, 314, **520**

KANSAS

Allen County Community College, 78
Barclay College, 88
Barton County Community College, 88
Butler Community College, 99
Fort Hays State University, 147
Johnson County Community College, 175
Kansas State University, 176, **402**
Labette Community College, 179
Ottawa University, 223
Pratt Community College, 231
Southwestern College, 257
The University of Kansas, 286
Washburn University, 318
Wichita State University, 324

KENTUCKY

Campbellsville University, 103
Clear Creek Baptist Bible College, 115
Eastern Kentucky University, 136
Elizabethtown Community and Technical
  College, 140
Henderson Community College, 159
Hopkinsville Community College, 163
Kentucky State University, 178
Midway College, 197
Murray State University, 206
Spencerian College–Lexington, 257
Sullivan University, 263
University of Louisville, 287
Western Kentucky University, 320

LOUISIANA

Elaine P. Nunez Community College, 139
Louisiana State University and Agricultural
  and Mechanical College, 186
Louisiana State University and Agricultural
  and Mechanical College, 186
Loyola University New Orleans, 187
Northwestern State University of Louisiana,
  218
University of New Orleans, 294

MAINE

Saint Joseph's College of Maine, 242, **438**
Southern Maine Community College, 254
Thomas College, 267
The University of Maine at Augusta, 287
University of Maine at Fort Kent, 287
University of Maine at Machias, 287
University of Southern Maine, 302
York County Community College, 326

MARYLAND

Anne Arundel Community College, 82
Baltimore City Community College, 87

Baltimore Hebrew University, 88
Carroll Community College, 105
College of Southern Maryland, 118
Garrett College, 150
Goucher College, 154
Hagerstown Community College, 157
Harford Community College, 158
The Johns Hopkins University, 174
University of Maryland, College Park, 288,
  500
University of Maryland University College,
  288

MASSACHUSETTS

Andover Newton Theological School, 81
Bridgewater State College, 96
Bristol Community College, 97
Cape Cod Community College, 104
Endicott College, 141
Fitchburg State College, 145
Framingham State College, 148
Gordon-Conwell Theological Seminary, 154
Greenfield Community College, 156
Hebrew College, 159
Holyoke Community College, 162
Massachusetts College of Art and Design, 191
Massachusetts College of Liberal Arts, 191
Massasoit Community College, 191
MGH Institute of Health Professions, 194
Middlesex Community College, 196
Mount Wachusett Community College, 205
Nichols College, 211
Northeastern University, 215
Simmons College, 251
Tufts University, 270
University of Massachusetts Boston, 289
University of Massachusetts Lowell, 290
Westfield State College, 321
Worcester Polytechnic Institute, 326
Worcester State College, 326

MICHIGAN

Alpena Community College, 79
Baker College of Flint, 87, **342**
Calvin College, 103
Calvin Theological Seminary, 103
Central Michigan University, 107, **356**
Eastern Michigan University, 136, **384**
Ferris State University, 144
Grand Rapids Community College, 155
Grand Rapids Theological Seminary of
  Cornerstone University, 155
Henry Ford Community College, 159
Kettering University, 179, **406**
Kirtland Community College, 179
Lawrence Technological University, 182
Michigan State University, 194
Michigan State University, 195
Michigan Technological University, 195
Monroe County Community College, 202
Montcalm Community College, 202
Northwestern Michigan College, 218
Northwood University, 219
St. Clair County Community College, 240
Siena Heights University, 251
Spring Arbor University, 258
University of Michigan, 290
University of Michigan–Dearborn, 290
University of Michigan–Flint, 290
Western Michigan University, 320
West Shore Community College, 322

MINNESOTA

Capella University, 104, **354**
The College of St. Scholastica, 118
Concordia University, St. Paul, 124
Crossroads College, 125
Crown College, 125
Hamline University, 157
Hibbing Community College, 160
Lake Superior College, 181
Metropolitan State University, 194
Minneapolis College of Art and Design, 198
Minnesota School of Business–Richfield, 198
Minnesota State Community and Technical
  College–Fergus Falls, 198
Northland Community and Technical College–
  Thief River Falls, 217
Northwest Technical College, 219
Pine Technical College, 230
St. Cloud State University, 240
University of Minnesota, Crookston, 291
University of Minnesota, Duluth, 291
University of Minnesota, Morris, 291
University of Minnesota, Twin Cities Campus,
  291, **502**
University of St. Thomas, 300
Walden University, 318, **526**

MISSISSIPPI

Alcorn State University, 78
Belhaven College, 89
East Central Community College, 135
Jackson State University, 171
Mississippi Delta Community College, 199
Mississippi State University, 200
Mississippi University for Women, 200
University of Southern Mississippi, 303

MISSOURI

Assemblies of God Theological Seminary, 84
Avila University, 86
Central Bible College, 106
Columbia College, 121
Conception Seminary College, 123
Covenant Theological Seminary, 125
Culver-Stockton College, 126
Fontbonne University, 147
Global University, 153
Grantham University, 156, **396**
Harris-Stowe State University, 158
Jefferson College, 173
Midwestern Baptist Theological Seminary,
  197
Missouri State University, 200
Missouri State University–West Plains, 201
Missouri University of Science and
  Technology, 201
Moberly Area Community College, 201
North Central Missouri College, 213
Northwest Missouri State University, 219
Park University, 226, **426**
Saint Charles Community College, 240
St. Louis Community College System, 243,
  440
Saint Louis University, 244
Southeast Missouri State University, 254
Three Rivers Community College, 268
University of Central Missouri, 278, **480**
University of Central Missouri, 278, **482**
University of Central Missouri, 278, **484**
University of Central Missouri, 279, **486**

University of Missouri–Columbia, 292
University of Missouri–Columbia, 292
Webster University, 319

MONTANA

Dawson Community College, 129
Flathead Valley Community College, 145
Montana Tech of The University of Montana, 202
The University of Montana–Western, 293

NEBRASKA

Bellevue University, 90, **344**
Chadron State College, 110
Clarkson College, 114
Nebraska Christian College, 208
Southeast Community College Area, 253
University of Nebraska at Kearney, 293
Wayne State College, 319
Western Nebraska Community College, 320

NEVADA

University of Nevada, Reno, 293

NEW HAMPSHIRE

Daniel Webster College, 128
Franklin Pierce University, 149
Granite State College, 155
New England College, 208
Plymouth State University, 231
Southern New Hampshire University, 255

NEW JERSEY

Bergen Community College, 90
Berkeley College, 91
Bloomfield College, 93
Burlington County College, 99
Cumberland County College, 126
Drew University, 132
Kean University, 178
Mercer County Community College, 193
Monmouth University, 202
New Jersey City University, 209
New Jersey Institute of Technology, 209
Passaic County Community College, 227
The Richard Stockton College of New Jersey, 236
Seton Hall University, 249, **448**
Seton Hall University, 249, **450**
Seton Hall University, 249, **452**
Seton Hall University, 250, **454**
Seton Hall University, 250, **456**
Stevens Institute of Technology, 262, **466**
Thomas Edison State College, 267, **472**
Union County College, 272
University of Medicine and Dentistry of New Jersey, 290

NEW MEXICO

Central New Mexico Community College, 108
New Mexico Highlands University, 209
New Mexico Institute of Mining and Technology, 210
New Mexico Junior College, 210
New Mexico State University, 210
University of the Southwest, 307

NEW YORK

Berkeley College–New York City Campus, 91
Berkeley College–Westchester Campus, 91
Broome Community College, 97
Bryant and Stratton Online, 97
Buffalo State College, State University of New York, 98
Canisius College, 103, **352**
Cayuga County Community College, 106
Clinton Community College, 117
Columbia-Greene Community College, 121
Columbia University, 122
Concordia College–New York, 123
Corning Community College, 124
Daemen College, 126
Erie Community College, 141
Erie Community College, North Campus, 142
Erie Community College, South Campus, 142
Eugenio María de Hostos Community College of the City University of New York, 143
Excelsior College, 144, **386**
Finger Lakes Community College, 145
Five Towns College, 145
Fulton-Montgomery Community College, 149
Genesee Community College, 151, **392**
Herkimer County Community College, 160
Hofstra University, 161
Iona College, 168
Jamestown Community College, 173
Jefferson Community College, 174
Manhattan School of Music, 188
Marist College, 190
Marist College, 189
Mercy College, 193
Monroe Community College, 202
Nassau Community College, 207
The New School: A University, 211, **414**
The New School: A University, 211, **416**
The New School: A University, 211, **418**
New York Institute of Technology, 211
Nyack College, 221
Pace University, 224
Rochester Institute of Technology, 237
Rockland Community College, 237
St. John's University, 242
St. John's University, 241
St. Joseph's College, Long Island Campus, 242
St. Joseph's College, New York, 242
Schenectady County Community College, 248
Skidmore College, 252, **458**
State University of New York at Binghamton, 259
State University of New York at Oswego, 259, **462**
State University of New York at Plattsburgh, 259
State University of New York College at Cortland, 260
State University of New York College at Potsdam, 260
State University of New York College of Agriculture and Technology at Morrisville, 260
State University of New York College of Technology at Canton, 260
State University of New York Empire State College, 261, **464**
State University of New York Institute of Technology, 261

State University of New York Institute of Technology, 261
State University of New York Institute of Technology, 261
Sullivan County Community College, 263
Syracuse University, 263
Syracuse University, 263, **470**
Tompkins Cortland Community College, 269
Unification Theological Seminary, 272
Utica College, 315
Westchester Community College, 320

NORTH CAROLINA

Appalachian State University, 82
Beaufort County Community College, 89
Blue Ridge Community College, 94
Caldwell Community College and Technical Institute, 100
Campbell University, 103
Cape Fear Community College, 104
Central Carolina Community College, 107
Cleveland Community College, 115
College of The Albemarle, 118
Duke University, 134, **380**
East Carolina University, 134, **382**
Edgecombe Community College, 139
Elizabeth City State University, 140
Halifax Community College, 157
Haywood Community College, 158
McDowell Technical Community College, 192
Montgomery Community College, 203
Mount Olive College, 205
North Carolina State University, 212
Pamlico Community College, 226
Piedmont Community College, 229
Randolph Community College, 233
Richmond Community College, 236
Southeastern Community College, 253
South Piedmont Community College, 256
Tri-County Community College, 270
The University of North Carolina at Chapel Hill, 295
The University of North Carolina at Chapel Hill, 295, **504**
The University of North Carolina at Charlotte, 295
The University of North Carolina at Greensboro, 295
The University of North Carolina Wilmington, 296
Wake Technical Community College, 317

NORTH DAKOTA

Dickinson State University, 132
Lake Region State College, 180
Mayville State University, 191
Minot State University, 199
Minot State University–Bottineau Campus, 199
North Dakota State College of Science, 214
North Dakota State University, 214, **420**
University of North Dakota, 296
Valley City State University, 316
Williston State College, 325

OHIO

Antioch University McGregor, 82
Belmont Technical College, 90
Bowling Green State University, 94
Cincinnati Christian University, 112

Cincinnati State Technical and Community College, 112
Clark State Community College, 114
Cleveland Institute of Electronics, 116
Cleveland State University, 116
College of Mount St. Joseph, 117
Columbus State Community College, 122
Cuyahoga Community College, 126
Defiance College, 130
Edison State Community College, 139
Franciscan University of Steubenville, 148
Franklin University, 149, **390**
Hocking College, 161
James A. Rhodes State College, 172
Jefferson Community College, 174
Lakeland Community College, 180
Malone College, 188
Marion Technical College, 189
Myers University, 206
North Central State College, 213
The Ohio State University, 221
Shawnee State University, 250
Sinclair Community College, 252
Tiffin University, 269
The University of Akron, 272
University of Cincinnati, 279
University of Cincinnati Raymond Walters College, 279
The University of Findlay, 282
University of Northwestern Ohio, 298
The University of Toledo, 307, **512**
Youngstown State University, 327

OKLAHOMA

Connors State College, 124
Murray State College, 205
Northwestern Oklahoma State University, 218
Oklahoma Panhandle State University, 221
Oklahoma State University, 222
Rose State College, 238
Southeastern Oklahoma State University, 253
University of Oklahoma, 298, **506**

OREGON

Blue Mountain Community College, 94
Central Oregon Community College, 108
Chemeketa Community College, 112
Clackamas Community College, 113
Clatsop Community College, 115
Corban College, 124, **370**
Eastern Oregon University, 137
Eugene Bible College, 143
George Fox University, 151
Linn-Benton Community College, 184
Mt. Hood Community College, 205
Oregon Institute of Technology, 223
Oregon State University, 223, **424**
Portland Community College, 231
Treasure Valley Community College, 269
University of Oregon, 298
Western Seminary, 321

PENNSYLVANIA

The American College, 79
Baptist Bible College of Pennsylvania, 88
Blackstone Career Institute, 93
Bloomsburg University of Pennsylvania, 93
Bryn Athyn College of the New Church, 98
Carlow University, 105
Chatham University, 111

Clarion University of Pennsylvania, 114, **362**
Community College of Beaver County, 123
Delaware County Community College, 130
DeSales University, 131
Drexel University, 133
Drexel University, 133, **378**
Duquesne University, 134
Eastern University, 137
Elizabethtown College, 140
Gratz College, 156
Harrisburg Area Community College, 158
Immaculata University, 165
Indiana University of Pennsylvania, 166
Lackawanna College, 179
Lehigh Carbon Community College, 182
Lehigh University, 183
Lock Haven University of Pennsylvania, 185, **408**
Luzerne County Community College, 187
Manor College, 188
Mansfield University of Pennsylvania, 188
Millersville University of Pennsylvania, 197
Misericordia University, 199
Montgomery County Community College, 203
Neumann College, 208
Northampton County Area Community College, 212
Peirce College, 228, **428**
Penn State University Park, 228, **430**
Pennsylvania College of Technology, 229, **432**
Pennsylvania Highlands Community College, 229
Philadelphia University, 229
Pittsburgh Technical Institute, 230
Reading Area Community College, 234
Saint Francis University, 241
Saint Joseph's University, 243
Shippensburg University of Pennsylvania, 250
Temple University, 265
Trinity Episcopal School for Ministry, 270
University of Pennsylvania, 298
University of Pennsylvania, 298
University of Pittsburgh, 299
University of Pittsburgh at Bradford, 299
University of Pittsburgh at Johnstown, 300
The University of Scranton, 301
University of the Sciences in Philadelphia, 307
Widener University, 324

RHODE ISLAND

New England Institute of Technology, 208
Roger Williams University, 237

SOUTH CAROLINA

Clemson University, 115
Columbia International University, 121
Greenville Technical College, 157
Limestone College, 184
Piedmont Technical College, 230
York Technical College, 327

SOUTH DAKOTA

Black Hills State University, 93
Dakota State University, 126
Mitchell Technical Institute, 201
Northern State University, 216
Presentation College, 232
Sioux Falls Seminary, 252
Southeast Technical Institute, 254

University of Sioux Falls, 301
The University of South Dakota, 301

TENNESSEE

Austin Peay State University, 86
Bethel College, 92
Cleveland State Community College, 116
East Tennessee State University, 138
Huntington College of Health Sciences, 163
Johnson Bible College, 174
Lipscomb University, 185
Middle Tennessee State University, 196
Motlow State Community College, 204
Nashville State Technical Community College, 207
Northeast State Technical Community College, 215
Pellissippi State Technical Community College, 228
Union University, 272
The University of Tennessee, 304
The University of Tennessee at Martin, 304
Vanderbilt University, 316
Williamson Christian College, 325

TEXAS

Abilene Christian University, 77
Amberton University, 79
Angelo State University, 81
Arlington Baptist College, 84
Brazosport College, 95
Central Texas College, 108
Dallas Baptist University, 127
Dallas Christian College, 127
Dallas County Community College District, 128
Frank Phillips College, 149
Galveston College, 150
Houston Community College System, 163
Lamar State College–Port Arthur, 181
Laredo Community College, 181
LeTourneau University, 183
McMurry University, 192
Midwestern State University, 197
Mountain View College, 204
North Central Texas College, 213
North Lake College, 216
Northwood University, Texas Campus, 219
Prairie View A&M University, 231
St. Edward's University, 241
St. Mary's University, 244
Sam Houston State University, 245
San Antonio College, 245
Southern Methodist University, 255, **460**
Southwestern Adventist University, 256
Stephen F. Austin State University, 262
Texas A&M University–Commerce, 265
Texas A&M University–Kingsville, 265
Texas Christian University, 266
Texas State Technical College Waco, 266
Texas State University–San Marcos, 266
Texas Tech University, 266
Texas Woman's University, 267
Tyler Junior College, 271
University of Dallas, 281, **492**
University of Houston–Downtown, 283
University of Houston–Victoria, 283, **498**
University of North Texas, 297
The University of Texas at Brownsville, 304
The University of Texas at Dallas, 305

The University of Texas at El Paso, 305
The University of Texas at San Antonio, 305
The University of Texas at Tyler, 305
The University of Texas of the Permian Basin, 306
The University of Texas System, 306, **508**
University of the Incarnate Word, 306, **510**
Wayland Baptist University, 318
West Texas A&M University, 322
Wharton County Junior College, 324

UTAH

Brigham Young University, 96
Independence University, 165
Midwives College of Utah, 197
University of Utah, 308
Utah State University, 314, **522**
Utah Valley State College, 315
Utah Valley State College, 315
Weber State University, 319, **530**

VERMONT

Burlington College, 99
Green Mountain College, 156
Johnson State College, 175
University of Vermont, 308
Vermont Technical College, 316

VIRGIN ISLANDS

University of the Virgin Islands, 307

VIRGINIA

Atlantic University, 86
The Catholic Distance University, 106
Central Virginia Community College, 109
Danville Community College, 128
Eastern Mennonite University, 136
George Mason University, 151
James Madison University, 172
Jefferson College of Health Sciences, 173
J. Sargeant Reynolds Community College, 176
Liberty University, 183
Marymount University, 190
Mountain Empire Community College, 204
New River Community College, 210
Northern Virginia Community College, 216
Old Dominion University, 222
Patrick Henry College, 227
Patrick Henry Community College, 227
Rappahannock Community College, 234
Regent University, 235
Southside Virginia Community College, 256
Southwest Virginia Community College, 257
University of Management and Technology, 288
University of Mary Washington, 289
University of Virginia, 309
The University of Virginia's College at Wise, 309

Virginia Polytechnic Institute and State University, 317, **524**
Wytheville Community College, 326

WASHINGTON

Bakke Graduate University, 87
Bellevue Community College, 89
Centralia College, 107
Central Washington University, 109
City University of Seattle, 113, **360**
Eastern Washington University, 137
Everett Community College, 143
Gonzaga University, 154
North Seattle Community College, 217
Peninsula College, 228
Seattle Central Community College, 248
Seattle Pacific University, 248
Tacoma Community College, 264
University of Washington, 309, **514**
Washington State University, 318, **528**
Western Washington University, 321

WEST VIRGINIA

American Public University System, 80, **334**
Eastern West Virginia Community and Technical College, 137
Glenville State College, 152
Marshall University, 190
Mountain State University, 204
West Virginia State University, 323
West Virginia University, 323
West Virginia University at Parkersburg, 323
Wheeling Jesuit University, 324

WISCONSIN

Blackhawk Technical College, 92
Cardinal Stritch University, 104
Carroll University, 105
Concordia University Wisconsin, 124
Fox Valley Technical College, 148
Gateway Technical College, 150
Lakeland College, 180
Maranatha Baptist Bible College, 189
Marian College of Fond du Lac, 189
Marquette University, 190
Medical College of Wisconsin, 192
Milwaukee School of Engineering, 198
Silver Lake College, 251
Southwest Wisconsin Technical College, 257
University of Wisconsin Colleges, 311
University of Wisconsin–Green Bay, 311
University of Wisconsin–La Crosse, 311
University of Wisconsin–Parkside, 311
University of Wisconsin–Platteville, 311
University of Wisconsin–Platteville, 312
University of Wisconsin–Platteville, 312
University of Wisconsin–Platteville, 312
University of Wisconsin–Platteville, 312
University of Wisconsin–Platteville, 312
University of Wisconsin–Platteville, 312
University of Wisconsin–Stout, 313

University of Wisconsin–Stout, 313
University of Wisconsin–Superior, 313, **516**
University of Wisconsin–Whitewater, 313
Wisconsin Indianhead Technical College, 325

WYOMING

Central Wyoming College, 109
Eastern Wyoming College, 138
University of Wyoming, 314, **518**
Western Wyoming Community College, 321

CANADA

ALBERTA

Athabasca University, 84, **338**
University of Calgary, 277
University of Lethbridge, 286

BRITISH COLUMBIA

Regent College, 234
Summit Pacific College, 263
The University of British Columbia, 276

MANITOBA

Providence College and Theological Seminary, 232
University of Manitoba, 288

NEW BRUNSWICK

Mount Allison University, 204

NEWFOUNDLAND AND LABRADOR

Memorial University of Newfoundland, 192

NOVA SCOTIA

Acadia University, 77
Nova Scotia Agricultural College, 220

ONTARIO

Brock University, 97
Centennial College, 106
Institute for Christian Studies, 167
Laurentian University, 182
Master's College and Seminary, 191
Nipissing University, 212
Queen's University at Kingston, 233
University of St. Michael's College, 300
University of Toronto, 308
University of Waterloo, 310
University of Windsor, 310
Wilfrid Laurier University, 324
York University, 327

SASKATCHEWAN

College of Emmanuel and St. Chad, 117
Horizon College & Seminary, 163
University of Saskatchewan, 301